THE
NAVY LIST
2002

Corrected to 9th April 2002
(See Notes on page iii)

LONDON: TSO

Published by The Stationery Office Limited and available from:

Online
www.tso.co.uk/bookshop

Mail, Telephone, Fax & E-mail
TSO
PO Box 29, Norwich NR3 1GN
Telephone orders/General enquiries: 0870 600 5522
Fax orders: 0870 600 5533
E-mail: book.orders@tso.co.uk
Textphone 0870 240 3701

TSO Shops
123 Kingsway, London WC2B 6PQ
020 7242 6393 Fax 020 7242 6394
68-69 Bull Street, Birmingham B4 6AD
0121 236 9696 Fax 0121 236 9699
9-21 Princess Street, Manchester M60 8AS
0161 834 7201 Fax 0161 833 0634
16 Arthur Street, Belfast BT1 4GD
028 9023 8451 Fax 028 9023 5401
18-19 High Street, Cardiff CF10 1PT
029 2039 5548 Fax 029 2038 4347
71 Lothian Road, Edinburgh EH3 9AZ
0870 606 5566 Fax 0870 606 5588

TSO Accredited Agents
(See Yellow Pages)

and through good booksellers

The Navy List is compiled and published by order of the Defence Council for the convenience of the Naval Service, but as errors may occasionally occur the Council must expressly reserve the right to determine the status of any Officer according to the actual circumstances of the case, independently of any entry in the Navy List

By Command of the Defence Council,

KEVIN TEBBIT

Printed in the United Kingdom for TSO
N118948 C17 11/02

PREFACE

The Navy List is on sale to the public and is published annually in July or as soon as possible thereafter. The Navy List of Retired Officers, also on sale to the public, is published separately and biennially in August.

This edition of the Navy List has been produced largely from the information held in the Naval Manpower Management Information System and is corrected to include those promotions, appointments etc. promulgated on or before 9 April 2002 as becoming effective on or before 30 June 2002. Section one is corrected as far as possible, up to the date of going to press.

Serving officers who notice errors or omissions in Sections 2 and 3 of the List should complete the form found on the final page of the Navy List and forward it to their Appointer. Other errors or omissions should be brought to the attention of the Editor of the Navy List. Any other reader who notices errors or omissions is invited to write to:

> Mrs Mary-Jane Carvil
> The Editor of the Navy List
> NMA Portsmouth
> Room 115
> Victory Building
> HM Naval Base
> Portsmouth
> Hampshire
> PO1 3LS

quoting the page(s) in question. Every effort will be made to include corrections and omissions received by the Editor before 28 March 2003. Regrettably, letters cannot be acknowledged.

Officers who succeed to peerages, baronetcies or courtesy titles should notify their appointer so that their computer records can be updated and the changes reflected in the Navy List. The degrees shown after Active Service Officers' names are not necessarily a complete list of those held, but are generally confined to degrees of an honorary nature conferred specially upon an Officer, and those that are so related to the professional duties of an Officer as to give some indication of his professional qualifications.

The master Allowance List for the free distribution of the Navy List is controlled by the Editor. DSDC(L) at Llangennech is responsible for the issue of this publication strictly according to the Allowance List. Units are asked to ensure that the Editor and DSDC(L) are informed of any reduction in requirement. Requests for additional copies and amendment to the master Allowance List should be addressed to DSDC(L) at Llangennech (using RN Form 53001(Demand for Naval Books)). Firmly attached to this demand should be a letter addressed to the Editor with a clear supporting case.

CONTENTS

CONTENTS

Her Majesty The Queen

LORD HIGH ADMIRAL OF THE UNITED KINGDOM 1964

MEMBERS OF THE ROYAL FAMILY

HIS ROYAL HIGHNESS PRINCE PHILIP THE DUKE OF EDINBURGH KG, KT, OM, GBE, AC, QSO

Admiral of the Fleet	15 Jan 53
Captain General Royal Marines	1 Jun 53
Admiral of the Fleet Royal Australian Navy	1 Apr 54
Admiral of the Fleet Royal New Zealand Navy	15 Jan 53
Admiral of the Royal Canadian Sea Cadets	15 Jan 53

HIS ROYAL HIGHNESS THE PRINCE OF WALES KG, KT, GCB, AK, QSO, ADC

Rear Admiral .... 14 Nov 98

HIS ROYAL HIGHNESS THE DUKE OF YORK CVO, ADC
Admiral of the Sea Cadet Corps .... 11 May 92

Commander Royal Navy .... 27 Apr 99

HER ROYAL HIGHNESS THE PRINCESS ROYAL KG, GCVO, QSO

Rear Admiral Chief Commandant for Women in the Royal Navy .... 1 Nov 93

HIS ROYAL HIGHNESS PRINCE MICHAEL OF KENT KCVO

Honorary Commodore Royal Naval Reserve .... 1 Apr 94

HER ROYAL HIGHNESS PRINCESS ALEXANDRA THE HON LADY OGILVY GCVO

Patron, Queen Alexandra's Royal Naval Nursing Service .... 12 Nov 55

VICE ADMIRAL OF THE UNITED KINGDOM AND LIEUTENANT OF
THE ADMIRALTY
Admiral Sir Jeremy Black GBE, KCB, DSO

REAR ADMIRAL OF THE UNITED KINGDOM
Admiral Sir Kenneth Eaton GBE, KCB

PERSONAL AIDES-DE-CAMP TO THE QUEEN
Rear Admiral His Royal Highness The Prince of Wales KG, KT, GCB, AK, QSO, ADC
Commander His Royal Highness The Duke of York CVO, ADC

FIRST AND PRINCIPAL NAVAL AIDE-DE-CAMP TO THE QUEEN

Admiral Sir Alan West KCB, DSC, ADC .... 30 Nov 00

FLAG AIDE-DE-CAMP TO THE QUEEN

Vice Admiral Sir Peter Spencer KCB, ADC .... 19 Jan 00

NAVAL AND MARINE AIDES-DE-CAMP TO THE QUEEN

Captain R.F.Cheadle (Commodore)	Appointed	25 May 00	Seniority	30 Jun 93
Captain S.R.J.Goodall (Commodore)	Appointed	10 Jan 00	Seniority	31 Dec 93
Captain R.P. Boissier (Commodore)	Appointed	28 Sep 00	Seniority	30 Jun 94
Captain M.J.Holmes (Commodore)	Appointed	13 Oct 00	Seniority	30 Jun 94
Captain R.S. Ainsley (Commodore)	Appointed	02 Nov 01	Seniority	31 Dec 94
Captain A.J.G. Miller (Commodore)	Appointed	30 Nov 01	Seniority	31 Dec 94
Captain P.L. Wilcocks (Commodore)	Appointed	30 Jan 02	Seniority	31 Jun 95
Captain H.R. Whitaker (Commodore)	Appointed	08 Jan 02	Seniority	31 Dec 95
Brigadier J.B. Dutton	Appointed	10 May 02	Seniority	31 Dec 98

EXTRA NAVAL AND MARINE EQUERRIES TO THE QUEEN

Vice Admiral Sir James Weatherall KCB, KCVO
Vice Admiral T Blackburn CB LVO
Lieutenant General Sir John Richards KCB, KCVO
Rear Admiral Sir Richard Trowbridge KCVO
Rear Admiral Sir Paul Greening GCVO
Rear Admiral Sir John Garnier KCVO, CBE
Rear Admiral Sir Robert Woodard KCVO
Commodore A.J.C.Morrow CVO Royal Navy

NAVAL AND MARINE RESERVE AIDES-DE-CAMP TO THE QUEEN

Commodore G.N.Wood JP, RD*, ADC	Appointed	28 Oct 99	Seniority	28 Oct 99
Captain A.C.Adams RD, ADC	Appointed	30 Sept 99	Seniority	30 Sep 99
Colonel P. A. Jobbins OBE, RD*, ADC	Appointed	6 Mar 01	Seniority	20 Jan 94
Commodore J.A. Ellis RD, RNR	Appointed	19 Nov 01	Seniority	8 Nov 01

HONORARY CHAPLAINS TO THE QUEEN

The Reverend A.T.Maze BSc
The Reverend Monsignor T.M.Burns SM, VG, BA, BD, MBIM
The Reverend B.K.Hammett MA

HONORARY PHYSICIANS TO THE QUEEN

Surgeon Commodore G.H.G.McMillan OStJ, MB BCH, FFOM, FRCP, FICSH, MRCP(UK) MD, QHP
Surgeon Commodore N.E.Baldock MB BS, FFOM, Dip Av Med, FRCP, QHP
Surgeon Commodore C.W. Evans, MB BS, MRCS LRCP, MFOM, MPH, DIH, DTMH, RCDS, QHP
Surgeon Rear Admiral R.D.Curr MB BS, DObst RCOG, FRCGP, AKC, QHP

HONORARY SURGEONS TO THE QUEEN

Surgeon Vice Admiral I.L.Jenkins CVO, OStJ, MB BCH, FRCS, QHS
Surgeon Captain M.A.Farquharson-Roberts MB BS, OStJ, FRCS, QHS

HONORARY DENTAL SURGEON TO THE QUEEN

Surgeon Commodore (D) J. Hargraves MSc, BDS, DGDP(UK), LDS RCS(Eng)

NAVAL RESERVE
HONORARY PHYSICIAN TO THE QUEEN

Surgeon Captain N.R.J.Hooper RD*, QHP

HONORARY NURSING SISTER TO THE QUEEN

Captain J.C.Brown ARRC, QHNS, QARNNS

HONORARY OFFICERS IN HER MAJESTY'S FLEET

ADMIRAL

His Majesty King Karl XVI Gustav of Sweden KG .... 25 Jun 75

His Majesty Sultan Haji Hassanal Bolkiah Mu'izzaddin Waddaulah Sultan and Yang Di-pertuan of Brunei Darussalam GCB, GCMG .... 2 Aug 01

HONORARY OFFICERS IN HER MAJESTY'S ROYAL MARINES

COLONEL

His Majesty King Harald V of Norway GCVO .... 18 Mar 81

THE DEFENCE COUNCIL

Chairman

THE RIGHT HONOURABLE GEOFF HOON MP

(Secretary of State for Defence)

THE RIGHT HONOURABLE ADAM INGRAM MP

(Minister of State for the Armed Forces)

LORD BACH

(Parlimentary Under Secretary of State and Minister for Defence Procurement)

DOCTOR LEWIS MOONIE MP

(Parliamentary Under-Secretary of State for Defence)

ADMIRAL SIR MICHAEL BOYCE GCB, OBE, ADC

(Chief of Defence Staff)

SIR KEVIN TEBBIT

(Permanent Under-Secretary of State)

ADMIRAL SIR ALAN WEST KCB, DSC, ADC

(First Sea Lord and Chief of the Naval Staff)

GENERAL SIR MICHAEL WALKER GCB, CMG, CBE, ADC Gen

(Chief of the General Staff)

AIR CHIEF MARSHAL SIR PETER SQUIRE GCB, DFC, AFC, ADC, DSc, FRAeS

(Chief of the Air Staff)

AIR CHIEF MARSHALL SIR ANTHONY BAGNALL KCB, OBE, FRAeS

(Vice Chief of the Defence Staff)

SIR ROBERT WALMSLEY KCB, FREng

(Chief of Defence Procurement)

PROFESSOR SIR KEITH O'NIONS FRS

(Chief Scientific Adviser)

MR IAN ANDREWS CBE, TD

(Second Permanent Under-Secretary of State)

AIR CHIEF MARSHAL SIR MALCOLM PLEDGER KCB, OBE, AFC, BSc, FRAeS

(Chief of Defence Logistics)

THE ADMIRALTY BOARD

Chairman

THE RIGHT HONOURABLE GEOFF HOON MP

(Secretary of State for Defence)

(Chairman of the Defence Council and Chairman of the

Admiralty Board of the Defence Council)

THE RIGHT HONORABLE ADAM INGRAM MP

(Minister of State for the Armed Forces)

LORD BACH

(Parlimentary Under Secretary of State and Minister for Defence Procurement)

DOCTOR LEWIS MOONIE MP

(Parliamentary Under-Secretary of State for Defence)

ADMIRAL SIR ALAN WEST KCB, DSC, ADC

(First Sea Lord and Chief of the Naval Staff)

ADMIRAL SIR JONATHON BAND KCB

(Commander in Chief Fleet)

VICE ADMIRAL SIR PETER SPENCER KCB, ADC

(Second Sea Lord and Commander in Chief Naval Home Command)

REAR ADMIRAL NIGEL C F GUILD

(Controller of the Navy)

REAR ADMIRAL TIM P MCCLEMENT OBE

(Assistant Chief of Naval Staff)

REAR ADMIRAL JONATHON REEVE

(Naval Member for Logistics)

MR IAN ANDREWS, CBE, TD

(Second Permanent Under-Secretary of State and Secretary of the Admiralty Board)

OFFICERS ON THE ACTIVE LIST
OF THE
ROYAL NAVY, THE ROYAL MARINES,
THE QUEEN ALEXANDRA'S ROYAL
NAVAL NURSING SERVICE; AND
RETIRED AND EMERGENCY OFFICERS
SERVING AND
LIST OF RFA OFFICERS' NAMES

Name	Rank	Branch	Spec	Seniority	Where Serving

A

Name	Rank	Branch	Spec	Seniority	Where Serving
Abbey, Michael Keith, MSc, CEng, MIMarEST,	CDR(FTC)	E	MESM	31.12.00	DRAKE SFM
Abbey, Michael Peter, MBE, pcea,	LT CDR(FTC)	X	P	01.10.88	750 SQN (HERON)
Abbot, Richard Leslie, BSc,	SLT(IC)	X		01.09.00	DARTMOUTH BRNC
Abbott, Charles Peregrine George, OBE, psc,	CDR(FTC)	S		30.06.84	NMA PORTSMOUTH
Abbott, David Anthony, BTech,	LT(FTC)	E	WE	24.02.95	ST ALBANS
Abbott, David,	LT RM(IC)	-	SO(LE)	01.04.00	CTCRM LYMPSTONE
Abbott, Grant Paul, MA,	LT RM(IC)	-		01.09.00	45 CDO RM
Abbot, Sir Peter (Charles) GBE, KCB, MA, rcds, pce	ADM	-		03.10.95	
Abbott, Robert James,	LT(IC)	X	ATCU/T	01.09.01	RNAS CULDROSE
Abbott, Simon Saint Clair,	LT CDR(FTC)	X	PWO(U)	01.06.92	MOD (LONDON)
Abbotts, Michael Charles, BEng,	SLT(IC)	E	ÆE	01.09.99	SULTAN
Abel, Lucy, BSc,	SLT(IC)	X		01.09.00	DARTMOUTH BRNC
Abel, Nigel Philip,	LT(CC)	X	P	16.08.96	848 SQN HERON
Abernethy, James Richard Gordon, PGDIPAN, pce,	LT CDR(FTC)	X	PWO(N)	01.08.96	MWS DRYAD
Abernethy, Lee John Francis, pce,	LT CDR(FTC)	X	PWO(C)	11.07.94	NORFOLK
Ablett, Simon David, BEng,	LT(FTC)	E	WE	01.01.98	WSA/CAPT MCTA
Abraham, Paul, pce(sm),	CDR(FTC)	X	SM	31.12.96	FOST CSST SEA
Ackerley, Richard St John, SM,	LT(IC)	X	SM	01.11.99	FWO FASLANE
Ackland, Heber Kemble, MA(OXON),	LT CDR(FTC)	S		01.11.99	JSCSC
Acland, David Daniel, pce, pcea,	LT CDR(FTC)	X	P	01.10.93	JCA IPT USA
Adair, Allan Alexander Shafto, pce, psc(a),	CAPT(FTC)	X	PWO	30.06.98	SA PARIS
Adam, Ian Kennedy, pce,	LT CDR(FTC)	X	PWO(A)	01.01.97	FLEET HQ PORTS 2
Adams, Alistair John, BSc, pce,	CDR(FTC)	X	PWO(C)	31.12.98	FOST SEA
Adams, Andrew Mark, BEng, CEng, MIMarEST,	CDR(FTC)	E	MESM	30.06.02	FOSM NWOOD HQ
Adams, Benjamin Mark,	LT(CC)	X	P	16.05.91	NELSON
Adams, Edwin Smyth, BEng,	LT(IC)	X	P	16.02.00	815 FLT 207
Adams, Geoffrey Hugh, BEng, MSc,	LT CDR(FTC)	E	ME	01.04.01	MOD (BATH)
Adams, George,	LT(FTC)	E	ME	01.05.97	FEARLESS
Adams, Ian, BA,	LT(CC)	X	P	01.11.90	RAF CRANWELL EFS
Adams, Peter Nigel Elliott, n,	LT(FTC)	X		01.07.96	MWS DRYAD
Adams, Peter, BSc, PGCE,	LT CDR(FTC)	E	TM	01.01.94	OCLC ROSYTH
Adams, Richard Anthony Skelton, BSc,	CDR(FTC)	E	MESM	30.06.92	MOD (BATH)
Adams, Richard Joseph, BEng, CEng, MIMarEST,	LT(FTC)	E	MESM	01.03.95	NP BRISTOL
Adams, William John,	LT(IC)	X	PT	01.05.02	DRAKE CBP(DLO)
Adamson, Stephen Edward,	LT(IC)	X		01.05.02	GUERNSEY
Adcock, Graham Edward,	CAPT RM(FTC)	-		01.01.01	1 ASSLT GP RM
Adlam, Gail Margaret, BA,	LT CDR(FTC)	S	BAR	01.10.00	FLEET HQ PORTS
Ager, Robin Gordon, BSc, CEng, MIMarEST, MIMechE, psc,	LT CDR(FTC)	E	ME	01.08.82	MOD (LONDON)
Agnew, Robert Le Page, BA, MPhil,	LT(IC)	X		01.09.01	MOD (LONDON)
Ahlgren, Edward Graham, SM(n), SM,	LT CDR(FTC)	X	SM	01.10.00	FOST CSST DEVPT
Aiken, Stephen Ronald, MA, pce, pce(sm), psc(j),	LT CDR(FTC)	X	SM	01.07.93	UKMARBATSTAFF
Ainscow, Anthony James,	LT(IC)	E		01.05.02	INVINCIBLE
Ainsley, Andrew Malcolm James,	LT(CC)	X		01.08.00	MANCHESTER
Ainsley, Roger Stewart, ADC, MA, (Commodore) jsdc, pce,hcsc,	CAPT(FTC)	X	AWO(A)	31.12.94	FWO PORTS SEA

Name	Rank	Branch	Spec	Seniority	Where Serving
Ainslie, Arthur Andrew, MBA, FCMI, (Act Capt) .... CDR(FTC)	S	SM	30.06.89	DA PEKING
Airey, Simon Edward, MA, jsdc, ... CDR(FTC)	S			31.12.94	MOD (LONDON)
Aitchison, Kenneth, MB, DObstRCOG, MRCGP, CHB, ... SURG CDR(SCC)	-	GMPP	04.02.96	RN GIBRALTAR
Aitken, Andrew John, BA, SM(n), SM, ... LT(FTC)	X	SM	01.09.94	SUPERB
Aitken, Kenneth Matthew, ... LT CDR(FTC)	S	(S)	01.10.96	DLO/DGDEF LOG SP
Aitken, Lee-Anne, ... SLT(IC)	X		01.01.02	MANCHESTER
Aitken, Steven Robert, MSc, ... LT(CC)	X	P	01.01.01	FLEET AV VL
Ajala, Ahmedrufai Abiodun, BEng, ... LT(FTC)	E	WE	01.09.94	RMC OF SCIENCE
Akers, Samuel John, ... MID(IC)	X		01.01.01	DARTMOUTH BRNC
Alabaster, Martin Brian, MA, MSc, rcds, psc, ... CDRE(FTC)	E	WE	30.04.02	DPA BRISTOL
Alberts, Paul William, ... LT(FTC)	E	WE	01.04.01	CORNWALL
Albon, Mark, BSc, Cert Ed, PGDip, ... LT CDR(FTC)	X	METOC	12.08.98	FLEET HQ PORTS
Albon, Ross, OBE, BSc, MBA, ... CAPT(FTC)	S	BAR	30.06.02	FLEET HQ NWD
Alcindor, David John, BSc, ... LT(CC)	X	SM	01.04.97	VENGEANCE(STBD)
Alcock, Christopher, OBE, pce, pcea, psc, ... LT(CC)	X	O	30.06.98	FLEET HQ PORTS
Alderson, Richard James, BSc, ... CAPT RM(CC)	-	P U/T	01.05.98	CTCRM
Alderton, Paul Alexander, BSc, ... SLT(IC)	E	WE	01.01.00	PORTLAND
Alderwick, Jason Royston Claude, BA, ... LT(IC)	X	HM2	01.12.99	SCOTT
Aldous, Benjamin Walker, LLB, ... LT(FTC)	X		01.11.99	WALNEY
Aldous, Robert James, ... SLT(IC)	X	ATCU/T	01.01.01	RAF SHAWBURY
Aldridge, Dean, ... LT(IC)	X	P U/T	01.05.01	RNAS YEOVILTON
Aldwinckle, Terence William, ... LT CDR(MCC)	Q	IC	01.10.01	RH HASLAR
Alexander, Amy, BA, ... LT(IC)	E	WE	01.09.99	MWS COLLINGWOOD
Alexander, Emma Jayne, ... SLT(IC)	X		01.05.00	MANCHESTER
Alexander, Giles David, BSc, ... CAPT RM(FTC)	-		01.05.99	NBC PORTSMOUTH
Alexander, Oliver Douglas Dudley, ... LT(CC)	X	MCD	01.11.97	DARTMOUTH BRNC
Alexander, Phillip Michael Duncan, MEng, ... LT(FTC)	E	MESM	01.01.01	SULTAN
Alexander, Robert Stuart, MA, pce, pcea, psc, ... CDR(FTC)	X	P	30.06.99	ILLUSTRIOUS
Alexander, Stephen James, ... CDR(FTC)	E	WESM	01.10.93	NEPTUNE SWS
Alison, Lynn Alexander, ... LT CDR(FTC)	E	WE	01.10.94	FLEET HQ PORTS
Allan, Chris Ruthven, BSc, ... LT(FTC)	X		01.09.98	MARLBOROUGH
Allan, Fraser, ... 2LT(IC)	-		01.09.98	CTCRM LYMPSTONE
Allan, Nicholas Simon John, BSc, ... SLT(IC)	S		01.01.01	DARTMOUTH BRNC
Allan, Robert William, ... MID(IC)	X		01.01.01	RALEIGH
Allcock, Edward Charles, (Act Surg Lt) .... SURG SLT(SCC)	-		10.07.01	DARTMOUTH BRNC
Allen, Anthony David, PGDIPAN, pce, ... LT CDR(FTC)	X	PWO(N)	01.02.98	MWS DRYAD
Allen, David Peter, ... LT(FTC)	E	WE	15.06.90	MWS DRYAD
Allen, David Robert, BEng, AMIEE, ... LT(FTC)	E	WE	01.11.95	EXCHANGE CANADA
Allen, Douglas James Keith, BEng, ... LT(CC)	X	P	16.01.94	MWS COLLINGWOOD
Allen, Leslie Bernard, ... LT(CC)	X	MW	01.10.92	RALEIGH
Allen, Patrick Lyons, pce, pcea, ... LT CDR(FTC)	X	O	01.06.99	SUTHERLAND
Allen, Paul Miles, ... LT(FTC)	X	O	01.05.91	815 SQN HQ
Allen, Richard Mark, pce(sm), ... CDR(FTC)	X	SM	30.06.99	MOD (LONDON)
Allen, Richard, pce(sm), SM(n), SM, ... LT CDR(FTC)	X	SM	20.07.99	FLEET HQ PORTS 2
Allen, Stephen Michael, pce, pcea, ... LT CDR(FTC)	X	O	01.12.97	820 SQN
Allfree, Joseph, BA, ... LT(FTC)	X		01.01.95	DARTMOUTH BRNC
Allibon, Mark Christopher, pce, psc(j), ... CDR(FTC)	X	PWO(A)	30.06.00	MOD (LONDON)
Allison, Aubrey Stuart Crawford, MSc, MB, BS, MRCGP,.SURGCDR(FCC) LRCP,MRCS,AFOM,psc	-	GMPP	30.06.91	MOD (LONDON)
Allison, Glenn, ... LT(CC)	X	P	16.11.94	815 FLT 246
Allison, Kenneth Richard, MBE, ... MAJ(FTC)	-		25.04.96	HQ NORTH
Allkins, Helen Louise, BSc, ... LT CDR(FCC)	Q	ACC/EM	31.12.97	DMTO HQ
Allsford, Karen Marie, BA, ... LT(CC)	S		01.12.97	2SL/CNH FOTR
Allsop, Alistair Roos Lonsdale, BA, MB, BCh, ... SURG LT(FCC) DipIMC RCSED,	-		05.08.98	MODHU DERRIFORD
Allwood, Christopher, BSc, PGCE, adp, (Act Capt) .... CDR(FTC)	E	IS	31.12.93	RMCS SHRIVENHAM
Almond, David Edwin Magor, BA, psc, ... LT CDR(FTC)	S		01.07.89	CSSG (SEA)
Alsop, Sweyn Hamish, ... LT(CC)	X	P	01.12.98	771 SQN
Alston, Richard, BA, ... LT RM(IC)	-		01.09.00	45 CDO RM
Ambler, Kerry Kirsten, BA, (Act Lt Cdr) .... LT(CC)	W	C	04.04.91	MOD (LONDON)
Ambrose, Rachel, (Act Surg Lt) .... SURG SLT(SCC)	-		15.07.01	DARTMOUTH BRNC
Ames, Jeremy Peter, BD, AKC, ... CHAPLAIN	CE		19.06.75	RH HASLAR

Name	Rank	Branch	Spec	Seniority	Where Serving
Ames, Karen Margaret Mary, LLB,	LT(IC)	S		01.10.99	NMA GOSPORT
Amey, John Miles, BA,	LT(IC)	X		01.09.98	NORFOLK
Ameye, Christopher Robin, pce, psc(j)o,	CDR(FTC)	X	MCD	31.12.97	MWS DEF DIV SCHL
Amorosi, Riccardo Guy Filippo Luigi,	SLT(UCE)(IC)	E	ME	01.09.01	DARTMOUTH BRNC
Amos, Julian Harvey James,	MAJ(FTC)	-		01.09.98	CTCRM
Amphlett, Nigel Gavin, BSc, MA, pce, pcea, psc(j),	LT CDR(FTC)	X	O	01.05.95	MOD (LONDON)
Ancona, Simon James, MA, pce, pcea, psc,	CDR(FTC)	X	O	30.06.98	MOD (LONDON)
Anderson, Andrew,	SLT(IC)	X	ATC	01.05.00	RNAS CULDROSE
Anderson, Christopher John, IEng, MIIE,	LT(IC)	E	WE	13.04.01	KENT
Anderson, Fraser Boyd, BSc,	LT CDR(FTC)	X	O	01.10.93	700M MERLIN OEU
Anderson, Garry Stephen, SM(n), SM,	LT(IC)	X	SM	01.10.98	SUPERB
Anderson, Hugh Alastair, LLB,	CDR(FTC)	S	BAR	30.06.02	RNP TEAM
Anderson, Lindsy Claire,	SLT(UCE)(FTC)	E	WE	01.09.00	DARTMOUTH BRNC
Anderson, Lynne Ann, BComm,	SLT(IC)	X		01.09.99	YORK
Anderson, Mark Edgar John, BSc,	LT(FTC)	X		01.12.97	SUTHERLAND
Anderson, Mark, BSc, pce, pce(sm),	CAPT(FTC)	X	SM	31.12.99	MWS DRYAD
Anderson, Melvin John,	CDR(FTC)	S	(S)	01.10.96	RN GIBRALTAR
Anderson, Robert Gordon, MSc, AMIEE, psc,	CDR(FTC)	E	WE	31.12.95	MOD (LONDON)
Anderson, Stephen Ronald,	LT(CC)	X	O	01.08.00	815 FLT 214
Anderson, Steven Thomas,	MAJ(FTC)	-	SO(LE)	01.10.96	CTCRM
Anderson, Stuart Christopher, pcea,	LT CDR(CC)	X	P	01.10.99	DHFS
Anderton, Simon William, BDS,	SG LT(D)(SCC)	-		06.09.99	40 CDO RM
Andrew, Peter, BEng,	LT(CC)	E	MESM	01.01.00	SULTAN
Andrew, William George, psc, pce,	CDR(FTC)	X	PWO(A)	30.06.93	STG BRISTOL
Andrews, Charles John, BSc,	LT(CC)	X	P	01.05.00	RNAS YEOVILTON
Andrews, Christopher, BSc,	LT(IC)	E	IS	01.05.00	RNEAWC
Andrews, Dominic Michel,	SLT(IC)	E	WE	01.05.00	DARTMOUTH BRNC
Andrews, Iain Stuart, DipEd,	LT(IC)	X		01.09.01	MWS DRYAD
Andrews, Ian,	LT CDR(FTC)	E	MESM	01.10.95	SPARTAN
Andrews, Justin Pierre,	LT(IC)	E	WE	01.05.02	DARTMOUTH BRNC
Andrews, Paul Nicholas, pce,	LT CDR(FTC)	X	PWO(A)	01.06.94	NEPTUNE
Aniyi, Christopher Bamidele Jost, BEng, MSc,	LT CDR(FTC)	E	ME	01.10.00	JSCSC
Ankah, Gregory Kofi Esiaw, BEng,	LT(FTC)	E	ME	01.12.96	SULTAN
Annett, Ian Gordon, BEng, MSc, FRGS, MIEE, gw,	CDR(FTC)	E	WE	30.06.02	JSCSC
Ansell, Christopher Neil, BA, SM, SM(n),	LT(CC)	X		01.01.99	SUPERB
Anstey, Robert James, pce(sm), pce, SM(n), SM,	LT CDR(FTC)	X	SM	01.05.98	FOST CSST SEA
Antcliffe, Graham Albert, BSc, CEng, MIEE,	CDR(FTC)	E	WESM	31.12.89	DRAKE NBSD
Anthony, Derek James, MBE, jsdc, pce, pce(sm), hcsc,	RADM	-	SM	08.08.00	FOSNNI/NBC CLYDE
Anthony, Nicholas Mark Kenwood, MBE, MA, MCGI, psc(j), mdtc,	LT COL(FTC)	-	LC	30.06.01	539 ASSLT SQN RM
Antrobus, Stuart Ronald, BEM,	LT(IC)	X	AV	05.08.01	JS PHOT SCHOOL
Aplin, Adrian Trevor, MBE, MCIT, MILT,	CDR(FTC)	S		30.06.02	JSCSC
Appelquist, Paul, BSc,	LT CDR(FTC)	E	WESM	01.10.99	SOVEREIGN
Appleyard, Timothy Paul, MA, MNI, MRIN, psc,	LT CDR(FTC)	X	FC	05.06.88	RNAS YEOVILTON
Archdale, Peter Mervyn,	LT CDR(FTC)	X	PWO(U)	16.03.85	NEPTUNE
Archer, Graham William, BEng,	CDR(FTC)	E	AE	30.06.02	JHCHQ
Archer, Timothy,	2LT(IC)	-		01.09.98	CTCRM LYMPSTONE
Archibald, Brian Robert, BSc, pce, psc(j),	CDR(FTC)	X	PWO(A)	30.06.94	WSA BRISTOL
Arden, Victoria Grace,	LT(FTC)	X	P U/T	01.07.97	845 SQN
Arding, Nicholas Miles Bennett, BSc, MA, psc,	LT COL(FTC)	-		30.06.98	CDO LOG REGT RM
Arend, Faye Marie, BA,	LT(FTC)	S		01.01.99	SACLANT USA
Argent-Hall, Dominic, BSc, psc, CEng, MIEE,	CDR(FTC)	E	WE	30.06.00	MOD (LONDON)
Arkle, Nicholas James, BA,	LT(CC)	X	P	01.04.99	801 SQN
Armour, Graeme Alexander, psc(j),	MAJ(FTC)	-		01.05.99	RM WARMINSTER
Armstrong, Charles Albert, pce, psc(a),	CDR(FTC)	X	PWO(U)	31.12.91	QHM CLYDE
Armstrong, Colin David,	LT(IC)	X		01.09.00	CUMBERLAND
Armstrong, David Morgan, BA,	SLT(IC)	X		01.01.01	DARTMOUTH BRNC
Armstrong, Euan McAlpine, MB, ChB,	SURG LTCDR(MCC)	-		05.02.02	MODHU DERRIFORD
Armstrong, Maxine Anne,	LT(SCC)	Q	REGM	28.04.97	RN GIBRALTAR
Armstrong, Neil Stanley,	LT(IC)	X	P	01.07.96	GANNET SAR FLT
Armstrong, Nicholas Peter Bruce, pcea, gdas,	LT CDR(FTC)	X	O	01.10.96	LOAN JTEG BSC DN
Armstrong, Roger Ian, psc(m),	LT COL(FTC)	-		31.12.92	MWC SOUTHWICK

Name	Rank	Branch	Spec	Seniority	Where Serving
Armstrong, Rory James, BSc,	SLT(IC)	X		01.01.00	BLYTH
Armstrong, Scott Thomas,	LT(FTC)	X	P	16.08.95	848 SQN HERON
Armstrong, Siobhan,	LT CDR(CC)	W		01.10.00	ES AIR BRISTOL
Armstrong, Stuart McAlpine, BSc, SM, SM(n),	LT(FTC)	X		01.09.00	VIGILANT(PORT)
Arnall-Culliford, Nigel David, AFC, MRAeS, psc, tp,	CDR(FTC)	X	P	01.10.92	FLEET AV VL
Arnell, Stephen John,	LT CDR(FTC)	E	WE	01.10.98	MWS COLLINGWOOD
Arnold, Andrew Stewart,	LT(FTC)	S	(W)	17.12.93	AFPAA(CENTURION)
Arnold, Bruce William Henry, MEng, MSc, CEng, MIMechE,	CDR(FTC)	E	MESM	31.12.92	MOD (BATH)
Arthur, Andrew Warren, BSc, CEng, MIMarEST, MIMechE,	LT CDR(CC)	E	ME	15.03.02	DRAKE SFM
Arthur, Calum Hugh Charles, MB, ChB,	SURG LT(SCC)	-		01.08.01	CTCRM
Arthur, Iain Davidson, pce(sm),	CDR(FTC)	X	SM	30.06.94	FOSM NWOOD OPS
Arwynck, Luke,	2LT(IC)	-		01.09.98	CTCRM LYMPSTONE
Asbridge, Jonathan Ian, MILT,	LT CDR(FTC)	S	SM	16.11.97	ENDURANCE
Ash, Timothy Claudius Vincent,	LT CDR(FTC)	X	MW	01.10.99	JSCSC
Ashby, Keith John, BEng,	LT(CC)	E	WE	01.09.97	RALEIGH
Ashby, Maxine Kim,	LT(CC)	S		01.12.97	ARGYLL
Ashby, Philip James Conyers, QGM, BSc,	MAJ(FTC)	-	MLDR	01.09.99	RMCS SHRIVENHAM
Ashcroft, Adam Charles, MA, pce, pcea, psc(j),	CDR(FTC)	X	P	31.12.00	MANCHESTER
Ashcroft, Christopher, pce,	CDR(FTC)	X	MW	30.06.01	MOD (LONDON)
Ashley, Paul David,	LT(IC)	S		01.05.00	JMOTS NORTHWOOD
Ashlin, James Matthew, BSc,	LT(IC)	X	P	16.09.98	846 SQN
Ashman, Rodney Guy, ACMA,	LT CDR(FTC)	S	CMA	28.02.00	MOD (LONDON)
Ashmore, Sir Edward, (Beckwith), GCB, DSC,	ADM OF FLEET	-		09.02.77	
Ashton Jones, Geraint, MSc, PGCE,	LT CDR(FTC)	E	IS	01.10.96	NMA PORTSMOUTH
Ashton, James, BEng,	SLT(IC)	E	ME	01.09.99	SULTAN
Ashton, Richard Eric, MA, MD, MB, BCh, FRCP,	SURG CDR(FCC)	-	(CK)	31.12.85	RH HASLAR
Ashton, Roy David,	LT CDR(FTC)	E	WE	01.10.96	SFM PORTSMOUTH
Ashworth, Helen Joanne, BEng,	LT(FTC)	E	ME	01.12.96	SFM PORTSMOUTH
Aspden, Andrew Mark, BA, pce, pcea, psc(j),	LT CDR(FTC)	X	O	01.12.95	FLEET HQ PORTS 2
Asquith, Simon Phillip, SM(n), SM,	LT(FTC)	X	SM	01.06.95	TIRELESS
Astle, Dawn Sandra,	LT(CC)	X	FC	01.12.98	JSCSC
Aston, James Alexander, BEng,	LT(IC)	E	TM	01.01.00	DEF SCH OF LANG
Aston, Mark William, BDS, MSc, MGDS RCS,	SGCDR(D)(FCC)	-		30.06.97	SULTAN
Athayde Banazol, Claire Victoria Norsworthy De, ACIS,	LT CDR(FTC)	S		04.04.99	FLEET HQ PORTS
Atherton, Bruce William,	CAPT RM(CC)	-	P	01.09.97	847 SQN
Atherton, Martin John, MA, psc(j),	CDR(FTC)	S		31.12.97	MOD (BATH)
Atkins, Ian, BEng, MSc, CEng, MIMarEST,	LT CDR(FTC)	E	ME	01.07.00	CORNWALL
Atkins, Paul Ronald,	SLT(IC)	E	MESM	01.05.00	DARTMOUTH BRNC
Atkinson, Charlotte Penelope, BSc,	LT(FTC)	X	H2	01.04.95	EXCHANGE N ZLAND
Atkinson, Garth Carson, BSc,	LT(FTC)	X	MW	01.02.92	FOST MPV(SEA)
Atkinson, Ian Neville,	LT(CC)	S		01.04.91	CALEDONIA DLO
Atkinson, Lee Vickerman,	LT(IC)	X		01.05.02	MANCHESTER
Atkinson, Mark, pce,	LT CDR(FTC)	X	MCD	01.02.96	ATHERSTONE
Atkinson, Neil Craig,	CAPT RM(FTC)	-		01.05.00	CTCRM
Atkinson, Penelope Ann, MB, ChB,	SURG LTCDR(MCC)	-		01.08.01	NELSON (PAY)
Atkinson, Richard Jonathan,	LT(FTC)	X	FC	01.07.96	MWS DRYAD
Atkinson, Simon Reay, BSc, MPhil, CEng,MIEE,MRIN, Eur Ing,	CDR(FTC)	E	WE	30.06.00	MOD (LONDON)
Atwill, John William Owen,	LT(CC)	S		22.10.98	RALEIGH
Aubrey-Rees, Adam William, BSc,	LT CDR(FTC)	E	WE	16.04.84	HQ DCSA
Auld, Douglas Martin, BEng,	LT(CC)	E	MESM	01.01.98	SPARTAN
Austen, Richard Mark,	LT(FTC)	S	(W)	08.04.94	FWO DEVONPORT
Austin, John Damien, BTech,	LT CDR(FTC)	X		01.10.92	ILLUSTRIOUS
Austin, Peter Nigel, BSc, BA(OU), IEng, MIIE.	LT CDR(FTC)	E	WESM	09.01.01	VIGILANT(PORT)
Austin, Simon Alexander,	MID(UCE)(IC)	X		01.09.01	CUMBERLAND
Austin, Stephen Timothy, MSc,	LT(FTC)	E	ME	01.05.00	MOD (BATH)
Austin, Stewart John, MBE, MA, psc,	LT CDR(FTC)	S	CMA	16.12.82	MOD (LONDON)
Auty, Stephen John, BSc, FRMS, MinstP, (Commodore) ARCS, rcds, jsdc, psc,	CAPT(FTC)	X	METOC	30.06.95	MOD(LONDON)
Avery, Malcolm Byrne, BSc, MRINA, (Act Cdre) pce, pce(sm), psc,	CAPT(FTC)	X	SM	31.12.97	SHAPE BELGIUM
Avison, Matthew James, pcea,	LT CDR(FTC)	X	O	01.10.99	MWC PORTSDOWN
Axcell, Matthew Frederick, BSc,	LT RM(IC)	-		01.09.00	CTCRM LYMPSTONE

Name	Rank	Branch	Spec	Seniority	Where Serving
Axon, David Brian, pce,	LT CDR(FTC)	X	AAWO	01.07.98	RAMSEY
Ayers, Dominic Edwin Bodkin, BA, MB, BS, MRCS,	SURG LTCDR(MCC)	-		03.08.00	NELSON (PAY)
Ayers, Richard Peter Beedom, BSc, CEng, MIEE, psc,	CDR(FTC)	E	WE	31.12.92	SA COPENHAGEN
Aylott, Peter Richard Frank Dobson, MA, PGDIPAN, pce, n,	LT CDR(FTC)	X	PWO(N)	29.01.00	OCEAN
Ayres, Christopher Paul, BSc, pce, psc, psc(j),	CDR(FTC)	X	PWO(U)	30.06.96	RNAS CULDROSE
Ayrton, Robert Edward,	SLT(IC)	X		01.09.99	ROEBUCK

B

Name	Rank	Branch	Spec	Seniority	Where Serving
Babbington, Peter Murray, CBE, MC, nadc, psc,	Lt Col	-	A/TK	30.06.86	FLEET HQ PORTS
Backhouse, Anthony Wynter, BSc, psc, odc(Aus),	CDR(FTC)	S	SM	31.12.90	JHQ SOUTHCENT
Backus, Alexander Kirkwood, OBE, jsdc, pce,	RADM	-	AWO(A)	07.09.99	FLEET HQ PORTS
Backus, Robert Ian Kirkwood, BEng,	LT(FTC)	X	P	01.03.96	814 SQN
Baden, James Martin, MB, BS, BDS, BMS, FDS RCPSGlas,	SURG LT(SCC)	-		02.08.00	40 CDO RM
Badrock, Bruce, n,	LT CDR(FTC)	X	H CH	05.07.98	MOD (LONDON)
Baggaley, Jason Antony Lloyd, BSc, MIEE,	LT CDR(FTC)	E	WE	01.10.01	T45 IPT
Bagnall, Sally Anne Elizabeth, BSc,	LT(SCC)	Q		28.05.96	RCDM
Bagshaw, Edward Frank, BSc,	LT(IC)	X		01.04.00	SPARTAN
Bagshaw, James Richard William, BA,	LT(CC)	X		01.09.98	MWS DRYAD
Bagworth, Joanna Frances, BSc,	LT(FTC)	S		01.07.96	NELSON
Baileff, Roger Ian, pce,	LT CDR(FTC)	X	PWO(U)	01.12.89	MOD (LONDON)
Bailes, Kenneth Peter, BA,	LT(IC)	X		01.09.00	LEDBURY
Bailey, Anthony Mark Savile, psc(m), (Act Lt Col)	MAJ(FTC)	-		01.08.82	FLEET HQ PORTS
Bailey, Daniel Standfast, (Act Maj)	CAPT RM(FTC)	-		01.09.96	FLEET HQ PORTS 2
Bailey, Ian John,	SLT(UCE)(FTC)	E	WE	01.09.00	DARTMOUTH BRNC
Bailey, James Walter, CEng, FIMarEST,	CDR(FTC)	E	ME	31.12.91	MOD (BATH)
Bailey, Jeremy James, BEng,	LT(FTC)	E	ME	01.01.96	SULTAN
Bailey, John, pce,	CDR(FTC)	X	PWO(U)	30.06.89	JSSU OAKLEY
Bailey, Jonathan James, BEng,	MAJ(FTC)	-		01.09.00	42 CDO RM
Bailey, Sian, BSc, PGCE,	LT(IC)	E	TM	01.08.99	NELSON RNSETT
Bailey, Timothy David,	SLT(IC)	E	WE	01.01.00	EXETER
Bailie, Dennis James, MSc, CEng, MRAeS, jsdc, gw,	CDR(FTC)	E	AE	31.12.87	FLEET HQ NWD
Baillie, Robbie William, BSc, PGCE,	LT(IC)	E	TM	01.05.00	SULTAN
Bain, David Iain,	MAJ(FTC)	-	SO(LE)	01.10.00	FPGRM
Bainbridge, John,	LT(IC)	X		30.06.98	MWS DRYAD
Bainbridge, Stuart Darryl,	LT(CC)	X	P	01.03.95	824 SQN
Baines, Andrew Richard, BSc,	LT(CC)	X	P	01.07.97	846 SQN
Baines, David Michael Llewellyn, BSc,	LT CDR(FTC)	E	IS	01.10.01	AGRIPPA AFSOUTH
Baines, Gary Anthony,	CAPT RM(FTC)	-	SO(LE)	01.01.01	CDO LOG REGT RM
Bains, Baldeep Singh, MB, ChB,	SURG LT(SCC)	-		01.08.01	CFLT MED(SEA)
Baird, George Mitchell,	SLT(IC)	X	P U/T	01.09.00	DARTMOUTH BRNC
Baker, Adrian Bruce, MB, ChB, DipAvMed,	SURG CDR(FCC)	-	GMPP	30.06.94	NELSON (PAY)
Baker, Adrian Paul, BEng, pcea,	LT CDR(FTC)	X	O	01.11.99	815 SQN HQ
Baker, Graham Reginald,	LT CDR(FTC)	E	ME	15.01.88	SFM PORTSMOUTH
Baker, James Edward Gunn, BA, MPhil,	SLT(IC)	X		01.09.00	DARTMOUTH BRNC
Baker, Kenneth, MSc, OStJ,	CDR(FTC)	MS	(RGN)	01.10.97	FORT BLOCKHOUSE
Baker, Michael Benson, BA,	CAPT RM(CC)	-	P U/T	01.09.98	847 SQN
Baker, Michael John, BEng, CEng, MIEE,	LT CDR(FTC)	E	WE	01.06.98	MONMOUTH
Baker, Nicholas James,	LT(FTC)	S	(W)	20.09.99	CUMBERLAND
Baker, Peter Guest, Eur Ing, BSc, CEng, MIEE,	CDR(FTC)	E	WE	30.06.00	MOD (LONDON)
Bakewell, Timothy David,	MAJ(FTC)	-		01.09.00	JSCSC
Balcombe, Jeremy Stephen, BEng,	LT(CC)	E	AE	01.09.94	LOAN DSTL
Baldie, Steven Anthony Hamilton, BEng,	LT(IC)	X	P	01.05.99	846 SQN
Baldock, Nicolas Edwin, QHP, MB, (Commodore) ChB, FRCP, FFOM, MRCS, DipAvMed,	SURG CAPT(FCC)	-	(CO/M)	1.12.92	INM ALVERSTOKE
Baldwin, Christopher Martin, BA,	LT CDR(FTC)	X	MCD	01.03.95	MWS DRYAD
Baldwin, Simon Frederic, BSc, psc,	CAPT(FTC)	E	AE	31.12.99	ES AIR YEO
Balhetchet, Adrian Stephen, BEng,	LT CDR(FTC)	E	AE	01.03.00	ES AIR BRISTOL
Ball, Andrew David, SM(n),	LT(IC)	X		01.01.99	CUMBERLAND
Ball, Matthew Peter, BEng,	LT(CC)	E	MESM	01.12.99	SUPERB
Ball, Michael Peter, BSc, MIEE, CEng,	LT CDR(FTC)	E	WESM	01.09.91	MOD (BATH)
Ball, Stephen James, (Act Lt Cdr)	LT(FTC)	E	ME	13.02.92	NORTHUMBERLAND

Name	Rank	Branch	Spec	Seniority	Where Serving
Ball, Ursula Elizabeth,	SLT(IC)	S		01.01.01	DARTMOUTH BRNC
Ball, William John Edgar,	SLT(IC)	E	ME	01.05.00	SULTAN
Ballantyne, Craig,	LT(IC)	X		01.05.02	TRIUMPH
Ballard, Adam Paul Vince,	SLT(IC)	X		01.09.01	TYNE
Ballard, Mark Lewis, BEng, MIEE, CEng,	LT CDR(FTC)	E	WESM	01.12.00	MWS COLLINGWOOD
Ballard, Stephen Alexis,	CAPT RM(FTC)	-		01.09.96	UKLFCSG RM
Baller, Charles Rupert, MSc,	LT CDR(FTC)	E	ME	01.06.01	MOD (BATH)
Balletta, Rene James, n,	LT(FTC)	X		01.11.96	FOST MPV(SEA)
Balm, Stephen Victor, psc(a),	LT COL(FTC)	-	LC	30.06.92	RHQ AFNORTH
Balmer, Anthony Victor, MB, BS, BSc, MRCGP, DA, DipAvMed,	SURG CDR(FCC)	-	GMPP	31.12.93	SULTAN
Balmer, Guy Austin,	MAJ(FTC)	-		24.04.02	847 SQN
Balston, David Charles William, BA, pce, pce(sm), psc,	CDR(FTC)	X	SM	30.06.97	VENGEANCE(PORT)
Bamforth, Christian John Milton, BEng,	LT(FTC)	E	WESM	01.12.97	SOVEREIGN
Bance, Nicholas David, BSc,	LT(FTC)	X	P	16.02.89	RNAS YEOVILTON
Band, James Wright, BEng, psc(j),	LT CDR(FTC)	E	AE	01.09.98	845 SQN
Band, *Sir* Jonathon, KCB, BA, jsdc, pce, hcsc,	ADM	-	PWO	11.01.00	FLEET HQ NWD
Bane, Nicholas St John, BEng,	LT(IC)	X	P U/T	01.01.01	RNAS YEOVILTON
Banham, Alexander William Debower, BEng,	LT(CC)	E	AE	01.12.97	RNAS CULDROSE
Bankier, Stewart,	LT CDR(FTC)	X		19.02.96	QHM CLYDE
Banks, Matthew Charles, BSc,	LT(IC)	X		01.05.00	EDINBURGH
Banks, Morven Janet, BSc,	SLT(IC)	X		01.01.01	DARTMOUTH BRNC
Bannister, Andrew Neil,	LT CDR(FTC)	E	WE	01.10.01	MWS COLLINGWOOD
Bannister, Jonathan,	SLT(IC)	X		01.04.00	ATHERSTONE
Barber, Christopher James Harrison, BA,	LT(CC)	X	O	01.02.95	EXCHANGE RAF UK
Barber, Mark, BSc,	SLT(IC)	X	P U/T	01.09.00	DARTMOUTH BRNC
Barber, Ralph Warwick, BA,	LT(IC)	S		01.04.96	RNAS CULDROSE
Barclay, John Harrison Buchanan, BSc, CEng,	LT CDR(FTC)	E	AE	01.05.91	FLEET HQ PORTS
Barfoot, Peter Michael, BSc,	SLT(IC)	X		01.09.00	DARTMOUTH BRNC
Bark, Alexander Martyn, BSc, pce, n,	LT CDR(FTC)	X	PWO(C)	01.11.98	FLEET HQ NWD
Bark, James Spencer, pce(sm), SM,	LT CDR(FTC)	X	SM	01.09.96	SCEPTRE
Barker, Charles Philip Geoffrey, MB, BS, MS, FRCS, FICS, DipTh, GB,	SURG CAPT(FCC)	-	(CGS)	30.06.01	NELSON (PAY)
Barker, David Charles Kingston, pce, pcea,	CDR(FTC)	X	O	30.06.01	ST ALBANS
Barker, John Edward,	LT(CS)RM(CAS)	-		01.05.98	DNR EC 2
Barker, John Wilson, MBE,	LT CDR(FTC)	X	O	01.10.99	LYNX OEU
Barker, Nicholas James, MA, pce, pcea, psc,	LT CDR(FTC)	X	P	01.05.90	LOAN OMAN
Barker, Paul David, BEng,	LT(FTC)	E	P U/T	01.04.00	DHFS
Barker, Piers Thomas, BSc, pce(sm), SM,	LT CDR(FTC)	X	SM	01.04.97	FLEET HQ PORTS 2
Barker, Richard Demetrious John, OBE, MA, pce, pce(sm), psc(j),	CDR(FTC)	X	SM	30.06.97	MOD (LONDON)
Barker, Ruth,	SURG SLT(SCC)	-		01.07.01	DARTMOUTH BRNC
Barker, Timothy John,	LT(CC)	X	O	16.10.99	771 SQN
Barker, Victoria, (Act Surg Lt)	SURG SLT(MDC)	-		11.07.01	DARTMOUTH BRNC
Barlow, Bruce Michael,	LT(CC)	X		01.12.00	CATTISTOCK
Barlow, David, BA,	CHAPLAIN	CE		04.04.78	MWS DRYAD
Barlow, Martin John,	LT(FTC)	X	O	01.03.97	EXCHANGE USA
Barnard, Toby James, BEng,	LT(IC)	X	P U/T	01.01.02	DHFS
Barnbrook, Jeremy Charles, pcea,	LT CDR(FTC)	X	P	16.12.96	FOST SEA
Barnes, James Richard,	LT CDR(FTC)	X	AAWO	01.08.99	EXETER
Barnes, Nicholas John,	SLT(IC)	S		01.05.00	RALEIGH
Barnes, Patrick Alan Lambeth, BSc,	LT(CC)	X	P	01.04.94	847 SQN
Barnes, Paul Illingworth,	LT(CC)	X		01.08.00	INVINCIBLE
Barnes, Rex Warwick, psc,	LT COL(FTC)	-	LC	31.12.00	FLEET HQ NWD
Barnes-Yallowley, Jonathan James Hugh, pce, pcea,	LT CDR(FTC)	X	P	16.07.92	MWC SOUTHWICK
Barnett, Alan Clive, BA, MSc,	LT CDR(FTC)	E	AE	01.02.02	HARRIER IPT
Barnwell, Alan,	CAPT RM(IC)	-	SO(LE)	21.07.01	847 SQN
Barnwell, Keith Leigh, GCIS,	LT CDR(FTC)	S		23.04.91	WSA BRISTOL
Barnwell, Nicholas Andrew Michael,	SLT(IC)	X		01.05.00	ARK ROYAL
Barr, Calum Alexander, BEng,	SLT(IC)	E	ME U/T	01.09.00	LANCASTER
Barr, David Jonathan,	MID(IC)	X		01.09.00	IRON DUKE
Barr, Derek Desmond,	LT(IC)	E	AE	01.04.02	DARTMOUTH BRNC

Name	Rank	Branch	Spec	Seniority	Where Serving
Barr, Simon Peter, BSc,	LT(IC)	X	P	01.09.99	845 SQN
Barraclough, Carole Denise,	LT(FTC)	X	REG	24.07.97	2SL/CNH FOTR
Barrand, Stuart Martin, pce,	CDR(FTC)	X	AAWO	30.06.02	FLEET HQ PORTS
Barratt, Stephen Mitchell,	LT(FTC)	S	(W)	03.04.97	MOD (LONDON)
Barrett, David Leonard, IEng, MIIE,	LT CDR(FTC)	E	AE(M)	01.10.01	SULTAN
Barrett, Samantha Jane, BA,	SLT(IC)	S		01.05.00	ILLUSTRIOUS
Barrett, Scott,	SLT(IC)	X	SM	01.01.01	DARTMOUTH BRNC
Barrett, Stephen James,	LT CDR(FTC)	E	WE	01.10.99	MOD (LONDON)
Barrick, Paul Vincent,	LT CDR(FTC)	X	EW	01.10.98	FLEET HQ NWD
Barritt, Michael Kenneth, MA, FNI, FRGS, rcds, jsdc,	CAPT(FTC)	X	H CH	30.06.96	FWO DEVONPORT
Barritt, Olivier David, BA,	LT(IC)	X		01.04.00	MWS RNHMS CULD
Barron, Jeremy Mark,	LT(IC)	E	WE U/T	01.05.01	DARTMOUTH BRNC
Barron, Patrick Joseph, BSc,	LT CDR(FTC)	X	C	01.10.00	UKMARBATSTAFF
Barron, Philip Robert,	SLT(IC)	X	O U/T	01.01.01	702 SQN HERON
Barrow, Charles Michael,	LT(IC)	X		01.01.02	MWS DRYAD
Barrows, David Malcolm, BEng,	LT(FTC)	E	WE	01.06.95	WSA BRISTOL
Barrows, Susan Mary, BEng,	LT(FTC)	E	WE	01.04.96	WSA BRISTOL
Barry, John Peter,	LT(FTC)	X	MW	11.10.94	QUORN
Bartholomew, David John, BSc,	LT(IC)	E	TM	01.05.00	SULTAN
Bartholomew, Ian Munro, ARICS, psc,	CDR(FTC)	X	H CH	31.12.92	SVHO IPT
Bartlett, David Stephen George, BSc,	LT CDR(FTC)	E	AE(P)	01.03.97	RNAS CULDROSE
Bartlett, Ian David, BEng, MSc,	LT CDR(FTC)	E	MESM	01.01.98	TURBULENT
Bartlett, Mark John, BEng,	LT(FTC)	E	WE	01.05.98	WSA BRISTOL
Bartley, David James, BSc,	LT RM(IC)	-		01.09.00	42 CDO RM
Barton, Jane Emmeline, BSc,	LT(CC)	X	HM	01.03.99	RNAS CULDROSE
Barton, Keith Jeffrey Atkinson, BEng, MSc,	LT(CC)	E	P U/T	01.03.99	DHFS
Barton, Mark Alfred, BEng, CEng, MIMechE, MRINA,	LT CDR(FTC)	E	ME	01.07.00	EXETER
Barton, Peter Glenn, MSc,	CDR(FTC)	E	WE	30.06.99	OCEAN
Barton, Sarah Jane, MB, BS,	SURG LT(MCC)	-		04.08.99	RALEIGH
Barton, Timothy John, pce, psc, (Commodore)	CAPT(FTC)	X	AWO(U)	30.06.94	NMA PORTSMOUTH
Bartram, Gregory James,	LT(IC)	X	WE	01.05.02	DARTMOUTH BRNC
Bartram, Richard James,	LT(CC)	X	P	01.04.01	702 SQN HERON
Bass, Andrew Simon, BA,	SLT(IC)	X	P U/T	01.05.00	DARTMOUTH BRNC
Bass, Paul William,	SLT(IC)	E	WESM	01.01.00	RALEIGH
Bassett, Dean Anthony, BA, AMNI, n,	LT(FTC)	X		01.11.95	MOD (LONDON)
Bassett, Neil Edward,	LT CDR(FTC)	E	WE	01.10.99	MWS COLLINGWOOD
Basson, Andrew Paul, MSc, MDA, psc,	CDR(FTC)	E	TM	30.06.00	SULTAN
Bastiaens, Paul Alexander,	LT(IC)	X	AE	01.05.02	DARTMOUTH BRNC
Bate, Christopher,	LT CDR(FTC)	X	PT	01.10.93	NELSON
Bate, David Ian George,	LT CDR(FTC)	X	MCD	01.10.95	FLEET HQ PORTS 2
Bateman, Richard Michael, MB, ChB,	SURG LTCDR(MCC)	-		02.08.00	NELSON (PAY)
Bateman, Stephen John Francis,	CDR(FTC)	X	AAWO	30.06.93	LOAN OMAN
Bates, Andrew James, BSc,	LT(CC)	X	P	16.04.98	824 SQN
Bates, Nicholas Stuart, BSc,	LT(IC)	X	O	01.04.00	CAMPBELTOWN FLT
Bath, Edward George,	LT CDR(FTC)	X	AAWO	27.12.95	EXCHANGE CANADA
Bath, Michael Anthony William, BSc,	CDR(FTC)	S	SM	30.06.00	JSCSC
Batho, William Nicholas Pakenham, pce, psc,	CAPT(FTC)	X	AWO(A)	31.12.95	JSU NORTHWOOD
Bathurst, Sir (David) Benjamin, GCB, DL, rcds,	ADM OF FLEET	-	P	10.07.95	
Batten, Andrew John, BEng,	LT(FTC)	E	WE	19.02.93	ARK ROYAL
Battrick, Richard Robert,	LT(FTC)	X	MCD	01.04.96	MWS DRYAD
Baudains, David Percival, pce, psc, psc(j),	CDR(FTC)	X	O	30.06.87	FLEET HQ PORTS
Baudains, Terence John, BSc, pce,	LT CDR(FTC)	X	P	01.04.89	2SL/CNH FOTR
Baum, Stuart Richard, BSc, pce, pce(sm),	CDR(FTC)	X	SM	30.06.97	ASM IPT
Baverstock, Andrew Peter,	SLT(IC)	X	AV	01.10.99	JARIC
Baxendale, Adrian Graham, BEng,	SLT(IC)	X		01.01.01	DARTMOUTH BRNC
Baxendale, Robert Fred, BSc,	MAJ(FTC)	-		01.09.99	FLEET HQ NWD
Baxendale, Rodney Douglas, BA, DipTh,	CHAPLAIN	CE		14.07.83	DRAKE CBP(CNH)
Baxter, Arran Charles,	LT(IC)	E	MESM	01.05.02	TRENCHANT
Baxter, Frederick Joseph,	LT(FTC)	E	AE(L)	29.04.01	EXCHANGE GERMANY
Baxter, Graham Francis, nadc, pce,	CAPT(FTC)	X	AAWO	31.12.96	UKNMR SHAPE
Baxter, Iain Menzies, BEng, CEng, MRAeS,	LT CDR(FTC)	E	AE	01.01.00	ES AIR WYTON
Baxter, John Charles, SM,	LT(FTC)	X	SM	27.09.95	FLEET CIS PORTS

Name	Rank	Branch	Spec	Seniority	Where Serving
Bayntun, David Andrew, BSc,	SLT(IC)	X		01.05.00	ARGYLL
Beacham, Philip Robert, BA,	LT(FTC)	X	P	01.07.95	824 SQN
Beadle, John Thomas,	CHAPLAIN	SF		30.03.95	DRAKE CBP(CNH)
Beadling, David John,	LT(IC)	E	MESM	01.09.01	VENGEANCE(PORT)
Beadnell, Robert M, MSc,	LT(CC)	E	TM	01.01.92	MWS COLLINGWOOD
Beadon, Colin John Alexander, MBE, psc(a),	LT COL(FTC)	-		30.06.94	EXCHANGE USA
Beadsmoore, Emma Jane, MB, BS,	SURG LT(MCC)	-		06.08.97	MODHU DERRIFORD
Beadsmoore, Jonathan Edgar, pce, n,	LT CDR(FTC)	X	AAWO	01.02.98	FOST SEA
Beale, Michael Dean,	LT(FTC)	X	MCD	23.07.98	WALNEY
Beales, Nicola Susan,	SLT(IC)	S		01.01.00	SUTHERLAND
Beanland, Peter Louis, BSc,	LT(CC)	X		01.06.00	GRIMSBY
Beard, David John, MB, ChB,	SURG LT(SCC)	-		01.08.01	NEPTUNE NT
Beard, Graham Thomas Charles, BA, psc,	CDR(FTC)	S		31.12.98	ELANT/NAVNORTH
Beard, Hugh Dominic, pce(sm), pce, SM(n), SM,	LT CDR(FTC)	X	SM	01.09.99	VENGEANCE(PORT)
Beard, Richard Geoffrey,	LT(FTC)	X	C	10.12.98	CMSG IPT
Beard, Stephen Anthony,	SLT(IC)	X		01.01.01	DARTMOUTH BRNC
Beardall, John, MA, psc,	CDR(FTC)	X	REG	01.10.97	NMA PORTSMOUTH
Beardall, Michael John Doodson, pce,	LT CDR(FTC)	X	AAWO	01.09.95	JSCSC
Beare, Amanda Louise,	LT(SCC)	Q	IC	10.10.97	MODHU Derriford
Bearne, Jeremy Peter, pce, psc,	CDR(FTC)	X	PWO(U)	31.12.90	2SL/CNH FOTR
Beats, Kevan Ashley, pce,	LT CDR(FTC)	X	PWO(U)	16.02.90	FOST DPORT SHORE
Beattie, Kathryn Elizabeth, MSc,	LT(IC)	E	TM	01.01.00	SULTAN
Beattie, Michael Ross, BA,	SLT(IC)	X	O U/T	01.01.01	DARTMOUTH BRNC
Beattie, Paul Spencer, pce, n,	LT CDR(FTC)	X	PWO(A)	01.10.01	MWS DRYAD
Beaumont, Ian Hirst, pce, pcea,	CDR(FTC)	X	O	31.12.95	NMA PORTSMOUTH
Beaumont, Steven John,	LT CDR(FTC)	X	C	01.10.00	LOAN DSTL
Beautyman, Andrew John, BEng,	LT(FTC)	E	MESM	01.09.94	MOD (BATH)
Beaver, Robert Mark Steven, BSc, AMIMechE,	LT(CC)	E	ME	01.05.98	MOD (BATH)
Beavis, John Alexander, BSc,	LT(CC)	X		01.04.99	MWS DRYAD
Beazley, Phillip, sq,	MAJ(FTC)	-	SO(LE)	01.10.99	45 CDO RM
Beck, Simon Kingsley, pce,	LT CDR(FTC)	X	PWO(A)	01.04.99	SOUTHAMPTON
Becker, Robert Keith, BA,	SLT(IC)	X		01.05.00	SHOREHAM
Beckett, Keith Andrew, BSc, MDA,	CDR(FTC)	E	MESM	31.12.97	NP BRISTOL
Bedding, Darren, BA,	LT(IC)	X	P	01.06.00	FLEET AV VALLEY
Bedding, Simon William Edward, BEng, CEng, MIEE,	LT CDR(FTC)	E	WE	01.04.00	EDINBURGH
Bedelle, Stephen James,	LT(FTC)	E	WE	19.02.93	MWS COLLINGWOOD
Beech, Christopher Martin, pce,	LT CDR(FTC)	X	PWO(C)	01.07.98	JMOTS NORTHWOOD
Beech, Daymion John, BSc,	LT(CC)	X	P	16.03.98	820 SQN
Beedle, James Daniel Stephen,	MID(IC)	X		01.01.01	EXC BRISTOL
Beegan, Clive Francis, SM,	LT(IC)	X		01.01.02	FLEET HQ NWD
Beirne, Stephen,	LT(IC)	X	O	01.06.91	750 SQN SEAHAWK
Bell, Adrian Scott, pce, psc,	CAPT(FTC)	X	PWO(U)	30.06.02	MOD (LONDON)
Bell, Andrew Dawson, BSc, CEng, MRAeS,	CDR(FTC)	E	AE(P)	31.12.89	HQ NORTH
Bell, Catriona Mary, BSc,	LT(CC)	X		01.02.99	PORTLAND
Bell, Darrel Patrick,	LT CDR(FTC)	E	AE(L)	01.10.00	ES AIR YEO
Bell, Douglas William Alexander, BA,	MAJ(FTC)	-	MLDR	26.04.97	HQBF CYPRUS
Bell, Fiona Jean,	SLT(UCE)(IC)	E	ME	01.09.01	DARTMOUTH BRNC
Bell, Jeffrey Mark, BEng, CEng, MRAeS,	LT(FTC)	E	AE	01.05.96	HARRIER IPT
Bell, Lucy Jane,	LT(IC)	S		01.05.02	RALEIGH
Bell, Mark,	LT CDR(FTC)	S	SM	01.10.00	RICHMOND
Bell, Reginald Paul William,	LT CDR(FTC)	X	AAWO	01.10.90	MWS DRYAD
Bell, Robert Douglas, pce,	LT CDR(FTC)	X	PWO(U)	01.03.97	SDG PLYMOUTH
Bell, Scott William, MinstAM,	LT(FTC)	S	(W)	01.04.01	FLEET HQ PORTS
Bell-Davies, Richard William, BSc, pce, psc,	CDR(FTC)	X	PWO(U)	30.06.93	SACLANT USA
Bellfield, Robert James Astley, pce,	LT CDR(FTC)	X	PWO(U)	01.07.96	SUTHERLAND
Benarr, Christopher Michael,	SLT(UCE)(IC)	X		01.09.00	DARTMOUTH BRNC
Benbow, James Alexander Kennedy,	SLT(IC)	X		01.01.01	DARTMOUTH BRNC
Bence, David Elliott, pce,	LT CDR(FTC)	X	MCD	01.02.98	FLEET HQ PORTS 2
Benfell, Niall Andrew,	LT(FTC)	S	(S)	02.05.00	JSCSC
Benn, Stephen William, BEng, MAPM, MSc, CEng, MRAeS,	LT(FTC)	E	AE	01.01.95	899 SQN HERON
Bennet, George,	2LT(IC)	-		01.09.98	CTCRM LYMPSTONE
Bennett, Alan Reginald Courtenay, DSC, jsdc, pce, pcea, psc,	CAPT(FTC)	X	P	30.06.98	JHCHQ

Name	Rank	Branch	Spec	Seniority	Where Serving
Bennett, Anthony John,	LT CDR(FTC)	S	(W)	01.10.97	MWS COLLINGWOOD
Bennett, Christopher David, BSc,	LT(IC)	X	P	01.08.00	ARK ROYAL
Bennett, Douglas Prasad, BEng,	LT(IC)	E	IS	01.05.97	CINCFLEET FIMU
Bennett, Gavin,	SLT(IC)	MS		01.05.00	RH HASLAR
Bennett, Graham Lingley Nepean, pce,	LT CDR(FTC)	X	PWO(U)	01.07.93	FLEET HQ PORTS 2
Bennett, Ian David, BA,	SLT(IC)	X	P U/T	01.05.00	DARTMOUTH BRNC
Bennett, Mark Anthony, BEng,	SLT(IC)	E	WE	01.01.01	DARTMOUTH BRNC
Bennett, Neil Malcolm, BA, psc, psc(j)o,	MAJ(FTC)	-	C	01.09.96	FLEET HQ PORTS 2
Bennett, Paul Martin, BA, pce,	CDR(FTC)	X	PWO(A)	30.06.98	MOD (LONDON)
Bennett, Stephen Harry Guy, OBE, psc,	CDR(FTC)	X	H CH	31.12.86	RNLO GULF
Bennett, Stuart Albin Frances James, MB, BS,	SURG LT(SCC)	-		01.08.01	NEPTUNE NT
Bennett, William Dean, SM,	LT CDR(FTC)	X	C	01.10.00	AGRIPPA NAVSOUTH
Bennett, William Ellis, MEng,	LT(IC)	E	ME	01.09.00	ARK ROYAL
Bennetts, Neil,	LT(FTC)	X	C	03.04.97	JSCSC
Benson, Melanie Mercedes,	SLT(IC)	X		01.01.01	DARTMOUTH BRNC
Benson, Richard Austin, BEng,	LT(IC)	X		01.02.99	MWS DRYAD
Benstead, Neil William John, BEng,	LT(FTC)	E	ME	01.04.98	SULTAN
Bentham-Green, Nicholas Richard Heriot, psc,	MAJ(FTC)	-	LC	01.09.92	CDO LOG REGT RM
Bentley, David Alan, (Act Lt Cdr)	LT(FTC)	X	g	06.09.85	MWS DRYAD
Benton, Angus Michael, BSc,	LT CDR(FTC)	X	MCD	01.09.96	AGRIPPA AFSOUTH
Benton, Peter John, MB, BCh, FFOM,	SURG CDR(FCC)	-	(CO/M)	31.12.93	EXCHANGE USA
Benzie, Nichol James Emslie, BSc,	LT(IC)	X	P	01.10.98	845 SQN
Beresford-Green, Paul Maxwell,	LT CDR(FTC)	S		16.12.00	FLEET HQ PORTS
Berisford, Andrew William, LLB,	LT(FTC)	S	SM	01.06.97	MOD (LONDON)
Bernard, Alain Raymond, BA,	LT(IC)	X	H2	01.04.97	NP 1008 OFS SVY
Bernau, Jeremy Charles, pce, pce(sm), SM,	LT CDR(FTC)	X	SM	01.11.91	FWO FASLANE
Berry, James Thomas, BSc,	SLT(IC)	X	P U/T	01.09.00	DARTMOUTH BRNC
Berry, Paul,	LT CDR(FTC)	E	ME	01.10.00	FEARLESS
Berry, Steven Mark,	LT(IC)	E	WE	01.01.02	YORK
Berry, Timothy James, BSc,	LT(IC)	X		01.09.98	CHATHAM
Bessell, David Alexander, BA, SM(n), SM,	LT CDR(FTC)	X	SM	01.06.01	SOVEREIGN
Best, Peter, pdm, (Act Maj)	CAPT RM(FTC)	BS		01.01.98	MWS RM SCH MUSIC
Best, Robert Michael, BSc,	SLT(IC)	E	ME	01.09.99	SULTAN
Best, Russell Richard, OBE, BA, pce, psc,	CAPT(FTC)	X	PWO(U)	30.06.01	FLEET HQ PORTS 2
Bestwick, Michael Charles,	MAJ(FTC)	-		01.05.01	JSCSC
Betteridge, Jeremy Trevor, MCMI, pce, pcea, psc,	CDR(FTC)	X	P	30.06.96	SULTAN
Bettles, John,	SLT(IC)	X		01.09.00	ARK ROYAL
Betton, Andrew, BA, pce, pcea,	LT CDR(FTC)	X	O	01.02.99	GRAFTON
Betts, Andrew Thomas James,	MID(UCE)(IC)	E	AE U/T	01.09.01	NEWCASTLE
Bevan, Jeffrey Richard,	LT(CC)	X	P	16.12.99	824 SQN
Bevan, Noel Stuart, MB, BS, MRCGP, LRCP, MRCS,	SURG CAPT(FCC)	-	GMPP	31.12.99	DRAKE CBP(DLO)
Bevan, Simon, BSc, MBA, jsdc,	CDR(FTC)	X	METOC	31.12.93	SACLANT USA
Beveridge, Simon Alexander Ronald,	CHAPLAIN	CE		28.04.93	CTCRM
Beverstock, Mark Alistair, BSc, CEng, MIEE, (Act Capt)	CDR(FTC)	E	WESM	30.06.96	WSA BRISTOL
Bevis, Timothy John, psc,	LT COL(FTC)	-		31.12.98	45 CDO RM
Bewick, David John, pce, psc(j),	CDR(FTC)	X	PWO(U)	30.06.02	MCM3 SEA
Bewley, Nicholas John,	LT(FTC)	X	FC	01.08.99	ARK ROYAL
Bhattacharya, Debdash, BSc,	LT(FTC)	X	P	16.06.90	771 SQN
Bibbey, Mark William, BA, psc(m),	COL(FTC)	-		31.12.00	FLEET HQ PORTS 2
Bickley, Gary Neil,	SLT(IC)	X		01.01.00	LEDBURY
Biggs, Colin Richard,	LT CDR(FTC)	E	MESM	01.10.98	FLEET HQ PORTS
Biggs, David Michael, pcea, BSc,	LT CDR(FTC)	X	O	01.10.96	849 SQN B FLT
Biggs, Peter,	LT(IC)	X		01.05.02	SHETLAND
Biggs, William Patrick Lowther, BEng, MSc, MIEE,	LT CDR(FTC)	E	WE	01.04.98	MONTROSE
Bignell, Stephen, BEng,	LT CDR(FTC)	E	WE	01.04.00	MWS COLLINGWOOD
Billington, Nigel Stephen, BA, psc,	LT CDR(FTC)	S	SM	01.02.88	FLEET HQ PORTS
Billington, Sam, BEng,	LT(IC)	E	MESM	01.09.01	SULTAN
Billington, Tony John,	LT CDR(FTC)	X	EW	01.10.00	JSSU DIGBY
Bilson, John Michael Frederick, pce,	LT CDR(FTC)	X	AAWO	01.01.93	EXCHANGE USA
Bing, Neil Adrian, BSc,	LT(CC)	X	P	16.12.99	RAF LINTN/OUSE
Bingham, Alexander Anthony John, MEng,	SLT(IC)	E	ME U/T	01.05.00	MOD (BATH)
Bingham, David Spencer,	LT CDR(FTC)	X	PWO(A)	01.03.99	MWS DRYAD

Name	Rank	Branch	Spec	Seniority	Where Serving
Binns, John Brendon Harold, OBE, MSc, (Act Capt) FIMarEST, MINucE, jsdc,	CDR(FTC)	E	MESM	31.12.88	DRAKE CBS
Binns, John Richard,	LT(IC)	E	WE	01.01.02	GLASGOW
Binns, Jon Frank, BA,	LT(IC)	X		01.05.01	SHEFFIELD
Binns, Jonathan Brian, MSc, CEng, MIMarEST,	CDR(FTC)	E	MESM	30.06.87	ASM IPT
Binstead, Kenneth Nigel,	LT(CC)	X	P	01.02.93	848 SQN HERON
Birbeck, Keith,	LT CDR(FTC)	E	WESM	01.10.98	TALENT
Birch, Peter Laurence, BEng,	SLT(IC)	X	P U/T	01.01.00	RAF CRANWELL EFS
Birchall, James Charles, BSc,	LT(CC)	X	P	01.09.98	AACC MID WALLOP
Birchall, Stephen John, BSc, CEng, MIMarEST,	CDR(FTC)	E	MESM	30.06.02	MOD (BATH)
Bird, David Edward, pcea,	LT CDR(FTC)	X	P	01.10.93	DHFS
Bird, Gary Michael, BA,	CAPT RM(CC)	-		01.09.99	CDO LOG REGT RM
Bird, Jonathan Michael, BEng, pcea,	LT(CC)	X	O	01.05.92	RNAS CULDROSE
Bird, Matthew Graham James, BEng, CEng,MRAeS, (Act Lt Cdr)	LT(FTC)	E	AE	01.11.94	EXCHANGE USA
Bird, Richard Alexander James, n, PGDIP,	LT CDR(FTC)	X	H CH	01.07.98	ECHO
Bird, Toby Samuel Varnam, MA,	LT(IC)	E	TM	01.09.98	SULTAN
Birkin, Kay,	SLT(IC)	MS		01.01.01	NEPTUNE DLO
Birleson, Paul Denzil, BSc,	LT(FTC)	X		01.09.99	ECHO
Birley, Jonathan Hugh, pce,	LT CDR(FTC)	X	PWO(U)	01.05.95	LOAN DSTL
Birrell, Gavin Craig, BSc, MA,	LT(FTC)	X		01.07.97	PJHQ
Birrell, Stuart Martin, MA, psc(j),	MAJ(FTC)	-		01.09.96	42 CDO RM
Birse, Bronwen Louise,	LT(CC)	S		01.12.94	NELSON
Birse, Gregor James, BA, MSc, PGDip,	LT(FTC)	X	METOC	01.05.92	MWS DRYAD
Birt, David Jonathan, MB, BS, FRCA,	SURG CDR(FCC)	-	(CA)	30.06.01	ILLUSTRIOUS
Bishop, George Charles,	LT(FTC)	X	AV	27.07.95	FLEET CMSA UK
Bishop, Paul Richard, BSc, MIMechE, AMRAeS, (Act Capt)	CDR(FTC)	E	AE	30.06.93	HARRIER IPT
Bishop, Robert Johnstone, MNI, pce, psc,	CDR(FTC)	X	PWO(U)	31.12.91	DRAKE RELEASE
Bissett, Ian Michael,	LT CDR(FTC)	E	AE(L)	01.10.00	EXCHANGE AUSTLIA
Bissett, Phillip Keith, BSc,	LT CDR(FTC)	E	AE(L)	01.10.00	ES AIR YEO
Bissett, Roger William,	LT(FTC)	E	AE(L)	17.10.91	HARRIER IPT
Bisson, Ian Jean Paul, MSc, CEng, MIEE, psc, gw,	CDR(FTC)	X	WE	30.06.99	T45 IPT
Bithell, Ian Stephen,	LT CDR(FTC)	X	ATC	01.10.00	FLEET AV VL SEA
Black, Edward John, BA, MA(CANTAB),	LT(IC)	X		01.01.02	MARLBOROUGH
Black, Jeremy James McLaren, BA, pcea,	LT CDR(FTC)	X	P	01.02.01	MOD (LONDON)
Black, Joanna Mary, BSc,	SLT(IC)	X		01.01.00	PEMBROKE
Black, Sarah Beth, MA,	LT(IC)	S		01.10.99	GRAFTON
Blackburn, Andrew Roland James, BEng,	LT(FTC)	E	AE	01.12.98	JSCSC
Blackburn, Craig Jonathan,	SLT(IC)	X		01.09.01	QUORN
Blackburn, Lee Richard, BEng,	LT(FTC)	E	ME	01.09.00	MANCHESTER
Blackburn, Stephen Anthony, BSc, CEng, MIMarEST,	LT CDR(FTC)	E	ME	01.03.98	MOD (BATH)
Blackburn, Stuart James, SM(n), SM,	LT CDR(FTC)	X	SM	01.05.02	MWC PORTSDOWN
Blackett, Jeffrey, (Act Cdre)	CAPT(FTC)	S	BAR	30.06.98	2SL/CNH
Blackett, William Philip Harry,	MID(UCE)(IC)	X		01.09.01	EXETER
Blackham, *Sir* Jeremy, (Joe), KCB, BA, rcds, pce, psc,	VADM	-	D	24.06.97	MOD (LONDON)
Blackler, Steven, BSc,	LT(IC)	E	TM	01.01.01	DARTMOUTH BRNC
Blacklock, James Francis,	LT(FTC)	X	MW	26.04.99	BRIDPORT
Blackman, Nicholas Trevor, BSc, MA, CEng, MIEE, psc(j),	LT CDR(FTC)	E	AE	01.01.94	SULTAN
Blackmore, James, BSc,	LT(CC)	X	P	16.04.98	800 SQN
Blackmore, Mark Stuart, pce, pcea, psc(j),	CDR(FTC)	X	O	30.06.02	SACLANT USA(SEA)
Blackwell, Jason Mark,	LT(IC)	X	ATC	16.01.98	CHFHQ
Blackwell, Richard Edward,	LT CDR(FTC)	S	SM	01.12.96	RNAS CULDROSE
Blacow, Carl, BEng, CEng, MIMarEST,	LT CDR(FTC)	E	ME	24.04.02	EXCHANGE CANADA
Blair, Duncan Guy Sanderman, MB, BCh, MRCGP, DipFFP,	SURG LTCDR(FCC)	-	GMPP	01.08.97	NELSON (PAY)
Blair, Graeme John Livingston, BEng,	LT(FTC)	E	MESM	01.05.96	FLEET HQ NWD
Blair, Samuel Raymond, MSc, pce,	LT CDR(FTC)	X	N	01.05.86	NBC PORTSMOUTH
Blake, Gary Edmund, BSc,	CDR(FTC)	E	WESM	30.06.00	FWO DEVPT SEA
Blake, Matthew George,	MID(IC)	X		01.05.00	IRON DUKE
Blakeley, Anne Louise,	LT(SCC)	Q	CC	17.11.98	MODHU DERRIFORD
Blakey, Adrian Lawrence,	LT CDR(FTC)	X	MCD	01.03.92	RN GIBRALTAR
Blanchford, Daniel, BEng,	CAPT RM(FTC)	-		01.09.96	ASC WATCHFIELD

Name	Rank	Branch	Spec	Seniority	Where Serving
Bland, Christopher David, MEng, AMIEE,	LT(IC)	E	WESM	01.09.01	CSST RNSSS
Bland, Steven Aaron, MB, BSc, ChB, RCSEd,	SURG LTCDR(SCC)	-		07.08.01	NELSON (PAY)
Blethyn, Hugh Phillip, BSc,	LT(IC)	E	TM	01.01.00	MWS COLLINGWOOD
Blick, Sarah Louise,	LT(IC)	S		01.01.02	702 SQN HERON
Bligh, Sarah Louise,	SLT(IC)	X		01.05.01	MWS DRYAD
Block, Andrew William George, AMIEE, MA,	LT(FTC)	E	PWO(A)	01.07.94	MWS DRYAD
Blocke, Andrew David, (Act Lt Cdr)	LT(FTC)	MS	(AD)	04.04.96	CDO LOG REGT RM
Blois, Simon Dudley, BSc, AMIEE,	LT(FTC)	E	WE	01.04.01	MARLBOROUGH
Bloska, Robert Max,	LT(FTC)	X	EW	01.01.00	JSSU OAKLEY
Blount, Derek Raymond, BSc, CEng, MIMechE,	LT CDR(FTC)	E	MESM	01.04.94	FOST CSST SEA
Blount, Keith Edward, pce, pcea,	CDR(FTC)	X	P	31.12.00	SOMERSET
Blow, Philip Thomas, BSc,	LT(CC)	E	MESM	01.09.95	VENGEANCE(STBD)
Blowers, Michael David, pce, pcea, psc(a),	CDR(FTC)	X	O	31.12.00	FLEET HQ PORTS 2
Blunden, Jeremy Jonathan Frank, LVO, BSc, pce,	CDR(FTC)	X	PWO(N)	30.06.96	NEWCASTLE
Blyth, Michael,	CAPT RM(IC)	-		28.04.99	LN BMATT (CEE)
Blythe, James,	SLT(CC)	X		01.04.99	ARGYLL
Blythe, Paul Christopher, pce, pce(sm), SM,	LT CDR(FTC)	X	SM	01.10.99	SOVEREIGN
Blythe, Tom Stuart,	MAJ(FTC)	-	LC	01.09.00	COMAMPHIBFOR
Boakes, Philip John,	LT(IC)	E		01.05.02	EXETER
Boardman, Sarah Jane, BA,	LT(IC)	S		01.01.02	2SL/CNH
Boast, Mark Thomas, MBE, pcea, tp, (Act Cdr)	LT CDR(FTC)	X	P	01.09.89	FLEET AV VL
Boddington, Jeremy Denis Leonard, BSc, MRAeS, MDA, pcea, tp	LTCDR(FTC)	X	P	16.12.95	MERLIN IPT
Boddy, Katherine,	SURG SLT(SCC)	-		01.07.00	DARTMOUTH BRNC
Bodman, Simon Alexander, BEng,	LT(CC)	X		01.04.00	DULVERTON
Boeckx, Thomas Julius Francis, MSc,	LT(FTC)	X		01.01.00	BANGOR
Boissier, Robin Paul, ADC, MA, pce, (Commodore) pce(sm), psc,	CAPT(FTC)	X	SM	30.06.94	NBC PORTSMOUTH
Bolam, Andrew Guy, BSc, CEng, MIMarEST,	LT CDR(FTC)	E	ME	01.06.94	FLEET HQ PORTS 2
Bollen, Johanna Michelle,	LT(FTC)	S		01.01.96	MOD (LONDON)
Bolton, Jonathan Praed, BEng, CEng, MIMarEST,	LT CDR(FTC)	E	ME	01.09.99	ARGYLL
Bolton, Matthew Thomas William, BEng, MSc, CEng, MIMarEST, MIMechE,	LT CDR(FTC)	E	ME	06.02.00	NEWCASTLE
Bolton, Stephen Jack,	LT(CC)	X	P	16.10.93	EXCHANGE USA
Bond, Alan James, BEng,	LT CDR(FTC)	E	AE	09.06.00	RNAS YEOVILTON
Bond, Jason Eric, BA,	LT(IC)	X		01.05.02	MWS DRYAD
Bond, Nigel David,	CDR(FTC)	S		31.12.00	FLEET HQ PORTS 2
Bond, Robert Douglas Acton,	SLT(IC)	X	P U/T	01.09.01	DHFS
Bone, Christopher John, AMRAeS,	LT CDR(FTC)	E	AE	01.05.92	FLEET HQ PORTS
Bone, Darren Nigel, pce, psc(j),	CDR(FTC)	X	PWO(A)	31.12.99	MOD (LONDON)
Bone, Richard Charles, BSc,	LT CDR(FTC)	E	TMSM	01.05.98	RALEIGH
Bonnar, John Andrew, BEng, AMIEE,	LT CDR(FTC)	E	WE	01.06.01	WSA BRISTOL
Bonnar, Susan Mary,	LT(CC)	X	ATC	01.11.96	RNAS YEOVILTON
Bonner, Neil, BEng,	LT(FTC)	E	WESM	01.08.94	ASM IPT
Bonner, Timothy John, MB, ChB,	SURG LT(SCC)	-		09.08.01	CTCRM
Bonney, James Edward, BSc,	CAPT RM(IC)	-		01.09.01	CTCRM
Booker, Glenn Raymond,	LT CDR(FTC)	X	ATC	01.10.89	FLEET AV VL
Booker, Scott Richard,	LT(CC)	X	P	16.06.90	RAF SHAWBURY
Boon, Gareth John,	LT(IC)	X	HM	19.09.00	RFANSU (ARGUS)
Boon, Simon Edward, BSc,	SLT(IC)	S		01.09.00	DARTMOUTH BRNC
Booth, Michael Dennison, DSC, pce, psc,	CAPT(FTC)	X	P	30.06.95	BDLS CANADA
Booth, William Norman, IEng, MIEE, AMIMarEST,	LT(FTC)	E	ME	02.09.99	DRAKE SFM
Bootland, Erich Gustav, psc, (Act Capt)	CDR(FTC)	MS	(AD)	01.10.95	MOD (LONDON)
Boraston, Peter John, BSc, CEng, MIEE,	LT CDR(FTC)	E	WE	01.04.90	IA BRISTOL
Borbone, Nicholas,	LT(FTC)	X	PWO(A)	06.02.95	RICHMOND
Borland, Stuart Andrew, BSc, MA, CEng, MIEE,	CDR(FTC)	E	WE	30.06.01	NMA PORTSMOUTH
Borley, Kim John, MA, CEng, MIEE, rcds, jsdc, (Commodore)	CAPT(FTC)	E	WESM	31.12.95	FOSNNI/NBC CLYDE
Boschi, Paul Hamilton, BA,	CAPT RM(IC)	-		01.09.99	UKLFCSG RM
Bosley, Benjamin Daniel, n,	LT(FTC)	X		01.10.95	PJHQ
Bosley, Stuart Niki, BEng,	SLT(IC)	X	P U/T	01.01.00	RAF CRANWELL EFS
Bosshardt, Robert George, BSc, pce,	CDR(FTC)	X	AAWO	31.12.93	FLEET HQ PORTS
Bostock, Colin Edward,	CDR(FTC)	S		30.06.02	2SL/CNH FOTR

Name	Rank	Branch	Spec	Seniority	Where Serving
Boston, Justin, BA,	LT(CC)	E	TM	01.01.93	FLEET HQ PORTS 2
Bosustow, Antony Michael, BEng, CEng, MIEE,	LT CDR(FTC)	E	WE	01.06.98	FLEET HQ PORTS 2
Bosustow, Benjamin Francis, BEng,	LT(CC)	E	WESM	01.02.91	DCSA RADIOHQ FMR
Boswell, Daniel John, BEd,	LT(IC)	X	MW	01.03.99	BANGOR
Botterill, Hugh Walter Scott,	SLT(IC)	X		01.05.00	EDINBURGH
Botting, Neil Andrew, BSc,	SLT(IC)	X		01.09.99	ATHERSTONE
Bottomley, Steven,	LT(FTC)	E	AE(L)	06.09.96	AH IPT
Boughton, Jonathan Anthony Lee, BEng,	SLT(IC)	E	WE U/T	01.09.00	ARK ROYAL
Boughton, Timothy Frederick,	LT(CC)	X	P	01.07.97	847 SQN
Bougourd, Mark Anthony, BEng,	LT CDR(FTC)	E	AE	01.10.99	846 SQN
Boulind, Matthew Angus, LLB,	LT(IC)	X	P U/T	01.01.02	DHFS
Boullin, John Paul, BEng,	LT(IC)	X		01.09.01	RALEIGH
Boulton, Neil Andrew, BSc,	LT CDR(CC)	E	TM	20.11.98	RALEIGH
Bourn, Kelvin Edward, BSc, psc(a),	LT CDR(FTC)	X	PWO(N)	09.05.85	STG BRISTOL
Bourne, Christopher Michael, pce,	LT CDR(FTC)	X	O	16.08.97	LINDISFARNE
Bourne, Donald Sidney,	LT CDR(FTC)	E	AE(L)	01.10.98	CHFHQ(SHORE)
Bouyac, David Roger Louis, (Act Maj)	CAPT RM(FTC)	-	SO(LE)	01.01.96	42 CDO RM
Bouyac, David Roger Louis,	LT(IC)	X	P	01.04.01	RNAS YEOVILTON
Bowbrick, Richard Charles, pce,	LT CDR(FTC)	X	AAWO	01.04.97	JSCSC
Bowden, Matthew Neil, BSc, PGDip,	LT CDR(FTC)	E	TMSM	01.10.98	FLEET HQ PORTS
Bowden, Matthew Thomas Edward, BEng,	LT(FTC)	E	WE	01.02.95	OCEAN
Bowen, Christopher Nicholas, BSc, PGCE,	LT(IC)	X		01.10.99	BRIDPORT
Bowen, Michael, ARRC, BA, MSc,	CAPT(FCC)	Q	RNT	27.03.01	DMTO HQ
Bowen, Nigel Timothy, pce, pcea,	LT CDR(FTC)	X	O	01.11.96	SHEFFIELD
Bowen, Richard James,	SLT(UCE)(IC)	E	WE	01.09.01	DARTMOUTH BRNC
Bower, Andrew John, BSc, SM(n), SM,	LT CDR(FTC)	X	SM	01.08.01	SUPERB
Bower, John William,	LT(FTC)	S	(S)	24.07.97	HQBF CYPRUS
Bower, Nigel Scott, pce(sm),	LT CDR(FTC)	X	SM	01.04.97	FLEET HQ NWD
Bowers, John Paul,	LT CDR(FTC)	X	O	01.10.01	702 SQN HERON
Bowhay, Simon, BSc,	LT CDR(FTC)	E	WESM	01.05.99	MWC PORTSDOWN
Bowie, Alan Niven, MB, BCh, MRCGP,	SURG LTCDR(FCC)	-	GMPP	11.03.99	RN GIBRALTAR
Bowie, Richard,	LT(IC)	E	WE	01.05.02	DARTMOUTH BRNC
Bowker, Geoffrey Neil,	LT CDR(FTC)	X	ATC	01.10.93	MOD (LONDON)
Bowker, Iain Cameron, BEng,	LT CDR(FTC)	E	MESM	13.02.01	SULTAN
Bowker, Jane Mary, MA,	SLT(IC)	X		01.05.00	RICHMOND
Bowker, Michael Andrew, MSc, MIMarEST, MIMechE, jsdc,	CAPT(FTC)	E	MESM	30.06.97	RCDS
Bowman, Robert James, BEng,	LT(FTC)	E	AE	01.04.95	ES AIR WYTON
Bowman, Simon Kenneth James,	SLT(IC)	X		01.09.00	RALEIGH
Bowness, Paul,	LT(FTC)	E	AE(M)	15.10.93	SULTAN
Bowra, Mark Andrew,	CAPT RM(CC)	-		01.09.97	RM POOLE
Bowser, Nicholas John,	LT(FTC)	E	AE	02.05.00	700M MERLIN OEU
Bowyer, Richard John,	CAPT RM(CC)	-	MLDR	01.05.00	MOD (LONDON)
Boxall, Pauline, BEng,	LT(FTC)	E	ME	01.04.97	CAPT IST STAFF
Boxall-Hunt, Brian Paul, OBE, AMNI, pce,	CDR(FTC)	X	PWO(A)	30.06.91	DA SINGAPORE
Boyce, Sir Michael, (Cecil), GCB, OBE, ADC, rcds, psc,	ADM	-	SM	25.05.95	MOD (LONDON)
Boyd, James Alexander, jsdc, pce(sm),	CAPT(FTC)	X	SM	30.06.96	SA TOKYO
Boyd, Nicholas, MSc, CEng, MIMechE,	LT CDR(FTC)	E	ME	01.03.95	MOD (BATH)
Boyes, Gareth Angus, BA(OU), MEng,	LT(FTC)	E	ME	01.07.97	SULTAN
Boyes, Martyn Richard, BEng, MSc,	LT(FTC)	E	MESM	01.02.95	NP BRISTOL
Boyes, Norman,	LT CDR(FTC)	E	ME	11.08.88	FLEET HQ PORTS 2
Boyes, Richard Austen,	LT(FTC)	X	P	01.03.89	700 OEU T23 FLT
Boyle, Jonathan Bartley, BEng, CEng,	LT(FTC)	E	MESM	01.10.94	MOD (BATH)
Boynton, Stephen Justin, BSc,	LT CDR(FTC)	X	O	01.12.99	750 SQN SEAHAWK
Brace, Anna Frances, BA,	SLT(IC)	X	ATCU/T	01.01.01	DARTMOUTH BRNC
Bracher, Hugh,	LT CDR(FTC)	E	WESM	01.10.96	DRAKE CBS
Bradburn, James Anthony, BSc, SM,	LT(CC)	X		01.01.99	TORBAY
Bradburn, Stephen Joseph, pcea,	LT CDR(FTC)	X	P	01.10.93	824 SQN
Bradbury, James Edward David, MSc,	LT(CC)	X		01.01.01	ST ALBANS
Bradbury, Simon,	CHAPLAIN	RC		18.09.96	MWS COLLINGWOOD
Bradford, Giles Job, MEng,	SLT(IC)	X	P U/T	01.09.99	RNAS YEOVILTON
Bradford, Terrance Horace Colin,	LT(FTC)	MS	(AD)	04.04.96	2SL/CNH
Brading, Roland David,	LT RM(IC)	-		01.03.01	40 CDO RM

Name	Rank	Branch	Spec	Seniority	Where Serving
Bradley, Harriet,	SURG SLT(SCC)	-		03.07.00	DARTMOUTH BRNC
Bradley, Matthew Thomas, n,	LT CDR(FTC)	X	PWO(U)	01.05.02	SOMERSET
Bradley, Patrick Martin, BEng,	LT CDR(FTC)	E	WE	01.06.00	NORTHUMBERLAND
Bradley, Rupert Litherland, LLB,	LT(CC)	X	P	01.11.96	849 SQN B FLT
Bradley, Trevor Adrian, BEng,	LT(IC)	E	WE	01.05.02	MWS COLLINGWOOD
Brads, Wayne, BSc,	LT CDR(FTC)	E	TMSM	14.01.94	FLEET HQ PORTS 2
Bradshaw, Kevin Thomas, BSc,	LT(FTC)	E	WE	18.02.94	SFM PORTSMOUTH
Brady, Mark Rowland, BSc, pce,	LT CDR(FTC)	X		16.01.81	FLEET HQ PORTS 2
Brady, Sean Edward, pce,	LT CDR(FTC)	X	PWO(U)	01.09.96	EXCHANGE USA
Brady, Sean, BSc,	CAPT RM(CC)	-		01.09.97	HQ 3 CDO BDE RM
Brady, Thomas William,	LT(FTC)	S	(W)	01.04.01	CORNWALL
Braham, Stephen Wyn, MSc, CEng, FIMarEST, psc,	CDR(FTC)	E	ME	30.06.97	MOD (LONDON)
Brailey, Ian Stewart Fordyce,	LT(FTC)	X	AV	04.04.96	RNAS CULDROSE
Brain, William James, FHCIMA,	CAPT RM(CC)	-		01.09.00	45 CDO RM
Braithwaite, Geoffrey Charles,	SLT(IC)	E	ME	01.04.00	DARTMOUTH BRNC
Braithwaite, Jeremy Sean,	LT(FTC)	X	HM	01.01.95	MWS DRYAD
Bramall, Kieron Scott, BA,	LT(CC)	X		01.10.97	LIVERPOOL
Bramley, Stephen, pce, pcea, psc,	CDR(FTC)	X	P	31.12.91	RNP TEAM
Bramwell, John Gerald,	LT(CC)	X	O	01.04.93	ES AIR YEO
Brand, Simon Martin, BSc, MA, pce, pcea, psc(j),	CDR(FTC)	X	P	30.06.97	PJHQ
Bratby, Simon Paul,	LT(CC)	X	P	16.11.94	702 SQN HERON
Bratt, Adrian Richard, BSc, n,	LT(FTC)	X		01.01.96	CHARGER
Bravery, Martin Anthony Edward, pcea,	LT CDR(FTC)	X	P	01.05.99	824 SQN
Bray, Katherine Elizabeth, MB, BSc, BS,	SURG LT(SCC)	-		01.08.01	CTCRM
Bray, Matthew Robert, psc(j),	MAJ(FTC)	-		01.05.01	FPGRM
Bray, Nigel Godfrey Hensman, pce, (Commodore)	CAPT(FTC)	X	AWO(C)	30.06.95	FLEET CIS PORTS
Brayson, Mark,	LT(CC)	X	P	16.10.94	DHFS
Brazenall, Benjamin Crawford, BEng,	SLT(IC)	X	P U/T	01.01.01	DARTMOUTH BRNC
Brazier, Francis William Thomas, IEng, FIEIE, FIIE,	CDR(FTC)	E	WE	01.10.97	2SL/CNH FOTR
Brazier, Lars Frank, MA,	LT(IC)	X	P	01.01.99	846 SQN
Brearley, Rosalind Lydia, BSc,	LT(IC)	X		01.05.00	SOMERSET
Breckenridge, Iain Galloway, pce, pce(sm),	LT CDR(FTC)	X	SM	01.07.97	EXCHANGE USA
Bree, Stephen Edward Peter, MB, BCh, FRCA,	SURG CDR(FCC)	-	(CA)	30.06.00	MODHU DERRIFORD
Breen, John Edward, MEng, MRAeS,	LT(IC)	E	AE	01.09.01	899 SQN HERON
Brember, Peter Bruce,	LT(FTC)	X	AV	25.07.96	RNAS YEOVILTON
Brenchley, Nigel Gerard,	LT CDR(FTC)	S		17.02.00	FLEET HQ NWD
Brennan, Andrew John, SM,	LT(CC)	X	SM	01.09.95	FOSNNI OPS DLO
Brennan, Paul Anthony, BA, BSc, IEng, MIIE,	LT(FTC)	E	MESM	02.09.99	FWO DEVONPORT
Breslin, Michael John, BEM,	LT(CS)(CAS)	-		07.01.90	DNR NEE 1
Bretten, Nicholas John,	MID(IC)	X		01.01.01	DARTMOUTH BRNC
Brewer, Christopher Edward, BSc, SM,	LT(IC)	X		01.01.00	TRAFALGAR
Brewin, David John, BSc,	LT(IC)	X	P	01.03.99	846 SQN
Brian, Neil, pcea,	LT(FTC)	X	O	01.08.92	814 SQN
Bridger, David William, MSc, HND,	CDR(FTC)	E	TM	30.06.96	FLEET HQ PORTS 2
Bridger, Richard John, pcea,	LT CDR(FTC)	X	O	01.06.92	FLEET HQ PORTS 2
Brierley, Simon Paul John, BEng,	SLT(IC)	E	AE	01.09.99	SULTAN
Briers, Matthew Peter, pce, pcea,	LT CDR(FTC)	X	P	01.11.96	NMA PORTSMOUTH
Briggs, Andrew David, MA,	SLT(IC)	X	O U/T	01.09.00	DARTMOUTH BRNC
Briggs, Charmody Elizabeth, BSc,	SLT(IC)	X		01.09.99	BRECON
Briggs, Helen Claire,	SLT(IC)	S		01.01.99	ARK ROYAL
Briggs, Mark David, BEng,	LT(CC)	E	WE	01.06.97	MWS EXCELLENT
Brighouse, Neil George,	MAJ(FTC)	-	P	24.04.02	846 SQN
Brimacombe, Louise Marie, BSc,	LT(IC)	S		01.02.00	SULTAN AIB
Brimley, Keith Stuart, BSc, pce,	LT CDR(FTC)	X	AWO(C)†	01.12.80	MWS DRYAD
Brims, Fraser John Hall, MB, ChB,	SURG LT(MCC)	-		05.08.98	RH HASLAR
Brindley, Mark William,	SLT(IC)	E	WE	01.01.00	RICHMOND
Brinsden, Mark Dudley, MB, BS, MRCS,	SURG LTCDR(FCC)	-		01.08.99	NELSON (PAY)
Brint, Ian,	LT(IC)	S	SM	29.04.01	TURBULENT
Briscoe, James William Austen, BEng,	SLT(IC)	E	WE U/T	01.05.00	ILLUSTRIOUS
Bristow, Geoffrey David,	LT CDR(FTC)	X	SM	01.10.88	2SL/CNH FOTR
Bristow, Paul Christopher, BA,	LT(IC)	E	TM	01.09.98	ARK ROYAL
Bristowe, Paul Andrew, BSc, FRGS, pcea,	LT CDR(FTC)	X	P	01.03.01	MWS DRYAD

Name	Rank	Branch	Spec	Seniority	Where Serving
Britchfield, Alison Esther Phyllis, MA, BD,	CHAPLAIN	SF		01.10.92	DARTMOUTH BRNC
Britton, Nicholas John, MBE, BSc,	LT CDR(FTC)	X		01.04.90	CSIS IPT
Broad, Robert Oliver, BSc, CEng, MIMechE, psc,	CDR(FTC)	E	ME	30.06.90	MOD (BATH)
Broadbent, Peter Stephen, BSc, BA(OU),	LT CDR(FTC)	E	WE	01.03.02	MWS COLLINGWOOD
Broadhurst, Michael Robert, BA, MSc,	LT CDR(FTC)	X	AAWO	01.12.00	NOTTINGHAM
Broadley, Kevin James, BSc, MA, pce, pcea, psc,	CDR(FTC)	X	P	30.06.00	NELSON
Brock, Mathew Jonathan,	LT(IC)	X		01.01.02	PORTLAND
Brock, Raymond Frederick,	LT CDR(FTC)	S		01.03.02	RALEIGH
Brockington, Gordon Colin, BSc,	LT(FTC)	X	MW	01.11.97	SANDOWN
Brocklebank, Guy Philip, BSc, FRSA, pce, MIMgt,	CDR(FTC)	X	PWO(C)	31.12.92	EXCHANGE USA
Brocklehurst, Kelly Paul, BA,	LT RM(IC)	-		01.09.00	CDO LOG REGT RM
Brockwell, Paul Edward Norman, MBE, BSc, CEng,MIMarEST,	CDR(FTC)	E	MESM	30.06.94	FWO DEVPT SEA
Brodie, Duncan John, BEng,	LT(IC)	E	AE	01.01.02	SULTAN
Brodie, Ross William James, n,	LT(FTC)	X	PWO(U)	01.12.94	KENT
Brodier, Mark Ian,	LT(FTC)	E	AE(L)	04.09.98	JHCHQ
Brodribb, Timothy John, MB, BS,	SURG LT(SCC)	-		04.08.99	45 CDO RM
Brokenshire, Laurence Phillip, BA, BSc,(Commodore)	CAPT(FTC)	E	TM	30.06.94	RALEIGH
CertEd, MBCS, MIMA, AFIMA, jsdc,					
Bromage, Kenneth Charles,	CHAPLAIN	CE		02.08.92	DARTMOUTH BRNC
Bromige, Timothy Robert James, pce,	LT CDR(FTC)	X	AAWO	19.05.92	FLEET HQ NWD
Bromwell, Mark Steven, MEng, AMIEE,	SLT(IC)	E	WE	01.09.99	MWS COLLINGWOOD
Brook, John Gordon, BSc, CEng, MIEE, psc,	LT CDR(FTC)	E	WE	21.03.87	SCU LEYDENE ACNS
Brooking, Richard Robert,	LT(IC)	E	WE	01.05.02	DARTMOUTH BRNC
Brooks, Gary Lee, pce,	LT CDR(FTC)	X	H1	01.04.99	MWS RNHMS DRAKE
Brooks, Graeme Christian Gibbon,	LT(FTC)	X	MCD	01.04.97	LEDBURY
Brooks, Kirsten Mary Louise, BSc,	LT(IC)	E	TM	01.12.96	NELSON
Brooks, Mervyn Leigh,	LT CDR(FTC)	X	AV	01.10.97	DOSG BRISTOL
Brooks, Nicholas Robert, BEng,	LT(IC)	E	MESM	01.09.01	SULTAN
Brooks, Paul Neil,	SLT(IC)	E	WE	01.01.00	NEWCASTLE
Brooksbank, Richard James, BSc, pce, pcea,	CDR(FTC)	X	P	31.12.97	RNAS CULDROSE
Brooksbank, Richard,	MID(NE)(IC)	S		01.05.00	RALEIGH
Broom, Neil John, MBE,	LT CDR(FCC)	Q	OTSPEC	01.10.99	MODHU DERRIFORD
Brooman, Martin John,	LT(CC)	X	P	16.08.95	771 SQN
Brosnan, Mark Anthony, pcea,	LT(CC)	X	O	16.07.93	EXCHANGE CANADA
Broster, Mark, BA,	LT(IC)	X		01.05.01	IRON DUKE
Broster, Patrick Thomas, BSc,	LT CDR(FTC)	X	O	01.10.97	MOD (LONDON)
Brothers, Anthony Herbert George,	LT(FTC)	E	WE	18.02.94	MWS COLLINGWOOD
Brotherton, John Darren, QCBA,	LT CDR(FTC)	X	P	16.04.02	FLEET AV CU
Brotherton, Michael, MBE, BD,	CHAPLAIN	CE		04.09.84	RNAS CULDROSE
Brotton, Peter James, BSc,	LT(FTC)	X		01.04.98	CORNWALL
Brough, Geoffrey Alan,	CDR(FTC)	E	WESM	31.12.94	2SL/CNH FOTR
Brown, Aaron Richard Andrew,	LT(IC)	X	O	01.03.00	849 SQN B FLT
Brown, Andrew Martyn, BEng,	LT(FTC)	E	PWO(A)	01.12.96	WESTMINSTER
Brown, Andrew Paul,	LT(FTC)	X	ATC	01.02.92	RAF SHAWBURY
Brown, Andrew Paul,	MID(IC)	X		01.09.00	DARTMOUTH BRNC
Brown, Andrew Scott, MSc,	LT(IC)	X		01.09.01	RICHMOND
Brown, Andrew, BM, BCh,	SURG LT(MCC)	-		05.08.98	MODHU DERRIFORD
Brown, Bernard Craig,	LT(SCC)	Q		11.06.00	MODHU DERRIFORD
Brown, Christopher Dennis, pcea, (Act Cdr)	LT CDR(FTC)	X	P	01.09.87	LOAN JTEG BSC DN
Brown, David Campbell, MSc, MB, ChB, LRCP,	SURGCAPT(FCC)	-	CPDATE	30.06.02	LOAN OTHER SVCE
MRCS, MSRP, FFOM, OStJ,					
Brown, David John, BSc,	LT CDR(FTC)	X	SM	01.04.85	PJHQ
Brown, Howard Spencer, MBE, pce, pcea, psc(j),	CDR(FTC)	X	P	31.12.99	MOD (LONDON)
Brown, James Alexander, BEng, MSc,	SLT(IC)	E	WESM	01.01.00	OCLC ROSYTH
Brown, James Alexander, BSc,	LT(IC)	X		01.05.00	ALDERNEY
Brown, Leonard Anthony, BA, (Act Maj)	CAPT RM(FTC)	-	P	01.09.97	JHCHQ
Brown, Malcolm Keith, MBE, BSc, pce,	CDR(FTC)	X	AAWO	20.09.94	BDS WASHINGTON
Brown, Neil Logan, LLB,	CDR(FTC)	S	BAR	31.12.98	FLEET HQ PORTS
Brown, Nigel Peter, BSc, MA, psc(m),	LT COL(FTC)	-	C	30.06.98	JSCSC
Brown, Paul Alexander Everett, BA, pce, n,	LT CDR(FTC)	X	AAWO	01.08.99	MWS DRYAD
Brown, Paul Angus,	LT(FTC)	E	AE(M)	07.09.95	ARK ROYAL
Brown, Peter Richard, pce, psc,	LT CDR(FTC)	X	PWO(A)	16.03.85	SHAPE BELGIUM

Name	Rank	Branch	Spec	Seniority	Where Serving
Brown, Peter St John, BEng, CEng, MIMarEST,	LT CDR(FTC)	E	MESM	01.06.95	DRAKE SFM
Brown, Robert Andrew Mark, OBE, pce,	CAPT(FTC)	X	AAWO	30.06.02	FWO DEVPT SEA
Brown, Robert John,	MAJ(FTC)	-	SO(LE)	01.10.92	FLEET HQ PORTS 2
Brown, Scott James, BD,	CHAPLAIN	SF		20.04.93	SULTAN
Brown, Simon David, n, MSc,	LT(FTC)	X	PWO(A)	01.11.94	MANCHESTER
Brown, Stephen Glynn,	LT(CC)	X	P	04.08.00	845 SQN
Brown, Stephen, pce,	LT CDR(FTC)	X	PWO(U)	15.01.01	MARLBOROUGH
Brown, William Clarke, pce,	LT CDR(FTC)	X	AAWO	01.01.94	CAPT IST STAFF
Browning, Martin Lawrence Corbet,	LT CDR(FTC)	X	SM	21.09.86	CNH(R)
Browning, Rowan Susannah, BSc, adp,	LT CDR(CC)	E	IS	01.01.02	PJHQ
Bruce, Steven Leonard, BA(OU), MA, psc,	LT COL(FTC)	-		30.06.96	FEARLESS
Bruce-Jones, Nicholas William, BSc, psc(a),	LT COL(FTC)	-		31.12.00	FLEET HQ PORTS
Bruford, Robert Michael Charles, pce,	LT CDR(FTC)	X	AAWO	01.04.00	FOST SEA
Brundle, Paul Robert, MBE,	LT CDR(FTC)	X	ATC	01.10.95	RNAS YEOVILTON
Brunell, Paul Jonathan,	LT(FTC)	E	AE(M)	02.09.99	ES AIR YEO
Brunsden-Brown, Sebastian Edward, pcea,	LT CDR(FTC)	X	P	01.10.01	824 SQN
Brunskill, John Edmund Tanner,	LT(CC)	X	P	01.06.91	849 SQN B FLT
Brunton, Steven Buchanan, MSc, CEng, MIEE, MCGI, mdtc,	CAPT(FTC)	E	WESM	30.06.01	HQ DCSA
Brutton, Joseph Henry, BEng,	LT(IC)	E	MESM	01.08.97	VICTORIOUS(STBD)
Bryan, Rory John Lockton, BA,	LT CDR(FTC)	X	PWO(U)	01.01.00	FOST SEA
Bryant, Daniel John Grenfell,	LT(FTC)	S	SM	01.10.94	DARTMOUTH BRNC
Bryant, David John,	LT CDR(FTC)	X	PWO(U)	01.10.94	MWS COLLINGWOOD
Bryant, Graham David,	LT CDR(FTC)	S	CA	01.10.99	FLEET HQ PORTS
Bryars, Paul,	LT RM(IC)	-	SO(LE)	01.04.00	CTCRM
Bryce, Colin Gerard, BSc, PGCE, MBCS, adp,	LT CDR(CC)	E	IS	01.10.94	2SL/CNH
Bryce, Graeme Edward, BDS,	SG LT(D)(SCC)	-		29.06.00	CTCRM
Bryce, Neville Anthony, MBE,	LT(FTC)	E	MESM	14.10.94	NBC PORTSMOUTH
Bryce-Johnston, Fiona Lorraine Sterling, MA,	LT(SCC)	Q		16.07.01	RH HASLAR
Bryson, Susan Ainee, BA, n,	LT(CC)	X		01.03.94	NORFOLK
Bubb, Jonathan David,	CAPT RM(IC)	-		01.05.99	42 CDO RM
Buchan, John Alan, MA,	LT(IC)	X		01.09.99	CARDIFF
Buchan-Steele, Mark Anthony, BSc, MA, psc(j),	CDR(FTC)	S	SM	31.12.00	FOSNNI/NBC CLYDE
Buchanan, David,	SLT(IC)	E	ME	01.05.00	SULTAN
Buchanan, Robert Michael, BEng,	LT(IC)	E	AE	01.05.01	820 SQN
Buck, James Edward, PGDIPAN, pce, n,	LT CDR(FTC)	X	PWO(N)	01.04.00	ENDURANCE
Buck, Sarah Rachael, BSc,	LT(IC)	E	TM	01.05.98	SULTAN
Buckenham, Peter James, BEng, AMIMechE,	LT(CC)	E	ME	01.10.99	LIVERPOOL
Buckeridge, Vincent,	LT(FTC)	E	WESM	18.02.94	DRAKE SFM
Buckett, Edward Joseph,	LT CDR(FTC)	X	P	01.10.90	OCLC BRISTOL
Buckingham, Guy, SM(n), SM,	LT CDR(FTC)	X	SM	01.12.01	FOST CSST DEVPT
Buckland, Richard John Francis, pce, pcea,	CDR(FTC)	X	O	31.12.99	BDS WASHINGTON
Buckle, Iain Lawrence, BEng, MBA, CEng, MIMarEST,	LT CDR(FTC)	X	WE	01.07.96	FLEET HQ PORTS 2
Buckley, Dominic David George, BA,	LT(CC)	X	HM	01.02.94	MWS RNHMS DRAKE
Buckley, Martin John, MBE, BA, pce,	LT CDR(FTC)	X	SM	16.05.85	SULTAN
Buckley, Noel Christopher,	LT(FS)(CAS)	FS		19.09.97	NEPTUNE 2SL/CNH
Buckley, Phillip James Anthony, jsdc, pce(sm), pce,	CDR(FTC)	X	SM	31.12.96	FLEET HQ PORTS
Bucknall, Robin James Woolcott,	MAJ(FTC)	-		01.05.00	CDO LOG REGT RM
Buczkiewicz, Mathew,	2LT(IC)	-		01.09.98	CTCRM LYMPSTONE
Budd, Philip Richard, BA, pce,	LT CDR(FTC)	X	AWO(A)	16.12.80	2SL/CNH
Budge, Daniel Jordan, LLB,	SLT(IC)	X	ATCU/T	01.09.99	RNAS CULDROSE
Bugg, Kevin John,	LT CDR(FTC)	E	AE(M)	01.03.02	JCA IPT UK
Buggins, Brian, QGM,	LT(IC)	X	AV	01.05.02	RFANSU
Bukhory, Hamesh, BEng,	LT(IC)	E	AE	01.01.02	SULTAN
Bulcock, Michael, BEng,	LT CDR(FTC)	E	MESM	28.07.00	NEPTUNE DSA
Bull, Andrew John, pcea, psc,	CDR(FTC)	X	O	01.10.95	SA LISBON
Bull, Charlotte Vivienne Rachel, BA,	LT(IC)	S		01.11.97	AFPAA(CENTURION)
Bull, Christopher Martin Sefton, MA, CEng, MIEE,	LT CDR(FTC)	E	WESM	01.03.97	FLEET HQ PORTS 2
Bull, Geoffrey Charles, BEng, MSc, AMIMechE,	LT CDR(FTC)	E	MESM	01.11.94	SCEPTRE
Bull, Louis Paul, BA,	LT(IC)	X		01.07.00	VICTORIOUS(STBD)
Bull, Michael Antony John, BSc, SM(n), SM,	LT(CC)	X	SM	11.09.99	TALENT
Bullock, James Richard,	SLT(CC)	X	P	01.01.00	845 SQN
Bullock, Michael Peter, MBE,	CDR(FTC)	S	SM	31.12.95	NMA PORTSMOUTH

Name	Rank	Branch	Spec	Seniority	Where Serving
Bullock, Robert Arthur, BSc,	LT(CC)	X		01.09.00	RICHMOND
Bulmer, Renny John,	MAJ(FTC)	-	SO(LE)	01.10.00	40 CDO RM
Bulmer, William Elliot, MA,	SLT(IC)	S		01.01.00	CHATHAM
Bulter, Danielle Barbara, BEng,	LT(IC)	E		01.09.01	848 SQN HERON
Bunn, Malcolm Edward,	LT CDR(FTC)	X	P	01.10.91	FLEET AV VL
Bunn, Toby J,	SLT(IC)	X	P U/T	01.05.01	DARTMOUTH BRNC
Bunney, Graham John, BSc,	LT(IC)	X	P	01.02.94	GANNET SAR FLT
Bunt, Kevin John,	LT CDR(FTC)	S	(S)	01.10.00	CARDIFF
Burbidge, Kay,	LT(CC)	X	O	01.09.98	771 SQN
Burcham, Jason Richard,	LT RM(IC)	BS	SO(LE)	01.04.00	MWS RM SCH MUSIC
Burchell, Hannah Eve, BA,	LT(FTC)	S		01.08.99	MWS DRYAD
Burden, John Charles,	LT CDR(FTC)	X	MCD	01.11.91	NORTH DIVING GRP
Burdett, Richard Wyndham, BSc, CEng, MIMechE,	LT CDR(FTC)	E	MESM	01.06.92	DSQ ROSYTH
Burdett, Vincent Charles,	LT(IC)	E		01.05.02	GLASGOW
Burge, Roger George,	LT CDR(FTC)	E	WESM	01.10.00	MOD (BATH)
Burgess, Andrew James, BSc, MB, BCh, FRCA, FFARCS, DA,	SURG CDR(FCC)	-	(CA)	30.06.96	MOD HUDERRIFORD
Burgess, Darren James,	LT(IC)	X	O U/T	01.05.02	MWS COLLINGWOOD
Burgess, Gary Thomas Myles, BEng, MSc,	LT CDR(FTC)	E	MESM	01.02.00	TRIUMPH
Burgess, Jonathan David Allen, BSc, pcea,	LT CDR(FTC)	X	P	01.10.93	846 SQN
Burgess, Mark,	LT RM(IC)	-	SO(LE)	01.04.00	CTCRM LYMPSTONE
Burgess, Stanley, pcea,	LT CDR(FTC)	X	P	01.10.90	771 SQN
Burgess, William Charles,	CDR(FTC)	E	AE	01.10.96	NEPTUNE DLO
Burghall, Rebecca Clare, BSc,	LT(IC)	X		01.08.01	ANGLESEY
Burgon, Ross, BSc,	LT(IC)	X	P U/T	01.01.02	DHFS
Burke, David Edward, MA, SM(n), SM,	LT(FTC)	X	SM	01.07.96	VICTORIOUS(STBD)
Burke, Michael Christopher, BSc,	LT CDR(FTC)	X	SM	01.09.95	FLEET HQ PORTS
Burke, Paul Dominic, BA, pce, pce(sm),	CDR(FTC)	X	SM	30.06.02	SPLENDID
Burkett, Janis Ann, MB, BCH, BAO, DObstRCOG, Dip FFP, MRCGP, JCPTGP	SURGCDR(SCC)	-	GMPP	01.07.00	NELSON (PAY)
Burley, Matthew Richard, BEng,	LT(FTC)	E	MESM	01.06.97	TALENT
Burlingham, Brett Limmer, BSc, MA, CEng, MIMarEST, psc(j),	LT CDR(FTC)	E	ME	01.11.95	NMA PORTSMOUTH
Burnell, Jeremy Richard Jenner, fsc,	LT COL(FTC)	-		31.12.00	RHQ AFNORTH
Burnell-Nugent, James Michael, CBE, MA, jsdc, pce, pce(sm),	RADM	-	SM	06.12.99	UKMARBATSTAFF
Burnett, Gilbert Arthur,	LT CDR(FTC)	E	ME	01.10.99	SULTAN
Burnett, Paul Henry,	SLT(IC)	MS		01.05.00	INM ALVERSTOKE
Burnham, James Alistair Irby, MA,	LT(CC)	S		01.08.97	DLO/DGDEF LOG SP
Burningham, Michael Robert, BA,	LT CDR(FTC)	S	SM	01.01.98	FLEET HQ PORTS
Burnip, John Matthew, BSc,	LT CDR(FTC)	E	ME	01.08.93	MOD (BATH)
Burns, Adrian Conleth,	LT CDR(FTC)	S	SM	04.03.02	COMATG SEA
Burns, Andrew James, BEng,	SLT(IC)	X	P U/T	01.01.00	RAF CRANWELL EFS
Burns, Andrew Paul, BA,	LT CDR(FTC)	X	PWO(A)	01.04.00	ST ALBANS
Burns, David Ian, BSc, ARCS, pce, psc(j),	LT CDR(FTC)	X	PWO(C)	01.05.98	PJHQ
Burns, Euan Paterson, BEng,	LT(FTC)	E	WE	01.08.98	JSCSC
Burns, James Edward, BEng,	LT(FTC)	E	WE	01.02.99	OCEAN
Burns, Robin Douglas James, BSc, PGDip,	LT CDR(FTC)	X	METOC	01.03.99	ILLUSTRIOUS
Burns, Royston John, MHCIMA,	LT(FTC)	S	CA	20.09.99	RNAS CULDROSE
Burns, Thomas Matthew, QHC, BA, BD,	PR CHAPLAIN	RC		04.01.94	2SL/CNH
Burrell, Aleck Michael George,	CAPT RM(FTC)	-		28.04.98	FEARLESS
Burrell, David James, MEng,	SLT(IC)	X		01.09.99	ANGLESEY
Burrell, Philip Mark, BSc, psc,	CAPT(FTC)	E	TM	30.06.02	2SL/CNH FOTR
Burrows, John Campbell,	LT(FTC)	E	MESM	15.10.93	TRENCHANT
Burrows, Michael John,	LT CDR(FTC)	X	P	01.10.94	FLEET HQ PORTS
Burrows, Michael John, jsdc, pce, psc(j),	CDR(FTC)	X	AAWO	31.12.94	MTS IPT
Burston, Richard John King, pce(sm),	CDR(FTC)	X	SM	30.06.92	NSRS IPT
Burstow, Richard Stanley, pce,	LT CDR(FTC)	X	PWO(U)	01.05.99	DARTMOUTH BRNC
Burt, Douglas James,	SLT(IC)	E	MESM	01.10.99	SPLENDID
Burt, Paul Ronald, BA,	LT CDR(FTC)	S	(S)	01.10.93	MOD (LONDON)
Burton, Alex, BSc,	LT(FTC)	X		01.11.00	NOTTINGHAM
Burton, Alexander James, BSc, pce, psc(j),	CDR(FTC)	X	PWO(U)	30.06.01	NORTHUMBERLAND
Burton, David Stephen, MSc, (Act Capt)	CDR(FTC)	E	IS	31.12.95	AFPAA(CENTURION)

Name	Rank	Branch	Spec	Seniority	Where Serving
Burton, Paul Richard,	LT(FTC)	E	ME	02.05.00	RALEIGH
Burton, Tanya Jane, BDS,	SG LT(D)(SCC)	-		05.07.99	NELSON
Burvill, Justin Paul, BEng, MSc, CEng, MIMarE,	LT(FTC)	E	MESM	01.03.95	MOD (BATH)
Burwin, Harvey Lee, BEng,	LT CDR(FTC)	E	WE	01.11.96	2SL/CNH
Bush, Alexander John Taylor, pce,	LT CDR(FTC)	X	PWO(U)	01.06.99	MWS DRYAD
Bush, Natalie,	LT(CC)	X		01.12.01	SHEFFIELD
Bush, Stephen John Duyland, OBE, psc,	LT COL(FTC)	-		31.12.86	SULTAN AIB
Bushell, Gary Robert,	LT CDR(FTC)	X	PT	09.07.99	TEMERAIRE
Bussey, Emma Louise, BA,	LT(FTC)	X		01.09.99	EXCHANGE SPAIN
Butcher, David,	LT RM(IC)	-	SO(LE)	01.04.00	UKLFCSG RM
Butcher, Linda Joan, ARRC, MA(Ed), Cert Ed, (Act Cdr)	LT CDR(FCC)	Q	RNT	08.01.88	MOD (LONDON)
Butcher, Martin Charles, pce,	LT CDR(FTC)	X	PWO(C)	16.11.85	MWS DRYAD
Butcher, Martin William, MBE, pce, psc,	CDR(FTC)	X	P	30.06.91	MOD (LONDON)
Butler, Ian Anthony,	LT(FTC)	E	AE(L)	12.09.97	HARRIER IPT
Butler, Jonathon Edward, MEng,	SLT(IC)	E	WESM	01.09.00	MONTROSE
Butler, Lee Peter, IEng, AMRAeS,	LT(FTC)	E	AE(L)	15.10.93	ES AIR BRISTOL
Butler, Nicholas Abraham Marsh, pce, pcea,	CAPT(FTC)	X	P	31.12.97	SA THE HAGUE
Butler, Philip Michael, BSc,	LT(IC)	X	P	01.01.01	RAF LINTN/OUSE
Butler, Rachel, BSc,	LT(IC)	X	HM2	01.07.99	MWS RNHMS CULD
Butler, Simon, BA,	LT RM(IC)	-		01.09.00	40 CDO RM
Butterfield, Neil Philip, MB, BS, DA, DipAvMed,	SURG CDR(FCC)	-	GMPP	31.12.92	ARK ROYAL
Butterworth, Leslie,	LT(FS)(CAS)	FS		16.01.99	DRAKE CBP(CNH)
Butterworth, Paul Gerard, LLB,	LT(FTC)	X		01.03.97	FLEET HQ NWD
Buxton, David Adrian, BEng, AMIEE,	LT(IC)	E	WESM	01.09.01	RALEIGH
Buxton, Peter John, BA, BM, BCh, FRCR,	SURG CDR(FCC)	-	CPDATE	31.12.95	RH HASLAR
Bye, Marc David, BEng, CEng,	LT CDR(FTC)	E	ME	01.05.00	AGRIPPA AFSOUTH
Byers, Hannah Rebecca,	MID(UCE)(IC)	E	AE	01.09.00	DARTMOUTH BRNC
Byrne, Adrian Charles, IEng, MIPlantE,	LT(FTC)	E	ME	18.06.93	ENDURANCE
Byrne, Terence Michael, (Act Lt Cdr)	LT(FTC)	X	REG	13.12.95	NP 1061
Byron, Douglas Charles,	SLT(IC)	S		01.09.00	DARTMOUTH BRNC
Byron, James David,	LT(FTC)	X	MW	01.05.95	PURSUER
Bywater, Richard Lewis, BEng, MSc, CEng, MIEE, gw,	LT CDR(FTC)	E	WE	01.03.99	CUMBERLAND

C

Name	Rank	Branch	Spec	Seniority	Where Serving
Cable, Phillip Mark, LLB,	LT(CC)	X		01.11.99	MWS DRYAD
Cackett, Thomas Edward Robert,	MID(NE)(IC)	X		01.05.01	CUMBERLAND
Caddick, Andrew,	SLT(IC)	E	ME	01.09.00	CUMBERLAND
Cahill, Karen Ann, BA,	LT(FTC)	X	FC	01.08.95	NOTTINGHAM
Cailes, Michael John,	MAJ(FTC)	-		10.02.81	RMB STONEHOUSE
Cain, Christopher William,	LT(FTC)	E	WESM	07.02.97	FWO FASLANE
Caldicott-Barr, Victoria Anne,	LT(IC)	X		01.02.97	OCLC BRISTOL
Caldwell, Daniel,	2LT(IC)	-		01.09.98	CTCRM LYMPSTONE
Calhaem, Richard Tahi, BEng,	LT(CC)	X	P	15.03.98	845 SQN
Callaghan, Paul Fraser, MBE, BSc,	LT CDR(FTC)	X	P	01.10.99	700 OEU T23 FLT
Callis, Gregory, BEng,	SLT(IC)	E		01.09.99	SULTAN
Callister, David Roy, pcea,	LT CDR(FTC)	X	O	01.10.95	UKMFTS IPT
Callon, Andrew McMillan,	CHAPLAIN	CE		05.06.90	AFCC
Calter, Mark,	LT(FTC)	X	EW	26.04.99	EXCHANGE USA
Cambridge, Grant Andrew, BA,	CAPT RM(IC)	-		01.09.99	45 CDO RM
Cameron, Andrew John Brunt, pce,	CAPT(FTC)	X	PWO(U)	30.06.98	JMOTS NORTHWOOD
Cameron, Fiona, BSc,	LT(IC)	E	TM	24.04.98	MWS DRYAD
Cameron, Iain,	LT CDR(FTC)	X	P	01.09.99	MOD (LONDON)
Cameron, Mark John, BEng, CEng, MIEE,	LT CDR(FTC)	E	WE	01.04.00	CORNWALL
Cameron, Peter Stuart, BA, psc(j),	LT COL(FTC)	-		30.06.02	FLEET HQ PORTS
Campbell, Alistair Lamont, BEM,	LT(IC)	X		12.04.02	FLEET PHOT PORTS
Campbell, David John, MB, BS,	SURG CDR(FCC)	-	GMPP	30.06.02	FOSM GOSPORT
Campbell, Iain Angus,	LT(CC)	X	P	16.04.96	EXCHANGE CANADA
Campbell, James Colin, Cert Ed, HNC,	LT CDR(CC)	E	IS	01.09.01	CINCFLEET FTSU
Campbell, James Kininmonth, MB, BS,	SURG CAPT(FCC)	-	(CGS)	30.06.02	MODHU DERRIFORD
LRCP, FRCS, FRCSEd,					
Campbell, Katrina Louise,	LT CDR(CC)	W	X	01.10.97	RNAS YEOVILTON
Campbell, Leslie Michael, BA,	LT CDR(FTC)	X	MW	01.07.00	NP 1061

Name	Rank	Branch	Spec	Seniority	Where Serving
Campbell, Malcolm Alexander, BEd, MSc, ... LT CDR(CC)	E	IS		01.01.00	CINCFLEET FIMU
Campbell, Mark Alan McMillian, BEng, ... LT(CC)	X	P		01.09.96	702 SQN HERON
Campbell, Peter Robert, ... LT(CC)	X	O		01.01.94	LYNX OEU
Campbell, Robin David Hastings, BEng, ... LT CDR(FTC)	E	WESM		01.02.95	FWO DEVONPORT
Campbell, Timothy Ross, BSc, ... LT(IC)	X			01.06.00	HURWORTH
Campbell-Balcombe, Andre Alexander, BEng, AMIEE, ... LT(FTC)	E	WE		01.07.94	DCSA NWD REGION
Campbell-Baldwin, James William, BA, ... SLT(IC)	X			01.05.00	CORNWALL
Canale, Andrew James, BA, ... LT(FTC)	X			01.07.97	IRON DUKE
Cannell, Graham Martin, BSc, ... LT(IC)	X	P		01.05.00	702 SQN HERON
Canning, Christopher Paul, BSc, pcea, ... LT(FTC)	X	O		01.03.92	700 OEU T23 FLT
Canning, William Andrew, OBE, psc(m), ... LT COL(FTC)	-			30.06.93	CTCRM
Cannon, Leslie Brian, BSc, MB, BS, FRCS, ... SURG LTCDR(FCC)	-			01.08.97	NELSON (PAY)
Cantellow, Richard Barry, ... SLT(IC)	X			01.01.00	MWS DRYAD
Cantellow, Stuart John, BEng, ... LT(FTC)	E			01.09.01	801 SQN
Cantrill, Richard John, BSc, ... CAPT RM(FTC)	-	MLDR		01.09.98	RM Poole
Canty, Nigel Robert, BSc, ... LT CDR(FTC)	E	MESM		01.09.91	FWO FASLANE
Canty, Thomas Alexander, BEng, ... SLT(IC)	E	ME		01.09.99	SULTAN
Capes, Stuart George, SM(n), SM, ... LT(FTC)	X	SM		01.04.96	DULVERTON
Capewell, David Andrew, OBE, psc(m), fsc, ... COL(FTC)	-			31.12.99	PJHQ
Caple, Jonathan Neil, ... LT(CC)	S			01.07.99	MOD (BATH)
Carbery, Stephen James, ... LT(IC)	E	WE		01.01.02	MONMOUTH
Carcone, Paul Nicholas, BSc, ... LT(IC)	S			01.12.99	MANCHESTER
Carcone, Suzy Helen, BA, ... LT(IC)	S			01.03.99	RALEIGH
Carden, Peter David, pce, pcea, psc(j), ... CDR(FTC)	X	O		30.06.99	COMAMPHIBFOR
Carey, Trevor James, ... LT(IC)	E	ME		01.05.02	DARTMOUTH BRNC
Cargen, Malcolm Robert, BSc, psc, ... CDR(FTC)	E	AE		31.12.00	JHCHQ
Carlisle, Christopher Richard, BEng, MSc, ... LT(FTC)	E	ME		01.03.95	SULTAN
Carlton, Ian Philip, ... LT CDR(FTC)	X	g		01.10.89	MOD (LONDON)
Carne, Richard James Power, pcea, ... LT(FTC)	X	O		16.05.87	824 SQN
Carnell, Gregory James, pcea, ... LT(CC)	X	O		01.09.91	815 FLT 208
Carnell, Richard Paul, BA, ... LT(SCC)	Q			06.11.98	FORT BLOCKHOUSE
Carnew, Sean Frederick, BA, ... SLT(IC)	X	O U/T		01.09.00	DARTMOUTH BRNC
Carnie, Manson John, BA, ... LT(FTC)	X	P U/T		01.09.99	RAF CRANWELL EFS
Carolan, Kevin Stuart, BEng, ... LT(IC)	X	MCD		08.08.98	ATHERSTONE
Carpenter, Bryony Helen, BSc, PGCE, ... LT(CC)	E	TM		01.01.95	MWS COLLINGWOOD
Carpenter, Christopher John, BSc, CEng, MIEE, ... LT CDR(FTC)	E	WESM		01.09.90	RALEIGH
Carpenter, George Edward, ... SLT(UCE)(FTC)	X			01.09.99	DARTMOUTH BRNC
Carr, David Leslie, pcea, ... LT CDR(FTC)	X	O		01.10.89	FLEET HQ PORTS
Carr, Martin Paul, ... LT CDR(FTC)	X	WE		01.10.98	HQ DCSA
Carr, Robert Alexander, BA, ... LT(CC)	X	P		13.04.91	848 SQN HERON
Carretta, Mark Vincent, BSc, pcea, ... LT CDR(FTC)	X	P		01.10.95	848 SQN HERON
Carrick, James Paul, BSc, SM, ... LT(FTC)	X	SM		01.12.97	SPARTAN
Carrick, Richard James, BEng, MBA, MSc, ... LT CDR(FTC)	E	MESM		01.05.97	TRAFALGAR
CEng, MIMechE,					
Carrigan, Jonathan Andrew, ... LT(FTC)	S			01.01.98	RALEIGH
Carrington, Victoria Louise, BA, ... LT(IC)	X			01.01.99	OCEAN
Carrington-Wood, Clive Gordon, pce, ... LT CDR(FTC)	X	AAWO		01.10.91	CV(F) IPT
Carroll, Benjamin John, BA, pce, n, ... LT CDR(FTC)	X	PWO(U)		01.02.98	MOD (LONDON)
Carroll, Paul Christopher, BEng, MSc, CEng, MIMarEST, ... LT CDR(FTC)	E	ME		01.03.02	WSA BRISTOL
Carroll, Peter William Mark, pce, pce(sm), (Act Cdr) ...... LT CDR(FTC)	X	SM		01.10.89	FOSM NWOOD HQ
Carroll, Philip John, BSc, ... LT CDR(CC)	X	H1		01.01.98	ACE SRGN TURKEY
Carroll, Stephen Laurence, BEng, MSc, ... LT(CC)	E	AE		01.01.99	814 SQN
Carson, Neil Douglas Ernest, BSc, pce(sm), SM, ... LT CDR(FTC)	X	SM		01.01.97	EXCHANGE AUSTLIA
Carter, Ashley Francis Rees, BSc, CEng, MIEE, ... CDR(FTC)	E	WE		31.12.97	MOD (LONDON)
Carter, Graham Richard, ... LT(IC)	S			01.06.00	JSU NORTHWOOD
Carter, Ian Paul, pce, ... CDR(FTC)	X	AAWO		30.06.00	FLEET CIS PORTS
Carter, Jonathon Mark, BSc, ... CDR(FTC)	X	WESM		01.06.96	NEPTUNE SWS
Carter, Kendall, BSc, pce, ... CDR(FTC)	X	PWO(N)		30.06.95	SACLANT USA
Carter, Kevin Stanley, ... LT(FTC)	X	PT		29.07.94	JSCSC
Carter, Nigel Robin, ... LT(IC)	X	AV		29.04.01	SULTAN
Carter, Paul, ... LT(FTC)	E	WESM		01.04.01	RALEIGH
Carter, Robert Ian, ... LT CDR(FTC)	X	ATC		01.10.95	RNAS CULDROSE

Name	Rank	Branch	Spec	Seniority	Where Serving
Carter, Simon Neil, psc(j),	LT CDR(FTC)	S	SM	01.02.96	MOD (BATH)
Carter, Simon Peter,	LT(FTC)	S	CA	04.04.96	UKSU SHAPE
Carter, Stephen Frank, FFA, CDipAF, psc,	CDR(FTC)	S	SM	31.12.89	NMA GOSPORT
Carthew, Richard James, BA,	LT(IC)	S	SM	01.05.01	SPLENDID
Cartwright, Darren, pce, pcea,	LT CDR(FTC)	X	O	01.09.98	ALDERNEY
Cartwright, James Andrew, BEng,	LT(FTC)	E	MESM	01.08.98	TURBULENT
Carty, Jonathan, MB, ChB,	SURG LT(SCC)	-		05.08.98	MODHU DERRIFORD
Carty, Michael Gareth,	2LT(IC)	-		01.09.00	45 CDO RM
Carver, Anthony Graham, BSc,	LT CDR(FTC)	E	WESM	01.05.89	MOD (LONDON)
Carvosso-White, Anna-Louise, BEng,	SLT(IC)	E	ME	01.09.99	SULTAN
Case, Alexander Charles, BSc, psc(j),	MAJ(FTC)	-		24.04.99	JSCSC
Case, Anthony,	LT(FTC)	S	CA	26.04.99	SOVEREIGN
Case, Paul, MILog,	LT CDR(FTC)	S	(S)	01.10.98	NELSON
Cass, Paul Stuart,	LT CDR(FTC)	S		11.02.89	MWS COLLINGWOOD
Cassar, Adrian Peter Felix, MA, pce, psc(j),	CDR(FTC)	X	MCD	30.06.98	MCMFORNORTH
Cassidy, Mark James,	CHAPLAIN	RC		24.09.00	RALEIGH
Cassidy, Stuart Martin, BEng,	SLT(IC)	X	P U/T	01.09.00	DARTMOUTH BRNC
Casson, Neil Philip, BSc,	LT CDR(FTC)	E	TMSM	01.03.99	MWS COLLINGWOOD
Casson, Paul Richard, BEng, MBA, psc(j),	CDR(FTC)	E	ME	30.06.01	BDS WASHINGTON
Casson, Roy Frederick,	LT(CC)	E	ME	01.09.00	DARTMOUTH BRNC
Castle, Alastair Stuart, BSc,	LT CDR(FTC)	X	P	01.12.01	814 SQN
Castle, Colin David,	LT(FTC)	X	PWO(A)	19.09.00	CHATHAM
Catherall, Mark Leslie,	CHAPLAIN	CE		01.09.98	FWO PORTS SEA
Cattroll, David,	LT(FTC)	E	MESM	13.06.97	NP DNREAY
Cattroll, Iain Murdo, BSc,	LT CDR(FTC)	E	WE	01.03.94	FLEET CIS PORTS
Causton, John Fraser,	SLT(IC)	X		01.09.99	MWS DRYAD
Cave, Joseph Henry James, MA,	LT(IC)	X	P U/T	01.05.01	RNAS CULDROSE
Cavill, Niki Richard Dalgliesh,	CAPT RM(IC)	-		01.05.01	42 CDO RM
Cawthorne, Matthew William Southworth, MA, psc(m),	LT COL(FTC)	-	MLDR	30.06.00	MOD (LONDON)
Cessford, Richard Ian, BEng,	LT(CC)	E	WE	01.12.99	LIVERPOOL
Chacksfield, Edward Nicholas, BA,	LT(IC)	X	HM2	01.11.99	FLEET HQ NWD
Chadfield, Laurence James, BA,	LT(FTC)	X	PWO(C)	01.03.94	ARK ROYAL
Chadwick, Kara, BA,	LT(IC)	S		01.01.02	DRAKE NBC
Challis, Sarah Elizabeth,	LT(IC)	S		01.04.01	RNAS CULDROSE
Chalmers, Donald Peter, MA, pce, psc(j),	CDR(FTC)	X	PWO(U)	31.12.99	FLEET HQ PORTS
Chalmers, Paul, BSc,	LT CDR(FTC)	X	FC	01.10.99	ARK ROYAL
Chamberlain, Nicholas Richard Lawrence, BEng,	LT CDR(FTC)	E	WE	01.11.01	HQ DCSA
Chambers, Christopher Paul, BSc,	LT(IC)	X	P	01.12.99	RNAS CULDROSE
Chambers, Ian Richard, BEng, CEng, MIEE, CDipAF,	LT CDR(FTC)	E	WESM	01.05.00	FOSM FASLANE
Chambers, Nigel Maurice Christopher, BSc, pce, (Act Capt)	CDR(FTC)	X	PWO(U)	30.06.91	2SL/CNH
Chambers, Paul David, BEng,	LT(CC)	E	WE	01.12.97	EDINBURGH
Chambers, Richard, BSc,	LT(IC)	X	HM	01.04.00	RFANSU
Chambers, Thomas George,	LT CDR(FTC)	X	MCD	01.10.88	FDG
Chambers, William John, pce,	CDR(FTC)	X	MCD	30.06.93	LOAN BMATT(EC)
Chan-A-Sue, Stephen Sangster,	LT CDR(CC)	X	P	15.04.02	845 SQN
Chandler, Marcus Ffrench Hamilton,	MAJ(CC)	-	P	01.05.98	845 SQN
Chandler, Nigel James, pce,	LT CDR(FTC)	X	PWO(C)	01.03.97	COMATG SEA
Chandler, Philip John, BEng,	LT(IC)	X		01.01.02	SULTAN
Chandler, Stephen Arthur,	LT CDR(FTC)	X	PWO(U)	01.01.87	VIVID
Chang, Christopher Joseph,	SLT(IC)	S		01.05.00	OCEAN
Chang, Hon Weng, BEng,	SLT(IC)	X	P U/T	01.01.00	DARTMOUTH BRNC
Chapell, Andrew, BA,	LT CDR(FTC)	S	SM	01.03.97	RALEIGH
Chapman, Charles Leslie, BEng,	LT CDR(FTC)	E	WESM	29.11.99	MTS IPT
Chapman, Darren Andrew,	LT CDR(CC)	X	P	01.10.98	845 SQN
Chapman, Geoffrey John Douglas, MSc, CMath, MIMA,	LT CDR(CC)	E	TM	01.10.95	NELSON RNSETT
Chapman, James Lawrence John, BSc,	LT(IC)	X		01.01.02	MWS DRYAD
Chapman, Martin Stuart,	LT(IC)	S		01.09.01	UKMARBATSTAFF
Chapman, Nicholas John, BA, MBA, pce(sm),	LT CDR(FTC)	X	SM	01.05.90	LOAN DSTL
Chapman, Nolan Phillip,	LT CDR(FTC)	S	(W)	01.10.92	RNAS YEOVILTON
Chapman, Peter, BEng, MSc,	LT CDR(FTC)	E	WE	01.09.01	MOD (LONDON)
Chapman, Simon James,	LT(FTC)	X		01.01.01	MWS DRYAD
Chapman, Simon John, pce,	LT CDR(FTC)	X	AAWO	01.04.98	ARK ROYAL

Name	Rank	Branch	Spec	Seniority	Where Serving
Chapman, Simon, BA,	MAJ(FTC)	-		01.09.98	RMCS SHRIVENHAM
Chapman-Andrews, Peter Charles, LVO, MBE, (Act Capt)	CDR(FTC)	X	PWO(N)†	30.06.89	MOD(BATH)
pce, psc,					
Chapple, Colin Peter, BSc, PGCE,	LT CDR(FTC)	X	METOC	01.05.90	MWS RNHMS CULD
Charlesworth, Graham Keith, MSc, CEng, MIEE, MCGI,	CDR(FTC)	E	WESM	30.06.91	FOST CSST SEA
Charlier, Simon Boyce, pce, pcea, psc,	CAPT(FTC)	X	P	30.06.00	MOD (LONDON)
Charlton, Christopher Robin Arthur MacGaw, BA,	CDR(FTC)	S		31.12.97	PJHQ
Charlton, Kevin William, BSc,	LT(SCC)	Q		14.01.00	RCDM
Chartres, David,	LT CDR(FC)	X		01.10.93	FLEET HQ NWD
Chaston, Stephen Paul, SM,	LT CDR(FTC)	X	SM	01.03.01	TURBULENT
Chatterjee, Shatadeep,	SLT(IC)	E	ME	01.09.99	SULTAN
Chattin, Antony Paul, BEng,	MAJ(FTC)	-	MLDR	01.05.00	HQ 3 CDO BDE RM
Chatwin, Nicholas John, BSc, pce, pcea, (Act Cdr)	LT CDR(FTC)	X	P	01.07.90	NP 1064
Chaudhary, Rahul,	SLT(UCE)(IC)	E	ME	01.01.02	DARTMOUTH BRNC
Chaudhry, Karen Ann, BM, MRCP,	SURG LTCDR(MCC)	-		01.08.98	NELSON (PAY)
Chawira, Denis Nyarono, BSc,	LT(CC)	X	MCD	01.08.97	PENZANCE
Cheadle, Richard Frank, ADC, MSc, CEng, (Commodore)	CAPT(FTC)	E	MESM	30.06.93	DRAKE NBC
FCMI, MIMechE, jsdc,					
Cheater, Christopher John,	MID(UCE)(IC)	E	ME	01.09.00	DARTMOUTH BRNC
Cheesman, Christopher John, BEng, MSc,	CDR(FTC)	E	AE	30.06.02	AFPAA(CENTURION)
Cheesman, Daniel James Edward, BSc,	CAPT RM(FTC)	-		01.09.98	COMAMPHIBFOR
Chelton, Simon Roger Lewis, BA, MIL, CDipAF, OCDS(JAP),	CDR(FTC)	S	SM	30.06.94	JSCSC
Cheseldine, David,	LT(FTC)	E	AE(M)	16.10.92	824 SQN
Cheshire, Thomas Edward, BEng, CEng, MIMechE,	LT(FTC)	E	MESM	01.02.94	SULTAN
Chesterman, Graham John, pce, pcea,	LT CDR(FTC)	X	O	01.02.93	NORTHUMBERLAND
Chesters, David Martin Brandon,	SLT(FTC)	S		01.09.98	RALEIGH
Chestnutt, James Muir, BEng,	LT(FTC)	E	P U/T	01.01.98	846 SQN
Cheyne, Roger Duncan, BEng,	LT(FTC)	E		01.09.01	RNAS YEOVILTON
Chichester, Mark Arlington Raleigh, BSc, pce, pce(sm),	LT CDR(FTC)	X	SM	01.10.90	ASM IPT
Chick, Nicholas Stevens,	LT(FTC)	X	P	16.11.95	DHFS
Chick, Stephen John, BSc, pce,	CAPT(FTC)	X	PWO(A)	30.06.01	MOD (LONDON)
Chicken, Simon Timothy, MBE, MA, psc,	COL(FTC)	-	LC	31.12.00	45 CDO RM
Chidley, Timothy James, BEng, CEng, MIMarEST, psc(j),	CDR(FTC)	E	ME	31.12.98	FWO DEVPT SEA
Chilcott, Peter Leslie Herbert, MISM, (Act Lt Cdr)	LT(FTC)	MS	SM	02.04.93	DMTO HQ
Childs, David Geoffrey, BSc, CEng,	LT(FTC)	E	AE(P)	30.06.02	JSCSC
Childs, John Richard,	LT CDR(FTC)	X	PWO(A)	01.04.02	LIVERPOOL
Chilton, Denise June,	LT(FTC)	S	(S)	01.04.01	DLO/DGDEF LOG SP
Chilton, Jerard, BEng,	LT(CC)	E	WE	01.07.98	ILLUSTRIOUS
Chilvers, Leah,	LT(SCC)	Q	ACCEM*	14.11.99	MODHU DERRIFORD
Chittenden, Timothy Clive, MA, MSc, CEng,(Commodore)	CAPT(FTC)	E	MESM	31.12.94	MOD (BATH)
MIMechE, MINucE, jsdc,					
Chittick, William Brian Oliver, BDS, MSc,	SG LT(D)(MCC)	-		10.07.97	FEARLESS
Chivers, Paul Austin, MA, pce, pcea, psc(j),	CDR(FTC)	X	O	30.06.00	PJHQ
Choat, Jeffery Hugh,	LT(CC)	X	O	16.08.93	750 SQN SEAHAWK
Choules, Barrie, MEng,	LT(CC)	E	TMSM	01.09.90	SULTAN
Chrishop, Timothy Ian, pce, pcea,	LT CDR(FTC)	X	PWO(U)	01.04.96	DUMBARTON CASTLE
Christian, David,	LT CDR(FTC)	E	ME	01.05.98	LPD(R) IPT
Christie, Andrew Bell,	LT(IC)	S	(S)	29.04.01	INVINCIBLE
Christie, Campbell Stuart, BEd, psc, psc(j),	CAPT(FTC)	E	TM	30.06.01	2SL/CNH FOTR
Christmas, Stephen Peter,	LT(CC)	X	P	16.08.91	824 SQN
Chubb, John James, BEng, MSc, CEng, MIEE, psc(j), gw,	CDR(FTC)	E	WE	30.06.02	MOD (LONDON)
Chudley, Ian Vernon,	SLT(IC)	X	P U/T	01.05.00	DARTMOUTH BRNC
Church, Alan David,	CDR(FTC)	S		31.12.96	BDS WASHINGTON
Church, Carl Robert, (Act Lt Cdr)	LT(FTC)	S	SM	01.09.90	FLEET HQ PORTS 2
Church, Stephen Cofield,	LT(CC)	X	P	16.07.96	815 SQN HQ
Churcher, Jeremy Edward, pce, n,	LT CDR(FTC)	X	H1	01.08.99	FLEET HQ PORTS 2
Churcher-Brown, Christopher John, LRCP, MRCS,	SURG CAPT(FCC)	-	CPDATE	31.12.97	RH HASLAR
DPM, FRC. Psych,					
Churchill, Timothy Charles, BA, pce,	CDR(FTC)	X	PWO(N)	31.12.93	MOD (LONDON)
Churchill, William John,	LT CDR(FTC)	E	HULL	01.10.86	DRAKE CBP(DLO)
Churchward, Matthew James,	CAPT RM(CC)	-	LC	01.05.98	ASC WATCHFIELD
Ciaravella, Timothy James, BEng,	SLT(IC)	E	ME	01.01.01	DARTMOUTH BRNC

Name	Rank	Branch	Spec	Seniority	Where Serving
Clague, John Joseph, MEng, n,	LT(CC)	X		15.01.97	WESTMINSTER
Clapham, Grantley Thom, BEng,	LT(IC)	X	P U/T	01.09.01	DHFS
Clapp, Richard Julian, BSc, jsdc, pce, pcea, (Commodore)	CAPT(FTC)	X	P	30.06.95	RN GIBRALTAR
Clapson, Keith, osc,	MAJ(FTC)	-		01.07.85	ATTURM
Clare, Jonathan Francis,	CAPT RM(FTC)	-	SO(LE)	01.01.99	CTCRM
Clare, Katharine, BSc, PhD,	LT(IC)	E	IS	29.06.96	MOD (LONDON)
Clark, Alan Sutherland, SM,	LT(IC)	X	SM	03.04.97	FLEET HQ NWD
Clark, Alastair William Charles, MA, pce, pcea, psc(j),	CDR(FTC)	X	O	31.12.98	JSCSC
Clark, Andrew Nelham, BSc, CEng, MIMechE,	LT CDR(FTC)	E	MESM	01.09.91	ASM IPT
Clark, Anthony Ivo Harvey, BSc, CEng, (Commodore) MIEE, psc,	CAPT(FTC)	E	WE	31.12.94	NC3 AGENCY
Clark, Dennis Michael James, MA, psc,	LT COL(FTC)	-	SO(LE)	31.12.99	CTCRM
Clark, Donald Kennedy, BSc, CEng, MIMarEST,	CDR(FTC)	E	MESM	30.06.98	NEPTUNE DSA
Clark, Douglas,	2LT(IC)	-		01.09.99	CTCRM LYMPSTONE
Clark, Ian David, MSc, CEng, MIMarEST,	LT CDR(FTC)	E	MESM	01.11.94	NP BRISTOL
Clark, James Lea, n,	LT CDR(FTC)	X		01.10.01	NMA PORTSMOUTH
Clark, Kenneth Ian MacDonald, pce(sm),	CDR(FTC)	X	SM	31.12.94	FOST CSST SEA
Clark, Kevin Charles, BEng, MSc, CEng, MIMarEST, MCGI,	LT CDR(FTC)	E	ME	01.11.94	MOD (BATH)
Clark, Matthew Thomas,	LT CDR(FTC)	S	SM	01.11.98	PJHQ
Clark, Michael Howard, n,	LT(FTC)	X	PWO(A)	01.03.96	EXCHANGE AUSTLIA
Clark, Paul Anthony,	CAPT RM(FTC)	-	SO(LE)	01.01.97	FLEET HQ PORTS 2
Clark, Paul Michael Colin,	LT CDR(FTC)	X	ATC	01.10.93	CV(F) IPT
Clark, Robert William,	LT CDR(FTC)	S		01.07.88	MOD (BATH)
Clark, Russell Anthony,	LT(FTC)	X	FC	01.08.99	750 SQN SEAHAWK
Clark, Simon Mansfield,	LT CDR(FTC)	S	CMA	01.12.98	ARK ROYAL
Clark, Simon Richard, BEng, adp, PGDip, CEng, MIEE,	LT CDR(FTC)	E	IS	01.05.97	CINCFLEET FTSU
Clark, Stephen Michael,	SLT(IC)	S		01.01.01	DARTMOUTH BRNC
Clark, Stephen, BSc,	LT(CC)	E	TM	01.09.97	RMB STONEHOUSE
Clark, Timothy Hubert Vian, MA, pce, psc,	CDR(FTC)	X	AWO(U)	30.06.91	MOD (LONDON)
Clarke, Adam Gregory, BSc,	LT(CC)	S		01.11.99	800 SQN
Clarke, Andrew Patrick,	LT CDR(FTC)	X	P	01.10.00	847 SQN
Clarke, Andrew Richard, BEng,	LT CDR(FTC)	E	AE	03.01.01	SULTAN
Clarke, Bernard Ronald, MA, FRGS,	CHAPLAIN	CE		30.06.81	MWS COLLINGWOOD
Clarke, Charles Maxwell Lorne, pce,	CDR(FTC)	X	PWO(U)	30.06.95	PJHQ
Clarke, Daniel, pcea,	LT(FTC)	X	O	16.03.94	848 SQN HERON
Clarke, Daniel, SM(n), SM,	LT(FTC)	X	SM	01.01.99	RALEIGH
Clarke, Ian Bruce, n,	LT CDR(FTC)	X		01.10.01	MWS DRYAD
Clarke, James,	LT CDR(FTC)	E	WE	01.10.98	CHATHAM
Clarke,John Martin, MB, BS, MRCGP, DObstRCOG, Dip FFP,	SURG CDR(FCC)	-	GMPP	30.06.02	DARTMOUTH BRNC
Clarke, Mark, SM, SM(n),	LT(FTC)	X	SM	01.04.01	VICTORIOUS(PORT)
Clarke, Matthew David, BSc,	LT(CC)	E	TM	01.05.98	45 CDO RM
Clarke, Matthew,	LT(IC)	X		01.01.02	EXETER
Clarke, Nicholas John, pce, pcea,	CDR(FTC)	X	P	30.06.99	RNAS YEOVILTON
Clarke, Peter Martin,	CAPT RM(IC)	-	P	01.01.02	815 FLT 212
Clarke, Richard William, BEng,	LT CDR(FTC)	E	AE	01.03.02	FLEET HQ PORTS
Clarke, Richard, BA, MBA,	LT CDR(FTC)	E	TM	01.10.96	JSCSC
Clarke, Robert,	LT(CC)	X	P	16.08.96	820 SQN
Clarke, Roger Donald, MSc,	LT CDR(FTC)	E	WE	27.05.92	CSIS IPT
Clarkson, Antony Michael,	SLT(IC)	E	WE	01.01.00	CUMBERLAND
Clarkson, Suzanne Jane, MB, BCh, DObstRCOG,	SURG LTCDR(SCC)	-		01.08.01	NELSON (PAY)
Claxton, Andrew Geoffery Douglas, BSc,	SLT(IC)	X		01.01.01	DARTMOUTH BRNC
Claxton, Martin Geoffrey,	LT CDR(FTC)	E	MESM	18.02.93	FOST CSST SEA
Clay, Jason Christopher, BSc, SM(n), SM,	LT(FTC)	X	SM	01.03.96	EXAMPLE
Clay, Toby Charles De Candole, BSc,	LT(CC)	X	P	01.05.98	815 FLT 214
Clayton, Christopher Hugh Trevor, pce, psc, (Commodore)	CAPT(FTC)	X	P	31.12.95	FLEET HQ PORTS
Clayton, Michael James, BA,	CAPT RM(CC)	-	LC	01.09.97	45 CDO RM
Clayton, Steven,	LT CDR(FTC)	X	P	01.07.96	899 SQN HERON
Clear, Nichola Jane, BEng,	LT(CC)	E	ME	01.11.99	ARK ROYAL
Cleary, Christopher Mycroft,	SLT(IC)	S		16.01.99	CHATHAM
Cleary, Stephen Peter, pce,	CAPT(FTC)	X	AAWO	30.06.00	MOD (LONDON)
Cleaver, James Patrick, BSc,	CAPT RM(IC)	-		24.04.99	42 CDO RM

Name	Rank	Branch	Spec	Seniority	Where Serving
Clee, James Stefan,	LT(IC)	X		01.05.02	RALEIGH
Cleeve, Kelly Ann,	MID(NE)(IC)	X		01.05.00	MWS DRYAD
Clegg, Martin Leslie, BSc, FRGS,	LT CDR(FTC)	X	H CH	01.06.90	NP 1008 OFS SVY
Clelland, Graham,	LT(FTC)	X	REG	23.07.98	DISC
Clement, Colin James, BSc,	LT CDR(FTC)	E	ME	01.10.89	WSA/CAPT MCTA
Clements, Elizabeth Joanne,	LT(CC)	S		01.05.99	815 SQN HQ
Clements, Stephen James, (Act Lt Cdr)	LT(FTC)	X	g	02.04.93	FLEET HQ PORTS 2
Cleminson, Mark David, BEng,	LT(FTC)	E	MESM	01.02.93	SPARTAN
Clemson, Anthony James, BSc,	LT(IC)	X	MW	01.08.97	BLYTH
Clifford, Clive,	LT(FTC)	X	EW	25.09.96	UKLFCSG RM
Clifford, Timothy John, BEng, MSc, CEng, MRAeS,	CDR(FTC)	E	AE	30.06.02	JSCSC
Clink, Adam Duncan, BSc,	LT CDR(FTC)	X	P	01.10.01	899 SQN HERON
Clink, John Robert Hamilton, PGDIPAN, pce,	CDR(FTC)	X	PWO(N)	30.06.99	FLEET HQ NWD
Cloney, Justin William John, BA,	SLT(IC)	X		01.09.00	DARTMOUTH BRNC
Clough, Christopher Ralph, MSc, CEng, MIEE, gw,	CDR(FTC)	E	WE	31.12.00	JSCSC
Clucas, Malcolm Richard, pcea,	LT CDR(FTC)	X	P	01.10.97	JHCHQ
Clucas, Paul Richard,	LT(FTC)	X	PT	04.04.91	NEPTUNE DLO
Cluett-Green, Stephen Mark, pce, pcea,	CDR(FTC)	X	P	30.06.02	ALBION
Coatalen-Hodgson, Ryan, BA,	MID(UCE)(IC)	X		01.09.00	DARTMOUTH BRNC
Coates, Adam James, BEng,	SLT(IC)	E	WE	01.09.00	OCEAN
Coates, Philip James Barton, MB, BS,	SURG LT(MCC)	-		04.08.99	RNAS CULDROSE
Coats, Daniel Simon, LLB,	CAPT RM(IC)	-		01.09.98	CDO LOG REGT RM
Cobb, Jill Elizabeth,	LT CDR(FTC)	W	S	01.10.97	MWS DRYAD
Cobban, Michael James, BSc, SM,	LT(IC)	X	SM	01.09.99	SUPERB
Cobbett, James Frank, pcea,	LT(FTC)	X	P	16.05.90	FEARLESS
Cochrane, Malcolm David,	LT CDR(FTC)	E	AE	09.08.91	ES AIR YEO
Cochrane, The Honourable Michael (Charles Nicholas), OBE, pce	CAPT(FTC)	X	PWO(N)	30.06.02	MWS DRYAD
Codd, Justin Sandell, BSc, SM(n), SM,	LT(CC)	X	SM	01.02.97	VIGILANT(PORT)
Cogan, Robert Edward Charles, BSc,	LT(CC)	S		01.11.92	JMOTS NORTHWOOD
Cogdell, Phillip Charles, HND,	LT CDR(CC)	E	IS	01.01.01	SHAPE BELGIUM
Coldrick, Simon Alexander,	MAJ(FTC)	-	C	01.05.97	NELSON
Cole, Alan Charles, BA,	LT CDR(FTC)	S	BAR	01.02.00	NEPTUNE 2SL/CNH
Cole, Benjamin Barry, LLB,	LT(IC)	S		01.09.01	SFM PORTSMOUTH
Cole, David John, BA,	LT(CC)	X	O	01.04.97	GANNET SAR FLT
Cole, Simon Philip,	LT CDR(FTC)	E	WE	01.10.97	MWS COLLINGWOOD
Coleman, Helen Louise, BA,	LT(IC)	X		01.05.02	MWS DRYAD
Coles, Adam John,	SLT(IC)	X		01.05.01	SOMERSET
Coles, Andrew Laurence, MA, pce, psc(j), pce(sm),	LT CDR(FTC)	X	SM	01.08.96	FLEET HQ NWD
Coles, Christopher John, BEng,	LT CDR(FTC)	E	MESM	01.09.96	NMA PORTSMOUTH
Coles, Christopher Paul, BEng,	LT(FTC)	E	AE	01.05.00	702 SQN HERON
Coles, Geoffrey William Grenville, MSc,	CDR(FTC)	E	ME	30.06.90	DRAKE SFM
Coles, Simon Phillip, BSc,	LT(IC)	E	TM	01.09.98	CAMPBELTOWN
Coley, Anthony Richard, MRIN, pce, psc,	LT CDR(FTC)	X	PWO(A)	16.04.84	MWC PORTSDOWN
Colin-Thome, Nicola Jill, BA,	LT(FTC)	X		01.09.98	DRAKE CBP(DLO)
Collacott, Jonathan Steven, BSc,	LT(CC)	S	SM	01.03.99	VENGEANCE(PORT)
Collen, Sara Jean, BEng,	LT(CC)	E	ME	01.12.97	NEPTUNE FD
Collett, Stuart Mark, BM,	SURG LT(SCC)	-		05.08.98	RH HASLAR
Colley, Ian Paul,	SLT(UCE)(IC)	E	WE	01.09.01	DARTMOUTH BRNC
Colley, Robert,	LT(IC)	X	REG	01.09.01	FLEET HQ NWD
Collier, Andrew Sheldon, BA, FRGS,	LT CDR(FTC)	X		01.06.93	MOD (LONDON)
Collighan, Giles Thomas, pce,	LT CDR(FTC)	X	AAWO	01.04.99	LOAN DSTL
Collin, Martin, (Act Maj)	CAPT RM(FTC)	-		28.04.98	LN SIERRA LEONE
Collins, Andrew Charles,	LT(CC)	X	O	01.11.00	815 FLT 210
Collins, Dale,	LT(IC)	E		01.05.02	814 SQN
Collins, Darren,	LT(FTC)	E	WE	09.01.01	WSA BRISTOL
Collins, David Andrew,	LT(FTC)	E	MESM	02.05.00	SUPERB
Collins, David Anthony, MSc, PGCE,	LT CDR(FTC)	X	METOC	01.10.95	FLEET HQ NWD
Collins, David Rudolf, BSc, PhD,	LT(IC)	E	TM	01.01.97	NELSON
Collins, Graham John Simon, pce,	LT CDR(FTC)	X	PWO(U)	07.04.96	EXCHANGE CANADA
Collins, John,	CAPT RM(FTC)	-	SO(LE)	01.01.01	RM POOLE
Collins, Lorna Jane, BSc,	LT(IC)	E	TM	01.09.00	NORTHUMBERLAND
Collins, Mark Andrew,	LT(FTC)	E	WE	09.01.01	DITMTC SHRIVNHAM

Name	Rank	Branch	Spec	Seniority	Where Serving
Collins, Mark Christopher,	LT(FTC)	X	tas	24.07.97	CALEDONIA DLO
Collins, Paul Nicholas, pce, pcea, psc,	CAPT(FTC)	X	P	30.06.02	EUMS
Collins, Paul Reginald, BSc,	LT CDR(FTC)	E	WESM	01.09.95	FLEET HQ NWD
Collins, Peter Ronald,	MAJ(FTC)	-	SO(LE)	01.10.96	FLEET HQ PORTS
Collins, Richard John, CEng, MRAeS,	CDR(FTC)	E	AE(M)	01.10.98	LOAN DARA
Collins, Sarah Jane, BSc, PGDip,	LT(CC)	E	IS	27.06.88	AFPAA(CENTURION)
Collins, Simon Jonathan Peter, BA,	LT(IC)	X	O	01.09.01	815 FLT 219
Collins, Stephen Anthony,	LT(FTC)	E	WESM	07.02.97	FOSM FASLANE
Collins, Tamar Louise, BEng, MSc, PhD,	LT(CC)	E	IS	01.01.96	NMA GOSPORT
Collis, Martin John, BEng,	LT CDR(FTC)	E	ME	01.08.99	YORK
Coltman, Timothy Patrick, MB, BS,	SURG LTCDR(MCC)	-		01.08.00	MOD (LONDON)
Combe, Gavin Robert, BEng,	LT(FTC)	E	WE	01.08.94	WSA BRISTOL
Combe, Stephen Anthony Nicholson, BA,	CAPT RM(IC)	-	P	01.09.97	847 SQN
Compain, Craig Herbert,	LT(IC)	X		21.03.98	RNAS YEOVILTON
Concarr, David Terry,	LT(CS)(CAS)	-		19.09.99	RNSR BOVINGTON
Congreve, Steven Chistopher, BSc,	MAJ(FTC)	-		01.05.00	CTCRM
Conlin, John Anthony, BA,	LT(CC)	X		01.01.99	CATTISTOCK
Conneely, Steven Andrew,	LT(FTC)	E	WE	09.01.01	OCLC BIRM
Connell, John Andrew, MBE, psc, (Act Capt)	CDR(FTC)	X	EW	01.10.93	MOD (LONDON)
Connell, Martin John,	LT CDR(FTC)	X	O	01.01.00	UKMARBATSTAFF
Connolly, Christopher John, BSc, MA, pce, psc(j),	CDR(FTC)	X	PWO(A)	31.12.00	MOD (LONDON)
Connolly, Michael Henry,	LT(CS)(CAS)	-		19.09.97	DNR SWE 2
Connor, Daniel James, BMS, BM, BS, FRCA,	SURG LTCDR(MCC)	-		01.08.97	NELSON (PAY)
Conran, Nicholas William Douglas, BSc,	SLT(IC)	S		01.01.00	MARLBOROUGH
Conroy, David Alexander,	CHAPLAIN	RC		24.09.00	FWO PORTS SEA
Conroy, Tim,	2LT(IC)	-		01.09.98	CTCRM LYMPSTONE
Considine, Keith John,	LT(IC)	X	P	01.08.00	RNAS YEOVILTON
Conway, Julian John,	LT CDR(FTC)	X	PWO(C)	01.11.93	EXCHANGE CANADA
Conway, Michael John, (Act Lt Cdr)	LT(FTC)	X	EW	03.04.97	JSSU OAKLEY
Conway, Stephen Andrew, jsdc,	LT COL(FTC)	-	C	30.06.97	RMR SCOTLAND
Conyers, Wendy Lee, BSc,	LT(CC)	X		01.02.00	PENZANCE
Cook, Christian, SM(n), SM,	LT(FTC)	X	SM	01.04.97	RALEIGH
Cook, Christopher Buchan, MSc,	LT CDR(FTC)	E	IS	01.10.00	NELSON RNSETT
Cook, David John, gdas,	LT CDR(FTC)	X	O	01.10.97	LOAN JTEG BSC DN
Cook, Gordon Edward,	LT CDR(FTC)	X	O	01.10.00	815 SQN HQ
Cook, Harry, MBE,	LT CDR(FTC)	X	PWO(N)	10.08.83	MWS DRYAD
Cook, James Steele,	MID(NE)(IC)	X	SM	01.01.02	DARTMOUTH BRNC
Cook, Michael, BEng,	LT(CC)	E	TM	01.07.90	SULTAN
Cook, Myles Fitzpatrick, BA,	MAJ(FTC)	-	C	01.05.00	HQ 3 CDO BDE RM
Cook, Neville John Hunter, MILT,	LT(IC)	S		01.05.02	PJHQ
Cook, Paul Roger, pce,	CDR(FTC)	X	AAWO	31.12.98	MOD (LONDON)
Cook, Peter William John, sq,	MAJ(FTC)	-		01.05.92	HQ SOUTHLANT
Cook, Simon Geoffrey, BA,	SLT(IC)	X	O U/T	01.09.00	DARTMOUTH BRNC
Cook, Timothy Arnold, BA,	MAJ(FTC)	-	C	01.09.97	NELSON (PAY)
Cooke, Darren Christopher James, BSc,	LT(IC)	X		01.05.02	MWS DRYAD
Cooke, David John, MBE, pce, pce(sm), hcsc, (Commodore)	CAPT(FTC)	X	SM	31.12.95	MOD (LONDON)
Cooke, Graham John,	LT CDR(FTC)	X	PT	01.10.99	SHAPE BELGIUM
Cooke, Graham Spencer, BSc,	LT CDR(FTC)	X	O	01.10.01	702 SQN HERON
Cooke, Joanne Madeleine, MB, ChB,	SURG LT(SCC)	-		02.08.00	CFLT MED(SEA)
Cooke, Jonathan Edward, n,	LT(FTC)	X	PWO(U)	18.02.95	ARGYLL
Cooke, Martin Yeats, BA(OU), psc(m), osc,	LT COL(FTC)	-	C	30.06.91	JACIG
Cooke, Michael John,	LT(FTC)	E	AE(M)	16.10.92	FLEET AV VL
Cooke, Robert Neale,	LT(IC)	E	AE	29.04.01	HARRIER IPT
Cooke, Stephen Neil, BEng,	LT(IC)	X	P U/T	01.01.02	RNAS YEOVILTON
Cooke-Priest, Nicholas Charles Richard, pcea,	LT(CC)	X	O	01.05.95	JSCSC
Cooksley, Richard Edgar Charles,	LT(IC)	X	C	08.04.01	HQ DCSA
Cooling, Robert George, BA, jsdc, pce,	CAPT(FTC)	X	PWO(N)	30.06.98	MOD (LONDON)
Coomber, Jonathan Martin, BA,	MAJ(FTC)	-	MLDR	01.09.01	EXCHANGE ARMY UK
Coomber, Mark Andrew,	LT CDR(FTC)	X	FC	18.07.95	RNAS YEOVILTON
Coombes, Derek, MIIE,	CDR(FTC)	E	WE	31.12.93	SFM PORTSMOUTH
Coope, Philip James, BEng,	LT(FTC)	E	WE	01.03.95	JSCSC
Cooper, Adam, BA,	LT(IC)	S		01.08.98	FWO FASLANE

Name	Rank	Branch	Spec	Seniority	Where Serving
Cooper, Adam, BEng,	SLT(IC)	E	WE U/T	01.09.00	KENT
Cooper, Christopher John, BSc, PGDip,	LT CDR(FTC)	X	METOC	01.10.98	FOST SEA
Cooper, John Arnold, BSc, CEng, MIMarEST, MINucE,	CDR(FTC)	E	MESM	31.12.92	MOD (BATH)
Cooper, Kevin Philip, BSc,	LT CDR(FTC)	E	WE	01.10.96	FOST SEA
Cooper, Mark Andrew, pce, pce(sm),	CDR(FTC)	X	SM	31.12.00	TORBAY
Cooper, Neil Philip,	LT CDR(FTC)	E	ME	01.10.97	LOAN OMAN
Cooper, Neil,	CAPT RM(FTC)	-	SO(LE)	01.01.00	CTCRM
Cooper, Peter Frank, MBE, MSc, CEng, MIMechE,	LT CDR(FTC)	E	MESM	21.04.89	RN GIBRALTAR
Cooper, Robert Terence, MBE,	MAJ(FTC)	-	SO(LE)	01.10.96	1 ASSLT GP RM
Cooper, Simon John, pcea, psc,	CDR(FTC)	X	O	30.06.01	NEPTUNE
Cooper, Simon Stanway, BEng, CEng, MIMarEST,	LT CDR(FTC)	E	WESM	01.05.99	MOD (BATH)
Cooper-Simpson, Roger John,	MAJ(FTC)	-	C	01.05.00	FLEET CIS PORTS
Cope, Marcus Adrian,	LT(FTC)	E	WESM	09.01.01	VIGILANT(PORT)
Copeland, Stephen Nicholas, BEng, psc(j),	LT CDR(FTC)	E	AE	01.02.99	849 SQN HQ
Copinger-Symes, Rory Sandham, psc(j),	LT COL(FTC)	-		30.06.02	CTCRM
Coppin, Nigel James,	SLT(IC)	S		01.01.00	FEARLESS
Coppin, Paul David,	LT CDR(FTC)	E	AE(L)	01.10.92	SULTAN
Copsey, Nicholas,	2LT(IC)	-		01.09.98	CTCRM LYMPSTONE
Corbett, Andrew Scott, pce, pce(sm), psc(j),	LT CDR(FTC)	X	SM	01.06.96	FOST CSST SEA
Corbett, Gerard John,	LT CDR(FTC)	X	ATC	01.10.96	RNAS YEOVILTON
Corbett, Mark Thomas,	LT(IC)	X		01.05.01	MIDDLETON
Corbett, Paul,	SLT(IC)	X	AV	01.10.99	RFANSU (ARGUS)
Corbett, Thomas James,	LT(CC)	X	FC	01.04.94	MWS DRYAD
Corbett, William Roger, BSc, FRMS, psc(m),	CDR(FTC)	X	METOC	30.06.01	ELANT/NAVNORTH
Corbidge, Stephen John,	MAJ(FTC)	-	SO(LE)	01.10.97	RALEIGH
Corder, Ian Fergus, MA, jsdc, pce, pce(sm),	CAPT(FTC)	X	SM	30.06.99	CUMBERLAND
Corderoy, John Roger, MSc, BEng,	CDR(FTC)	E	MESM	30.06.01	JSCSC
Corderoy, Richard Ian, MEng, AMIEE,	LT(FTC)	E	WESM	01.01.00	SPARTAN
Cordner, Michael, MB, BMS, CHB, (Act Surg Lt)	SURG SLT(SCC)	-		11.07.01	DARTMOUTH BRNC
Corkett, Kerry Stephen,	LT(FTC)	X	REG	24.07.97	SULTAN
Cormack, Andrew James Ross, BSc, MB, ChB,	SURG LT(MCC)	-		05.08.98	MODHU DERRIFORD
Cornberg, Malcolm Arthur, OBE, MBA, FCMA, CDipAF,	CAPT(FTC)	S	CMA	30.06.02	FLEET HQ PORTS 2
Corner, Gordon Charles, pce, (Act Cdr)	LT CDR(FTC)	X	PWO(C)	01.12.90	MOD (LONDON)
Corner, Ian Lindsey Ferguson, fsc, osc,	MAJ(FTC)	-	P	01.11.83	CTCRM
Cornford, Marc, BEng,	LT(CC)	X	P	01.04.00	846 SQN
Cornick, Robin Michael,	LT CDR(FTC)	X	MCD	01.10.97	MOD (LONDON)
Cornish, Michael Christopher, pce,	LT CDR(FTC)	X	AAWO	01.07.95	EXCHANGE CANADA
Corps, Stephen David,	LT CDR(FTC)	E	WE	01.03.02	WSA/CAPT MCTA
Corrigan, Niall Richard, BSc, pce,	CDR(FTC)	X	PWO(A)	30.06.96	2SL/CNH
Corrin, Colby St John, LLB, jsdc, psc,	MAJ(FTC)	-	MLDR	01.09.92	PJHQ AUGMENTEES
Corry, Simon Myles, BSc, MA, AMIEE, psc(j),	CDR(FTC)	E	WE	31.12.00	T45 IPT
Coryton, Oliver,	2LT(IC)	-		01.09.98	CTCRM LYMPSTONE
Cosby, Richard Ashworth De Sausmarez, LVO, jsdc, pce,	CAPT(FTC)	X	PWO	30.06.94	NATO MEWSG VL
Costello, Gerard Thomas, BSc, MDA,	CDR(FTC)	E	WESM	31.12.93	WSA BRISTOL
Cottee, Benjamin Richard John,	LT(CC)	X	ATC	01.09.94	RNAS YEOVILTON
Cotterill, Bruce Maxwell, BEng, MSc,	LT CDR(FTC)	E	WESM	01.03.00	FLEET HQ PORTS 2
Cottis, Mathew Charles,	LT CDR(FTC)	S	SM	01.10.01	CHATHAM
Cotton, Emma Louise,	LT(FTC)	S	(W)	01.04.01	FLEET HQ PORTS 2
Couch, Paul Henry Reginald Benedict,	CHAPLAIN	RC		05.05.92	RNAS YEOVILTON
Couch, Paul Jonathan, MSc, CEng, MRAeS,	CAPT(FTC)	E	AE	30.06.02	FLEET HQ PORTS
Coughlan, Scott, BA,	SLT(IC)	X		01.09.00	DARTMOUTH BRNC
Coulson, Jeremy Richard, BEng, PGCE,	LT CDR(FTC)	E	IS	08.12.85	NMA PORTSMOUTH
Coulson, Peter, BEng, MSc, CEng, MIEE,	LT CDR(FTC)	E	WE	01.12.97	FOST SEA
Coulthard, Adrian, BSc, MinstP, CMath, MIMA,	LT(CC)	E	TM	11.05.91	SULTAN
Coulthard, John Kinnear, MSc, CEng, MIMechE, jsdc,	CDR(FTC)	E	MESM	31.12.93	MOD (BATH)
Coulton, Ian Christopher, MA, MBA, psc(j),	CDR(FTC)	MS		30.06.01	MOD (LONDON)
Coulton, Jamie Robert Spencer,	LT(CC)	X	P	16.06.98	702 SQN HERON
Counter, Paul Richard, MB, BS, MRCS,	SURG LTCDR(MCC)	-		01.08.99	NELSON (PAY)
Course, Andrew James, MBE, MSc, AMIEE, gw,	CDR(FTC)	E	WE	30.06.02	JSCSC
Courtney, Timothy Paul,	SLT(IC)	E	WESM	01.05.00	DARTMOUTH BRNC
Coverdale, Anthony, MSc, CEng, psc,	CDR(FTC)	E	MESM	31.12.93	MOD (BATH)
Coverdale, Paul, BSc,	LT(IC)	X	HM	01.03.00	FWO DEVPT SEA

Name	Rank	Branch	Spec	Seniority	Where Serving
Covington, William MacArtney, pce, pcea, psc, (Commodore)	CAPT(FTC)	X	P	31.12.96	RNAS YEOVILTON
Cowan, Aidan Roland,	LT(FTC)	X	C	19.09.00	MWS DRYAD
Cowan, Christopher John, LLB,	LT(FTC)	S		01.07.95	OCLC ROSYTH
Cowan, Kenneth Gordon,	CAPT RM(IC)	-		23.04.99	45 CDO RM
Cowdrey, Mervyn Charles,	CDR(FTC)	S		30.06.93	FLEET HQ PORTS
Cowell, Richard James, BSc,	SLT(IC)	E	WE U/T	01.09.00	LIVERPOOL
Cowie, Andrew David, BSc,	LT(IC)	E	WE	01.01.02	MWS COLLINGWOOD
Cowie, Kevin Michael,	LT CDR(FTC)	X	C	01.10.99	RALEIGH
Cowin, Timothy James, BSc,	LT(IC)	X	P	01.11.98	846 SQN
Cowley, Nigel Jonathan, pcea, psc,	CDR(FTC)	X	P	31.12.89	NMA GOSPORT
Cowley, Richard Merlin, BSc,	LT CDR(FTC)	X	MCD	01.04.97	MWS DEF DIV SCHL
Cowper, Ian Robert, BSc, CEng, MIMarEST,	LT CDR(FTC)	E	ME	01.10.00	CUMBERLAND
Cowton, Elliott Neil, BEd, adp,	LT CDR(FTC)	E	IS	01.10.91	AFPAA(CENTURION)
Cox, David John, BEng, MSc, CEng, MIEE,	LT CDR(FTC)	E	WE	01.10.01	MWS COLLINGWOOD
Cox, Gillian Fay, BSc,	LT(CC)	S		01.04.98	NELSON
Cox, Jonathan Peter,	LT CDR(FTC)	X	MCD	01.10.95	WSA BRISTOL
Cox, Mark Bamber,	LT(FTC)	S		03.07.97	DRAKE DPL
Cox, Matthew David, BEng,	SLT(IC)	E	ME	01.01.01	DARTMOUTH BRNC
Cox, Matthew James, BA,	LT(IC)	X	HM	01.01.99	ROEBUCK
Cox, Pieter William Studley, BSc, CEng, MIEE,	CDR(FTC)	X	WESM	30.06.93	NMA PORTSMOUTH
Cox, Rex John, n,	LT CDR(FTC)	X	AAWO	01.03.01	LIVERPOOL
Cox, Sean Adrian Joel,	LT(CC)	X	P	16.08.93	848 SQN HERON
Cox, Stephen John, psc(m),	COL(FTC)	-	MOR	30.06.99	RMB STONEHOUSE
Coxon, Helen Elizabeth Mary,	MID(UCE)(IC)	X		01.09.00	DARTMOUTH BRNC
Coyle, Gavin James, BSc, n,	LT CDR(FTC)	X	PWO(U)	01.08.01	RICHMOND
Coyle, Phillip John, BSc,	LT(IC)	S		24.09.99	NEPTUNE NT
Coyle, Ross Daniel,	LT(IC)	E	WE	01.05.02	DARTMOUTH BRNC
Coyne, John Derek,	LT(FTC)	X	AV	17.12.93	RNAS YEOVILTON
Crabb, Antony John, MSc,	LT(FTC)	X		01.04.96	MWS DRYAD
Crabbe, Robert James, BSc,	LT(CC)	X		01.12.98	SUTHERLAND
Crabtree, Ian Michael, BSc, pce,	CDR(FTC)	X	AAWO	31.12.90	NMA PORTSMOUTH
Crabtree, Peter Dixon, OBE, BA, ACIS,	CAPT(FTC)	S	BAR	31.12.00	MOD (LONDON)
Cragg, Richard Darryl, BEng,	LT(FTC)	E	MESM	01.01.95	FOSM GOSPORT
Craggs, Stuart, BEng, CEng, MIMechE,	LT(FTC)	E	AE	01.12.94	ES AIR YEO
Crago, Philip Thomas, BSc, CEng, MIMarEST,	CDR(FTC)	E	ME	30.06.02	RMCS SHRIVENHAM
Craib, Alfred George,	LT(FTC)	E	WE	05.06.92	ELANT/NAVNORTH
Craig, Clare Lucy, BSc,	LT(IC)	X		01.12.95	MWS DRYAD
Craig, John Antony,	LT CDR(FTC)	X	MCD	01.05.02	EDINBURGH
Craig, Kenneth Mitchell, BSc,	MAJ(FTC)	-		01.05.01	CTCRM
Craig, Michael Jon, BSc,	SLT(IC)	X	P U/T	01.05.00	DARTMOUTH BRNC
Craig, Peter Daniel, BEng, PGDIPAN, pce,	LT CDR(FTC)	X	PWO(N)	01.02.96	BRIDPORT
Craig, Rodney William Wilson, MNI, jsdc, pce,	CDR(FTC)	X	PWO(A)	30.06.90	PJHQ AUGMENTEES
Cramp, Anthony Michael, pce, pcea,	LT CDR(FTC)	X	P	01.01.96	815 SQN HQ
Cran, Barrie Charles, BEng, CEng, MIMechE,	LT CDR(FTC)	E	MESM	01.12.96	NP DNREAY
Crane, Oliver Richard, BSc,	LT(IC)	X	P	01.10.98	846 SQN
Craner, Matthew John, MB, BCh, MRCP,	SURG LTCDR(MCC)	-		01.08.98	NELSON (PAY)
Crascall, Stephen John, (Act Lt Cdr)	LT(FTC)	X	AV	23.07.93	FLEET HQ PORTS
Craven, Dale,	SLT(IC)	E	WESM	01.01.00	CSST RNSSS
Craven, John Arthur Graham, MIL, MCMI,	LT CDR(FTC)	S		01.09.85	2SL/CNH FOTR
Craven, Martin William, BEng,	LT(CC)	X	P	01.08.98	815 FLT 229
Craven, Oliver Edward,	MID(UCE)(IC)	X		01.09.00	DARTMOUTH BRNC
Craven-Phillips, Thomas Charles Dale,	MAJ(FTC)	-		01.02.79	RM CONDOR
Crawford, Adam Timothy Stephen, BSc,	CAPT RM(IC)	-		01.05.98	MOD (LONDON)
Crawford, Keith,	LT(IC)	X		01.09.01	MWS DRYAD
Crawford, Leslie,	LT CDR(FTC)	E	WE	01.10.01	WSA BRISTOL
Crawford, Paul Ian, MB, BS,	SURG CDR(FCC)	-	SM	31.12.98	LOAN BRUNEI
Crawford, Valerie Elizabeth, LLB,	LT(IC)	X		01.01.02	SHEFFIELD
Crawley, David Anthony,	LT(IC)	E	ME	01.04.01	CAMPBELTOWN
Creates, Keith Ian, BA, pce,	LT CDR(FTC)	X	PWO(U)	01.04.87	TCM IPT
Cree, Andrew Martin, BEng, MSc,	LT CDR(FTC)	E	TM	01.09.97	FLEET HQ PORTS
Cree, Malcolm Charles, BA, pce, fsc,	CDR(FTC)	X	AAWO	30.06.98	JSCSC
Creech, Richard David, gdas,	LT CDR(FTC)	X	O	01.10.96	700M MERLIN OEU

Name	Rank	Branch	Spec	Seniority	Where Serving
Creek, Stephen Brian,	LT(IC)	E	WESM	01.01.02	TRIUMPH
Crew, Julian Maynard, BA,	LT(IC)	X	P	01.01.00	815 FLT 211
Criddle, Gary David James,	LT(CC)	X	O	01.06.96	FLEET AV SUPPORT
Crimmen, David John, pcea,	LT(CC)	X	P	01.03.91	771 SQN
Cripps, Michael James, MEng, MRAeS,	SLT(IC)	E	AE	01.09.99	SULTAN
Crispin, Toby Alexander Baldwin, BSc, pcea,	LT CDR(FTC)	X	O	01.04.94	RNAS YEOVILTON
Crockatt, Stephen Richard James,	LT(FTC)	X	P	01.09.90	LOAN JTEG BSC DN
Croft, David Francis, MA,	LT(IC)	X		01.01.99	ECHO
Crofts, David Jeffrey, BEng, MSc, AMIEE,	LT CDR(FTC)	E	WE	01.02.99	GLASGOW
Croke, Anthony, pce, pcea, psc, ocds(Can),	CAPT(FTC)	X	P	30.06.99	SA MADRID
Cromie, John Martin, MSc,	LT(CC)	X	FC	01.05.00	SOUTHAMPTON
Crompton, Andrew Paul James, BSc,	SLT(IC)	X	ATCU/T	01.09.99	RNAS YEOVILTON
Crompton, Philip John,	LT(CC)	X	P	01.11.00	820 SQN
Crook, Andrea Susan, BA, jsdc,	CDR(FTC)	S		30.06.97	FEARLESS
Crookes, Waveney Alan,	LT(FTC)	X	MCD	01.07.97	FDU1
Croome-Carroll, Michael Patrick John, MBE,	LT CDR(FTC)	X	MCD	27.01.90	NELSON
Cropley, Andrew, BSc, MA(Ed), MA, psc(j),	LT CDR(FTC)	E	TM	01.09.94	2SL/CNH FOTR
Cropper, Fraser Brunel Nicholas, BEng, MSc,	LT CDR(FTC)	E	AE	24.06.01	LOAN DSTL
Cropper, Martin Andrew Keith, BA,	LT CDR(FTC)	S	SM	16.05.90	DRAKE DPL
Crosbie, Donald Ernest Frederick,	LT CDR(FTC)	X	PWO(U)	01.02.00	FOSNNI OPS DLO
Crosby, John Paul, psc, (Act Col)	LT COL(FTC)	-		30.06.93	HQ NORTH
Crosland, Stephen Andrew,	SLT(IC)	E	WE	01.01.01	MWS COLLINGWOOD
Cross, Alexander Leigh, BEng,	LT(FTC)	E	WESM	01.07.98	VICTORIOUS(PORT)
Cross, Andrew George,	CAPT RM(IC)	-	SO(LE)	01.04.02	45 CDO RM
Cross, Eric John,	CAPT RM(IC)	-	P	01.01.02	847 SQN
Cross, Martin George, BSc, psc,	LT CDR(FTC)	E	MESM	01.04.88	ASM IPT
Crossley, Charles Crispin, BSc, CEng, MIMarEST, MIMechE,	CDR(FTC)	E	ME	31.12.99	NMA PORTSMOUTH
Crossley, Guy Antony,	LT(CC)	X	P	16.05.93	RAF CRANWELL EFS
Crouch, Matthew, BSc,	LT(IC)	X		01.05.01	GRIMSBY
Crouden, Stephen Frederick,	MAJ(FTC)	-	SO(LE)	01.10.98	JSCSC
Crowe, David Michael, n,	LT(FTC)	X		01.08.99	ARGYLL
Crowther, Kevin Wayne, BSc, pce,	LT CDR(FTC)	X	AAWO	29.03.91	MWC PORTSDOWN
Crozier, Stuart Ross McDonald, BA,	CDR(FTC)	S	BAR	30.06.01	MWS COLLINGWOOD
Crudgington, Paul, AFC, pcea,	LT CDR(FTC)	X	F	01.09.87	824 SQN
Crumplin, Carolyn Anne,	LT CDR(FTC)	X	C	01.10.92	MWS COLLINGWOOD
Crundell, Richard John, BEng, MSc, gw,	LT CDR(FTC)	E	WE	01.07.00	MOD (LONDON)
Cryar, Timothy Martin Craven, pce, n,	LT CDR(FTC)	X	AAWO	01.08.98	FOST SEA
Cubbage, Jamie, BEng,	LT CDR(FTC)	E	WE	01.04.02	NELSON RNSETT
Cull, Iain, n,	LT CDR(FTC)	X	PWO(N)	01.05.02	FOST SEA
Cullen, Nicola Leonie, BSc,	LT(CC)	E	TM	01.09.95	MWS COLLINGWOOD
Cullis, Christopher John, sq,	MAJ(FTC)	-	LC	25.04.96	NELSON
Culshaw, Joanne, BA,	SLT(IC)	X		01.01.01	DARTMOUTH BRNC
Culwick, Peter Francis, BDS, MSc, MGDS RCS,	SGCDR(D)(FCC)	-		31.12.96	JSCSC
Cummin, Michael Antony, BSc, CEng, MIMarEST,	CDR(FTC)	E	MESM	31.12.95	MOD (BATH)
Cumming, Frazer Smith, MEng,	SLT(IC)	X	O U/T	01.09.00	DARTMOUTH BRNC
Cumming, Robert Angus, BEng,	LT(FTC)	E	MESM	01.04.97	TRIUMPH
Cummings, Alan Thomas, pce, pcea, ocds(USN),	LT CDR(FTC)	X	O	01.03.97	WALNEY
Cummings, David John, BEng, MSc,	LT(FTC)	E	WE	01.11.94	DOSG BRISTOL
Cunane, John Richard, MCIT, MILT,	LT CDR(FTC)	S	SM	01.10.98	UKMARBATSTAFF
Cundy, Robert Graham, psc(j),	MAJ(FTC)	-		01.09.96	RM POOLE
Cunnane, Keith John, BEng, MSc, CEng, MIEE,	LT CDR(FTC)	E	WESM	01.10.01	MOD (LONDON)
Cunnell, Rachael Louise, BA,	SLT(IC)	S		01.01.00	ILLUSTRIOUS
Cunningham, Andrew Nicholas, BA,	CAPT RM(FTC)	-		01.09.96	NP 1061
Cunningham, Craig, HND,	LT CDR(CC)	E	TMSM	01.10.95	NEPTUNE 2SL/CNH
Cunningham, David Andrew, MB, BS, LRCP, MRCS,	SURG CAPT(FCC)	-	GMPP	30.06.94	NELSON
Cunningham, David Andrew, pcea,	LT CDR(FTC)	X	O	15.12.95	ARK ROYAL
Cunningham, David Brand,	LT(IC)	E	MESM	01.09.01	VANGUARD(PORT)
Cunningham, John Gavin, BA, pce, pcea, PSC(ONDC),	LT CDR(FTC)	X	O	01.12.93	FWO PORTS SEA
Cunningham, John Stewart,	MAJ(FTC)	-	SO(LE)	01.10.98	RM POOLE
Cunningham, Justin Thomas, MA, psc(j),	MAJ(FTC)	-		01.05.99	MOD (LONDON)
Cunningham, Nigel John Whitworth,	LT(FTC)	X	O	27.07.95	815 FLT 202
Cunningham, Paul, FCIPD, CDipAF,	CDR(FTC)	S		31.12.97	OCEAN

Name	Rank	Branch	Spec	Seniority	Where Serving
Cunningham, Rachel Ann, BEng,	SLT(IC)	E	WE U/T	01.01.01	DARTMOUTH BRNC
Cunningham, Richard Alister, MBE, pce, pcea, psc,	CDR(FTC)	X	P	30.06.00	MWC PORTSDOWN
Cunningham, Thomas Anthony, pce, pcea, psc,	CAPT(FTC)	X	O	31.12.00	FEARLESS
Curd, Timothy Allan, pce, psc,	CDR(FTC)	X	MCD	31.12.93	LOAN KUWAIT
Curlewis, Andrew John, BEng, MSc,	LT CDR(FTC)	E	ME	01.04.00	ALBION
Curnow, Michael David, BSc, CEng, MIMechE, psc,	CDR(FTC)	E	ME	31.12.98	ILLUSTRIOUS
Curr, Ralph Donaldson, MB, BS, DObstRCOG, FRCGP, AKC,	SURG RADM	-	GMPP	03.10.02	2SL/CNH
Currass, Timothy David, BEng, MSc,	LT CDR(FTC)	E	WE	01.03.99	WSA BRISTOL
Currie, David William, BSc, pce,	LT CDR(FTC)	X	AAWO	01.04.90	LOAN DSTL
Currie, Duncan Gordon,	LT CDR(FTC)	X	P	16.12.01	NMA PORTSMOUTH
Currie, Michael John, BSc,	LT(CC)	X	O	16.08.99	824 SQN
Currie, Stuart McGregor, BEng,	LT CDR(FTC)	E	MESM	01.08.99	SUPERB
Curry, Benedict Rodney, MBE, psc,	LT COL(FTC)	-	C	30.06.02	FLEET HQ NWD
Curry, Jamie Hunter, BA, n,	LT(CC)	X		01.02.98	YORK
Curry, Robert Edward, BSc, n,	LT CDR(FTC)	X		01.11.01	EXCHANGE NORWAY
Curtis, David,	LT(FTC)	E	WESM	04.09.98	FOST CSST FSLN
Curtis, Paul Anthony, HND, IEng, MIIE, (Act Lt Cdr)	LT(FTC)	E	WE	18.10.85	FLEET CIS PORTS
Curtis, Robert John,	LT CDR(FTC)	X	AAWO	01.10.00	LOAN OMAN
Curtis, Suzannah Elizabeth Hayton, BMus,	LT(IC)	S		01.09.99	ILLUSTRIOUS
Curwood, Jenny Elizabeth, BSc,	LT(CC)	S		01.11.98	MOD (BATH)
Cusack, Nicholas James, MSc, jsdc,	LT COL(FTC)	-	C	30.06.99	BDS WASHINGTON
Cust, David Robert, nadc, jsdc, pce(sm), (Commodore)	CAPT(FTC)	X	SM	30.06.94	HQ SOUTHLANT
Cutler, Tristan Paul, BSc,	LT(CC)	S		01.10.99	NELSON WF
Cutt, John James Douglas, pce(sm), psc,	CDR(FTC)	X	SM	30.06.94	NMA PORTSMOUTH

D

Name	Rank	Branch	Spec	Seniority	Where Serving
D'Arcy, Paul Andrew,	LT(FTC)	X	O	16.08.90	FLEET AV VL
D'Silva, Daniel Mark, BEng, AMIEE,	LT(FTC)	E	WE	01.02.98	WSA BRISTOL
Da Gama, Joseph Anthony Jude, BSc, CEng, MIEE, MRAeS, psc,	CDR(FTC)	E	AE	30.06.96	2SL/CNH
Dabell, Guy Lester, BSc,	CDR(FTC)	E	MESM	30.06.02	MOD (BATH)
Dacombe, Carl Andrew,	SLT(UCE)(IC)	X		01.09.01	DARTMOUTH BRNC
Dadwal, Rajesh Kimle, BA,	SLT(IC)	X		01.08.99	ARK ROYAL
Daglish, Hugh Blyth, LVO, pce, psc,	CAPT(FTC)	X	AAWO	31.12.96	TEMERAIRE
Dailey, Paul George Johnson, MSc, CEng, MIEE, MCMI, Eur Ing,	LT CDR(FTC)	E	WESM	01.04.97	VANGUARD(PORT)
Dainton, Steven, pce, n,	LT CDR(FTC)	X	PWO(C)	01.03.98	NMA PORTSMOUTH
Dainty, Robin Christopher, SM,	LT(IC)	X	SM	29.04.01	TURBULENT
Dale, Alistair,	LT(FTC)	X	ATC	23.02.92	ARK ROYAL
Dale, Jamie Richard,	MID(NE)(IC)	X	O U/T	01.09.01	DARTMOUTH BRNC
Dale, Michael John, pce, psc, (Act Capt)	CDR(FTC)	X	PWO(C)	30.06.93	FLEET CIS PORTS
Dale, Nathan Andrew,	SLT(IC)	X	P U/T	01.09.01	DHFS
Dale, Nigel,	LT(FTC)	X	SM	25.07.96	STRS IPT
Dale, William David John, BSc, n,	LT(IC)	X	HM2	01.08.98	SCOTT
Dale-Smith, Guy, BA, PGDIPAN, pce,	LT CDR(FTC)	X	PWO(N)	01.12.97	EXCHANGE CANADA
Dalglish, Kenneth Michael,	SLT(UCE)(IC)	E	WE	01.09.01	DARTMOUTH BRNC
Dallamore, Rebecca Ann,	LT(IC)	X		01.01.01	FLEET HQ PORTS
Dalton, David John,	LT CDR(FTC)	E	AE(L)	01.10.92	MERLIN IPT
Dalton, Feargal John, BEng,	LT(CC)	E	WESM	01.07.95	TORPEDO IPT
Daly, Andrew, BEng, AMIEE,	LT CDR(FTC)	E	WE	01.12.00	MWS COLLINGWOOD
Daly, Julie Margaret, BEd, (Act Lt Cdr)	LT(CC)	E	TM	04.01.93	2SL/CNH FOTR
Daly, Michael Philip,	SLT(IC)	E	WE	01.01.01	MWS COLLINGWOOD
Daly, Paul,	LT(CC)	X		01.05.99	LEEDS CASTLE
Danbury, Ian Gerald, BSc, AMIEE,	CDR(FTC)	E	WE	30.06.98	MOD (LONDON)
Dando, Jonathon Neil, n,	LT CDR(FTC)	X	PWO(A)	01.08.00	2SL/CNH FOTR
Dane, Richard Martin Henry, MBE,	LT CDR(FTC)	X	P	01.10.94	814 SQN
Daniel, Andrew Gordon,	LT CDR(FTC)	X	SM	01.10.95	2SL/CNH FOTR
Daniel, Benjamin James Edward, BA,	SLT(IC)	X	P U/T	01.01.01	DARTMOUTH BRNC
Daniell, Christopher John, pcea,	LT CDR(FTC)	X	O	01.10.95	LOAN OTHER SVCE
Daniels, Ian James Russel, BSc, pcea, gdas,	LT CDR(FTC)	X	O	01.10.95	849 SQN B FLT
Daniels, Stephen Anthony, pcea, psc, tp,	CDR(FTC)	X	P	30.06.00	LOAN JTEG BSC DN

Name	Rank	Branch	Spec	Seniority	Where Serving
Daniels, Stuart Paul,	LT(FTC)	X	PT	01.04.01	RNAS YEOVILTON
Daniels, Timothy Nicholas, BA, psc(j),	MAJ(FTC)	-	C	01.09.93	PJHQ
Dann, Ace, BA,	LT(FTC)	X		01.04.99	MWS DRYAD
Dann, Adrian Stuart,	LT CDR(FTC)	X	MCD	01.10.98	MCME IPT
Dannatt, Timothy Mark, MSc, CEng, MIMechE, jsdc,	CDR(FTC)	E	ME	30.06.93	FLEET HQ PORTS 2
Daramola, Olufunmilayo, MB, MRCOG, CHB,	SURG LTCDR(SCC)	-		01.12.98	CFLT MED(SEA)
Darch, Brian Nicholas, BSc, CEng,	CDR(FTC)	E	ME	31.12.83	MOD (BATH)
MIMechE, MDA, CDipAF, psc,					
Darkins, Colin Richard, BSc,	LT(IC)	E	TM	01.01.98	NELSON RNSETT
Darley, Matthew Edward, BSc,	CAPT RM(IC)	-	P U/T	01.09.01	RAF CRANWELL EFS
Darling, James Ian,	LT CDR(FTC)	E	WE	01.10.98	FLEET HQ PORTS 2
Darlington, Mark Robinson, BSc, pce,	CDR(FTC)	X	AAWO	30.06.98	MOD (LONDON)
Darlow, Paul Raymond,	LT(FTC)	S	CA	03.04.97	RNAS YEOVILTON
Dart, Duncan James,	SLT(IC)	X	P U/T	01.09.01	DHFS
Darwent, Andrew, BSc, MDA, CEng, MIEE,	CDR(FTC)	E	WE	30.06.99	FLEET CIS PORTS
Darwent, Sean Anthony, BSc,	LT(CC)	X	O	01.03.93	GANNET SAR FLT
Dashfield, Adrian Kenneth, MB, BCh, MD, FRCA,	SURG CDR(FCC)	-	(CA)	30.06.00	MODHU DERRIFORD
Dathan, Timothy James, BEng, MSc,	LT CDR(FTC)	E	ME	01.03.95	PJHQ
Daukes, Nicholas Michael, BSc,	MAJ(FTC)	-		01.09.01	RM POOLE
Daulby, Darron James, BEng,	LT(IC)	X	FC	01.05.00	CARDIFF
Daveney, David Alan, BA, BSc, SM(n),	LT(FTC)	X	SM	01.10.97	SOVEREIGN
Davenport, Nigel Jefferson, BDS,	SGLTCDR(D)(MCC)	-		16.01.97	MWS COLLINGWOOD
Davey, Christopher Stephen, BSc,	SLT(IC)	X	P U/T	01.01.01	DARTMOUTH BRNC
Davey, Gary Stuart, BEng,	LT CDR(FTC)	E	AE	01.11.98	702 SQN HERON
Davey, Paul John, BSc, CEng, FIMarEST,	LT CDR(FTC)	E	ME	01.06.89	MOD (BATH)
Davey, Timothy James, BSc,	LT(IC)	X	MCD	01.10.97	RAMSEY
David, Simon Evan James, MA, psc(j),	LT CDR(FTC)	S		16.10.94	NMA PORTSMOUTH
Davidson, Allan Miller,	LT CDR(FTC)	X	P	01.06.98	RNAS CULDROSE
Davidson, Neil Richard,	LT(FTC)	X	P	01.04.91	JSCSC
Davies, Andrew James Albert, gdas,	LT(CC)	X	O	01.08.90	NELSON
Davies, Anthony Robin, MA, psc, pce,	CDR(FTC)	X	PWO(A)	31.12.94	ELANT/NAVNORTH
Davies, Christopher John, BSc, MIExpE, ACMI, pce, isc,	CDR(FTC)	X	MCD	30.06.02	COMSTRIKFORSTH
Davies, Christopher Ronald,	CAPT RM(CC)	-		01.05.99	ASC WATCHFIELD
Davies, Christopher Stanley, MA,	LT CDR(FTC)	X	METOC	01.09.90	BDLS INDIA
Davies, Gary,	LT(FC)	E	WESM	15.06.90	MWS COLLINGWOOD
Davies, Geraint William Tudor,	LT(CC)	X	FC	01.12.97	ILLUSTRIOUS
Davies, Henry George Alexander,	LT(IC)	X	P	01.07.96	849 SQN B FLT
Davies, Huan Charles Ayrton, BSc,	MAJ(FTC)	-	MLDR	01.09.00	FLEET HQ PORTS
Davies, Ian Ellis, n,	LT CDR(FTC)	X	H CH	01.12.98	MWS DRYAD
Davies, Ian Hugh, BSc, pce,	LT CDR(FTC)	X	SM	16.10.83	FLEET HQ NWD
Davies, Jason Lee,	LT(IC)	MS		01.09.01	MODHU DERRIFORD
Davies, John Huw, BA, psc(j),	CDR(FTC)	X	METOC	31.12.00	HQ SOUTHLANT
Davies, John Robert, osc(us),	LT COL(FTC)	-		31.12.98	CTCRM
Davies, Jonathan Peter, BSc, MA, psc(j),	LT CDR(FTC)	S		01.10.92	MOD (LONDON)
Davies, Justin Wayne, BEng,	LT CDR(FTC)	E	ME	11.05.01	CV(F) IPT
Davies, Lee, BEng,	LT CDR(FTC)	E	AE(P)	01.01.02	815 FLT 209
Davies, Lyndon James,	LT CDR(FTC)	E	ME	01.10.98	RALEIGH
Davies, Mark Bryan, pce, pcea, psc(j)o,	LT CDR(FTC)	X	O	24.01.97	NMA PORTSMOUTH
Davies, Michael Charles, BSc,	LT(IC)	X		01.07.00	SUTHERLAND
Davies, Nicholas Mark Samuel, BSc,	LT(CC)	X	HM	01.09.98	FWO DEVPT SEA
Davies, Paul Nicholas Michael, pce, psc(m).	CAPT(FTC)	X	AAWO	31.12.98	NEPTUNE DLO
Davies, Peter Roland, CBE, MSc, CEng, FIEE, nadc, gw,	RADM	-	WESM	31.07.01	2SL/CNH FOTR
Davies, Stephen Philip,	LT CDR(FTC)	E	WESM	01.10.01	DRAKE SFM
Davies, Timothy Christopher, BSc,	LT(IC)	X	P	16.04.00	RAF LINTN/OUSE
Davies, Timothy Gordon, BSc, MRAeS, odc(Fr),	CDR(FTC)	E	AE(P)	31.12.98	ILLUSTRIOUS
Davies, Trevor Martin, BEng, MSc, MIExpE,	LT CDR(FTC)	E	WE	01.10.97	MOD (LONDON)
Davis, Andrew Richard,	LT CDR(CC)	X	P	18.10.95	800 SQN
Davis, Bernard James, OBE, LLB,	CDR(FTC)	S	BAR	31.12.90	NMA PORTSMOUTH
Davis, Christopher John,	LT COL(FTC)	BS		30.06.02	RM BAND PTSMTH
Davis, Edward Grant Martin, MBE, MA, psc(m),	LT COL(FTC)	-		31.12.98	MOD (LONDON)
Davis, Gary,	LT(IC)	X	EW	01.01.02	RNU RAF DIGBY
Davis, Martin Philip, BSc, pce, pcea, psc,	LT CDR(FTC)	X	O	01.07.88	T45 IPT

Name	Rank	Branch	Spec	Seniority	Where Serving
Davis, Richard, BSc,	LT(CC)	X		01.01.99	CUMBERLAND
Davis, Stephen Rickard, BEng,	LT(FTC)	E	WESM	01.11.96	FLEET HQ NWD
Davis-Marks, Michael Leigh, BSc, MA, pce, pce(sm), psc, MNI,	CDR(FTC)	X	SM	31.12.95	UKMARBATSTAFF
Davison, Andrew Paul, BSc, PGDip PGCE,	LT CDR(FTC)	X	METOC	01.10.94	MOD (LONDON)
Davison, Gregory James,	LT(FTC)	X	P	01.04.91	815 FLT 239
Davison, James Charles, PGDIPAN, pce,	LT CDR(FTC)	X	PWO(N)	01.11.98	FOST MPV(SEA)
Davison, Jeffrey Edward, pce,	LT CDR(FTC)	X	AAWO	06.04.97	SA MALAYSIA
Davison, Laura Marie,	MID(NE)(IC)	X		01.09.01	DARTMOUTH BRNC
Davison, Terence John,	LT(FTC)	E	WE	13.06.86	2SL/CNH
Daw, Simon James, pcea,	LT CDR(CC)	X	O	01.10.97	ARK ROYAL
Dawe, Christopher John,	SLT(IC)	X		01.01.02	RALEIGH
Dawkins, Martin William, BSc, MRAeS,	LT CDR(CC)	X	P	01.10.97	LOAN JTEG BSC DN
Daws, Richard Patrick Anthony, MSc, MIEE,	CDR(FTC)	E	WESM	30.06.99	MOD (LONDON)
Dawson, Alan James, BTech,	LT(FTC)	E	WESM	24.02.95	RALEIGH
Dawson, Allan,	LT RM(IC)		SO(LE)	30.03.00	RM POOLE
Dawson, Edward William, MSc, CEng, MIEE, jsdc, gw,	CAPT(FTC)	E	AE	31.12.95	RCDS
Dawson, Graham Alexander Edward, BSc, BEng,	LT(IC)	X	P	01.09.00	SULTAN
Dawson, Nigel Julian Frederick, BSc,	LT(CC)	E	TM	01.09.94	MOD (LONDON)
Dawson, Paul,	LT(FTC)	E	MESM	01.04.01	VENGEANCE(STBD)
Dawson, Peter John,	LT CDR(FTC)	X	ATC	01.10.89	MOD (LONDON)
Dawson, Phillip Mark David,	LT(IC)	X		01.01.02	RALEIGH
Dawson, Stephen Lee, MA, PGCE, MDA, psc,	CDR(FTC)	E	TM	30.06.02	2SL/CNH
Dawson, Stewart Neville, BEng, MIIE,	LT CDR(FTC)	E	WE	01.10.98	NOTTINGHAM
Dawson, William, pce,	LT CDR(FTC)	X	AAWO	01.11.98	CARDIFF
Day, Anthony,	SLT(IC)	X	REG	01.01.00	MOD (LONDON)
Day, Benjamin Thomas, BA,	LT(IC)	X		01.01.02	MWS DRYAD
Day, Christopher Philip, BSc,	SLT(IC)	X		01.05.98	COTTESMORE
Day, Michael Kershaw, BSc,	LT(CC)	X	P	15.06.95	848 SQN HERON
Day, Nigel Richard, MA, FInstAM, MCIT, MILT, psc, psc(j),	CDR(FTC)	S		31.12.91	RHQ AFNORTH
Day, Simon Nicholas, BEng, MSc,	LT(FTC)	E	ME	01.10.96	MOD (BATH)
Day, Timothy Mark, MSc,	LT CDR(CC)	E	TM	01.10.94	MWS COLLINGWOOD
de Jager, Hendrikus, psc,	LT COL(FTC)	-		31.12.91	FLEET HQ PORTS 2
De Jonghe, Paul Trevor, IEng, HNC, MIIE,	LT CDR(FTC)	E	WE	01.10.94	LOAN OMAN
De La Mare, Richard Michael,	LT CDR(FTC)	S		01.10.94	MOD (LONDON)
De La Rue, Andrew Nicholas, BA,	LT(IC)	S		01.09.01	VANGUARD(PORT)
De Reya, Anthony Luciano,	MAJ(FTC)	-		01.09.01	HQ 3 CDO BDE RM
De Sa, Philip John, pce, psc,	CDR(FTC)	X	PWO(A)	31.12.91	SACLANT USA
de Val, Kevin Leslie, rcds, psc,	LT COL(FTC)	-		31.12.86	FLEET HQ PORTS 2
De-Yoxall, James,	SLT(IC)	X	P U/T	01.09.00	DARTMOUTH BRNC
Deacon, Phillip Reginald,	SLT(IC)	S		01.09.01	RALEIGH
Deacon, Stephen,	LT CDR(FTC)	X	O	01.06.98	824 SQN
Deakin, David John, BSc,	LT(IC)	X	P	01.01.00	815 FLT 227
Deakin, Johanna, BEng,	LT(FTC)	E	AE	01.01.95	LYNX OEU
Deal, Charlotte, BEng,	LT(CC)	E	WE	01.06.99	SOUTHAMPTON
Deam, Paul Andrew Victor, SM(n), SM,	LT(FTC)	X	SM	23.07.98	FLEET HQ NWD
Dean, James Robert, (Act Lt Cdr)	LT(FTC)	S		01.10.95	NMA GOSPORT
Dean, Michael Robin, MB, BCh, MFOM, MRCGP, DObstRCOG,	SURG CDR(FCC)	-	(CO/M)	30.06.93	INM ALVERSTOKE
Dean, Simon Ian Robert,	LT RM(IC)	-		01.09.00	FPGRM
Dean, Timothy Charles, BDS,	SG LT(D)(SCC)	-		22.07.97	LOAN BRUNEI
Dean, William Michael Henry, BSc, gdas,	LT CDR(FTC)	X	P	01.10.95	EXCHANGE USA
Deaney, Mark Nicholas, BSc, CEng, MRAeS,	CDR(FTC)	E	AE	31.12.00	HARRIER IPT
Dearden, Steven Roy, MSc, CEng, FIMechE,	CAPT(FTC)	E	MESM	30.06.02	NP BRISTOL
Dearling, Peter Charles,	LT(FTC)	X	MW	29.07.88	FLEET HQ PORTS
Deavin, Matthew James,	LT(CC)	X	O	01.07.95	FLEET AV VALLEY
Debenham, Leslie Allen, BEng, CEng, MRAeS, CGIA, mdtc,	LT CDR(FTC)	E	AE	20.10.82	MOD (BATH)
Dechow, William Ernest, BSc, jsdc,	LT COL(FTC)	-		30.06.99	PJHQ
Dedman, Nigel John Keith, pce, pcea, fsc,	CAPT(FTC)	X	O	30.06.01	MOD (LONDON)
Deighton, Alastair William Greenway, BA,	LT(FTC)	X		01.09.99	ST ALBANS
Deighton, Derek Simpson, pce,	LT CDR(FTC)	X	PWO(A)	01.05.92	MOD (LONDON)
Dekker, Barrie James, MB, BS,	SURG LTCDR(MCC)	-		01.08.99	NELSON (PAY)

Name	Rank	Branch	Spec	Seniority	Where Serving
Delahay, Jonathon Edward, BSc,	LT RM(IC)	-		01.09.00	FPGRM
Dell, Iain Martin, MSc, (Act Lt Cdr)	LT(FTC)	MS	(AD)	23.07.93	PJHQ AUGMENTEES
Deller, Mark Gareth, pce, pcea, psc,	LT CDR(FTC)	X	P	01.03.94	COMSTRIKFORSTH
Delvin, Sarah Louise,	SLT(IC)	X		01.09.00	DARTMOUTH BRNC
Dembrey, Mark Nicholas Scott, BSc,	LT(IC)	X	O	16.12.94	RNAS YEOVILTON
Dempsey, Sean Patrick,	LT(FTC)	X		01.02.99	KENT
Denham, Daniel John,	LT(CC)	X	P	01.06.98	FLEET AV VALLEY
Denham, Nigel John,	CDR(FTC)	X	SM	31.12.00	ELANT/NAVNORTH
Denholm, Iain Glenwright, pce,	LT CDR(FTC)	X	AAWO	13.08.94	FOST SEA
Denholm, James Lovell, MB, ChB,	SURG LTCDR(MCC)	-		07.08.01	NELSON (PAY)
Denison, Alan Rae Van Tiel, MSc, CEng, MIMechE,	LT CDR(FTC)	E	ME	01.02.89	MCME IPT
Denney, Andrew,	2LT(IC)	-		01.09.01	CTCRM LYMPSTONE
Denney, James Robert, BA,	LT(CC)	X		01.02.99	NOTTINGHAM
Denning, Paul Richard, MA, psc(m),	LT COL(FTC)	-	P	31.12.96	MOD (LONDON)
Dennis, James Alexander, BSc,	CAPT RM(IC)	-		01.09.99	CHFHQ
Dennis, Mark John, BSc, PGCE,	LT(IC)	E	TM	01.01.97	DISC
Dennis, Matthew John, SM(n),	LT CDR(FTC)	X	SM	01.10.01	VIGILANT(PORT)
Dennis, Philip Edward, BSc,	LT(FTC)	X	FC	01.07.96	FOST SEA
Denovan, Paul Andrew, BSc, CEng, MIEE,	LT CDR(FTC)	E	WESM	01.01.94	ASM IPT
Densham, Martin Philip John, BA, BSc,	LT(IC)	X	HM	01.10.98	FLEET HQ NWD
Denton, Adrian Matthew, BSc,	LT(IC)	X	FC	01.10.97	EXETER
Depledge, Ian George, BSc, CEng, MIEE,	LT CDR(FTC)	E	WE	01.04.94	MOD (BATH)
Derby, Byron Dylan, BEng, CEng, MIEE, MIIE, NDipM,	LT CDR(FTC)	E	WE	01.04.02	MOD (BATH)
Derby, Peter John, MAPM,	LT CDR(FTC)	MS	(PD)	01.10.98	2SL/CNH
Dermody, Ryan Thomas,	LT(IC)	X	FC	01.12.00	NOTTINGHAM
Derrick, Gareth Gwyn James, BSc, CEng, MIEE, psc(j)o,	CDR(FTC)	E	WESM	30.06.97	MOD (LONDON)
Derrick, Matthew John George, BEng,	LT(IC)	E	TM	01.12.99	SULTAN
Despres, Julian,	SLT(SCC)	Q		19.11.98	RH HASLAR
Devereux, Michael Edwin, BA,	CAPT RM(FTC)	-	P	01.09.97	ASC WATCHFIELD
Deverson, Richard Timothy Mark, pcea,	LT CDR(FTC)	X	P	01.10.01	UKMFTS IPT
Devine, Alexander Robert,	SLT(IC)	X		01.05.01	NORFOLK
Devlin, Hugh Francis Gerard,	MAJ(FTC)	-	SO(LE)	01.10.00	42 CDO RM
Dew, Anthony Michael, MB, BCh,	SURG LT(SCC)	-		02.08.00	VIGILANT(STBD)
Dewar, Duncan Andrew, BSc, psc(j),	MAJ(FTC)	-		01.03.99	40 CDO RM
Dewar, Joanna Clare, BM,	SURG LTCDR(SCC)	-		30.04.02	FOSM GOSPORT
Dewar, Michael James, BSc,	SLT(IC)	X		01.01.01	DARTMOUTH BRNC
Dewsnap, Michael David,	LT CDR(FTC)	E	WE	01.10.01	WSA/CAPT MCTA
Di Maio, Mark David, BSc,	SLT(IC)	S		01.01.00	MARLBOROUGH
Dible, James Hunter, pce,	LT CDR(FTC)	X	P	16.11.96	GUERNSEY
Dick, Colin Michael, BEng,	LT(IC)	E	TM	01.01.97	FOST CSST FSLN
Dickens, David James Rees, pce, psc,	CAPT(FTC)	X	PWO(U)	30.06.02	FWO PORTS SEA
Dickens, David Stephen, BEng,	LT(IC)	E	WE	01.11.92	PORTLAND
Dicker, Nicholas Martin,	SLT(IC)	X		01.05.01	HURWORTH
Dickins, Benjamin Russell, BA,	LT(FTC)	X		01.11.96	RAIDER
Dickinson, Pamela Hepple, BEng,	LT(IC)	E	TM	01.07.00	PORTLAND
Dickinson, Philip Neville, BA,	LT CDR(FTC)	X	O	01.05.82	2SL/CNH FOTR
Dickinson, Richard John, BSc, MA, psc, (Act Cdr)	LT CDR(FTC)	E	AE	01.04.90	JCA IPT USA
Dickson, Andrew McGillivray,	MID(IC)	X	P U/T	01.01.01	DARTMOUTH BRNC
Dickson, Andrew Peat, pce, (Commodore)	CAPT(FTC)	X	AAWO	30.06.96	MOD (LONDON)
Dickson, James Ian, BSc,	LT(FTC)	S	SM	01.08.94	AGRIPPA NAVSOUTH
Dickson, James Peter Edward, MSc,	LT CDR(FTC)	X	METOC	01.10.96	MWC PORTSDOWN
Dickson, Stuart James, MB, ChB, DTM&H, MRCP,	SURG LTCDR(MCC)	-		02.08.00	NELSON (PAY)
Dillon, Ben, BEng,	SLT(IC)	E	WE U/T	01.09.00	ST ALBANS
Dilloway, Philip John, BA,	LT(SCC)	Q	RMN	07.12.96	RH HASLAR
Dineen, John Michael George, MA,	LT CDR(FTC)	X	PWO(A)	01.04.02	NORFOLK
Dingley, Paul Alexander,	LT(FTC)	X	O	01.01.01	820 SQN
Dinham, Alan Colin, BSc, PhD,	LT CDR(FTC)	E	TM	01.10.88	MOD (LONDON)
Dinsdale, Andrew Malcolm, BEng, MSc, CEng, MIEE,	LT CDR(FTC)	E	WESM	01.02.00	WSA/CAPT MCTA
Disney, Peter William, pcea,	LT CDR(FTC)	X	O	01.10.94	824 SQN
Diver, Paul Harry, HND,	LT(IC)	E	TM	01.01.91	ASM IPT
Dixon, Arthur Kenneth, BEng,	LT(IC)	E	MESM	01.09.00	SULTAN
Dixon, Mark Edward, BEng,	SLT(IC)	E	ME U/T	01.01.01	DARTMOUTH BRNC

Name	Rank	Branch	Spec	Seniority	Where Serving
Dixon, Raymond Francis, HNC, IEng, MITE, psc,	LT CDR(FTC)	E	WE	08.06.84	MOD (BATH)
Dixon, Richard Andrew,	LT(IC)	X	P	01.01.01	CORNWALL FLT
Dixon, Robert James,	SLT(IC)	X		01.01.02	FLEET HQ PORTS
Dixon, Simon Peter,	SLT(IC)	X		01.05.01	MWS DRYAD
Dobbin, Vincent William,	LT CDR(FTC)	E	WESM	01.10.96	ACDS(POL) USA
Dobbins, Stuart James, BA,	LT(IC)	S		01.06.97	CNH(R)
Dobie, Fiona Elizabeth,	LT(FTC)	W	X	01.09.96	COMATG SEA
Dobson, Amy Clare,	SLT(IC)	X	O U/T	01.04.00	702 SQN HERON
Dobson, Brian John,	LT CDR(FTC)	S	SM	01.10.95	CHFHQ
Dobson, Richard Andrew, BSc,	LT CDR(FTC)	X	H CH	01.04.91	LOAN HYDROG
Docherty, Paul Thomas, BA, MNI, pce, psc,	CAPT(FTC)	X	AAWO	31.12.98	2SL/CNH FOTR
Dodd, Kevin Michael, QCBA, pcea,	LT CDR(FTC)	X	O	01.04.99	824 SQN
Dodd, Laura, BEng,	LT(CC)	E		01.09.01	MONMOUTH
Dodd, Nicholas Charles,	LT CDR(FTC)	S		01.04.99	2SL/CNH
Dodd, Peter Michael,	SLT(IC)	X		01.01.01	PJHQ
Dodd, Stuart Eric, SM(n),	LT(CC)	X	SM	01.10.00	RM POOLE
Dodds, Malcolm, jsdc, pce,	CDR(FTC)	X	PWO(N)†	31.12.90	DA MANAMA
Dodds, Matthew Lewis, BSc,	LT(FTC)	X		01.04.99	INVERNESS
Dodds, Ralph Scott, pce, pcea,	LT CDR(FTC)	X	O	01.05.93	MWS DRYAD
Dodgson, Stephen John, BA, MSc,	CDR(FTC)	E	WESM	31.12.98	MOD (LONDON)
Doe, James Richard, BSc,	SLT(IC)	X		01.09.00	DARTMOUTH BRNC
Doherty, Kenneth,	LT CDR(FTC)	X	P	01.10.93	702 SQN HERON
Doig, Barry John, BSc,	LT(CC)	X		01.12.97	OCEAN
Dolby, Michael John, MIIE, AMIEE,	LT CDR(FTC)	E	WE	01.10.99	2SL/CNH FOTR
Dominy, David John Douglas, n,	LT CDR(FTC)	X	AAWO	01.03.00	EDINBURGH
Donaldson, Andrew Michael,	LT(FTC)	E	WE	09.01.01	WSA BRISTOL
Donaldson, James, FCMI, jsdc, pce, MBA,	CDR(FTC)	X	PWO(A)	30.06.92	JSCSC
Donaldson, Stuart Bruce, pce(sm),	LT CDR(FTC)	X	SM	01.09.91	FWO DEVONPORT
Donegan, Claire Louise, LLB,	LT(CC)	X	P	01.10.96	771 SQN
Donnelly, James Stephen, BEng, CEng, MRAeS,	LT CDR(FTC)	E	AE	22.11.98	800 SQN
Donnelly, Samantha, BSc, HND,	LT(IC)	E	TM	17.09.96	EXCHANGE RAF UK
Donovan, Patrick, BEng,	LT(FTC)	E	MESM	01.11.91	SULTAN
Donovan, Paul Anthony,	CHAPLAIN	RC		22.04.85	EXCHANGE USA
Donovan, Robin John, BA,	LT CDR(FTC)	S	SM	01.01.01	SHEFFIELD
Donovan, Sally Jane,	LT(CC)	X	ATC	01.07.97	FOST DPORT SHORE
Donovan, Simon James, BA,	LT(IC)	X		01.05.02	MWS DRYAD
Donworth, Desmond Maurice Joseph, n,	LT(CC)	X		01.12.96	MWS DRYAD
Doolan, Martin, MA, pce, psc(j),	CDR(FTC)	X	PWO(U)	30.06.01	MWC SOUTHWICK
Dooley, Martin Edward,	SLT(IC)	E	WE	01.01.01	MWS COLLINGWOOD
Doran, Iain Arthur Gustav, BA,	LT(FTC)	X		01.07.95	MWS DRYAD
Doran, Katie Elizabeth, BSc,	LT(IC)	X		01.09.01	BRECON
Doran, Shane Edmund, BEng,	LT(FTC)	E	ME	01.07.94	T45 IPT
Dorricott, Alan Joseph,	CDR(FTC)	E	ME	30.06.02	SFM PORTSMOUTH
Doubleday, Steven,	LT(CC)	X	P	16.10.98	RAF SHAWBURY
Douglas, Emma Elizabeth, BEng,	SLT(IC)	E	ME	01.09.99	SULTAN
Douglas, Francis Robin, BSc, CEng, MIEE, MIMarEST,	CDR(FTC)	E	MESM	31.12.89	DRAKE CBS
Douglas, Patrick John,	LT CDR(FTC)	X	P	01.12.00	MWS DRYAD
Douglas, Paul Gordon, SM(n), SM,	LT CDR(FTC)	X	SM	03.12.00	SPLENDID
Douglas-Riley,Timothy Roger, MB, BS, LRCP, MRCS, DA, MRCGP, jsdc,	SURGCAPT(FCC)	-	GMPP	31.12.96	MOD (LONDON)
Douglass, Martin Colin Marc, BEng,	LT CDR(FTC)	E	ME	01.03.99	FOST SEA
Doull, Donald James Murray, BEng, MSc, CEng, MIMarEST, BS,	LT(FTC)	E	MESM	01.11.94	MOD (BATH)
Dow, Andrew James Royston,	2LT(IC)	-		01.09.00	FPGRM
Dow, Clive Stewart,	LT(FTC)	S	BAR	01.01.97	2SL/CNH
Dow, William Allister McGowan, MB, ChB,	SURG LT(MCC)	-		06.08.97	NELSON (PAY)
Dowd, Jonathan Wyn, BSc,	MAJ(FTC)	-		01.09.01	NMA PORTSMOUTH
Dowdell, Robert Edmund John, BSc,	LT CDR(FTC)	X	P	01.10.94	LOAN JTEG BSC DN
Dowell, Paul Henry Neil, BSc, MA, psc(j),	LT CDR(FTC)	E	WE	01.08.94	FLEET HQ PORTS 2
Dowie, Matthew Edwin, BSc,	LT(IC)	X		01.01.02	RALEIGH
Dowling, Andrew Jonathan,	LT(IC)	X	O	01.09.01	815 FLT 202
Downes, Colin Henry, BSc,	LT CDR(FTC)	X	MW	01.09.01	FOST MPV(SEA)
Downie, Alan John, FIEE,	LT CDR(FTC)	E	WE	01.10.97	JACIG

Name	Rank	Branch	Spec	Seniority	Where Serving
Downing, Iain Michael,	LT(CC)	X	P	16.09.94	RAF CRANWELL EFS
Downing, Phaedra Louise, BSc,	LT(IC)	E	TM	01.02.99	2SL/CNH FOTR
Downing, Stephen Jamie, BSc,	LT(CC)	X		01.11.98	CAMPBELTOWN
Downing-Waite, Jeanette Ann, LLB,	LT(FTC)	S		01.05.99	CTCRM
Dowrick, Michael Paul, BA(OU), MA,	LT RM(IC)	BS	SO(LE)	01.04.00	MWS RM SCH MUSIC
Dowsett, Patrick Giles, pce, n,	LT CDR(FTC)	X	PWO(C)	01.09.01	ARK ROYAL
Doxsey, Roland Arthur, MSc, CEng, MIMechE, jsdc,	CDR(FTC)	E	ME	30.06.89	CV(F) IPT
Doyle, Gary Lawrence, pce, pcea, psc(j),	CDR(FTC)	X	O	31.12.99	SOUTHAMPTON
Doyle, Nicholas Patrick,	LT(FTC)	X	g	17.12.93	GUERNSEY
Doyne-Ditmas, Philip Simon, MBE, pce, pcea, psc, psc(j),	CDR(FTC)	X	P	31.12.95	DRAKE DPL
Drake, Charlotte Louise, BMus,	LT(FTC)	S		01.02.98	2SL/CNH
Drake, Edwin Denis,	CDR(FTC)	E	WESM	30.06.96	JSU NORTHWOOD
Dransfield, Joseph Asa James, BSc,	LT(CC)	X	O	01.05.99	815 FLT 246
Draper, Stephen Perry, pce,	LT CDR(FTC)	X	AAWO	26.02.96	MWS DRYAD
Dray, Jake,	SLT(IC)	X		01.05.00	MWS DRYAD
Dreelan, Michael Joseph, MSc, pce,	LT CDR(FTC)	X	PWO(U)	01.08.99	WESTMINSTER
Dresner, Rupert James,	MAJ(FTC)	-	P	24.04.02	RNAS YEOVILTON
Drewett, Colin Edward, BEM,	LT(CS)(CAS)	-		19.09.98	DNR RCHQ SOUTH
Drewett, Robin Edward, MBE, pce, pcea, (Act Capt)	CDR(FTC)	X	O	30.06.99	DA KIEV
Driscoll, Robert, BSc, PGCE,	LT(CC)	E	TM	22.07.97	CDO LOG REGT RM
Drodge, Andrew Paul Frank,	LT(FTC)	X	O	01.10.94	JSCSC
Drodge, Kevin Nigel, BSc,	LT(IC)	X	P	01.10.98	CAMPBELTOWN FLT
Drummond, Henrietta, BSc,	LT(IC)	E	TM	01.09.96	RALEIGH
Drummond, Karl Bruce, BDS,	SG LT(D)(MCC)	-		13.07.98	OCEAN
Drury, Martin Herbert,	LT CDR(FTC)	X	PT	01.10.93	KING ALFRED
Dry, Ian, BSc,	LT(IC)	E	TM	31.01.99	CINCFLEET FIMU
Drylie, Andrew John, BSc,	LT CDR(FTC)	X	SM	01.02.92	MOD (LONDON)
Drysdale, Steven Ronald, pce(sm), SM,	LT CDR(FTC)	X	SM	01.02.97	PJHQ
Drywood, Tobias, BEng, MSc,	LT CDR(FTC)	E	ME	01.04.01	MOD (BATH)
Duce, Matthew,	LT(IC)	X		01.05.01	QUORN
Duff, Andrew Patrick,	LT(FTC)	X	SM	01.09.00	MWS DRYAD
Duffy, Henry, pce,	LT CDR(FTC)	X	PWO(C)	01.05.99	JSCSC
Duffy, Mari Louise,	SLT(IC)	X		01.01.00	TEMERAIRE
Dufosee, Sean William, pcea,	LT CDR(FTC)	X	P	01.10.00	LOAN OTHER SVCE
Duke, Ronald Michael,	LT CDR(FCC)	Q	CPN	31.12.96	MOD (LONDON)
Dumbell, Phillip, BSc, MA, CEng, MIEE, psc,	CDR(FTC)	E	WESM	30.06.02	NEW IPT
Dumbleton, David William,	LT(FTC)	E	WE	01.04.01	MONTROSE
Duncan, Colin John,	LT(FTC)	X	P	01.09.93	815 FLT 219
Duncan, Giles Spencer, BSc,	CAPT RM(FTC)	-		01.05.98	CTCRM
Duncan, Ian Stewart, BSc,	LT CDR(FTC)	E	MESM	01.06.94	DRAKE CBS
Duncan, Jeremy,	LT CDR(FTC)	X	P	01.10.01	FLEET AV CU
Duncan, Kathryn Claire Louise, BSc,	LT(CC)	X		01.10.99	NORFOLK
Dunham, Mark William, BSc, psc(m),	COL(FTC)	-		30.06.02	FPGRM
Dunkley, Simon Charles,	LT(FTC)	X	AV	26.04.99	RNAS YEOVILTON
Dunlop, Peter Francis, BSc, pce,	LT CDR(FTC)	X	PWO(U)	01.04.91	MWS DRYAD
Dunn, Andrew James Patrick,	LT CDR(FTC)	E	AE(M)	01.10.00	NMA PORTSMOUTH
Dunn, Anthony,	LT(FTC)	X	AV	01.04.01	RNAS CULDROSE
Dunn, Gary Russell, BEng, MSc, CEng, Eur Ing,	LT CDR(FTC)	E	WESM	01.05.98	TRENCHANT
Dunn, Nicholas Geoffrey, BSc, pcea,	LT CDR(FTC)	X	P	01.10.92	ARK ROYAL
Dunn, Paul Edward, SM, SM(n),	LT CDR(FTC)	X	SM	01.07.01	FOST CSST DEVPT
Dunn, Paul Ernest,	LT CDR(FTC)	X	PT	01.10.01	PJHQ AUGMENTEES
Dunn, Robert Alexander Phillip, BEng,	LT(IC)	X	P	01.12.99	FLEET AV VALLEY
Dunn, Robert Paul, pce(sm),	LT CDR(FTC)	X	SM	02.01.98	SHAPE BELGIUM
Dunne, Michael Gerard, BEM, (Act Lt Cdr)	LT(FTC)	X	AV	03.04.97	FLEET AV SUPPORT
Dunningham, Stephen, IEng, (Act Lt Cdr)	LT(FTC)	E	ME	10.06.94	NOTTINGHAM
Dunsby, Nicholas Byron,	LT CDR(FTC)	E	MESM	01.10.01	TRAFALGAR
Dunt, Peter Arthur, CB, rcds,	VADM	-	(S)	30.04.02	MOD (LONDON)
Dunthorne, Julie Agnes,	LT CDR(FTC)	S		04.01.00	CSSG (SEA)
Durham, Paul Christopher Langton, BEng, MRAeS, n,	LT(FTC)	E		18.05.95	HQ3GP HQSTC
Durkin, Jane,	SURG SLT(SCC)	-		01.07.01	DARTMOUTH BRNC
Durkin, Mark Thomas Gilchrist, BSc, pce, psc(j),	CDR(FTC)	X	MCD	31.12.00	EXETER
Durning, William Munro,	LT CDR(FTC)	MS		01.10.99	NMA GOSPORT

Name	Rank	Branch	Spec	Seniority	Where Serving
Durston, David Howard, pce, pcea, psc, psc(j), ... CDR(FTC)	X	P	30.06.92	MWS COLLINGWOOD
Durup, Jason Michael Stanley, ... CAPT RM(IC)	-	LC	01.09.00	539 ASSLT SQN RM
Dustan, Andrew John, ... LT CDR(FTC)	E	AE	19.02.93	FLEET HQ PORTS
Dutton, Andrew Colin, ... LT(FTC)	S	SM	01.02.95	TRIUMPH
Dutton, David, MA, pce, psc(j), ... CDR(FTC)	X	PWO(C)	31.12.00	GLASGOW
Dutton, James Benjamin, BSc, rcds, psc(m), ... BRIG(FTC)	-	C	31.12.98	HQ 3 CDO BDE RM
Dutton, Philip John, ... LT CDR(FTC)	E	WESM	01.10.99	DCSA RADIOHQ FMR
Dwane, Christopher Malcolm Robin, BSc, ... LT CDR(FTC)	S		01.01.89	DRAKE NBC
Dyer, Graham Richard, ... LT(FTC)	E	WE	05.06.92	MOD (BATH)
Dyer, Jonathan David Thomas, BTech, MSc, ... LT CDR(CC)	E	IS	01.09.99	RMCS SHRIVENHAM
Dyer, Michael David James, BEng, MSc, CEng, MIEE, ... CDR(FTC)	E	WESM	30.06.00	ASM IPT
Dyer, Shani Danyell, ... MID(NE)(IC)	X		01.09.01	DARTMOUTH BRNC
Dyer, Simon John, BSc, psc, ... CDR(FTC)	E	WE	30.06.92	MOD (LONDON)
Dyke, Christopher Leonard, MA, pce, psc(j), ... LT CDR(FTC)	X	PWO(C)	01.02.96	FLEET CIS PORTS
Dyke, Kenneth Andrew, BEng, ... LT CDR(FTC)	E	MESM	01.10.00	VICTORIOUS(PORT)
Dymock, Anthony Knox, BA, pce, psc, ... RADM	-	AWO(C)	19.01.00	COMSTRIKFORSTH
Dymond, Justin Roy Melville, BEng, ... SLT(IC)	E	WE	01.09.00	CHATHAM
Dymond, Nicholas Robert John, ... LT CDR(FTC)	E	WE	18.02.94	OCLC BIRM
Dyter, Ross Courtney, ... SLT(UCE)(FTC)	E	ME	01.09.99	DARTMOUTH BRNC

E

Name	Rank	Branch	Spec	Seniority	Where Serving
Eagles, Anthony James, AFC, MA, pcea, psc, ... LT CDR(FTC)	X	P	01.03.84	FLEET AV VL
Eaglestone, Stephen, ...LT(IC)	E	MESM	01.05.02	VICTORIOUS(STBD)
Eardley, John Mark, ... LT(FTC)	E	WE	07.02.97	HQ DCSA
Earle-Payne, Gareth Ellis, BEng, ... SLT(IC)	E	ME U/T	01.09.00	ARK ROYAL
Eastaugh, Andrew Charles, MSc, adp, (Act Cdr) .... LT CDR(FTC)	E	IS	01.10.89	RMCS SHRIVENHAM
Eastaugh, Timothy Colin, pcea, ... CDR(FTC)	X	P	30.06.02	899 SQN HERON
Easterbrook, Kevin Ivor Edgar, BEng, CEng, MIEE, ... LT CDR(FTC)	E	WE	11.12.99	MOD (BATH)
Eastlake, Amanda Clare, ... LT CDR(CC)	W	X	01.10.98	DISC
Eastley, Barry Roger, BSc, CEng, MIMechE, MRAeS, jsdc, ... CAPT(FTC)	E	AE	30.06.96	MOD (BATH)
Easton, Derek William, ... LT(FTC)	X	PT	04.04.96	JSCSC
Easton, Richard William, ... CDR(FTC)	X	PWO(C)	01.10.96	HQ SOUTHLANT
Eastwood, Richard Noah, MEng, ...LT(IC)	X	P	15.02.98	727 NAS
Eaton, David Charles, BA, ...LT(IC)	X	ATCU/T	01.01.02	RNAS YEOVILTON
Eaton, Paul Graham, BSc, ... LT CDR(FTC)	X	METOC	01.06.94	MOD (LONDON)
Eatwell, Russell Andrew, ... LT CDR(FTC)	X	P	01.10.01	HQ3GP HQSTC
Ebbens, Andrew John, sq, ...MAJ(FTC)	-		01.09.87	HQ NORTH
Eberle, Peter James Fuller, pce, psc, (Commodore) .... CAPT(FTC)	X	PWO(C)	30.06.97	MOD (LONDON)
Eddie, Alan George Watt, BTech, ... LT(FTC)	E	WE	24.02.95	WSA BRISTOL
Edey, Michael John, BSc, n, ... LT CDR(FTC)	X		01.12.01	IRON DUKE
Edge, Helen Ruth, BEng, ... SLT(IC)	E	AE	01.09.99	SULTAN
Edge, John Howard, MA, MILT, psc(j), (Act Cdr) .... LT CDR(FTC)	S	SM	01.06.97	NMA GOSPORT
Edge, Philippa Anne, BA, ... LT CDR(CC)	W	X	01.10.99	2SL/CNH
Edgell, John Nicholas, OBE, pce, pce(sm), psc, ... CDR(FTC)	X	SM	31.12.93	JDCC
Edgley, Andrew David, BA, ... LT CDR(FTC)	X	METOC	15.10.96	FLEET HQ NWD
Edinburgh, His Royal Highness The Prince Philip, Duke of, ... ADM OF FLEET			15.01.53	
KG, KT, OM, GBE, AC, QSO					
Edleston, Hugh Anthony Harold Greswell, ... RADM	-	AWO(A)	01.01.02	NP 1061
MNI, AMBIM, jsdc, pce, hcsc,					
Edmonds, Gerald, ... LT CDR(FTC)	X	C	02.08.85	HQ NORTH
Edmonds, Rebecca Mary, BEng, ... LT CDR(FTC)	E	TM	01.11.99	NP 1066
Edmondson, James Andrew, ... LT(FTC)	X		01.04.01	DEF SCH OF LANG
Edmondson, Simon Peter, BA, ... CAPT RM(IC)	-	P U/T	01.05.99	847 SQN
Edmondstone, William Mark, MB, BS, ... SURG CAPT(FCC)	-	(CM)	30.06.96	RH HASLAR
FRCP, AFOM, DIH,					
Edney, Andrew Ralph, MBE, BEng, pce, pcea, psc, ... CDR(FTC)	X	P	31.12.96	FLEET AV CRANWEL
Edson, Mark Andrew, HNC, ... LT(FTC)	E	WE	22.02.96	BULWARK
Edward, Amanda Michelle, (Act Surg Lt) .... SURG SLT(SCC)	-		02.07.01	DARTMOUTH BRNC
Edward, Gavin James, BEng, CEng, MIEE, ... LT(FTC)	E	WE	01.07.95	RMC OF SCIENCE
Edwardes, Geoffrey, pce, (Commodore) .... CAPT(FC)	X		31.12.91	NBC PORTSMOUTH
Edwards, Andrew Donald Pryce, MBE, BSc, ... LT CDR(FTC)	E	MESM	01.02.88	DRAKE NBSD
Edwards, Andrew George, BEng, CEng, MRAeS, ... LT(FTC)	E	AE(L)	01.09.95	MERLIN IPT

Name	Rank	Branch	Spec	Seniority	Where Serving
Edwards, Carlos Carew, BSc,	LT CDR(FTC)	S		01.07.85	DARTMOUTH BRNC
Edwards, Charles John Albert, MB, BS, FRCA,	SURG CDR(FCC)	-	(CA)	31.12.97	RH HASLAR
Edwards, David,	LT(IC)	MS		01.01.02	DRAKE CBS
Edwards, James Eustice, BEng,	LT(CC)	E	WE	01.06.97	JSCSC
Edwards, James, BSc, PGCE,	LT(IC)	E	TM	01.09.96	40 CDO RM
Edwards, Janice Mary,	LT CDR(FTC)	S		01.04.86	AFPAA(CENTURION)
Edwards, John Paul Thomas, BSc, pcea,	LT CDR(FTC)	X	P	01.10.97	EXCHANGE USA
Edwards, John, BEng, MRAeS,	LT(CC)	E	AE	01.08.97	ES AIR NAML
Edwards, Philip Douglas, MA, BChir, FRCSEd, FRCR,	SURG LTCDR(FCC)	-	(CX)	21.12.95	RH HASLAR
Edwards, Philip John, BSc,	LT CDR(FTC)	X	METOC	01.05.93	MOD (LONDON)
Edwards, Richard,	LT CDR(FTC)	X	EW	01.10.99	FOST SEA
Edwards, Richmond Arthur,	LT CDR(FTC)	E	WE	01.10.95	DISC
Edwards, Thomas Hugh Hamish, MPhil,	SLT(IC)	X		01.05.00	ST ALBANS
Edwins, Mark Richard,	LT(FTC)	E	ME	02.05.00	SULTAN
Edye, Robin Francis,	CAPT RM(CC)	-		01.05.00	40 CDO RM
Eedle, Richard John, BA, psc(j)o,	LT CDR(FTC)	X	SM	01.03.91	EXCHANGE AUSTLIA
Egeland-Jensen, Finn Adam, PGDIPAN, pce,	LT CDR(FTC)	X	PWO(N)	01.04.95	MWS DRYAD
Egerton, Paul Michael, BSc, CEng, MIMarEST, MIMechE,	CDR(FTC)	E	ME	31.12.88	DRAKE NBC
Egerton, Stephen Brian,	LT(FTC)	X	C	10.12.98	DCSA NWD REGION
Eglin, Caroline Anne, BA,	CHAPLAIN	SF		10.09.90	MWS COLLINGWOOD
Eglin, Ian, BA,	CHAPLAIN	CE		27.01.87	SULTAN
Elborn, Teresa Kathleen, MHCIMA,	LT(FTC)	W	S	11.12.92	DRAKE DPL
Eldridge, Gareth,	2LT(IC)	-		01.09.01	CTCRM LYMPSTONE
Eldridge, Timothy John,	LT(FTC)	X	P	01.04.91	DHFS
Elford, David Graham, MSc, CEng, MRAeS, AMIEE, psc(j),	CDR(FTC)	E	AE	30.06.98	ES AIR BRISTOL
Eling, Richard James, BA,	SLT(IC)	X		01.09.99	CHATHAM
Elkins, Stuart Spencer,	LT(IC)	S		01.05.02	FOSNNI/NBC CLYDE
Ellerton, Paul,	LT(CC)	X	P	16.10.94	RAF CRANWELL EFS
Ellett, Keith Geoffrey,	LT(CC)	X	ATC	01.06.84	FOST DPORT SHORE
Elliman, Simon Mark, pce,	LT CDR(FTC)	X	PWO(U)	01.10.94	NELSON
Ellingham, Richard Edwin,	CHAPLAIN	SF		17.04.00	FWO PORTS SEA
Ellins, Stuart John, BSc, CEng, FIMechE, psc,	CAPT(FTC)	E	ME	31.12.99	NMA PORTSMOUTH
Elliot-Smith, Teilo John, BA,	SLT(IC)	X		01.09.99	NOTTINGHAM
Elliott, James Alistair,	LT(CC)	E	AE	01.07.00	DARTMOUTH BRNC
Elliott, Mark,	2LT(IC)	-		01.09.01	CTCRM LYMPSTONE
Elliott, Stephen Peter,	SLT(IC)	E	WE	01.01.01	MWS COLLINGWOOD
Elliott, Steven, BEng, AMIEE,	LT(FTC)	E	WESM	01.07.93	FOST CSST FSLN
Elliott, Thomas Fitzgerald, MBE, TEng, IEng, AMIMarEST,	LT CDR(FTC)	E	ME	01.10.90	MOD (BATH)
Elliott, Timothy Douglas,	SLT(UCE)(IC)	X		01.09.01	DARTMOUTH BRNC
Ellis, Andrew Christopher, BA,	LT(CC)	X	P	01.05.99	845 SQN
Ellis, Charles Richard, BEng,	LT(FTC)	E	WESM	01.03.00	VICTORIOUS(PORT)
Ellis, David Robert, BEng,	SLT(IC)	E	AE	01.09.99	SULTAN
Ellis, David, BSc, CEng, MBCS,	LT(CC)	E	IS	09.07.92	2SL/CNH
Ellis, James Paul, BEng,	LT(FTC)	E	ME	01.09.93	SULTAN
Ellis, Michael Philip, psc(a),	LT COL(FTC)	-	P	31.12.98	CHFHQ
Ellis, Neil James, BA,	LT(CC)	X		01.08.98	MIDDLETON
Ellis, Nicholas Mark,	LT CDR(FTC)	X		18.07.97	ALBION
Ellis, Richard William, BSc,	CDR(FTC)	E	AE	30.06.99	HARRIER IPT
Ellis-Morgan, Roger Terrence,	LT(IC)	X	EW	01.05.02	JSSU OAKLEY
Ellison, Toby George,	LT(FTC)	X		01.06.97	COTTESMORE
Ellwood, Peter George, SM,	LT(FTC)	X	SM	29.07.91	FLEET HQ NWD
Elmer, Timothy Brendan, BDS,	SGCDR(D)(FCC)	-		30.06.02	RN GIBRALTAR
Elmore, Graeme Martin,	CHAPLAIN	CE		30.09.86	FWO PORTS SEA
Elsey, David John, BSc,	LT(CC)	E	TM	01.09.97	MWS DRYAD
Elsom, Geoffrey Keith,	LT CDR(FTC)	X	C	01.10.00	FLEET CIS PORTS
Elston, Adrian John,	LT(FTC)	X	REG	16.12.94	VICTORY
Elvin, Andrew James, pce,	LT CDR(FTC)	X	MCD	06.11.93	FLEET HQ NWD
Elwell-Deighton, Dean Carl, pcea,	LT(FTC)	X	P	16.09.93	771 SQN
Emerson, Martin John,	SLT(IC)	X		01.01.02	MWS DRYAD
Emery, Christian Stanley,	SLT(IC)	E	WE	01.05.00	DARTMOUTH BRNC
Emmerson, Graham John, pce,	LT CDR(FTC)	X	AAWO	01.06.92	LOAN OMAN
Emms, Stuart Michael,	LT(FTC)	E	WE	09.01.01	DNR PRES TEAMS

Name	Rank	Branch	Spec	Seniority	Where Serving
Enever, Shaun Andrew,	LT(CC)	X	O	01.09.96	815 FLT 228
Engeham, Paul Richard, MA, pce,	LT CDR(FTC)	X	AWO(C)	16.01.81	MOD (LONDON)
England, Lorraine,	LT(MCC)	Q	REGM	11.01.91	UKSU AFSOUTH
England, Philip Morgan, MSc,	LT(IC)	X		01.04.00	MWS RNHMS CULD
English, Colin Richard, MSc, CEng, FIMarEST, jsdc,	CDR(FTC)	E	ME	30.06.88	MOD (BATH)
Enticknap, Kenneth, QGM,	CDR(FTC)	E	ME	30.06.98	NELSON
Entwisle, William Nicholas, MVO, BA, psc(j),	CDR(FTC)	X	P	30.06.02	MOD (LONDON)
Entwistle, Stephen Charles, pce, psc(j),	CDR(FTC)	X	AAWO	30.06.00	EUMS
Epps, Matthew Paul, BSc,	LT(IC)	E	IS	17.07.99	RMCS SHRIVENHAM
Errington, Ridley James Bentley,	MID(UCE)(IC)	E	ME	01.09.00	DARTMOUTH BRNC
Erskine, Peter Anthony, BA, MSc, MIMechE, psc,	CDR(FTC)	E	ME	30.06.96	FSC IPT
Essenhigh, Angus Nigel Patrick, BA,	LT(FTC)	X		01.11.96	TRACKER
Essenhigh, *Sir* Nigel, (Richard), GCB, ADC, rcds, pce, psc, hcsc,	ADM	-	PWO(N)†	11.09.98	
Etchells, Stephen Barrie, BEng, CEng, MIEE,	LT CDR(FTC)	E	WESM	03.07.00	RALEIGH
Ethell, David Ross, BEng, (Act Maj)	CAPT RM(CC)	-	LC	28.04.95	FEARLESS
Euden, Christopher Peter, BA, n,	LT(FTC)	X		01.06.95	DASHER
Evans, Andrew William,	LT CDR(CC)	X	SM	01.10.95	MWC PORTSDOWN
Evans, Barry David,	LT(FTC)	X	REG	02.05.00	2SL/CNH
Evans, Benjiman Gwynn, BSc,	SLT(FTC)	X		01.01.01	DARTMOUTH BRNC
Evans, Charles Alexander, BA,	LT(FTC)	S	SM	01.06.96	NMA PORTSMOUTH
Evans, Charles William, MPH, MB, BS, MFOM, LRCP, MRCS, DIH, DTM&H, rcds,	SURGCAPT(FCC)	-	(CO/M)	30.06.89	DRAKE CBS
Evans, Christopher Anthony, BSc,	SLT(IC)	X	SM U/T	01.05.00	LANCASTER
Evans, Craig Hamilton, MSc,	LT CDR(CC)	E	IS	01.11.00	RMCS SHRIVENHAM
Evans, David Anthony,	LT(CC)	X	ATC	20.12.95	RNAS YEOVILTON
Evans, David John, BSc, CEng, MIEE, MRAeS, psc,	LT CDR(FTC)	E	AE(P)	30.06.95	NMA PORTSMOUTH
Evans, David Mark Mortimer, psc(m),	LT COL(FTC)	-	C	30.06.01	FLEET CIS PORTS
Evans, David Melville, BSc, MPhil, pce,	CDR(FTC)	X	PWO(A)	30.06.94	MWS DRYAD
Evans, Desmond John,	LT CDR(FTC)	X	AV	01.10.96	RNAS YEOVILTON
Evans, Edward Thomas, MinstAM, MCIT, MILT,	LT CDR(FTC)	S	SM	16.08.97	OCEAN
Evans, Gareth Charles, BA, MB, ChB,	SURG LT(MCC)	-		05.08.98	NELSON (PAY)
Evans, Geraint, BEng, AMIEE,	LT CDR(FTC)	E	WE	01.06.98	LOAN BRUNEI
Evans, Graham Roy, BSc, pce,	LT CDR(FTC)	X	PWO(U)	01.12.90	AGRIPPA AFSOUTH
Evans, Ivan Charles,	LT(IC)	X	SM	01.01.02	VENGEANCE(PORT)
Evans, John Walter,	LT CDR(FTC)	X	PWO(C)	06.05.86	NBC PORTSMOUTH
Evans, Karl Nicholas Meredith, pce, pce(sm), psc(j),	CDR(FTC)	X	SM	31.12.98	BDS WASHINGTON
Evans, Laura Jane, BSc,	SLT(IC)	X		01.09.99	MONTROSE
Evans, Lee Stewart,	LT(IC)	X	P	01.05.01	RNAS CULDROSE
Evans, Marc David, MILDM, AMIAM,	LT CDR(FTC)	S		16.05.98	2SL/CNH
Evans, Martin Joseph, BSc, pce,	LT CDR(FTC)	X	PWO(U)	01.09.95	FLEET HQ NWD
Evans, Martin Lonsdale,	CHAPLAIN	CE		01.09.98	JSCSC
Evans, Martyn Alun, BA, sq,	MAJ(FTC)	-		01.09.93	AGRIPPA AFSOUTH
Evans, Michael Clive, BSc, MA, MNI, MCMI, pce, pcea, psc,	CDR(FTC)	X	P	31.12.94	SACLANT BELGIUM
Evans, Michael Edward, BEng,	LT(FTC)	E	MESM	01.08.97	TRAFALGAR
Evans, Peter Colin, MSc,	LT(CC)	E	IS	01.05.96	MWS COLLINGWOOD
Evans, Peter John, BSc, psc(j), mdtc,	MAJ(FTC)	-	LC	01.09.99	40 CDO RM
Evans, Robert Paul,	SLT(IC)	E	WE	01.01.01	MWS COLLINGWOOD
Evans, Sarah Jane, BSc,	LT CDR(CC)	E	IS	01.10.97	MWS DRYAD
Evans, Stephen, BTech,	LT CDR(FTC)	E	WESM	01.10.01	MOD (LONDON)
Evans, Thomas, (Act Surg Lt)	SURG SLT(MDC)	-		09.07.01	DARTMOUTH BRNC
Evans, William Quennell Frankis, MNI, pce,	CDR(FTC)	X	PWO(N)	30.06.02	FLEET HQ PORTS
Eve, Laurie,	2LT(IC)	-		01.09.99	CTCRM LYMPSTONE
Evelyn, Richard Hugh, BSc,	SLT(IC)	X	P U/T	01.05.00	DARTMOUTH BRNC
Everett, Edward Jason,	CAPT RM(FTC)	-		24.04.96	42 CDO RM
Everitt, Claire Julia, BDS, LDS RCS(Eng),	SGLTCDR(D)(MCC)	-		11.03.97	MWS DRYAD
Everitt, Tobyn,	LT(CC)	X	P	19.08.96	RNAS YEOVILTON
Everritt, Richard, BSc, psc(j),	MAJ(FTC)	-	SO(LE)	01.10.98	FLEET HQ PORTS 2
Evershed, Marcus Charles, MB, BCh, MRCGP, Dip FFP,	SURG CDR(SCC)	-	GMPP	30.06.02	2SL/CNH
Every, Mark, BM, BSc, MRCGP, Dip FFP, (Act Surg Cdr)	SURG LTCDR(MCC)	-	GMPP	03.02.98	NEPTUNE DLO
Ewen, Andrew Philip, BEng, MSc,	LT CDR(FTC)	E	AE	01.07.00	824 SQN
Ewen, Raymond John,	LT CDR(FTC)	S	(W)	01.10.96	AFPAA WTHY DOWN
Ewence, Martin William, MA, pce, psc(j),	CDR(FTC)	X	AAWO	30.06.98	LIVERPOOL

Name	Rank	Branch	Spec	Seniority	Where Serving
Ewer, Jonathan Edward,	SLT(IC)	X	P	01.04.00	DHFS
Ewing, Andrew David, pce, psc, psc(j),	CDR(FTC)	X	AWO(U)	30.06.91	SHAPE BELGIUM
Ewins, Graeme Power, pce,	CDR(FTC)	X	AWO(C)	30.06.89	LPD(R) IPT
Exworthy, Damian Andrew Giles, BSc, MA,	LT(FTC)	S		01.06.97	DARTMOUTH BRNC

F

Name	Rank	Branch	Spec	Seniority	Where Serving
Fabik, Andre Nicholas, BA,	LT(IC)	X		01.05.01	GUERNSEY
Fairbairn, William David Murray, MA, rcds, jsdc,(Commodore)	CAPT(FTC)	E	WE	30.06.95	MOD (LONDON)
Fairbank, Brian Douglas Seeley, AKC,	CHAPLAIN	CE		03.09.91	NELSON
Fairclough-Kay, Matthew, BA,	SLT(IC)	X		01.05.00	SANDOWN
Fairnie, David William,	LT(FTC)	X	PR	02.05.00	RALEIGH
Falk, Benedict Hakan Geoffrey, MNI, pce,	CDR(FTC)	X	PWO(A)	30.06.02	JSCSC
Fallowfield, Jonathan Paul, BTech,	LT(FTC)	E	WE	24.02.95	2SL/CNH
Fancy, Robert, pce, pce(sm),	CDR(FTC)	X	SM	31.12.00	TRAFALGAR
Fanshawe, Edward Leo,	SLT(IC)	E	WESM	01.05.00	DARTMOUTH BRNC
Fanshawe, James Rupert, jsdc, pce, (Commodore) hcsc, l(2)Fr,	CAPT(FTC)	X	PWO(U)	30.06.96	UKMARBATSTAFF
Farmer, Paul Adrian,	SLT(CC)	X	P U/T	01.04.00	RNAS YEOVILTON
Farquhar, John William, FRGS, nadc, jsdc,	CDR(FTC)	S		30.06.87	NATO DEF COL
Farquharson-Roberts, Michael Atholl, CBE, MB, MA, rcds, FRCS, OStJ	SURGCAPT(FCC)	-	(CO/S)	30.06.93	DMTO HQ
Farr, Ian Raymond,	LT(CC)	X	P	01.04.01	824 SQN
Farrage, Michael Edward, BSc, psc,	CDR(FTC)	E	TM	31.12.96	MOD (LONDON)
Farrant, James Derek,	SLT(UCE)(FTC)	S		01.09.00	DARTMOUTH BRNC
Farrell, Jamie Andrew, SM,	SLT(CC)	X	SM	01.09.99	CAPTAIN SM2
Farrington, John Lewis, BEng, MSc, AMIEE,	LT CDR(FTC)	E	WESM	01.10.01	DPA BRISTOL
Farrington, Richard, OBE, BA, jsdc, pce,	CDR(FTC)	X	PWO(C)	30.06.96	NOTTINGHAM
Farrington, Stephen Paul, QGM, MPhil, IEng, FIMarEST, FRINA, psc,	CDR(FTC)	E	ME	30.06.96	FEARLESS
Faulconbridge, David, MSc, CEng, MIMarEST, AMIEE, psc,	CDR(FTC)	E	MESM	31.12.94	MOD (BATH)
Faulkner, Daniel William, BEng, CEng, MRAeS,	LT CDR(FTC)	E	AE	29.11.97	2SL/CNH FOTR
Faulkner, Jeffrey James, ARICS,	CDR(FTC)	X	H CH	30.06.01	LOAN HYDROG
Faulkner, Richard Ian, BSc,	LT CDR(FTC)	E	ME	01.08.89	NMA GOSPORT
Faulkner, Stuart Glen,	SLT(UCE)(FTC)	E	AE	01.09.00	DARTMOUTH BRNC
Faulks, David John,	CDR(FTC)	S		30.06.02	FLEET HQ NWD
Fawcett, Fiona Patricia, BA,	LT CDR(FTC)	E	TM	01.05.98	JSCSC
Fear, Richard Keith, BSc, MDA,	CDR(FTC)	E	WESM	30.06.99	HQ DCSA
Fearnley, Andrew Thomas,	LT CDR(FTC)	S	(S)	01.10.01	YORK
Fearon, David John,	SLT(IC)	E	WE U/T	01.09.00	INVINCIBLE
Feasey, Ian David,	SLT(CC)	X		01.09.99	PORTLAND
Febbraro, Nicholas Robert,	CDR(FTC)	E	MESM	30.06.93	DRAKE SFM
Fedorowicz, Richard,	LT CDR(CC)	X	ATC	16.10.00	RNAS CULDROSE
Feeney, Matthew Blake, BA,	LT(FTC)	X		01.04.00	PORTLAND
Feeney, Michael Leonard, BEng, CEng, MIMarEST,	LT CDR(FTC)	E	ME	01.05.97	FLEET HQ PORTS
Felfel, Sammy Ibrahim,	SLT(IC)	X	SM	01.05.00	MWS DRYAD
Felgate, Howard, BSc,	LT CDR(FTC)	X		01.05.83	MOD (LONDON)
Felters, Adam William, BSc,	LT(CC)	X	P U/T	01.05.99	RAF CRANWELL EFS
Fennell, Charles Benjamin, BSc,	LT(CC)	X		01.07.99	COTTESMORE
Fenwick, John, OBE, BEng,	CDR(FTC)	E	WESM	30.06.83	WSA BRISTOL
Fenwick, Julie Cheryl, BDS,	SGLTCDR(D)(MCC)	-		03.09.95	JSU NORTHWOOD
Fenwick, Robin John, BSc,	CAPT RM(CC)	-	P	01.05.97	RNAS YEOVILTON
Ferguson, Gordon Henry, IEng,	LT CDR(FTC)	E	MESM	01.10.98	TRENCHANT
Ferguson, Julian Norman, BA, BSc, pce, pce(sm),	CDR(FTC)	X	SM	30.06.91	VENGEANCE(STBD)
Ferguson, Robert Grant,	LT CDR(FTC)	X	C	12.12.90	MOD (LONDON)
Ferguson, Vikki Sara,	LT(MCC)	Q	CC	21.01.95	CTCRM
Fergusson, Andrew Christopher, BSc,	MAJ(FTC)	-		01.05.99	COMAMPHIBFOR
Fergusson, Duncan Campbell McGregor, (Commodore) jsdc, pce, pcea, psc,	CAPT(FTC)	X	P	30.06.97	NMA GOSPORT
Fergusson, Houston James,	CDR(FTC)	S	SM	30.06.00	NMA PORTSMOUTH
Fergusson, Iain Buchan,	LT(IC)	X		01.05.02	MWS DRYAD
Fergusson, Nigel Andrew, MSc, CEng, MIEE,	LT CDR(FTC)	E	WE	01.02.99	IRON DUKE
Fergusson, Richard Routledge, MA, adp, (Act Cdr)	LT CDR(FTC)	E	IS	01.05.85	PJHQ

Name	Rank	Branch	Spec	Seniority	Where Serving
Fernihough, Michael Robert, BSc, MIMechE,	LT CDR(FTC)	E	AE	08.12.82	RNAS YEOVILTON
Ferns, Timothy David, LLB,	LT CDR(FTC)	S		01.06.99	FLEET HQ NWD
Ferran, Simon Harold Michael,	SLT(IC)	X		01.05.00	NEPTUNE
Ferrey, Robert,	2LT(IC)	-		01.09.98	CTCRM LYMPSTONE
Ferris, Daniel Peter Sefton, BEng, MSc, CEng, MIEE, gw,	LT CDR(FTC)	E	WE	01.04.98	CAMPBELTOWN
Fewtrell, Malcolm, psc,	LT CDR(FTC)	X	PWO(U)	01.09.84	FLEET HQ NWD
Fiander, Peter John, BSc,	LT CDR(FTC)	E	MESM	01.02.87	EAGLET
Fiddock, Matthew Lee, BEng,	SLT(IC)	E	ME U/T	01.09.00	DRAKE SFM
Fidler, John Quentin, BSc,	LT RM(IC)	-		01.09.00	FPGRM
Field, Charles Richard Howard, BEng,	LT(FTC)	E	ME	01.01.96	SFM PORTSMOUTH
Field, John Dobson, pce,	LT CDR(FTC)	X	AAWO	16.04.87	T45 IPT
Field, Stephen Nigel Crawford,	LT CDR(FTC)	X	MCD	01.09.86	MWS DRYAD
Fields, David Graham, pce,	LT CDR(FTC)	X	PWO(A)	01.06.94	JSCSC
Fieldsend, Mark Andrew, BEng, fsc,	LT CDR(FTC)	E	ME	01.03.96	FLEET HQ PORTS 2
Fifield, David James, jsdc, pce, ocds(Can),	CAPT(FTC)	X	P	30.06.96	IMS BRUSSELS
Fillmore, Raymond Jeffrey,	LT(IC)	X	SM	01.12.00	VENGEANCE(PORT)
Filshie, Sarah Jane, BA,	LT(IC)	X	ATCU/T	01.01.02	RNAS CULDROSE
Filtness, David Mark, BSc,	LT(IC)	X		01.09.01	TIRELESS
Finch, Bruce Andrew, BA, MIL, MInsD, MinstAM,	LT CDR(FTC)	S		01.08.01	SULTAN
Finch, Craig Richard,	LT(CC)	X	P	16.11.91	RAF SHAWBURY
Finch, Iain Robert,	LT(CC)	X		01.11.99	LANCASTER
Finch, Robert Leonard, BEng, MSc, CEng, MIMarEST, AMIMechE,	LTCDR(FTC)	E	ME	01.05.97	IRON DUKE
Finch, Steven,	LT(IC)	E	AE	29.04.01	849 SQN A FLT
Finch, Timothy Stuart Aubrey,	LT CDR(FTC)	S	CA	01.10.97	SULTAN
Fincher, Kevin John, pce,	LT CDR(FTC)	X	PWO(C)	01.10.95	ARGYLL
Finlayson, Alasdair Grant, MA, fsc,	CDR(FTC)	S		30.06.96	DPA BRISTOL
Finlayson, Ronald Didrik, MA, MBA, (Commodore), CEng, FIEE, rcds, psc,	CAPT(FTC)	E	WE	31.12.94	MOD (LONDON)
Finley, Paul Michael, MEng, AMIEE,	LT(IC)	E	WE	01.09.01	SUTHERLAND
Finn, David William, OStJ,	LT(FTC)	MS	(AD)	03.04.97	NELSON (PAY)
Finn, Emma Jane,	LT(CC)	S		01.04.99	2SL/CNH
Finn, Graham John, pcea,	LT CDR(FTC)	X	P	01.10.00	COMSTRIKFORSTH
Finn, Ivan Richard, BEng,	LT CDR(FTC)	E	AE	01.10.00	JCA IPT UK
Finn, James Sutherland, BSc,	LT(IC)	X	P	01.01.01	824 SQN
Finn, Stuart Andrew, BSc,	LT(FTC)	X		01.09.01	CATTISTOCK
Finnemore, Richard Andrew, AMBIM, pce,	LT CDR(FTC)	X	PWO(U)	09.07.90	PCRS IPT
Finney, Michael Edwin, pce, pce(sm),	CDR(FTC)	X	SM	30.06.94	MOD (LONDON)
Finnie, Harry Morrison,	LT(FTC)	E	ME	13.06.97	539 ASSLT SQN RM
Firth, John Simon, BSc,	LT(IC)	X		01.05.00	EDINBURGH
Firth, Nigel Richard, pce, pce(sm),	LT CDR(FTC)	X	SM	01.03.95	RHQ AFNORTH
Firth, Rachel Jane Gardner,	LT CDR(FTC)	X	ATC	08.04.00	HQ STC
Firth, Stephen Kenneth, MSc, CEng, MIEE,	CDR(FTC)	E	MESM	31.12.90	DRAKE SFM
Fisher, Aaron George, BSc,	CAPT RM(CC)	-		01.09.98	CTCRM
Fisher, Charles Edward David, BSc,	SLT(IC)	X		01.01.01	DARTMOUTH BRNC
Fisher, Clayton Richard Allan,	LT CDR(FTC)	S		06.10.98	2SL/CNH
Fisher, Matthew Robert,	SLT(IC)	X		01.01.01	DARTMOUTH BRNC
Fisher, Morleymor Alfred Leslie, MBE,BSc,CEng, FIMarEST, MIMechE, MCMI,	CDR(FTC)	E	MESM	30.06.94	AGRIPPA AFSOUTH
Fisher, Nicholas Douglas,	SLT(UCE)(IC)	E	WE	01.09.01	DARTMOUTH BRNC
Fisher, Nicholas Gorden, MB, BS, MRCP,	SURG LTCDR(MCC)	-		01.08.97	NELSON (PAY)
Fisher, Pamela Clare, BEng,	LT(FTC)	E	AE	01.03.95	DARTMOUTH BRNC
Fisher, Robert James,	LT(IC)	X	P	01.06.96	845 SQN
Fisher, Robert,	LT(FTC)	E	WE	10.06.88	MWS COLLINGWOOD
Fisher, Rupert Vincent,	SLT(IC)	X	ATCU/T	01.01.01	RNAS YEOVILTON
Fisher, Stephen John, BA,	LT(IC)	X	P	01.09.99	845 SQN
Fishlock, Geoffrey Norman,	LT CDR(FTC)	S		16.04.86	CALLIOPE
Fitter, Ian Stuart Thain, BSc, pcea,	CDR(FTC)	X	O	30.06.02	820 SQN
Fitzgerald, Brian,	MAJ(FTC)	-	SO(LE)	01.10.98	1 ASSLT GP RM
Fitzgerald, Colin,	LT(FTC)	E	AE(M)	12.09.97	FLEET HQ PORTS
Fitzgerald, Gary Samuel,	LT(IC)	E	WE	01.01.02	EXETER

Name	Rank	Branch	Spec	Seniority	Where Serving
Fitzgerald, Marcus Peter, OBE, BSc, (Commodore) .... CAPT(FTC) CEng, MIEE, rcds,	E		WESM	30.06.95	MOD (LONDON)
Fitzgerald, Nicholas John, ... LT(CC)	X		P	01.12.92	846 SQN
Fitzjohn, David, BEng, MSc, CEng, MIEE, ... LT CDR(FTC)	E		AE	01.05.96	ES AIR BRISTOL
Fitzpatrick, John Aloysius Joseph, ... LT(FTC)	X		O	01.07.97	815 FLT 204
Fitzpatrick, Neil James, BSc, ... SLT(IC)	X			01.05.00	CHATHAM
Fitzpatrick, Paul, ... CAPT RM(FTC)	-		SO(LE)	01.01.01	CHFHQ
Fitzsimmons, Mark Brown, pce, ... LT CDR(FTC)	X		PWO(A)	01.09.95	FLEET HQ NWD
Fitzsimons, Diane Elizabeth, BA, MB, ChB, ... SURG LT(SCC)	-			03.09.98	MODHU DERRIFORD
Flaherty, Christopher Lynton, BSc, ... LT(IC)	X			01.05.02	MWS DRYAD
Flannagan, Donna Louise, LLB, ... SLT(IC)	S			01.01.01	DARTMOUTH BRNC
Flannery, James, ... LT RM(IC)	-			01.09.00	42 CDO RM
Flatman, Timothy David, BSc, ... LT(IC)	X		P	16.05.99	RNAS YEOVILTON
Flatt, Leslie Declan, ... LT(FTC)	E		WE	02.09.99	WSA/CAPT MCTA
Flegg, Matthew James, BEng, ... LT(FTC)	E		AE	01.09.01	847 SQN
Fleisher, Simon Matthew, MEng, CEng, MIMechE, ... LT CDR(FTC)	E		ME	01.06.00	MOD (BATH)
Fleming, Kevin Patrick, BSc, pcea, ... LT CDR(FTC)	X		O	01.10.97	RNAS YEOVILTON
Fleming, Ruth Ernestine, BSc, ... LT(IC)	S			01.08.00	OCEAN
Fleming, Stephen Anthony, ... LT CDR(FTC)	X			30.09.94	MOD (LONDON)
Fletcher, Andrew Stuart, ... MID(UCE)(IC)	X			01.09.00	DARTMOUTH BRNC
Fletcher, Helene, ... LT(SCC)	Q			24.12.00	RH HASLAR
Fletcher, Ian James, BSc, ... LT(IC)	X		HM2	01.10.98	ENDURANCE
Fletcher, Nicholas Edgar, BA(OU), pce, psc, ... CDR(FTC)	X		PWO(A)	31.12.94	FLEET HQ PORTS
Fletcher, Richard John, BA, ... LT CDR(FTC)	S		CMA	16.03.00	LANCASTER
Flinn, John, ... LT RM(IC)	-		SO(LE)	01.04.00	CTCRM
Flint, Helen Anne, BSc, ... LT CDR(FTC)	E		TM	01.05.02	NP 1061
Flintham, Jason Edward, ... LT(FTC)	X		P	16.03.96	899 SQN HERON
Float, Roger Andrew, MA, MSc, MCGI, AMIEE, psc(j), ... CDR(FTC)	E		WE	30.06.02	MOD (LONDON)
Flower, Neil, ... LT RM(IC)	-		SO(LE)	01.04.00	847 SQN
Flynn, Andrew, ... LT(FTC)	E		AE(L)	01.05.96	LOAN JTEG BSC DN
Flynn, Michael Thomas, ... LT CDR(FTC)	S			01.11.93	RALEIGH
Flynn, Simon John, ... LT CDR(FTC)	X		O	09.01.01	RNAS CULDROSE
Foale, Simon John, BA, pce, ... LT CDR(FTC)	X		O	01.04.89	MERLIN IPT
Fogell, Andrew David, (Act Lt Cdr) .... LT(FTC)	S		SM	01.11.92	RNAS CULDROSE
Fogg, Duncan Stuart, MA, MSc, CEng, MIEE, gw, ... LT CDR(FTC)	E		WE	01.04.93	BULWARK
Follington, Daniel Charles, ... LT(FTC)	MS			23.07.98	MSA
Fomes, Christopher John Henry, ... CAPT RM(CC)	-			01.04.01	OPTAG
Fooks-Bale, Matthew Edward, ... SLT(IC)	X		P U/T	01.09.01	DARTMOUTH BRNC
Foote, Andrew Steven, ... LT(CC)	E		ME	01.08.00	DARTMOUTH BRNC
Forbes, Duncan Graham, LLB, ... CAPT RM(IC)	-			01.09.01	42 CDO RM
Forbes, Ian Andrew, CBE, rcds, pce, psc(a), ... ADM	-		AWO(A)	01.12.01	SACLANT USA
Forbes, Paul Thomas, ... LT(CC)	X		P	16.07.96	771 SQN
Ford, Anthony John, SM(n), SM, ... LT(CC)	X		SM	04.04.96	FWO FASLANE
Ford, Anthony, AMIMarEST, ... LT CDR(FTC)	E		ME	01.10.99	NBC PORTSMOUTH
Ford, Barry Emerson, ... SLT(IC)	E		MESM	08.10.99	TRENCHANT
Ford, Graham Ronald, MSc, CEng, PGDip, MIMarEST, ... LT(FTC)	E		MESM	14.10.94	NP BRISTOL
Ford, James Anthony, pcea, ... LT CDR(FTC)	X		P	01.10.00	EXCHANGE USA
Ford, Joanna Sophie, BEng, ... LT(CC)	E		ME	01.07.99	EDINBURGH
Ford, Jonathan Douglas, BEng, MIEE, ... LT CDR(FTC)	E		WE	01.12.01	CSIS IPT
Ford, Martin John, ... LT CDR(FTC)	X		O	05.08.98	FLEET HQ PORTS
Ford, Nicholas Paul, MBE, TEng, ... LT CDR(FTC)	E		MESM	01.10.93	DRAKE CBP(DLO)
Foreman, John Lewis Rutland, MA, pce, psc(j), ... CDR(FTC)	X		PWO(C)	30.06.01	MOD (LONDON)
Foreman, Simon Michael, BEng, CEng, MIEE, ... LT(FTC)	E		WE	01.04.97	WSA/CAPT MCTA
Foreman, Susan Louise, BSc, (Act Lt Cdr) .... LT(FTC)	X			01.05.92	FLEET CIS PORTS
Forer, Duncan Anthony, BSc, PGCE, ... LT CDR(FTC)	E		TM	01.10.98	NELSON RNSETT
Forester-Bennett, Rupert Michael William, ... LT CDR(FTC)	X		H CH	24.07.97	ENDURANCE
Forge, Stephen Mieczyseaw, BSc, ... LT(FTC)	S			01.05.00	NEPTUNE DLO
Forrester, Timothy Rae, pcea, ... LT CDR(FTC)	X		O	01.12.86	RNAS CULDROSE
Forsey, Christopher Roy, MSc, AMIEE, ... CDR(FTC)	E		WE	31.12.95	FOST SEA
Forshaw, David Roy, ... LT(FTC)	E		ME	02.09.99	SULTAN
Forster, Raymond Adrian, ... LT CDR(FTC)	X		ATC	01.10.01	RNAS YEOVILTON
Forster, Robin Makepeace, MA, psc(j), ... MAJ(FTC)	-			01.09.94	EXCHANGE ARMY UK

Name	Rank	Branch	Spec	Seniority	Where Serving
Forster, Steven,	CHAPLAIN	RC		08.08.94	NEPTUNE 2SL/CNH
Forsyth, Andrew Richard, BSc,	CDR(FTC)	S		30.06.94	NMA PORTSMOUTH
Fortescue, Paul Wyatt, BSc,	CDR(FTC)	X	METOC	31.12.91	AGRIPPA NAVSOUTH
Fortescue, Robert Christopher, MA, pce, pcea, psc(j),	LT CDR(FTC)	X	O	01.03.93	AGRIPPA AFSOUTH
Forward, David James,	LT(FTC)	E	AE(L)	19.10.90	792 NAS
Fosbury, Clare Fraser, HNC,	LT(IC)	X	O U/T	01.05.02	750 SQN SEAHAWK
Foster, Alan James,	SLT(IC)	E	MESM	01.05.00	SULTAN
Foster, Benjamin,	CAPT RM(IC)	-		01.09.00	40 CDO RM
Foster, Bruce Michael Trevor, BSc,	LT CDR(FTC)	E	TM	07.12.98	DHFS
Foster, Crawford Richard Muir, MB, ChB, MRCGP, AFOM, Dip FFP,	SURG CDR(FCC)	-	(CO/M)	31.12.00	INM ALVERSTOKE
Foster, David Hugh,	LT CDR(FTC)	X	MCD	01.05.99	DEF EXP ORD SCHL
Foster, Duncan Graeme Scott, BSc, PGDIPAN, pce,	LT CDR(FTC)	X	PWO(N)	01.07.95	YORK
Foster, Geoffrey Russell Nicholas, psc,	CDR(FTC)	X	P	30.06.91	MOD (LONDON)
Foster, Graeme Russell, BSc, psc(m),	LT COL(FTC)	-	LC	31.12.97	MOD (LONDON)
Foster, Graham James, BSc, AMIMechE,	LT CDR(FTC)	E	MESM	01.10.96	FWO DEVONPORT
Foster, Jeremy Stephen, MBE, BA, MSc,	LT CDR(CC)	E	IS	01.10.98	2SL/CNH FOTR
Foster, Mark Andrew, BSc, MA, CEng, MIMarE, psc,	CDR(FTC)	E	TM	30.06.97	LOAN OMAN
Foster, Nicholas Paul,	CAPT RM(FTC)	-		01.05.00	EXCHANGE ARMY UK
Foster, Nicholas Paul, BSc, MA,	LT(IC)	X	HM	01.02.97	MWS RNHMS CULD
Foster, Peter James, BEng,	LT(FTC)	E	MESM	01.09.95	DRAKE SFM
Foster, Simon James Harry, BEng, MSc, CEng, MIMarEST, MIMechE,	LT CDR(FTC)	E	MESM	01.04.99	VENGEANCE(PORT)
Foster, Stephen,	CDR(FTC)	E	ME	01.10.97	NMA GOSPORT
Foster, Toby George, BSc,	LT(FTC)	X	HM	01.04.95	FWO PORTS SEA
Foubister, Robert, IEng, FIIE,	LT(FTC)	E	WESM	18.06.87	HQ DCSA
Foulger, Thomas Edward, BDS,	SG LT(D)(MCC)	-		11.06.99	DRAKE CBP(CNH)
Foulis, Niall David Alexander, BSc,	LT(FTC)	X	HM	01.03.95	ENDURANCE
Fowler, Peter James Shakespeare, MSc,	LT CDR(FTC)	E	MESM	01.04.90	NEPTUNE DSA
Fox, David John,	SLT(IC)	X		01.01.01	DARTMOUTH BRNC
Fox, Jonathan Paul, BA,	SLT(IC)	X		01.09.00	DARTMOUTH BRNC
Fox, Kevin Andrew, BSc, CEng, MIEE,	CDR(FTC)	E	AE(P)	30.06.94	2SL/CNH FOTR
Fox, Richard George, pcea,	LT CDR(FTC)	X	P	01.10.92	COMATG SEA
Fox, Trefor Morgan,	LT(CC)	X	HM	01.07.96	FLEET HQ PORTS 2
France, Sean Charles, BSc,	LT(SCC)	Q		25.08.99	RH HASLAR
Francis, Derek Edward,	LT(FTC)	X	PWO(U)	10.01.00	GRAFTON
Francis, John,	LT CDR(FTC)	X	AV	01.10.94	RNAS CULDROSE
Francis, Steven John, BA, psc(j),	MAJ(FTC)	-		25.04.96	JHQ NORTHEAST
Francis, Thomas Dewolfe Hamlin, BA,	CAPT RM(IC)	-		01.09.01	HQ 3 CDO BDE RM
Frankham, Peter James, BSc, BEng, CEng, MIMarEST, MDA,	CDR(FTC)	E	WE	31.12.00	WSA BRISTOL
Franklin, Benjamin James, pcea, psc(j),	LT CDR(FTC)	X	O	01.10.98	814 SQN
Franklin, George Durnford, BEng, MPhil, pce,	LT(FTC)	X	PWO(C)	01.02.95	EXCHANGE FRANCE
Franklin, William Henry, MA,	CHAPLAIN	CE		10.01.89	MWS EXCELLENT
Franklyn-Miller, Andrew David, MB, BS,	SURG LT(SCC)	-		04.08.99	MODHU DERRIFORD
Franks, Christopher Stephen, BSc,	LT CDR(FTC)	E	WESM	01.02.98	MOD DIS SEA
Franks, Donald Ian, adp,	LT CDR(FTC)	E	IS	01.10.94	SHAPE BELGIUM
Franks, Jeremy Peter, BSc, CEng, MRAeS,	LT CDR(FTC)	E	AE	01.12.85	ES AIR YEO
Franks, Peter Dennis, MSc,	LT CDR(FTC)	E	IS	01.10.93	IMS BRUSSELS
Fraser, Alasdair Graham,	LT(IC)	X	FC	01.05.02	SOUTHAMPTON
Fraser, Donald Kennedy, pce, MRIN,	LT CDR(FTC)	X	PWO(U)	01.07.84	FLEET HQ NWD
Fraser, Eric, BSc, pce, psc,	CAPT(FTC)	X	PWO(C)	30.06.02	BDS WASHINGTON
Fraser, Graeme William, MA,	MAJ(FTC)	-	LC	01.10.01	FLEET AV SUPPORT
Fraser, Heather Lee, BEng,	LT(FTC)	E	WE	01.07.96	WSA BRISTOL
Fraser, Ian David, MSc,	LT(CC)	E	AE	01.07.90	SABR IPT
Fraser, Ian Edward,	LT(CC)	X	P	16.04.96	771 SQN
Fraser, James Michael, BA,	SLT(IC)	X	P U/T	01.09.00	DARTMOUTH BRNC
Fraser, Michael John Simon, MSc,	LT(IC)	X		01.09.01	MWS RNHMS CULD
Fraser, Patrick,	LT(FTC)	E	AE(L)	01.05.96	ES AIR WYTON
Fraser, Peter Timothy, pcea,	LT CDR(CC)	X	O	01.10.94	RNAS CULDROSE
Fraser, Robert William, MVO, LLB,	CAPT(FTC)	S	BAR	31.12.99	RCDS
Fraser, Timothy Peter, pce,	CAPT(FTC)	X	PWO(N)	31.12.00	CARDIFF
Fraser, Wilson Cameron,	LT CDR(FTC)	E	WESM	01.10.96	FOST CSST SEA

Name	Rank	Branch	Spec	Seniority	Where Serving
Frazer, Hamish Forbes,	LT(CC)	X	FC	01.08.99	800 SQN
Frean, James Peter, BA,	LT(CC)	X	P	16.05.97	847 SQN
Free, Andrew Stuart, BSc, HNC, MIIE,	LT(IC)	E	TM	01.05.00	MWS COLLINGWOOD
Freegard, Ian Paul, MBE,	LT CDR(FTC)	S	(W)	01.10.99	HQ SOUTHLANT
Freeman, David Andrew Kenneth, LVO, pce,	CAPT(FTC)	X	PWO(N)†	30.06.99	ELANT/NAVNORTH
Freeman, David Russel, pce,	LT CDR(FTC)	X	O	01.06.96	JSCSC
Freeman, Mark Edward,	MAJ(FTC)	-		01.09.96	ELANT/NAVNORTH
Freeman, Martin John, AMIIE,	LT(FTC)	E	MESM	01.04.01	TIRELESS
French, James Thomas,	CDR(FTC)	E	ME	30.06.02	LOAN OMAN
French, Jeremy Hugh, BEng,	LT(IC)	X	P U/T	01.01.02	RAF LINTN/OUSE
French, Kevin Lawrence, pce,	LT CDR(FTC)	X	AAWO	09.07.93	ARK ROYAL
French, Stephen Amos, BEng, MSc, CEng,	CDR(FTC)	E	MESM	31.12.99	FWO FASLANE SEA
MIMarEST, MCGI, psc(j),					
Freshwater, Dennis Andrew, MB, BS, MRCP,	SURG LTCDR(FCC)	-		09.08.98	NELSON (PAY)
Fries, Charles,	SURG SLT(SCC)	-		01.12.00	DARTMOUTH BRNC
Frost, Mark Adrian, BSc,	LT(IC)	E	TM	01.01.91	NELSON RNSETT
Frost, Michael John,	CAPT RM(IC)	-	P	01.01.01	847 SQN
Fry, Jonathan Mark Stewart, MSc, CEng,	CDR(FTC)	E	ME	31.12.98	INVINCIBLE
FIMarEST, MCGI, psc, CDipAF,					
Fry, Robert Allan, CBE, BSc, MA, psc(m),	MAJ GEN	-		16.03.01	COMAMPHIBFOR
Fry, Timothy Graham,	LT(IC)	E	WESM	01.01.02	VENGEANCE(STBD)
Fryer, Adrian Clifford, BSc,	LT CDR(FTC)	X	PWO(A)	01.02.02	EXETER
Fulford, John Philip Henry, BSc, psc(m),	CDR(FTC)	E	WESM	31.12.95	MOD CSSE USA
Fulford, Robin Nicholas, IEng,	LT(FTC)	E	WE	07.02.97	FOST SEA
Full, Richard John,	LT(CC)	X	O	01.06.98	750 SQN SEAHAWK
Fuller, Charles Edward,	LT(CC)	X	P	16.08.97	GANNET SAR FLT
Fuller, James Bruce, BSc,	CAPT RM(CC)	-	LC	01.09.99	OCEAN
Fuller, James Edward,	LT(IC)	X	FC	01.03.02	YORK
Fuller, Simon Roland,	MAJ(FTC)	-		01.09.01	JSCSC
Fuller, Stephen Paul, (Act Lt)	SLT(IC)	E		01.05.99	849 SQN HQ
Fullman, Gemma, BSc,	SLT(IC)	X		01.09.99	ENDURANCE
Fulton, Craig Robert, pce, pce(sm),	CDR(FTC)	X	SM	31.12.00	SOVEREIGN
Fulton, David Marc,	LT(IC)	E	MESM	01.05.02	DARTMOUTH BRNC
Fulton, Robert Henry Gervase, BA, rcds, psc(m), hcsc,	MAJ GEN	-	C	23.10.98	MOD (LONDON)
Funnell, Nicholas Charles, BSc, pce, pcea, psc(m),	CDR(FTC)	X	O	30.06.96	INVINCIBLE
Furlong, Keith, pce,	LT CDR(FTC)	X	AAWO	01.03.96	GRIMSBY
Furness, Stuart Brian, MSc, MIMA, pce, pcea,	CDR(FTC)	X	O	30.06.96	NELSON (PAY)
Fyfe, Karen Sabrina,	LT(IC)	X	HM	01.10.00	MWS RNHMS CULD
Fyfe, Peter Matthew, MNI, psc, MInsD,	CDR(FTC)	X	AWO(U)	31.12.86	SHAPE BELGIUM

G

Name	Rank	Branch	Spec	Seniority	Where Serving
Gabb, John Harry, MB, BS,	SURG CAPT(FCC)	-	GMPP	31.12.00	2SL/CNH
Gabriel, Colin James, BSc, AMIEE,	LT CDR(FTC)	E	WE	01.12.88	HQ DCSA
Gadie, Philip Anthony, sq,	MAJ(FTC)	-		01.05.97	COMSTRIKFORSTH
Gadsden, Andrew Christopher, BA,	LT(IC)	X		01.09.00	WESTMINSTER
Gair, Simon David Henley, BEng, AMIEE,	LT(FTC)	E	WE	01.02.95	CSIS IPT
Galbraith, Lee,	2LT(IC)	X		01.09.98	CTCRM LYMPSTONE
Gale, Crystal Violet,	LT CDR(FTC)	S		24.12.00	KENT
Gale, Henry Nelson, pce,	CDR(FTC)	X	PWO(U)	30.06.88	NELSON
Gale, Mark Andrew, MA, MSc,	LT CDR(FTC)	E	MESM	01.02.00	VICTORIOUS(STBD)
Gale, Sandra Lillian,	LT CDR(FTC)	W	X	01.10.00	801 SQN
Gale, Simon Philip, pce,	LT CDR(FTC)	X	PWO(U)	01.11.96	FOST SEA
Gall, Michael Robert Carnegie, BDS, MSc, MGDS RCS,	SGCDR(D)(FCC)	-		30.06.95	DRAKE CBP(CNH)
Gallimore, John Martin,	LT(FTC)	X	EW	01.04.01	CHATHAM
Gallimore, Richard,	LT(IC)	X	P	16.02.01	702 SQN HERON
Galvin, David,	LT CDR(FTC)	E	WE	01.10.96	HQ DCSA
Gamble, Ian William, BA,	SLT(IC)	X	P U/T	01.05.00	DARTMOUTH BRNC
Gamble, John, (Act Lt Cdr)	LT(FTC)	E	AE(L)	02.11.84	SULTAN
Gamble, Mark John,	LT(IC)	X		01.08.01	ALBION
Gamble, Neil,	LT(CC)	X	P	01.11.93	820 SQN
Gamble, Phillip, BSc,	LT(CC)	X	O	15.05.93	849 SQN HQ
Gamble, Richard,	LT(FTC)	E	WE	10.06.88	NSE NORTHWOOD

Name	Rank	Branch	Spec	Seniority	Where Serving
Gamble, Stephen Boston, BA, BEng,	LT(CC)	X	P	01.06.97	815 FLT 203
Game, Philip Gordon, BEng, MSc gw, CEng, MIEE,	LT CDR(FTC)	E	WE	01.10.00	MOD (LONDON)
Gardiner, Dermott,	SURG SLT(SCC)	-		24.06.99	DARTMOUTH BRNC
Gardiner, Peter Fredrick David,	LT CDR(FTC)	X	ATC	01.10.00	RAF SHAWBURY
Gardner, Callum Brian, MB, ChB,	SURG LT(SCC)	-		02.08.00	MODHU DERRIFORD
Gardner, Christopher Reginald Summers, LLB, psc,	CDR(FTC)	S	SM	31.12.99	FOST DPORT SHORE
Gardner, John Edward, BA, pce,	LT CDR(FTC)	X	PWO(A)	01.07.00	OCEAN
Gardner, Louis Philip,	SLT(IC)	X	P U/T	01.01.01	DARTMOUTH BRNC
Gardner, Michael Peter, BSc,	LT(IC)	X		01.05.00	GRAFTON
Gardner, Suzanne Lorraine,	LT(SCC)	Q		05.11.98	RCDM
Gare, Christopher James,	LT(CC)	X		01.07.00	EXCHANGE NLANDS
Garland, Andrew Neil,	CAPT RM(FTC)	-	SO(LE)	01.01.00	CTCRM
Garland, Nicholas, BSc,	CDR(FTC)	S	CMA	30.06.02	HQ DCSA
Garlick, Edward Christian,	LT CDR(FTC)	X	AV	01.10.00	MWS COLLINGWOOD
Garner, Michael Edward,	SLT(IC)	X		01.09.99	BLYTH
Garner, Sean Martin, BA,	LT(CC)	X	ATC	01.08.94	RNAS CULDROSE
Garnett, *Sir* Ian, (David Graham), KCB, psc,	ADM	-	P	11.09.01	SHAPE BELGIUM
Garnham, Simon William, BA,	CAPT RM(IC)	-		01.05.99	45 CDO RM
Garratt, John Kenneth, BA, pce, n,	LT CDR(FTC)	X	AAWO	01.05.99	2SL/CNH
Garratt, Mark David, pce, pcea,	CDR(FTC)	X	P	30.06.97	MOD (LONDON)
Garreta, Carlos Eduardo, BSc,	LT(IC)	X		01.05.01	NBC PORTSMOUTH
Garrett, Stephen Walter, OBE, pce, pce(sm),	CDR(FTC)	X	SM	31.12.97	JSCSC
Gascoigne, James, BA,	SLT(IC)	X		01.01.00	RALEIGH
Gaskell, Harvey David, BEng,	LT(IC)	X	P	16.10.98	845 SQN
Gaskin, Daniel Edward,	SLT(IC)	X		01.09.00	CHIDDINGFOLD
Gaskin, Simon Edward, MNI, MRIN, pce,	LT CDR(FTC)	X		01.11.87	OCEAN
Gass, Colin Joseph, BSc, psc, pce,	CAPT(FTC)	X	AAWO	30.06.97	MWS DRYAD
Gasson, Nicholas Simon Charles, pce, ocds(US),	CDR(FTC)	X	PWO(U)	30.06.95	PJHQ
Gater, James Clive, BSc,	SLT(IC)	X		01.01.00	NOTTINGHAM
Gates, Daniel Alexander, BSc, SM, SM(n),	LT(IC)	X		01.12.99	SOVEREIGN
Gates, Nigel Sinclair, BEng,	LT(CC)	X	P	16.03.93	848 SQN HERON
Gaunt, Neville Raymond, pce, pcea, psc, psc(j),	CDR(FTC)	X	O	30.06.98	RNAS YEOVILTON
Gay, David Allin Thomas, MB, BS,	SURG LT(MCC)	-		05.08.98	MODHU DERRIFORD
Gayfer, Mark Ewan, MA, MSc, CEng, MIEE,	LT CDR(FTC)	E	WESM	01.12.99	MOD (LONDON)
Gaytano, Ronald Troy McDonald, BEng, MSc,	LT(IC)	E	AE	01.01.02	SULTAN
Gazard, Philip Neil, BEng, MBCS,	LT CDR(FTC)	E	WE	01.10.99	HQ DCSA
Gazzard, Julian Henry, PGDIPAN, pce,	LT CDR(FTC)	X	PWO(N)	01.06.96	FOST SEA
Geary, Timothy William, BEng,	LT CDR(FTC)	E	ME	01.08.96	MOD (BATH)
Geddes, William Bruce, jssc,	CDR(FTC)	E	AE	30.06.90	RNAS YEOVILTON
Geddis, Richard Duncan, BEng, CDipAF,	LT CDR(FTC)	E	WESM	01.09.96	SPARTAN
Geldard, Michael Andrew,	MAJ(FTC)	-		01.05.01	FLEET HQ PORTS 2
Gelder, George Arthur, psc,	LT COL(FTC)	-		31.12.93	UKMILREP BRUSS
Geneux, Nicholas Steven, BSc,	SLT(IC)	X		01.05.00	WESTMINSTER
Gennard, Anthony, BA,	LT(FTC)	S		01.03.95	FLEET HQ PORTS 2
Gent, Richard Peter St John, MA, MB, BCh, MRCGP,	SURG CDR(FCC)	-	GMPP	31.12.99	RN GIBRALTAR
George, Alan Peter, pcea,	LT CDR(FTC)	X	O	16.01.95	815 SQN HQ
George, Christopher Alan, BSc,	SLT(IC)	X	O U/T	01.01.00	750 SQN SEAHAWK
George, David Mark,	LT CDR(FTC)	X	PWO(A)	13.03.01	WESTMINSTER
George, Seth Duncan, BSc, PGCE,	LT(IC)	E	TM	01.06.00	SULTAN
Geraghty, Felicity,	LT(SCC)	Q		01.09.00	RN GIBRALTAR
Gerrell, Frederick John,	LT CDR(FTC)	MS		01.10.00	MODHU PORTSMOUTH
Gershater, Stefan Craig, BSc,	SLT(IC)	S		01.01.01	DARTMOUTH BRNC
Getgood, James Ashley, BA, psc(m),	LT COL(FTC)	-		30.06.95	RMR LONDON
Gething, Jonathan Blair, pce(sm),	CDR(FTC)	X	SM	30.06.02	SHAPE BELGIUM
Gibb, Alexander,	LT RM(IC)	-	SO(LE)	30.03.00	MOD (LONDON)
Gibb, Roger Walter, BSc,	CDR(FTC)	E	WESM	31.12.91	SACLANT USA
Gibbon, Lynne,	CDR(FCC)	Q	ONC	31.12.00	2SL/CNH
Gibbons, Nicholas Philip,	LT(FTC)	X	O	01.10.92	FLEET AV CU
Gibbs, Anthony Edward,	LT(IC)	X	ATC	08.04.01	RNAS YEOVILTON
Gibbs, Anthony Maurice,	LT(IC)	X	P	01.03.99	815 FLT 208
Gibbs, David John Edward, BEng,	LT(IC)	X	P	01.02.98	848 SQN HERON
Gibbs, Mark Peter, BEng,	SLT(IC)	E	ME	01.09.99	SULTAN

Name	Rank	Branch	Spec	Seniority	Where Serving
Gibbs, Neil David, BSc,	LT CDR(FTC)	E	ME	01.07.95	DEF SCH OF LANG
Gibbs, Philip Norman Charles, MSc,	LT CDR(FTC)	X	PWO(U)	01.02.89	MOD (LONDON)
Gibson, Adrian,	SLT(IC)	X	WE	27.01.01	MWS COLLINGWOOD
Gibson, Alastair David, MA,	LT CDR(FTC)	S		16.11.97	COMATG SEA
Gibson, Alexander James, BSc,	CAPT RM(FTC)	-		01.01.01	539 ASSLT SQN RM
Gibson, Andrew Richard, MB, BS, MRCS,	SURG LTCDR(MCC)	-		01.08.99	NELSON (PAY)
Gibson, Andrew,	LT CDR(FTC)	E	AE	08.06.91	ES AIR YEO
Gibson, David Thomas, BSc,	LT CDR(FTC)	E	AE	01.06.91	LAIPT
Gibson, Ian Alexander, pce,	CDR(FTC)	X	PWO(A)	31.12.92	HQ NORTH
Gibson, Jennifer Blair, BSc,	LT(IC)	X	MW	01.01.96	MWS DRYAD
Gibson, Martin Jonathan Stuart, AMRAeS,	LT(FTC)	E	AE(M)	01.04.01	JSCSC
Gibson, Sarah Jane, BA, MSc,	LT(IC)	E	IS	01.01.99	AFPAA(CENTURION)
Gibson, Terence Anthony,	LT(IC)	E	WE	01.01.02	LANCASTER
Gibson, Timothy Andrew, MBE, pce,	LT CDR(FTC)	X	N	16.03.87	EXC BRISTOL
Gidney, Nigel, osc,	MAJ(FTC)	-		01.09.88	RM WARMINSTER
Gilbert, Lee Graham, BSc, MBA, FRSA, AMIMechE,	LT CDR(FTC)	E	AE	01.10.94	ES AIR YEO
Gilbert, Peter David, BEng, MA, MSc, CEng,	LTCDR(FTC)	E	ME	01.03.96	PJHQ
MIMarEST, MIMechE, MCGI, psc(j),					
Gilbert, Ross Grant, LLB,	LT(FTC)	S		01.06.98	2SL/CNH
Gilbert, Stephen Anthony, BEng, psc(j),	CDR(FTC)	E	ME	30.06.00	SFM ROSYTH
Gilding, Douglas Robert, BSc,	MAJ(FTC)	-		01.09.98	EXCHANGE NLANDS
Giles, Andrew Robert,	LT CDR(FTC)	S	(S)	21.07.92	NMA PORTSMOUTH
Giles, David William, MBE, MSc, CEng, MIEE,	LT CDR(FTC)	E	WE	01.07.93	FLEET HQ PORTS 2
Giles, Gary John,	CAPT RM(FTC)	-	SO(LE)	01.01.01	CTCRM
Giles, Kevin David Lindsay, BSc, pce,	LT CDR(FTC)	X	MCD	01.05.92	EXCHANGE USA
Giles, Robert Keith, BEng,	LT CDR(FTC)	X	PWO(A)	01.03.01	ARGYLL
Gill, Christopher David, SM,	LT(FTC)	X	SM	01.01.00	VENGEANCE(PORT)
Gill, Christopher Michael,	LT CDR(CC)	X	METOC	01.10.89	RALEIGH
Gill, Mark Hansen, BEng, pcea,	LT(FTC)	X	O	01.07.94	849 SQN HQ
Gill, Martin Robert, BEng, MSc, psc(j),	LT CDR(FTC)	E	MESM	01.04.95	MOD (BATH)
Gill, Paul Simon, MA,	LT(IC)	E	TM	01.01.00	SULTAN
Gill, Steven Clark,	LT(FTC)	X	(S)	12.12.91	UKSU JHQ NORTH
Gillam, Richard Leslie, BSc,	LT CDR(FTC)	E	ME	01.12.88	MOD (BATH)
Gillan, Gordon Maxwell, BEng, MSc, gw,	LT CDR(FTC)	E	WE	01.04.95	SHEFFIELD
Gillanders, Fergus Graeme Roy, pce,	CDR(FTC)	X	AAWO	31.12.94	JDCC
Gillard, Victoria Anne,	LT(FTC)	X	HM	01.07.99	GLEANER
Gillett, David Alexander,	LT(FTC)	X		01.11.98	750 SQN SEAHAWK
Gillett, Nathan David,	SLT(IC)	X		01.01.01	DARTMOUTH BRNC
Gillham, Paul Robert,	LT CDR(FTC)	E	WE	02.03.95	MOD (BATH)
Gillies, Elizabeth Mary, BSc,	LT(IC)	S		01.01.98	OCLC BIRM
Gillies, Robert Ross, BEng, CEng, MIMarEST,	LT CDR(FTC)	E	MESM	01.02.97	SULTAN
Gilliland, Samuel Saunderson,	LT(FTC)	E	WE	13.06.91	WSA/CAPT MCTA
Gillingham, George,	MID(NE)(IC)	X	O U/T	01.01.02	DARTMOUTH BRNC
Gilmartin, Kieran,	SURG SLT(SCC)	-		04.10.99	DARTMOUTH BRNC
Gilmore, Jeremy Edward,	SLT(IC)	X	P U/T	01.09.00	DHFS
Gilmore, Martin Paul,	LT(FTC)	X	P	01.06.96	815 SQN HQ
Gilmore, Steven John, BEng,	LT(CC)	E	WE	01.04.00	ARK ROYAL
Gilmour, Craig James Murray, MNI, pce,	CDR(FTC)	X	PWO(A)	30.06.02	MWS DRYAD
Ginn, Robert Nigel,	CAPT RM(FTC)	-	SO(LE)	01.01.95	RM POOLE
Ginn, Robert,	2LT(FTC)	-		01.09.01	CTCRM LYMPSTONE
Gittoes, Mark Anthony Warren,	MAJ(FTC)	-		01.09.90	LOAN OTHER SVCE
Gladston, Stephen Anderson,	LT(CC)	X	P	01.07.91	DHFS
Gladwell, Trevor John, SM,	LT CDR(FTC)	X	SM	01.12.93	MOD (LONDON)
Gladwin, Michael David, BSc,	LT(CC)	X	ATC	01.01.01	RNAS CULDROSE
Glancy, James,	2LT(UCE)(IC)	-		01.09.01	CTCRM LYMPSTONE
Glass, Jonathan Eric, BSc,	LT CDR(FTC)	X		01.09.94	JHQ NORTHEAST
Glaze, John William, BSc, psc,	MAJ(FTC)	-	SO(LE)	01.10.92	2SL/CNH FOTR
Glendinning, Christopher James Alexander,	SLT(IC)	X		01.05.00	MWS DRYAD
Glennie, Andrew Michael Gordon, BSc, CEng, MIMarEST,	CDR(FTC)	E	ME	31.12.00	FLEET HQ PORTS 2
Glennie, Brian William, MBA,	LT CDR(FTC)	E	WE	01.10.99	INVINCIBLE
Glover, Mark Alec, BA, BM, BCh, MRCGP, AFOM,	SURG CDR(FCC)	-	GMPP	31.12.00	INM ALVERSTOKE
Gobey, Christopher Graham,	LT CDR(CC)	X	SM	01.10.95	HQ SOUTHLANT

Name	Rank	Branch	Spec	Seniority	Where Serving
Goble, Ian John,	LT CDR(FTC)	E	WE	01.10.95	NMA PORTSMOUTH
Goddard, David Jonathan Sinclair, BSc, pce,	LT CDR(FTC)	X	PWO(N)	01.10.87	MWS DRYAD
Goddard, Ian Aleksis, BSc,	LT(IC)	X		16.11.01	OCEAN
Goddard, Ian Kenneth, pce, psc,	CAPT(FTC)	X	PWO(U)	31.12.97	UKMILREP BRUSS
Goddard, Paul,	LT(IC)	E	WESM	01.05.02	RALEIGH
Godfrey, Kim Richard, BSc, pce,	LT CDR(FTC)	X	MCD	01.09.93	SUPT OF DIVING
Godfrey, Simeon David William, SM, SM(n),	LT(FTC)	X	SM	01.04.01	VIGILANT(PORT)
Godley, David John,	LT(IC)	E	WE	01.01.02	CHATHAM
Godwin, Christopher Anthony, pcea,	LT CDR(FTC)	X	P	01.02.99	NOTTINGHAM
Gokhale, Stephen,	SURG SLT(SCC)	-		01.07.00	DARTMOUTH BRNC
Gold, John William, (Act Lt Cdr)	LT(FTC)	X	EW	06.04.95	MWC PORTSDOWN
Golden, Charles Alexander,	SLT(UCE)(IC)	E	ME	01.09.01	DARTMOUTH BRNC
Golden, Dominic St Clair,	LT CDR(FTC)	X	FC	01.06.99	RNAS YEOVILTON
Goldman, Paul Henry Louis, BEng, MSc,	LT CDR(FTC)	E	WE	01.04.99	ARK ROYAL
Goldsmith, Darran, pcea,	LT CDR(FTC)	X	O	01.10.99	824 SQN
Goldsmith, David Thomas, BEng,	LT CDR(FTC)	E	WE	01.01.02	CESM IPT
Goldsmith, Simon Victor William, BSc, pce,	LT CDR(FTC)	X	PWO(C)	01.05.95	UKMARBATSTAFF
Goldstone, Richard Samuel, BA, n,	LT(FTC)	X		01.08.94	DARTMOUTH BRNC
Goldsworthy, Elaine Tania, (Act Lt Cdr)	LT(CC)	S		01.08.95	MAS BRUSSELS
Goldsworthy, Peter Jarvis, BEng,	LT(FTC)	S	BAR	01.09.94	MONTROSE
Goldthorpe, Michael,	LT CDR(FTC)	S		06.06.96	RNAS YEOVILTON
Gomm, Kevin, BSc, pce, pce(sm),	LT CDR(FTC)	X	SM	01.06.91	RALEIGH
Gooch, Michael David, BEng,	SLT(IC)	E	ME	01.09.99	SULTAN
Goodacre, Ian Royston, pce,	LT CDR(FTC)	X	PWO(U)	01.05.98	UKMARBATSTAFF
Goodall, David Charles, pce, pcea, psc,	CAPT(FTC)	X	P	31.12.98	CJPS
Goodall, Joanne Claire, BA,	LT(IC)	E	TM	01.05.00	DARTMOUTH BRNC
Goodall, Michael Antony, BEng,	LT(IC)	E		01.05.98	GLOUCESTER
Goodall, Simon Richard James, CBE, ADC,BA,(Commodore) psc(m), MSc,	CAPT(FTC)	E	TM	31.12.93	2SL/CNH FOTR
Goode, Alun Nicholas,	LT CDR(FTC)	X	PWO(A)	01.09.99	DARTMOUTH BRNC
Goodenough, Robert Henry, BEng,	SLT(IC)	E	ME	01.09.99	SULTAN
Gooder, Simon Philip, MNI,	LT CDR(FTC)	X	N†	01.05.83	DRAKE DPL
Gooding, David Christopher,	MID(NE)(IC)	X		01.01.02	DARTMOUTH BRNC
Goodings, George James,	LT CDR(FTC)	E	MESM	01.10.96	NEPTUNE NT
Goodman, Andrew Theodore, BSc, pce, n,	LT CDR(FTC)	X	PWO(U)	01.03.98	MWC PORTSDOWN
Goodman, David Frederick, SM,	LT(FTC)	X	SM	09.05.01	SOVEREIGN
Goodman, Peter Robert,	LT(FTC)	S		01.10.94	ARK ROYAL
Goodrich, David Leslie,	LT CDR(FTC)	E	WE	01.10.93	HQ DCSA
Goodridge, Terence James, (Act Maj)	CAPT RM(FTC)	-	SO(LE)	01.01.93	CTCRM
Goodrum, Simon Edward,	LT(FTC)	MS		19.09.99	PJHQ AUGMENTEES
Goodsell, Christopher David, MNI, pce, pce(sm),	LT CDR(FTC)	X	SM	01.02.99	EXCHANGE USA
Goodsell, David Lee,	SLT(IC)	E	WE	01.01.00	IRON DUKE
Goodship, Mark Thomas, BEng,	LT(CC)	E	ME	01.01.98	ILLUSTRIOUS
Goodwin, David Robert, pce,	CDR(FTC)	X	PWO(U)	31.12.93	MWC SOUTHWICK
Goodwin, Lincoln Bryan,	LT(FTC)	S	(S)	03.04.98	DRAKE DPL
Goosen, Richard Davidson,	SLT(IC)	X		01.05.01	EDINBURGH
Gopsill, Brian Richard, MIL,	LT CDR(FTC)	S	SM	01.07.85	AGRIPPA NAVSOUTH
Gordon, Andrew Jon,	SLT(UCE)(IC)	E	ME	01.09.00	DARTMOUTH BRNC
Gordon, David Iain, BSc,	LT(IC)	X		01.05.01	VENGEANCE(STBD)
Gordon, David, BA, BSc, psc,	CDR(FTC)	E	TM	30.06.01	FLEET HQ PORTS
Gordon, John, (Act Lt)	SLT(IC)	X		01.05.00	MWS COLLINGWOOD
Gordon, Neil Leslie, BSc,	LT(CC)	E	ME	01.11.92	INVINCIBLE
Gordon, Robert Stuart,	LT RM(IC)	-	SO(LE)	01.04.00	45 CDO RM
Gordon, Stuart Ross, MA, pce, pcea, psc,	CDR(FTC)	X	P	30.06.02	JHCHQ
Gorman, Darren Ashley, BSc,	SLT(IC)	X	P U/T	01.09.99	RAF CRANWELL EFS
Gorman, Glenn Kieran,	SLT(IC)	X	P U/T	01.09.00	DARTMOUTH BRNC
Gorrod, Peter Charles Alfred,	LT(FTC)	X	PR	06.09.85	FOST DPORT SHORE
Goscomb, Paul Andrew, BA,	SLT(IC)	S		01.01.01	DARTMOUTH BRNC
Gosden, Daniel Richard,	SLT(UCE)(FTC)	E	ME	01.09.01	DARTMOUTH BRNC
Gosden, Stephen Richard, MSc, CEng, FIMarEST, psc,	CAPT(FTC)	E	ME	30.06.02	NELSON
Gosling, Darren John,	LT(IC)	S		01.04.01	2SL/CNH
Gosney, Christopher,	CAPT RM(FTC)	-	SO(LE)	01.01.99	TRAINTEAM BRUNEI

Name	Rank	Branch	Spec	Seniority	Where Serving
Gothard, Andrew Mark, BEng,	LT(FTC)	E	ME	01.11.96	NEPTUNE NT
Gotke, Christopher Torben, BEng,	LT(CC)	X	P	16.01.94	800 SQN
Gott, Stephen Bruce,	SLT(IC)	S		01.05.00	MARLBOROUGH
Goudge, Simon David Philip, BA,	LT CDR(FTC)	S		01.04.02	NOTTINGHAM
Gough, Martyn John,	CHAPLAIN	CE		01.09.98	AFCC
Gough, Steven Roy,	LT CDR(FTC)	X	PT	01.10.01	TEMERAIRE
Gould, Amelia Alice, MEng,	LT(FTC)	E	WE	01.09.01	ARK ROYAL
Gould, Ian,	SLT(IC)	E	AE	01.05.00	SULTAN
Gould, James David,	LT(FTC)	X		01.10.98	SOUTHAMPTON
Goulder, Jonathan David, BEng,	LT(CC)	X		01.11.97	TYNE
Goulding, Jonathan Paul, BA, ACMI, n,	LT(FTC)	X		01.03.95	MWS DRYAD
Gourlay, James Stewart, BSc, psc,	CDR(FTC)	E	AE	30.06.96	HUMS IPT
Govan, Richard Thomas, OBE, pce, psc,	CDR(FTC)	X	PWO(U)	30.06.92	DSTL CDA HLS
Goward, Rachel Jane, BSc, PGCE,	LT(IC)	E	TM	01.05.98	SULTAN
Gower, John Howard James, OBE, BSc, MNI, pce, pce(sm),	CAPT(FTC)	X	SM	31.12.99	BDS WASHINGTON
Grace, Nicholas John, pdm,	CAPT RM(FTC)	BS		01.01.01	CTCRM BAND
Grace, Trevor Paul,	LT CDR(FTC)	E	WE	01.10.98	SOUTHAMPTON
Grafton, Martin Nicholas, BSc, CEng, MIMechE, MINucE,	CDR(FTC)	E	MESM	31.12.96	NEPTUNE FD
Graham, Alastair Neil Spencer, BSc, AMIEE,	LT CDR(FTC)	E	WESM	01.08.01	MOD (LONDON)
Graham, David Edward, pce,	LT CDR(FTC)	X	AAWO	01.10.91	FLEET HQ PORTS 2
Graham, David Winston Stuart, BEng, CEng, MIMechE,	LT CDR(FTC)	E	MESM	01.08.97	VENGEANCE(PORT)
Graham, Gordon Russell, BSc, psc(m),	CDR(FTC)	E	WE	30.06.97	ARK ROYAL
Graham, Ian Edmund, pce, n,	LT CDR(FTC)	X	PWO(A)	01.08.98	FOST SEA
Graham, James Edward, PSC(ONDC),	CDR(FTC)	S	SM	30.06.00	JHQSW MADRID
Graham, Mark Alexander, pcea,	LT CDR(FTC)	X	O	01.10.01	MWC PORTSDOWN
Graham, Penelope Jane, BA,	LT CDR(FTC)	W	S	22.10.99	ELANT/NAVNORTH
Graham, Robert,	LT CDR(FTC)	E	ME	01.10.97	INVINCIBLE
Grainge, Christopher Leonard, BSc, MB, BS,	SURG LT(SCC)	-		04.08.99	ENDURANCE
Grandison, John Alexander Steele,	LT CDR(FTC)	X	AAWO	01.03.86	MWS DRYAD
Grange, Alan Benjamin,	SLT(IC)	X		01.05.00	ARGYLL
Granger, Christopher Ronald,	LT CDR(FTC)	E	MESM	01.10.97	DRAKE SFM
Grant, Alan Kenneth, OBE, MA, pcea, pce,	CDR(FTC)	X	O	30.06.93	MOD (BATH)
Grant, Brian Gerald,	LT(TC)	E	MESM	10.06.94	NEPTUNE FD
Grant, David James,	LT(FTC)	E	MESM	14.06.96	SCEPTRE
Grant, Ian William, psc(m), psc(j),	LT COL(FTC)	-	LC	30.06.91	FLEET HQ PORTS
Grant, Roland Stephen, MBE, psc,	LT COL(FTC)	-		30.06.90	CTCRM
Grant, Wayne Graham, BEng,	LT(FTC)	E	AE	01.06.00	899 SQN HERON
Grantham, Stephen Mark, MSc, CEng, MIMechE, MCGI,	CDR(FTC)	E	MESM	30.06.01	NP BRISTOL
Gratton, Stephen William, MIIE,	LT CDR(FTC)	E	WE	01.10.96	WSA/CAPT MCTA
Graves, Michael Edward Linsan, BSc,	CAPT(FTC)	E	WESM	30.06.98	NMA PORTSMOUTH
Gray, Anthony James, MA, psc(j),	CDR(FTC)	E	AE(P)	31.12.98	ES AIR BRISTOL
Gray, Anthony John, MSc, CEng, MIMechE,	CDR(FTC)	E	MESM	30.06.02	MOD (BATH)
Gray, David Kingston, BEng, AMIEE,	LT CDR(FTC)	E	WE	01.04.95	FLEET HQ PORTS
Gray, Dennis,	LT CDR(FTC)	E	ME	01.10.93	FOST DPORT SHORE
Gray, Emma Jane, BA,	LT(IC)	S		01.09.01	FOST SEA
Gray, James Alan, (Act Maj)	CAPT RM(FTC)	-		29.04.97	BDS WASHINGTON
Gray, James Michael, MEng,	SLT(IC)	E	AE U/T	01.09.00	IRON DUKE
Gray, James Nelson Stephen,	LT(CC)	X	O	01.04.95	702 SQN HERON
Gray, John Allan, BEng, pce,	LT CDR(FTC)	X	AAWO	01.06.00	PENZANCE
Gray, John Arthur, BSc,	LT(CC)	X	SM	01.03.98	TRENCHANT
Gray, Karl Daniel,	CAPT RM(FTC)	-		01.05.00	40 CDO RM
Gray, Mark Nicholas, MBE, MA, osc(us),	LT COL(FTC)	-		30.06.02	PJHQ
Gray, Michael John Henry,	LT(FTC)	X	AV	09.01.01	800 SQN
Gray, Nathan John, BEng,	LT(CC)	X	P	01.12.99	RNAS CULDROSE
Gray, Paul Reginald,	LT(CC)	X	P	01.08.91	PJHQ
Gray, Richard Laurence,	SLT(IC)	X		01.09.00	DARTMOUTH BRNC
Gray, Richard, SM(n), BSc,	LT CDR(FTC)	E	IS	01.03.99	DITMTC SHRIVNHAM
Gray, Robert Stanley, BSc,	CDR(FTC)	S	BAR	31.12.99	DARTMOUTH BRNC
Gray, Simon Anthony Neatham, BSc,	LT RM(IC)	-		01.09.00	FPGRM
Gray, Yvonne Michelle, BEd,	LT(FTC)	X	MW	01.02.95	NMA PORTSMOUTH
Grears, Jonathan, BSc,	LT CDR(FTC)	E	IS	01.09.99	RMC OF SCIENCE
Greatwood, Ian Mark, BEng, MSc,	LT CDR(FTC)	E	WESM	01.01.99	TURBULENT

Name	Rank	Branch	Spec	Seniority	Where Serving
Greaves, Martin Richard,	SLT(IC)	X		01.05.01	NORTHUMBERLAND
Greedus, David Arthur, psc(j),	MAJ(FTC)	-	SO(LE)	01.10.96	HQ 3 CDO BDE RM
Green, Adrian Richard, MSc, CEng, MIMechE, MCGI,	CDR(FTC)	E	MESM	31.12.98	NMA PORTSMOUTH
Green, Andrew John, BA,	LT CDR(FTC)	E	TMSM	01.05.98	MOD (LONDON)
Green, Andrew Michael, BSc,	LT CDR(FTC)	E	ME	01.07.01	CARDIFF
Green, David Patrick Savage, BEng, MSc,	LT CDR(FTC)	E	WESM	01.05.95	MOD (LONDON)
Green, David Paul, SM,	LT CDR(FTC)	X	SM	13.08.93	FOSM GOSPORT
Green, Gareth Mark, BA,	MAJ(FTC)	-		01.09.98	EXCHANGE FRANCE
Green, Gary Edward,	MAJ(FTC)	-	SO(LE)	01.10.01	UKLFCSG RM
Green, Ian Andrew,	LT(CC)	X	ATC	01.04.97	ARK ROYAL
Green, Janette Lesley, (Act Lt Cdr)	LT(FTC)	W	AV	11.12.92	2SL/CNH FOTR
Green, Jayne Hannah, BSc,	LT(IC)	X	O U/T	01.09.99	750 SQN SEAHAWK
Green, John Anthony, BSc, CEng, MIEE, MInstP, AMInstP, CDipAF, jsdc,	CAPT(FTC)	X	WESM	31.12.97	NEPTUNE NT
Green, John,	CHAPLAIN	CE		04.06.91	ARK ROYAL
Green, Jonathan,	SLT(IC)	X	P	01.01.00	771 SQN
Green, Jonathan,	LT CDR(FTC)	X		01.06.98	COMSTRIKFORSTH
Green, Leslie David,	SLT(IC)	E	MESM	01.05.00	SULTAN
Green, Michael Gerald Hamilton, MA, psc(j),	MAJ(FTC)	-	LC	01.09.98	40 CDO RM
Green, Michael Ronald,	MAJ(FTC)	-	SO(LE)	01.10.99	RMB STONEHOUSE
Green, Patrick George, (Act Lt)	SLT(IC)	MS		01.10.99	FORT BLOCKHOUSE
Green, Peter James, pce(sm), SM,	LT CDR(FTC)	X	SM	01.07.96	MOD (LONDON)
Green, Philip Daniel, BSc,	LT(CC)	X	P	16.10.97	849 SQN B FLT
Green, Roger Richard, BA,	LT(IC)	E		08.01.00	42 CDO RM
Green, Stephen Noel, BSc, CEng, MIEE, psc, psc(j),	CDR(FTC)	E	WE	31.12.98	WSA BRISTOL
Green, Timothy Cooper, BA, SM(n), SM,	LT CDR(FTC)	X	SM	01.10.01	VENGEANCE(PORT)
Green, Timothy John, pce(sm), psc(a),	CDR(FTC)	X	SM	31.12.98	FOST CSST SEA
Greenaway, Nicholas Mark, pce,	LT CDR(FTC)	X	AAWO	01.08.95	ST ALBANS
Greenberg, Neil, BSc, BM, MRCPsych,	SURG LTCDR(MCC)	-		01.09.99	NELSON (PAY)
Greene, Michael John, BEd, MSc, psc,	CDR(FTC)	E	TM	31.12.98	NELSON
Greener, Carl, MEng, MSc, CEng, MIEE,	LT CDR(FTC)	E	WE	01.09.99	EXCHANGE USA
Greenfield, Kenneth,	LT CDR(FTC)	E	ME	01.10.93	DRAKE SFM
Greenhill, Matthew Charles, BA,	SLT(IC)	X		01.01.01	DARTMOUTH BRNC
Greenish, Philip Duncan, BSc, CEng, MIEE, rcds, jsdc,	RADM	-	WE	24.11.00	FLEET HQ PORTS
Greenland, Michael Richard, pce, pcea,	LT CDR(FTC)	X	P	16.04.95	RICHMOND
Greenlees, Iain Wallace, BSc, pce,	CDR(FTC)	X	PWO(A)	30.06.93	NMA PORTSMOUTH
Greenop, Jeremy Peter Spencer, OBE, jsdc, pce, psc,	CDR(FTC)	X	P	31.12.89	IMS BRUSSELS
Greenway, Stephen Anthony, BEng, CEng, MIMarEST, MIMechE, CDipAF,	LT CDR(FTC)	E	ME	01.02.00	YORK
Greenwood, Antony Wyn, BSc,	LT(CC)	X	HM	01.02.99	FWO DEVPT SEA
Greenwood, Benjamin Charles John, BEng,	LT(IC)	X	ATCU/T	01.09.01	RAF SHAWBURY
Greenwood, Michael John, BA,	LT CDR(FTC)	X	METOC	01.09.91	RNAS YEOVILTON
Greenwood, Peter Adam,	LT(CC)	X	P	16.10.99	824 SQN
Greenwood, Peter, pce,	CDR(FTC)	X	MCD	30.06.01	MOD (LONDON)
Greenwood, Stephen, BSc, CEng, MRAeS, MDA,	CDR(FTC)	E	AE(P)	31.12.97	ARK ROYAL
Gregan, David Carl, psc,	CDR(FTC)	X	H CH	30.06.92	MOD (LONDON)
Gregory, Alastair Stuart, BEng, MSc, CEng, MIMarEST, MRINA,	LT CDR(FTC)E	M	E	01.06.00	NORFOLK
Gregory, James Russell Clement, MB, ChB,	SURG LT(SCC)	-		02.08.00	42 CDO RM
Gregory, Timothy Maurice, BA, rcds, psc(m),	BRIG(FTC)	-	C	31.12.00	HQ DCSA
Greig, Judith Anne, BEng,	LT(FTC)	E	ME	01.11.98	SULTAN
Grenfell-Shaw, Mark Christopher, MA,	LT CDR(FTC)	E	WESM	01.06.95	TORBAY
Grennan, Eamonn Fergal, BEng, MSc,	LT(IC)	E	AE	01.05.98	EXCHANGE ARMY UK
Grey, Christopher Sidney, BSc,	LT(IC)	X	O U/T	01.01.02	702 SQN HERON
Grey, Edward John William, BA,	LT(IC)	E	TM	03.04.99	CTCRM
Grice, Matthew Gordon, BEng,	SLT(IC)	E	AE	01.09.00	CUMBERLAND
Grieve, Steven Harry, BSc, MA, CEng, MRAeS, psc,	CDR(FTC)	E	AE	30.06.01	CV(F) IPT
Griffen, David John, BSc,	LT(IC)	X		01.04.00	GRAFTON
Griffin, Niall Robert,	LT CDR(CC)	X	P	01.10.01	JHCNI
Griffin, Peter John,	LT(FTC)	X	ATC	19.09.00	OCEAN
Griffin, Stephen,	LT(IC)	X	AV	01.09.01	RFANSU
Griffiths, Alan Richard,	LT(FTC)	E	WE	09.06.89	MWS COLLINGWOOD

Name	Rank	Branch	Spec	Seniority	Where Serving
Griffiths, Andrew John, MSc, psc(j),	LT CDR(FTC)	E	TM	26.07.94	FWO PORTS SEA
Griffiths, Anthony,	LT CDR(FTC)	X	MW	01.10.97	SAUDI AFPS SAUDI
Griffiths, Christopher John James,	LT(IC)	E	ME	29.04.01	FEARLESS
Griffiths, Colin Stuart Henry, BSc,	LT(CC)	X	P U/T	01.04.00	845 SQN
Griffiths, David Anthony, MSc,	LT CDR(FTC)	MS	SM	01.10.99	FLEET HQ PORTS 2
Griffiths, David Michael, BSc, CEng, FIMarEST, (Act Cdr)	LT CDR(FTC)	E	ME	01.06.91	2SL/CNH FOTR
Griffiths, David Price, BEng,	LT(FTC)	E	WE	01.09.97	MWS COLLINGWOOD
Griffiths, David Thomas, BSc, pce,	LT CDR(FTC)	X	MCD	01.04.90	ENDURANCE
Griffiths, Francis Mark,	MID(UCE)(IC)	E	ME U/T	01.09.01	ARK ROYAL
Griffiths, Gareth Heaton, BSc, SM,	LT(IC)	X	SM	01.10.98	SPARTAN
Griffiths, Glyn,	SLT(IC)	E	WESM	28.01.00	RALEIGH
Griffiths, Lloyd, MEng,	LT(FTC)	E	MESM	01.04.98	TURBULENT
Griffiths, Michael Owen John,	LT CDR(FTC)	X	PWO(U)	16.01.00	DEF SCH OF LANG
Griffiths, Neil, BA,	LT(CC)	X	MW	01.09.98	PEMBROKE
Griffiths, Nicholas Alan,	CAPT RM(CC)	-		01.05.00	NMA WHALE ISLAND
Griffiths, Nigel Colin,	SLT(IC)	E	WE	01.01.00	INVINCIBLE
Griffiths, Nigel Mills, QGM, (Act Lt)	SLT(IC)	X		01.01.01	ELANT/NAVNORTH
Griffiths, Richard Hywel, SM(n), SM,	LT(FTC)	X	SM	01.06.96	TIRELESS
Grigg, Shelton Kent,	LT(IC)	S	(W)	08.01.01	RNAS CULDROSE
Grimley, Daemon Marcus John, pce, pce(sm),	LT CDR(FTC)	X	SM	01.11.89	DALRIADA
Grimshaw, Ernest,	CHAPLAIN	SF		02.05.00	FWO FASLANE
Grindel, David John Stuart, BEd, MSc, psc(j),	CDR(FTC)	E	TM	30.06.02	JSCSC
Grindon, Matthew Guy, BEng,	LT CDR(CC)	X	P	01.10.00	LOAN JTEG BSC DN
Grinnell, Jason, BSc, HND,	LT(IC)	E	IS	01.10.01	SULTAN
Gritt, Louisa Ann, BSc,	LT CDR(FTC)	X	H2	01.10.01	JSCSC
Grixoni, Martin Reynold Roberto,	MAJ(FTC)	-		01.09.90	FLEET HQ PORTS 2
Grocott, Peter Clark,	LT CDR(FTC)	S	(W)	01.10.00	NEPTUNE DLO
Groom, Ian Stuart, BEng, CEng, MIMarEST,	LT CDR(FTC)	E	ME	01.03.99	NOTTINGHAM
Groom,Mark Richard, MB, ChB, MRCGP, MRAeS, DipAvMed, AFOM, aws,	SURG CDR(FCC)	-	GMPP	30.06.00	RNAS YEOVILTON
Grosse, Sarah Elizabeth Kingsbury, BDS, BSc,	SG LT(D)(SCC)	-		25.06.99	MWS COLLINGWOOD
Groves, Christopher Keith, pce(sm), SM(n),	LT CDR(FTC)	X	SM	01.04.99	TIRELESS
Gubbins, Victor Robert, BSc, CEng, MIMarEST, fsc,	CDR(FTC)	E	ME	31.12.93	MOD (BATH)
Gubby, Adrian William, BEng,	SLT(IC)	E	WE	01.09.99	MWS COLLINGWOOD
Guest, Samuel,	2LT(IC)	-		01.09.98	CTCRM LYMPSTONE
Guild, Nigel Charles Forbes, BA, PhD, MIEE, AFIMA, jsdc,	RADM	-	WE	06.01.00	DPA BRISTOL
Guilfoyle, Victoria Marion,	LT(CC)	X		15.11.00	CORNWALL
Guiver, Paul, BEM,	LT(FTC)	X	MCD	03.04.97	BANGOR
Gullett, Humphrey Richard, MA,	LT(CC)	S	SM	01.02.97	MOD (LONDON)
Gulley, Trevor James, MSc, CEng, MCGI,	CDR(FTC)	E	ME	30.06.98	BULWARK
Gulliford, Kerry Anne, BA,	LT(CC)	S		01.01.00	SOUTHAMPTON
Gulliver, Jeffrey William, BEng,	SLT(IC)	X		01.09.99	NOTTINGHAM
Gunn, William John Simpson, BSc, PGDip,	LT CDR(FTC)	X	METOC	01.11.94	MWS DRYAD
Gunther, Paul Thomas,	LT CDR(FTC)	E	WESM	01.10.99	NMA GOSPORT
Gurmin, Stephen John Albert, pce,	LT CDR(FTC)	X	PWO(C)	18.05.95	CHATHAM
Gurr, Andrew William George, pce,	LT CDR(FTC)	X	AAWO	01.05.00	SOUTHAMPTON
Gutteridge, Jeffery,	LT(FTC)	E	WE	20.12.90	WSA BRISTOL
Guy, Charles Richard, BA, n,	LT(IC)	X		01.03.98	GRAFTON
Guy, Frances Louisa,	MID(NE)(IC)	X		01.01.02	DARTMOUTH BRNC
Guy, Mark Andrew, BEng,	LT CDR(FTC)	E	WE	13.11.98	MWS COLLINGWOOD
Guy, Philip Stuart, BA,	CAPT RM(FTC)	-	MLDR	01.09.97	UKLFCSG RM
Guy, Richard John, MB, BCh,	SURG CDR(FCC)	-	(CGS)	30.06.01	MODHU PETERBRGH
Guy, Terry John, MIExpE, psc,	CDR(FTC)	E	WESM	30.06.93	MOD (BATH)
Guy, Thomas Justin, pce, n,	LT CDR(FTC)	X	PWO(U)	01.05.00	SHOREHAM
Guyer, Simon Thomas Glode, psc(m),	LT COL(FTC)	-	LC	30.06.95	JDCC
Guyver, Paul Michael, MB, BS,	SURG LT(SCC)	-		04.08.00	CDO LOG REGT RM
Gwatkin, Nicholas John,	LT(IC)	X		29.04.01	MWS DRYAD
Gwillim, Vivian George,	MAJ(FTC)	-	ML2@	01.09.93	1 ASSLT GP RM

H

Habershon, David Broadhurst, pce, psc,	CDR(FTC)	X	PWO(U)	30.06.90	2SL/CNH FOTR
Hackland, Andrew Stuart,	LT(IC)	X	P U/T	01.05.01	RNAS CULDROSE

Name	Rank	Branch	Spec	Seniority	Where Serving
Haddacks, Sir Paul, Paul Kenneth, KCB, rcds, pce, psc, hcsc, ... VADM	-	PWO(N)†	24.02.97	IMS BRUSSELS
Haddon, Richard William James, MB, BS, DipAvMed, ... SURGLTCDR(FCC)	-		19.10.87	MODHU DERRIFORD
LRCP, FRCA, MRAeS, MRCGP, MRCS, AFOM,					
Haddow, Fraser, psc, ... COL(FTC)	-	MLDR	30.06.00	MOD (BATH)
Haddow, Timothy Rowat, BEng, ... LT(FTC)	E	WE	01.03.97	MWS DRYAD
Hadfield, David, MSc, CEng, MIMarEST, ... CDR(FTC)	E	MESM	30.06.99	MOD (LONDON)
Hadland, Giles Vincent, ... LT(CC)	X		01.10.00	DULVERTON
Hadlow, David Keith, ... CAPT RM(FTC)	-	SO(LE)	01.01.99	RM POOLE
Haggard, Amanda, BA, ... LT(FTC)	S		01.03.98	FEARLESS
Haggerty, Shaun Michael, BEng, ... LT(FTC)	E	AE	01.10.97	JCA IPT UK
Haggo, Jamie Robert, BSc, ... LT(CC)	X	P	16.04.98	LOAN OTHER SVCE
Haigh, Alastair James, BSc, ... LT(FTC)	X	P	01.12.92	OCEAN
Haigh, Julian Joseph, BA, ... LT(CC)	S	SM	01.02.98	VICTORIOUS(STBD)
Hailstone, Jonathan Henry Steven, BA, pce, pcea, psc(m), ... LT CDR(FTC)	X	O	16.05.94	RMC OF SCIENCE
Haines, Paul Roger, ... CDR(FTC)	E	WE	30.06.01	MOD (LONDON)
Haines, Russell James, ... LT(CC)	S		01.02.99	CALEDONIA DLO
Haines, Steven William, MA, PhD, FNI, FRGS, ... CDR(FTC)	E	TM	30.06.93	JDCC
FRSA, MRIN, MIMgt, psc,					
Hains, Justin, BSc, ... LT(FTC)	X	MCD	01.04.96	EXCHANGE FRANCE
Hale, Amanda Diane, BSc, ... SLT(IC)	X	O U/T	01.09.00	DARTMOUTH BRNC
Hale, Bradley William, BEng, ... SLT(IC)	E	ME	01.09.00	OCLC MANCH
Hale, John Nathan, BSc, ... MAJ(FTC)	-	LC	27.04.02	ALBION
Haley, Colin William, MA, pce, psc(a), ... CDR(FTC)	X	AAWO	30.06.99	MOD (LONDON)
Haley, Timothy John, MSc, CEng, FIMarEST, ... CDR(FTC)	E	ME	30.06.96	WSA BRISTOL
Hall, Alexander Peter, BSc, pce, pcea, ... LT CDR(FTC)	X	O	01.03.93	RMC OF SCIENCE
Hall, Andrew Jeremy, BSc, ... LT CDR(FTC)	E	AE	01.08.98	MERLIN IPT
Hall, Barry James, BEng, MSc, CEng, MIMechE, ... LT CDR(FTC)	E	MESM	01.11.98	TIRELESS
Hall, Christopher John, ... LT(IC)	X		01.12.00	ALBION
Hall, Christopher Langford, BEng, AMIMechE, ... SLT(IC)	E	ME	01.09.99	SULTAN
Hall, Christopher Mark Ian, ... CAPT RM(SCC)	-		01.04.01	40 CDO RM
Hall, Darren, ... LT(CC)	X	P	16.08.96	848 SQN HERON
Hall, David James, BDS, MSc, MGDS RCSEd, ... SGCDR(D)(FCC)	-		31.12.99	EXCHANGE USA
Hall, David William, BSc, gdas, ... LT CDR(FTC)	X	O	01.10.90	RNAS CULDROSE
Hall, Derek Alexander, ... LT CDR(FTC)	S	(W)	01.10.00	RALEIGH
Hall, Eleanor Louise, BA, (Act Lt Cdr) .... LT(FTC)	X		01.05.95	MWS DRYAD
Hall, Elizabeth Clair, BSc, PGCE, ... CDR(FTC)	S		30.06.02	2SL/CNH
Hall, Graham William Russell, BSc, ... SLT(IC)	X		01.01.00	EXC BRISTOL
Hall, James Edward, BSc, ... SLT(IC)	X	O U/T	01.05.00	750 SQN SEAHAWK
Hall, John, ... LT(CS)(CAS)	-		19.09.97	2SL/CNH FOTR
Hall, Kilian John Darwin, BSc, ... LT(IC)	X		01.05.01	LEEDS CASTLE
Hall, Neil Jeremy, pce, ... LT CDR(FTC)	X	PWO(A)	01.03.93	HQBF CYPRUS
Hall, Richard Mark, MA, psc, ... MAJ(FTC)	-		01.09.90	CTCRM
Hall, Robert Langford, BSc, pce, (Act Cdr) .... LT CDR(FTC)	X	PWO(C)	01.05.93	MOD (LONDON)
Hall, Sasha Louise, ... LT(IC)	X		01.05.02	MWS DRYAD
Hall, Simon Jeremy, MSc, psc, ... LT COL(FTC)	-	MLDR	31.12.99	RM POOLE
Hall, Steven Brian, BSc, ... CAPT RM(IC)	-		28.04.95	CTCRM
Hallett, Simon John, BA, ... LT CDR(FTC)	S		01.03.01	SOMERSET
Halliday, David Alistair, BA, jsdc, pce, ... CAPT(FTC)	X	AAWO	30.06.00	FLEET HQ PORTS 2
Halliwell, David Colin, BEng, MSc, ... LT CDR(FTC)	E	MESM	01.03.00	VIGILANT(PORT)
Halls, Bernard Charles, MSc, IEng, HNC, MIIE, (Act Lt Cdr) .... LT(FTC)	E	WE	18.10.85	DOSG BRISTOL
Hally, Philip John, BSc, ... LT CDR(FTC)	S	CMA	01.11.00	LIVERPOOL
Halpin, Andrew, ... SURG SLT(SCC)	-		01.07.01	DARTMOUTH BRNC
Halsey, Karen Elizabeth, BSc, ... LT(IC)	S		01.01.01	NEWCASTLE
Halsted, Benjamin Erik, BA, ... CAPT RM(IC)	-		01.09.01	FPGRM
Halton, Paul Vincent, pce, pce(sm), ... LT CDR(FTC)	X	SM	01.12.97	FLEET HQ PORTS 2
Hambly, Brian John, BEng, MIEE, ... LT(FTC)	E	WESM	01.09.95	TURBULENT
Hamiduddin, Iqbal, BA, ... LT(IC)	X		01.05.02	MWS DRYAD
Hamilton, Angus John Burnside, BEng, ... LT CDR(FTC)	E	AE(P)	01.04.98	LOAN DARA
Hamilton, Graham Douglas, ... LT(IC)	E	AE	29.04.01	JF HARROLE OFF
Hamilton, Gregory Robert, ... LT CDR(FTC)	X		01.10.94	MOD (LONDON)
Hamilton, Ivan James, ... LT(CC)	X	P	16.11.91	849 SQN A FLT
Hamilton, Mark Ian, BEng, ... LT(CC)	E	ME	01.12.99	LANCASTER

Name	Rank	Branch	Spec	Seniority	Where Serving
Hamilton, Matthew Sean, BDS,	SG LT(D)(SCC)	-		26.06.01	DRAKE CBP(CNH)
Hamilton, Richard Alexander, MSc, CEng, MBCS,	LT CDR(FTC)	E	IS	01.10.93	2SL/CNH
Hamilton, Susanna Mary, BEng,	LT(FTC)	E	ME	01.07.94	MOD (BATH)
Hamilton-Bruce, Emma Catherine, BEng, MSc,	LT(CC)	E	AE	01.07.99	824 SQN
Hammersley, James Michael, MSc, PGCE, (Act Cdr)	LT CDR(FTC)	E	IS	01.10.94	MOD (LONDON)
Hammett, Barry Keith, QHC, MA,	DGNCS CE	CE		01.06.02	2SL/CNH
Hammock, Simon George, BEng,	LT(CC)	X	P	16.08.98	CARDIFF
Hammon, Mark Alexander, BSc,	LT(IC)	X		01.10.99	HURWORTH
Hammond, David Evan, BSc,	CAPT RM(FTC)	-	P	01.09.96	COMAMPHIBFOR
Hammond, Mark Christopher,	MAJ(FTC)	-	P	01.05.00	847 SQN
Hammond, Meirion Mark Vivian, BSc,	LT(IC)	X	P	16.08.00	RNAS YEOVILTON
Hammond, Nicholas John, MBE, BTech, PGCE, psc,	LT CDR(FTC)	X	METOC	01.09.85	SACLANT USA
Hammond, Paul Adrian, BEng, MSc, MIEE, gw,	CDR(FTC)	E	AE	31.12.99	CASOM IPT
Hammond, Paul John, n,	LT(FTC)	X		01.05.96	ARCHER
Hamp, Colin John, BSc, pce, pcea, psc,	CDR(FTC)	X	O	31.12.96	UKMARBATSTAFF
Hampshire, Tony,	LT(CC)	X		01.10.00	MWS DRYAD
Hampson, Alexander Glendinning,	SLT(IC)	X		01.01.02	BANGOR
Hancock, Andrew Philip, pce,	LT CDR(FTC)	X	PWO(U)	01.01.99	JSCSC
Hancock, James Henry, BA,	LT(IC)	X		01.10.00	ARGYLL
Hancock, Robert Thomas Alexander, BEng, AMIEE,	LT CDR(FTC)	E	WE	01.10.01	MWS COLLINGWOOD
Hancox, Michael John, BEng, CEng, MIMarEST,	LT CDR(FTC)	E	MESM	01.02.99	FLEET HQ NWD
Hand, Christopher John, MB, BS, FRCS, FRCSTr&Orth,	SURG LTCDR(FCC)	-		04.01.95	NELSON (PAY)
Handley, Jonathan Mark, MA, jsdc, pce, psc(j),	CDR(FTC)	X	PWO(U)	31.12.96	PORTLAND
Handoll, Guy Nicholas George, MEng,	SLT(IC)	E	MESM	01.09.99	SULTAN
Hands, Adrian Peter, pcea,	LT CDR(FTC)	X	P	01.10.94	DHFS
Hands, Anthony James, BDS,	SG LT(D)(MCC)	-		26.06.97	FWO DEVONPORT
Hanks, Paul Eric, BSc,	LT(CC)	X	P	01.04.99	FLEET AV VALLEY
Hannah, William Ferguson, MBE,	MAJ(FTC)	-	SO(LE)	01.10.01	45 CDO RM
Hannam, Darrell Brett, BSc,	LT(CC)	X	O	01.08.99	849 SQN B FLT
Hanneman, Martin Nicholas, BSc,	LT(CC)	X	P	01.10.95	846 SQN
Hannigan, Paul Francis, pcea,	LT CDR(FTC)	X	P	01.10.01	EXCHANGE AUSTLIA
Hanrahan, Martin William, pcea,	LT CDR(FTC)	X	P	01.10.01	DHFS
Hansen, Christopher John, LLB, MSc,	SLT(IC)	X	O U/T	01.09.00	DARTMOUTH BRNC
Hanslip, Michael Richard,	LT CDR(FTC)	E	WE	01.10.91	ACE SRGN GIBLTAR
Hanson, Mark Nicholas, BA,	LT(FTC)	S		01.03.96	RALEIGH
Hanson, Nicholas Anthony, BEng, CEng, AMIEE, MIMarEST,	LT CDR(FTC)	E	WE	01.06.98	MOD (BATH)
Hanson, Sven Christopher, BSc,	CAPT RM(IC)	-		01.05.01	CTCRM
Harborth, Julia Ann,	LT(IC)	X	P	01.08.99	846 SQN
Harbour, John Robert MacKay, jsdc, psc,	CDR(FTC)	S		31.12.93	EUMS
Harbroe-Bush, Robert Douglas, BSc, CEng, MIEE, psc,	CDR(FTC)	E	WESM	31.12.88	2SL/CNH
Harcombe, Andrew, BSc,	LT(IC)	X	P	01.09.00	AACC MID WALLOP
Harcourt, Robert James, BSc, PGCE, PGDip,	LT CDR(FTC)	X	PWO(U)	01.01.00	CUMBERLAND
Hardacre, Paul Vincent, BSc, SM,	LT CDR(FTC)	X	SM	01.06.94	FOST DPORT SHORE
Hardern, Simon Paul, MNI, pce, psc(j),	CDR(FTC)	X	PWO(U)	30.06.01	KENT
Hardie, Mark John, BA,	CAPT RM(IC)	-		01.09.00	45 CDO RM
Hardiman, Nicholas Anthony, BEng,	LT(FTC)	E	MESM	01.05.95	SULTAN
Harding, Carl Sinclair, BEng, MBA,	LT(CC)	E	TM	01.09.92	NELSON RNSETT
Harding, David Malcolm, BSc, CEng,	LT CDR(FTC)	E	AE	01.05.95	HQ3GP HQSTC
Harding, David Victor, BEng,	SLT(IC)	E	WE	01.09.99	MWS COLLINGWOOD
Harding, Ellen Louise, (Act Lt)	SLT(IC)	S		01.10.99	FLEET HQ PORTS 2
Harding, Gary Alan, BEng, AMIEE, psc,	LT CDR(FTC)	E	WE	01.12.94	FOST SEA
Harding, Hadrian Robert, BEng,	LT(CC)	E	ME	01.04.97	ARK ROYAL
Harding, Russell George, BSc, pce, pcea,	CDR(FTC)	X	O	31.12.95	MOD (LONDON)
Hardman, Mathew James, BSc,	LT(FTC)	X		01.09.99	BLYTH
Hardwick, Mark John,	LT(FTC)	S	SM	01.09.98	RALEIGH
Hardy, Duncan Mark,	MAJ(FTC)	-	C	24.04.02	UKLFCSG RM
Hardy, Lee Charles, pce,	CDR(FTC)	X	AAWO	30.06.02	MOD (LONDON)
Hardy, Leslie Brian,	LT(FTC)	X	PWO(U)	16.12.94	EXETER
Hardy, Robert John,	LT(IC)	E	ME	29.04.01	IRON DUKE
Hare, John Herbert, BA, PGDip,	LT CDR(CC)	X	METOC	01.09.97	OCEAN

Name	Rank	Branch	Spec	Seniority	Where Serving
Hare, Nigel James, pce,	CDR(FTC)	X	PWO(N)	30.06.02	RNLO JTF4
Harford Cross, Peter James, MA, SM,	LT(IC)	X	SM	01.02.00	VICTORIOUS(STBD)
Hargreaves, Neale,	LT CDR(FTC)	X	O	01.10.97	LOAN JTEG BSC DN
Harland, Nicholas Jonathan Godfrey, BSc, jsdc, pce,	CAPT(FTC)	X	O	30.06.99	SACLANT BELGIUM
Harlow, Simon Richard,	LT(FTC)	X	P	01.05.93	LOAN JTEG BSC DN
Harman, Michael John,	CHAPLAIN	CE		20.09.79	RN GIBRALTAR
Harman, Stephen John, BSc,	SLT(IC)	S		01.09.99	RALEIGH
Harmer, Jason Neil Jonathon,	LT CDR(FTC)	X	P	01.10.97	FLEET AV VL
Harms, James Graeme,	LT(CC)	X	P	01.03.95	EXCHANGE RAF UK
Harold, Richard St John, BSc, SM,	LT(IC)	X		01.01.99	2SL/CNH
Harper, Christopher Hodges, BSc,	LT CDR(FTC)	X	H CH	01.09.95	MOD (LONDON)
Harper, Ian Lorimer,	LT(FTC)	X	AV	23.07.93	DOSG BRISTOL
Harper, James Andrew,	LT CDR(FTC)	X	O	01.10.97	EXCHANGE N ZLAND
Harper, Kevan James,	MID(NE)(IC)	X		01.05.01	ARK ROYAL
Harper, Philip Robert, BA, n,	LT(FTC)	X		01.02.97	NORTHUMBERLAND
Harradine, Paul Anthony, psc(j),	LT COL(FTC)	-	SO(LE)	30.06.02	CTCRM
Harrall, Phillip Anthony Robertson, AFC, MPhil, (Act Cdr) MRAeS, MRIN, MCMI, psc,	LT CDR(FTC)	X	O	03.03.85	FLEET AV VL
Harrap, Nicholas Richard Edmund, OBE, MNI, jsdc, pce, pce(sm),	CDR(FTC)	X	SM	31.12.95	MOD (LONDON)
Harries, Jon Michael Henry, BSc, CEng, FIEE, jsdc,	CAPT(FTC)	E	WE	31.12.91	DRAKE NBC
Harriman, Peter,	LT(FTC)	X	C	26.04.99	EXCHANGE CANADA
Harriman, Suzanne Jane,	LT(SCC)	Q	IC	20.02.96	RH HASLAR
Harrington, Jonathan Barratt, BEng,	LT(FTC)	E	WE	01.08.95	JSCSC
Harrington, Lee, BEng,	LT(FTC)	E	ME	01.03.98	CUMBERLAND
Harris, Andrew Gordon, BEng, MAPM, AMIEE,	LT CDR(FTC)	E	WE	12.04.97	MANCHESTER
Harris, Andrew Ian, MA, pce, pcea, psc(j),	CDR(FTC)	X	O	31.12.99	FOST DPORT SHORE
Harris, Carl Christian, BA,	MAJ(FTC)	-		01.09.01	FPGRM
Harris, Keri John, BEng, pcea,	LT CDR(FTC)	X	O	01.04.99	MONTROSE
Harris, Michael Trevor,	LT CDR(FTC)	S	CA	01.10.99	SUTHERLAND
Harris, Nicholas Henry Linton, MBE, (Commodore) pce, pce(sm), ocds(US),	CAPT(FTC)	X	SM	30.06.95	BDS WASHINGTON
Harris, Philip Norman, OBE, MPhil, MNI, pce, psc,	CDR(FTC)	X	O	31.12.85	LOAN BMATT GHANA
Harris, Richard Paul, BA,	LT(CC)	S		01.09.96	DPA BRISTOL
Harris, Timothy Ronald, pce,	CAPT(FTC)	X	PWO(U)	31.12.98	PJHQ
Harris, Tristan,	CAPT RM(FTC)	-		01.09.96	RM POOLE
Harrison, Adrian, BEng, MSc,	LT CDR(FTC)	E	MESM	01.02.01	VENGEANCE(PORT)
Harrison, Andrew David,	LT(IC)	E	AE	29.04.01	824 SQN
Harrison, Clive Anthony, AIL, pce,	LT CDR(FTC)	X	AAWO	01.03.94	ELANT/NAVNORTH
Harrison, David, BEng,	LT CDR(FTC)	E	WESM	05.01.97	TRAFALGAR
Harrison, Ian,	SLT(IC)	X	O U/T	01.10.99	750 SQN SEAHAWK
Harrison, James Colin, MB, BS,	SURG LT(SCC)	-		02.08.00	VICTORIOUS(PORT)
Harrison, John Andrew George,	LT(IC)	X		01.05.02	MWS DRYAD
Harrison, Leigh Elliot, BSc,	SLT(IC)	X		01.01.00	WESTMINSTER
Harrison, Mark Andrew, BEng, AMIEE,	LT(CC)	E	WESM	01.11.97	VENGEANCE(PORT)
Harrison, Matthew Sean, BEng, MSc, CEng, MIEE, psc(j), gw,	CDR(FTC)	E	WE	31.12.99	BDS WASHINGTON
Harrison, Paul Dominic, gdas,	LT(FTC)	X	O	01.10.90	LOAN JTEG BSC DN
Harrison, Paul Geoffrey, BTech, CEng, MRAeS, BEng,	LT CDR(FTC)	E	AE(L)	12.09.96	846 SQN
Harrison, Richard Anthony, CDipAF, psc, gw, MDA, MSc,	CDR(FTC)	E	WESM	31.12.89	MOD (BATH)
Harrison, Richard Simon, BA,	LT(CC)	X	P	15.09.95	MWS DRYAD
Harrison, Roger Geoffrey, psc,	CDR(FTC)	X	P	31.12.87	FLEET AV VL
Harrison, Thomas Iain, BEng, MPhil,	LT(IC)	E	TM	01.01.96	FOST CSST FSLN
Harrop, Ian, BEng, MSc,	LT CDR(FTC)	E	MESM	01.05.96	SULTAN
Harry, Andrew David, BEng,	LT CDR(FTC)	X		01.04.96	ES AIR YEO
Harry, Peter Norman, MILog, AMIAM,	CDR(FTC)	S	(S)	01.10.98	RHQ AFNORTH
Hart, Acland Paul Withiel, BSc,	CAPT RM(IC)	-		01.05.01	NEPTUNE
Hart, Derek John, BSc, CEng, FIEE,	CAPT(FTC)	E	WE	30.06.01	2SL/CNH
Hart, Jonathan, MSc, CEng, MIEE, psc,	CAPT(FTC)	E	WESM	31.12.99	MOD (LONDON)
Hart, Mark Alan, BSc, MA, pce, psc(j),	LT CDR(FTC)	X	AAWO	01.12.94	MIDDLETON
Hart, Neil Lawrence Whynden,	LT(FTC)	S	SM	01.05.94	DRAKE DPL
Hart, Paul Andrew, BSc,	LT CDR(FTC)	E	TM	01.10.98	LOAN BRUNEI
Hart, Stephen John Eric, BA,	CAPT RM(FTC)	-		01.09.99	CTCRM

Name	Rank	Branch	Spec	Seniority	Where Serving
Hart, Steven David,	SLT(FTC)	X		01.04.00	COTTESMORE
Hart, Steven James,	LT(IC)	X	P U/T	01.05.02	RNAS YEOVILTON
Hart, Tobin Giles De Burgh,	LT CDR(FTC)	X	P	01.10.00	848 SQN HERON
Hart, Willem Cornelis, CEng, IEng, FIMarEST, MIMgt, AMIMarEST,	CDR(FTC)	E	ME	01.10.98	FLEET HQ PORTS 2
Hartley, Andrew Paul, BEng,	LT CDR(FTC)	E	ME	02.03.00	FLEET HQ PORTS 2
Hartley, Benjamin Paul Iles, BSc,	LT(IC)	X	P	01.12.98	849 SQN B FLT
Hartley, James Henry Dean, BSc, PhD,	LT(IC)	E	TM	01.05.98	DARTMOUTH BRNC
Hartley, John Laurence, BSc,	LT CDR(FTC)	X	P	01.10.99	FLEET AV VL
Hartley, Stephen William, BSc, PGCE, MA(Ed),	LT CDR(CC)	E	TM	01.10.96	NELSON RNSETT
Hartnell, Stephen Thomas, OBE, MA, psc,	COL(FTC)	-		30.06.98	MOD (LONDON)
Harvey, Barrie, BEng,	LT(FTC)	E	ME	01.06.97	2SL/CNH FOTR
Harvey, Colin Ashton, BSc,	CDR(FTC)	E	MESM	30.06.00	FOST CSST SEA
Harvey, Gary,	LT CDR(FTC)	E	ME	25.05.98	KENT
Harvey, Graham Anthony,	SLT(IC)	E	WE	01.01.00	NORFOLK
Harvey, Keith, pce,	CDR(FTC)	X	MCD	30.06.93	2SL/CNH
Harvey, Paul Anthony, BSc,	LT CDR(FTC)	X	ATC	01.10.91	MOD (LONDON)
Harvey, Paul Geoffrey,	SLT(IC)	E	WE	01.01.01	MWS COLLINGWOOD
Harvey, Paul John,	LT(IC)	S	CA	08.01.01	AFPAA HQ
Harvey, Robert Matthew Malvern Jolyon, pce,	LT CDR(FTC)	X	AAWO	01.03.97	CARDIFF
Harwood, Christopher George, HNC, BTech,	LT(FTC)	E	WE	24.02.95	WSA BRISTOL
Harwood, Lee Brian,	LT(IC)	X		01.02.00	EDINBURGH
Haseldine, Stephen George,	LT CDR(FTC)	X	ATC	01.02.98	MOD (LONDON)
Haskell, Eric Thomas,	LT CDR(FTC)	E	WE	01.10.94	WSA/CAPT MCTA
Haslam, Clair Louise,	LT(SCC)	Q		24.10.01	MODHU DERRIFORD
Haslam, Philip James, pce,	LT CDR(FTC)	X	PWO(A)	01.10.98	MARLBOROUGH
Hassall, Harry, MEng, MSc, MA(Ed),	LT CDR(CC)	E	TM	01.10.95	EXCHANGE ARMY UK
Hassall, Ian, BEng,	LT(FTC)	E	ME	01.12.97	COMSTRIKFORSTH
Hasted, Daniel,	CAPT RM(IC)	-	C	01.05.99	40 CDO RM
Hatch, Giles William Hellesdon, pce,	CDR(FTC)	X	PWO(A)	31.12.98	MOD (LONDON)
Hatchard, John Paul, FRAeS,	LT(CC)	X	P	04.03.92	845 SQN
Hatchard, Peter John, BSc, MBA, jsdc, pce,	CDR(FTC)	X	PWO(C)	30.06.94	SACLANT USA
Hatcher, Rhett Slade, pce,	LT CDR(FTC)	X	P	01.03.98	PENZANCE
Hatcher, Timothy Robert,	LT CDR(FTC)	E	WESM	01.10.00	ASM IPT
Hattle, Prideaux McLeod,	LT(IC)	X		29.04.01	NORFOLK
Haughey, John,	LT(FTC)	MS		01.04.01	MOD (BATH)
Havron, Paul Richard,	LT(FTC)	E	WE	01.04.01	GLOUCESTER
Haw, Christopher Edward, BSc,	CAPT RM(CC)	-	MLDR	01.05.98	UKLFCSG RM
Hawes, Grace Elaine, psc,	LT CDR(FTC)	W	C	01.01.91	RHQ AFNORTH
Hawkes, Jonathan Derrick,	LT(FTC)	X	PT	23.07.93	NELSON
Hawkins, Ian,	CDR(FTC)	E	AE	31.12.98	SABR IPT
Hawkins, James Seymour, pcea,	LT CDR(FTC)	X	O	16.08.98	FLEET HQ PORTS 2
Hawkins, Martin Adam Jeremy, pce, pcea,	LT CDR(FTC)	X	O	01.05.95	JSCSC
Hawkins, Richard Culworth, BA, jsdc, pcea,	CAPT(FTC)	X	P	30.06.01	HQ3GP HQSTC
Hawkins, Robert Henry, pce,	LT CDR(FTC)	X	MCD	01.10.91	IRON DUKE
Hawkins, Shane Robert, BEng,	LT(FTC)	E	WE	01.12.97	DRAKE SFM
Hawkins, Stuart,	LT(IC)	E	WE	01.01.02	SOUTHAMPTON
Haworth, John, IEng, MIIE,	CDR(FTC)	E	ME	30.06.99	MOD (BATH)
Haworth, Jonathan Hywel Tristan, BEng,	LT(FTC)	E	WE	01.10.96	SFM ROSYTH
Hawthorn, Emma Maudie, BA,	LT(IC)	S		01.12.98	ARK ROYAL
Hawthorne, Michael John, MA, pce(sm), psc(j), pce,	CDR(FTC)	X	SM	31.12.97	MOD (LONDON)
Hay, James Donald, BSc,	CDR(FTC)	E	WE	30.06.97	MOD (LONDON)
Hay, Michael, BEng,	LT(FTC)	E	WE	01.03.98	SHEFFIELD
Hayashi, Luke Ronald, BSc,	LT(CC)	X		01.11.99	CARDIFF
Haycock, Timothy Paul, BSc, pce, pcea, psc,	LT CDR(FTC)	X	O	01.06.94	FOST SEA
Hayde, Phillip John, BSc, MRAeS,	LT CDR(FTC)	X	P	01.10.99	899 SQN HERON
Hayden, Timothy William, BSc,	LT(CC)	X	P	01.12.96	814 SQN
Hayes, Brian John,	LT(FTC)	X	PT	03.04.98	MWS COLLINGWOOD
Hayes, Claire Louise, BSc,	LT(FTC)	S		01.09.97	RNSR BOVINGTON
Hayes, David John,	LT CDR(FTC)	MS	(AD)	01.10.90	RNAS YEOVILTON
Hayes, James Victor Buchanan, BSc, psc(j),	CDR(FTC)	E	WESM	31.12.98	FWO FASLANE SEA
Hayes, Mark Andrew,	SLT(IC)	X		01.01.00	TYNE

Name	Rank	Branch	Spec	Seniority	Where Serving
Hayes, Sean, BSc,	LT(IC)	X		01.07.01	MWS RNHMS CULD
Hayes, Stuart John, pce,	CDR(FTC)	X	MCD	30.06.00	LOAN OMAN
Hayle, Elizabeth Anne, BA, MSc,	LT CDR(FTC)	W	X	01.10.98	FOSNNI OPS DLO
Hayle, James Kenneth,	LT CDR(FTC)	S	SM	01.04.96	UKMARBATSTAFF
Hayler, Benjamin,	2LT(IC)	-		01.09.01	CTCRM LYMPSTONE
Hayman, Paul Stephen, MIIE,	LT(FTC)	E	WE	09.01.01	DRAKE SFM
Haynes, John Graham,	MID(IC)	X		01.01.01	MONTROSE
Haynes, John William,	LT CDR(FTC)	X	PT	01.10.98	WILDFIRE
Hayton, James Charles, BA, MB, ChB,	SURG LT(SCC)	-		02.08.00	UKLFCSG RM
Hayton, Stephen Robert Charles,	LT(FTC)	X	O	05.09.95	824 SQN
Hayward, Clive Edward William, BA, SM,	LT CDR(FTC)	X	SM	01.06.96	EXCHANGE FRANCE
Hayward, Geoffrey,	LT(FTC)	X	O	16.07.91	849 SQN HQ
Hayward, James Andrew David, BSc,	SLT(IC)	X		01.01.01	DARTMOUTH BRNC
Hayward, Peter James,	LT CDR(FTC)	S		01.04.86	RH HASLAR
Haywood, Guy, pce, pcea,	CDR(FTC)	X	P	30.06.02	MWS DRYAD
Haywood, Peter James, BEng,	LT(CC)	X	P	01.01.94	814 SQN
Haywood, Simon Anthony,	CDR(FTC)	E	WESM	30.06.02	FLEET HQ PORTS 2
Hazard, Lee,	SLT(IC)	MS		27.01.01	DARTMOUTH BRNC
Hazelwood, Christopher David,	CAPT RM(FTC)	-	SO(LE)	01.01.00	CTCRM
Head, Rupert Richmond D Esterre,	CDR(FTC)	S		30.06.89	SA RIYADH
Head, Steven Andrew, BEng, MSc,	LT CDR(FTC)	E	WE	01.03.01	FLEET CIS PORTS
Headley, Mark James, BSc,	LT(IC)	X		01.04.00	LINDISFARNE
Heal, Jeremy Phillip Carlton, psc,	COL(FTC)	-		31.12.99	MOD (LONDON)
Heal, Tristan Stephen, MEng,	LT(IC)	E	WESM	01.09.01	RALEIGH
Healey, Mark Jon,	LT(CC)	E	AE	01.10.99	SULTAN
Healy, Anthony John,	CDR(FTC)	X	EW	31.12.99	RNEAWC
Heames, Richard Mark, BM, FRCA,	SURG LTCDR(MCC)	-		01.08.99	NELSON (PAY)
Heaney, Martin Joseph, BSc,	LT(CC)	X	O	16.04.97	824 SQN
Heap, Justin Timothy, BEng,	LT(FTC)	X	SM	01.05.98	TRAFALGAR
Hearn, Samuel Peter, BA,	LT(IC)	X		01.09.00	SPLENDID
Hearnden, Graham Eric, pce,	LT CDR(FTC)	X	AWO(C)	01.04.79	MWS DRYAD
Heath, Stephen Philip Robert, MEng,	SLT(IC)	E	MESM	01.09.99	SULTAN
Heatly, Robert Johnston, MBE, osc(us),	LT COL(FTC)	-		31.12.95	MOD (LONDON)
Heaton, Henry Gerald, BSc,	LT(IC)	X		01.05.02	MWS DRYAD
Heaver, David Gerard Verney, MA, psc(m),	COL(FTC)	-		30.06.96	1 ASSLT GP RM
Hecks, Ian James, BA,	LT RM(IC)	-		01.09.00	42 CDO RM
Hedgecox, David Colin, BEng,	LT(FTC)	E	WE	01.06.96	CESM IPT
Hedges, Justin William, BSc,	MAJ(FTC)	-		01.09.01	RM POOLE
Hedworth, Anthony Joseph, BComm,	LT(CC)	X	P	01.06.94	702 SQN HERON
Hefford, Christopher John, BSc,	LT(CC)	S		01.03.97	FLEET HQ PORTS
Heighway, Martin Richard, MSc, PGCE, MA(Ed),	LT(IC)	E	TM	01.01.96	MWS COLLINGWOOD
Heirs, Gavin George, MA,	LT(CC)	X	P	01.08.98	820 SQN
Helby, Philip Faulder Hasler, MBE, BSc, MBA, AMIEE, CDipAF,	LT CDR(FTC)	E	MESM	16.07.82	DRAKE CBS
Heley, David Nicholas, pce,	CDR(FTC)	X	PWO(U)	30.06.00	MOD (LONDON)
Heley, Jonathan Mark, BEng, MSc, CEng, MIMarEST,	CDR(FTC)	E	MESM	31.12.00	MOD (BATH)
Helliwell, Michael Andrew, BEng,	LT CDR(FTC)	E	AE	01.05.98	824 SQN
Hellyn, David Robert,	LT CDR(FTC)	E	WE	01.10.97	PORTLAND
Helps, Adrian Robin, BEng, MSc,	LT CDR(FTC)	E	MESM	01.06.00	DRAKE SFM
Hember, Marcus James Christopher, n,	LT(CC)	X		01.05.00	RICHMOND
Hembrow, Terence,	MAJ(FTC)	-	SO(LE)	01.10.97	HQ 3 CDO BDE RM
Hembury, Lawrence,	LT RM(IC)	-	SO(LE)	01.04.00	CDO LOG REGT RM
Hemingway, Darren Graham, BSc,	LT(IC)	E		01.01.00	MWS COLLINGWOOD
Hemingway, Ross, (Act Surg Lt)	SURG SLT(SCC)	-		11.07.01	DARTMOUTH BRNC
Hempsell, Adrian Michael, n,	LT(FTC)	X	PWO(A)	01.06.94	SOMERSET
Hemsworth, Kenneth John, BEng, CEng,	LT CDR(FTC)	E	ME	01.01.98	SULTAN
Hemsworth, Michael Kim, BSc,	CAPT(FTC)	S		30.06.97	2SL/CNH
Henaghen, Stephen John,	LT(IC)	X		13.07.01	MWS DRYAD
Henderson, Andrew David,	CAPT RM(FTC)	BS		01.01.93	HQ BAND SERVICE
Henderson, Peter Philip, HNC,	LT(FTC)	E	WE	24.02.95	WSA BRISTOL
Henderson, Robert John,	LT(FTC)	E	AE(M)	04.09.98	FWO PORTS SEA
Henderson, Sam Charles, BA,	LT(IC)	S		01.10.00	OCEAN

Name	Rank	Branch	Spec	Seniority	Where Serving
Henderson, Stuart Philip, BEng, MSc,	LT CDR(FTC)	E	ME	01.03.99	SOUTHAMPTON
Henderson, Thomas Maxwell Philip, BSc, pce,	LT CDR(FTC)	X	PWO(U)	01.04.91	ELANT/NAVNORTH
Hendrickx, Christopher John, BEng,	LT(FTC)	E	WE	01.01.96	NP 1061
Hendy, Laurence Samuel, BEng,	LT CDR(FTC)	E	WE	28.09.00	LOAN DSTL
Hendy, Richard,	LT(FTC)	S		23.09.97	OCLC BIRM
Heneghan, John Francis, BEng, adp,	LT CDR(CC)	E	IS	01.10.97	RNEAWC
Henley, Simon Michael, MBE, BSc, CEng, (Commodore)	CAPT(FTC)	E	AE	30.06.97	JCA IPT UK
MRAeS, jsdc,					
Hennell, Nigel Jeffrey, AFC, pcea,	LT CDR(FTC)	X	P	01.03.80	771 SQN
Hennessey, Timothy Patrick David, BSc, pce, psc,	CDR(FTC)	X	O	30.06.93	MOD (LONDON)
Henry, Gavin Paul, BA,	LT(IC)	X		01.01.02	MARLBOROUGH
Henry, Mark Frederick, MB, BCh,	SURG LT(MCC)	-		06.08.97	MODHU DERRIFORD
Henry, Timothy Michael,	LT CDR(FTC)	X	PWO(U)	01.10.00	PJHQ
Hepburn, John, BA, LLB, MInstAM, MCMI,	LT CDR(FTC)	S		01.02.83	DRAKE DPL
Hepplewhite, Mark Barrie,	LT(CC)	E	AE	01.09.99	702 SQN HERON
Hepworth, Andrew William David, BEng,	LT CDR(FTC)	E	IS	01.05.98	RMC OF SCIENCE
Herbert, Lara,	SURG SLT(SCC)	-		01.07.01	DARTMOUTH BRNC
Heritage, Lee James, BSc, CEng, MIMarEST, psc,	CDR(FTC)	E	ME	30.06.96	MOD (BATH)
Herman, Thomas Rolf, OBE, BSc, pce(sm),	CDR(FTC)	X	SM	30.06.92	RNAS YEOVILTON
Hermer, Jeremy Peter,	MAJ(FTC)	-		01.09.01	FLEET HQ PORTS 2
Herridge, Daniel Jonathon,	MID(IC)	X		01.05.00	NEWCASTLE
Herridge, Peter Gary, BSc, MA, CEng, MRAeS, psc,	CDR(FTC)	E	AE	31.12.95	FLEET HQ PORTS
Herriman, John Andrew, BSc, MA, DipEd, FCIPD, MIMgt,	LT(CC)	X	MCD	01.04.91	FDU3
Herring, Jonathan James Auriol, BSc, MA, psc,	LT COL(FTC)	-		30.06.98	MOD (LONDON)
Heselton, Branden Lawrence, MA, CEng, (Commodore)	CAPT(FTC)	E	WE	30.06.96	FLEET HQ PORTS 2
MIEE, psc,					
Hesketh, John James, BSc,	SLT(IC)	X		01.09.99	SANDOWN
Hesling, Gary, n,	LT CDR(FTC)	X	H1	28.02.02	GLEANER
Hester, James Francis William, BA,	CAPT RM(IC)	-		01.09.01	40 CDO RM
Hetherington, Thomas Angus, BSc,	SLT(IC)	E	ME	01.09.00	NORFOLK
Hett, David Anthony, BSc, FRCA, LRCP, MRCS, DA,	SURG CDR(FCC)	-	(CA)	31.12.93	RH HASLAR
Heward, Alan Frank, (Act Maj)	CAPT RM(FTC)	-	SO(LE)	01.01.95	FLEET HQ PORTS 2
Heward, Mark George,	SLT(IC)	X		01.01.01	RALEIGH
Hewit, Stephanie,	SLT(IC)	X		01.09.01	SOMERSET
Hewitson, Jonathan George Austin, BSc,	LT(IC)	X		01.08.00	TURBULENT
Hewitt, Antony, BEng,	LT CDR(FTC)	E	MESM	01.06.95	NEPTUNE DSA
Hewitt, David Leslie, pce,	LT CDR(FTC)	X	AAWO	01.07.99	EXETER
Hewitt, Ian Rhoderick, OBE, nadc, jsdc, pce,	CAPT(FTC)	X	SM	31.12.93	SULTAN AIB
pce(sm), odc(US),					
Hewitt, Lloyd Russell,	LT CDR(FTC)	S		16.11.97	AFPAA WTHY DOWN
Hewitt, Mark John,	LT(IC)	E	ME	29.04.01	ARK ROYAL
Hewitt, Richard Paul,	SLT(IC)	X		01.01.01	DARTMOUTH BRNC
Heycocks, Christian John, MA,	CHAPLAIN	CE		24.09.00	UKLFCSG RM
Heyworth, James Edward, BSc,	LT(IC)	X		01.03.00	GLASGOW
Hibberd, Karen Michelle, BA, n,	LT(FTC)	X		01.05.97	RNP TEAM
Hibberd, Nicholas James, pce, pce(sm),	LT CDR(FTC)	X	SM	01.11.97	FLEET HQ NWD
Hibbert, Martin Christopher,	LT CDR(FTC)	X		01.10.96	DRAKE SFM
Hibbert, Nicola Jane,	LT CDR(FTC)	S		29.07.96	DRAKE CBP(DLO)
Hibbert, Peter Nigel, MNI, MInsD, jsdc, pce, pce(sm),	CDR(FTC)	X	SM	31.12.90	BDS WASHINGTON
Hicking, Neil, BSc, ARCS,	LT CDR(FTC)	X	METOC	01.10.94	FLEET HQ NWD
Hickman, Simon Michael, BEd,	MAJ(FTC)	-		01.09.00	40 CDO RM
Hicks, Anna Rachael, BM,	SURG LT(SCC)	-		01.08.01	RALEIGH
Hicks, Nicholas John Ivatts, BSc, SM,	LT(IC)	X	SM	01.06.98	TALENT
Hickson, Michael Stuart Harris, BEng, MRAeS,	LT(FTC)	E	(AE)	01.08.95	EXCHANGE CANADA *
Higgins, Andrew John,	LT(CC)	X	FC	01.08.95	899 SQN HERON
Higgins, Godfrey Nigel, BEng,	LT CDR(FTC)	X	AE	01.11.96	JF HARROLE OFF
Higgins, Peter Martin, BEng,	SLT(IC)	X	P U/T	01.09.99	DHFS
Higginson, Nicholas John, BEng,	LT(IC)	X		01.06.00	SANDOWN
Higgs, Robert James,	LT CDR(FTC)	X	C	01.10.00	HQ SOUTHLANT
Higgs, Thomas Arthur, BSc,	LT CDR(FTC)	S		01.02.02	ARGYLL
Higham, Anthony, pce, psc,	CDR(FTC)	X	PWO	30.06.89	NBC PORTSMOUTH
Higham, James Godfrey, BEng, MSc, AMIEE, gw,	LT CDR(FTC)	E	WE	01.01.00	MWS COLLINGWOOD

OFFICERS - ACTIVE LIST

Name	Rank	Branch	Spec	Seniority	Where Serving
Higham, Stephen William James, MA,	LT(FTC)	X		01.05.98	GUERNSEY
Higson, Beverly Lynn, BSc, PGDip, MIMA, CMath,	LT(CC)	E	TM	01.01.93	SULTAN
Hill, Adrain Jason, BSc,	LT(CC)	X	O	01.10.96	EXCHANGE RAF UK
Hill, Christopher John, BSc,	SLT(IC)	X	SM	01.01.01	DARTMOUTH BRNC
Hill, David, BEng, CEng, MRAeS, psc(j)o,	LT CDR(FTC)	E	AE	01.03.99	RNAS YEOVILTON
Hill, George Alexander,	LT CDR(FTC)	E	WESM	01.10.98	SPLENDID
Hill, Giulian Francis, BEng, MSc, MCGI, MIMarEST,	LT CDR(FTC)	E	ME	01.01.98	EXCHANGE CANADA
Hill, Graham Allen, MB, ChB, FRCS, FRCS(ORTH),	SURG CDR(FCC)	-	(CO/S)	31.12.00	RH HASLAR
Hill, John,	CHAPLAIN	CE		17.01.94	2SL/CNH
Hill, Jonathan Paul, BSc,	CAPT RM(FTC)	-		01.05.99	DNR PRES TEAMS
Hill, Mark Robert, pce, pcea,	LT CDR(FTC)	X	P	22.06.96	MWC PORTSDOWN
Hill, Philip John, BEng,	LT CDR(FTC)	E	WESM	01.06.96	TORPEDO IPT
Hill, Richard Andrew,	LT CDR(FTC)	X	MW	01.09.95	MWS DRYAD
Hill, Roy Keith John, MA, ACMA, psc(j), (Act Cdr)	LT CDR(FTC)	S	CMA	16.02.97	2SL/CNH FOTR
Hill, Thomas Edward, BEng,	SLT(IC)	X	O U/T	01.05.00	750 SQN SEAHAWK
Hill-Norton, The Lord, GCB,	ADM OF FLEET	-		12.03.71	
Hilliard, Robert Godfrey, BA, DipTh,	CHAPLAIN	CE		01.08.80	NELSON
Hillier, Colin,	2LT(IC)	-		01.09.98	CTCRM LYMPSTONE
Hillman, Christopher,	SURG SLT(SCC)	-		18.10.00	DARTMOUTH BRNC
Hills, Anthony Alexander, pce, pcea,	LT CDR(FTC)	X	P	01.12.94	RAF CRANWELL EFS
Hills, Ian Edward,	LT(IC)	X	P	01.09.97	820 SQN
Hills, Michael John,	CHAPLAIN	CE		21.04.98	45 CDO RM
Hills, Richard Brian, BA,	MAJ(FTC)	-		01.05.99	45 CDO RM
Hilson, Steven Millar,	LT(CC)	X	O	01.10.91	702 SQN HERON
Hilton, James,	2LT(IC)	-		01.10.01	CTCRM LYMPSTONE
Hilton, Simon Thomas, BEng,	LT(CC)	X	O	01.04.99	849 SQN B FLT
Hinch, David Graham William,	LT CDR(FTC)	X	P	01.10.00	801 SQN
Hinch, Neil Eric,	LT CDR(FTC)	X	PT	01.10.93	TEMERAIRE
Hinchcliffe, Alan, BSc,	LT(IC)	X	P	01.03.94	GANNET SAR FLT
Hindmarch, Stephen Andrew, BA,	LT(CC)	X	P	01.09.96	GANNET SAR FLT
Hindson, Craig Lee, BEng, CEng, MIMarEST,	LT(FTC)	E	ME	01.04.94	UKLFCSG RM
Hine, Nicholas William, BSc, MA, pce, pce(sm), psc(j),SM(n),	CDR(FTC)	X	SM	30.06.00	TALENT
Hinks, Karl James, BEng, CEng, MIMarEST,	LT CDR(FTC)	E	ME	25.08.98	EXETER
Hinton, Lee, BSc,	LT(IC)	X	ATC	01.09.99	RNAS YEOVILTON
Hinxman, Matthew Alex, LLB,	LT(IC)	X		01.04.00	OCEAN
Hipsey, Stephen Jon, MSc,	LT CDR(CC)	X	METOC	01.10.89	HQ NORTH
Hirons, Francis Durham, BSc,	LT(CC)	X		01.02.99	SHETLAND
Hirst, Robert Thomas,	LT CDR(FTC)	X	SM	01.09.88	DISC
Hirstwood, John Laurence,	LT(IC)	X		01.09.01	ARGYLL
Hiscock, Stephen Richard Blackler, BEng,	LT(FTC)	E	WE	01.05.96	MWS COLLINGWOOD
Hitchings, Deborah Louise, BA,	LT(CC)	X	FC	01.01.94	RNAS YEOVILTON
Hoare, Dion Wyn,	LT(FTC)	E	WE	09.01.01	MOD (BATH)
Hoare, Peter James Edward, pcea,	LT(FTC)	X	O	01.05.94	702 SQN HERON
Hoare, Peter,	CAPT RM(IC)	-	SO(LE)	21.07.01	45 CDO RM
Hoath, Moira Elizabeth Jane, MA, MSc, CEng, CMath, MBCS, MIMA,	CDR(FTC)	W	E	01.10.96	NMA PORTSMOUTH
Hoather, Martin Stephen, MA(CANTAB), MEng,	LT(FTC)	E	WE	01.09.99	JSCSC
Hobbs, Alan Ronald,	LT CDR(FTC)	X	PWO(A)	01.04.93	STG BRISTOL
Hobbs, Richard, IEng, FIIE,	CDR(FTC)	E	WE	01.10.98	NMA PORTSMOUTH
Hobbs, Thomas Peter,	SLT(UCE)(IC)	E	WE	01.09.01	DARTMOUTH BRNC
Hobson, Charles William Peter, psc, hcsc,	COL(FTC)	-		31.12.98	PJHQ
Hobson, Ian Stuart, BTech,	LT CDR(FTC)	E	WESM	01.10.00	VENGEANCE(STBD)
Hocking, Mark John Eldred,	LT(FTC)	E	WE	01.04.01	IRON DUKE
Hockley, Christopher John, MSc, CEng, MIMarEST, psc,	CAPT(FTC)	E	ME	30.06.99	CV(F) IPT
Hodder, Philip James,	SLT(IC)	X		01.09.00	DARTMOUTH BRNC
Hodge, Christopher Michael, MSc, BEng,	LT(FTC)	E	MESM	01.09.94	SULTAN
Hodgkins, Jonathan Mark, pce, pcea, psc(j),	CDR(FTC)	X	O	30.06.02	LN BMATT SAFRICA
Hodgson, Jonathan Richard,	LT(FTC)	E	ME	02.05.00	FLEET HQ PORTS 2
Hodgson, Richard Stephen, BSc,	LT(IC)	X	SM	01.03.00	TRAFALGAR
Hodgson, Timothy Charles, MBE, MA, CEng, MIMarEST, MIMechE, psc(j),	CDR(FTC)	E	MESM	31.12.99	MOD (LONDON)
Hodkinson, Christopher Brian, pce, MA, psc(j),	CDR(FTC)	X	PWO(A)	30.06.02	COMATG SEA

Name	Rank	Branch	Spec	Seniority	Where Serving
Hofman, Alison Jayne, BSc,	LT(SCC)	Q	IC	26.10.98	RCDM
Hogan, Terence,	LT CDR(FTC)	X	AV	01.10.00	MOD (BATH)
Hogben, Andrew Lade, pce,	LT CDR(FTC)	X	AAWO	01.03.99	MWS DRYAD
Hogg, Adam James,	SLT(IC)	X	P U/T	01.05.00	RNAS YEOVILTON
Hogg, Christopher William, BSc,	LT CDR(FTC)	X	PWO(A)	01.03.97	DARTMOUTH BRNC
Holberry, Anthony Paul, psc, psc(j),	CDR(FTC)	E	WE	31.12.94	MOD (BATH)
Holden, John Lloyd, BA, SM,	LT(IC)	X	SM	01.12.99	VICTORIOUS(PORT)
Holden, Neil,	LT CDR(FTC)	X	MCD	01.04.01	MWS DRYAD
Holden, Paul Andrew,	LT(FTC)	E	AE(L)	07.09.95	HARRIER IPT
Holden, Robert John,	LT CDR(FTC)	X	O	01.10.99	849 SQN A FLT
Holder, John Michael, BSc,	LT(IC)	X	P	01.08.97	700M MERLIN OEU
Holdsworth, Howard William,	CDR(FTC)	E	AE	30.06.97	ES AIR YEO
Holford, Stephen James, BEng,	LT(FTC)	E	MESM	01.05.01	SULTAN
Holgate, James Alan,	SLT(CC)	E	WESM	01.04.00	DARTMOUTH BRNC
Holihead, Philip Wedgwood, pce, psc(a),	CDR(FTC)	X	AAWO	30.06.93	SA CAIRO
Holland, Charlotte Claire, BA,	LT(IC)	S		01.05.02	NEPTUNE DLO
Holland, Christopher,	SLT(IC)	E	AE	01.05.00	SULTAN
Holland, Nicholas Roy, BSc,	LT CDR(FTC)	S	(S)	01.10.99	CUMBERLAND
Holland, Simon Martin Walkington, BSc,	LT CDR(CC)	E	TM	01.05.01	PJHQ
Holley, Andrew John, pcea,	LT CDR(CC)	X	P	01.10.95	DHFS
Hollidge, John Howard, BSc, CEng, FIMarE,	CAPT(FTC)	E	ME	30.06.98	NELSON
MBIM, MCMI, psc,					
Holliehead, Craig Lewis, BSc,	LT(IC)	X	O U/T	01.01.02	750 SQN SEAHAWK
Hollins, Rupert Patrick, MA,	LT CDR(FTC)	S	BAR	01.12.96	2SL/CNH
Holloway, Jonathan Toby, MSc, CEng, MIMechE, jsdc,	CAPT(FTC)	E	MESM	30.06.02	NELSON
Holloway, Nicholas, BEM, (Act Maj)	CAPT RM(FTC)	-	SO(LE)	01.01.98	RMDIV LECONFIELD
Holloway, Steven Andrew,	LT(FTC)	X	PWO(U)	01.10.97	CORNWALL
Hollyfield, Peter Richard, BSc,	LT(IC)	E	TM	01.05.00	DARTMOUTH BRNC
Holmes, Annabel Mary,	LT(CC)	X	ATC	16.07.00	RNAS YEOVILTON
Holmes, Ashley Neil, BA,	LT(IC)	X	P	01.01.01	RNAS CULDROSE
Holmes, Christopher John,	MAJ(FTC)	-	C	01.05.98	JSCSC
Holmes, Graham, pce(sm),	LT CDR(FTC)	X	SM	01.12.87	MWC PORTSDOWN
Holmes, Helen Jane, LLB,	LT(IC)	S		01.01.02	FLEET CIS PORTS
Holmes, Jonathan David,	LT CDR(FTC)	X	H1	04.02.99	SCOTT
Holmes, Mark Daniel,	SLT(IC)	X	P U/T	01.04.00	RNAS CULDROSE
Holmes, Matthew John, BA, psc(j),	MAJ(FTC)	-		01.09.96	HQ 3 CDO BDE RM
Holmes, Michael John, ADC, BSc, CEng, (Commodore)	CAPT(FTC)	E	WESM	30.06.94	WSA BRISTOL
MIEE, MCMI, jsdc,					
Holmes, Patrick James Mitchell, BA, BSc,	LT(IC)	X	P U/T	01.05.02	RNAS YEOVILTON
Holmes, Paul Stewart, BDS,	SG LT(D)(SCC)	-		20.07.98	42 CDO RM
Holmes, Robert Andrew Gordon, BEng,	LT(FTC)	E	AE	01.03.95	FLEET HQ PORTS
Holmes, Robert, pce, psc(a),	CDR(FTC)	X	PWO(A)	31.12.95	MWS COLLINGWOOD
Holmes, Rupert Womack, BEng,	LT CDR(FTC)	E	AE	01.04.95	RNAS YEOVILTON
Holmwood, Mark Alan, BEng,	LT(CC)	E	ME	01.08.99	FEARLESS
Holroyd, Jonathon Edward James, BSc,	LT(CC)	X	O	16.02.98	CORNWALL FLT
Holt, Andrew Frederick, BSc,	LT CDR(FTC)	X	H CH	01.10.88	MOD (LONDON)
Holt, John David, BSc, BA, MIIE,	LT(IC)	E	TM	01.05.00	MWS COLLINGWOOD
Holt, Justin Sefton, MA, psc(j),	MAJ(FTC)	-	LC	27.08.99	40 CDO RM
Holt, Steven, PGDIPAN, pce,	LT CDR(FTC)	X	PWO(N)	01.04.97	MWS DRYAD
Holvey, Paul Jonathan,	LT(FTC)	E	MESM	01.04.01	TORBAY
Holyer, Raymond John, MSc,	CDR(FTC)	MS	(P)	01.10.98	NMA PORTSMOUTH
Honey, John Philip, BSc, CEng, MIMarE, MIMechE,	LT CDR(FTC)	E	MESM	01.03.88	DRAKE SFM
Honnoraty, Mark Robert, pce(sm), SM(n),	LT CDR(FTC)	X	SM	01.07.99	NMA PORTSMOUTH
Hood, Kevin Christopher,	LT CDR(FTC)	S		16.01.98	JSCSC
Hood, Kevin Michael, BEng, MSc,	LT CDR(FTC)	E	MESM	01.04.98	VENGEANCE(STBD)
Hood, Matthew John,	MAJ(FTC)	-		25.04.96	DARTMOUTH BRNC
Hook, David Arnold, psc(m),	LT COL(FTC)	-	C	31.12.97	42 CDO RM
Hoole, Robert John, MBA, MIExpE, ACMI,	LT CDR(FTC)	X	MCD	01.03.84	MWC PORTSDOWN
Hooper, Gary Peter, IEng, MIIE,	LT CDR(FTC)	E	WE	01.10.01	FOST SEA
Hooper, Johanna,	LT(FTC)	S		01.07.99	HARRIER IPT
Hooton, David Richard, BA,	LT(CC)	X	P	16.04.97	RNAS YEOVILTON
Hope, Karl, BSc, CEng, PGDip, MBCS,	LT CDR(CC)	E	IS	01.09.96	FLEET CIS PORTS

Name	Rank	Branch	Spec	Seniority	Where Serving
Hope, Mark Roger, BEng,	LT(FTC)	E	AE(L)	01.07.96	FLEET HQ PORTS
Hoper, Paul Roger, MCGI, pcea, gdas,	LT CDR(FTC)	X	O	01.10.96	ARK ROYAL
Hopkins, Anthony Edward Tobin, BSc,	LT(IC)	X		01.01.02	LINDISFARNE
Hopkins, Catherine,	LT(IC)	X	ATC	01.05.01	RNAS YEOVILTON
Hopkins, Rhys, BA, BSc,	CAPT RM(IC)	-		01.09.01	45 CDO RM
Hopkins, Richard Michael Edward,	CAPT RM(IC)	-		01.09.99	RMR TYNE
Hopkins, Steven David,	LT(FTC)	X	P	16.07.94	846 SQN
Hopley, David Alan, OBE, jsdc, psc,	COL(FTC)	-		31.12.96	RHQ AFNORTH
Hopper, Gary,	SLT(IC)	E	WE	01.01.01	MWS COLLINGWOOD
Hopper, Ian Michael,	LT CDR(FTC)	X	MW	09.04.02	RAMSEY
Hopper, Simon Mallam, BA, pce, n,	LT CDR(FTC)	X	PWO(A)	01.02.01	FOST SEA
Hopper, Stephen Owen, pce, psc(j),	CDR(FTC)	X	PWO(N)	31.12.99	MWS DRYAD
Hore, Robert Charles, psc,	CDR(FTC)	E	ME	31.12.93	2SL/CNH FOTR
Horn, Peter Barrick, MBE, pce,	CDR(FTC)	X	PWO(A)	30.06.99	MOD (LONDON)
Horne, Archibald,	LT CDR(FTC)	X	C	01.10.99	STRS IPT
Horne, Coralie Ann,	LT(IC)	S		01.12.99	NEPTUNE DLO
Horne, Jason Richard, SM(n),	LT(FTC)	X	PWO(U)	01.10.95	SOMERSET
Horne, Timothy George, MA, MSc, pce, psc, psc(j),	CDR(FTC)	X	PWO(A)	30.06.97	NMA PORTSMOUTH
Horne, Trevor Kingsley, MA, PGDip, FRICS, FCMI, pce, psc,	CDR(FTC)	X	H CH	31.12.94	ELANT/NAVNORTH
Horner, Patrick Andrew, pce,	LT CDR(FTC)	X	AAWO	01.08.94	UKMARBATSTAFF
Horrell, Michael Ian, OBE, BSc, CEng, FIMarEST, rcds, psc,	CAPT(FTC)	E	ME	30.06.97	DRAKE SFM
Horsley, Alan Malcolm Ronald, pce,	LT CDR(FTC)	X	PWO(N)	01.07.94	JSCSC
Horsted, James Alexander, MEng,	SLT(IC)	E	ME	01.09.99	SULTAN
Horsted, Peter James, MAPM, MSc, CEng, (Commodore)	CAPT(FTC)	E	ME	31.12.96	MOD (BATH)
FIMarEST, MIMechE, MINucE, rcds, psc, Eur I,					
Horswill, Mark Nicholas,	LT CDR(FTC)	S		01.08.97	AGRIPPA NAVSOUTH
Horton, James Robert, BEng,	LT(IC)	X	P U/T	01.09.01	DHFS
Horton, Peter Adam, BSc, MBA, CEng, MIEE,	LT CDR(FTC)	E	WE	01.01.94	WSA BRISTOL
Horton, Simon, BA,	LT(IC)	X		01.12.01	WALNEY
Horwell, Brian Bernard,	LT CDR(FTC)	E	WE	01.10.01	MCM1 SEA
Horwood, Neil Anthony,	LT(IC)	S		01.01.02	NELSON
Hosker, Timothy James, MA, psc,	CDR(FTC)	S		30.06.92	MOD (LONDON)
Hosking, David Blaise, MBE, MA, pce, psc,	CDR(FTC)	X	MCD	31.12.94	PJHQ AUGMENTEES
Hougham, Thomas Neil,	MID(IC)	X	P U/T	01.09.00	DARTMOUTH BRNC
Houghton, Philip John, MA, pce,	LT CDR(FTC)	X	PWO(U)	01.07.94	PJHQ
Houlberg, Kenneth Mark Torben, pce, n,	LT CDR(FTC)	X	PWO(A)	01.11.97	ALBION
Houlberg, Kristian Anthony Niels, BM, MRCP,	SURG LTCDR(MCC)	-		01.08.99	MODHU DERRIFORD
Hounsom, Timothy Rogers, n,	LT(IC)	X		01.04.97	PORTLAND
Hounsome, Jonathan Robert,	SLT(IC)	X	O U/T	01.01.01	750 SQN SEAHAWK
Hourigan, Mark Peter,	LT(CC)	X	P	16.06.96	845 SQN
House, Nigel Patrick Joseph, psc, jssc,	LT COL(FTC)	-		31.12.91	FLEET HQ PORTS 2
Houston, Darren John McCaw, n,	LT CDR(FTC)	X	PWO(A)	01.10.01	CAMPBELTOWN
Houvenaghel, Ian Michael,	CAPT RM(FTC)	-		01.09.98	FOST SEA
Howard, Charles William Wykeham, BTh	CHAPLAIN	CE		28.09.82	RNAS YEOVILTON
Howard, Daniel Gordon, MBA, MIL,	LT CDR(FTC)	X	ATC	01.10.99	NELSON
Howard, Keith Anthony, MSc, CEng, MIMarEST,	LT CDR(FTC)	E	ME	01.07.90	DRAKE SFM
Howard, Naomi Avice, BSc,	LT(IC)	X	HM	01.09.98	ROEBUCK
Howard, Neil, BEng, MRAeS, psc(j)o,	LT CDR(FTC)	E	AE	31.10.94	MOD (LONDON)
Howard, Nicholas Henry, BSc,	LT CDR(FTC)	E	AE	01.06.00	SABR IPT
Howard, Oliver Melbourne, MB, BS, FRCP, OStJ,	SURG CAPT(FCC)	-	(CM)	31.12.94	FORT BLOCKHOUSE
Howard, Peter MacArthy, pce, pcea,	LT CDR(FTC)	X	P	16.08.96	PJHQ
Howard, Richard David,	CAPT RM(CC)	-		01.05.00	42 CDO RM
Howarth, Dillon Wharton, MSc, pce, pcea, gdas,	LT CDR(FTC)	X	O	01.06.90	MERLIN IPT
Howarth, John,	CAPT RM(FTC)	-	SO(LE)	01.01.00	CHFHQ
Howarth, Stephen Joseph,	CAPT RM(FTC)	-		01.09.99	CTCRM
Howe, Craig Michael, BSc,	LT(CC)	X	P	01.07.98	820 SQN
Howe, Julian Peter, BA,	LT CDR(FTC)	X	PWO(A)	01.10.01	IRON DUKE
Howe, Paul Alfred, BSc, MA, psc(j),	MAJ(FTC)	-	MLDR	01.05.94	CDO LOG REGT RM
Howe, Sarah Elizabeth, BDS,	SGCDR(D)(MCC)	-		31.12.98	RALEIGH
Howe, Scott,	CAPT RM(CC)	-		01.04.01	ASC WATCHFIELD
Howe, Thomas, BSc, SM(n),	LT(FTC)	X	SM	01.11.97	SPLENDID
Howe, Tokunbo Akinlabi Irorunula Olusegun, BA,	LT(IC)	X	MCD	01.12.98	LEDBURY

Name	Rank	Branch	Spec	Seniority	Where Serving
Howell, Gwynne Evan Daniel, MB, BS, ... SURG CDR(FCC)	-	(CO/S)		30.06.98	RH HASLAR
FRCS, FRCS(ORTH),					
Howell, Henry Roderick Gwynn, MSc, PGDip, ... LT CDR(CC)	X	METOC		01.10.00	EXCHANGE USA
Howell, Michael Alfred, MB, BS, MA(CANTAB), FRCS, ... SURG CDR(FCC)	-	(CA/E)		30.06.99	RH HASLAR
Howell, Michael, MinstAM, MCMI, MILT, ... LT CDR(FTC)	S	(W)		01.10.93	2SL/CNH
Howell, Simon Brooke, pce, psc(j), ... LT CDR(FTC)	X	PWO(A)		01.11.93	FLEET HQ PORTS
Howells, Gary Russell, BSc, BA(OU), CEng, MIMarEST, adp, ... LT CDR(CC)	E	IS		01.10.90	AFPAA(CENTURION)
Howells, Martin John, ... LT(FTC)	MS	SM		29.07.94	MOD (LONDON)
Howells, Sian Louise, BEng, ... LT(IC)	E	TM		01.05.96	DARTMOUTH BRNC
Howells, Simon Murray, ... LT(FTC)	X	EW		19.09.00	PJHQ
Howes, Francis Hedley Roberton, BSc, MA, psc, ... COL(FTC)	-	MLDR		30.06.02	RCDS
Howes, Nicholas James, ... LT CDR(FCC)	Q	ACC/EM		01.10.99	RH HASLAR
Howorth, Georgina Mary Rumney, ... SLT(CC)	X			01.04.00	ST ALBANS
Howorth, Keith, BSc, MNI, pce, pcea, ... LT CDR(FTC)	X	O		01.12.92	DARTMOUTH BRNC
Hoyle, John Jefferson, ... LT CDR(FTC)	E	AE(M)		01.10.99	ES AIR MASU
Hubbard, Charles, ... 2LT(IC)	-			01.09.98	CTCRM LYMPSTONE
Hubbarde, Simon David, ... LT(FTC)	S	(W)		09.01.01	JFHQ STAFF NWOOD
Hubschmid, Spencer Raymond, BSc, ... LT(IC)	E	WESM		01.11.99	VIGILANT(PORT)
Hucker, Oliver Charles, ... MID(IC)	X			01.05.00	CUMBERLAND
Hudson, Andrew Ian, SM(n), ... LT(IC)	X	SM		01.02.01	TRIUMPH
Hudson, Jeremy David, MA, psc(j), ... LT COL(FTC)	-	MLDR		30.06.02	NMA WHALE ISLAND
Hudson, Jonathan David Piers, (Act Surg Cdr) .... SURG LTCDR(SCC)	-			02.08.00	MWS COLLINGWOOD
MB, ChB, MRCGP, Dip FFP,					
Hudson, Nicholas Graeme, jsdc, pce, ... CDR(FTC)	X	PWO(U)		30.06.91	NMA PORTSMOUTH
Hudson, Peter Derek, BSc, pce, ... CAPT(FTC)	X	PWO(N)		31.12.00	SULTAN AIB
Hudson, Peter John, BA, ... LT(IC)	X			01.10.99	NP 1061
Hudson, Philip Trevor, ... LT CDR(FTC)	X	AV		01.10.96	FLEET HQ PORTS
Huggett, Clare Louise, ... SLT(UCE)(IC)	E	WE		01.09.01	DARTMOUTH BRNC
Hughes, Andrew Simon, MB, BCh, MRCGP, ... SURG CDR(FCC)	-	GMPP		31.12.95	UKSU AFSOUTH
Hughes, Benjamin Frederick Mostyn, BA, ... SLT(IC)	S			01.01.00	EDINBURGH
Hughes, Christopher Bryan, BSc, ... LT(IC)	X	O		01.06.99	849 SQN A FLT
Hughes, David James, MB, ChB, ... SURG LTCDR(MCC)	-	SM		01.08.99	NELSON (PAY)
Hughes, Frank Charles, ... SLT(IC)	E	WE		01.01.00	CARDIFF
Hughes, Gareth David, BEng, ... LT(IC)	E	ME		01.01.02	SULTAN
Hughes, Gareth Llewelyn, psc, ... CDR(FTC)	S			31.12.00	ES AIR WYTON
Hughes, Gary Edward, ... LT(IC)	X	AV		01.05.02	RFANSU
Hughes, Gary George Henry, ... LT CDR(FTC)	X	C		01.10.98	FLEET CIS PORTS
Hughes, Geoffrey Alan, BA, ... SLT(IC)	S			01.09.00	DARTMOUTH BRNC
Hughes, John James, BEng, ... LT(IC)	X	P		01.08.99	845 SQN
Hughes, Jon-Paul Hudson, ... MAJ(FTC)	-	C		01.09.97	JSCSC
Hughes, Mark Jonathan, ... MAJ(FTC)	-			01.09.01	HQ 3 CDO BDE RM
Hughes, Nicholas David, ... LT(FTC)	E	ME		01.12.95	SUPT OF DIVING
Hughes, Nicholas Justin, pce, pce(sm), ... CDR(FTC)	X	SM		31.12.96	SUPERB
Hughes, Paul Antony, MB, BS, MRCGP, ... SURG CDR(FCC)	-	GMPP		30.06.98	JSU NORTHWOOD
DObstRCOG, Dip FFP,					
Hughes, Peter John, LVO, pce, psc, ... CDR(FTC)	X	PWO(N)†		31.12.87	NMA PORTSMOUTH
Hughes, Robert Ian, BSc, CEng, MIEE, jsdc, ... CAPT(FTC)	E	WESM		30.06.02	ASM IPT
Hughes, Scott Maurice, BSc, ... LT(CC)	X	P		16.07.97	750 SQN SEAHAWK
Hughes, Stephen John, psc(m), ... LT COL(FTC)	-			30.06.94	SA OSLO
Hughes, Thomas William, BEng, ... SLT(IC)	E	ME U/T		01.01.01	DARTMOUTH BRNC
Hughes, Timothy, ... LT(FTC)	E	MESM		01.04.01	FOST CSST FSLN
Hughesdon, Mark Douglas, BEng, MSc, CEng, MIEE, ... LT CDR(FTC)	E	WE		01.02.98	NC3 AGENCY
Hugo, Ian David, pce, pce(sm), ... CDR(FTC)	X	SM		31.12.96	MOD (LONDON)
Hulme, Timothy Mark, BA, pce, pcea, ... LT CDR(FTC)	X	O		01.03.97	HQ3GP SEA
Hulse, Anthony William, ... CAPT RM(CC)	-			01.04.01	COMAMPHIBFOR
Hulse, Royston Matthew, BA, ... SLT(IC)	X			01.09.00	DARTMOUTH BRNC
Hulston, Lauren Marie, BSc, ... LT(IC)	X	O U/T		01.09.01	824 SQN
Hume, Charles Bertram, BSc, CEng, MIMechE, ... CDR(FTC)	E	MESM		31.12.91	NEPTUNE NT
Hume, Kenneth John, BEng, ... LT(IC)	X	HM		01.03.99	RFANSU
Humphery, Duncan, BEng, ... LT(CC)	E	ME		01.06.98	DRAKE SFM
Humphrey, Ian Robert, ... LT(IC)	X			01.12.01	KENT
Humphrey, Ivor James, ... LT CDR(FTC)	E	WE		01.03.02	MOD (BATH)

Name	Rank	Branch	Spec	Seniority	Where Serving
Humphreys, John Illingworth, MNI, pce(sm),	CDR(FTC)	X	SM	30.06.94	VICTORIOUS(PORT)
Humphries, Graham David,	LT(IC)	X	P U/T	01.05.01	RNAS CULDROSE
Humphries, Jason Eric, n,	LT(FTC)	X		01.04.95	MWS DRYAD
Humphries, Mark, MSc,	LT(IC)	X	P	01.07.00	FLEET AV VALLEY
Humphrys, James Alan, BSc, MA, pce, psc,	CDR(FTC)	X	PWO(U)	31.12.93	ARK ROYAL
Hunkin, David John, pce,	LT CDR(FTC)	X	MCD	01.12.99	UKMARBATSTAFF
Hunt, Ben Paul, BSc,	SLT(IC)	X	P U/T	01.09.00	DARTMOUTH BRNC
Hunt, Charles James, BEng, MSc, BS,	LT CDR(CC)	X	METOC	01.10.97	MWS DRYAD
Hunt, Darren, MM,	CAPT RM(IC)	-	P	01.01.01	846 SQN
Hunt, Fraser Brain George,	LT(CC)	X	P	01.03.96	814 SQN
Hunt, Gerald Clive, pce, (Act Capt)	CDR(FTC)	X	O	30.06.85	JSU NORTHWOOD
Hunt, Jeremy Simon Paul, BSc, PGDip,	LT CDR(FTC)	X	METOC	05.02.95	ARK ROYAL
Hunt, Patrick Edward Robin David, HNC,	LT(FTC)	E	WE	05.06.92	HQ DCSA
Hunt, Patrick Simon, BEng,	LT(FTC)	E	WE	01.01.99	NORFOLK
Hunt, Paul Roland, BSc,	SLT(IC)	X	O U/T	01.01.01	DARTMOUTH BRNC
Hunt, Rachel Eleanor, MA,	SLT(IC)	X		01.01.00	YORK
Hunt, Robert James Campbell, LLB,	SLT(IC)	S		01.09.99	RALEIGH
Hunt, Stephen Christopher,	LT(FTC)	X	FC	01.07.94	EXCHANGE RAF UK
Hunter, Clare, (Act Surg Lt)	SURG SLT(SCC)	-		15.07.01	DARTMOUTH BRNC
Hunter, Kevin Patrick, BSc, CEng, FIMarEST, MIMechE,	LT CDR(FTC)	E	ME	01.08.87	HQ NORTH
Hunter, Neil Mitchell, QCBA, BSc, pce, pcea,	LT CDR(FTC)	X	P	01.01.94	BDLS CANADA
Hunter, Nicholas John, BEng,	LT(IC)	E	TM	01.09.95	SULTAN
Hunter, Toby Charles Graeme, psc(m),	LT COL(FTC)	-		30.06.90	SHAPE BELGIUM
Huntingford, Damian John, BA,	CAPT RM(CC)	-	MLDR	01.09.00	42 CDO RM
Huntington, Simon Peter, BSc, pce, n,	LT CDR(FTC)	X	PWO(U)	01.10.98	PJHQ
Huntley, Ian Philip, BA, psc(m), psc(j),	COL(FTC)	-		30.06.02	NMA PORTSMOUTH
Hunwicks, Sarah Elizabeth, BEng,	LT(CC)	E	AE	01.01.97	MERLIN IPT
Hurford, Peter Giles, OBE, BSc, FIMechE,	CAPT(FTC)	E	MESM	31.12.94	CNNRP BRISTOL
Hurley, Christopher, BSc,	LT(FTC)	X	PWO(A)	01.06.94	FEARLESS
Hurley, Karl Antony,	LT(SCC)	Q	ACC/EM	26.05.99	MODHU DERRIFORD
Hurman, Richard Nicholas,	MID(IC)	X		01.09.00	GUERNSEY
Hurrell, Piers Richard, pce, n,	LT CDR(FTC)	X	AAWO	01.07.98	FLEET HQ PORTS 2
Hurry, Andrew Patridge, pcea,	LT CDR(FTC)	X	P	01.11.94	815 SQN HQ
Hurst, Charles Nicholas Somerville,	LT(IC)	X	SM	01.02.01	VIGILANT(PORT)
Hussain, Amjad Mazhar, MSc, CEng, MIEE, jsdc,	CAPT(FTC)	E	WE	31.12.97	NELSON
Hussain, Shayne, BSc, PhD, PGDip,	LT CDR(FTC)	X	METOC	01.03.99	MOD (LONDON)
Hussey, Steven John, BSc,	MAJ(FTC)	-	P	01.09.99	RM WARMINSTER
Hutchings, James Stewart,	LT CDR(FTC)	E	AE(M)	01.10.00	FLEET AV VL
Hutchings, Justin Robert, MA, SM,	LT(IC)	X		01.04.99	TALENT
Hutchings, Richard Peter Hugh, MA, SM(n),	LT(FTC)	X	SM	01.12.97	FLEET HQ NWD
Hutchings, Sam David, BM, DipIMC RCSED,	SURG LT(MCC)	-		06.08.97	RH HASLAR
Hutchins, Iain David MacKenzie, n,	LT(FTC)	X		01.09.98	DEF SCH OF LANG
Hutchins, Richard Frank, BEng, MSc,	LT CDR(FTC)	E	MESM	01.06.01	NP BRISTOL
Hutchins, Timothy Paul, BSc,	LT CDR(FTC)	E	AE(P)	01.06.96	FLEET HQ PORTS
Hutchins, Timothy Simon, BSc,	LT(CC)	X	HM	16.06.96	FWO DEVPT SEA
Hutchinson, Christopher John, BSc, PGDip,	LT CDR(FTC)	X	METOC	01.09.00	RALEIGH
Hutchinson, Michael Robert,	SLT(IC)	X		01.01.02	MWS DRYAD
Hutchinson, Nicholas James, BA,	LT(IC)	X		01.01.02	ARGYLL
Hutchinson, Oliver James Procter,	LT CDR(FTC)	X	AAWO	01.09.97	UKMARBATSTAFF
Hutchinson, Peter, IEng, AMIMarEST,	LT(FTC)	E	ME	14.06.96	FLEET HQ PORTS 2
Hutchinson, Thomas Stanley,	LT CDR(FTC)	S	SM	01.07.83	FLEET HQ PORTS
Hutchinson, Timothy James, BSc, CEng, MIMarEST, MINucE,	CDR(FTC)	E	MESM	30.06.91	ASM IPT
Hutchison, George Bruce, pcea,	LT CDR(FTC)	X	O	01.02.95	849 SQN HQ
Hutchison, Paul Gordon, BEng, MSc, MIMarEST, CEng,	LT CDR(FTC)	E	MESM	01.05.98	TURBULENT
Hutton, Graham, pcea,	LT(FTC)	X	O	01.11.91	MWS DRYAD
Hutton, James Kyle, psc(m),	LT COL(FTC)	-		30.06.97	40 CDO RM
Hutton, Katharine Denise, BEd,	LT CDR(CC)	E	TM	01.10.01	MWS DRYAD
Hutton, Simon John, pce, SM,	LT CDR(FTC)	X	SM	01.11.95	FSC IPT
Huxford, Stephen, BSc,	LT(IC)	X		01.08.01	LANCASTER
Huxtable, Barrie James, BChD,	SG LT(D)(SCC)	-		22.07.97	RALEIGH
Huynh, Cuong Chuong, BA,	LT(IC)	S		01.03.02	WESTMINSTER
Hyde, Debra Marie, BSc,	LT(SCC)	Q	ONC	22.06.00	MODHU DERRIFORD

Name	Rank	Branch	Spec	Seniority	Where Serving
Hyde, James William, MEng,	SLT(IC)	E	WE	01.09.99	MWS COLLINGWOOD
Hyde, Trevor,	LT CDR(FTC)	E	WESM	01.10.94	MOD (BATH)
Hygate, Alison Margaret, BEng,	LT CDR(FTC)	X		01.05.02	PJHQ
Hyland, Roger Alan, BSc, PGDip,	LT(FTC)	E	WE	22.02.96	MOD (BATH)
Hyldon, Christopher John, BSc, MIEE, jsdc,	CAPT(FTC)	E	AE	30.06.96	BDLS INDIA
Hynde, Claire Louise, BSc,	LT(IC)	S		01.07.00	NELSON
Hynett, William Anthony,	LT(CC)	X	P	16.05.95	899 SQN HERON

I

Name	Rank	Branch	Spec	Seniority	Where Serving
Ibbotson, Richard Jeffery, DSC, MSc,CGIA,pce,(Commodore)	CAPT(FTC)	X	PWO(U)	30.06.97	BFFI
Iliffe, David Ian, BD, MLITT,	LT(IC)	X	O	16.11.98	849 SQN B FLT
Imrie, Peter Blain, DSM,	LT(FTC)	X	AV	14.12.90	SULTAN
Imrie, Samantha Jane, BD,	SLT(IC)	S		01.09.00	DARTMOUTH BRNC
Ince, David Peter,	LT CDR(FTC)	X	MCD	01.12.97	JSCSC
Ingamells, Stephen David, BSc,	SLT(IC)	X	P U/T	01.01.01	DARTMOUTH BRNC
Inge, Daniel Jon,	LT(CC)	X	ATC	01.05.95	JSCSC
Ingham, Andrew Richard, BEng,	LT(FTC)	X		01.09.98	NOTTINGHAM
Ingham, Lee-Anne Elizabeth, LLB,	LT(IC)	X		01.09.01	LEEDS CASTLE
Ingham, Nicholas Hampshire,	SLT(IC)	X		01.09.01	COTTESMORE
Ingham, Phillip Clayton, pce, psc,	CDR(FTC)	X	PWO(N)	30.06.92	MOD (LONDON)
Inglis, David John, BSc,	LT(IC)	X	P U/T	01.01.02	DHFS
Ingram, Gareth John, BSc,	LT(FTC)	X	O	01.12.95	815 FLT 201
Ingram, Richard Gordon, pce, psc(a),	CDR(FTC)	X	AAWO	30.06.98	2SL/CNH FOTR
Inness, Matthew John, BEng,	SLT(IC)	E	MESM	01.01.00	FWO FASLANE
Instone, Malcolm John, BA,	LT(CC)	X		01.11.98	SOUTHAMPTON
Ireland, Alasdair Robbie, MNI, pce, psc(j),	CDR(FTC)	X	AAWO	30.06.99	MOD (LONDON)
Ireland, John Mitchell,	LT(FTC)	E	MESM	15.10.93	MOD (BATH)
Ireland, Philip Charles, pce,	LT CDR(FTC)	X	PWO(U)	01.03.97	BROCKLESBY
Ireland, Roger Charles, MBE, MILT, ACIS,	CDR(FTC)	S	SM	31.12.95	PJHQ AUGMENTEES
Irons, Paul Andrew,	LT CDR(FTC)	X		01.07.97	NS OBERAMMERGAU
Irons, Rupert Charles St John, BSc, n,	LT(FTC)	X		01.10.95	MONTROSE
Irving, David,	LT(FTC)	X	PWO(C)	10.01.00	CAMPBELTOWN
Irving, Thomas Charles, BA,	SLT(IC)	S		01.05.00	LIVERPOOL
Irwin, Mark Andrew, BEng, CEng, MIMechE,	LT CDR(FTC)	E	ME	09.01.97	FOST SEA
Irwin, Stuart Gordon,	LT(CC)	X		01.06.00	SULTAN
Isaac, Philip, ACIS,	CDR(FTC)	S		31.12.99	2SL/CNH FOTR
Isbister, Elspeth,	SURG SLT(SCC)	-		01.08.99	DARTMOUTH BRNC
Issitt, Barry David,	LT(IC)	X	P U/T	01.01.02	RAF LINTN/OUSE
Issitt, David James, BA, BSc, jsdc,	CDR(FTC)	E	AE(P)	30.06.90	PJHQ
Ives, David Jonathan, BSc,	LT(CC)	X		01.06.00	GRAFTON
Iyamu, Osakue Benjamin, MSc,	SLT(IC)	E	TM	01.09.99	EXETER

J

Name	Rank	Branch	Spec	Seniority	Where Serving
Jackman, Andrew Warren, pce,	CDR(FTC)	X	PWO(C)	30.06.98	SCU LEYDENE ACNS
Jackman, Richard William, BSc, psc,	CAPT(FTC)	E	WE	31.12.98	SACLANT USA
Jackson, Andrew Stephen, BSc, MSc,	LT CDR(FTC)	E	MESM	01.01.97	MOD (BATH)
Jackson, Anthony,	LT(IC)	S		21.12.01	801 SQN
Jackson, Daniel James, BEng,	SLT(IC)	X		01.01.00	MWS DRYAD
Jackson, David John, BEng, MSc,	LT CDR(FTC)	E	AE	01.03.00	EXCHANGE RAF UK
Jackson, Gary Kevin, MA, MISM, psc(j),	CDR(FTC)	X	REG	30.06.02	2SL/CNH
Jackson, Howard Charles, BEng,	LT(IC)	X	P U/T	01.05.01	DHFS
Jackson, Ian Anthony, MSc, psc(j)o,	LT CDR(FTC)	E	ME	01.04.96	BDLS INDIA
Jackson, Ian, SM,	LT(CC)	X	SM	01.03.97	SCEPTRE
Jackson, Mark Harding, BA,	CHAPLAIN	CE		19.04.83	RNAS YEOVILTON
Jackson, Matthew John Andrew, MA,	CAPT RM(FTC)	-		01.09.96	CTCRM
Jackson, Pamela, BSc,	LT(IC)	X		01.02.00	EXETER
Jackson, Paul Anthony, MISM,	LT CDR(FTC)	S	(W)	01.10.01	AFPAA WTHY DOWN
Jackson, Peter Neil, BEng, MIEE,	LT CDR(FTC)	E	AE	01.02.99	848 SQN HERON
Jackson, Richard Anthony, BA,	SLT(IC)	X	SM	01.01.01	DARTMOUTH BRNC
Jackson, Stephen Michael,	LT CDR(FTC)	E	ME	09.02.89	SAUDI AFPS SAUDI
Jackson, Stephen Norman, BSc,	LT(IC)	E	IS	01.01.00	PJHQ

Name	Rank	Branch	Spec	Seniority	Where Serving
Jackson, Stevan Kenneth, FRGS,	CDR(FTC)	MS		31.12.00	MODHU DERRIFORD
Jackson, Stuart Harry, BSc, MBA, MRAeS, (Act Cdr)	LT CDR(FTC)	E	AE	01.07.89	2SL/CNH
Jackson-Smith, Stuart Paul,	LT(IC)	X	ATC	01.09.01	EXCHANGE RAF UK
Jacob, Andrew William, BA,	LT(CC)	X	HM	01.07.00	ARK ROYAL
Jacobs, Benjamin,	MID(IC)	X	P U/T	01.01.01	RAF CRANWELL EFS
Jacobs, Matthew Philip, BEng,	LT(CC)	E	ME	01.02.98	MOD (LONDON)
Jacques, Marcus James,	LT(FTC)	X	AAWO	01.07.94	CARDIFF
Jacques, Nicholas Adrian,	LT(FTC)	X	O	01.06.93	702 SQN HERON
Jagger, Charles Edward, BSc, pcea, psc,	LT CDR(FTC)	X	P	16.04.83	LAIPT
Jagger, Paul Richard Albert, MSc, AMIEE,	CDR(FTC)	E	WESM	30.06.95	MOD (LONDON)
Jaggers, Gary George, pcea,	LT CDR(FTC)	X	O	01.10.01	824 SQN
Jaini, Andrew,	LT(IC)	X		01.10.96	MOD (LONDON)
James, Adam Jon,	LT CDR(FTC)	X	H CH	01.10.97	ROEBUCK
James, Alexander Williams, BSc,	LT(FTC)	X	FC	01.04.99	EDINBURGH
James, Andrew George, BEng,	SLT(FTC)	E	ME	01.09.99	SULTAN
James, Christopher William, pce,	LT CDR(FTC)	X	AAWO	27.10.93	MWS DRYAD
James, Christopher, BSc, CEng, MIMarEST, MIMechE,	LT CDR(FTC)	E	MESM	01.06.91	ASM IPT
James, David Russell, pce, pcea, psc,	CDR(FTC)	X	O	31.12.94	MWC SOUTHWICK
James, Gareth Clark Miguel,	SLT(IC)	S		01.05.00	FEARLESS
James, Ian, BChD, MFGDP(UK),	SGLTCDR(D)(MCC)	-		09.01.99	CTCRM
James, Katherine Jeanette,	LT(MCC)	Q	CC	26.11.96	RCDM
James, Mark,	LT(FTC)	E	WE	01.04.01	CHATHAM
James, Paul Melvyn,	MAJ(FTC)	-		01.09.01	RMCS SHRIVENHAM
James, Richard Michael, BSc,	SLT(IC)	X		01.09.99	CATTISTOCK
James, Stuart Alain,	MAJ(FTC)	-		01.09.96	CTCRM
Jameson, Andrew Charles, LLB, psc(j),	CDR(FTC)	S	BAR	31.12.98	ARK ROYAL
Jameson, Andrew John, BA,	LT(IC)	E	TM	01.09.98	DARTMOUTH BRNC
Jameson, Roger Mark, BSc,	LT(FTC)	X	P	16.07.92	702 SQN HERON
Jamieson, Paul Andrew,	MID(IC)	X		01.01.01	BANGOR
Janaway, Paul, BSc, CEng, MIEE,	LT CDR(FTC)	E	WE	01.10.93	2SL/CNH FOTR
Jappy, Gavin William George, BA,	LT(CC)	X		01.08.97	DEF SCH OF LANG
Jaques, David Anthony,	LT(CC)	X	O	16.08.92	FLEET CMSA UK
Jaques, Simon,	SURG SLT(SCC)	-		18.10.00	DARTMOUTH BRNC
Jardine, Darren Scott, MRIN, n, MSc,	LT(FTC)	X	PWO(A)	01.11.95	MWS DRYAD
Jardine, Graham Andrew, pce, pcea, psc(j),	CDR(FTC)	X	O	30.06.98	ELANT/NAVNORTH
Jarman, Paul Richard,	LT(IC)	E	WESM	01.01.02	VIGILANT(PORT)
Jarrett, Michael Thomas John, n,	LT(FTC)	X		01.06.95	BITER
Jarvis, David John, BSc, CEng, MIEE, psc,	CAPT(FTC)	E	WESM	31.12.99	ACDS(POL) USA
Jarvis, Ian Lawrence, BSc, psc,	CAPT(FTC)	E	WE	30.06.97	LOAN DSTL
Jarvis, Laurence Richard, BSc,	CDR(FTC)	E	ME	30.06.02	T45 IPT
Jarvis, Lionel John, MB, BS, MRCS, LRCP, FRCR,	SURG CAPT(FCC)	-	CPDATE	31.12.99	RH HASLAR
Jayes, Neil John,	LT(FTC)	X	REG	01.04.01	MWS COLLINGWOOD
Jaynes, Peter Robert William, BSc, CEng, FIMechE, psc,	CAPT(FTC)	E	ME	30.06.99	NBC PORTSMOUTH
Jeffcoat, Stewart Murray, BA, CEng, FIMarEST, GradIMA, MCMI, MDA,	CDR(FTC)	E	ME	31.12.93	FOST SEA
Jefferson, Peter Mark, pcea,	LT CDR(FTC)	X	O	01.10.96	849 SQN HQ
Jefferson, Toby Simon, BEng,	LT(FTC)	E	AE	01.02.97	RMCS SHRIVENHAM
Jeffrey, Ian, BA, BSc, CEng, MIEE, MIL, nadc, psc, (Act Capt)	CDR(FTC)	E	WE	30.06.85	SHAPE BELGIUM
Jellyman, Paul Anthony, BSc, psc,	CDR(FTC)	X	METOC	30.06.89	2SL/CNH
Jemmeson, Susannah Hazel, BA,	SLT(IC)	S		01.05.00	CORNWALL
Jenkin, Alastair Michael Hugh, BSc, MA, CEng,MIEE, psc(m),	CDR(FTC)	E	WE	31.12.96	NMA PORTSMOUTH
Jenkin, James Richard Saint Lawrence,	LT CDR(FTC)	X	SM	01.05.92	LOAN DSTL
Jenking-Rees, Damian, LLB,	LT(CC)	S		01.10.97	RALEIGH
Jenkins, Alastair Rodney, BSc,	LT(CC)	X	P	16.06.98	JSCSC
Jenkins, David Gareth, BSc,	LT(IC)	X		01.09.01	RALEIGH
Jenkins, Gari Wyn, BEng, MSc, gw,	LT CDR(FTC)	E	WE	01.09.95	MOD (BATH)
Jenkins, Gwyn,	MAJ(FTC)	-		01.09.01	MOD (LONDON)
Jenkins, Ian Francis, BSc, CEng, MIEE, psc,	CAPT(FTC)	E	WE	31.12.96	2SL/CNH FOTR
Jenkins, Ian Lawrence, CVO, MB, BCh, FRCS, OStJ,	SURG VADM	-	CPDATE	21.10.02	2SL/CNH
Jenkins, Robert Christopher, BSc,	LT(IC)	X	ATCU/T	01.12.99	RNAS YEOVILTON
Jenkins, Thomas Richard,	MID(IC)	X		01.09.00	DARTMOUTH BRNC
Jenks, Anthony William Jervis, FIMarEST, CMarSci,	LT.CDR(FTC)	X	H CH	16.04.87	MWS RNHMS DRAKE

Name	Rank	Branch	Spec	Seniority	Where Serving
Jenner, Andrew Christopher, BEng,	LT(IC)	E	TM	16.09.97	OCLC MANCH
Jennings, Christian Rubin, MBE,	SLT(IC)	S		01.01.01	DARTMOUTH BRNC
Jennings, Matthew Paul, BTech, MA, MRAeS, pcea, psc,	LT CDR(FTC)	X	P	01.10.89	FLEET AV VL
Jennings, William, BEng,	LT(FTC)	E	ME	01.03.95	UNOMIG
Jenrick, Martin Frederick,	LT CDR(FTC)	X	MCD	01.10.95	SUPT OF DIVING
Jepson, Nicholas Henry Martin,	CAPT RM(FTC)	-	C	01.09.97	45 CDO RM
Jermy, Stephen Charles, BSc, MPhil, pce,	CAPT(FTC)	X	O	31.12.97	MOD (LONDON)
Jermyn, Nicholas Charles, BA,	MAJ(FTC)	-	LC	01.09.00	MWS DRYAD
Jerrold, William Harry, MEng,	SLT(IC)	E	ME U/T	01.09.00	ARK ROYAL
Jervis, Neil David, pce(sm),	CDR(FTC)	X	SM	30.06.99	FLEET HQ PORTS 2
Jess, Aran Ernest Kingston, BSc, MPhil,	CAPT RM(CC)	-		01.09.98	MOD (LONDON)
Jess, Ian Michael, MA, MSc, CEng, MIMarEST, psc,	CAPT(FTC)	E	ME	31.12.00	MOD (BATH)
Jessiman, Sarah Irene, BDS,	SG LT(D)(SCC)	-		20.06.97	SULTAN
Jessop, Paul Edward, MBE, BEng, MSc, CEng, MIMechE,	CDR(FTC)	E	MESM	31.12.00	MOD (BATH)
Jewitt, Charles James Bagot, MSc,	LT CDR(FTC)	S		01.07.96	ES AIR BRISTOL
John, Gareth David, BSc, PGDip, CEng, MIEE,	LT CDR(FTC)	E	WE	01.09.92	2SL/CNH
Johns, Adrian James, CBE, BSc, pce, pcea, psc, hcsc,	CAPT(FTC)	X	P	31.12.94	OCEAN
Johns, Andrew William, SM(n), SM,	LT(FTC)	X	SM	01.03.98	VENGEANCE(STBD)
Johns, Leslie Ernest,	LT(FTC)	X	REG	23.07.98	NEPTUNE 2SL/CNH
Johns, Michael Glynn, BSc, pcea,	LT CDR(FTC)	X	O	01.10.99	JMOTS NORTHWOOD
Johns, Sarah Alice Bedford, MSc,	LT CDR(FTC)	E	IS	01.10.96	DARTMOUTH BRNC
Johns, Tony, MSc, psc,	CAPT(FTC)	E	MESM	31.12.00	MOD (BATH)
Johnson, Alan David,	MAJ(IC)	-		29.05.97	JACIG
Johnson, Alan David, BSc,	LT(IC)	X		01.08.97	PJHQ
Johnson, Alex David, BSc,	LT(CC)	X	P	01.01.99	815 FLT 221
Johnson, Amanda Constance,	LT(CC)	S		01.09.00	SHEFFIELD
Johnson, Andrew Stephen, pce,	CDR(FTC)	X	AAWO	31.12.99	FLEET HQ PORTS
Johnson, Anthony Robert,	LT(CC)	X	O	16.02.95	LANG TRNG(UK)
Johnson, Bryan, BSc, pce,	LT CDR(FTC)	X	PWO(U)	01.05.88	MWC PORTSDOWN
Johnson, Chad Colin Burnett, BEng,	LT CDR(FTC)	E	AE(P)	01.04.02	RNAS YEOVILTON
Johnson, Graham Robert, BPharm, (Act Capt)	CDR(FTC)	X	AWO(C)	30.06.87	HQ DCSA
Johnson, Grenville Philip, MBE, jsdc, pce,	CDR(FTC)	X	MCD	31.12.91	LOAN ABU DHABI
Johnson, James Charles, MBE, BEng, MBA, CEng, MIEE,	CDR(FTC)	E	WESM	31.12.99	LPD(R) IPT
Johnson, Kevin, MBE,	LT(FTC)	S	(S)	09.01.01	CAMPBELTOWN
Johnson, Lee Samuel, n,	LT CDR(FTC)	X	PWO(A)	01.03.00	EDINBURGH
Johnson, Mark Ralph Edward, BSc,	LT(FTC)	X		01.07.98	EXCHANGE NLANDS
Johnson, Mark William, BSc,	SLT(IC)	X		01.09.99	ROEBUCK
Johnson, Mark,	CAPT RM(IC)	-		01.09.99	OCLC BRISTOL
Johnson, Michael David, ACMI, (Act Lt Cdr)	LT(FTC)	S	(W)	17.12.93	MOD (LONDON)
Johnson, Michael John,	LT CDR(FTC)	E	WE	01.10.01	LANCASTER
Johnson, Paul Raymond, BEng,	LT(CC)	E	AE U/T	01.02.99	750 SQN SEAHAWK
Johnson, Scott, SM(n), SM,	LT(CC)	X	SM	01.09.99	TURBULENT
Johnson, Sharon,	SLT(SCC)	Q		26.09.99	RH HASLAR
Johnson, Symon,	LT(CC)	X	P	16.01.97	CHFHQ
Johnson, Voirrey,	LT(SCC)	Q		25.01.96	FORT BLOCKHOUSE
Johnston, Alan George, BEng, AMIEE,	SLT(IC)	E	WESM	01.09.99	MWS COLLINGWOOD
Johnston, Charles Gardner, MB, BCh, BAO, FFARCSI,	SURG CAPT(FCC)	-	(CA)	31.12.00	MODHU DERRIFORD
Johnston, David Raymond,	LT(IC)	S		01.05.02	PORTLAND
Johnston, Gavin Stewart, MA,	LT(IC)	X	P	01.12.98	820 SQN
Johnston, James Angus, BEng, SM(n), SM,	LT(FTC)	X	SM	01.04.96	TURBULENT
Johnston, Jeffrey Joseph,	SLT(IC)	X		01.01.00	MWS DRYAD
Johnston, Karl,	2LT(IC)	-		01.09.98	CTCRM LYMPSTONE
Johnston, Richard Patrick, MB, BS, MRCP, AFOM, DipAvMed	SURG CDR(FCC)	-	(CO/M)	30.06.97	RNAS CULDROSE
Johnston, Timothy Alan, pce, pcea,	LT CDR(FTC)	X	P	01.06.95	JSCSC
Johnstone, Clive Charles Carruthers, BA, BSc, pce,	CDR(FTC)	X	PWO(A)	31.12.97	MWS DRYAD
Johnstone-Burt, Charles Anthony, OBE, MA, pce, pcea, hcsc	CDRE(FTC)	X	P	10.01.02	DARTMOUTH BRNC
Joll, Simon Mark, BA,	LT CDR(FTC)	S	SM	01.10.01	MARLBOROUGH
Jolly, John Edward Ian, (Act Cdr)	LT CDR(FTC)	X	H CH	16.12.84	LOAN OMAN
Jones, Adam Edward, BEng,	LT(FTC)	X	P	01.11.94	846 SQN
Jones, Alan Frank, MSc, Cert Ed, (Act Lt Cdr)	LT(CC)	E	TM	28.08.91	2SL/CNH FOTR

Name	Rank	Branch	Spec	Seniority	Where Serving
Jones, Aled,	SURG SLT(SCC)	-		30.11.00	DARTMOUTH BRNC
Jones, Alun David, BA, pce, pcea,	LT CDR(FTC)	X	P	01.11.97	FOST SEA
Jones, Anthony, psc,	CDR(FTC)	S		31.12.91	CALEDONIA DLO
Jones, Carolyn Jane,	LT(CC)	S		28.04.95	CHFHQ
Jones, Christopher David,	LT(IC)	E	WE	01.01.02	GRAFTON
Jones, Collin Raymond,	LT(CS)(CAS)	-		08.01.99	DNR NWE 2
Jones, Craig Antony, n,	LT CDR(FTC)	X	PWO(C)	01.11.99	MWS COLLINGWOOD
Jones, David Allen, MSc,	LT CDR(FTC)	E	MESM	01.10.99	NP BRISTOL
Jones, David Bryan, BEng, MSc, AMIMechE,	LT CDR(FTC)	E	MESM	01.07.99	SOVEREIGN
Jones, David Kenneth,	SLT(IC)	S		01.05.00	RALEIGH
Jones, David Lloyd, BTech, (Act Lt Cdr)	LT(FTC)	E	WE	24.02.95	JSSU AY NIK
Jones, David Michael, BEng, AMIEE,	LT(FTC)	E	WE	01.07.96	DARTMOUTH BRNC
Jones, Derrick John, SM(n), SM,	LT(IC)	X	SM	01.12.00	TRAFALGAR
Jones, Emmanuel Nelson Lomotetteh,	SLT(IC)	X		01.01.00	MARLBOROUGH
Jones, Gareth David, BSc,	LT(CC)	E	TM	01.09.91	NELSON RNSETT
Jones, Gary James,	CAPT RM(FTC)	-	SO(LE)	01.01.97	RMR MERSEYSIDE
Jones, Glyn Robert, MA, pce,	LT CDR(FTC)	X	METOC	01.09.95	JSCSC
Jones, Gordon James Lyn, BSc,	SLT(IC)	X		01.09.00	DARTMOUTH BRNC
Jones, Huw Ashton, MSc,	CDR(FTC)	E	MESM	31.12.00	CNNRP BRISTOL
Jones, Ian Michael, BEng,	LT(CC)	E	AE	01.11.99	846 SQN
Jones, Jenny, BA,	LT(IC)	X	FC	01.05.97	EXCHANGE RAF UK
Jones, Lyndsey Helan, BEng,	LT(IC)	E	TM	14.02.99	JSCSC
Jones, Mark Andrew,	LT(IC)	S	(W)	10.12.98	AFPAA(CENTURION)
Jones, Mark Anthony, BSc,	SLT(IC)	X	ATCU/T	01.05.99	FOST DPORT SHORE
Jones, Mark Douglas, BEng,	LT(CC)	X	O	16.01.95	LYNX OEU
Jones, Mark Roger,	LT(CC)	E	WE	01.05.00	MWS COLLINGWOOD
Jones, Martin Clifford, BSc, pce, psc(j), n,	CDR(FTC)	X	H CH	30.06.01	ECHO
Jones, Martin David, BA,	LT(FTC)	X	FC	01.01.95	MWS DRYAD
Jones, Martyn Aubrey, BA, IEng, MIPlantE, MSE,	LT(FTC)	E	ME	13.06.97	MWS DEF DIV SCHL
Jones, Matthew Robert, BSc,	LT(IC)	X		01.01.02	MWS DRYAD
Jones, Matthew Russell, BA,	MAJ(FTC)	-		01.09.98	40 CDO RM
Jones, Michael, pce,	LT CDR(FTC)	X	AAWO	01.03.95	SOMERSET
Jones, Nicholas Thomas Edward, BA,	SLT(IC)	X		01.09.00	DARTMOUTH BRNC
Jones, Nigel Patrick, SM(n), SM,	LT CDR(FTC)	X	SM	01.02.99	FOST CSST FSLN
Jones, Nikki Sarah,	LT(IC)	S		01.07.00	YORK
Jones, Oliver Christian, BSc,	SLT(IC)	X		01.05.00	CORNWALL
Jones, Paul Andrew,	LT(FTC)	E	WE	09.01.01	MWS COLLINGWOOD
Jones, Paul David, SM(n), SM,	LT(FTC)	X	SM	01.11.95	SPARTAN
Jones, Paul, pce,	LT CDR(FTC)	X	PWO(A)	01.07.92	JSCSC
Jones, Peter Haydn, OBE, jsdc, (Act Capt)	CDR(FTC)	X	H CH	30.06.89	DA BRUNEI
Jones, Philip Andrew, MA, jsdc, pce,	CAPT(FTC)	X	PWO(C)	31.12.99	MOD (LONDON)
Jones, Richard James, BSc,	LT(IC)	X	SM	01.12.99	SPLENDID
Jones, Richard John, BA,	LT(IC)	X		01.05.01	SOVEREIGN
Jones, Richard William, MSc, CEng, MIMarEST,	CDR(FTC)	E	ME	30.06.02	JSCSC
Jones, Robert Peter Martyn, BSc,	2LT(FTC)	-		01.09.01	CTCRM LYMPSTONE
Jones, Roderick Vernon,	LT(FTC)	E	ME	14.06.96	SULTAN
Jones, Russell Keenan, IEng, MIEE,	LT(FTC)	E	MESM	19.06.98	SCEPTRE
Jones, Simon Sean,	LT(FTC)	X	AV	01.04.01	ILLUSTRIOUS
Jones, Stephen,	SLT(IC)	E	ME	01.05.00	SULTAN
Jones, Timothy Mark,	LT(FTC)	MS		01.04.01	NEPTUNE NT
Jones-Thompson, Michael John,	LT(FTC)	X		01.04.01	MWS DRYAD
Jordan, Adrian Mark, BDS, MSc, LDS RCS(Eng),	SGCDR(D)(FCC)	-		31.12.98	DDA TE
Jordan, Andrew Aidan, BA, pce, n,	LT CDR(FTC)	X	PWO(U)	01.10.00	BRECON
Jordan, Anna Frances, LLB,	LT(FTC)	X	O U/T	01.09.99	702 SQN HERON
Jordan, Craig, BEng, MSc, (Act Lt Cdr)	LT(CC)	E	IS	01.01.95	2SL/CNH
Jordan, Louis,	LT CDR(FTC)	E	ME	01.10.00	FLEET HQ PORTS 2
Jordan, Mark David, BSc,	LT(IC)	E	WE	01.05.01	DARTMOUTH BRNC
Jordan, Nicholas Stuart,	LT CDR(FTC)	E	WE	01.10.98	YORK
Jose, Steven, BA,	LT CDR(FTC)	E	P	01.03.02	815 FLT 206
Joyce, David Andrew, BEng, MSc, CEng, MIEE,	LT CDR(FTC)	E	WE	01.10.00	NELSON RNSETT
Joyce, Philip, BSc, psc(j),	MAJ(FTC)	-		25.04.98	45 CDO RM
Joyce, Thomas Jeremy,	LT CDR(FTC)	X	P	01.11.99	FOST SEA

Name	Rank	Branch	Spec	Seniority	Where Serving
Joyner, Adam, pce, pcea,	LT CDR(FTC)	X	P	01.05.89	SA MALAYSIA
Juckes, Martin Anthony,	LT CDR(FTC)	E	AE(L)	16.08.95	847 SQN
Julian, Timothy Mark, (Act Lt Cdr)	LT(FTC)	X	P	16.11.92	RNAS CULDROSE

K

Name	Rank	Branch	Spec	Seniority	Where Serving
Kadinopoulos, Benjamin Alexander,	SLT(UCE)(FTC)	E	WE	01.09.00	DARTMOUTH BRNC
Karsten, Thomas Michael, BA, jsdc, pce,	CAPT(FTC)	X	PWO(U)	31.12.00	FLEET HQ PORTS 2
Kassapian, David Lee, BA, psc(j),	MAJ(FTC)	-		01.09.97	MOD (LONDON)
Kay, Paul Stuart, SM(n), SM,	LT(FTC)	X	SM	01.04.01	TIRELESS
Keane, Brendan Michael,	SLT(IC)	E	WE	01.05.00	DARTMOUTH BRNC
Kearney, Paul Leonard, BDS,	MAJ(FTC)	-		27.04.02	CTCRM
Keble, Kenneth Wayne Latimer, jsdc, pce, pcea,	CDR(FTC)	X	O	31.12.95	RICHMOND
Keefe, Patrick Charles, BSc,	CDR(FTC)	S		31.12.95	NELSON
Keefe, Sally-Anne, BA,	CDR(FTC)	W	S	30.06.01	2SL/CNH FOTR
Keegan, William John, BSc, CEng, MIEE, psc,	CAPT(FTC)	E	WE	31.12.98	FLEET HQ NWD
Keeley, Stephen Peter,	LT(FTC)	E	MESM	15.06.95	TORBAY
Keen, Neil, BEng, AMIEE,	LT CDR(FTC)	E	WE	01.06.01	CV(F) IPT
Keenan, Benjamin, BEng, MSc,	SLT(IC)	E		01.09.99	SULTAN
Keeping, Daniel James, BEng,	LT(IC)	X	P	01.09.00	RNAS YEOVILTON
Kehoe, Anthony Desmond, MB, ChB,	SURG LTCDR(MCC)	-		01.12.00	MODHU FRIMLEY
Keillor, Stuart James,	SLT(IC)	X		01.09.01	RALEIGH
Keith, Benjamin Charles, BSc,	LT(CC)	X	P	01.05.00	815 FLT 246
Kelbie, Ewan, MA, pce, pcea, psc(j),	CDR(FTC)	X	P	30.06.02	HQ3GP HQSTC
Kellett, Andrew, BEng,	LT(FTC)	E	ME	01.02.95	MOD (BATH)
Kelly, Anthony Paul,	MAJ(FTC)	-	SO(LE)	01.10.01	RM NORTON MANOR
Kelly, Grant Jason, MA,	LT(IC)	E	TM	01.09.96	NELSON RNSETT
Kelly, Howard Clifton, BEng,	LT CDR(FTC)	E	MESM	01.04.02	SPARTAN
Kelly, John Anson, BEng,	LT CDR(FTC)	E	ME	01.02.00	KENT
Kelly, John Anthony,	CAPT RM(IC)	BS	SO(LE)	01.01.01	RM BAND SCOTLAND
Kelly, Nigel,	CHAPLAIN	CE		26.05.92	RALEIGH
Kelly, Philip Michael, BEng, MSc,	CAPT RM(FTC)	-	P	01.09.96	801 SQN
Kelly, Richard, pce(sm),	LT CDR(FTC)	X	SM	03.04.91	ASM IPT
Kelly, Simon Peter, BA,	LT(FTC)	X		01.07.99	NEWCASTLE
Kelly, Stephen,	SLT(IC)	X		01.01.00	CORNWALL
Kelly, Thomas James, BA,	CAPT RM(IC)	-		01.09.00	UKLFCSG RM
Kelynack, Mark Trevellyan, pcea,	LT(CC)	X	O	16.04.95	815 FLT 221
Kemp, Alexander Charles,	CAPT RM(CC)	-		01.04.02	1 ASSLT GP RM
Kemp, Peter John,	MAJ(FTC)	-	MLDR	01.09.98	PJHQ
Kempsell, Ian, BSc, CEng, MIMarEST,	LT CDR(FTC)	E	ME	26.06.96	GLOUCESTER
Kendall-Torry, Guyan Charles,	MID(UCE)(IC)	E	WE	01.09.00	DARTMOUTH BRNC
Kendrick, Alexander Michael, BEng,	LT(FTC)	E	WE	01.02.97	MOD (LONDON)
Kennan, Nicholas Paul,	SLT(IC)	S		01.06.99	ILLUSTRIOUS
Kennaugh, Alastair John, BSc, PGCE, psc,	CDR(FTC)	E	TM	31.12.88	SULTAN AIB
Kenneally, Sean Joseph,	CAPT RM(FTC)	-	SO(LE)	01.01.00	RM POOLE
Kennedy, Angelina, LLB,	LT(IC)	S		08.01.98	JSU NORTHWOOD
Kennedy, Catheryn Helena,	LT(SCC)	Q	CC	07.05.98	RH HASLAR
Kennedy, Ian James Andrew, BEng,	LT CDR(FTC)	E	ME	01.08.95	JSCSC
Kennedy, Ian, BEng,	LT(FTC)	E	WESM	01.07.97	MWS COLLINGWOOD
Kennedy, Inga Jane,	LT CDR(SCC)	Q		31.03.97	RCDM
Kennedy, Nigel Henry, BSc, MIMarEST, psc,	LT CDR(FTC)	E	ME	01.05.92	ENTERPRISE
Kennedy, Roger John, BEng,	LT(CC)	X	O	01.07.99	849 SQN A FLT
Kenney, Ronald Paul, OStJ, (Act Cdr)	LT CDR(FTC)	MS		01.10.97	RN GIBRALTAR
Kennington, Lee Alexander, BSc,	LT(CC)	X	O	01.05.94	815 FLT 217
Kennon, Stanley, BA, BD,	CHAPLAIN	SF		24.09.00	RNAS CULDROSE
Kenny, Stephen James, pce, MA,	CDR(FTC)	X	AAWO	31.12.97	EXCHANGE USA
Kent, Isabel Maria, BEd,	LT CDR(FTC)	W	X	01.10.96	2SL/CNH FOTR
Kent, Martin David, BSc, pce,	LT CDR(FTC)	X	PWO(N)	01.05.89	NBC PORTSMOUTH
Kent, Matthew John,	LT(IC)	E	ME	01.05.01	DARTMOUTH BRNC
Kenward, Peter David, BSc, MA, CEng, MRAeS, psc,	CDR(FTC)	E	AE(P)	30.06.95	MOD (LONDON)
Kenworthy, Leigh,	LT(SCC)	Q		01.04.99	RH HASLAR
Kenworthy, Richard Alan, sq,	MAJ(FTC)	-		30.04.98	UKLFCSG RM
Kenyon, Carolyn Marie, LLB,	LT(IC)	S		01.05.01	DRAKE SFM

Name	Rank	Branch	Spec	Seniority	Where Serving
Keogh, Joanna Mary Elizabeth, MB, BS,	SURG LT(MCC)	-		04.08.99	RNAS YEOVILTON
Keogh, Steven David, BSc,	SLT(IC)	E	TM	01.01.00	DARTMOUTH BRNC
Kerchey, Stephen John Victor, BSc, CEng, MIEE,	CDR(FTC)	E	WE	31.12.00	DLO MCBU/DGMIPT
Kerley, Benjamin John,	SLT(IC)	X	P U/T	01.05.00	DARTMOUTH BRNC
Kern, Alastair Seymour,	MAJ(FTC)	-		01.09.00	UNOMIG
Kerr, Adrian Nicholas, BEng, CEng, MIEE,	LT(FTC)	E	WESM	01.01.01	WSA/CAPT MCTA
Kerr, Alan Thomas Frederick,	LT CDR(FTC)	X	PWO(U)	01.10.01	NORTHUMBERLAND
Kerr, Jack,	LT CDR(FTC)	X	PR	01.10.01	INVINCIBLE
Kerr, Mark William Graham, BA, pce, psc,	RADM	-	PWO	22.01.02	NMA PORTSMOUTH
Kerr, William Malcolm McTaggart,	LT CDR(FTC)	X	MCD	09.03.90	EXCHANGE CANADA
Kershaw, Christopher Robert, MA, MB, BCh, FRCP, MRCS, DCH,	SURG CDR(FCC)	-	(CC)	30.06.85	RH HASLAR
Kershaw, Richard, BM, (Act Surg Lt)	SURG SLT(SCC)	-		06.07.01	DARTMOUTH BRNC
Kershaw, Simon Henry Christopher, BDS,	SG LT(D)(SCC)	-		18.07.01	SULTAN
Kershaw, Steven, MSc, CEng, MIEE,	CDR(FTC)	E	WESM	30.06.01	JSCSC
Kerslake, Richard William, pce,	LT CDR(FTC)	X	P	01.02.99	815 SQN HQ
Kerwood, Richard John, PGDIP, (Act Lt Cdr)	LT(FTC)	S	CA	25.07.91	NELSON
Kestle, Mark,	LT(IC)	E		01.05.02	SUTHERLAND
Kettle, Richard Andrew, BA, psc(j)o,	MAJ(FTC)	-		24.04.99	FLEET HQ PORTS 2
Kewley, Ian David, BA,	LT(FTC)	X		01.08.98	LEEDS CASTLE
Key, Benjamin John, BSc, pce,	CDR(FTC)	X	O	31.12.99	LANCASTER
Key, David Frank, pce, pcea, (Act Cdr)	LT CDR(FTC)	X	P	01.11.91	OCEAN
Khan, Liaqat Ali, BSc,	LT(CC)	X		01.02.99	NORTHUMBERLAND
Khan, Mansoor Ali, MB, BS,	SURG LT(SCC)	-		01.08.01	CFLT MED(SEA)
Kidd, James Christian, MSc, CDipAF, psc, gw,	CAPT(FTC)	E	WE	30.06.99	MWS COLLINGWOOD
Kidner, Peter Jonathan, BSc, CEng, FRAeS, psc, psc(m),	RADM	-	AE	02.04.02	DMTO HQ
Kiernan, Colin Graham, BEng,	LT(IC)	X	P U/T	01.05.02	RNAS YEOVILTON
Kierstan, Simon Janusz James, BEng,	LT(IC)	E	TM	01.01.02	SULTAN
Kies, Lawrence Norman, BSc, PGCE,	LT(FTC)	E	TM	01.01.94	SULTAN
Kiff, Ian William,	SLT(IC)	E	WE	01.01.00	EDINBURGH
Kilbane, Dominic Kevin John, BSc,	SLT(IC)	X	O U/T	01.01.00	DARTMOUTH BRNC
Kilby, Stewart Edward, MA, pce, pcea, psc(j),	LT CDR(FTC)	X	O	01.04.96	702 SQN HERON
Kilgour, Niall Stuart Roderick, pce, pce(sm), psc,	RADM	-	SM	18.09.01	FLEET HQ NWD
Kilmartin, Andrew, BSc,	LT(IC)	E	ME	01.02.99	SOMERSET
Kilmartin, Steven,	CAPT RM(IC)	-		04.04.97	CINCFLEET FTSU
Kimberley, Robert, BSc, n,	LT CDR(FTC)	X	PWO(U)	01.07.98	MWS DRYAD
Kimmons, Michael, BA,	CAPT(FTC)	S		30.06.97	RCDS
King, Anthony Michael, BSc, MDA, CEng, MRAeS,	CDR(FTC)	E	AE(P)	31.12.99	FLEET HQ PORTS
King, Antony Richard, gdas,	LT(FTC)	X	O	01.03.92	849 SQN A FLT
King, Charles Edward William, BA, MILT, jsdc,	CDR(FTC)	S		30.06.96	RALEIGH
King, David Christopher Michael, BSc, MA, psc(j),	LT COL(FTC)	-		30.06.01	FLEET HQ PORTS 2
King, Edward Michael, MSc, CEng, MIEE, CDipAF, gw,	CDR(FTC)	E	WE	31.12.96	MOD (LONDON)
King, Gordon Charles,	LT(FTC)	E	MESM	14.06.96	FWO FASLANE
King, Iain Andrew, BSc,	SLT(IC)	X	P U/T	01.09.99	RAF CRANWELL EFS
King, Michael Andrew,	MID(UCE)(IC)	E	WE	01.09.00	DARTMOUTH BRNC
King, Nicholas William, BEng, MSc,	LT CDR(FTC)	E	MESM	01.05.97	SPLENDID
King, Nigel Alan, pcea, psc(m),	LT CDR(FTC)	X	P	01.12.84	FLEET HQ PORTS
King, Paul Christopher, MSc,	LT CDR(FTC)	E	ME	01.09.92	SULTAN
King, Richard James, BSc, pcea,	LT CDR(FTC)	X	P	01.10.99	771 SQN
King, Richard John, BSc,	MAJ(FTC)	-		01.05.01	45 CDO RM
King, Richard William, BSc, pce, pcea,	CDR(FTC)	X	P	30.06.02	MOD (LONDON)
King, Steven John,	LT(CC)	X	P	16.06.92	849 SQN HQ
King, William Robert Charles, BSc,	LT(IC)	X		01.09.01	PEMBROKE
King, William Thomas Poole, BEng,	LT(IC)	E	MESM	01.09.01	SULTAN
Kingdom, Mark Andrew, BEng,	LT(FTC)	E	AE	01.02.97	HARRIER IPT
Kingdon, Simon Charles,	LT(IC)	S		01.01.02	FWO DEVONPORT
Kings, Simon John Nicholson, MBE, FCMI, pce, pcea,	CDR(FTC)	X	PWO(A)	30.06.98	MOD (LONDON)
Kingsbury, James Arthur Timothy, BSc, (Act Cdr)	LT CDR(FTC)	S	BAR	01.02.91	2SL/CNH
Kingsbury, Simon Hugh, BEng, MSc, CEng, MIEE,	LT CDR(FTC)	E	WE	01.04.96	DRAKE SFM
Kingsbury-Smith, Rosemary,	SURG SLT(SCC)	-		14.08.00	DARTMOUTH BRNC
Kingston, Earl Anthony, BEng,	SLT(IC)	X	P U/T	01.09.99	DHFS
Kingwell, John Matthew Leonard, BA, pce, psc(j),	CDR(FTC)	X	PWO(U)	30.06.99	ARGYLL

Name	Rank	Branch	Spec	Seniority	Where Serving
Kirby, Stephen Redvers, BSc, MA, pce, pcea,psc, cds(USN),	CAPT(FTC)	X	O	30.06.98	CORNWALL
Kirk, Adrian Christopher, BEng,	LT(FTC)	E	AE	01.05.97	ES AIR MASU
Kirk, Trevor Leslie, BSc, PGDip, psc,	LT CDR(FTC)	E	WE	01.06.87	DOSG BRISTOL
Kirkbright, Keith Leslie Mellor,	LT(CS)(CAS)	-		17.02.91	DNR WROUGHTON
Kirkby, Stephen James, BSc,	SLT(IC)	X		01.09.00	DARTMOUTH BRNC
Kirkham, Simon Philip, (Act Lt Cdr)	LT(CC)	X	P	16.08.94	RAF CRANWELL EFS
Kirkpatrick, John, OBE, BSc, AMIEE, jsdc,	CAPT(FTC)	E	WESM	31.12.95	WSA BRISTOL
Kirkup, John Paul, BSc, MA, psc(j),	LT CDR(FTC)	E	TM	01.03.94	DARTMOUTH BRNC
Kirkwood, James Alistair Delange, LLB, pce,	LT CDR(FTC)	X	PWO(A)	01.04.90	AGRIPPA NAVSOUTH
Kirkwood, Tristram Andrew Harry, BSc,	LT(FTC)	X	P	01.11.94	820 SQN
Kirwan, John Anthony,	LT(IC)	S		07.04.02	LAIPT
Kissane, Robert Edward Thomas, BEng, MSc,	LT CDR(FTC)	E	WE	01.04.97	UKCEC IPT
Kitchen, Bethan, BEng,	LT(IC)	E	AE	01.07.00	RNAS CULDROSE
Kitchen, Stephen Anthony, BEng,	LT CDR(FTC)	E	AE(P)	01.01.98	LOAN DARA
Kitson, Robert Henry,	SLT(IC)	X	ATCU/T	01.01.00	DARTMOUTH BRNC
Kitt, Robert George,	LT(FTC)	E	WE	01.09.99	WSA BRISTOL
Kitteridge, Daniel James, BA,	LT(IC)	X	P	01.01.00	845 SQN
Klidjian, Michael Jeffrey, BSc,	LT(IC)	X		01.05.01	MWS DRYAD
Knibbs, Mark, BA, pce, psc(j),	CDR(FTC)	X	PWO(U)	30.06.99	PJHQ
Knight, Alastair Cameron Fergus, BSc,	LT(IC)	X	P	01.03.94	849 SQN A FLT
Knight, Andrew Robert,	LT CDR(FTC)	X	P	01.10.01	FOST SEA
Knight, Anthony William, BSc, pce,	LT CDR(FTC)	X	PWO(C)	01.02.90	CINCFLEET FIMU
Knight, Damon Ashley, MBE, pce,	CDR(FTC)	X	AAWO	30.06.01	PJHQ
Knight, Daniel Simon, BSc, SM,	LT(FTC)	X	SM	01.09.99	TORBAY
Knight, David John, rcds, psc,	CDR(FTC)	S		31.12.89	RALEIGH
Knight, David William, BSc,	LT CDR(FTC)	X	AAWO	01.12.00	NEWCASTLE
Knight, Diane Joy,	LT CDR(MCC)	Q	IC	01.10.01	MODHU DERRIFORD
Knight, Emma Margaret, MB, ChB,	SURG LT(SCC)	-		05.08.98	MODHU DERRIFORD
Knight, Jeremy Denis,	LT(FTC)	X	EW	13.12.95	HQ NORTH
Knight, Jonathan Michael,	MID(IC)	X		01.01.01	DARTMOUTH BRNC
Knight, Keith John, BTech,	LT(FTC)	E	WESM	24.02.95	WSA BRISTOL
Knight, Paul James, BSc, psc(j),	LT CDR(FTC)	E	AE	01.05.97	CV(F) IPT
Knight, Paul Richard, BSc, psc,	LT CDR(FTC)	E	MESM	01.09.93	DRAKE SFM
Knight, Robert Harry,	LT(FTC)	E	MESM	15.06.95	SULTAN
Knight, Stephen David, MEng,	LT(CC)	X	P	01.09.99	RNAS YEOVILTON
Knights, Robin,	LT CDR(FTC)	X	PWO(U)	01.10.99	DL IPT
Knill, Robin Lloyd,	LT CDR(FTC)	S	(S)	01.10.97	FOST SEA
Knock, Gareth Paul,	LT CDR(FTC)	S	SM	01.10.01	CORNWALL
Knott, Michael Bruce, AMNI, pce,	LT CDR(FTC)	X	PWO(A)	01.02.01	FOST SEA
Knowles, Christopher James, BSc,	LT(IC)	X	P U/T	01.09.01	RAF CRANWELL EFS
Knowles, David,	SLT(IC)	X		01.09.01	MONTROSE
Knowles, John Michael, pce, pcea, psc,	CAPT(FTC)	X	P	30.06.99	RCDS
Knowles, Michael Mark,	LT CDR(FTC)	S	(W)	15.04.00	MWS COLLINGWOOD
Knowling, Philip John, MSc, CEng, MIEE, jsdc,	CDR(FTC)	E	AE	31.12.91	MOD (BATH)
Knox, Graeme Peter, LLB,	LT(IC)	S		01.10.99	NEPTUNE DLO
Knox, Margaret Mary,	LT(FS)(CAS)	FS		17.04.89	FLEET HQ PORTS
Koheeallee, Mohummed Cassim Rashid Charif, BEng,	SLT(IC)	X	P U/T	01.01.01	DARTMOUTH BRNC
Kohler, Andrew Philip,	LT CDR(FTC)	X	PWO(A)	01.04.02	YORK
Kohn, Patricia Anne,	LT(FTC)	X		01.07.00	MANCHESTER
Kongialis, James Allyn, BSc,	CAPT(FTC)	E	WESM	30.06.97	MOD (BATH)
Krosnar-Clarke, Steven Matthew, MSc,	LT CDR(FTC)	E	TM	01.10.98	MWS COLLINGWOOD
Kurth, Rolf, SBSTJ,	LT(IC)	X		18.05.98	MWS DRYAD
Kyd, Jeremy Paul, PGDIPAN, pce, n, BSc,	LT CDR(FTC)	X	PWO(N)	01.08.97	ARK ROYAL
Kyte, Andrew Jeffery, MA, psc(j), (Act Cdr)	LT CDR(FTC)	S		16.12.96	FOST DPORT SHORE

L

Name	Rank	Branch	Spec	Seniority	Where Serving
L'Amie, Christopher Andrew, BA,	SLT(IC)	X		01.01.00	BRECON
Lacey, Catherine Margaret, BEng,	LT CDR(FTC)	E	WE	01.10.00	MWS COLLINGWOOD
Lacey, Ian Nigel, MSc, PhD,	LT CDR(FTC)	E	IS	16.06.91	EXCHANGE USA
Lacey, Stephen Patrick, pcea,	CDR(FTC)	X	O	30.06.02	MOD (LONDON)
Lacy, Lynne Helen, BEng,	LT(CC)	X		01.12.96	EXPLORER
Lade, Christopher John, BSc, pce,	CDR(FTC)	X	MCD	30.06.98	FLEET HQ PORTS

Name	Rank	Branch	Spec	Seniority	Where Serving
Ladislaus, Cecil James, BEng,	LT(IC)	X		01.01.02	MWS DRYAD
Laggan, Peter John, BSc,	LT CDR(FTC)	S	(W)	01.10.98	MOD (LONDON)
Lai-Hung, Jeremy Jean Paul,	SLT(IC)	S		01.07.00	EDINBURGH
Laidler, Paul James, MEng,	SLT(IC)	E	WE	01.09.99	MWS COLLINGWOOD
Laing, Iain, BEng, CEng, MIEE, NDipM,	LT CDR(FTC)	E	WE	01.09.01	WSA/CAPT MCTA
Lake, Peter Howard,	LT CDR(FTC)	E	ME	01.10.01	SHEFFIELD
Lamb, Andrew Gordon, n,	LT(FTC)	X		01.12.94	TRUMPETER
Lamb, Caroline Jayne, BEng,	LT(FTC)	X		01.10.98	NORFOLK
Lamb, Robert John Favell,	MID(IC)	X		01.01.01	NORFOLK
Lamb, Robert, jsdc, pce, pcea, psc,	CDR(FTC)	X	P	31.12.90	SHAPE BELGIUM
Lambert, Allison,	LT(CC)	X	ATC	09.08.92	RNAS YEOVILTON
Lambert, Anthony Wayne, MB, BS, FRCS,	SURG CDR(FCC)	-	(CGS)	30.06.99	MODHU DERRIFORD
Lambert, Brian, pce,	CDR(FTC)	X	PWO(A)	31.12.96	MWC PORTSDOWN
Lambert, Nicholas Richard, BSc, pce,	CAPT(FTC)	X	AAWO	30.06.00	RHQ AFNORTH
Lambert, Paul, BSc, MPhil, rcds, pce, (Commodore) pce(sm), hcsc,	CAPT(FTC)	X	SM	30.06.96	MOD (LONDON)
Lambert-Humble, Stephen, BDS, MSc, DGDP(UK),	SGCAPT(D)(FCC)	-	DPHC	31.12.95	DDA HALTON
Lambourn, Peter Neil, pce, pcea, psc,	CDR(FTC)	X	O	31.12.96	MCM2 SEA
Lambourne, David John, BSc,	LT CDR(FTC)	X	P	01.10.97	849 SQN HQ
Lamont, Neil, SM(n),	LT(FTC)	X	SM	06.10.94	TRIUMPH
Lamont, Samuel Neville James, MB, BCh, BAO, BSc,	SURG LT(SCC)	-		02.08.00	CDO LOG REGT RM
Lancashire, Antony Craig, MA,	CAPT RM(CC)	-	LC	01.09.97	42 CDO RM
Lancaster, James Henry David, LLB,	SLT(IC)	X		01.01.00	NBC PORTSMOUTH
Lander, Daniel Timothy James, BEng,	LT(IC)	X	P	01.01.01	BFFI
Lander, Martin Christopher, MA, pce, pcea, psc, psc(j),	CDR(FTC)	X	O	30.06.95	JMOTS NORTHWOOD
Landrock, Graham John, pce,	LT CDR(FTC)	X	MCD	01.09.93	BLYTH
Lane, Michael George, BSc, FCMI, rcds, psc, (Commodore)	CAPT(FTC)	S		31.12.95	NELSON
Lane, Nicholas, BSc,	LT(IC)	S	SM	01.05.00	VIGILANT(PORT)
Lane, Richard Norton, BA, pce,	LT CDR(FTC)	X	PWO(U)	01.04.97	FOST SEA
Lane, Robert Michael,	LT(FTC)	E	ME	18.02.88	NBC PORTSMOUTH
Lane, Roger Guy Tyson, OBE, FCMI, rcds, jsdc, psc(m), fsc, hcsc,	BRIG(FTC)	-	WTO	30.06.99	HQ 3 CDO BDE RM
Lang, Andrew James Nicholas, BEng,	LT CDR(FTC)	E	AE	01.02.02	INVINCIBLE
Lang, Justine Suzanne,	LT(SCC)	Q		30.09.98	RN GIBRALTAR
Langbridge, David Charles, MSc, MCGI, jsdc,	CAPT(FTC)	E	MESM	30.06.01	NEPTUNE NT
Langhorn, Nigel,	CDR(FTC)	X	AAWO	30.06.96	FLEET HQ PORTS
Langley, Eric Steven, pce,	LT CDR(FTC)	X	AAWO	01.02.93	GRAFTON
Langrill, Mark Philip, BEng, MSc, CEng,	LT CDR(FTC)	E	AE	01.10.01	HARRIER IPT
Langrill, Tracey Jane, MA,	LT(IC)	X		01.02.95	DARTMOUTH BRNC
Langrish, Gary James, (Act Lt Cdr)	LT(CC)	X	P	01.10.92	899 SQN HERON
Langrishe, James Hoadly, pce,	LT CDR(FTC)	X	PWO(U)	16.04.81	SONAR 2087 IPT
Lanigan, Ben Ryan,	SLT(IC)	S		01.04.00	TRENCHANT
Lankester, Peter, BTech, pce, pcea, psc,	CDR(FTC)	X	P	30.06.92	RCDS
Lankester, Timothy John, BSc, CEng, MIMechE, psc,	CDR(FTC)	E	ME	30.06.92	DRAKE NBC
Lanni, Martin Nicholas, pcea,	LT(CC)	X	P	01.09.95	DHFS
Lanning, Roderick MacGregor, BSc,	LT(CC)	X		01.03.00	NEWCASTLE
Lansdale, Timothy John, BA,	SLT(IC)	X		01.01.00	LEEDS CASTLE
Large, John Lawrence, (Act Cdr)	LT CDR(FTC)	S	SM	17.01.90	DNR RCHQ SOUTH
Large, Stephen Andrew, BEng, MSc,	LT(FTC)	E	ME	01.03.95	MOD (BATH)
Larmour, David Rutherford, pce,	CAPT(FTC)	X	O	30.06.98	DRAKE CBP(DLO)
Latham, Lynne Barbara,	LT(FTC)	S	(S)	01.04.01	NELSON
Latham, Neil Degge, MSc, CEng, (Commodore) MIMechE, jsdc,	CAPT(FTC)	E	ME	30.06.96	SULTAN
Latus, Simon Harry, BSc,	LT(IC)	X		01.01.02	MWS DRYAD
Lauchlan, Robert Alexander, BSc,	LT CDR(FTC)	E	WESM	01.08.00	RALEIGH
Laughton, Peter,	LT(FTC)	X	MCD	01.04.96	GRIMSBY
Laurence, Simon Timothy,	LT(CC)	X	O	16.01.01	750 SQN SEAHAWK
Laurence, Timothy James Hamilton, MVO, (Commodore) BSc, Hf, pce,	CAPT(FTC)	X	PWO(U)	30.06.95	MOD (LONDON)
Lauste, William Emile, BA,	LT CDR(FTC)	E	TM	01.03.99	RNSR BOVINGTON
Laverty, Robert Edwin, BA, SM(n),	LT(FTC)	X	SM	01.02.95	VICTORIOUS(PORT)
Lavery, John Patrick, MVO,	CDR(FTC)	S		30.06.99	FLEET HQ PORTS

Name	Rank	Branch	Spec	Seniority	Where Serving
Lavin, Gerard Joseph, BEng, CEng, MIMarEST, MIMechE,	LT(IC)	E	ME	01.03.93	LEEDS CASTLE
Law, James Samuel,	SLT(IC)	E	WE	01.05.00	DARTMOUTH BRNC
Law, John,	LT CDR(FTC)	X	MCD	27.03.95	SACLANT ITALY
Law, Richard, BEng,	LT(FTC)	E	WE	01.01.00	ARGYLL
Law, Samuel James, MA,	SLT(IC)	S		01.09.00	DARTMOUTH BRNC
Lawler, Jon Andrew, MBE, (Act Cdr)	LT CDR(CC)	X	P	01.10.95	801 SQN
Lawrance, Gregory Michael,	LT(CC)	X	P	16.05.92	EXCHANGE GERMANY
Lawrence, Linda Jane, BA,	LT(IC)	X	HM	16.09.99	820 SQN
Lawrence, Marc Andrew, BSc,	LT(IC)	X	O	01.05.01	849 SQN B FLT
Lawrence, Richard Gywnne, MA,	SLT(IC)	S		01.09.99	MWS COLLINGWOOD
Lawrence, Stephen Paul, n,	LT CDR(FTC)	X	H CH	01.10.93	MWS RNHMS DRAKE
Lawrence, Steven Raymond,	LT CDR(FTC)	E	ME	01.10.97	DRAKE SFM
Lawrence, Stuart Peter,	LT CDR(FTC)	S		01.03.02	RALEIGH
Laws, Philip Eric Arthur, LLB, FCMA, ACMA,	CDR(FTC)	S	CMA	30.06.02	2SL/CNH FOTR
Lawson, Alexandra Florence, BA,	SLT(IC)	S		01.01.00	SUTHERLAND
Lawson, Geoffrey John,	LT(FTC)	X	tas	13.12.95	ANGLESEY
Lawson, Stephen Jonathan, pce, pce(sm),	LT CDR(FTC)	X	SM	01.09.91	RN GIBRALTAR
Lawton, Andrew Charles Richard, BSc,	LT CDR(FTC)	E	ME	01.11.85	2SL/CNH
Lawton, Peter, MBE,	CAPT RM(FTC)	-	SO(LE)	01.01.99	RM POOLE
Laycock, Antony, BSc,	LT(IC)	X	O	16.07.94	702 SQN HERON
Layland, Stephen, BSc, pce,	CDR(FTC)	X	PWO(N)	30.06.02	JSCSC
Layton, Christopher, BEng,	LT(IC)	E	MESM	01.05.01	SULTAN
Le Gassick, Peter James, BEng,	LT(CC)	E	TM	01.09.95	JSCSC
Lea, Jeffrey Henry Arthur, BSc, CEng, MIMarEST, psc,	CDR(FTC)	E	ME	31.12.94	DRAKE SFM
Lea, John, pce, pcea,	LT CDR(FTC)	X	O	01.01.98	NOTTINGHAM
Lea, Sebastian Augustine Pollard, n,	LT(FTC)	X	PWO(C)	01.11.91	FEARLESS
Leach, Sarah Jane, BEng,	LT(FTC)	E	ME	01.07.96	ECHO
Leach, *Sir* Henry, (Conyers). GCB, DL, jssc, psc	ADM OF FLEET	-		01.12.82	
Leadbetter, Andrew John, BA,	LT(IC)	X		01.11.97	OCLC BIRM
Leaman, Richard Derek, OBE, pce, hcsc, (Commodore)	CAPT(FTC)	X	AAWO	31.12.96	MOD (LONDON)
Leaney, Michael John, BSc,	LT CDR(FTC)	X	MCD	01.03.90	MWC PORTSDOWN
Leaning, David John,	LT CDR(FTC)	E	MESM	01.10.01	TALENT
Leaning, Mark Vincent, MA, MCMI, pcea, psc,	LT CDR(FTC)	X	P	01.09.91	RNAS YEOVILTON
Lear, Stuart Francis, BA,	LT(IC)	S		01.09.00	JHCHQ
Leason, Nicholas Charles,	LT(CC)	X		01.05.00	SOMERSET
Leatherby, James Hawton,	CDR(FTC)	S	SM	31.12.90	NEPTUNE DLO
Leaver, Andrew Michael,	LT(FTC)	E	AE(M)	02.09.99	ES AIR YEO
Leaver, Charmian Elizabeth Lucy, MA, MSc, PGDip,	LT(FTC)	X	METOC	01.07.91	ILLUSTRIOUS
Ledward, Karen Louise,	LT(IC)	S		01.04.01	NBC PORTSMOUTH
Lee, Christian James, BSc,	SLT(IC)	X		01.01.01	DARTMOUTH BRNC
Lee, Daniel John, MDA, pce, psc,	CDR(FTC)	X	AAWO	31.12.96	FLEET HQ PORTS 2
Lee, Jonathan Coling,	LT CDR(FTC)	X	MW	01.10.94	ELANT/NAVNORTH
Lee, Matthew Martin, MRAeS,	LT CDR(FTC)	X	ATC	01.10.91	MOD (LONDON)
Lee, Nicholas Foden, BEng, MIMechE, pcea,	LT CDR(FTC)	X	P	01.03.99	771 SQN
Lee, Nigel David, (Act Lt Cdr)	LT(FTC)	X	PWO(A)	16.06.95	MWS DRYAD
Lee, Oliver Andrew, BA,	CAPT RM(FTC)	-		01.05.98	NELSON (PAY)
Lee, Peter Alan, BEng,	LT CDR(FTC)	E	ME	01.08.99	LANCASTER
Lee, Philip Marsden, BSc,	LT(IC)	X	P	01.10.94	LOAN OTHER SVCE
Lee, Raymond Andrew,	SLT(IC)	E	WESM	01.01.01	MWS COLLINGWOOD
Lee, Steven Edward, MEng,	LT(CC)	E	WE	01.11.99	CUMBERLAND
Lee, Steven Patrick, MA, (Act Maj)	CAPT RM(FTC)	-		27.04.96	FPGRM
Lee, Steven Yiu Lam, BEng, CEng, MIEE,	LT(FTC)	E	WE	01.12.95	MWS COLLINGWOOD
Lee, Warren, BEng,	LT(FTC)	E	WE	01.06.97	MOD (LONDON)
Lee-Gallon, Timothy James, BSc,	SLT(IC)	X		01.09.99	SHETLAND
Leeder, Timothy Rupert,	LT(IC)	X		01.05.02	CHIDDINGFOLD
Leeming, Robert John, BSc, CEng,	CAPT(FTC)	E	ME	30.06.00	MOD (BATH)
Leeper, James Stephen, BSc,	SLT(IC)	X		01.01.99	MWS DRYAD
Lees, Edward Charles, n,	LT CDR(FTC)	X	PWO(C)	01.02.99	PJHQ
Lees, Simon Neville, BEd, (Act Lt Cdr)	LT(FTC)	E	TM	02.09.93	2SL/CNH FOTR
Leese, James,	LT(IC)	E		01.05.02	801 SQN
Leeson, Antony Richard,	SLT(IC)	X		01.04.00	EDINBURGH
Leggett, Stephen Edward, MBE,	LT CDR(FTC)	E	AE	13.01.88	ES AIR YEO

Name	Rank	Branch	Spec	Seniority	Where Serving
Leggett, Stephen John, BA,	SLT(IC)	X		01.05.00	LANCASTER
Leigh, Clara Jane,	MID(NE)(IC)	X		01.05.01	MANCHESTER
Leigh, John, osc(us),	LT COL(FTC)	-	MLDR	31.12.96	SACLANT USA
Leigh-Smith, Simon, BM, BCH, FRCS(ED)A&E, MRCGP, DObstRCOG, Dip FFP,	SURG LTCDR(MCC)	-	GMPP	01.12.96	NELSON (PAY)
Leightley, Simon Mark,	SLT(IC)	X		01.04.01	YORK
Leighton, Matthew Richard, BA,	LT(CC)	X	P	01.06.97	845 SQN
Leitch, Iain Robertson, BSc, pce,	LT CDR(FTC)	X	AAWO	01.10.96	EDINBURGH
Leivers, Andrew James,	LT(CC)	E	ME	01.09.99	NEWCASTLE
Lemkes, Paul Douglas, pce,	CDR(FTC)	X	AAWO	31.12.97	MOD (LONDON)
Lemon, Robert Gordon Arthur, BSc,	LT CDR(FTC)	E	WESM	01.09.84	MOD (LONDON)
Lenehan, David John,	MID(NE)(IC)	X		01.01.02	DARTMOUTH BRNC
Leonard, Mark,	LT CDR(FTC)	E	WE	01.10.97	FWO DEVPT SEA
Leonard, Thomas, BEng, AMIMechE,	SLT(IC)	E		01.09.99	SULTAN
Leslie, Bruce Duncan,	SLT(IC)	X	O U/T	01.05.00	750 SQN SEAHAWK
Lester, Rodney Leslie,	LT(FTC)	X		10.01.00	LINDISFARNE
Lett, Jonathan David, n, BA,	LT CDR(FTC)	X	PWO(U)	01.10.00	IRON DUKE
Letts, Andrew John, BEng, CEng, MIEE,	LT(FTC)	E	WE	01.08.95	RALEIGH
Lew-Gor, Simione Tomasi Warren, MB, ChB,	SURG LTCDR(MCC)	-		05.09.00	RH HASLAR
Lewins, Grant,	LT(FTC)	S	(W)	08.04.94	JFHQ STAFF NWOOD
Lewis, Andrew James, BEng, CEng,	LT(FTC)	E	MESM	01.03.96	SOVEREIGN
Lewis, Benjamin Charles, BSc,	LT(CC)	X	P	16.05.97	845 SQN
Lewis, Daniel, BEng,	LT(IC)	E	TM	19.07.98	LIVERPOOL
Lewis, David James,	LT CDR(CC)	X	O	01.10.98	815 SQN HQ
Lewis, David John, BEng, AMIEE,	LT CDR(FTC)	E	WE	01.09.01	MWS COLLINGWOOD
Lewis, David Malcolm John, MBE, FCMI,	CDR(FTC)	E	ME	31.12.96	SFM PORTSMOUTH
Lewis, Edward James, BSc,	LT(IC)	X	P U/T	01.05.02	RNAS YEOVILTON
Lewis, Gary David,	LT CDR(FTC)	S		01.09.89	MONTROSE
Lewis, Guy David, BEng, CEng, MIMarE,	LT CDR(FTC)	E	ME	03.02.00	ST ALBANS
Lewis, John Keene, BEng, MDA, AMIEE,	CDR(FTC)	E	WESM	30.06.99	NMA PORTSMOUTH
Lewis, Jonathan Munro,	SLT(IC)	X		01.09.01	CARDIFF
Lewis, Keith Alan, (Act Lt Cdr)	LT(FTC)	X	PWO(C)	03.04.97	LPD(R) IPT
Lewis, Mark David, MEng,	SLT(IC)	E	AE	01.09.99	SULTAN
Lewis, Paul Leonard,	LT(IC)	X	tas	08.01.01	RNU ST MAWGAN
Lewis, Peter Reginald, MBE, pce, (Act Cdr)	LT CDR(FTC)	X	PWO(U)	21.11.86	MWS DRYAD
Lewis, Simon John, MSc,	LT(CC)	E	IS	01.01.93	MWS COLLINGWOOD
Lewis, Stephen Bernard, pce, psc,	LT CDR(FTC)	X	PWO(U)	01.01.87	DRAKE CBP(CNH)
Lewis, Timothy John, pce,	LT CDR(FTC)	X	PWO(U)	05.02.95	MCM3 SEA
Lewis, Wesley Darren, BSc,	SLT(IC)	X	P U/T	01.09.00	DARTMOUTH BRNC
Ley, Alastair Blevins, SM(n), SM,	LT(FTC)	X	SM	01.11.95	TALENT
Ley, Jonathan Ashley, pce, n,	LT CDR(FTC)	X	PWO(A)	01.08.00	PJHQ
Leyden, Tristan Neil,	CAPT RM(FTC)	-		01.09.99	42 CDO RM
Leyland, Emma Margaret, BEng,	LT(IC)	E	WE	01.09.01	NORTHUMBERLAND
Leyshon, Robert John, BDS,	SGLTCDR(D)(SCC)	-		09.01.99	RNAS YEOVILTON
Lias, Carl David, BSc, MEng,	LT CDR(FTC)	E	MESM	01.10.96	VICTORIOUS(PORT)
Lidbetter, Scott, pce, hcsc,	RADM	-	P	24.07.01	HQ3GP HQSTC
Liddell, Matthew Lewis,	LT(FTC)	E	ME	02.05.00	MOD (BATH)
Liddle, Richard David, BEng,	LT(CC)	X	P	01.09.00	RNAS YEOVILTON
Liddle, Stephen Johnstone, BA,	MAJ(FTC)	-		01.09.01	FLEET HQ NWD
Liebnitz, Andrew Daniel, BEng,	SLT(IC)	E	WESM	01.01.00	FWO FASLANE SEA
Ligale, Eugene,	SLT(IC)	X		01.01.00	WESTMINSTER
Liggins, Michael Philip, BSc,	LT CDR(CC)	X	P	01.10.01	MWC PORTSDOWN
Liggins, Steven John, BDS, MB, BCh, FDS RCSEdin, FRCS, BSc,	SGCDR(D)(FCC)	-	(COSM)	31.12.97	MODHU DERRIFORD
Lightfoot, Charles David, BSc, pce, pce(sm), psc(j),	LT CDR(FTC)	X	SM	01.07.90	UPHLDER TRG TEAM
Lightfoot, Christopher Morrison, MA, MRIN, pce, psc, psc(j),	CDR(FTC)	X	PWO(N)†	30.06.89	NBC PORTSMOUTH
Lightfoot, Richard Alan,	LT(IC)	X	O	16.02.01	820 SQN
Lilley, David John, BSc, pce, pcea, psc(m),	CDR(FTC)	X	O	31.12.96	MOD (LONDON)
Lilly, David Mark, BSc,	LT(IC)	X	P	01.08.99	815 FLT 215
Lincoln, Keith James, BEng,	LT(FTC)	E	WE	01.07.95	MWS DRYAD
Linderman, Ian Ronald, BSc, MBA,	LT CDR(CC)	E	TM	01.10.99	MWS COLLINGWOOD
Lindeyer, Matthew James, BSc,	LT(IC)	X		01.05.02	MWS DRYAD

Name	Rank	Branch	Spec	Seniority	Where Serving
Lindley, Jeannine,	SLT(IC)	X		01.01.01	DARTMOUTH BRNC
Lindley, Nicholas Paul, BSc, MA, psc(m),	LT COL(FTC)	-		31.12.99	COMATG SEA
Lindsay, David Joseph, BEng,	LT(CC)	X	P	01.08.91	899 SQN HERON
Lindsay, Ian Barry,	LT(CC)	X	ATC	01.06.96	RNAS CULDROSE
Lindsay, Irvine Graham, MA, pce, pce(sm), psc(j),	LT CDR(FTC)	X	SM	01.04.96	FLEET HQ PORTS 2
Lindsay, Jonathan Mark, BSc,	CAPT RM(IC)	-		01.05.01	42 CDO RM
Lindsay, Michael,	SURG SLT(SCC)	-		14.04.00	DARTMOUTH BRNC
Lindsey, Richard, pce(sm), SM(n),	LT CDR(FTC)	X	SM	30.04.00	FOST CSST FSLN
Lineker, Robert John, BSc, Eur Ing, CEng, MIEE,	CDR(FTC)	E	WESM	30.06.93	MOD (LONDON)
Lines, James Micheal, MDA,	CDR(FTC)	S		30.06.02	FLEET HQ PORTS
Ling, Christopher, MSc, CEng, MA, MIMechE, MRAeS,	LT(FTC)	E	AE	01.03.96	ES AIR YEO
Ling, John William Legrys, BEng,	LT(CC)	X	O	16.09.94	RNAS YEOVILTON
Lintern, Robert David, BA, MSc, PGDIP, n,	LT CDR(FTC)	X	H1	01.10.01	ROEBUCK
Linton, Patrick John,	LT(SCC)	Q	OTSPEC	30.03.96	RH HASLAR
Lippiett, Richard John, MBE, rcds, jsdc, pce, psc,	RADM	-	PWO	07.07.97	JSCSC
Lippitt, Simon Thomas, BEng,	LT(CC)	X	ATC	01.04.98	FOST DPORT SHORE
Lipscomb, Paul, BSc, CEng, MIMarEST,	LT CDR(FTC)	E	MESM	01.11.95	NEPTUNE NT
Lison, Andrew Christopher, BEng, MSc, AMIEE,	LT(FTC)	E	AE	01.05.99	815 SQN HQ
Lister, Mark, pce(sm),	LT CDR(FTC)	X	SM	01.01.97	CHIDDINGFOLD
Lister, Simon Robert, OBE, MSc, AMIMechE,	CAPT(FTC)	E	MESM	31.12.99	SA MOSCOW
Lister, Simon, SM,	LT(FTC)	X	SM	08.04.94	MOD DIS SEA
Lister, Stephen Richard,	LT CDR(FTC)	S	SM	01.04.93	ARK ROYAL
Litchfield, Julian Felix,	CDR(FTC)	S		30.06.98	NMA PORTSMOUTH
Litster, Alan, MBE, BSc,	MAJ(FTC)	-	LC	01.09.98	BDS WASHINGTON
Little, Charles Stewart Anderson, BSc, pce, pce(sm),	LT CDR(FTC)	X	SM	01.02.90	FOST CSST DEVPT
Little, Craig Martin,	SLT(IC)	X	O U/T	01.10.99	824 SQN
Little, Graeme Terence, BEng, MSc, psc(j),	CDR(FTC)	E	ME	30.06.00	MOD (BATH)
Little, Matthew Iain Graham, BSc,	LT(IC)	X		01.05.01	BROCKLESBY
Little, Rhoderick McKeand, BSc, CDipAF, CEng, MIEE, psc,	CAPT(FTC)	E	WESM	31.12.98	SSIP IPT
Liva, Anthony John, BSc,	CAPT RM(IC)	-		01.09.01	NP 1002 DIEGOGA
Livesey, John Edward, SM(n), SM,	LT(FTC)	X	SM	01.10.97	SPLENDID
Livingston, Martin Philip James, BEng,	LT(IC)	E	AE	01.05.02	SULTAN
Livingstone, Alan James, MBE, ocds(No),	MAJ(FTC)	-		01.09.97	45 CDO RM
Livsey, Andrew Everard John, BA,	LT(FTC)	X		01.09.99	KENT
Llewellyn, Jonathan Gwyn,	LT(FTC)	X	AV	20.09.99	ARK ROYAL
Llewelyn, Kevin,	LT CDR(FTC)	X	ATC	01.10.97	RNAS YEOVILTON
Lloyd, Bruce Jeremy, BSc,	LT(CC)	X	P	01.04.00	RAF LINTN/OUSE
Lloyd, Christopher John, OStJ,	LT CDR(FTC)	MS		01.10.96	INM ALVERSTOKE
Lloyd, David Philip John,	LT CDR(FTC)	S		01.09.91	RALEIGH
Lloyd, Matthew Rome,	SLT(IC)	S		01.09.99	INVINCIBLE
Lloyd, Paul Robert, pce, psc(j),	CDR(FTC)	X	PWO(N)	31.12.97	OCEAN
Lloyd, Stephen John, MSc, CEng, MIMarEST, psc,	CAPT(FTC)	E	MESM	30.06.00	DRAKE SFM
Lloyd-West, Carolyn,	LT(SCC)	Q		21.09.01	MODHU DERRIFORD
Loane, Michael MacAire,	LT(CC)	X	MCD	01.06.93	FDU2
Lochrane, Alexandre Edmond Ross, pce,	LT CDR(FTC)	X	PWO(U)	01.07.95	DEF SCH OF LANG
Lock, Andrew Glen David, (Act Maj)	CAPT RM(FTC)	-		28.04.98	FLEET HQ PORTS 2
Lock, Willam Robert, BDS, MSc, MFGDP(UK), LDS RCS(Eng), OStJ,	SGCAPT(D)(FCC)	-		30.06.97	DDA PORTSMOUTH
Lock, William James, BSc,	LT(IC)	X	O U/T	01.05.02	750 SQN SEAHAWK
Lockett, David John, n,	LT(FTC)	X		01.04.96	MONMOUTH
Lockwood, Roger Graham, BA, FCIPD, rcds, jsdc,	RADM	-		22.08.00	2SL/CNH
Lofthouse, Ian, MA,	CDR(FTC)	E	MESM	31.12.96	FLEET HQ PORTS 2
Logan, John Gordon, BA, PGCE, MISM,	LT(SCC)	Q	RNT	27.07.96	RH HASLAR
Logan, Joseph Majella,	LT(FTC)	X	FC	01.10.91	MWS DRYAD
Lokai, Dario Steffan,	LT(SCC)	Q		14.09.00	RH HASLAR
Lombard, Didier, pce, pce(sm), odc(Fr), (Act Capt)	CDR(FTC)	X	SM	31.12.91	NELSON
London, Martin Richard, MBE,	LT CDR(FTC)	X	P	01.03.99	899 SQN HERON
Long, Adrian Montague, BEng, MSc, CEng, MIEE,	LT CDR(FTC)	E	WE	01.04.00	MOD (LONDON)
Long, Andrew Bruce Millett, BA, BD,	LT(IC)	X		01.05.02	MWS DRYAD
Long, Anthony Donald, pce, pcea,	LT CDR(FTC)	X	O	16.05.98	JSCSC
Long, Derek Ray,	LT CDR(FTC)	X	PWO(A)	17.02.83	NMA GOSPORT
Long, Michael Selden,	LT(FTC)	X	MW	01.04.96	MWS DRYAD

Name	Rank	Branch	Spec	Seniority	Where Serving
Long, Nicholas Andrew, MSc, CEng, MIEE, (Act Cdr)	LT CDR(FTC)	E	WE	01.05.91	SHAPE BELGIUM
Long, Philip John, MBE, jsdc, pce,	CDR(FTC)	X	PWO(U)	30.06.94	RH HASLAR
Longmore, David,	SURG SLT(SCC)	-		14.08.00	DARTMOUTH BRNC
Longstaff, Richard, MSRP,	LT(FTC)	E	WE	13.06.86	CFPS SEA
Longstaff, Thomas William,	LT(FTC)	S	SM	19.09.00	TRAFALGAR
Lonsdale, Robert James, MA,	CAPT RM(IC)	-		01.09.98	OCLC MANCH
Lord, Andrew Stephen, BA, PGCE, M ED, MCIPD,	LT CDR(FTC)	E	TM	01.09.87	SULTAN
Lord, Martin,	LT CDR(FTC)	E	WE	01.10.98	FLEET CIS PORTS
Lord, Richard James,	LT(CC)	X	P	01.10.94	815 FLT 209
Loring, Andrew, BSc, CEng, MIMechE,	LT CDR(FTC)	E	ME	01.03.93	NORTHUMBERLAND
Louden, Carl Alexander,	LT(FTC)	X	C	23.07.98	FLEET CIS PORTS
Loughrey, Neil Charles,	LT(IC)	E	AE	29.04.01	SULTAN
Louis, David Richard Anthony,	SLT(UCE)(FTC)	X		01.09.00	DARTMOUTH BRNC
Louw, Len,	LT(IC)	E	WESM	01.01.02	RALEIGH
Lovatt, Graham John,	LT(FTC)	X	PWO(A)	01.04.95	MONTROSE
Love, John James,	SLT(IC)	E	AE	01.05.00	DARTMOUTH BRNC
Love, Julie Dawn,	LT(FTC)	S	(W)	19.09.00	NELSON
Love, Richard J, BEng,	LT(FTC)	E	AE	01.08.98	ES AIR YEO
Love, Robert Thomas, BSc, CEng, FIMarEST, psc,	CAPT(FTC)	E	ME	30.06.98	MOD (BATH)
Love, Tristram Simon Nicholas, BEng, CEng, MIEE,	LT CDR(FTC)	E	WESM	01.10.00	MWS COLLINGWOOD
Lovegrove, Raymond Anthony, MSc, CEng, MIEE, gw,	LT CDR(FTC)	E	WE	01.10.96	MOD (LONDON)
Lovell, James Edward Charles, BA,	SLT(IC)	X		01.01.00	GUERNSEY
Lovelock, Richard Benjamin, psc(m),	LT COL(FTC)	-		30.06.94	EUMS
Loveridge, Paul James, MA,	LT(IC)	X		01.05.02	MWS DRYAD
Lovering, Tristan Timothy Alan, BSc, (Act Lt Cdr)	LT(CC)	E	TM	01.01.95	FLEET HQ PORTS 2
Lovett, Andrew Robert,	LT(CC)	E	AE	01.07.00	SULTAN
Lovett, Michael John, BSc,	CDR(FTC)	E	WE	30.06.96	FLEET HQ PORTS
Lovett, Stephen Andrew, SM,	LT(FTC)	X	SM	26.04.99	RALEIGH
Low, Christopher David Tullis, MB, ChB, FRCSEd,	SURG CDR(FCC)	-	(CO)	31.12.99	RH HASLAR
Low, Mark Edward,	LT CDR(FTC)	E	WESM	01.10.00	MOD (BATH)
Lowe, Christopher,	LT(FTC)	E	MESM	02.05.00	VICTORIOUS(PORT)
Lowe, Julian Charles, BEng, BTech, MSc,	LT CDR(FTC)	E	ME	01.08.99	MANCHESTER
Lowe, Stuart Michael, BEng, MSc,	LT CDR(FTC)	E	WE	01.12.00	MOD (LONDON)
Lowe, Timothy Miles, jsdc, pce,	CDR(FTC)	X	PWO(N)	31.12.95	COMATG SEA
Lower, Iain Stuart, BSc, pce, n,	LT CDR(FTC)	X	AAWO	01.10.99	SOUTHAMPTON
Lowes, Christopher,	LT CDR(FTC)	E	WE	01.10.99	MOD (LONDON)
Lowson, Roderick Mark, pce,	LT CDR(FTC)	X	AAWO	01.04.97	UKMARBATSTAFF
Lowther, James Marcus, BA, PGDIPAN, pce, n,	LT CDR(FTC)	X	PWO(N)	01.07.98	FOST SEA
Lucas, Darren Philip,	LT(IC)	E	WE	01.05.02	DARTMOUTH BRNC
Lucas, Simon Ulrick,	CAPT RM(FTC)	-	SO(LE)	01.01.01	40 CDO RM
Lucey, Richard Noel, pce,	CDR(FTC)	X	PWO(C)	30.06.89	NMA PORTSMOUTH
Luckraft, Christopher John, BD, AKC,	CHAPLAIN	CE		05.08.87	FLEET HQ PORTS
Lucocq, Nicholas James, BSc, n,	LT(FTC)	X		01.08.95	DARTMOUTH BRNC
Ludlow, Julian Andrew,	LT(IC)	X	SM	01.01.02	SPARTAN
Lugg, John Charles,	CAPT RM(FTC)	-	SO(LE)	01.01.98	ALBION
Luker, Geoffrey Peter, MBE,	LT CDR(FTC)	X	AAWO	01.03.83	EXCHANGE NLANDS
Lumsden, Peter Imrie, BEng,	LT(FTC)	X	P	01.04.97	RNAS CULDROSE
Lunn, Adam Christopher, pce, pcea,	LT CDR(FTC)	X	P	01.06.94	FLEET HQ NWD
Lunn, David Vaughan, MB, ChB, DA, FFARCS,	SURG CDR(FCC)	-	(CA)	30.06.91	MODHU DERRIFORD
Lunn, James Francis Clive, BSc, CEng, MIMarEST, MIMechE, psc,	CDR(FTC)	E	MESM	31.12.93	MOD (LONDON)
Lunn, Mark Henry Bernard, MSc, CEng, MIMarEST,	LT CDR(FTC)	E	MESM	01.07.00	SPLENDID
Lunn, Thomas Ramsay,	LT(FTC)	X		01.01.95	COTTESMORE
Lupini, James Martin, BA,	SLT(IC)	X		01.09.00	DARTMOUTH BRNC
Luscombe, Michael David, pcea,	LT CDR(FTC)	X	P	01.10.99	ARK ROYAL
Lusted, Roy Peter, BSc, (Act Lt Cdr)	LT(FTC)	E	AE(L)	13.10.89	RNAS YEOVILTON
Lustman, Arnold Marc, GCIS,	CDR(FTC)	S	SM	30.06.02	MOD (LONDON)
Lutman, Charles Robert, BEng,	LT(IC)	E	TM	01.01.01	SULTAN
Luxford, Charles Alexander, BA,	LT(IC)	X		01.05.02	NOTTINGHAM
Lydiate, Gary, pce,	LT CDR(FTC)	X	AAWO	01.01.95	PJHQ
Lye, David James, OBE, psc,	CAPT(FTC)	X	H CH	31.12.00	MOD (LONDON)
Lynas, Jonathan Francis Alistair,	LT(CC)	X	P	01.09.00	771 SQN

Name	Rank	Branch	Spec	Seniority	Where Serving
Lynch, Michael, MA, MCIT, MCMI, MILT, psc,	LT CDR(FTC)	S	SM	24.03.91	UKSU SOUTHLANT
Lynch, Paul Patrick, BA,	CAPT RM(CC)	-		01.05.98	40 CDO RM
Lynch, Rory Denis Fenton, BA,	LT CDR(CC)	X		16.04.02	CHFHQ
Lynch, Stephen, pcea,	LT CDR(FTC)	X	O	01.10.00	JSCSC
Lynn, Henry William,	LT(FTC)	X	tas	19.09.00	FOSM NWOOD OPS
Lynn, Ian Herbert,	LT(FTC)	X	PWO(U)	30.06.95	WESTMINSTER
Lynn, Sarah Louise, MSc,	SLT(IC)	X	O U/T	01.09.00	DARTMOUTH BRNC
Lynn, Steven Robert, BEng,	LT CDR(FTC)	E	WE	01.04.98	WSA BRISTOL
Lyons, Alan Gordon, BEng,	LT(CC)	E	MESM	01.10.98	TRIUMPH
Lyons, Michael John, BEng, AMIMechE,	LT(FTC)	E	MESM	01.06.96	VENGEANCE(PORT)

M

Name	Rank	Branch	Spec	Seniority	Where Serving
Mabbott, Keith Ian, BSc,	LT(CC)	X		01.01.00	EXETER
Mac Donald, Stuart Brewey,	LT(IC)	S		01.11.00	NMA PORTSMOUTH
MacAskill, Colin Hugh, (Act Lt Cdr)	LT(FTC)	S	CA	11.12.92	NEPTUNE DLO
Macaulay, Neil,	LT CDR(FTC)	E	WE	01.10.95	SFM PORTSMOUTH
Macaulay, Scott Charles,	MID(IC)	X		01.05.00	KENT
MacColl, Andrew Alexander James,	LT(FTC)	X	ATC	01.05.96	EXCHANGE GERMANY
MacCormick, Alexander Wright, psc,	COL(FTC)	-	C	31.12.95	MOD (LONDON)
MacCormick, James, BSc,	LT(IC)	E	WESM	01.05.02	RALEIGH
MacCorquodale, Mairi Ann, MA, MPhil,	LT(IC)	E	TM	01.09.98	NMA PORTSMOUTH
MacDonald, Alasdair Iain, BSc, MDA, CEng, MIEE, MCMI,	CDR(FTC)	E	WE	30.06.98	NBC PORTSMOUTH
MacDonald, Alastair James, BEng,	LT(FTC)	E	WE	01.09.94	PJHQ AUGMENTEES
MacDonald, Douglas Hugh Lawson, BSc, MA,	CDR(FTC)	X	MCD	30.06.91	MWC SOUTHWICK
MNI, pce, ocds(US),					
MacDonald, George Ewen, LLB,	CAPT(FTC)	S		30.06.00	2SL/CNH
MacDonald, Glen Dey, BA,	LT CDR(FTC)	X		01.05.91	ARK ROYAL
MacDonald, Ian Robert, MBE, sq,	MAJ(FTC)	-		08.02.93	HQ NORTH
MacDonald, John Robert, BEng, MSc, psc(j), gw,	LT CDR(FTC)	E	WESM	01.07.97	TRIUMPH
MacDonald, Katrina Louise,	SLT(IC)	X		01.09.00	DARTMOUTH BRNC
MacDonald-Robinson, Nicholas Ulric Spencer, pce,	LT CDR(FTC)	X	AAWO	01.04.98	ILLUSTRIOUS
MacDougall, Gavin Ross,	LT CDR(FTC)	S		01.10.98	DARTMOUTH BRNC
MacDougall, Stewart John,	LT(FTC)	E	WESM	19.02.93	RALEIGH
Mace, Stephen Barry, BEng,	LT CDR(FTC)	E	WE	01.02.96	FWO PORTS SEA
MacFarlane, Iain Stuart David, BSc,	LT(CC)	X	P	01.11.93	824 SQN
MacGillivray, Ian, BEng,	LT CDR(FTC)	E	WE	01.04.98	ST ALBANS
MacIntyre, Ian Douglas,	LT(IC)	E	WESM	01.01.02	SUPERB
MacIver, George, BSc, pce, SM,	LT CDR(FTC)	X	SM	01.02.98	FOSNNI OPS DLO
MacKay, Andrew Colin, BA,	LT(FTC)	S		01.02.96	AGRIPPA NAVSOUTH
Mackay, Colin Ross, BSc,	CDR(FTC)	E	IS	30.06.02	MOD (BATH)
MacKay, Graeme Angus, pce, pcea, ocds(Can),	CDR(FTC)	X	O	31.12.97	MWS DRYAD
MacKay, Peter, BEng,	LT CDR(FTC)	E	WE	01.12.98	FOST SEA
MacKenzie, Jessica-Rose Emily, BA,	LT(IC)	S		01.07.99	FEARLESS
MacKenzie, Michael David, BSc, pce(sm),	LT CDR(FTC)	X	SM	01.11.95	FLEET HQ PORTS 2
MacKett, Duncan Geoffrey, pce, (Act Cdr)	LT CDR(FTC)	X	PWO(A)	01.05.88	RHQ AFNORTH
Mackey, Martin Christopher, pce,	LT CDR(FTC)	X	PWO(U)	01.06.99	MANCHESTER
Mackie, David Francis Sarsfield, BEng, MSc, gw,	LT CDR(FTC)	E	WE	01.03.99	MOD (LONDON)
Mackie, Simon John, MB, BS, MRCS,	SURG LTCDR(MCC)	-		12.08.01	RH HASLAR
MacKinnon, Anne, BSc,	LT(CC)	E	TM	01.09.97	SULTAN
MacKinnon, Donald James, BEng,	LT CDR(FTC)	X		01.01.01	MWS DRYAD
MacLaughlin, Richard Adrian, BA,	LT(IC)	X	P	01.08.98	820 SQN
MacLean, David James, BTech, MSc, (Commodore)	CAPT(FTC)	E	ME	30.06.94	LPD(R) IPT
MRINA, jsdc,					
MacLean, Graham Francis,	SLT(IC)	X		01.09.00	ATHERSTONE
MacLean, Malcolm Thomas,	LT(FTC)	E	ME	02.09.99	LEEDS CASTLE
MacLean, Richard,	2LT(IC)	-		01.09.00	CTCRM LYMPSTONE
MacLean, Shamus MacFarlane,	SLT(IC)	X		01.09.01	RALEIGH
Macleod, James Norman, BEng, MSc, MIEE, CEng,	LT CDR(FTC)	E	WE	01.03.00	WESTMINSTER
Macleod, Mark Stuart, BEng,	LT CDR(FTC)	E	AE(P)	01.02.02	814 SQN
Macleod, Roderick Alexander Randle, BA, BD, MBA,	CHAPLAIN	SF		20.02.98	1 ASSLT GP RM
MacNaughton, Francis George, MBE, BA, pce,	LT CDR(FTC)	X	PWO(A)	01.05.87	COMATG SEA
MacNeil, Stephen William, pcea,	LT(FTC)	X	P	01.03.93	824 SQN

Name	Rank	Branch	Spec	Seniority	Where Serving
MacOwan, Andrew Stewart, MA,	CAPT RM(IC)	-		01.09.00	45 CDO RM
MacPhail, Neil MacTaggart, (Act Lt)	SLT(IC)	MS		01.05.00	INM ALVERSTOKE
MacPherson, Craig Alexander Cameron,	SLT(IC)	X		01.01.00	DULVERTON
MacPherson, William Gordon Clark,	CAPT RM(IC)	-	SO(LE)	01.04.02	42 CDO RM
MacQuarrie, Gary, BEng,	LT(IC)	E	ME	01.05.02	SULTAN
MacRae, Justin,	LT RM(IC)	-		05.09.99	CTCRM LYMPSTONE
MacRae, Kirsteen Louise, BSc, PGCE,	LT(CC)	X	HM	01.09.99	ENDURANCE
MacSephney, Tracy Lee Helen,	SLT(IC)	X	ATCU/T	01.01.00	RAF SHAWBURY
Madders, Brian Richard, MBE,	CHAPLAIN	RC		09.09.85	DRAKE CBP(CNH)
Maddick, Mark Jeremy, psc(j),	LT COL(FTC)	-	LC	30.06.02	COMAMPHIBFOR
Maddison, Hugh Richard, BEng,	SLT(IC)	E	ME U/T	01.09.00	CARDIFF
Maddison, John David,	CAPT RM(FTC)	-	SO(LE)	01.01.98	CTCRM
Madge, Anthony Willian John,	LT CDR(FTC)	X	PR	01.10.94	RNAS CULDROSE
Madgwick, Edward Charles Cowtan, BDS,	SGLTCDR(D)(MCC)	-		23.07.01	RH HASLAR
Madigan, Lee, BA,	LT(IC)	X		01.03.00	SHOREHAM
Maese, Philip Andrew,	MAJ(FTC)	-	SO(LE)	01.10.97	RM POOLE
Magan, Michael James Christopher, BEng, MA, MSc, CEng, MIEE, psc(j), gw,	CDR(FTC)	E	WE	30.06.02	WSA BRISTOL
Magill, Thomas Eugene,	LT(FTC)	X	AV	24.07.97	RNAS CULDROSE
Magill, William John, BSc, CEng, MIEE, MAPM,	CDR(FTC)	E	WE	30.06.89	WSA BRISTOL
Magowan, Robert Andrew, BSc, odc(US),	MAJ(FTC)	-		01.09.97	EXCHANGE ARMY UK
Maguire, Anton Paul Duncan, MIPD,	LT CDR(FTC)	S		01.11.81	GLOUCESTER
Magzoub, Mohayed Mohamed Mustafa,	MID(UCE)(IC)	E	ME	01.09.00	DARTMOUTH BRNC
Maher, Michael Patrick, pce,	LT CDR(FTC)	X	AAWO	16.05.96	MANCHESTER
Mahony, Christopher David Copinger,	LT CDR(FTC)	X	P	03.04.99	JSCSC
Mahony, David Grehan, pce, pcea,	LT CDR(FTC)	X	O	16.04.96	ANGLESEY
Maidment, Keith Charles, MSc, CEng, MIMarEST,	LT CDR(FTC)	E	ME	01.03.87	FWO DEVONPORT
Maidment, Phillip Charles,	LT CDR(FTC)	E	WE	01.10.95	MOD (BATH)
Mailes, Ian Robert Arthur, pcea,	LT(CC)	X	O	16.04.94	824 SQN
Main, Edward Stafford, BSc, CEng, MIMarEST,	CDR(FTC)	E	ME	30.06.98	OCEAN
Mains, Graham,	LT(IC)	X	O	18.03.99	820 SQN
Mair, Brian, pce,	CDR(FTC)	X	MCD	30.06.02	PJHQ
Makepeace, Philip Andrew, BEng, MSc, MIEE,	LT CDR(FTC)	E	WE	24.12.98	WSA BRISTOL
Malcolm, Paul Stuart, BA,	SLT(IC)	X		01.09.99	GUERNSEY
Malcolm, Stephen Robert, MA, FIMarEST, CMarSci, pce, psc(j),	CDR(FTC)	X	H CH	31.12.00	MWS RNHMS DRAKE
Maley, Catherine Elizabeth, LLB,	LT(CC)	X	O	16.01.98	815 FLT 204
Malin, Michael John,	LT CDR(FTC)	X	H CH	01.04.88	SHERWOOD
Malins, Damian Joseph Holland, BSc,	LT(FTC)	S		01.03.95	DARTMOUTH BRNC
Malkin, Sharon Louise, BA,	LT(FTC)	E	AE	01.05.95	NMA PORTSMOUTH
Mallabone, James John Kenneth, BSc,	LT(IC)	E	TM	01.08.97	RALEIGH
Mallalieu, Adam John, MA, psc,	LT COL(IC)	-		31.12.98	BDS WASHINGTON
Mallen, David John, BEng,	LT(FTC)	E	AE(P)	01.12.95	700M MERLIN OEU
Malley, Mark Paul, BEng,	LT CDR(FTC)	E	WESM	01.01.01	MOD (BATH)
Mallinson, Laurence John, BSc,	SLT(IC)	S		01.05.00	WESTMINSTER
Mallinson, Robert, BEng, MA, pcea, psc(j),	LT CDR(FTC)	E	AE(O)	01.03.97	814 SQN
Malone, Martin Thomas,	SLT(IC)	S		01.05.00	RALEIGH
Malone, Mick,	LT(IC)	X		29.07.01	MWS DRYAD
Malone, Roger William, BSc,	SLT(IC)	X		01.01.00	MWS DRYAD
Malster, Dudley Andrew,	MID(IC)	X		01.05.00	NEWCASTLE
Maltby, Michael Robert James, BSc,	CDR(FTC)	E	ME	31.12.99	FLEET HQ PORTS
Maltby, Richard James,	CAPT RM(FTC)	-		29.04.97	RM WARMINSTER
Mandley, Philip John, MSc,	LT CDR(CC)	E	TM	01.05.02	JSCSC
Manfield, Michael David, pce(sm), SM,	LT CDR(FTC)	X	SM	01.01.99	VICTORIOUS(PORT)
Manger, Garth Stuart Cunningham, osc(us),	LT COL(FTC)	-	C	30.06.02	MWC SOUTHWICK
Mann, Andrew William,	LT(IC)	E	WE	01.01.02	CARDIFF
Mann, Colin Andrew,	SLT(UCE)(CC)	E	AE	01.09.99	DARTMOUTH BRNC
Mann, David Michael, BEng,	LT(IC)	X		01.06.99	WESTMINSTER
Mann, Gary Digby, BA, FCMA,	LT CDR(CC)	E	TMSM	01.10.97	RALEIGH
Manning, Duncan, MA,	CAPT RM(FTC)	-		01.09.97	RM POOLE
Manning, Gary Paul,	LT(IC)	S		01.09.01	ROEBUCK

Name	Rank	Branch	Spec	Seniority	Where Serving
Manning, Martin Graham Bickley, AFC, FIMgt, (Commodore) .... CAPT(FTC)	X	O		31.12.95	JSCSC
pce, pcea, psc, psc(j),					
Mannion, Robert Victor, pce, SM, ... LT CDR(FTC)	X	SM		01.06.95	FOSM GOSPORT
Mannion, Timothy Shaun, ... LT CDR(FTC)	X	P		01.09.86	FLEET AV VL
Manoy, Stephen, BSc, ...LT(IC)	X			01.04.99	MWS DRYAD
Manser, Darren Nicholas, ...LT(IC)	X	P		01.04.94	771 SQN
Mansergh, Andrew Christopher, BA, ... CAPT RM(IC)	-			01.09.01	OCLC BIRM
Mansergh, Michael Peter, BA, pce, ... CAPT(FTC)	X	PWO(C)		31.12.00	MOD (LONDON)
Mansergh, Robert James, LLB, pce, pce(sm), ... CAPT(FTC)	X	SM		30.06.00	MOD (LONDON)
Mansfield, James Alexander, BA, ... LT(CC)	X			01.10.97	LEEDS CASTLE
Manson, Colin Robert, BSc, PGDip, ... LT CDR(FTC)	X	METOC		01.10.98	FLEET HQ NWD
Manson, Peter Duncan, BA, ... MAJ(FTC)	-	P		01.09.99	847 SQN
Manson, Thomas Edward, BSc, psc(j), ... LT CDR(FTC)	E	AE(P)		07.09.98	RNAS YEOVILTON
Mant, James Nicholas, BSc, CEng, MIEE, ... LT CDR(FTC)	E	WE		01.10.89	FLEET HQ PORTS
Mantella, Dante Nevil, BSc, ... CAPT RM(IC)	-	MLDR		01.09.98	MOD (LONDON)
Mantle, Mark, MB, BS, ... SURG LTCDR(MCC)	-			07.08.01	MODHU DERRIFORD
Mantri, Anand Harishankar, BEng, ...LT(IC)	E	TM		22.05.00	MOD (LONDON)
Manwaring, Roy Geoffrey, ... LT(FTC)	MS			26.04.99	JSCSC
Maples, Andrew Thomas, MB, ChB, ... SURG LT(SCC)	-			01.08.01	CTCRM
Marchant, Timothy Alan Cardew, pce, ... LT CDR(FTC)	X	PWO(U)		01.02.91	FWO DEVPT SEA
Marden, Tony, MEng, ... SLT(IC)	E	WE		01.09.99	MWS COLLINGWOOD
Mardlin, Stephen Andrew, ... LT CDR(FTC)	S			01.04.99	FLEET HQ PORTS 2
Mardon, Karl Fraser, ... LT CDR(FTC)	X	PWO(U)		02.09.92	EXCHANGE USA
Marino, David Jones, MBE, MA, MCMI, psc, ... LT COL(FTC)	-	SO(LE)		01.10.98	SHAPE BELGIUM
Marjoram, Gareth Keri, BEng, ... LT(FTC)	E	WESM		01.05.96	TIRELESS
Marjoram, Joseph William, BSc, SM, ... LT(CC)	X	SM		01.02.00	VENGEANCE(STBD)
Marjoribanks, Charlotte, ... SLT(IC)	X			01.09.00	DARTMOUTH BRNC
Mark, Robert Alan, MSc, MNI, MRIN, (Commodore) .... CAPT(FTC)	X	H CH		31.12.96	MOD (BATH)
Markey, Adrian Philip, BEng, ... LT CDR(FTC)	X	O		01.08.01	MWS DRYAD
Markwick, Kenneth William, BSc, ... SLT(IC)	X			01.05.00	ARK ROYAL
Marland, Eunice Elizabeth, BSc, ...LT(IC)	S	S		01.01.02	RNAS YEOVILTON
Marley, Peter Shaun, BSc, MA, PGCE, FCMI, (Act Capt) .... CDR(FTC)	E	TM		31.12.87	2SL/CNH FOTR
MIPD, jsdc, psc(m),					
Marmont, Kerry Lewis, BSc, ... CDR(FTC)	E	WESM		31.12.00	FLEET CMSA UK
Marok, Jani, BSc, MA, psc(j), ... LT COL(FTC)	-			30.06.02	COMAMPHIBFOR
Marquis, Adrian Colin, BEng, ... LT(CC)	X	P		01.12.93	CAMPBELTOWN FLT
Marr, James, BEng, ... LT(FTC)	E	MESM		01.05.97	NEPTUNE DSA
Marratt, Richard James, BSc, ...LT(FTC)	E	TM		01.09.90	RM POOLE
Marriott, Mark Nicholas, BEng, MSc, ... LT CDR(FTC)	E	AE		01.04.99	801 SQN
Marriott, Matthew James, ... SLT(FTC)	X			01.09.99	ALDERNEY
Marriott, Neil Kenneth, ... LT(CC)	X	MCD		01.12.95	MWS DEF DIV SCHL
Marsh, Brian Henry, MBE, BSc, pcea, ... LT CDR(FTC)	X	O		01.10.99	FLEET HQ PORTS 2
Marsh, David Julian, BSc, MCMI, ... CDR(FTC)	S			31.12.93	FLEET HQ PORTS
Marsh, David Richard, ... SLT(IC)	S			01.01.01	DARTMOUTH BRNC
Marsh, Michael Peter Alan, ... LT(FTC)	X			13.12.95	NEPTUNE
Marsh, Stephen William, ... SLT(IC)	S			01.01.01	DARTMOUTH BRNC
Marsh, Stuart David, BA, ...LT(IC)	X			01.05.02	MWS DRYAD
Marshall, Alistair John, BA, ...LT(IC)	X	SM		01.12.99	TIRELESS
Marshall, Colin George, ... SLT(UCE)(FTC)	E	WE		01.09.00	QUORN
Marshall, Fleur Tiffany, MB, ChB, ... SURG LTCDR(MCC)	-			07.08.01	NELSON (PAY)
Marshall, Gavin Peter, MEng, ...LT(IC)	E	ME		01.01.02	SULTAN
Marshall, Jason, ... SLT(IC)	X			01.01.01	RNAS CULDROSE
Marshall, Matthew, BEng, ...LT(IC)	X	P		01.05.98	845 SQN
Marshall, Paul, BEng, MSc, ... LT CDR(FTC)	E	ME		01.09.00	WESTMINSTER
Marshall, Richard Anthony, pce, psc(m), ... CDR(FTC)	X	MCD		31.12.92	DARTMOUTH BRNC
Marshall, Richard George Carter, pce, ... LT CDR(FTC)	X	PWO(C)		01.05.95	LIVERPOOL
Marson, Gary Michael, ... LT CDR(FTC)	E	WE		14.10.96	DARTMOUTH BRNC
Marston, Peter Alan, BA, ... LT CDR(FTC)	S			16.04.96	RN GIBRALTAR
Marten, Andrew David, ... LT(FTC)	X	ATC		01.04.95	OCEAN
Martin, Antony John, ... LT(FTC)	X	C		10.12.98	FOST SEA
Martin, Bruce Anthony, BSc, CEng, ... LT CDR(FTC)	E	MESM		01.05.97	FLEET HQ PORTS
Martin, Colin John, pce, pcea, ocds(Can), ... CDR(FTC)	X	O		30.06.00	SACLANT USA

Name	Rank	Branch	Spec	Seniority	Where Serving
Martin, David Charles Sarsfield,	LT(IC)	X		01.09.01	MWS DRYAD
Martin, David Leslie,	MID(NE)(IC)	X		01.09.01	DARTMOUTH BRNC
Martin, Elizabeth Janet, BSc,	LT CDR(FTC)	E	TM	01.04.91	FLEET CMSA UK
Martin, Lisa,	SURG SLT(SCC)	-		01.07.01	DARTMOUTH BRNC
Martin, Michael Peter,	CDR(FTC)	E	AE(L)	30.06.01	ES AIR YEO
Martin, Michael Terence, BEng, psc,	CDR(FTC)	E	ME	30.06.01	MOD (BATH)
Martin, Neil Douglas, BSc, pcea, psc, gdas,	LT CDR(FTC)	X	O	01.06.87	LOAN JTEG BSC DN
Martin, Neil, MB, ChB, BSc,	SURG LT(SCC)	-		04.08.99	VENGEANCE(STBD)
Martin, Nicholas Peter, MB, BS,	SURG LT(SCC)	-		26.08.99	MODHU DERRIFORD
Martin, Nigel,	LT(FTC)	X	C	20.09.99	DCSA COMMCEN PLY
Martin, Paul John, BSc, psc(m), (Act Col)	LT COL(FTC)	-	C	31.12.93	HQ DCSA
Martin, Robert James, BEng,	LT(CC)	E	AE	01.02.00	848 SQN HERON
Martin, Roger Graham,	LT CDR(FTC)	X	AAWO	01.09.95	JMOTS NORTHWOOD
Martin, Ronald Charles John Richard, BA,	CHAPLAIN	SF		03.09.96	40 CDO RM
Martin, Simon Charles, LVO, pce, pce(sm), psc,	CAPT(FTC)	X	SM	30.06.98	JSCSC
Martin, Simon James, BEng, MSc, CEng, MIEE,	LT CDR(FTC)	E	WESM	01.02.00	JSSU OAKLEY
Martin, Stuart William, MSc,	LT(IC)	E	AE	01.08.99	771 SQN
Martin, Timothy Frederick Wilkins, LLB, MA, rcds,	CAPT(FTC)	S	BAR	31.12.98	NELSON
Martyn, Alan Wallace, MSc, CEng, MRAeS,	CDR(FTC)	E	AE	31.12.00	MOD (LONDON)
Martyn, Daniel, BA, MSc,	LT(IC)	X		01.05.01	SOVEREIGN
Masilamani, Nithyanand Samuel, MB, BS, FRCS,	SURG LTCDR(SCC)	-		14.01.98	RH HASLAR
Maskell-Bott, John Malcolm, adp, (Act Lt Cdr)	LT(FTC)	E	MESM	16.02.84	MOD (LONDON)
Mason, Alexander Malcolm, CBE, ocds(No), fsc,	COL(FTC)	-	RL	30.06.94	MOD (LONDON)
Mason, Andrew Clive, BSc,	LT(CC)	X		01.07.98	RICHMOND
Mason, Andrew Harold, MSc,	CDR(FTC)	E	AE	31.12.99	MERLIN IPT
Mason, Colin Edward, ACMA, (Act Cdr)	LT CDR(FTC)	S	CMA	16.11.83	FLEET HQ PORTS
Mason, Darren Jon, BEng, SM(n),	LT(FTC)	X	SM	01.03.97	SPARTAN
Mason, Jeffrey Sinclair, MBE, psc,	COL(FTC)	-	LC	30.06.01	CDO LOG REGT RM
Mason, Lindsay, MSc,	LT(FTC)	E	TM	01.11.89	NELSON
Mason, Mark John, BSc,	LT(IC)	X		01.01.00	MWS DRYAD
Mason, Martin,	LT CDR(FTC)	E	AE(M)	01.10.99	OCEAN
Mason, Maxwell James, BA,	LT(IC)	X	HM	01.05.98	SCOTT
Mason, Michael Miles David, BSc, MPhil, pce, pcea,	CDR(FTC)	X	O	30.06.93	MOD (LONDON)
Mason, Nicholas Hugh, BSc, MinstP, C PHYS,	CDR(FTC)	E	TM	31.12.98	2SL/CNH FOTR
Mason, Richard James, BSc,	SLT(IC)	X		01.05.01	DARTMOUTH BRNC
Mason, Richard William, BSc, MA, CEng, MIEE, psc,	CAPT(FTC)	E	WE	30.06.01	NMA PORTSMOUTH
Mason-Matthews, Angela,	SLT(IC)	X		01.12.01	MWS DRYAD
Massey, Alan Michael, BA, rcds, pce, psc,	CAPT(FTC)	X	PWO(A)	30.06.96	ILLUSTRIOUS
Massey, Paul, (Act Lt Cdr)	LT(FTC)	X	AV	23.07.93	DISC SEA
Massie-Taylor, Christopher Gerald, OBE, pce, psc,	CAPT(FTC)	X	MCD/MW	31.12.93	2SL/CNH FOTR
Masson, Neil Graham, BSc,	LT(IC)	X		01.05.02	MWS DRYAD
Masterman, Andrew Paul, BA, MLITT,	SLT(IC)	X		01.09.99	INVERNESS
Masters, James Christopher, pce,	LT CDR(FTC)	X	AAWO	01.05.96	LEEDS CASTLE
Masters, Nicholas Norman John, MA, MRCVS,	CAPT RM(IC)	-		01.09.98	FLEET AV SUPPORT
Masters, Richard Hilary, BTech, MA(Ed), MA, FCIPD, psc(j),	LT CDR(FTC)	E	TM	01.01.92	SULTAN
Mather, Graeme Philip,	LT CDR(FTC)	E	ME	01.07.97	MOD (BATH)
Mather, Richard Hedley, BM, BS, BMS,	SURG LTCDR(SCC)	-		07.08.01	MODHU DERRIFORD
Mathews, Andrew David Hugh, MSc, CEng, MIMechE, rcds, psc,	CAPT(FTC)	E	MESM	30.06.97	DPA BRISTOL
Mathias, Philip Bentley, MBE, pce, pce(sm), psc,	CAPT(FTC)	X	SM	31.12.99	FLEET HQ PORTS 2
Mathias-Jones, Peter David, pce,	LT CDR(FTC)	X	PWO(U)	01.09.90	SACLANT ITALY
Mathieson, Kevin Richard, pcea,	LT CDR(FTC)	X	P	01.10.95	824 SQN
Mathieson, Neil Braid, BEng,	LT(CC)	E	AE	01.03.00	800 SQN
Matters, Andrew Charles, BSc, CEng, FIMechE,	CDR(FTC)	E	ME	30.06.92	MOD (BATH)
Matthew, Mark Jonathan,	LT(CC)	S	SM	01.09.99	TORBAY
Matthews, David William, BEng, MSc,	LT CDR(FTC)	E	WESM	01.01.98	TALENT
Matthews, Duncan Neil, MBE, BSc, pce, pcea, psc(j),	CDR(FTC)	X	P	31.12.99	CFPS SHORE
Matthews, Gary Anthony, MB, BCh, FRCA, MRCP,	SURG LTCDR(MCC)	-		01.08.98	NP 1064
Matthews, George, psc,	LT COL(FTC)	-	SO(LE)	31.12.00	CTCRM
Matthews, Jonathan James, MB, ChB,	SURG LTCDR(MCC)	-		01.08.01	RH HASLAR
Matthews, Justin,	LT(CC)	X	O	16.05.94	MWS DRYAD
Matthews, Paul Brian, BEng, PGDip,	LT CDR(FTC)	E	TM	01.10.99	NELSON RNSETT

Name	Rank	Branch	Spec	Seniority	Where Serving
Matthews, Paul Kinley,	LT(FTC)	S		01.10.95	RALEIGH
Matthews, Peter Ronald,	LT(FTC)	E	AE(M)	01.04.01	ES AIR MASU
Matthews, Peter, BSc, pce, psc(j),	CDR(FTC)	X	AWO(A)	30.06.89	WSA/CAPT MCTA
Mattin, Paul Roger,	MAJ(FTC)	-	MLDR	01.05.00	UKLFCSG RM
Mattock, Nicholas John,	SLT(IC)	X	P U/T	01.01.02	DARTMOUTH BRNC
Maude, Christopher Philip, BSc(Eng), MRAeS, pcea, tp,	LT CDR(FTC)	X	P	01.10.92	700M MERLIN OEU
Maude, Colin David, BEng,	SLT(IC)	E	AE U/T	01.09.00	EDINBURGH
Maude, David Howard,	LT CDR(FTC)	E	AE(L)	01.10.99	ES AIR YEO
Maw, Martyn John, BSc, CEng, MIEE,	LT CDR(FTC)	E	WESM	01.12.90	MOD (BATH)
Mawdsley, Gareth Richard,	SLT(FTC)	S		01.09.99	RALEIGH
Mawson, John Robert, BA,	CAPT RM(IC)	-	LC	01.05.99	ALBION
Maxwell, Alexander Matthew,	LT(CS)RM(CAS)	-		10.01.97	DNR RCHQ NORTH
Maxwell, Rachel, BA, n,	LT CDR(FTC)	X	PWO(U)	01.05.02	PORTLAND
May, Caroline Louise,	LT(IC)	S		01.08.00	KENT
May, Colin,	LT(FTC)	X		01.07.96	SHEFFIELD
May, Damien John,	CAPT RM(IC)	-	P U/T	01.04.02	RAF CRANWELL EFS
May, David Mark,	SLT(IC)	X	REG	01.10.99	2SL/CNH
May, Dominic Peter,	MAJ(FTC)	-		01.05.00	42 CDO RM
May, John William,	LT(CC)	X	P	01.07.95	RNAS YEOVILTON
May, Nigel Peter, pce, pcea,	LT CDR(FTC)	X	P	01.09.98	820 SQN
May, Peter James,	LT(FTC)	X	C	29.10.93	HQ DCSA
May, Steven Charles, BEng, MSc,	LT(FTC)	E	ME	01.07.95	SULTAN
May-Clingo, Martin Stephen,	LT(FTC)	X	AV	04.04.91	JFHQ STAFF NWOOD
Maybery, James Edward,	MAJ(FTC)	-		01.05.97	JSCSC
Mayell, Julie Ann, BA,	LT(FTC)	W	S	14.07.92	SULTAN AIB
Mayhew, Nicholas Morvaren, pce, pcea, psc,	LT CDR(FTC)	X	P	16.08.90	771 SQN
Maynard, Andrew Thomas Westenborg, MA, osc(us),	LT COL(FTC)	-		30.06.02	NMA PORTSMOUTH
Maynard, Charles Ian, BA, n,	LT(FTC)	X		01.02.95	SMITER
Maynard, Paul Andrew, BSc,	CAPT RM(IC)	-		01.09.01	DNR DISP TEAM
Maze, Andrew Terence, QHC, BSc,	PR CHAPLAIN	SF		11.09.79	2SL/CNH
Mc Allister, Steven Edward,	LT(IC)	X		01.01.02	MWS DRYAD
Mc Currach, Robert Henry,	LT(IC)	X	FC	01.08.00	RNAS YEOVILTON
Mc Laren, James Patrick,	MAJ(FTC)	-		30.04.98	PJHQ
McAlpine, Paul Anthony, pce, psc(j),	CDR(FTC)	X	MCD	31.12.98	MOD (LONDON)
McArthur, Calum James Gibb, BM, BCh, BAO, MRCPG, LRCP, DObstRCOG, Dip FFP,	SURG CAPT(FCC)	-	GMPP	30.06.02	NELSON
McAulay, Paul John, BSc,	LT(IC)	X		01.02.00	SANDOWN
McAuslin, Thomas McDonald, MSc,	LT CDR(FTC)	MS	SM	01.10.98	2SL/CNH
McBain, Mandy Sheila,	LT(CC)	W	S	11.12.92	SULTAN AIB
McBarnet, Thomas Francis, BSc, pce,	CDR(FTC)	X	PWO(U)	31.12.97	MOD (LONDON)
McBratney, James Alexander Grant, SM(n), SM,	LT(FTC)	X	SM	01.11.96	VIGILANT(PORT)
McCabe, Daniel Stewart, HNC,	LT(FTC)	E	WE	19.02.93	MCM2 SEA
McCabe, Garry Patrick, BA,	CAPT RM(IC)	-		01.09.97	OCLC ROSYTH
McCabe, Joseph, BA, psc,	LT COL(FTC)	-		31.12.92	NMA PORTSMOUTH
McCabe, Shane Edward Thomas, MB, BS, BSc,	SURG LTCDR(MCC)	-		01.08.00	MODHU DERRIFORD
McCaffery, George Frederick,	LT CDR(FTC)	E	AE(M)	01.10.98	HQ DCSA
McCall, Gary, BA,	LT(CC)	X	P	01.11.98	815 FLT 244
McCall, Iain Robert, PGDIPAN, pce,	LT CDR(FTC)	X	PWO(N)	01.07.96	ARK ROYAL
McCallum, Guy Peter, BSc,	SLT(IC)	X	P U/T	01.09.00	DARTMOUTH BRNC
McCallum, Malcolm Donald, BA,	SLT(IC)	X		01.05.00	ST ALBANS
McCallum, Neil Ritchie, BEng,	LT(FTC)	E	ME	01.06.97	SULTAN
McCallum, Nicola,	MID(IC)	X		01.05.00	CHATHAM
McCamphill, Paul Joseph, BEng,	LT(IC)	E	WE	01.01.02	MWS COLLINGWOOD
McCann, Toby, BEng,	LT(FTC)	E	AE	01.12.98	771 SQN
McCardle, John Alexander, BSc, jsdc,	LT COL(FTC)	-	P	30.06.02	847 SQN
McCartain, Michael Brendon William, BSc, pce, pcea, psc,	CDR(FTC)	X	O	31.12.98	MWS DRYAD
McCarthy, Daniel John, BEng,	SLT(IC)	E	ME	01.09.99	SULTAN
McCarthy, Steven James, BEng, MSc,	LT(FTC)	E	ME	01.01.95	MOD (BATH)
McCaughey, Vincent Joseph, BComm, PGCE,	LT(CC)	E	IS	01.03.93	2SL/CNH
McCauley, Linda Jane, BA,	LT(IC)	X		01.05.01	MWS RNHMS DRAKE
McCleary, Simon Paul, BEng,	LT(FTC)	E	WESM	01.03.98	FOST CSST FSLN
McClement, Duncan Lewis, BEng,	LT(FTC)	E	MESM	01.09.99	SCEPTRE

Name	Rank	Branch	Spec	Seniority	Where Serving
McClement, Timothy Pentreath, OBE, jsdc, pce, pce(sm), hcsc,	RADM	-	SM	23.04.01	MOD (LONDON)
McCloskey, Ian Michael,	LT(FTC)	E	ME	01.06.96	SULTAN
McClurg, Robert James, BEng,	SLT(IC)	E	WE	01.09.99	MWS COLLINGWOOD
McCombe, John, MIMarEST,	LT(FTC)	E	ME	01.09.96	MOD (BATH)
McConochie, Andrew David, BSc,	LT CDR(FTC)	S		16.04.96	MOD (BATH)
McConville, Claire,	LT(SCC)	Q		28.03.00	RH HASLAR
McCormack, Conor Patrick,	MAJ(FTC)	-	LC	30.04.98	EXCHANGE NLANDS
McCormack, Gary,	SLT(UCE)(FTC)	E	ME	01.09.00	DARTMOUTH BRNC
McCormick, Peter Edward, MEng,	LT(CC)	X	P	15.03.98	820 SQN
McCowan, David James,	LT(CC)	X	P	16.06.95	CHFHQ
McCowen, Polly Anne Charlotte, BA,	LT(IC)	S		01.05.01	NEPTUNE
McCoy, Mark, BEng,	LT(CC)	E	AE	01.11.98	824 SQN
McCue, Duncan, MA, MSc, CEng, MIMarEST,	LT CDR(FTC)	E	ME	01.10.98	ILLUSTRIOUS
McCulley, Steven Cameron,	CAPT RM(CC)	-		01.04.01	NEPTUNE
McCutcheon, Graeme,	LT(FTC)	X	P	01.02.95	EXCHANGE DENMARK
McDermott, Mark, pcea, (Act Lt Cdr)	LT(CC)	X	P	01.01.90	GANNET SAR FLT
McDermott, Owen David, BEng,	LT CDR(FTC)	E	WE	01.10.99	NORFOLK
McDermott, Paul Andrew,	LT(FTC)	X	MCD	24.07.97	MWS DRYAD
McDicken, Ian Neil, BDS, (Act Sgltcdr(D))	SG LT(D)(SCC)	-		08.01.02	RNAS CULDROSE
McDonald, Andrew, BEng,	LT(CC)	E	AE	01.03.00	849 SQN B FLT
McDonald, Duncan James, BEng,	LT(IC)	E		01.09.98	NOTTINGHAM
McDonald, Ian Gordon,	LT(CC)	X	O	01.05.91	750 SQN SEAHAWK
McDonald, James,	LT(CS)(CAS)	-		06.02.94	DNR RCHQ NORTH
McDonald, John James Bruce,	LT CDR(FTC)	X	P	01.05.84	CHFHQ
McDonald, Norman,	LT(CC)	X	P	01.09.94	849 SQN HQ
McDonnell, David Shaw, BEng, PGDIP,	LT CDR(FTC)	X	METOC	01.03.99	UKMARBATSTAFF
McDonnell, Peter William, pce, pce(sm),	CDR(FTC)	X	SM	30.06.98	FWO FASLANE SEA
McDonough, Ambrose Gerrard, BSc, pce,	LT CDR(FTC)	X	PWO(U)	01.07.96	FOST SEA
McElwaine, Richard Ian, BSc,	CDR(FTC)	E	AE(P)	31.12.94	MERLIN IPT
McEvoy, Lee Patrick,	LT(FTC)	X	EW	24.07.97	UKMARBATSTAFF
McEwan, Andrea Morrison, BA,	LT(IC)	X		01.10.96	ENDURANCE
McEwan, Rory Daniel, BEng,	SLT(IC)	E	WESM	01.09.99	RALEIGH
McFadden, Andrew,	CHAPLAIN	RC		01.09.98	SULTAN
McFadyen, Howard, OBE, MSc, CEng, MIMechE,	CAPT(FTC)	E	MESM	31.12.96	MOD (BATH)
McFadzean, Iain, MA, BD,	CHAPLAIN	SF		01.07.99	FWO PORTS SEA
McFarland, Noeleen,	LT(SCC)	Q	REGM	14.01.99	RN GIBRALTAR
McFarlane, Andrew Lennox, OBE, BSc, CEng, MIMechE,	CAPT(FTC)	E	MESM	30.06.00	NEPTUNE DSA
McFarlane, Robert William Archibald,	LT(SCC)	Q		02.07.01	RCDM
McGannity, Colin Stephen, BEng,	LT(CC)	X	O	16.03.00	849 SQN B FLT
McGarel, David Francis, (Act Cdr)	LT CDR(FTC)	S	CA	01.10.96	MOD (BATH)
McGhee, Craig, BEng,	CAPT RM(FTC)	-	P	01.09.96	HQ 3 CDO BDE RM
McGhie, Ian Andrew, pce, pce(sm),	CDR(FTC)	X	SM	31.12.99	SPLENDID
McGill, Emma Jane, BDS,	SG LT(D)(SCC)	-		17.06.98	DRAKE CBP(CNH)
McGinley, Christopher Thomas, BSc, PGCE,	LT(IC)	E	TM	01.05.97	CTCRM
McGlory, Stephen Joseph, BA,	LT(FTC)	X	FC	01.06.94	MWS DRYAD
McGowan, Angela Bridget, BA,	LT(IC)	X	O	01.09.01	771 SQN
McGrane, Richard John, pce,	LT(FTC)	X	C	03.04.97	DULVERTON
McGrath, Wayne James,	LT(IC)	S	(S)	08.01.01	MWS DRYAD
McGreal, Benjamin, BEng,	SLT(IC)	X	P U/T	01.01.00	DARTMOUTH BRNC
McGrenary, Andrew,	LT CDR(FTC)	X		01.01.94	1 PBS SEA
McGuire, James, SM(n), SM,	LT(CC)	X	SM	01.10.96	VICTORIOUS(STBD)
McGuire, Michael Joseph, pce, n,	LT CDR(FTC)	X	PWO(A)	31.08.98	EXCHANGE GERMANY
McGunigall, Roy,	LT(FTC)	MS	(AD)	03.04.97	INM ALVERSTOKE
McHale, Gareth John, BSc, pce, pcea,	LT CDR(FTC)	X	O	01.12.91	MOD (LONDON)
McHale, Kevan,	LT CDR(FTC)	E	AE(M)	01.10.97	ES AIR YEO
McHugh, Richard Henry, BEng,	LT(FTC)	E	ME	01.03.97	ST ALBANS
McHugh, Terence Patrick, BSc,	LT CDR(CC)	X		01.08.01	JPS UK
McInerney, Andrew Jonathon, BSc,	MAJ(FTC)	-		01.09.99	RMC OF SCIENCE
McInnes, James Gerard Kenneth, BSc,	LT CDR(FTC)	E	WESM	01.06.95	NMA PORTSMOUTH
McIntosh, James Declan, BA, MB, BS,	SURG LT(MCC)	-		26.08.97	MODHU DERRIFORD

Name	Rank	Branch	Spec	Seniority	Where Serving
McIntyre, Alastair William, (Act Lt Cdr)	LT(FTC)	X	tas	25.07.91	PJHQ
McIntyre, Louise, MA, ...	LT(CC)	X		01.01.00	BLYTH
McJarrow, Duncan James, BDS, MGDS	SGCDR(D)(FCC)	-		30.06.00	RNAS YEOVILTON
RCS, LDS RCS(Eng),					
McKay, Paul Anthony, pcea, ...	LT CDR(FTC)	X	O	16.08.85	MOD (LONDON)
McKay, Thomas Westley, LLB, ...	LT(IC)	X		01.01.02	NORFOLK
McKeating, Paul, ...	2LT(IC)	-		01.09.98	CTCRM LYMPSTONE
McKee, Hamish McLeod, BA, BComm, ...	LT(CC)	X	O	01.07.97	814 SQN
McKendrick, Andrew Michael, pce, pce(sm), ...	CDR(FTC)	X	SM	31.12.98	TURBULENT
McKenna, Danelle Rosanne, ...	SLT(IC)	X		01.01.01	PEMBROKE
McKenzie, David, BSc, CEng, MIMarEST, ...	CDR(FTC)	E	ME	30.06.00	NATO DEF COL
McKenzie, Ian Scott, MBE, jsdc, pce, ...	CDR(FTC)	X	P	31.12.87	MOD (LONDON)
McKenzie, Malcolm, pce, pcea, ...	LT CDR(FTC)	X	O	03.03.98	849 SQN A FLT
McKeown, Justin Reaney, ...	MAJ(FTC)	-		01.09.97	CTCRM
McKernan, James, ...	LT CDR(FTC)	X	C	01.10.01	FLEET CIS PORTS
McKie, Andrew, MBE, MA, pcea, psc, ...	CDR(FTC)	X	P	31.12.00	RNAS CULDROSE
McKillop, Helenora Elisabeth Lang, (Act Lt Cdr)	LT(MCC)	Q	OTSPEC	14.02.86	RH HASLAR
McKinlay, Jayne, ...	SURG SLT(SCC)	-		01.12.00	DARTMOUTH BRNC
McKinney, Mark Douglas, ...	MAJ(FTC)	-	MLDR	01.05.97	LOAN OTHER SVCE
McKnight, Derek James Stewart, ...	LT(FTC)	X	PWO(A)	01.07.91	LANCASTER
McKnight, Nicholas William, MSc, ...	LT CDR(FTC)	S		01.10.93	AFPAA(CENTURION)
McLachlan, Jennifer Kim, MB, ChB, ...	SURG LTCDR(MCC)	-		17.08.00	NELSON (PAY)
McLachlan, Michael Paul, AMIMarE, ...	LT(FTC)	E	ME	18.06.93	OCEAN
McLarnon, Christopher Patrick Charles, BSc, ...	LT CDR(FTC)	E	TM	01.09.99	ARK ROYAL
McLaughlan, Charles John, MBA, ...	LT CDR(FTC)	MS	(PD)	01.10.00	MOD (LONDON)
McLaughlin, Steven, MEng, PhD, ...	LT(IC)	E	TM	01.12.98	DARTMOUTH BRNC
McLean, David, BSc, BD, ...	CHAPLAIN	RC		18.09.96	FWO PORTS SEA
McLean, Rory Alistair Ian, OBE, pce, hcsc, ...	RADM	-	P	09.04.01	MOD (LONDON)
McLellan, James Douglas, BEng, AMIEE, ...	LT(CC)	E	WE	01.11.97	WSA BRISTOL
McLelland, Peter Holmes, ...	CAPT RM(IC)	-	SO(LE)	01.04.02	771 SQN
McLennan, Andrew, ...	LT(CC)	X	O	01.04.95	814 SQN
McLennan, Richard Glenn, BSc, fsc, ...	CDR(FTC)	E	AE	30.06.98	NMA PORTSMOUTH
McLeod, Katherine Yvonne Louise, ...	SLT(IC)	X		01.09.00	DARTMOUTH BRNC
McLocklan, Lee Michael, ...	LT(IC)	S		01.04.00	IRON DUKE
McMahon, Daniel Steven, BSc, ...	SLT(IC)	X		01.01.01	DARTMOUTH BRNC
McMaster, Garry Thomas, BSc, ...	SLT(IC)	X		01.01.00	LEEDS CASTLE
McMeekin, Nicola Sarah, BDS, BSc, ...	SGLT(D)(MCC)	-		15.07.95	ARK ROYAL
McMenamin, Diarmaid, ...	SURG SLT(SCC)	-		01.10.99	DARTMOUTH BRNC
McMichael, James Stewart, BSc, ...	LT(CC)	X	O	01.01.98	815 SQN HQ
McMichael-Phillips, Scott James, BSc, ARICS, pce, ...	CDR(FTC)	X	H CH	31.12.99	SCOTT
McMillan, George Harrison Grant, (Commodore)	SURG CAPT(FCC)	-	(CO/M)	31.12.92	2SL/
QHP, MD, MSc, Bch, FRCP, FRCPGlas, FFOM, jsdc, GB, OStJ,					
McMillan, Nelson, ...	SLT(IC)	X		01.09.01	WESTMINSTER
McMulkin, John Patrick, BA, ...	CAPT RM(IC)	-		01.09.98	42 CDO RM
McMullan, Neil Leslie, BA, MSc, ...	LT CDR(FTC)	E	TM	01.01.01	RALEIGH
McNab, Gillian Jane, ...	SG SLT(D)(SCC)	-		01.01.01	DARTMOUTH BRNC
McNair, Euan Alan, AFC, pce, pcea, psc, ...	CDR(FTC)	X	P	30.06.95	LOAN DSTL
McNair, James, ...	LT(FTC)	E	AE	02.05.00	MERLIN IPT
McNally, Neville James, ...	LT CDR(FTC)	S		01.11.98	COMAMPHIBFOR
McNamara, Ian Martin, BEng, ...	LT(FTC)	E	WESM	01.08.96	MOD DIS SEA
McNaughton, John Alistair, BSc, adp, SM, ...	LT CDR(FTC)	E	IS	01.07.93	MOD (LONDON)
McNeile, Rory Hugh, MA, pce, pcea, psc(j), ...	CDR(FTC)	X	P	30.06.00	MOD (LONDON)
McNeill Love, Robin Michael Cox, MB, BS, ...	SURG CDR(FCC)	-	GMPP	30.06.96	2SL/CNH
MRCGP, DA, DObstRCOG, DipAvMed, DipFFP,					
McParland, Joanne Margaret, BSc, ...	SLT(IC)	X		01.01.01	DARTMOUTH BRNC
McPhail, Thomas Cameron, BSc, ...	SLT(IC)	X		01.05.01	DARTMOUTH BRNC
McQuaker, Stuart Ross, PGDIPAN, pce, psc(j), ...	CDR(FTC)	X	PWO(N)	31.12.98	MOD (LONDON)
McQueen, Jason Bedwell, BSc, n, ...	LT(IC)	E	TM	01.07.93	1 ASSLT GP RM
McQuire, Duncan Ewen Alexander, BEng, MSc, ...	SLT(IC)	E	ME	01.01.00	SULTAN
McRae, Philip Compton, BEng, CEng, MIEE, ...	LT CDR(FTC)	E	WESM	01.12.99	MOD (BATH)
McTaggart, Douglas Alexander, ...	LT(FTC)	E	WE	07.02.97	MOD (BATH)
McTear, Karen, BSc, ...	LT CDR(FTC)	E	TM	16.05.93	SA MOSCOW

Name	Rank	Branch	Spec	Seniority	Where Serving
McTear, Nigel James,	LT(FTC)	X	AV	11.12.92	NELSON
McTeer, Ian James, BA,	LT(IC)	X	P	16.08.98	CARDIFF
McWilliams, Adrian Robert,	LT(CC)	X	O	01.05.98	MWS DRYAD
McWilliams, Jacqueline Elizabeth, BA, MSc,	LT(FTC)	X	MW	01.09.95	BLYTH
Meacher, Paul Graham, BA,	SLT(IC)	X		01.01.00	ALDERNEY
Meachin, Michael Charles, BTh	CHAPLAIN	SF		07.07.97	RALEIGH
Meadows, Brian,	LT CDR(FTC)	X	PT	01.10.98	FORWARD
Meaken, John, BSc, CEng, MIEE, psc,	CDR(FTC)	E	MESM	31.12.89	DRAKE CBS
Meakin, Brian Richard, BSc, MBA, pcea,	LT CDR(FTC)	X	O	01.10.96	JSCSC
Mealing, David William, BEng,	LT(FTC)	E	AE	01.04.97	RNAS YEOVILTON
Mealing, Steven, BEng,	LT(CC)	E	ME	01.12.97	WESTMINSTER
Mearns, Craig McDonald, MA, psc(j),	LT CDR(FTC)	S		01.05.97	NEPTUNE DLO
Mears, Kristian Paul, BA, BMS, (Act Surg Lt)	SURG SLT(SCC)	-		11.07.01	DARTMOUTH BRNC
Mears, Richard John, BSc,	CAPT RM(CC)	-	C	01.05.00	42 CDO RM
Meatyard, Christopher George Brandon, psc,	CDR(FTC)	X	MCD	31.12.88	AST(E)
Meeds, Kevin, pce, pcea,	LT CDR(FTC)	X	O	16.12.95	SOUTHAMPTON
Meek, Camilla Simpson, BEng,	LT CDR(FTC)	E	ME	01.03.02	FLEET HQ PORTS
Mehta, Kim Louise, BEng,	LT(IC)	E	TM	01.09.95	NELSON RNSETT
Meikle, Kevin Edward James,	LT(FTC)	X		01.04.01	MARLBOROUGH
Meikle, Robert,	LT(IC)	X		01.04.01	FLEET HQ PORTS
Meikle, Stuart Andrew, BA, BSc, IEng, MIEE,	LT(FTC)	E	AE(L)	01.04.01	MERLIN IPT
Mellor, Adrian John, MB, BCh, FRCA,	SURG LTCDR(FCC)	-	SM	06.09.96	NELSON (PAY)
Mellor, Barry John, MA, MCMI, psc(j),	LT CDR(FTC)	S		16.05.93	ELANT/NAVNORTH
Melly, Richard Graham, MSc, CEng, (Commodore) FIMarEST, rcds, psc,	CAPT(FTC)	E	ME	31.12.95	NMA PORTSMOUTH
Melville, Arran, IEng, AMIMarEST,	LT(IC)	E		01.02.01	CARDIFF
Melville-Brown, Martin Giles,	LT CDR(FTC)	S	CA	01.10.01	NEWCASTLE
Menlove-Platt, Christopher John, BSc, CEng, FIMarEST,	CDR(FTC)	E	ME	31.12.93	AMC
Menzies, Angus,	CAPT(FTC)	S	SM	31.12.98	MOD (LONDON)
Menzies, Anthony John, BSc,	LT CDR(FTC)	E	AE(P)	01.05.90	RNAS CULDROSE
Menzies, Bruce, BSc,	LT(IC)	X	P	01.09.00	702 SQN HERON
Menzies, Gregor Malcolm, BSc,	LT RM(IC)	-		01.09.00	42 CDO RM
Mercer, Andrew Jude,	SURG LT(SCC)	-		01.08.01	FLEET AV SULTAN
Mercer, David Crispian,	LT(FTC)	X	P	16.01.93	EXCHANGE FRANCE
Mercer, Simon Jude, MB, ChB,	SURG LT(SCC)	-		02.08.00	CAPTAIN SM2
Mercer, Stuart James, BM, BCh, MRCS,	SURG LTCDR(MCC)	-		03.08.00	RH HASLAR
Merchant, Ian Charles,	CDR(FTC)	S		31.12.00	RNAS CULDROSE
Merchant, Jeremy Mark,	CAPT RM(FTC)	-	SO(LE)	01.01.98	RM POOLE
Meredith, Nicholas, BSc, pce(sm),	LT CDR(FTC)	X	SM	01.04.94	FLEET HQ NWD
Merewether, Henry Alworth Hamilton, pce, pcea,	LT CDR(FTC)	X	O	01.05.98	INVERNESS
Merriman, Peter Orrill, BSc, CEng, MIMechE,	CDR(FTC)	E	MESM	30.06.99	NEPTUNE NT
Merritt, Jonathan James, BEng, MSc, CEng, MCGI, MIMarEST,	LT CDR(FTC)	E	ME	01.05.96	SULTAN
Mervik, Christopher Fields, OBE, pce, pcea, ocds(Can),	CAPT(FTC)	X	P	31.12.99	FLEET HQ PORTS
Messenger, Gordon Kenneth, OBE, BSc, psc,	COL(FTC)	-	MLDR	30.06.02	40 CDO RM
Metcalf, Robin,	LT CDR(FTC)	E	ME	01.10.01	EXCHANGE N ZLAND
Metcalf, Stephen William, IEng, AMIMarEST,	LT(FTC)	E	MESM	01.04.01	VICTORIOUS(STBD)
Metcalfe, Anthony Paul Warren, pce,	LT CDR(FTC)	X	PWO(U)	01.12.91	FLEET HQ PORTS 2
Metcalfe, Liam,	2LT(IC)	-		01.09.98	CTCRM LYMPSTONE
Metcalfe, Michael Peter, BEM,	LT CDR(FTC)	X	EW	01.10.01	JSCSC
Metcalfe, Philip Geoffrey, BEng, MSc, MIEE,	LT CDR(FTC)	E	WESM	01.02.96	MOD (LONDON)
Metcalfe, Richard John,	LT(FTC)	E	WE	04.09.98	WSA BRISTOL
Methven, Paul, BEng, MSc, CEng, MIMarEST,	LT CDR(FTC)	E	MESM	01.11.99	TIRELESS
Mettam, Samuel Richard, MSc(Econ),	SLT(IC)	S		01.09.00	DARTMOUTH BRNC
Mewes, David Bruce,	CAPT RM(IC)	-	SO(LE)	01.04.02	40 CDO RM
Meyer, Alexander James, BA,	LT(CC)	X	FC	01.12.98	801 SQN
Meyer, Stephen Richard, pce, psc, hcsc,	RADM		PWO(N)	01.07.99	PJHQ
Miall, Merlin Christopher, BSc,	SLT(IC)	X		01.05.00	WALNEY
Michie, Anthony Richard, BSc,	CDR(FTC)	E	WE	30.06.99	CV(F) IPT
Mickleburgh, Allan,	LT CDR(FTC)	X	REG	01.10.97	2SL/CNH
Middlemas, Simon Robert, BSc, CEng, MIMechE,	CDR(FTC)	E	MESM	30.06.96	NP DNREAY
Middleton, Christopher Sydney, BEd,	CAPT RM(CC)	-	LC	01.09.98	1 ASSLT GP RM

Name	Rank	Branch	Spec	Seniority	Where Serving
Middleton, Judith, BSc,	LT(SCC)	Q	IC*	26.04.01	RN GIBRALTAR
Middleton, Simon,	SURG SLT(SCC)	-		30.04.99	DARTMOUTH BRNC
Middleton, Toby Patrick Windsor, BSc, psc(m),	LT COL(FTC)	-	LC	21.11.00	PJHQ
Middleton, Wayne Trevor,	LT(CC)	S		01.08.00	ES AIR YEO
Midmore, Martin Jonathan,	LT(FTC)	E	AE(M)	14.10.94	ES AIR BRISTOL
Midwinter, Mark John, MB, BSc, BS, MD, FRCS,	SURG CDR(FCC)	-	(CGS)	31.12.98	RH HASLAR
Mifflin, Michelle Jane,	SLT(IC)	X	X	01.01.02	MWS DRYAD
Miklinski, Anthony Stanley, BSc, DipEd, psc,	CAPT(FTC)	E	TM	31.12.98	2SL/CNH FOTR
Milburn, Philip Kenneth, pce,	CDR(FTC)	X	AAWO	31.12.00	MWC SOUTHWICK
Milburn, Victoria,	LT(FTC)	MS	(AD)	01.04.01	INM ALVERSTOKE
Miles, Graham John, BSc, BEng,	LT CDR(FTC)	E	AE	07.08.00	ES AIR BRISTOL
Miles, Philip John, BA,	LT(CC)	S		01.08.98	FLEET HQ PORTS
Miles, Rebecca Lewis, BSc,	LT(FTC)	X	HM	01.01.97	814 SQN
Miles, Richard, MB, BS, MRCP,	SURG LTCDR(FCC)	-	(CX)	01.08.96	NP 1067 KOSOVO
Miles, Sean,	SURG SLT(SCC)	-		01.05.01	DARTMOUTH BRNC
Millar, Gordon Craig, BEng,	LT CDR(FTC)	E	AE	15.05.94	771 SQN
Millar, Kevin Ian, MIIE,	LT(FTC)	E	MESM	02.09.99	NEPTUNE NT
Millar, Stuart William Sinclair, MB, BS, MRCGP, Dip FFP,	SURG CDR(FCC)	-	GMPP	30.06.02	RALEIGH
Millard, Andrew Robert,	LT CDR(FTC)	X		01.01.99	ELANT/NAVNORTH
Millard, Jeremy Robert, BEng, AMIEE,	LT(IC)	E	ME	01.02.98	PJHQ
Millen, Ian Stuart,	LT CDR(FTC)	X	EW	01.10.99	MOD (LONDON)
Millen, Stuart Charles William,	LT(FTC)	X	P	01.04.93	849 SQN B FLT
Miller, Andrew James Gildard, ADC, pce, (Commodore)	CAPT(FTC)	X	PWO(A)	31.12.94	COMATG SEA
Miller, Colin Robert, pcea,	LT CDR(FTC)	X	O	01.10.99	MWC PORTSDOWN
Miller, David Edward,	LT(FTC)	MS	(AD)	25.07.96	NELSON (PAY)
Miller, Gary, (Act Lt Cdr)	LT(FTC)	X	AV	17.12.93	RFANSU (ARGUS)
Miller, Ian, MEng,	LT(FTC)	E	MESM	01.09.00	SPLENDID
Miller, John Charles, IEng, MIMarEST,	LT(FTC)	E	MESM	17.10.86	SULTAN
Miller, Kevin Roy,	LT(IC)	E	WE	01.05.01	DARTMOUTH BRNC
Miller, Mandy Catherine, BEng,	LT(FTC)	E	WE	01.02.97	WSA/CAPT MCTA
Miller, Paul David,	LT CDR(FTC)	X	PWO(A)	01.02.01	PORTLAND
Milles, Olivia Kate, BA,	LT(IC)	X	P	01.01.01	RNAS YEOVILTON
Milligan, Robert James Charles, pcea,	LT(CC)	X	O	16.04.92	815 FLT 229
Millington, Isobel Rose,	LT(FS)(FCC)	FS		08.01.99	NELSON
Millman, Dominic John, BSc, PGDip,	LT(FTC)	X	METOC	01.01.92	FLEET HQ NWD
Mills, Andrew, BEng,	LT CDR(FTC)	E	WESM	01.05.95	OCLC MANCH
Mills, Barrie, BA(OU), pdm,	MAJ(FTC)	BS		01.10.99	RM BAND PLYMOUTH
Mills, Gary Anthony,	LT(FTC)	X	PT	19.09.00	MWS DRYAD
Mills, Gordon William,	LT CDR(FTC)	E	WE	01.10.98	MWS COLLINGWOOD
Mills, Ian, BEng, CEng, MIEE,	LT CDR(FTC)	E	WE	01.10.01	NEW IPT
Mills, Sydney David Gareth,	LT(CC)	X	P	01.01.95	FLEET AV VALLEY
Mills, Thomas Clark, BSc, MA, psc(j),	LT CDR(FTC)	E	TM	01.10.93	2SL/CNH FOTR
Millward, Jeremy, MBE, pcea,	CDR(FTC)	X	P	31.12.99	HQ3GP HQSTC
Milne, Andrew Richard, BA,	MAJ(FTC)	-	MLDR	01.09.88	RM WARMINSTER
Milne, David Murray Ferguson, BSc, AMIEE,	LT CDR(FTC)	E	WE	16.08.79	MOD (BATH)
Milne, Peter Barkes, BEng,	LT(CC)	X	P	16.09.91	800 SQN
Milne, William John Connington, BEng,	LT(FTC)	E	MESM	01.09.00	SULTAN
Milner, Hugh Christopher, ocds(No),	MAJ(FTC)	-		01.09.89	40 CDO RM
Milner, Robert Adrian, MB, BS,	SURG LTCDR(MCC)	-		07.08.01	42 CDO RM
Milnes, John Lee, nadc, pce, pce(sm), (Commodore)	CAPT(FTC)	X	SM	31.12.93	SA ATHENS
Milsom, Jonathan, BEng,	LT CDR(FTC)	E	AE	01.10.99	SULTAN
Milton, Anthony Arthur, CB, OBE, MPhil, rcds, jsdc, psc(m),	MAJ GEN	-	C	01.04.99	JDCC
Milton, Gary Peter, pcea,	LT(FTC)	X	O	01.05.93	824 SQN
Milton, George James Gordon, BSc, CEng, MIEE, psc,	CDR(FTC)	X	WESM	31.12.90	NEPTUNE SWS
Milton, Graham Boyd McCullough, pcea,	LT CDR(FTC)	X	P	01.10.89	UKMFTS IPT
Mimpriss, Graham Donald, n,	LT CDR(FTC)	X	H1	01.04.99	FLEET HQ PORTS 2
Minall, Mark Lee,	LT(IC)	X		01.05.02	CORNWALL
Mincher, David Joseph Francis, BEng,	LT(FTC)	E	MESM	01.07.94	FOST CSST SEA
Minshall, Darren,	SURG SLT(SCC)	-		27.11.01	DARTMOUTH BRNC
Mitchell, Bernard Anthony, BSc, MIEE,	LT CDR(FTC)	E	WESM	01.11.79	MOD (BATH)
Mitchell, Christopher David,	LT(FTC)	X	MW	01.12.96	PENZANCE
Mitchell, Henry George Murray, pcea, psc(j),	CDR(FTC)	X	P	30.06.01	MOD (LONDON)

Name	Rank	Branch	Spec	Seniority	Where Serving
Mitchell, James Robert, BA,	LT(IC)	X	P	01.07.95	DHFS
Mitchell, Jamie Dundas,	LT(IC)	X		01.09.01	RALEIGH
Mitchell, Jamie Murray, BSc,	LT(IC)	X	O U/T	01.01.02	750 SQN SEAHAWK
Mitchell, Michael, (Act Lt Cdr)	LT(FTC)	X	AV	11.12.92	FLEET HQ PORTS
Mitchell, Patrick, IEng, MIIE,	LT(FTC)	E	WESM	05.06.92	WSA/CAPT MCTA
Mitchell, Paul Jeffrey,	SLT(IC)	X		01.05.00	CORNWALL
Mitchell, Richard Hannay, pce,	CDR(FTC)	X	PWO(A)	31.12.88	HQ SOUTHLANT
Mitchell, Stephen Derek, IEng, AMIMarEST,	LT CDR(FTC)	E	MESM	01.10.01	SULTAN
Mitchinson, Leslie,	LT CDR(FTC)	X	C	01.10.96	HQ DCSA
Mittins, Simon,	SLT(IC)	X	ATCU/T	01.05.00	RAF SHAWBURY
Moberly, Nigel George Hamilton, BSc, MIEE, CEng, psc,	CDR(FTC)	E	WE	30.06.91	DOSG BRISTOL
Mockford, James Arthur,	LT CDR(FTC)	E	AE(M)	01.10.96	ES AIR YEO
Moffat, John William, BEng,	CAPT RM(IC)	-		23.04.99	40 CDO RM
Moffatt, Danny,	2LT(IC)	-		01.09.01	CTCRM LYMPSTONE
Moffatt, Neil Robert, BSc, CEng, MIMarEST,	CDR(FTC)	E	MESM	30.06.02	MOD (BATH)
Moffatt, Roger, pcea, tp,	LT CDR(FTC)	X	P	01.10.95	LOAN JTEG BSC DN
Moir, Simon, BSc, CEng, MIEE, jsdc,	CDR(FTC)	E	WESM	30.06.87	DRAKE SFM
Mole, Andrew James, MEng,	SLT(IC)	E	ME U/T	01.09.00	SOMERSET
Moll, Andrew Gerald, jsdc, pce,	CAPT(FTC)	X	AAWO	30.06.00	CHATHAM
Mollard, Michael Joseph, BSc,	LT(IC)	X	P	01.07.94	815 FLT 201
Molloy, Lynne, BSc,	SLT(IC)	X	ATCU/T	01.09.99	RNAS CULDROSE
Molnar, Richard Mark,	LT(FTC)	X		01.04.01	JSCSC
Molyneaux, Dean George, BSc, CEng, MIEE, psc,	CDR(FTC)	E	WE	30.06.94	MWS COLLINGWOOD
Molyneux, Ian Thomas, BEng, AMIEE,	LT(CC)	E	WESM	01.08.99	VICTORIOUS(STBD)
Molyneux, Mark Edward, BSc,	SLT(IC)	X		01.05.00	CUMBERLAND
Monachello, Paolo Gino, BSc, SM,	LT(IC)	X		01.01.99	VICTORIOUS(PORT)
Moncrieff, Ian, BA, pce,	CAPT(FTC)	X	PWO(C)	30.06.99	ENDURANCE
Monday, Julia Elizabeth, BA,	LT(IC)	S		01.09.01	NBC PORTSMOUTH
Money, Christopher John, BA,	LT(IC)	X		01.06.00	RAMSEY
Monger, Paul David, MSc, PGDip,	LT CDR(FTC)	X	METOC	01.10.94	RFANSU
Monk, Christopher David, BSc,	LT CDR(FTC)	E	TM	01.10.97	CTCRM
Monk, Colin Roy, BSc,	LT(FTC)	X		01.06.96	CFPS SHORE
Monk, Kevin Neil,	SLT(IC)	X	O U/T	01.10.99	702 SQN HERON
Monk, Stephen, n,	LT(CC)	X	PWO(U)	01.06.95	ST ALBANS
Monnox, Jill,	LT(IC)	X		01.09.01	GLASGOW
Montague, Richard James, BSc,	LT(IC)	X		01.09.01	RALEIGH
Montgomery, Charles Percival Ross, BEng, pce, psc,	CAPT(FTC)	X	PWO(U)	31.12.97	MOD (LONDON)
Montgomery, Michael Henry, SM,	LT CDR(FTC)	X	SM	01.12.97	AST(N)
Moodie, Graeme Russell, jsdc, pce, pcea,	CAPT(FTC)	X	O	31.12.96	LOAN OMAN
Moody, Alistair Charles, BEng, MSc,	LT(FTC)	E	MESM	01.01.00	TRAFALGAR
Moody, David Christopher, BEng, AMIEE,	LT CDR(FTC)	E	WE	01.07.00	MOD (LONDON)
Moon, Ian Langland,	LT(IC)	E	ME	01.05.01	DARTMOUTH BRNC
Moore, Christian Benedict,	MAJ(FTC)	-		01.09.96	JSCSC
Moore, Christopher Ian, pce,	CDR(FTC)	X	AAWO	30.06.99	FLEET HQ PORTS 2
Moore, Christopher, BA, MSc,	LT CDR(CC)	X		05.12.99	MWS DRYAD
Moore, David Duncan Vincent,	LT CDR(FTC)	S	(W)	01.10.99	RMB STONEHOUSE
Moore, Martin Nicholas, MBE,	CDR(FTC)	E	WESM	31.12.00	MOD (LONDON)
Moore, Martin, BA,	LT CDR(FTC)	X	PWO(U)	01.06.00	CAMPBELTOWN
Moore, Matthew James,	LT(CC)	X		01.04.01	BROCKLESBY
Moore, Michael Ronald, IEng, MIL,	LT(FTC)	E	WE	29.10.82	HQ DCSA
Moore, Nicholas James, BSc,	LT(IC)	X	P	01.04.00	FLEET AV VALLEY
Moore, Paul Grenville, BDS,	SGLTCDR(D)(MCC)	-		31.12.98	DRAKE CBP(CNH)
Moore, Piers Henry George,	LT CDR(FTC)	X	SM	01.06.96	RN GIBRALTAR
Moore, Sean Barry, LLB,	LT CDR(FTC)	S	BAR	01.04.02	2SL/CNH
Moore, Suzanne Kathryn, BEd, n, MSc,	LT CDR(FTC)	X	PWO(U)	01.11.01	SHEFFIELD
Moores, Colin Peter, BEng, CEng, MIMarEST,	LT(CC)	E	ME	01.09.91	SULTAN
Moores, John Keith, BSc, pce, pce(sm),	CDR(FTC)	X	SM	30.06.97	MOD (LONDON)
Moores, John,	LT(FTC)	S	(S)	03.04.97	RALEIGH
Moorey, Christopher George, pce, psc(j),	LT CDR(FTC)	X	PWO(A)	01.03.94	MOD (LONDON)
Moorhouse, Edward James,	MAJ(FTC)	-		24.04.02	EXCHANGE ARMY UK
Moorhouse, Stephen Mark Richard, BSc,	LT(FTC)	X	PWO(C)	01.02.96	CHATHAM
Moran, Benjamin Michael,	LT(IC)	X		01.01.02	SHETLAND

Name	Rank	Branch	Spec	Seniority	Where Serving
Moran, Craig Andrew,	LT(FTC)	X	REG	10.01.00	MWS COLLINGWOOD
Moran, Julian Toby,	CAPT RM(CC)	-		28.04.99	EXCHANGE ARMY UK
Moran, Russell James,	LT(IC)	X		01.06.99	YORK
Moreby, Martin Francis,	LT(FTC)	X	AV	02.04.93	CHFHQ
Moreland, Michael John, BSc, CEng, MIMarEST, psc(m),	CDR(FTC)	E	MESM	30.06.00	FOSM FASLANE
Morey, Kevin Norton,	SLT(IC)	X		01.09.98	PEMBROKE
Morgan, Andrew Kevin Glyn, MSc, Cert Ed, (Act Cdr)	LT CDR(FTC)	E	IS	06.02.92	MOD (LONDON)
Morgan, Benjamin Penoyre, BSc,	LT(IC)	X	P U/T	01.01.02	DHFS
Morgan, Christopher William,	LT(IC)	X		01.05.02	MWS DRYAD
Morgan, David Henry, BSc,	LT CDR(FTC)	X		01.10.94	MWS DRYAD
Morgan, David, (Act Lt)	SLT(IC)	X	EW	01.05.99	SCU LEYDENE ACNS
Morgan, David, BSc, MBA, CEng, MRAeS, jsdc, (Act Capt)	CDR(FTC)	E	AE	30.06.90	2SL/CNH FOTR
Morgan, Forbes Scott, BEng, MSc,	LT CDR(FTC)	E	ME	01.11.97	FLEET HQ PORTS 2
Morgan, Frances Antonia, BA,	LT(FTC)	X		01.08.98	GLASGOW
Morgan, Gareth Lee,	SLT(IC)	X	P U/T	01.09.01	DHFS
Morgan, Huw Lloyd, BSc,	CAPT RM(IC)	-		01.09.01	CTCRM
Morgan, Nicholas Vaughan, MB, BS, Dip SM, FRCSEd, jsdc,	SURG CAPT(FCC)	-	GMPP	30.06.00	NMA PORTSMOUTH
Morgan, Peter Thomas, DSC, pce, psc,	CDR(FTC)	X	PWO(A)	30.06.97	MOD (LONDON)
Morgan, Rachel Sara,	LT(SCC)	Q	REGM	06.09.99	MODHU DERRIFORD
Morgan, Stephen Alexander, HNC,	LT CDR(FTC)	E	WE	01.10.97	GLOUCESTER
Morgan-Hosey, John Noel, BEng, CEng, MIMarEST,	LT CDR(FTC)	E	MESM	01.10.01	VIGILANT(PORT)
Morisetti, Neil, BSc, jsdc, pce,	CDRE(FTC)	X	PWO(A)	26.03.02	NMA PORTSMOUTH
Morley, Adrian, BA,	CAPT RM(FTC)	-	P	29.04.97	RAF LINTN/OUSE
Morley, Anthony Derek, BSc,	CDR(FTC)	E	IS	31.12.99	SACLANT USA
Morley, James David, pce,	LT CDR(FTC)	X	PWO(A)	01.08.99	MARLBOROUGH
Morley, James Ian, BSc,	LT(FTC)	E	ME	01.11.97	NP 1061
Morley-Smith, Nigel Humphrey, MA,	LT CDR(FTC)	E	WE	01.02.78	HQ DCSA
Morphet, Kathryn, BSc, MA,	LT(IC)	E	TM	01.01.01	MWS COLLINGWOOD
Morrell, Andrew John, (Act Lt Cdr)	LT(FTC)	X	SM	25.07.91	FLEET HQ NWD
Morris, Andrew Julian, BSc, MDA,	CDR(FTC)	E	WESM	31.12.99	FLEET HQ PORTS 2
Morris, Anthony Martin,	LT(CC)	X	P	01.07.93	824 SQN
Morris, Daniel Rowland,	SLT(IC)	X		01.04.00	SHETLAND
Morris, Daniel William, BEng,	LT(IC)	E	ME	01.01.02	SULTAN
Morris, David Simon, pce, pce(sm),	CAPT(FTC)	X	SM	30.06.02	MOD (LONDON)
Morris, Harriet Sophie, BA,	SLT(IC)	S		01.09.99	RALEIGH
Morris, James Andrew John, BSc,	MAJ(FTC)	-		01.09.98	JSCSC
Morris, John Owen, BComm,	CHAPLAIN	CE		06.10.92	DRAKE CBP(CNH)
Morris, Kevin Ian,	LT(FTC)	S	CA	24.07.97	FLEET HQ PORTS
Morris, Louisa,	SURG SLT(SCC)	-		01.07.00	DARTMOUTH BRNC
Morris, Nigel Jonathan, BSc, CEng, MIEE,	CDR(FTC)	E	WE	30.06.00	MOD (BATH)
Morris, Paul Edward Mannering,	MAJ(FTC)	-	P	01.05.97	CHFHQ
Morris, Paul John, BA,	LT(IC)	X		01.09.01	IRON DUKE
Morris, Paul Nigel, MSc,	CDR(FTC)	E	TM	31.12.90	BRNC RNSU SOTON
Morris, Paul, BSc, MA(Ed), PGDip, PGCE,	LT CDR(CC)	E	TM	01.10.99	NELSON RNSETT
Morris, Peter John, BEng, CEng, MIEE,	LT CDR(FTC)	E	WESM	10.06.92	DRAKE SFM
Morris, Philip John,	LT CDR(FTC)	X	C	01.10.97	MWS COLLINGWOOD
Morris, Richard John, pce,	LT CDR(FTC)	X	PWO(A)	01.04.97	FWO PORTS SEA
Morris, Richard,	2LT(IC)	-		01.09.98	CTCRM LYMPSTONE
Morris, Simon Timothy, BEng, CEng, MIEE,	LT CDR(FTC)	E	WESM	01.10.97	TORBAY
Morrison, Graham Lindsay, BDS, MBA, DRD, FDS RCSEdin, jsdc,	SGCAPT(D)(FCC)	-		31.12.96	DDA HALTON
Morrison, Kenneth William, IEng, AMIMarEST,	CDR(FTC)	E	ME	31.12.99	HQ DCSA
Morrison, Paul,	LT(FTC)	X	O	13.12.95	MWS DRYAD
Morrison, Robert William,	LT CDR(FTC)	E	ME	01.10.97	SULTAN
Morritt, Dain Cameron, BEng, MA, MSc, psc,	CDR(FTC)	E	WE	31.12.98	FWO DEVPT SEA
Morse, Andrew Charles, pcea,	LT CDR(FTC)	X	O	01.01.92	RNAS YEOVILTON
Morse, James Anthony, BSc, pce,	CDR(FTC)	X	PWO(N)	30.06.97	ILLUSTRIOUS
Morse, Jeremy, BSc,	LT(IC)	X	P	16.04.00	RNAS YEOVILTON
Morshead, Christopher, BEng, CEng, MRAeS,	LT CDR(FTC)	E	AE	14.05.98	FLEET HQ PORTS
Mortimer, Philip Robert,	SLT(IC)	E	WESM	01.01.01	MWS COLLINGWOOD
Mortimer, Richard Peter, BEd,	LT(FTC)	X	H1	01.08.94	EXCHANGE AUSTLIA

Name	Rank	Branch	Spec	Seniority	Where Serving
Mortlock, Philip Alun, BEng, AMIEE,	LT(CC)	E	WESM	01.01.00	VENGEANCE(STBD)
Morton, Justin Clarke,	CAPT RM(IC)	-	SO(LE)	01.04.02	RMB STONEHOUSE
Morton, Nigel Peter Bradshaw, BSc, MA, psc,	CDR(FTC)	S		30.06.99	RNAS YEOVILTON
Moseley, Stephen Huw, BEng,	SLT(IC)	X	P U/T	01.09.99	RAF CRANWELL EFS
Moss, Patrick John, MIIE,	LT CDR(FTC)	E	WESM	01.10.00	WSA BRISTOL
Moss, Peter, psc(m),	LT CDR(FTC)	X	O	18.02.92	OCLC BIRM
Moss, Richard Ashley, BSc, pce,	LT CDR(FTC)	X	O	01.03.99	ARK ROYAL
Moss, Timothy Edward, MBE, IEng, AMIMarEST,	LT CDR(FTC)	E	ME	01.10.97	LOAN BMATT(EC)
Mould, Philip,	LT(FTC)	X	P	01.05.93	899 SQN HERON
Mould, Timothy Paul,	LT CDR(FTC)	E	WE	16.03.99	HQ SOUTHLANT
Moules, Clare Elizabeth, LLB,	LT(IC)	X		01.08.96	FOST DPORT SHORE
Moules, Matthew Alexander John, BSc, SM(n),	LT(FTC)	X	SM	01.08.96	VENGEANCE(PORT)
Moulton, Simon John, BSc,	LT(CC)	X	O	01.01.92	CAMPBELTOWN FLT
Mount, James Bruce,	LT(CC)	X	P	01.06.00	849 SQN HQ
Mountford, Penny Claire, BEng,	LT(FTC)	E	ME	01.04.98	SULTAN
Mountjoy, Brian John, MIOSH,	LT CDR(FTC)	E	WESM	01.10.01	MOD (BATH)
Mountney, Gemma Ann, BSc,	LT(IC)	X		01.01.02	MWS DRYAD
Mourant, Raegan Elizabeth,	MID(UCE)(IC)	E	WE	01.09.00	DARTMOUTH BRNC
Mowat, Andrew Duncan John, MA,	SLT(IC)	S		01.01.00	DARTMOUTH BRNC
Mowatt, Patrick, PGDip,	LT(FTC)	X	HM(AS)	01.05.96	ECHO
Moy, David Keith,	LT(FTC)	E	ME	02.05.00	1 PBS SEA
Moys, Andrew John, BSc,	LT CDR(FTC)	X	METOC	01.10.97	EXCHANGE USA
Muddiman, Andrew Robert, BA,	CAPT RM(FTC)	-		01.09.97	FPGRM
Mudford, Hugh Christopher, psc,	LT COL(FTC)	-		30.06.99	MWC SOUTHWICK
Mudge, Adrian Michael, BSc,	LT(FTC)	X	O	01.07.93	849 SQN HQ
Mugridge, Anthony Robert, MB, ChB, FRCSEd,	SURG CAPT(FCC)	-	(CGS)	30.06.98	MODHU DERRIFORD
Mugridge, David Robert, BA, MNI, pce,	LT CDR(FTC)	X	PWO(A)	01.02.98	MWS DRYAD
Muir, Keith, pce, pcea, psc(j),	CDR(FTC)	X	O	31.12.98	BDS WASHINGTON
Muirhead, Barry George, BEng,	LT(CC)	X	P	01.08.98	824 SQN
Mules, Anthony John, n,	LT CDR(FTC)	X	H2	01.03.98	FWO DEVPT SEA
Mullen, Andrew John, MA, psc, psc(j),	CDR(FTC)	S	SM	30.06.95	DRAKE DPL
Mullen, Jason John, BA,	LT(FTC)	X	MCD	01.10.94	MWS DEF DIV SCHL
Mullen, Matthew Lee, BA,	LT(IC)	X		01.07.00	MIDDLETON
Mullins, Andrew Dominic, BEng,	LT(FTC)	E	MESM	01.12.96	VIGILANT(PORT)
Mullowney, Paul, BEng,	LT(CC)	X	O	01.02.99	849 SQN A FLT
Mulvaney, Paul Andrew, BSc,	LT CDR(FTC)	E	AE	01.06.00	ES AIR BRISTOL
Muncer, Richard A, BSc,	CAPT RM(IC)	-		01.09.00	CTCRM
Munday, Ian Vernon, MBE, pce, pcea, psc,	LT CDR(FTC)	X	O	01.04.85	824 SQN
Munday, Stephen William, BSc,	SLT(IC)	X		01.01.01	DARTMOUTH BRNC
Munden, Cathryn Sarah,	LT(SCC)	Q	OTSPEC	07.07.95	MODHU DERRIFORD
Mundin, Adrian John, BSc, CEng, MIMechE,	LT CDR(FTC)	E	ME	01.04.92	MARLBOROUGH
Mundy, Alan Richard, (Act Lt)	SLT(IC)	MS		01.05.99	CDO LOG REGT RM
Munns, Andrew Robert, BEng, CEng, MIMarEST, (Act Cdr)	LT CDR(FTC)	E	ME	01.01.96	MOD (BATH)
Munns, Christopher Ronald, jsdc, pce, (Commodore) pce(sm), hcsc,	CAPT(FTC)	X	SM	31.12.96	PJHQ
Munns, Edward Neil,	MID(UCE)(IC)	X		01.09.01	OCEAN
Munro, Kenneth, BEng, CEng, MIMarEST,	LT CDR(FTC)	E	ME	01.04.95	NBC PORTSMOUTH
Munro, Niall Frank Hamilton, LLB,	LT(IC)	X		01.01.99	MWS DRYAD
Munro-Lott, Peter Robert John, BA, pcea,	LT CDR(FTC)	X	O	01.10.96	ILLUSTRIOUS
Murch, Julian David, MSc, CEng, FIEE, psc, (Act Capt)	CDR(FTC)	E	WE	30.06.90	MOD (LONDON)
Murchie, Alistair Duncan, BEng,	LT(FTC)	E	ME	01.05.97	INVINCIBLE
Murchison, Ewen Alexander, BSc,	MAJ(FTC)	-		01.09.00	40 CDO RM
Murdoch, Andrew Peter, BSc,	LT(FTC)	S	BAR	01.11.94	2SL/CNH
Murdoch, Andrew William, MSc, AMIEE,	LT CDR(FTC)	E	WESM	01.06.93	MOD (LONDON)
Murdoch, Gillian Agnes, BDS,	SG LT(D)(MCC)	-		20.07.98	CDO LOG REGT RM
Murdoch, Stephen John,	CDR(FTC)	S		31.12.99	DLO/DGDEF LOG SP
Murgatroyd, Andrew Clive, MBE, BSc, jsdc, pce,	CDR(FTC)	X	AAWO	31.12.94	MOD (LONDON)
Murgatroyd, Kevin John, BEng,	LT(IC)	X	O	01.04.00	824 SQN
Murison, Lisa Campbell, MA, n,	LT(FTC)	X		01.05.95	JSCSC
Murnane, Paul Martin, MBE, pce,	CDR(FTC)	X	AAWO	01.10.98	2SL/CNH FOTR
Murphie, John Dermot Douglas, pce, psc(m),	CDR(FTC)	X	MCD	31.12.95	MWS DRYAD
Murphy, Andrew, IEng, MIIE,	LT(FTC)	E	WE	09.01.01	SCU LEYDENE ACNS

Name	Rank	Branch	Spec	Seniority	Where Serving
Murphy, Anthony, MBA,	CDR(FTC)	MS		30.06.02	MOD (LONDON)
Murphy, Diccon Andrew, BSc,	LT(CC)	X	P	01.04.92	702 SQN HERON
Murphy, James, BSc,	LT CDR(FTC)	S	SM	01.06.92	RALEIGH
Murphy, Kian Stuart, BA,	CAPT RM(CC)	-		01.05.98	EXCHANGE ARMY UK
Murphy, Nicholas, MBE, MNI, pce,	LT CDR(FTC)	X	PWO(U)	01.09.90	BFFI
Murphy, Paul Anthony, BA,	LT CDR(FTC)	S	SM	01.03.00	GLASGOW
Murphy, Peter William, MSc, BEng,	LT CDR(FTC)	E	MESM	01.09.95	MOD (BATH)
Murphy, Richard James, BA,	LT(IC)	X		01.09.99	SOMERSET
Murphy, Stephen Mark, BEng,	LT(FTC)	E	ME	01.08.96	FOST SEA
Murphy, Steven Robert Anthony, BA, pce(sm),	LT CDR(FTC)	X	SM	01.09.98	TRIUMPH
Murray, Alexander Bruce,	MAJ(FTC)	-		26.04.00	FLEET HQ PORTS 2
Murray, Alister,	LT(IC)	MS		01.09.01	DEF MED TRG CTR
Murray, Andrew Sidney,	LT CDR(FTC)	X	P	01.10.99	820 SQN
Murray, Grant McNiven, BEng,	LT CDR(FTC)	E	WESM	01.06.98	SCEPTRE
Murray, Greig Martin, BSc,	SLT(IC)	X		01.09.99	WALNEY
Murray, Robert Henry, MBE, BSc, MIMechE,	LT CDR(FTC)	E	MESM	01.01.82	CNNRP BRISTOL
Murray, Simon Christopher, BSc,	LT(IC)	E	TM	01.01.98	NEPTUNE 2SL/CNH
Murray, Stephen John, pcea, gdas,	LT CDR(FTC)	X	O	01.10.89	814 SQN
Murray, William Richard Charles, BA,	MAJ(FTC)	-		01.09.01	CDO LOG REGT RM
Murrison, Richard Anthony, MA, GCIS, ACIS, psc(j),	LT CDR(FTC)	S		01.03.97	2SL/CNH
Murton, William Maurice, BSc, pcea,	LT CDR(FTC)	X	P	01.10.92	727 NAS
Muscroft, Paul James Victor,	LT CDR(FTC)	E	WE	01.10.93	2SL/CNH FOTR
Musto, Edward Charles, BA, psc(m),	LT COL(FTC)	-		31.12.96	COMAMPHIBFOR
Mutch, Jonathan Rocliffe, BSc,	LT(CC)	X	P	01.09.94	815 SQN HQ
Muxworthy, Angela Mary Blythe, psc,	CAPT(FTC)	W	IS	30.06.02	MOD (BATH)
Muyambo, Nomalanga Nosizo, MSc,	LT(IC)	E	TM	01.01.00	SULTAN
Myers, Geoffrey William, OBE, QHDS, (Commodore) BChD, MSc, MFGDP(UK), LDS RCS(Eng), jsdc,	SGCAPT(D)(FCC)	-		31.12.94	DDA HALTON
Myerscough, Andrew Paul, BEng,	LT CDR(FTC)	E	AE(P)	01.10.96	RNAS CULDROSE

N

Name	Rank	Branch	Spec	Seniority	Where Serving
Naden, Andrew Charles Keith, BSc, CEng, MIMarEST,	CDR(FTC)	E	ME	30.06.02	JSCSC
Naden, James Ralph, MSc, BA, PGDip, Cert Ed,	LT CDR(FTC)	E	IS	01.10.94	AFPAA(CENTURION)
Nail, Vaughan Anthony, MA, psc,	CDR(FTC)	X	H CH	31.12.97	FWO DEVONPORT
Nairn, Alan Barclay, BSc,	LT CDR(FTC)	S		01.02.99	FLEET HQ PORTS
Nairn, Robert, OBE, psc,	CDR(FTC)	S		31.12.96	MOD (LONDON)
Naismith, David Hamilton, BSc, pcea,	LT CDR(FTC)	X	O	01.05.91	824 SQN
Naldrett, Geoffrey Clive,	LT(IC)	X	C	08.01.01	HQ DCSA
Nance, Adrian Ralph, OBE, BSc, pce, (Commodore)	CAPT(FTC)	X	PWO(A)	30.06.97	MOD (LONDON)
Napier, Graham Andrew,	LT CDR(FTC)	E	AE(M)	01.07.01	MERLIN IPT
Nash, Philip David, BSc,	LT(FTC)	X	O	01.08.95	815 FLT 219
Nash, Robin David Cory, BSc,	LT(IC)	X		01.01.02	DRAKE CBP(DLO)
Nash, Rubin Piero, BSc,	LT(IC)	X		01.01.02	MWS DRYAD
Nash, Russell Frank Roger,	SLT(IC)	E	WESM	01.01.01	MWS COLLINGWOOD
Nathanson, Helen, BA,	LT(CC)	S		01.02.97	NOTTINGHAM
Naylor, Andrew James,	LT(CC)	X	P	16.06.94	824 SQN
Naylor, Ian Frederick, MA, AKC,	CHAPLAIN	CE		16.09.86	MWS EXCELLENT
Neal, Alistair John Duncan, MB, ChB, DipAvMed,	SURG CDR(FCC)	-	GMPP	30.06.96	MOD (LONDON)
Neal, Simon Matthew, pcea,	LT(IC)	X	O	16.01.92	EXCHANGE USA
Neave, Andrew Michael,	LT CDR(FTC)	X	ATC	01.10.98	FOST DPORT SHORE
Neave, Christopher Bryan, OBE, BSc, pcea,	CAPT(FTC)	E	AE(P)	30.06.01	MOD (LONDON)
Necker, Carl Dominic, PGDIPAN,	LT CDR(FTC)	X	PWO(N)	01.11.99	ALBION
Needham, Phillip David, DSC, MCGI, gdas,	LT CDR(FTC)	X	O	01.10.92	ES AIR YEO
Neil, David Alexander,	MID(IC)	X		01.05.00	DARTMOUTH BRNC
Neil, Simon John, MA, pce, psc(j),	CDR(FTC)	X	MCD	31.12.97	2SL/CNH
Neild, Timothy, n,	LT(FTC)	X		01.11.95	EXPRESS
Nekrews, Alan Neil Laurence Michael,	SLT(IC)	X		01.01.01	DARTMOUTH BRNC
Nelson, Andrew,	LT CDR(FTC)	E	WESM	01.10.95	MWC PORTSDOWN
Nelson, Christopher Stuart, BSc, n,	LT CDR(FTC)	X	PWO(U)	01.03.01	CHATHAM
Nelson, David Lawrence,	LT CDR(FTC)	X	P	01.10.92	FLEET HQ PORTS
Nelson, Digby Theodore, BSc, psc,	CDR(FTC)	S		30.06.94	NMA PORTSMOUTH
Nelson, Dominic Edward, BSc,	LT CDR(FTC)	X	PWO(A)	01.04.88	DRAKE DPL

Name	Rank	Branch	Spec	Seniority	Where Serving
Nelson, Lisa Marie, BEng,	LT(FTC)	E	ME	01.01.95	SVHO IPT
Nelson, Matthew Rodney,	LT(CC)	X	P	16.11.98	JSCSC
Nelson, Paul Moffat, BA, PGCE,	LT(CC)	E	TM	01.01.97	JSCSC
Nelson, Timothy Brian, pce,	LT CDR(FTC)	X	AAWO	16.06.83	MOD (BATH)
Nelson, Victoria, BA,	LT(FTC)	S		01.03.96	JSCSC
Nelstrop, Andrew Marcus, BCh,	SURG LT(SCC)	-		10.02.99	MODHU DERRIFORD
Neofytou, Andrew George Klropas, BEng,	LT(IC)	X	P	01.08.99	RNAS CULDROSE
Nethercott, Eoin Robert, BEng,	LT(IC)	X		01.05.99	NEPTUNE
Netherwood, Lyndsey Dawn, BA,	LT(FTC)	X		15.09.99	DUMBARTONCASTLE
Neve, Piers Charles, pce(sm),	LT CDR(FTC)	X	SM	11.02.94	VICTORIOUS(STBD)
New, Christopher Maxwell, BEng,	LT CDR(FTC)	E	ME	01.04.97	MWS EXCELLENT
New, Richard Ashley,	LT(IC)	S		01.02.01	VICTORIOUS(STBD)
Newall, Jeremy Andrew,	LT CDR(CC)	X	ATC	01.03.94	HQ AIRNORTH
Newall, Paul John, MA,	SLT(IC)	E	TM	01.09.99	CHATHAM
Newby Stubbs, Rebecca Louise,	LT(SCC)	Q	IC	15.08.99	UKSU SOUTHLANT
Newell, Gary David,	LT(IC)	E	ME	29.04.01	GRAFTON
Newell, Jonathan Michael, MSc, CEng, FIMarEST, MIL, fsc,	CDR(FTC)	E	ME	31.12.97	ALBION
Newell, Phillip Russell, BEng,	LT CDR(FTC)	X	H1	01.06.01	FWO DEVONPORT
Newing, Stephen Geoffrey, psc,	LT COL(FTC)	-	MOR	30.06.98	LOAN KUWAIT
Newland, Mark Ian, BSc, pce,	LT CDR(FTC)	X	PWO(U)	01.10.96	QUORN
Newlands, George Alexander, BSc, pce, pcea, psc,	LT CDR(FTC)	X	O	01.02.89	824 SQN
Newman, Christopher Richard Spencer,	LT(IC)	X		01.05.02	MWS DRYAD
Newman, David,	LT(CC)	E	AE	01.01.99	RNAS CULDROSE
Newman, Paul Henry, MBE, BSc,	LT CDR(FTC)	X	METOC	01.05.89	HQ SOUTHLANT
Newman, Sally,	LT(SCC)	Q	OTSPEC	18.08.97	JSU NORTHWOOD
Newport, David James,	MID(IC)	X		01.09.00	DARTMOUTH BRNC
Newport, Janet Daveen McDiarmid,	LT(CS)(CAS)	-		09.01.98	DNR SEE 1
Newth, Christopher, BSc,	LT(IC)	E	IS	01.05.00	OCEAN
Newton, David John, pce, psc,	CDR(FTC)	X	P	31.12.98	MOD (LONDON)
Newton, Garry Arnold, pce(sm),	CDR(FTC)	X	SM	30.06.00	VIGILANT(PORT)
Newton, James Lloyd,	LT(CC)	X	P	16.09.95	847 SQN
Newton, Michael Ronald, FIEIE, FIIE,	LT CDR(FTC)	E	WE	22.09.87	MOD (BATH)
Newton, Nicholas,	SURG SLT(SCC)	-		11.01.00	DARTMOUTH BRNC
Newton, Robert,	2LT(IC)	-		01.09.98	CTCRM LYMPSTONE
Nguyo, David Ngibuini, MEng,	SLT(IC)	E	WE	01.09.99	MWS COLLINGWOOD
Nicholas, Bryan John, BSc, pcea,	LT CDR(FTC)	X	P	01.10.01	DHFS
Nicholas, Jeremy Richard,	LT RM(IC)	-	SO(LE)	01.04.00	FEARLESS
Nicholas, Stephen Paul, BEng,	LT(CC)	E	MESM	01.04.94	DARTMOUTH BRNC
Nicholls, Barry Austin,	CAPT RM(FTC)	-	SO(LE)	01.01.95	UKLFCSG RM
Nicholls, Guy Anthony,	LT CDR(FTC)	E	WE	01.10.99	MARLBOROUGH
Nicholls, Larry Roy,	SLT(IC)	E	WE	01.05.00	DARTMOUTH BRNC
Nichols, Elizabeth Anne, MB, BS, MRCGP, DObstRCOG,	SURG CDR(FCC)	-	GMPP	31.12.00	HQ 3 CDO BDE RM
Nicholson, Brian Harold,	LT(IC)	E	AE	29.04.01	RNAS YEOVILTON
Nicholson, David Andrew Gore, BEng,	LT(IC)	X		01.01.02	WALNEY
Nicholson, David Peter, BSc,	CAPT RM(FTC)	-	LC	01.09.99	1 ASSLT GP RM
Nicholson, Graeme, MB, BCh, MRCGP, AFOM,	SURG CDR(FCC)	-	GMPP	31.12.00	CNNRP BRISTOL
Nicholson, Heather, BSc,	LT CDR(FTC)	S		06.04.97	INVINCIBLE
Nicholson, Jonathan Craig,	LT(FTC)	E	WE	02.09.99	FOST SEA
Nicholson, Kristin James, BA,	LT(FTC)	S		01.08.94	FWO PORTSMOUTH
Nicholson, Paul James,	LT(FTC)	E	WE	10.06.88	DCSA RADIO PLY
Nicholson, Shaun Raymond, BA,	LT(FTC)	X	PWO(U)	22.11.94	EXCHANGE AUSTLIA
Nicholson, Simon Charles Lawrence, pce,	CDR(FTC)	X	MCD	30.06.96	SUPT OF DIVING
Nickisson, David John,	LT(CS)RM(CAS)	-		02.05.97	DNR SCO 2
Nicklas, Colin James, BEng, MSc, CEng, MIEE,	LT CDR(FTC)	E	WE	01.06.00	SUTHERLAND
Nicklin, Gareth James Edward, BEng,	LT(CC)	E	MESM	01.01.00	VIGILANT(PORT)
Nickolls, Kevin Paul, BEng,	LT CDR(FTC)	E	AE	01.01.00	AFPAA(CENTURION)
Nicol, Peter James Stewart, MB, BS, LRCP, MRCS, JCPTGP,	SURG CDR(FCC)	-	GMPP	30.06.94	NMA PORTSMOUTH
Nicoll, Andrew John, BEng,	LT(FTC)	E	WE	01.04.97	GLASGOW
Nicoll, Steve Kenneth, (Act Maj)	CAPT RM(FTC)	-	SO(LE)	01.01.96	DCTA
Nimmo-Scott, Sarah Jane, BEng,	LT(FTC)	X		01.09.00	LIVERPOOL

Name	Rank	Branch	Spec	Seniority	Where Serving
Nimmons, Paul, BEng,	LT(FTC)	E	MESM	01.06.96	TRIUMPH
Nisbet, James Henry Thomas, pce, BSc,	LT CDR(FTC)	X	PWO(U)	01.07.95	SUPT OF DIVING
Nitsch, Karl David,	LT(IC)	X		01.10.99	FEARLESS
Nixon, Michael Charles, OBE, FRAeS, jsdc, pce, pcea,	CAPT(FTC)	X	P	31.12.99	AGRIPPA NAVSOUTH
Nixon, Paul William, BSc, CEng, MIMechE,	CDR(FTC)	E	MESM	30.06.96	FWO DEVONPORT
Nixon, Sophie Elizabeth Kate,	SLT(IC)	X		01.09.00	MANCHESTER
Noakes, Kevin Massie, BEng, MSc, CEng, MIEE, gw,	LT CDR(FTC)	E	WE	01.05.02	LOAN DSTL
Noble, Kevan Leslie,	LT RM(IC)	-	SO(LE)	01.04.00	CTCRM
Noble, Mark Jonathan Dean, psc,	COL(FTC)	-	P	31.12.99	FLEET HQ PORTS
Noblett, Peter Gordon Arthur, MNI, pce, pce(sm),	LT CDR(FTC)	X	SM	01.10.01	SPLENDID
Nokes, Oliver,	MID(NE)(IC)	X		01.09.01	DARTMOUTH BRNC
Nolan, Anthony Laurence,	CDR(FTC)	X	C	30.06.01	FLEET CIS PORTS
Nolan, Gareth John, BSc,	SLT(IC)	X	P U/T	01.01.00	RAF CRANWELL EFS
Nolan, Paul Ernest,	CAPT RM(IC)	-	SO(LE)	01.04.02	AACC MID WALLOP
Nolton, James Raymond, MBE, BSc,	LT CDR(FTC)	E	ME	01.02.86	SCOTIA
Noon, David,	LT(FTC)	S	CA	23.07.98	RNAS CULDROSE
Noonan, Charles Daniel, BA,	LT(IC)	X		01.05.01	SHEFFIELD
Norford, Michael,	LT(FTC)	X	PT	03.04.97	RALEIGH
Norgan, David James, BA, n,	LT CDR(FTC)	X	PWO(C)	01.07.01	ARK ROYAL
Norgate, Andrew Thomas, BSc, SM,	LT(FTC)	X	SM	01.11.98	VENGEANCE(PORT)
Norgate, Perry Raymond Edward,	LT(FTC)	E	ME	19.06.98	ENTERPRISE
Norman, Jaimie McCoy, BA,	LT RM(IC)	-		01.09.00	FPGRM
Norman, Phillip Douglas,	LT CDR(FTC)	E	WE	01.10.99	MWS DRYAD
Norman, Shaun Lindsay, BEng,	LT CDR(FTC)	E	AE	01.10.98	820 SQN
Norman, Toby Benjamin,	SLT(IC)	X		01.01.00	LEEDS CASTLE
Norris, Edmund,	2LT(IC)	-		01.09.98	CTCRM LYMPSTONE
Norris, Guy Patrick,	LT(CC)	X	O	16.07.93	DARTMOUTH BRNC
Norris, James Garnet, BA,	LT CDR(FTC)	E	AE	01.11.00	MOD (LONDON)
Norris, Richard Edward, BDS, MGDS RCS, LDS RCS(Eng), MA, psc(j),	SGCDR(D)(FCC)	-		30.06.96	DDA PORTSMOUTH
Norris, Robert John, pce,	CDR(FTC)	X	PWO(A)	30.06.95	2SL/CNH
Norriss, William Desmond, PhD, MB, ChB, BSc,	SURG LTCDR(FCC)	-		20.05.02	RH HASLAR
Norriss, Mark William,	SLT(IC)	X	P U/T	01.01.02	DARTMOUTH BRNC
Northcote, Mark Richard,	LT(IC)	X	MCD	01.12.00	QUORN
Northcott, Michael Kevin, BEng,	LT(CC)	E	WE	01.03.99	CUMBERLAND
Northcott, Philip James, BEng,	SLT(IC)	E	ME	01.09.99	SULTAN
Northeast, Paul,	LT(FTC)	S	SM	01.04.01	SUPERB
Northover, Adam Frederick, BSc, n,	LT(FTC)	X		01.08.97	MWS DRYAD
Northwood, Gerard Rodney, pce,	CDR(FTC)	X	AAWO	30.06.99	BFFI
Norton, Alexandra Louise Elizabeth, MEng,	SLT(IC)	E	ME	01.09.99	SULTAN
Norton, Andrew Jonathan, BSc, CEng, MIEE, psc,	CDR(FTC)	E	WE	30.06.87	FLEET HQ NWD
Norton, Thomas Charles Horatio,	2LT(FTC)	-		01.09.97	CTCRM
Norwood, James Kenneth, BSc,	SLT(IC)	X		01.01.01	DARTMOUTH BRNC
Norwood, Jeffrey,	SURG CDR(SCC)	-		01.03.97	DARTMOUTH BRNC
Notley, Edward John, LLB,	SLT(IC)	X		01.01.00	ANGLESEY
Notley, Louis Paul, MDA,	LT CDR(FTC)	S	SM	01.03.96	DLO/DGDEF LOG SP
Nottley, Simon Matthew,	LT(FTC)	E	WESM	01.04.01	SPLENDID
Nowosielski, Frank, MBE,	LT CDR(FTC)	X	AV	01.10.93	VICTORY
Noyce, Nigel Roderick,	LT CDR(FTC)	X		15.01.97	DISC
Noyce, Roger Grenville, MRINA,	LT(CC)	X		01.06.95	PJHQ
Noyce, Vincent Robert Amos, pce,	LT CDR(FTC)	X	PWO(A)	01.11.01	NOTTINGHAM
Noye, Charles Lovell, MBE, AMINucE,	LT CDR(FTC)	E	MESM	21.02.84	FWO DEVONPORT
Noyes, David James,	CDR(FTC)	S		30.06.01	FLEET HQ PORTS 2
Nugent, Colin James,	LT CDR(FTC)	X	EW	01.10.01	ELANT/NAVNORTH
Nunn, Christopher John, OBE, nadc, psc(a),	LT COL(FTC)	-	P	30.06.88	NELSON (PAY)
Nunn, Gerald Eric, BSc, CEng, PGCE, PGDip,	LT CDR(CC)	X	TM	01.10.95	NELSON RNSETT
Nunnen, Catherine Rebecca, MA,	LT(IC)	X	O	01.05.01	815 FLT 208
Nurse, Michael Talbot, BSc,	LT CDR(FTC)	E	AE	01.06.88	ES AIR WYTON
Nursey, Adrian Paul, IEng, MIIE,	LT(FTC)	E	MESM	02.09.99	DRAKE SFM
Nurton, Katherine Emma, BDS,	SGLTCDR(D)(SCC)	-		09.08.00	MWS EXCELLENT

Name	Rank	Branch	Spec	Seniority	Where Serving

O

O'Brien, Ian Patrick, BTech, IEng, MIIE,	LT(FTC)	E	WE	24.02.95	FLEET HQ PORTS 2
O'Brien, Kieran John, BEng,	LT CDR(FTC)	E	AE	01.02.00	ES AIR YEO
O'Brien, Patrick Michael Christopher, BEng, MSc, CEng, MIEE	LT CDR(FTC)	E	IS	01.10.96	NMA PORTSMOUTH
O'Brien, Peter Charles, BSc, PGCE, adp, (Act Cdr)	LT CDR(FTC)	E	IS	23.04.88	AFPAA HQ
O'Brien, Thomas Patrick,	SLT(IC)	E	WESM	01.01.01	MWS COLLINGWOOD
O'Byrne, Patrick Barry Mary, pce(sm), SM(n),	LT CDR(FTC)	X	SM	01.11.00	VIGILANT(PORT)
O'Callaghan, Patrick Francis,	LT(IC)	X		01.05.02	LANCASTER
O'Callaghan, Sean Tiernan,	LT CDR(FTC)	MS		01.10.00	INM ALVERSTOKE
O'Connor, David Paul,	SLT(IC)	E	WESM	01.01.00	CSST RNSSS
O'Donnell, Ian Mark, MA, psc,	MAJ(FTC)	-	P	01.10.97	847 SQN
O'Flaherty, Christopher Patrick John, pce,	LT CDR(FTC)	X	PWO(U)	01.03.99	UKMARBATSTAFF
O'Grady, Matthew James, fsc,	CDR(FTC)	S	SM	30.06.01	FLEET HQ NWD
O'Hara, Gerard Connor,	CAPT RM(FTC)	-		01.09.97	FPGRM
O'Kane, Robert James, BSc,	LT(IC)	X	O	16.05.00	820 SQN
O'Keefe, Thomas,	2LT(IC)	-		01.09.00	CTCRM LYMPSTONE
O'Neill, Conor Mark,	SLT(UCE)(IC)	X		01.09.01	DARTMOUTH BRNC
O'Neill, Henry Larence,	SLT(IC)	X	P U/T	01.01.00	DARTMOUTH BRNC
O'Neill, Patrick John, MA, MSc,	CDR(FTC)	E	WESM	30.06.97	MOD (LONDON)
O'Neill, Paul Joseph, BEng,	LT(FTC)	E	MESM	01.10.95	DRAKE CBS
O'Neill, Richard Kim, pce, psc,	CDR(FTC)	X	O	31.12.89	SHAPE BELGIUM
O'Neill, Timothy James,	LT(IC)	X		01.01.02	MWS DRYAD
O'Nyons, Yorick Ian, BA, SM(n),	LT(FTC)	X	SM	01.07.94	RALEIGH
O'Reilly, Sean Anthony, pce, psc,	CDR(FTC)	X	MCD	31.12.95	SAUDI AFPS SAUDI
O'Reilly, Terence Michael, MRAeS, psc(j),	CDR(FTC)	X	AE	31.12.98	LAIPT
O'Riordan, Michael Patrick, BSc, pce, pcea,	LT CDR(FTC)	X	P	01.04.89	LYNX OEU
O'Rourke, Richard Michael,	LT(IC)	S		01.05.02	UKMARBATSTAFF
O'Shaughnessy, David John, BEng,	LT(FTC)	E	ME	01.06.97	OCLC MANCH
O'Shaughnessy, Patrick Joseph,	LT CDR(FTC)	E	WE	01.10.99	CV(F) IPT
O'Shaughnessy, Paul Charles, BEng,	LT(CC)	E	WE	01.01.99	SOMERSET
O'Shea, Eamon Patrick, BEng,	LT CDR(FTC)	E	AE	01.07.98	ES AIR BRISTOL
O'Shea, Matthew Kent, BSc,	SURG SLT(SCC)	-		17.05.99	DARTMOUTH BRNC
O'Sullivan, Aidan Marian, pcea,	CDR(FTC)	X	O	30.06.02	RAF AWC
O'Sullivan, Barrie Oliver,	LT CDR(FTC)	X	P	01.10.00	846 SQN
O'Sullivan, Matthew Richard John,	LT RM(IC)	-		01.09.01	CDO LOG REGT RM
O'Sullivan, Michael Louis James, BSc,	LT CDR(FTC)	X	H1	01.08.01	MOD (LONDON)
O'Sullivan, Paul Benedict, BEng,	SLT(IC)	E	ME U/T	01.09.00	KENT
O'Toole, Mathew Charles, BEng,	LT(FTC)	E	MESM	01.10.97	VIGILANT(PORT)
Oakes, Ian James,	LT(IC)	X	P	16.06.94	848 SQN HERON
Oakes, Michael Carson,	LT(IC)	X		01.05.02	COTTESMORE
Oakley, Andrew J, BSc,	LT(IC)	E	TM	01.01.01	DARTMOUTH BRNC
Oakley, Claire Marie,	LT(IC)	X		01.05.01	CORNWALL
Oakley, Sarah Ellen, MA, n,	LT(FTC)	X		01.05.97	NORFOLK
Oatley, Timothy Peter,	LT(FTC)	X	O	16.07.94	824 SQN
Oddy, David Mark,	LT CDR(FTC)	X	P	01.10.00	848 SQN HERON
Oden, Mark, BA,	CAPT RM(IC)	-		01.09.99	AGRIPPA AFSOUTH
Officer, Robert Lennie,	LT(CC)	X	MW	01.02.96	FOSNNI OPS DLO
Offord, Matthew Ronald,	LT CDR(FTC)	X	MCD	01.04.02	BROCKLESBY
Oflaherty, John Stephen, BEng,	LT CDR(FTC)	E	ME	03.10.97	GRAFTON
Oherlihy, Simon Ian, MA,	CAPT RM(FTC)	-		01.09.96	1 ASSLT GP RM
Okukenu, Dele,	LT(IC)	X	P	01.01.96	846 SQN
Oldfield, Paul Henry, MSc, MBCS,	LT CDR(CC)	E	IS	01.10.95	PJHQ
Oliphant, William, psc(j),	LT CDR(FTC)	S		01.10.98	PJHQ
Olive, Peter Nicholas, pce, n,	LT CDR(FTC)	X	PWO(A)	01.11.98	LEDBURY
Oliver, Graeme John, BSc,	LT(IC)	S		01.12.99	AFPAA(CENTURION)
Oliver, Graham, PGDip, BSc,	LT(CC)	X	METOC	01.05.91	GANNET SAR FLT
Oliver, Kevin Brian, BEng, MSc, psc(j), mdtc,	MAJ(FTC)	-	MLDR	01.09.97	MOD (LONDON)
Olivey, Timothy Douglas,	LT(IC)	X	O U/T	01.05.02	815 FLT 244
Ollerton, Justin Clive,	LT(CC)	X	P	16.11.96	771 SQN
Ollis, Victoria,	LT(IC)	S		01.05.01	ELANT/NAVNORTH

Name	Rank	Branch	Spec	Seniority	Where Serving
Olliver, Adrian John, MILT,	LT CDR(FTC)	S	SM	01.10.96	NORTHUMBERLAND
Oneill, James, BA,	LT(CC)	X	HM	22.11.99	FEARLESS
Onions, Judith Mary, ARRC,	CDR(FCC)	Q	IC	30.06.02	MODHU DERRIFORD
Onyike, Chinyere Eme, NDipM, BEng, MSc, CEng, MIEE, MCMI,	LT CDR(FTC)	E	WE	01.01.02	MWS COLLINGWOOD
Orchard, Adrian Paul,	LT CDR(FTC)	X	P	16.01.99	EXCHANGE USA
Ordway, Christopher Norman Maurice Patrick,	CAPT RM(FTC)	-		01.09.99	FLEET AV SUPPORT
Orme, William Benjamin,	LT(IC)	X	P U/T	01.05.02	RAF CRANWELL EFS
Orr, Keith John, BEng,	LT(IC)	E	MESM	01.12.99	VENGEANCE(PORT)
Orr, Simon David,	CAPT RM(IC)	-	SO(LE)	01.04.02	FLEET HQ PORTS 2
Orton, David Michael, BSc, DPhil,	LT CDR(FTC)	E	TM	01.10.00	FOST CSST FSLN
Osbaldestin, Richard Alan,	LT(FTC)	X	MCD	01.10.98	INVERNESS
Osborn, Colvin Graeme, BSc, SM,	LT(FTC)	X	SM	01.06.94	JARIC
Osborn, Richard Marcus,	LT CDR(FTC)	X	AAWO	01.02.99	NOTTINGHAM
Osborne, John Michael, BSc,	LT(IC)	E	TM	01.10.99	MWS COLLINGWOOD
Osbourn, Simon Edwin John, pce,	LT CDR(FTC)	X	PWO(U)	01.04.93	MWS DRYAD
Osman, Mark Ronald, pcea, psc,	LT CDR(FTC)	X	P	01.09.86	824 SQN
Osmond, Justin Bruce, BEng, MSc,	LT CDR(FTC)	E	AE	01.02.99	JSCSC
Oswald, *Sir* (John) Julian (Robertson), GCB, rcds, psc,	ADM OF FLEET	-	G	02.03.93	
Ottaway, Thomas Arthur,	SLT(IC)	X		01.05.00	SOUTHAMPTON
Ottewell, Paul Steven, BSc, SM(n),	LT(IC)	X	SM	01.01.97	TORBAY
Oulds, Keith Antony, BEng,	LT CDR(FTC)	X	MCD	01.09.00	FLEET HQ PORTS 2
Oura, Adrian Nicholas, BA,	CAPT RM(FTC)	-		01.09.00	40 CDO RM
Ouvry, Janet Elisabeth Delahaize,	LT(SCC)	Q		25.03.97	DARTMOUTH BRNC
Ovenden, Neil Stephen Paul, pce,	LT CDR(FTC)	X	PWO(U)	01.02.95	MWS DRYAD
Ovens, Jeremy John, BSc, pce, pcea, psc,	CDR(FTC)	X	O	31.12.99	EXCHANGE USA
Ovens, Michael James,	LT CDR(FTC)	X	PWO(U)	20.08.97	FLEET HQ NWD
Overington, Nigel, BSc, pce,	CDR(FTC)	X	PWO(U)	31.12.90	FLEET HQ PORTS
Owen, Andrew,	2LT(IC)	-		01.09.98	CTCRM LYMPSTONE
Owen, Douglas Philip Collinson,	SLT(IC)	X		01.09.99	PENZANCE
Owen, Glyn,	LT(CC)	X	O	16.02.97	702 SQN HERON
Owen, Nigel Richard, jsdc, pce, psc(j), (Commodore)	CAPT(FTC)	X	AWO(U)	30.06.93	NATO DEF COL
Owen, Peter Clive, pcea,	LT CDR(FTC)	X	P	01.10.91	824 SQN
Owen, Samuel Thomas Louis,	LT(IC)	X	SM	01.11.00	SPLENDID
Owen, Vincent Frederick,	LT(IC)	X		01.05.02	MWS DRYAD
Owens, Daniel Tudor, BEng, CEng, MIMechE,	LT CDR(FTC)	E	ME	01.08.99	GLASGOW

P

Name	Rank	Branch	Spec	Seniority	Where Serving
Packham, Craig Nicholas Ronald,	LT(CC)	X	P	01.03.96	815 FLT 202
Page, David Michael, MDA, BSc, CEng, MIEE,	CDR(FTC)	E	WE	30.06.97	INVINCIBLE
Page, Durward Charles Miller, BSc,	MAJ(FTC)	-		01.09.01	CTCRM
Page, Lewis, BA,	LT(CC)	X	MCD	01.04.94	SDG PLYMOUTH
Page, Mark Robert,	LT(CC)	X	O	01.05.00	849 SQN HQ
Page, Michael Christian, MA, psc,	LT COL(FTC)	-	LC	30.06.99	MOD (LONDON)
Page, Trevor Andrew,	LT(FTC)	E	ME	10.06.94	SULTAN
Paget, Simon James,	LT(FTC)	X	PT	02.05.00	JARIC
Painter, Christopher John, MBE, BSc, MInstPS, MCMI, MILog,	LT CDR(FTC)	S		23.02.87	RNAS YEOVILTON
Pakes, Danyel Tobias, BEng,	LT(FTC)	E	WESM	01.01.96	FLEET HQ NWD
Palethorpe, Nicholas, BSc,	LT(CC)	X		01.09.97	NEWCASTLE
Palin, Giles Roland, LLB,	LT(FTC)	X		01.12.97	NEWCASTLE
Pallett, Angela Julie,	SLT(IC)	S		01.01.00	RALEIGH
Palmer, Alan Charles, MB, ChB,	SURG LTCDR(FCC)	-	GMPP	01.03.97	OCEAN
Palmer, Christopher Laurence, BSc, MCMI, pce, pcea, psc,	CAPT(FTC)	X	O	31.12.00	MOD (LONDON)
Palmer, Christopher Richard,	LT(IC)	E	MESM	01.09.01	SUPERB
Palmer, James Ernest, MSc, CEng, MIEE, AMBCS,	CDR(FTC)	E	WE	31.12.96	CSIS IPT
Palmer, John, MA, CEng, MIEE,	LT(CC)	E	WE	01.07.95	2SL/CNH
Palmer, Martin David, BSc,	SLT(IC)	X		01.01.00	RALEIGH
Palmer, Michael Edward, BEng, MSc, CEng, MIEE,	LT CDR(FTC)	E	WE	01.11.01	MWS COLLINGWOOD
Palmer, Phillip Alan, BA, SM,	LT CDR(FTC)	X	SM	01.07.89	BDS WASHINGTON
Palmer, Rhoderick Adrian Nigel, BSc, (Commodore) ACGI, psc,	CAPT(FTC)	E	AE	31.12.96	ES AIR YEO

Name	Rank	Branch	Spec	Seniority	Where Serving
Pamphilon, Michael John, pcea, psc,	LT CDR(FTC)	X	P	01.03.88	824 SQN
Pancott, Brian Michael, BSc, FRGS, MCGI, psc, mdtc,	CDR(FTC)	E	WE	31.12.91	2SL/CNH
Panic, Alexander, BSc,	LT(CC)	E	TM	15.04.95	TALENT
Pannett, Leonard William, BSc, BEng, AIL, AMIEE,	LT(CC)	E	WESM	01.06.97	TURBULENT
Panther, Andrew Mark, BEng, MSc,	LT CDR(FTC)	E	WE	01.07.00	GLOUCESTER
Pardoe, Elton Ramsey, BSc,	SURG SLT	-		12.09.99	DARTMOUTH BRNC
Paris, William, BEng,	LT CDR(FTC)	E	WE	15.04.98	WSA/CAPT MCTA
Park, Brian Campbell, BA,	LT(FTC)	S		01.06.94	DLO/DGDEF LOG SP
Park, Ian David, MA,	LT(CC)	S		01.08.98	2SL/CNH
Parker, Henry Hardyman, MA, PhD, CEng, MIEE, psc,	CAPT(FTC)	E	WESM	30.06.02	MOD (LONDON)
Parker, Ian Robert, BSc, CEng, MIMechE,	CDR(FTC)	E	MESM	31.12.93	NMA PORTSMOUTH
Parker, Jeremy Vaugn Vernham, BSc, psc(m),	LT COL(FTC)	-		30.06.92	FLEET HQ PORTS 2
Parker, Jonathan Donald, BEng,	SLT(IC)	E	WE U/T	01.09.00	GRAFTON
Parker, Mark Neal, BEng, MSc, CEng, FIMarEST, MCGI,	CDR(FTC)	E	ME	30.06.01	AFPAA(CENTURION)
Parker, Matthew Charles, BA,	LT RM(IC)	-		01.09.00	42 CDO RM
Parker, Matthew James, BA,	SLT(IC)	X		01.01.01	DARTMOUTH BRNC
Parker, Sarah Anne Marie, BA,	LT(IC)	X		01.09.00	CUMBERLAND
Parker, Stephen John, MB, BS, BSc, FRCS, FRCSEd,	SURG CDR(FCC)	-	(GS)UT	30.06.02	NELSON (PAY)
Parker, Timothy Stephen, BSc, CMath,	LT(CC)	X	IS	01.11.95	MWS COLLINGWOOD
Parkin, James Miles Benjamin, MA,	LT(FTC)	X	FC	01.09.98	MANCHESTER
Parkin, Malcolm Ian, BEng,	LT CDR(FTC)	E	ME	01.07.99	LIVERPOOL
Parkinson, Andrew Phillip,	LT(FTC)	X	AV	23.07.98	SULTAN
Parkinson, Henry Michael Larissa,	SLT(UCE)(FTC)	E	AE	01.09.00	DARTMOUTH BRNC
Parkinson, James Hugh George,	SLT(FTC)	X		01.09.98	YORK
Parks, Edward Patrick, jsdc, psc,	MAJ(FTC)	-		01.09.90	PJHQ
Parmenter, Alan John,	LT(FTC)	E	AE(M)	01.04.01	EXCHANGE ARMY UK
Parnell, Adam David, BEng,	LT CDR(FTC)	X	AAWO	01.04.01	MANCHESTER
Parr, Matthew John, BSc, pce, pce(sm),	CAPT(FTC)	X	SM	30.06.02	MONTROSE
Parr, Michael John Edward,	LT(FTC)	X	HM	01.10.96	OCEAN
Parrett, John William,	LT CDR(FTC)	E	MESM	01.10.00	NEPTUNE DSA
Parris, Kevin John, BSc, jsdc, pce,	CDR(FTC)	X	PWO(U)	31.12.88	DPA BRISTOL
Parrock, Neil Graham,	LT(CC)	X	P	01.07.95	814 SQN
Parrott, James Philip,	LT(FTC)	X	FC	01.07.96	MWS DRYAD
Parry, Alexander Keith Illiam, BSc,	LT CDR(FTC)	S		01.02.98	JSCSC
Parry, Christopher Adrian, MB, BS, BSc, MRCS,	SURG LTCDR(MCC)	-		12.08.99	MODHU DERRIFORD
Parry, Christopher John, MA, rcds, pce, (Commodore) pcea, psc,	CAPT(FTC)	X	O	30.06.97	MOD (LONDON)
Parry, Jonathan Allan, BSc,	CAPT RM(CC)	-	P	27.04.96	ASC WATCHFIELD
Parry, Jonathan David Frank,	LT CDR(FTC)	X	P	01.05.00	MWS DRYAD
Parry, Mark Roderick Raymond, BEng, MSc,	LT(FTC)	E	AE	01.05.96	JCA IPT UK
Parry, Nicholas Thomas, BSc, AMIEE, CGIA, psc, mdtc,	CDR(FTC)	E	WESM	31.12.94	NEPTUNE NT
Parry, Roger John,	LT(FTC)	E	AE(M)	16.10.92	GANNET SAR FLT
Parry, Stuart David, LLB,	LT(IC)	S		05.03.02	MWS COLLINGWOOD
Parsons, Andrew David, BSc, n,	LT CDR(FTC)	X	PWO(C)	01.01.00	MWS DRYAD
Parsons, Brian Robert, BSc, MBA,	CDR(FTC)	E	AE	31.12.00	NMA PORTSMOUTH
Parsons, Christopher Graham, BSc, MDA, CEng, MIEE,	CDR(FTC)	E	WE	31.12.00	MOD (LONDON)
Parsons, Geoffrey, MSc, CEng, MIEE, MCMI, gw,	CDR(FTC)	E	WE	30.06.93	NC3 AGENCY
Parsons, Patrick Hugh, osc(us),	LT COL(FTC)	-	MLDR	31.12.92	RMR TYNE
Parsons, Robert John, BSc,	LT(IC)	X		01.11.00	YORK
Parsons, Robert Martin James,	LT(IC)	X		01.01.02	MWS DRYAD
Parton, Alan,	LT(FTC)	X	MCD	19.09.00	BANGOR
Partridge, Simon Christopher, BSc,	LT(IC)	X		01.12.00	MWS RNHMS CULD
Parvin, Philip Stanley, BEng, MSc, CEng, FIMarEST, MIMechE,	LT CDR(FTC)	E	MESM	01.02.97	TORBAY
Parvin, Richard Alan, BA,	CAPT RM(FTC)	-		01.05.97	45 CDO RM
Pascoe, James Roderick Munro,	LT RM(IC)	-		01.09.00	CTCRM LYMPSTONE
Passingham, Rodney Edris, MSc, CEng, MIEE,	CDR(FTC)	E	WE	31.12.89	WSA/CAPT MCTA
Paston, William Alexander,	LT(IC)	X		01.05.02	MWS DRYAD
Pate, Christopher Michael,	SLT(IC)	X		01.01.01	GRIMSBY
Patel, Devang Ramesh,	SURG LT(SCC)	-		01.08.01	RH HASLAR
Paterson, Fergus James Blair,	LT CDR(FTC)	X	PWO(C)	01.08.99	ALBION
Paterson, Michael Paul, PGDIPAN, n,	LT CDR(FTC)	X	PWO(N)	01.06.01	FEARLESS

Name	Rank	Branch	Spec	Seniority	Where Serving
Paterson, Thomas John,	CAPT RM(IC)	-	SO(LE)	01.04.02	FPGRM
Paton, Alan John Malcolm,	LT(FTC)	E	ME	19.06.98	OCLC MANCH
Paton, Christopher Mark, BEng,	CAPT RM(FTC)	-		01.09.96	DARTMOUTH BRNC
Patrick, James, MSc, psc,	CAPT(FTC)	E	TM	31.12.97	RCDS
Patterson, Andrew James, BSc,	LT(IC)	X	P	16.11.92	GANNET SAR FLT
Patterson, David, BEng,	LT(FTC)	E	WE	01.12.94	DARTMOUTH BRNC
Patterson, John David, BSc, n,	LT(FTC)	X		01.08.96	ST ALBANS
Patterson, Scott Douglas, BEng,	LT(FTC)	E	WE	01.07.97	NEPTUNE NT
Patterson-Hollis, Christopher, BEng, AMIEE,	LT CDR(FTC)	E	WE	01.04.97	LPD(R) IPT
Pattinson, Ian Howard, MSc,	CDR(FTC)	S		30.06.98	FLEET HQ PORTS
Patton, Richard, (Act Lt)	SLT(IC)	MS		01.05.99	FORT BLOCKHOUSE
Paul, Russell William Fordyce, MA, psc,	LT COL(FTC)	-	LC	30.06.01	CTCRM
Paulet, Michael Raoul,	LT(IC)	X	P	01.02.01	820 SQN
Paulson, Richard Brian, BEng, MSc, AMIEE,	LT(FTC)	E	WE	01.08.95	MWS COLLINGWOOD
Pavey, Emma Lesley, LLB,	LT(IC)	X	HM	01.05.97	RFANSU
Payne, Daniel,	LT CDR(FTC)	E	ME	01.10.99	FLEET HQ PORTS 2
Payne, John Durley, BSc, pce, n,	LT CDR(FTC)	X	PWO(U)	01.06.98	MWS DRYAD
Payne, Matthew John,	LT(FTC)	X	PWO(C)	01.05.93	JFHQ STAFF NWOOD
Payne, Michael,	2LT(IC)	-		01.05.98	CTCRM LYMPSTONE
Payne, Philip John, BA,	LT(FTC)	X	H1	01.07.94	SCOTT
Payne, Richard Charles, pce, pcea,	CDR(FTC)	X	P	30.06.01	800 SQN
Payne, William Dudley,	SLT(IC)	X		01.05.00	CORNWALL
Peace, Richard William,	LT CDR(FTC)	E	MESM	02.07.97	TALENT
Peach, Christopher Charles, pce,	CAPT(FTC)	X	O	30.06.97	MOD (LONDON)
Peach, Graham Leslie, BSc, psc,	CAPT(FTC)	E	WE	30.06.00	WSA/CAPT MCTA
Peachey, Richard Matthew, BSc,	LT(IC)	X	P	01.11.94	847 SQN
Peacock, Michael Robert,	LT CDR(FTC)	E	MESM	01.10.96	DRAKE CBS
Peacock, Stephen, BSc, MDA, CEng, MIEE,	LT CDR(FTC)	E	WESM	01.06.92	WSA/CAPT MCTA
Peacock, Timothy James, BA, MA, pcea,	LT CDR(FTC)	X	P	01.01.98	MWS COLLINGWOOD
Peak, Martyn,	LT(FTC)	X	g	03.04.98	BRECON
Pear, Ian Keith, BSc, CEng, MIMarEST,	LT CDR(FTC)	E	MESM	01.04.96	TIRELESS
Pearce, Jonathan Kenneth Charles,	CAPT(FTC)	S		31.12.97	MOD (BATH)
Pearce, Jonathan,	SLT(IC)	E	WE	01.01.01	MWS COLLINGWOOD
Pearce, Robert James, BA,	LT(IC)	X		01.01.02	LEDBURY
Pearce, Sarah Louise,	MID(IC)	X		01.09.00	PENZANCE
Pearch, Sean Michael,	LT(FTC)	X	ATC	26.04.99	RNAS CULDROSE
Pearey, Michael Scott, DSC, BSc, jsdc, pce, pcea,	CDR(FTC)	X	O	31.12.96	INVINCIBLE
Pearmain, Stephanie Rosina, BSc,	LT(IC)	E	TM	14.05.00	RALEIGH
Pears, Ian James, BSc,	LT CDR(FTC)	E	IS	01.10.00	DITMTC SHRIVNHAM
Pearson, Charles Peter Bellamy, BEng,	LT CDR(FTC)	E	ME	01.10.00	CAMPBELTOWN
Pearson, Christopher Robert, MA, MBA, MB, BChir, FRCS, DLO,	SURG CDR(FCC)	-	(CE)	30.06.02	RH HASLAR
Pearson, Gareth, BEng,	CAPT RM(IC)	-		01.09.98	1 ASSLT GP RM
Pearson, James Carden,	LT(CC)	X	MCD	01.12.00	SHOREHAM
Pearson, Michael Forbes,	LT CDR(FTC)	X	O	01.03.01	MWS DRYAD
Pearson, Neil, BEng, CEng, MIMarEST,	LT CDR(FTC)	E	ME	01.08.97	SULTAN
Pearson, Stephen John, MA, pce, psc(j),	CDR(FTC)	X	O	30.06.00	NEWCASTLE
Pearson, Susie, BEd,	LT(IC)	S		01.05.01	NELSON
Peattie, Ian William, BSc,	LT(IC)	S		01.05.02	800 SQN
Peck, Ian John, BSc, CEng, MRAeS, MDA,	CDR(FTC)	E	AE	31.12.97	MOD (LONDON)
Peck, Simon Russell, MEng,	SLT(IC)	E	AE	01.09.99	SULTAN
Peckham, David Reginald, BSc, Eur Ing, CEng, MIEE, psc,	CDR(FTC)	E	WE	31.12.94	PAAMS PARIS
Pedler, Mark David, BEng,	LT(CC)	X	P	01.07.97	846 SQN
Pedre, Robert George, BSc, ARCS,	LT(FTC)	X		01.10.97	EDINBURGH
Peel, Giles Robert, BSc, FCIS,	CAPT(FTC)	S		30.06.01	MOD (BATH)
Peerman, Stephen John, (Act Cdr)	LT CDR(FTC)	E	WE	01.10.95	MOD (LONDON)
Pegg, Russell Montfort, pce, fsc,	CDR(FTC)	X	PWO(U)	31.12.95	MOD (LONDON)
Pegg, Stephen Michael, pce, psc,	CDR(FTC)	X	AWO(A)	30.06.88	SA ANKARA
Pegrum, Terrence Allen,	LT CDR(FTC)	X	P	01.10.99	846 SQN
Peilow, Benjamin Francis, BA, MILT, psc,	CDR(FTC)	S		31.12.92	DLO/DGDEF LOG SP
Pelly, Gilbert Ralph,	MAJ(FTC)	-		25.04.96	NEPTUNE DLO
Penalver, Warren Craig,	SLT(IC)	X		01.01.01	MWS DRYAD

Name	Rank	Branch	Spec	Seniority	Where Serving
Pendle, Martin Erle John, BSc, CEng, MIMarEST, jsdc,	CDR(FTC)	E	ME	30.06.95	T45 IPT
Penfold, Michael Jamie, HNC,	LT(FTC)	E	WE	18.02.94	SFM PORTSMOUTH
Pengelly, Steven,	SURG SLT(MDC)	-		16.05.99	DARTMOUTH BRNC
Penketh, Mark Geoffrey,	LT(FTC)	E	ME	02.09.99	SFM PORTSMOUTH
Penkman, William Alfred Vincent, BSc,	CAPT RM(FTC)	-	P	01.09.98	847 SQN
Penn-Barwell, Jowan,	SURG SLT(SCC)	-		11.01.00	DARTMOUTH BRNC
Pennefather, William Jonathan Richard, jsdc,	CAPT(FTC)	S		31.12.96	FLEET HQ NWD
Penney, Lisa Marie,	LT(SCC)	Q		16.09.01	MODHU DERRIFORD
Pennington, Charles Edmond, BSc,	CAPT RM(IC)	-		01.09.01	CTCRM
Penniston, John Raymond, BSc,	CDR(FTC)	E	MESM	31.12.97	NEPTUNE DSA
Penny, Anthony David, MSc, CEng, MIEE,	CAPT(FTC)	E	WE	31.12.00	MOD (LONDON)
Penprase, Jason Michael,	LT(CC)	X		01.10.94	LOAN SAUDI ARAB
Penson, Jonathan George,	LT(IC)	X		01.09.01	RICHMOND
Pentreath, Jonathan Patrick, BSc, pce, pcea, psc(j),	LT CDR(FTC)	X	P	01.12.95	845 SQN
Peppe, Alasdair George,	LT(FTC)	X		01.06.95	SOUTHAMPTON
Pepper, Martin Richard, BSc, pce, pcea, psc,	CDR(FTC)	X	O	31.12.92	JDCC
Pepper, Philip Michael,	LT(IC)	X	P U/T	01.09.01	DHFS
Percharde, Michael Robert, BSc, pce, psc(j),	CDR(FTC)	X	AAWO	31.12.98	MOD (LONDON)
Percival, Fiona,	LT(FTC)	S		01.09.96	ES AIR YEO
Percival, Michael Christopher,	LT CDR(FTC)	S		01.07.99	EXCHANGE USA
Percy, Nicolas Andrew, BSc,	LT(CC)	X		01.04.99	MWS DRYAD
Perkins, Ben, BEng,	LT(FTC)	E	AE	01.09.01	RNAS YEOVILTON
Perkins, Michael Jonathan, BA, MDA, pce,	CDR(FTC)	X	AAWO	30.06.96	MOD (BATH)
Perkins, Ross John, BEng,	LT(FTC)	E	ME	01.01.96	MOD (BATH)
Perks, James Le Seelleur, MSc, pce(sm), SM(n),	LT CDR(FTC)	X	SM	01.09.00	TALENT
Perrin, Mark Stephen, BA,	CAPT RM(IC)	-		01.09.01	FPGRM
Perry, Andrew James,	LT CDR(FTC)	S	SM	16.07.99	RALEIGH
Perry, Emma Marie, BSc,	LT(IC)	X		01.08.98	MWS DRYAD
Perry, Jonathan Neil, MB, ChB, FRCR,	SURG CDR(FCC)	-	(CX)	31.12.96	MODHU DERRIFORD
Perry, Richard, BSc, BA(OU), psc,	LT CDR(FTC)	E	MESM	01.11.90	JSCSC
Perry, Robert William,	MAJ(FTC)	-	SO(LE)	01.10.00	NMA WHALE ISLAND
Perry, Russell John,	LT(CC)	X	MW	01.11.93	DARTMOUTH BRNC
Perryman, Ian, BSc,	LT(IC)	E	TM	01.01.00	SULTAN
Perryment, Claire Patricia,	LT(CC)	X		01.08.01	TYNE
Peskett, Daniel Mark, BEng,	SLT(IC)	E	ME U/T	01.09.00	NORTHUMBERLAND
Petch, Alan Napier, BEng,	SLT(IC)	X	P U/T	01.09.00	DARTMOUTH BRNC
Peters, Adam John Urlin, BSc, (Act Cdr)	LT CDR(FTC)	X		01.08.87	NP 1002 DIEGOGA
Peters, Andrew Douglas,	LT RM(IC)	-	SO(LE)	01.04.00	40 CDO RM
Peters, William Richard, BA, n,	LT(FTC)	X		01.03.96	PUNCHER
Peterson, Keith Andrew, BEng,	SLT(IC)	E	WE U/T	01.09.00	EXETER
Petheram, Anthony John, pce,	LT CDR(FTC)	X	PWO(C)	01.09.97	CAMPBELTOWN
Petheram, Michael John, MBE, MA, pce, psc(j),	CDR(FTC)	X	PWO(U)	30.06.02	FLEET HQ PORTS
Petherick, Jason Stewart, pce,	LT CDR(FTC)	X	AAWO	01.04.98	HURWORTH
Pethybridge, Richard Alan, PGDIPAN, pce, n,	LT CDR(FTC)	X	PWO(N)	01.05.97	EXCHANGE USA
Petitt, Simon Richard, BEng, MBA, CEng, MIEE,	LT CDR(FTC)	E	WE	01.02.98	FLEET HQ PORTS 2
Pett, Jeremy Graham, BSc, MinstP, C PHYS,	CDR(FTC)	E	TM	30.06.99	MOD (LONDON)
Pettigrew, Thomas Robert, BEng, IEng, MIIE,	LT(CC)	E	TM	01.09.97	FOST CSST FSLN
Pettitt, Gary William, pce,	CDR(FTC)	X	PWO(U)	31.12.97	FOST SEA
Petzer, Garth Stephen, MBE, DipTh,	CHAPLAIN	CE		09.01.96	FOST SEA
Peyman, Tracy Anne,	LT(IC)	S		01.09.00	ARK ROYAL
Pheasant, John Christian Stephen, BSc,	LT CDR(FTC)	S	BAR	01.10.00	RALEIGH
Phenna, Andrew, BEng,	CDR(FTC)	E	WE	30.06.01	MWS COLLINGWOOD
Phesse, John Paul Lloyd, IEng, AMRAeS,	LT CDR(FTC)	E	AE(M)	01.10.00	NMA GOSPORT
Philip, Alistair David, BSc,	LT(CC)	X	HM	01.03.97	BEAGLE
Phillips, Andrew Graham,	CHAPLAIN	CE		14.02.00	CHFHQ
Phillips, Andrew Ralph, IEng, MIIE,	LT CDR(FTC)	E	AE(M)	01.10.01	HARRIER IPT
Phillips, Christopher John, BA,	LT(IC)	X		01.09.00	RALEIGH
Phillips, David George, pce, pce(sm),	CDR(FTC)	X	SM	30.06.95	NELSON
Phillips, David Guy,	LT RM(IC)	-	SO(LE)	01.04.00	CDO LOG REGT RM
Phillips, Ian Michael,	LT CDR(FTC)	MS		01.10.01	PJHQ
Phillips, James Charles, MB, CHB, (Act Surg Lt)	SURG SLT(SCC)	-		19.07.01	DARTMOUTH BRNC
Phillips, James Nicholas, BEng, ACMI, MIEE, Ceng,	LT(FTC)	E	WE	01.03.95	2SL/CNH FOTR

Name	Rank	Branch	Spec	Seniority	Where Serving
Phillips, Jason Peter, pcea,	LT CDR(FTC)	X	O	01.10.00	EXCHANGE AUSTLIA
Phillips, Laura Claire,	SLT(IC)	X		01.09.01	DARTMOUTH BRNC
Phillips, Mark Christopher, (Act Maj)	CAPT RM(FTC)	-	SO(LE)	01.01.99	RM POOLE
Phillips, Matthew Benjamin, BSc,	LT(IC)	X	P	16.08.95	FLEET AV VALLEY
Phillips, Richard Edward,	SLT(IC)	X	P U/T	01.09.00	RAF LINTN/OUSE
Phillips, Richard Mark, MSc,	LT(IC)	X		01.01.00	MWS DRYAD
Phillips, Stephen John, MA, psc, (Act Lt Col)	MAJ(FTC)	-		01.09.90	2SL/CNH
Philo, Julian Quentin, BEng, CEng,	LT CDR(FTC)	E	ME	01.06.98	FLEET HQ NWD
Philpot, David John, BEng,	LT CDR(FTC)	E	WESM	18.07.00	FLEET HQ PORTS 2
Philpott, Ashley Michael, SM(n), SM,	LT(FTC)	X	SM	01.03.96	RALEIGH
Philpott, Geoffrey Richard, BA,	CDR(FTC)	S		30.06.90	AFPAA(CENTURION)
Philpott, Nigel Edward, psc(j),	LT CDR(FTC)	S		01.11.96	MOD (LONDON)
Phipps, Tracey Anne, BA,	LT(CC)	X	H1	01.02.94	MWS RNHMS DRAKE
Piaggesi, Gareth Fiorenzo,	SLT(UCE)(IC)	E	AE	01.09.01	DARTMOUTH BRNC
Pickard, David Malcolm,	CAPT RM(FTC)	-	SO(LE)	01.01.99	42 CDO RM
Pickard, Donna Marie, BA,	LT(CC)	S		01.03.99	FOST DPORT SHORE
Pickard, Stephen Richard,	LT(CC)	E	AE	01.10.00	DARTMOUTH BRNC
Pickbourne, Martin, IEng, AMIMarEST,	LT CDR(FTC)	E	ME	01.10.95	CV(F) IPT
Picken, Christopher, MB, BCH, (Act Surg Lt)	SURG SLT(SCC)	-		09.07.01	DARTMOUTH BRNC
Pickering, Ian Jeffery, BA, SM(n),	LT(CC)	X	SM	01.07.96	TORBAY
Pickering, Martin John, BA,	CDR(FTC)	X	METOC	01.10.92	2SL/CNH FOTR
Pickering-Wheeler, Christopher William, BSc, SM(n),	LT(FTC)	X	SM	01.01.98	VIGILANT(STBD)
Pickles, David Richard,	LT(CC)	X	ATC	01.01.01	RNAS YEOVILTON
Pickles, Ian Seaton, pce, pce(sm),	CDR(FTC)	X	SM	30.06.97	SPARTAN
Pickles, Martin Richard, BSc,	LT(IC)	X	P U/T	01.05.01	RNAS CULDROSE
Picksley, Michael Raymond,	LT CDR(FTC)	E	WE	01.10.00	SIFF IPT
Pickthall, David Nicholas, BSc, CEng, MIEE,	CDR(FTC)	E	WE	31.12.97	EXCHANGE FRANCE
Pickup, Richard Allan, BSc, MA, psc(m), psc(j)o,	LT COL(FTC)	-		31.12.97	RM POOLE
Picton, Annette Mary, psc,	CAPT(FTC)	W	SEC	30.06.96	MOD (LONDON)
Pierce, Adrian Kevern Maxwell, PGDIPAN, n,	LT CDR(FTC)	X	PWO(N)	01.02.00	STANAVFORMED
Pierson, Matthew Fraser, odc(Fr),	MAJ(FTC)	-		01.09.99	MOD (LONDON)
Pike, Martin Stephen, BSc,	LT CDR(FTC)	S		01.03.91	JHQ NORTHEAST
Pike, Robin Timothy,	SLT(IC)	E	WESM	01.01.01	MWS COLLINGWOOD
Pilkington, Alex, BSc,	CAPT RM(IC)	-		01.07.96	ASC WATCHFIELD
Pillar, Andrew Robert, OBE, psc(a),	BRIG(FTC)	-		30.06.98	CTCRM
Pillar, Christopher David, pce,	LT CDR(FTC)	X	PWO(U)	01.03.95	RANGER
Pilley, Michael Anthony, pce,	LT CDR(FTC)	X	PWO(U)	16.09.84	MWS DRYAD
Pilsworth, Dermod Scott, MSc, CGIA,	LT CDR(FTC)	E	WE	01.06.85	HQ DCSA
Pimpalnerkar, Ashvin Lakshman, MB, BS, FRCS(ORTH),	SURG LTCDR(SCC)	-		04.01.98	NELSON (PAY)
Pinckney, Matthew,	2LT(UCE)(IC)	-		01.09.99	CTCRM LYMPSTONE
Pinder, Christopher David, BEng,	LT(CC)	E	TM	01.02.96	NELSON RNSETT
Pine, Paul Martin, BSc,	LT(IC)	E	TM	06.12.98	RALEIGH
Pinhey, Andrew David,	LT(IC)	MS		01.01.02	DRAKE CBS
Pink, Simon Edward, n,	LT CDR(FTC)	X	PWO(A)	01.01.02	DARTMOUTH BRNC
Piper, Benjamin James,	MID(NE)(IC)	X		01.05.01	EDINBURGH
Piper, Neale Derek, ARRC, BSc,	LT(MCC)	Q	IC	23.11.95	RCDM
Pipkin, Christopher, MB, BS, MRCPath,	SURG CDR(FCC)	-	CPDATE	30.06.94	RH HASLAR
Pipkin, Peter John, AMIEE, BEng,	LT(FTC)	E	WE	01.04.00	NEWCASTLE
Pipkin, Simon Christian,	LT CDR(FTC)	X	P	01.10.95	OCEAN
Pirie, Scott Keith,	CAPT RM(CC)	-		01.05.99	CDO LOG REGT RM
Pirrie, James Alexander,	LT(FTC)	X	C	19.09.00	OCLC ROSYTH
Pitcher, James,	LT CDR(FTC)	E	AE(L)	01.10.93	ES AIR BRISTOL
Pitcher, Paul, BA,	LT(FTC)	X	PWO(C)	01.11.94	CUMBERLAND
Pitman, Lisa Jill, BEd,	SLT(IC)	S		01.01.00	MONTROSE
Pitt, Johnathan Mark, SM(n), SM,	LT CDR(FTC)	X	SM	17.02.99	TRAFALGAR
Pitt, William,	SLT(IC)	X		01.01.00	MWS DRYAD
Pittard, David Campbell, BSc,	LT(IC)	X		01.06.99	EXETER
Pittock, Stephen James,	SLT(IC)	X		01.01.02	MWS DRYAD
Plackett, Andrew John, MA,	LT(CC)	E	TM	01.05.92	MOD (LONDON)
Plaice, Graham Conyers,	LT CDR(FTC)	S	SM	01.10.00	AGRIPPA NAVSOUTH
Plant, Ian Robert, BSc,	LT CDR(FTC)	E	AE	01.07.90	FLEET HQ PORTS

Name	Rank	Branch	Spec	Seniority	Where Serving
Plant, Jeremy Neil Melrose, BSc, MDA,	CDR(FTC)	E	AE	31.12.99	MOD (LONDON)
Plant, Martin Gary,	LT CDR(FTC)	E	WE	13.06.91	MWS DRYAD
Platt, Jonathan Howard, BSc,	LT(CC)	X	P	16.06.96	GANNET SAR FLT
Platt, Nicola,	LT(FTC)	S	(W)	03.04.98	RH HASLAR
Pledger, David,	LT(FTC)	X	AV	16.12.94	OCEAN
Plenty, Andrew Justin,	SLT(IC)	X	ATCU/T	01.09.00	DARTMOUTH BRNC
Plewes, Andrew Burns, BSc,	MAJ(FTC)	-		27.04.02	NMA WHALE ISLAND
Plummer, Russell William John, BEng,	LT(IC)	E	WE	01.05.02	MWS COLLINGWOOD
Pocock, David,	LT CDR(FTC)	S		16.10.00	MONMOUTH
Podger, Kevin Gordon Ray, BSc, psc,	CDR(FTC)	E	MESM	30.06.95	NP BRISTOL
Podmore, Anthony, BSc,	CDR(FTC)	E	TM	30.06.01	MWS DRYAD
Polding, Martin, BA,	LT(CC)	X	P	01.11.93	848 SQN HERON
Poll, Martin George, BA,	CHAPLAIN	CE		14.06.90	NEPTUNE 2SL/CNH
Pollard, Alexandra Eleanor, BA,	LT(CC)	X	FC	01.08.98	CARDIFF
Pollard, Andrew John,	LT(FTC)	E	ME	01.04.01	1 ASSLT GP RM
Pollard, Jonathan Richard, BEng, AMIEE,	LT(CC)	E	WE	01.12.99	NOTTINGHAM
Pollitt, David Nigel Anthony, pce, pce(sm), psc,	LT CDR(FTC)	X	SM	01.04.89	JMOTS NORTHWOOD
Pollock, Christopher Jon, BA,	LT(IC)	X		01.01.00	OCLC ROSYTH
Pollock, David John, BSc, pce, pce(sm),	CDR(FTC)	X	SM	30.06.99	MWC PORTSDOWN
Pollock, Malcolm Philip, pce, pcea,	LT CDR(FTC)	X	O	01.07.95	CORNWALL
Pollock, Susan, BSc,	SLT(IC)	X	O U/T	01.09.99	750 SQN SEAHAWK
Pollock, Sir Michael, (Patrick), GCB, LVO, DSC, psc	ADM OF FLEET	-		01.03.74	
Pomeroy, Mark Anthony,	LT CDR(FTC)	E	ME	01.10.98	FOST SEA
Pomeroy, Philippa Mary, BEd,	LT CDR(FTC)	S		01.02.00	FOST SEA
Pond, David William, BEd, MCMI, rcds,	CAPT(FTC)	X	METOC	30.06.98	SHAPE BELGIUM
Pond, Robert James,	SLT(IC)	E	MESM	01.05.00	SULTAN
Ponsford, Philip Kevin, BSc, MInsD,	LT CDR(FTC)	X	SM	01.01.99	MWS DRYAD
Poole, Jason Lee, pce,	LT CDR(FTC)	X	MCD	01.04.94	PJHQ
Poole, Timothy James, BSc, MRAeS, MCGI, pcea, gdas,	LT(CC)	X	O	16.01.92	LOAN JTEG BSC DN
Pooley, Steven William, BSc,	LT CDR(FTC)	E	WESM	01.07.96	FOST CSST SEA
Pope, Catherine Manuela, MA, MSc, psc,	CDR(FTC)	X	METOC	31.12.97	MOD (LONDON)
Porrett, Johnathan Anthony,	LT CDR(FTC)	S	SM	14.11.95	FLEET HQ PORTS
Porritt, Colin,	LT(IC)	E		01.05.02	820 SQN
Port, Leslie Alan, MBE,	LT CDR(FTC)	X	P	15.04.83	LAIPT
Porter, Christopher William,	LT CDR(FTC)	X	O	01.10.94	ES AIR YEO
Porter, Derek Lowry, BA,	LT(IC)	S	SM	01.06.97	OCLC MANCH
Porter, Matthew Edward, MBE, BSc, psc(j),	MAJ(FTC)	-		01.05.98	RM POOLE
Porter, Simon Paul, pce, psc(j),	CDR(FTC)	X	AAWO	31.12.99	PJHQ
Porter, Suzanne, MB, ChB, BSc,	SURG LTCDR(MCC)	-		01.08.01	NELSON (PAY)
Porter, Timothy Benedict, BA,	LT CDR(FTC)	S		01.05.02	RALEIGH
Postgate, Michael Oliver,	2LT(IC)	-		01.09.00	FPGRM
Pothecary, Richard Edward, FCMI, MNI, pce,	CDR(FTC)	X	AAWO	31.12.93	SACLANT USA
Potter, David John,	LT(FTC)	X	O	24.07.97	700M MERLIN OEU
Potter, David,	SURG SLT(SCC)	-		01.07.00	DARTMOUTH BRNC
Potter, Michael John, MA, MSc, CEng,	CAPT(FTC)	E	TM	30.06.97	MOD (LONDON)
MIMarEST, MINucE, MinstP, C PHYS, psc,					
Potter, Stephen,	MAJ(FTC)	-	SO(LE)	01.10.98	RM POOLE
Potts, Duncan Laurence, BSc, pce,	CAPT(FTC)	X	PWO(U)	30.06.00	MARLBOROUGH
Potts, Gary, BEng,	LT(FTC)	E	WESM	01.06.96	RMC OF SCIENCE
Potts, Kevin Maxwell,	LT CDR(FTC)	X	P	01.02.92	RAF CRANWELL EFS
Pounds, Nicholas Ernest, ADC, psc(m),	BRIG(FTC)	-	A/TK	31.12.99	CTCRM
Powell, Benjamin Michael Etherton,	MID(IC)	X		01.01.01	DARTMOUTH BRNC
Powell, David Charles, MSc,	CDR(FTC)	E	ME	31.12.95	FWO PORTS SEA
Powell, Gregory Mark John,	MID(NE)(IC)	X		01.01.02	DARTMOUTH BRNC
Powell, Mark Andrew, BSc,	LT CDR(FTC)	E	WESM	01.03.98	TIRELESS
Powell, Rebecca Jane,	SLT(IC)	X		01.04.98	MWS DRYAD
Powell, Richard Laurence, MA, pce, pcea, psc(j),	CDR(FTC)	X	P	31.12.00	YORK
Powell, Roger Norman, BA, BSc, CEng, psc,	CAPT(FTC)	E	AE	30.06.02	ES AIR YEO
Powell, Steven Richard, pce,	LT CDR(FTC)	X	PWO(C)	01.07.98	FLEET HQ PORTS
Powell, Steven, MA, pce, pcea, psc(a),	LT CDR(FTC)	X	O	16.04.92	750 SQN SEAHAWK
Powell, William Glyn, pce, pcea,	LT CDR(FTC)	X	O	16.12.98	FOST SEA
Powis, Jonathan, pce, pce(sm),	CDR(FTC)	X	SM	31.12.92	FLEET HQ NWD

Name	Rank	Branch	Spec	Seniority	Where Serving
Powles, Derek Anthony, MEng,	LT(FTC)	E	ME	01.02.96	SCOTT
Powne, Simon Philip Watts,	LT(IC)	E		01.05.02	DARTMOUTH BRNC
Pratt, Ian Heggie, BSc, CEng, MIEE,	LT CDR(FTC)	E	WE	01.03.93	MOD (BATH)
Preece, David Graeme, BA,	LT CDR(FTC)	S	SM	01.08.01	CAMPBELTOWN
Prendergast, Matthew Patrick, BM, BS, BMS,	SURG LT(SCC)	-		04.08.99	RM POOLE
Prendergast, Sally Ann, BSc, PGDip,	LT CDR(CC)	E	TM	26.02.02	DEF SCH OF LANG
Prentice, David Charles, QCVS,	LT CDR(FTC)	X	PWO(C)	22.12.97	NEWCASTLE
Prescott, Shaun, BEng, CEng, MIEE, psc(j),	CDR(FTC)	E	WE	30.06.01	RHQ AFNORTH
Pressdee, Simon John,	LT(CC)	X	MCD	01.07.98	GRIMSBY
Pressly, James Winchester, BSc, psc(j),	MAJ(FTC)	-		25.04.98	HQ 3 CDO BDE RM
Prest, Neal Andrew,	LT(FTC)	S	(W)	10.12.98	ECHO
Prest, Stephen Frederick, MEng, AMIEE,	LT(IC)	E	WE	01.06.01	HQ DCSA
Preston, Mark Richard, BEng, CEng, MIMechE,	LT CDR(FTC)	E	ME	01.10.99	FLEET HQ PORTS 2
Preston, Ross Walker, BSc,	CAPT RM(FTC)	-		01.09.96	ASC WATCHFIELD
Preston, Thomas Edward, MA,	LT RM(IC)	-		01.09.00	45 CDO RM
Preston-Jones, Noel Clisby, (Commodore)	CAPT(FTC)	S		31.12.94	MOD (LONDON)
Price, Andrew Michael, sq,	MAJ(FTC)	-	C	01.05.97	UKMARBATSTAFF
Price, David Glyn,	CAPT RM(FTC)	-	SO(LE)	01.01.00	845 SQN
Price, David John, pce,	LT CDR(FTC)	X	AAWO	01.04.93	MWC PORTSDOWN
Price, David William,	LT CDR(FTC)	X	REG	01.10.98	MWS EXCELLENT
Price, Frederick Earle Francis, MBE, MA, MSc, PhD,	CDR(FTC)	E	TM	30.06.95	MOD (LONDON)
CEng, MIOA, psc,					
Price, James Edward Owen, BSc,	LT RM(IC)	-		01.09.00	45 CDO RM
Price, John Philip, MA, MInsD, psc,	CDR(FTC)	E	ME	30.06.96	SULTAN
Price, Joseph Charles, BSc,	LT(IC)	X		05.03.01	MWS DRYAD
Price, Martin John, MA, psc,	LT COL(FTC)	-	MLDR	31.12.98	NMA PORTSMOUTH
Price, Raymond Terence,	CAPT RM(IC)	-	SO(LE)	01.04.02	UKLFCSG RM
Price, Tania Lucille, BSc, MA(Ed), Cert Ed, MCIPD,	LT CDR(FTC)	W	TM	01.10.92	JSCSC
Price, Terence Peter,	LT CDR(FTC)	E	WE	01.10.97	SOMERSET
Price, Timothy Andrew, pce, n,	LT CDR(FTC)	X	AAWO	01.07.98	MWS DRYAD
Price, Tracie Evelyn, BSc,	LT(CC)	E	TM	01.12.93	MWS DRYAD
Price, Trevor William, BSc, MA, psc(j),	LT CDR(FTC)	X	METOC	01.01.92	MOD (LONDON)
Price, Victoria Juliette, MB, ChB, BSc,	SURG LT(SCC)	-		04.08.99	CFLT MED(SEA)
Priddle, Alexandria C, BA,	LT(IC)	E	TM	01.01.02	DARTMOUTH BRNC
Priest, James Edward, BEng,	LT(IC)	X	P	15.02.98	845 SQN
Priestley, Catherine, BSc,	LT(IC)	E	TM	14.01.00	SULTAN
Prime, John Roger Martin, pce, psc, psc(a),	CDR(FTC)	X	PWO(N)†	30.06.88	2SL/CNH FOTR
Prince, Mark Edward, BEng, CEng, MIMarE,	LT CDR(FTC)	E	MESM	01.10.00	TRENCHANT
Pring, Stuart James, BSc,	LT(CC)	S		14.08.97	ELANT/NAVNORTH
Pringle, Anthony, pce, pcea,	LT CDR(FTC)	X	P	01.07.90	PJHQ
Prinsep, Timothy John, BEng, CEng, MIEE,	LT CDR(FTC)	E	WE	01.06.00	DL IPT
Prior, Grant Michael, IEng, FIIE,	LT CDR(FTC)	E	WE	02.06.96	FWO PORTSMOUTH
Prior, Iain Alexander,	LT(FTC)	E	ME	01.04.01	ARGYLL
Prior, Kate Rebecca Edna Jane, MB, BS,	SURG LT(MCC)	-		06.08.97	MODHU DERRIFORD
Pritchard, Alison Margaret, BA,	LT(IC)	X		01.05.00	KENT
Pritchard, Gavin Scrimgeour, pce,	CDR(FTC)	X	PWO(U)	30.06.01	MOD (LONDON)
Pritchard, Irene Joanne, BSc,	LT(IC)	S		01.02.00	RALEIGH
Pritchard, Rayson Cann,	MAJ(FTC)	-		01.08.85	RM BICKLEIGH
Pritchard, Simon Andrew, MA, psc,	MAJ(FTC)	-		18.04.94	COMAMPHIBFOR
Procter, Jamie Edward, BEng, MSc, Cert Ed, PGDip,	LT CDR(FTC)	E	TM	01.10.01	NMA PORTSMOUTH
Procter, Kathryn Joanne,	LT(SCC)	Q	CC	15.01.01	DRAKE CBP(DLO)
Proctor, Nicholas Stephen,	SLT(IC)	S		01.05.00	RALEIGH
Proctor, William John Gibbon, BEng, AMIEE,	LT CDR(FTC)	E	WE	01.03.02	MWS COLLINGWOOD
Prodger, Andrew Phillip,	SLT(IC)	E	WESM	01.01.00	RALEIGH
Proffitt Burnham, Julia Marie, BSc,	LT(CC)	E	TM	01.09.95	SULTAN
Prole, Nicholas Mark,	LT(CC)	X	P	16.09.97	846 SQN
Prosser, Matthew James,	LT(CC)	X		01.08.01	ARK ROYAL
Proud, Andrew Douglas, BEng,	LT CDR(FTC)	E	AE	11.06.99	FLEET HQ PORTS
Prowse, David George,	LT(FTC)	E	ME	01.04.01	DRAKE SFM
Pruden, Ian, BSc,	CAPT RM(CC)	-		01.05.98	RM POOLE
Pryde, Colin Swinton, BEng, CEng, Eur Ing,	LT CDR(FTC)	E	AE	01.07.94	RNAS CULDROSE
Pugh, Geoffrey Noel John, BEng,	SLT(IC)	X	P U/T	01.05.00	DARTMOUTH BRNC

Name	Rank	Branch	Spec	Seniority	Where Serving
Pugh, Jonathan, BEng,	LT CDR(FTC)	E	WE	08.03.00	NEWCASTLE
Pugh, Martin Reginald,	LT CDR(FTC)	X	C	01.10.00	SHAPE BELGIUM
Pulvertaft, Rupert James, odc(Fr),	MAJ(FTC)	-		01.05.97	MWC PORTSDOWN
Punch, Gerard Kevin, BEng, AMIMechE,	LT(IC)	E	MESM	01.03.96	SPLENDID
Punch, John Matthew, BSc,	LT(IC)	X	P U/T	01.09.01	RNAS CULDROSE
Punton, Ian Matthew, BEng, CEng, MRAeS, psc(j),	LT CDR(FTC)	E	AE	01.09.99	899 SQN HERON
Purchase, Louis Oliver,	MID(IC)	X		01.05.00	ARK ROYAL
Purdy, Richard John,	SLT(UCE)(IC)	E	AE	01.09.01	DARTMOUTH BRNC
Purvis, David Mark, MEng,	LT(FTC)	E	AE(P)	16.10.96	845 SQN
Purvis, Stephen Graham,	MID(IC)	X		01.05.00	CUMBERLAND
Puxley, Michael Edward, BEng, CEng,	LT(FTC)	E	WESM	01.09.96	WSA BRISTOL
Pye, Philip Martin,	LT CDR(FTC)	S	CA	01.10.98	EXETER
Pyne, Robert Leslie, BA, DipTh,	CHAPLAIN	CE		23.01.90	FEARLESS

Q

Name	Rank	Branch	Spec	Seniority	Where Serving
Quade, Nicholas Alexander Clive, BEng,	LT(FTC)	E	MESM	01.10.97	VIGILANT(PORT)
Quaite, David Geoffrey, BSc,	SLT(IC)	X		01.01.00	RALEIGH
Quantrill, Steven William, BSc,	LT(CC)	S		01.03.97	NEPTUNE
Quaye, Duncan Thomas George, MSc,	CDR(FTC)	E	ME	30.06.98	FLEET HQ NWD
Quekett, Ian Peter Scott, BEng, MSc, AMIEE,	LT CDR(FTC)	E	WE	01.08.99	ILLUSTRIOUS
Quemby, Sarah,	SLT(SCC)	Q		20.02.99	RCDM
Quick, Neville Hellins, BSc, CEng, MIEE,	LT CDR(FTC)	E	WE	01.05.91	WSA/CAPT MCTA
Quick, Stephen James, BA,	LT(IC)	X		01.05.01	WALNEY
Quince, Anthony Gary, BEng,	SLT(IC)	E	WE	01.01.01	DARTMOUTH BRNC
Quine, Nicholas John, MA, psc,	LT CDR(FTC)	E	WE	01.12.88	MWS COLLINGWOOD
Quinn, Martin Edward, (Act Lt Cdr)	LT(CC)	S	SM	01.02.92	DNR N IRELAND
Quinn, Michael Gerard, BA,	LT(IC)	X		01.01.02	MWS DRYAD
Quinn, Paul Anthony, BA, FCMI, FHCIMA, FCIPD, MHCIMA, MInstPS, CDipAF, jsdc,	CAPT(FTC)	S	SM	30.06.00	FLEET HQ PORTS
Quinn, Shaun Andrew, pcea,	LT(FTC)	X	O	16.05.92	824 SQN
Quirk, Anthony Thomas,	LT(FTC)	E	WE	02.09.99	MWS COLLINGWOOD

R

Name	Rank	Branch	Spec	Seniority	Where Serving
Raby, Nigel John Francis, MSc, jsdc, (Commodore)	CAPT(FTC)	E	WE	30.06.95	DPA BRISTOL
Race, Nigel James, MA, pce, psc(j),	CDR(FTC)	X	PWO(C)	31.12.99	MWC SOUTHWICK
Rackham, Anthony David Henry, BSc,	LT(FTC)	X	FC	01.11.95	MWS DRYAD
Rackham, Katharine, BSc, n,	LT(FTC)	X		01.03.97	MANCHESTER
Radakin, Antony David, LLB, pce, psc(j),	CDR(FTC)	X	PWO(U)	30.06.02	MWS DRYAD
Radbourne, Neville Ian,	LT(FTC)	E	WE	05.06.92	AGRIPPA AFSOUTH
Radcliffe, Nicholas, LLB, LMIPD,	LT CDR(FTC)	S		16.02.91	DLO/DGDEF LOG SP
Radford, Andrew James, BEng,	LT(CC)	X	P	01.06.92	DHFS
Rae, Alistair Lewis, BEng, CEng, AMIEE,	LT(FTC)	E	WE	01.04.97	HQ DCSA
Rae, Anthony James William, BSc,	LT CDR(FTC)	X	P	01.10.99	LOAN JTEG BSC DN
Rae, Derek Gordon, BSc, PGDip,	LT(FTC)	X	HM(AS)	01.03.96	MWS DRYAD
Rae, Fraser, BEng,	LT(IC)	X		01.04.00	BRIDPORT
Rae, Scott MacKenzie, MBE, BD,	CHAPLAIN	SF		02.02.81	NEPTUNE 2SL/CNH
Rae, Stephen Gordon, AGSM,	LT CDR(FTC)	S		01.02.00	MOD (BATH)
Raeburn, Craig, BSc, SM(n),	LT(FTC)	X		01.09.96	SOMERSET
Raeburn, Mark, n,	LT(FTC)	X		07.04.94	MWS DRYAD
Raffaelli, Philip Iain, MSc, MB, BCh, FFOM, MRCGP, jsdc,	SURG CAPT(FCC)	-	CPDATE	31.12.98	2SL/CNH
Rahman, Junia, MB, BS,	SURG LT(SCC)	-		06.08.97	MODHU DERRIFORD
Raisbeck, Paul Temple, MA, pce, psc(j),	LT CDR(FTC)	X	MCD	01.11.93	STANAVFORMED
Raitt, James Edwin, BSc,	CAPT RM(FTC)	-		01.09.97	42 CDO RM
Ralphson, Mark David, BEng, MSc,	LT CDR(FTC)	E	WE	01.10.00	CESM IPT
Ramm, Steven Charles, pce, pce(sm), psc,	CAPT(FTC)	X	SM	31.12.98	DA BRIDGETOWN
Ramsay, Graham Patrick, pce, ocds(US),	CDR(FTC)	X	PWO(N)	30.06.92	RALEIGH
Ramsey, Jeremy Stephen, BSc,	LT CDR(FTC)	S		16.04.89	FORT BLOCKHOUSE
Ramsey, Ryan Trevor, pce(sm), SM(n),	LT CDR(FTC)	X	SM	01.11.00	TORBAY
Ramshaw, George William Lilwall, BSc, CEng, FCMI, MIEE,	CDR(FTC)	E	WE	30.06.99	RMC OF SCIENCE
Rance, Maxwell George William, MA, psc(j),	CDR(FTC)	S		31.12.99	MOD (LONDON)

Name	Rank	Branch	Spec	Seniority	Where Serving
Rand, Marc James, BEng, MSc,	LT CDR(FTC)	E	ME	01.05.01	EXCHANGE NLANDS
Rand, Mark Andrew,	LT(IC)	E	WESM	01.01.02	VICTORIOUS(STBD)
Randall, David Frederick, BA, MSc,	CDR(FTC)	S		30.06.02	AFPAA WTHY DOWN
Randall, Nicholas John, BSc, PGDIPAN, pce,	LT CDR(FTC)	X	PWO(N)	01.10.97	FLEET HQ PORTS 2
Randall, Richard David, BSc,	LT CDR(FTC)	E	MESM	01.08.92	MOD (BATH)
Randles, Steven, BA,	LT(IC)	X		01.06.00	DUMBARTON CASTLE
Ranger, John Leonard, (Act Lt Cdr)	LT(FTC)	E	WE	18.10.85	WSA BRISTOL
Rankin, Graham Johnathon,	LT(IC)	X		01.09.01	SHOREHAM
Rankin, Ian Gordon, MSc, CEng, MIEE, (Commodore)	CAPT(FTC)	E	WESM	31.12.96	RCDS
CGIA, mdtc,					
Rankin, Suzanne Jayne,	LT(MCC)	Q	ONC	15.08.96	JSCSC
Rankine, Ivor Matthew,	LT(FTC)	E	MESM	19.06.98	NEPTUNE NT
Ransom, Benjamin Robert James,	LT(IC)	X		01.09.00	CHIDDINGFOLD
Ranson, Christopher David, MSc, CEng, MIEE,	CDR(FTC)	E	WE	30.06.99	FLEET CIS PORTS
Rant, Oliver James, BA, SM,	LT(IC)	X	SM	01.01.00	VICTORIOUS(PORT)
Rapp, James Campsie, pce, pcea, psc,	RADM	-	O	20.11.01	FOST SEA
Rasor, Andrew Martin,	LT(FTC)	X	P	01.07.92	ALBION
Ratcliffe, John Paul, BSc, PGDip,	CDR(FTC)	E	TM	30.06.92	NELSON RNSETT
Rawal, Krishna, MB, BS, DObstRCOG,	SURG LTCDR(MCC)	-		01.11.96	RN GIBRALTAR
Rawles, Julian Roy,	LT(CC)	X	ATC	01.04.99	RNAS CULDROSE
Rawlings, Damian Paul, BEng, CEng, MIMarEST,	LT CDR(FTC)	E	ME	01.08.95	SULTAN
Rawlings, Gary Andrew,	LT(FTC)	E	ME	01.04.01	DRAKE SFM
Rawlings, Gary Charles, HND, MCIPD,	LT CDR(CC)	E	TM	01.10.89	2SL/CNH
Rawlins, Simon Terence,	SLT(IC)	X	P	01.04.99	RNAS CULDROSE
Rawlinson, David,	LT(IC)	X	P	16.03.95	845 SQN
Rawlinson, Stephen James, BEng, CEng, MIMarEST,	LT CDR(FTC)	E	MESM	01.03.99	FLEET HQ PORTS 2
Rawson, Clive, AFC,	LT CDR(FTC)	X	O	01.10.94	824 SQN
Rawson, Scott Michael, BEng,	LT(FTC)	E	MESM	01.04.95	MOD (BATH)
Ray, Martin William, LLB,	LT(IC)	S		01.10.97	RNAS YEOVILTON
Ray, Pallab, BSc,	LT(IC)	E	TM	01.01.99	DARTMOUTH BRNC
Raybould, Adrian Glyn, BSc, CEng, MIEE, psc(j),	CDR(FTC)	E	WESM	30.06.01	WSA BRISTOL
Rayner, Brett Nicholas, psc,	CAPT(FTC)	S		30.06.99	AGRIPPA NAVSOUTH
Raynes, Christopher, BSc,	LT(IC)	X	P	16.09.98	846 SQN
Raynor, Sean David,	LT(FTC)	E	WE	04.09.98	CINCFLEET FIMU
Rea, Stephen Dennis,	LT(IC)	X		01.07.00	BRIDPORT
Read, Alun John,	LT(FTC)	X	P	01.09.84	815 SQN HQ
Read, Clinton Derek,	CAPT RM(FTC)	-		01.05.00	UKLFCSG RM
Read, Crispin Toby, BA,	LT(CC)	X	P	16.05.92	849 SQN A FLT
Read, Jonathan Mabyn, MSc, CEng, MIEE,	LT CDR(FTC)	E	WESM	23.05.97	VENGEANCE(PORT)
Read, Jonathon Asher Jason Marcus, MB, BS,	SURG LT(SCC)	-	O U/T	04.08.99	VIGILANT(PORT)
Read, Matthew Richard, BEng, CEng,	LT(FTC)	E	ME	01.02.96	FLEET ROSYTH
Read, Paul Steven, BEng, AMIEE,	LT(FTC)	E	WE	01.03.97	RALEIGH
Read, Richard John, BA,	CAPT RM(FTC)	-	LC	01.09.96	539 ASSLT SQN RM
Readwin, Roger Roy, BA,	LT(FTC)	X	MCD	01.04.96	DARTMOUTH BRNC
Reah, Stephen, BEng,	LT CDR(FTC)	E	ME	02.05.00	MONMOUTH
Rearden, Richard Joseph, (Act Maj)	CAPT RM(FTC)	-	SO(LE)	01.01.96	CDO LOG REGT RM
Reason, Ian Malcolm, MBE, BEng, MA, MSc, isc, psc(j),	CDR(FTC)	E	AE	30.06.00	JCA IPT UK
Reaves, Charles Edward, LLB,	SLT(IC)	S		01.01.00	FEARLESS
Redgrove, Mark Anthony,	LT(FTC)	E	WE	01.09.99	IMS BRUSSELS
Redman, Charles Jeremy Rufus, n,	LT CDR(FTC)	X		23.11.98	FOSNNI OPS DLO
Redman, Christopher Douglas Jeremy, BDS,	SGCDR(D)(FCC)	-		31.12.00	DDA HALTON
MSc, LDS RCS(Eng), MGDS RCS, MFDS,RCS,					
Redmayne, Mark Edward, BA,	LT(CC)	X		01.06.99	IRON DUKE
Redmayne, Michael Julian, BSc,	SLT(IC)	X		01.01.00	MWS DEF DIV SCHL
Redstone, Colin,	CDR(FTC)	S	SM	31.12.98	NEPTUNE DLO
Reece, Nigel David, BEng, MSc, CEng, MIMechE,	LT CDR(FTC)	E	MESM	01.03.00	TURBULENT
Reed, Andrew William, BSc, pce,	CDR(FTC)	X	AAWO	31.12.00	FLEET HQ NWD
Reed, Darren Keith, BA,	LT(FTC)	S		01.12.96	2SL/CNH
Reed, Frank, OBE, BA, MSc, psc, OStJ,	CDRE(FTC)	MS	(P)	12.06.02	DEF MED TRG CTR
Reed, James Hamilton, pce, pcea,	LT CDR(FTC)	X	P	01.04.95	NELSON (PAY)
Reed, James William,	MAJ(FTC)	-	SO(LE)	01.10.99	CTCRM
Reed, Jonathan Charles,	LT(FTC)	E	AE(M)	07.09.95	RNAS CULDROSE

Name	Rank	Branch	Spec	Seniority	Where Serving
Reed, Mark, BSc, PGDip,	LT CDR(CC)	X	METOC	01.10.98	FLEET HQ NWD
Reed, Nicholas,	LT(FTC)	S	(W)	26.04.99	TALENT
Reed, Peter Kirby,	SLT(UCE)(IC)	E	ME	01.09.01	DARTMOUTH BRNC
Reeder, Robert, OBE, BSc, MIMechE,	CDR(FTC)	E	AE	31.12.91	ES AIR MASU
Reehal, Thomas Gerald, BA,	SLT(IC)	X	O U/T	01.01.01	DARTMOUTH BRNC
Rees, Adam Martin, BA, MSc,	LT(IC)	E	TM	01.09.98	RALEIGH
Rees, Daniel Simon James, LLB,	SLT(IC)	X		01.09.99	PORTLAND
Rees, John Blain Minto, BSc, jsdc,	CAPT(FTC)	E	TM	31.12.99	2SL/CNH FOTR
Rees, John Patrick,	LT CDR(FTC)	S		29.06.99	NELSON WF
Rees, Paul Stuart Chadwick, MB, BS,	SURG LT(MCC)	-		06.08.97	RH HASLAR
Rees, Richard Thomas, BEng,	LT(FTC)	X		01.12.95	LANCASTER
Rees, Simon Geoffrey,	MID(IC)	X		01.09.00	RAMSEY
Reese, David Michael, BSc,	LT(FTC)	X	O	01.09.94	815 FLT 203
Reeve, Jonathon, MA, CEng, MIEE, rcds, psc,	RADM	-	MESM	13.03.00	MOD (BATH)
Reeves, Andrew Philip,	SLT(IC)	X	(X)	01.09.00	VIGILANT(PORT)
Reeves, Kurt, BEng, CEng, MIMarE,	LT CDR(FTC)	E	ME	04.12.00	MOD (BATH)
Reeves, Paul Kieth,	LT(CC)	E	ME	01.08.00	DARTMOUTH BRNC
Reid, Charles Ian, BSc, pce, pce(sm), psc(j),	CDR(FTC)	X	SM	31.12.99	VICTORIOUS(STBD)
Reid, Duncan, MBE, BA, BA(OU),	CAPT(IC)	E	AE(L)	31.12.00	AH IPT
Reid, James Lyle, BSc,	LT(IC)	X		01.05.00	NORTHUMBERLAND
Reid, Jason Charles James, BEng,	LT CDR(FTC)	E	WESM	01.04.01	FOST CSST DEVPT
Reid, Martyn Richard,	LT(CC)	X		01.04.95	OCLC MANCH
Reid, Martyn, pce, pcea, psc,	CDR(FTC)	X	O	30.06.94	HQ3GP HQSTC
Reid, Paul Frederick, SM,	LT CDR(FTC)	X	SM	01.10.01	MWS COLLINGWOOD
Reidy, Paul Alan, pce(sm), SM,	LT CDR(FTC)	X	SM	01.11.98	VICTORIOUS(STBD)
Reilly, Thomas Gerald, (Act Lt Cdr)	LT(FTC)	X	C	03.06.92	HQ DCSA
Reindorp, David Peter, PGDIPAN, MRIN, pce,	CDR(FTC)	X	PWO(N)	30.06.02	WESTMINSTER
Relf, Kerry Marie, BA,	LT(CC)	S		01.07.99	LANCASTER
Renaud, Gavin Andrew Richard,	LT(IC)	X	O	16.10.01	820 SQN
Rendell, Derrick John, MSc,	LT(FTC)	E	MESM	14.06.96	MOD (BATH)
Rennie, James Gibson,	LT(CS)RM(CAS)	-		18.09.98	DNR W CENTRAL
Rennison, William Ross, OBE, MSc,	CDR(FTC)	E	TM	31.12.86	NMA PORTSMOUTH
Renwick, John,	CDR(FTC)	S	SM	30.06.02	RALEIGH
Reston, Samuel Craig, MB, ChB,	SURG LTCDR(MCC)	-		07.08.01	RH HASLAR
Retter, Rachael Louise, BA,	LT(IC)	X	HM	01.07.00	SCOTT
Revens, Carl Andrew,	CAPT RM(FTC)	-		01.05.97	HQ BAND SERVICE
Rex, Colin Antony,	LT(CC)	X	P	01.10.99	846 SQN
Reynolds, Andrew Charles James, BEng,	SLT(IC)	E		01.09.99	SULTAN
Reynolds, Andrew Graham, BEng, MSc, CEng, MIMechE, MCGI,	LT CDR(FTC)	E	ME	01.08.97	MONMOUTH
Reynolds, Huw Francis, BEng,	SLT(IC)	E	AE	01.09.99	SULTAN
Reynolds, James,	SLT(IC)	X		01.01.00	SCOTT
Reynolds, Mark Edward,	SLT(UCE)(FTC)	E	ME	01.09.00	DARTMOUTH BRNC
Reynolds, Matthew Jowan,	LT(IC)	X		01.05.01	BANGOR
Reynolds, Peter Anthony, BSc, psc,	COL(FTC)	-		30.06.97	SA BUENOS AIRES
Reynolds, Timothy Edward, MA,	CDR(FTC)	X	METOC	30.06.98	MOD (LONDON)
Reynolds, Timothy Paul, BSc,	LT CDR(FTC)	E	IS	30.04.95	RMC OF SCIENCE
Reynolds, Zoe Anne,	SLT(IC)	X		01.09.00	DARTMOUTH BRNC
Rhodes, Andrew Gregory, BEng,	CDR(FTC)	E	WE	30.06.02	NELSON
Rhodes, Andrew William,	LT(FTC)	E	WE	01.04.01	FEARLESS
Rhodes, Martin James,	LT(FTC)	X	O	01.09.95	RNAS YEOVILTON
Rhodes, Paul Edwin,	CAPT RM(IC)	-	SO(LE)	21.07.01	CHFHQ
Rich, Alvin Arnold, pce, pcea,	CDR(FTC)	X	O	30.06.90	TEMERAIRE
Rich, David Charles, pce(sm), pce,	LT CDR(FTC)	X	SM	20.05.97	VENGEANCE(STBD)
Rich, Jonathan George, MIPD, pcea, psc(j),	LT CDR(FTC)	X	P	01.10.89	CV(F) IPT
Richards, Adam Vivian, BA,	LT(IC)	X		01.03.99	ANGLESEY
Richards, Alan David, jsdc, pce, pcea,	CDRE(FTC)	X	P	24.06.02	MOD (LONDON)
Richards, Anthony Jeremy,	LT(IC)	S		01.10.00	NEPTUNE 2SL/CNH
Richards, Bryan Robert, DEH, MIOSH,	LT CDR(FTC)	MS	(AD)	01.10.00	2SL/CNH
Richards, Catherine Duncan, BA,	LT(IC)	X		01.11.99	WESTMINSTER
Richards, Christopher Martin, pce, psc,	CDR(FTC)	X	AAWO	30.06.95	MOD (LONDON)
Richards, Fraser Charles, SM, (Act Lt Cdr)	LT(FTC)	X	SM	25.07.96	MOD DIS SEA

Name	Rank	Branch	Spec	Seniority	Where Serving
Richards, Guy Benjamin,	SLT(IC)	S		01.01.01	DARTMOUTH BRNC
Richards, James Ian Hanson, BEng,	LT(FTC)	E	WESM	01.07.97	VANGUARD(PORT)
Richards, Paul,	LT(IC)	E	ME	29.04.01	SHEFFIELD
Richards, Stephen William,	MAJ(FTC)	-	SO(LE)	01.10.99	JSCSC
Richards, Steven Charles Arthur,	LT(IC)	E	WE	01.01.02	MANCHESTER
Richardson, Adrian Paul,	LT(CC)	E	WE	01.02.01	DARTMOUTH BRNC
Richardson, Douglas, BEng,	LT(FTC)	E	MESM	01.10.94	RM POOLE
Richardson, Gavin Andrew, BSc, pcea,	LT CDR(CC)	X	O	01.10.01	824 SQN
Richardson, Geoffrey Leslie, BSc,	LT(IC)	X	P	01.08.91	846 SQN
Richardson, George Nicholas, BA,	LT CDR(FTC)	S		01.07.01	SOUTHAMPTON
Richardson, Ian Hayden,	LT(CC)	X	MCD	01.03.00	SANDOWN
Richardson, Ian James Ward, BSc, CEng, FIEE, rcds, psc,	CAPT(FTC)	E	WE	31.12.95	JDCC
Richardson, Mark Anthony, BSc,	LT CDR(CC)	E	IS	01.09.97	EXCHANGE USA
Richardson, Michael Colin,	CAPT RM(FTC)	-	SO(LE)	01.01.95	RM CHIVENOR
Richardson, Michael Peter, FHCIMA,	CDR(FTC)	S		30.06.97	ALBION
Richardson, Peter Stephen Mark, BEng, AMIEE,	LT CDR(FTC)	E	WE	01.08.99	WSA BRISTOL
Richardson, Peter,	LT(FTC)	X	P	16.01.92	EXCHANGE RAF UK
Richardson, Philip Charles, BSc,	LT(FTC)	X	P U/T	01.03.98	NORTHUMBERLAND
Richardson, Sophie Charlotte,	SLT(UCE)(FTC)	S		01.09.00	DARTMOUTH BRNC
Riches, Anthony Ian, BA,	SLT(IC)	X		01.05.00	CUMBERLAND
Riches, Ian Charles, pce(sm),	LT CDR(FTC)	X	SM	01.10.90	FOSM FASLANE
Richford, Terence Fitzpatrick,	LT CDR(FTC)	X	C	01.10.92	FOSNNI OPS DLO
Richman, Paul George, BA,	LT(IC)	X	P	16.11.97	846 SQN
Richman, Philip Jonathan,	LT CDR(FTC)	E	WESM	01.10.00	RALEIGH
Richmond, Iain James Martin, BA, pce, pcea,	CDR(FTC)	X	P	31.12.96	SACLANT USA(SEA)
Richter, Alwyn Stafford Byron, BEng, CEng, MIEE,	LT CDR(FTC)	E	WE	01.09.00	LIVERPOOL
Rickard, Jack, BSc,	LT(CC)	S		12.11.97	RALEIGH
Rickard, Rory Frederick, MB, BCh, BAO, FRCSEd,	SURG LTCDR(MCC)	-		03.08.98	NELSON (PAY)
Riddett, Adam Owen, BSc,	SLT(IC)	X		01.09.99	GRIMSBY
Riden, Donald Keith, BM, BDS, LDS,	SGCDR(D)(FCC)	-	(COSM)	30.06.02	RH HASLAR
FRCS, FDS RCS(Eng),					
Rider, John Charles Raymon, BSc,	LT(IC)	X		01.01.02	RALEIGH
Ridge, Mervyn Henry,	LT(FTC)	E	WESM	07.02.97	RALEIGH
Rigby, Jeremy Conrad, MA, MILDM, psc(j),	CDR(FTC)	S		31.12.00	HQ3GP HQSTC
Riggall, Andrew Derek,	LT(CC)	X	P	01.05.96	702 SQN HERON
Riggs, Matthew George Winston, BA,	SLT(IC)	S		01.01.01	DARTMOUTH BRNC
Riley, Graeme Alexander,	LT(FTC)	E	MESM	14.06.96	MOD (BATH)
Riley, Jansen,	LT(FTC)	X	AV	09.01.01	RNAS CULDROSE
Riley, Michael Jaeger, BSc, jsdc, pce,	CDR(FTC)	X	AAWO	31.12.93	BDS WASHINGTON
Riley, Ralph, BA,	SLT(IC)	X	O U/T	01.01.01	DARTMOUTH BRNC
Rimington, Anthony Kingsmill, BA,	LT(FTC)	X	P	01.02.96	815 FLT 210
Rimington, John Anthony, jsdc, pce,	CAPT(FTC)	X	AWO(U)	31.12.92	SULTAN AIB
Rimmer, Heather Elizabeth, BA, psc(j),	LT CDR(FTC)	E	TM	22.07.96	2SL/CNH FOTR
Rimmer, Michael, pce,	CDR(FTC)	X	PWO(C)	31.12.97	BDS WASHINGTON
Rimmer, Owen Francis, BA,	LT(IC)	X		01.01.02	RALEIGH
Rimmer, Robin,	LT CDR(FTC)	E	WE	01.10.98	MWS EXCELLENT
Riordan, Shaun Paul,	MID(UCE)(IC)	E	WE U/T	01.09.01	MONTROSE
Ripley, Benjamin Edward, n,	LT(FTC)	X	PWO(U)	01.11.94	NORFOLK
Rippingale, Stuart Nicholas, MSc, PGCE,	LT CDR(FTC)	E	IS	01.10.95	MOD (LONDON)
Risdall, Jane Elizabeth, MA, MB, BS, DA,	SURG CDR(FCC)	-	(CA)	31.12.98	INM ALVERSTOKE
Risley, James Grant, BEng,	LT(CC)	E	MESM	01.03.00	TIRELESS
Risley, Jonathan, BSc, MA, CEng, MBCS, CDipAF, adp,	CDR(FTC)	E	IS	31.12.00	CINCFLEET FTSU
Ritchie, Douglas Brian,	LT(IC)	E	MESM	01.09.01	TORBAY
Ritchie, Iain David, BSc,	LT(IC)	X		01.05.02	MWS DRYAD
Ritchie, John Noble, SM,	LT CDR(FTC)	X	SM	01.04.02	MOD (LONDON)
Ritchie, William James,	MAJ(FTC)	-	SO(LE)	01.10.97	RMC OF SCIENCE
Ritsperis, Athos, MSc, DIC, PGCE, MIL, ACGI, ARCS,	LT(CC)	E	TM	01.07.92	AFPAA(CENTURION)
Rix, Anthony John, pce, psc, (Commodore)	CAPT(FTC)	X	PWO(U)	30.06.97	FWO DEVPT SEA
Robb, Matthew Cruickshanks, OBE, BA, (Act Capt)	CDR(FTC)	E	WE	30.06.92	T45 IPT
CGIA, psc, mdtc,					
Robb, Michael Edward, BA,	LT(CC)	S		01.08.97	UKSU AFSOUTH
Robbins, Harry Vincent,	CAPT RM(IC)	-	P	01.01.02	847 SQN

Name	Rank	Branch	Spec	Seniority	Where Serving
Robbins, Jeremy Matthew Francis, MBE, BSc, hcsc, psc(m),	COL(FTC)	-	C	30.06.99	COMAMPHIBFOR
Robbins, Margaret Joy, psc,	CDR(FTC)	W	X	31.12.92	AFPAA HQ
Robert, Iain Andrew,	LT(IC)	E	AE	29.04.01	SULTAN
Roberts, Andrew Paul,	LT(IC)	E	AE	01.05.02	DARTMOUTH BRNC
Roberts, Annabel Mary, BSc,	LT(IC)	E	TM	01.01.95	NELSON
Roberts, Benjamin, BA,	SLT(IC)	S		01.09.00	DARTMOUTH BRNC
Roberts, Daniel Llewellyn,	MID(UCE)(IC)	E	MESM	01.09.01	SOUTHAMPTON
Roberts, David Alan, pce,	LT CDR(FTC)	X	PWO(A)	01.05.92	SACLANT USA(SEA)
Roberts, David Howard Wyn, BA, pce,	LT CDR(FTC)	X	AAWO	01.04.91	FLEET HQ NWD
Roberts, Dean, BEng,	LT CDR(FTC)	E	WE	04.04.99	WSA BRISTOL
Roberts, Ellis William,	LT CDR(FTC)	E	AE(M)	01.10.95	ES AIR YEO
Roberts, Iain Gordon, BSc, BEng,	LT(FTC)	E	WESM	01.10.91	WSA BRISTOL
Roberts, Ian Thomas, pce(sm), psc(j),	CDR(FTC)	X	SM	30.06.02	TRIUMPH
Roberts, Kenneth Eric, BEng, MSc, CEng, MIEE, gw,	LT CDR(FTC)	E	WE	01.01.99	EXETER
Roberts, Martin Alan,	LT(CC)	X	O	01.11.94	849 SQN A FLT
Roberts, Martyn, BEng,	LT(FTC)	X	O	01.10.88	EXCHANGE RAF UK
Roberts, Nicholas Steven, BEng, MSc, psc(j),	CDR(FTC)	E	WE	30.06.99	WSA BRISTOL
Roberts, Nigel David,	LT(IC)	X	O	10.02.98	815 FLT 211
Roberts, Peter Stafford,	LT CDR(FTC)	X	AAWO	01.10.01	YORK
Roberts, Selvin Clive, BEng,	LT CDR(FTC)	E	MESM	01.10.99	SUPERB
Roberts, Stephen David, BEng, MSc, CEng, MIEE,	LT CDR(FTC)	E	WE	01.04.98	NMA PORTSMOUTH
Roberts, Stephen Richard,	LT(IC)	E		01.02.01	FLEET HQ NWD
Roberts, Stephen,	LT CDR(FTC)	X	AV	01.10.01	CHFHQ
Roberts, Suzanne Marie, BA, (Act Lt Cdr)	LT(FTC)	S		01.06.94	MWS COLLINGWOOD
Roberts, Timothy John, BEng, MSc,	LT CDR(FTC)	E	MESM	01.07.95	FOST CSST SEA
Robertshaw, Ian Weston, BEng,	LT(FTC)	E	WESM	01.04.96	TALENT
Robertson Gopffarth, Alexander Alistair John, BSc, SM(n),	LT(IC)	X	SM	01.02.97	TIRELESS
Robertson, Adam Joseph,	MID(UCE)(IC)	E	WE	01.09.00	DARTMOUTH BRNC
Robertson, David Cameron, BSc, n, PGDIPAN, MRIN,	LT CDR(FTC)	X	H CH	01.06.97	SCOTT
Robertson, David Colin, BSc,	LT CDR(FTC)	E	AE	01.10.90	ES AIR BRISTOL
Robertson, Douglas Malcolm, BSc,	LT CDR(FTC)	X	ATC	01.10.93	RNAS CULDROSE
Robertson, Frederick William, MBE, pcea,	LT CDR(FTC)	X	P	01.03.86	CHFHQ
Robertson, Ian Wallace, BEng,	SLT(IC)	E	WESM	01.05.00	ILLUSTRIOUS
Robertson, Kevin Francis, pce,	CDR(FTC)	X	PWO(C)	30.06.98	MWS COLLINGWOOD
Robertson, Malcolm Nairn,	LT CDR(FTC)	E	MESM	01.10.99	SULTAN
Robertson, Michael George, BSc, pce,	LT CDR(FTC)	X	O	01.04.94	JSCSC
Robertson, Neil Bannerman,	MAJ(FTC)	-		01.05.00	FLEET HQ PORTS 2
Robertson, Paul Noel, pcea,	LT CDR(FTC)	X	O	01.10.00	771 SQN
Robertson, Stuart Thomas, BA,	LT(IC)	S		01.03.99	SOVEREIGN
Robey, James Christopher,	LT(IC)	X		01.10.00	LIVERPOOL
Robin, Christopher Charles Edward, pce, pcea, psc(j),	LT CDR(FTC)	X	P	01.09.94	UKMARBATSTAFF
Robin, Julie Isobel, MB, ChB,	SURG LT(SCC)	-		02.08.00	DRAKE CBP(DLO)
Robins, Mark Duncan, MBE,	LT(IC)	X	C	01.01.01	BOWMAN IPT
Robinson, Andrew,	LT(FTC)	MS		01.04.01	INM ALVERSTOKE
Robinson, Andrew, BSc, jsdc,	CDR(FTC)	X	METOC	30.06.97	2SL/CNH FOTR
Robinson, Charles Edward Thayne, pce, psc(j),	CDR(FTC)	X	PWO(U)	30.06.99	ELANT/NAVNORTH
Robinson, Christopher Paul, MBE, pce, pcea, psc, (Act Capt)	CDR(FTC)	X	O	31.12.87	MOD (LONDON)
Robinson, David Ian, MSc, AMIEE, psc, gw,	LT CDR(FTC)	E	WE	01.02.84	T45 IPT
Robinson, David Paul,	LT(FTC)	E	WESM	01.04.01	TORBAY
Robinson, David, (Act Lt)	SLT(IC)	S		01.10.99	DLO/DGDEF LOG SP
Robinson, Guy Antony, MA, pce, psc(j),	CDR(FTC)	X	PWO(A)	30.06.02	EDINBURGH
Robinson, James Stuart, pce,	CDR(FTC)	X	PWO(U)	31.12.97	FSC IPT
Robinson, Matthew Steven,	SLT(IC)	X	P U/T	01.05.01	RNAS YEOVILTON
Robinson, Melanie Suzanne, MSc,	LT CDR(FTC)	X		04.03.01	MWS DRYAD
Robinson, Michael Peter, MSc, CEng, MIMarEST, psc(j),	CDR(FTC)	E	MESM	30.06.02	FLEET HQ NWD
Robinson, Paul Henry, pce, pce(sm),	CAPT(FTC)	X	SM	30.06.00	FLEET HQ NWD
Robinson, Philip James Owen, BSc,	CAPT RM(IC)	-		01.09.01	45 CDO RM
Robinson, Pollyanna, BEng,	LT(CC)	E	AE	01.01.00	845 SQN
Robinson, Richard John,	LT(IC)	X	ATC	01.04.01	RNAS CULDROSE
Robinson, Steven Leslie, BEng,	LT(IC)	E	WE	01.09.01	MANCHESTER
Robinson, Timothy,	SURG SLT(SCC)	-		01.07.01	DARTMOUTH BRNC
Robison, Garry Stuart, MPhil, psc(m), psc(j),	COL(FTC)	-		31.12.98	MOD (LONDON)

Name	Rank	Branch	Spec	Seniority	Where Serving
Robley, William Forster,	LT(CC)	X	P	01.06.96	771 SQN
Robson, Christine Jane,	LT CDR(MCC)	Q	IC/CC	01.10.00	RH HASLAR
Rochester, Andrew David, BSc,	LT RM(IC)	-		01.09.00	40 CDO RM
Roddy, Michael Patrick, BSc,	MAJ(FTC)	-		27.04.02	NELSON
Rodgers, Darren,	LT(CC)	X	P	01.07.93	RAF CRANWELL EFS
Rodgers, Steven,	LT CDR(FTC)	E	WE	01.10.96	ALBION
Rogers, Alan,	LT CDR(FTC)	X	AV	01.10.01	792 NAS
Rogers, Andrew Gavin, BEng, CEng, MIEE,	LT CDR(FTC)	E	WE	01.02.98	FLEET HQ NWD
Rogers, Anthony George, AFC,	CDR(FTC)	X	O	31.12.85	MOD (LONDON)
Rogers, Christopher Mark, BEng,	LT CDR(FTC)	E	WE	01.06.00	MWS COLLINGWOOD
Rogers, Ian Arthur, MSc, CEng, MIMechE,	LT CDR(FTC)	E	MESM	01.01.96	DRAKE CBS
Rogers, Julian Charles Everard, SM,	LT(FTC)	X	SM	01.03.91	SPARTAN
Rogers, Malcolm Stuart, BSc, AMIEE,	CDR(FTC)	E	TM	30.06.90	AGRIPPA AFSOUTH
Rogers, Philip Scott, BSc,	LT(IC)	E	TM	01.01.95	SULTAN
Rogers, Simon James Peter, BA,	LT(IC)	X		01.07.98	CHATHAM
Rogers, Simon M, BSc,	LT RM(IC)	-		01.09.00	FPGRM
Rogers, Stella Monica, BEd,	LT(IC)	E	TM	01.09.00	MANCHESTER
Rogers, Timothy Hugh Goddard,	LT CDR(FTC)	X		04.12.98	BDS WASHINGTON
Rollason, Caroline Anne,	LT(IC)	S		01.11.00	899 SQN HERON
Rolph, Andrew Peter Mark, pce,	LT CDR(FTC)	X	PWO(C)	16.11.97	PJHQ
Rom, Stephen Paul,	LT(FTC)	E	WE	02.09.99	MWS COLLINGWOOD
Romney, Paul David, PGDIPAN, MRIN, pce,	LT CDR(FTC)	X	PWO(N)	01.01.98	NMA PORTSMOUTH
Ronald, Euan Taylor, BSc,	SLT(IC)	X		01.05.01	ARK ROYAL
Ronaldson, Gordon Ian, MBE, BEng, MIMechE, AMIMechE,	LT(FTC)	E	ME	01.12.94	DARTMOUTH BRNC
Rook, David John,	LT CDR(FTC)	E	WE	01.10.96	NP 1066
Rook, Graeme Inglis, BSc,	LT CDR(FTC)	E	WE	01.04.98	WSA/CAPT MCTA
Rooney, Michael,	LT(CC)	E	WE	01.07.00	DARTMOUTH BRNC
Roots, Sally, BEng,	LT CDR(FTC)	E	AE	01.08.98	TEMERAIRE
Roper, Martin, pcea,	LT CDR(FTC)	X	O	01.11.90	AGRIPPA NAVSOUTH
Roscoe, David,	SURG SLT(SCC)	-		01.07.00	DARTMOUTH BRNC
Roscoe, Robert David, BEng,	LT CDR(FTC)	E	WE	01.04.99	ARGYLL
Rose, Alan, BSc,	SLT(IC)	E	WE	01.09.99	MWS COLLINGWOOD
Rose, Andrew Donald, BA,	LT(CC)	X	O	16.12.97	849 SQN HQ
Rose, Caroline Mary, BEng, MSc, CEng, MIMechE, AMIMarE,	LT CDR(FTC)	E	ME	07.06.02	SULTAN
Rose, John Gordon, MBE, psc(m),	BRIG(FTC)	-		30.06.00	MOD (LONDON)
Rose, Michael Frederick, BEng, MSc, CEng, MIMarEST,	LT CDR(FTC)	E	ME	28.12.99	SUTHERLAND
Rose, Simone, BA,	SLT(IC)	S		01.05.00	CORNWALL
Roskilly, Martyn, BSc,	CAPT RM(IC)	-		01.05.01	45 CDO RM
Ross, Andrew Charles Paterson, BSc, ocds(No), psc,	MAJ(FTC)	-		25.04.96	NMA WHALE ISLAND
Ross, Andrew Duncan, MIL, SM,	LT(FTC)	X	SM	01.04.01	VICTORIOUS(PORT)
Ross, Angus Allan, BA, MSc,	CAPT(FTC)	S		30.06.02	AFPAA WTHY DOWN
Ross, Gareth Donald Anthony,	SLT(IC)	X	AV	01.05.00	RFANSU
Ross, Gawain,	CAPT RM(FTC)	-	SO(LE)	01.01.99	RM POOLE
Ross, Ian, BEng, CEng, MIMarE,	LT CDR(FTC)	E	ME	01.08.00	OCEAN
Ross, Jonathan Hubert, BSc, MA, ACGI, psc(j),	LT COL(FTC)	-		30.06.02	FLEET HQ PORTS
Ross, Robert Alasdair, MB, BS, FRCS, Dip FFP,	SURG CDR(FCC)	-	GMPP	31.12.99	CTCRM
Ross, Sarah Joanne, MB, BCh, MRCGP, psc(j),	SURG CDR(FCC)	-	GMPP	14.10.99	FEARLESS
Roster, Shaun Patrick,	LT(CC)	X	O	16.11.94	815 FLT 244
Rostron, David William, BEng,	LT(FTC)	E	MESM	01.01.92	DRAKE CBS
Rostron, John Harry,	SLT(IC)	E	WESM	01.01.00	RALEIGH
Rothwell, John Francis,	LT CDR(FTC)	X	PWO(A)	01.09.82	WSA/CAPT MCTA
Roue, James Llewellyn, BA,	SLT(IC)	S		01.01.00	ILLUSTRIOUS
Round, Matthew James, BA, BSc, PGCE,	LT(IC)	X	O U/T	01.05.02	750 SQN SEAHAWK
Routledge, William David,	LT(FTC)	X	PT	10.12.98	SULTAN
Rowan, Mark Edward,	LT(FTC)	X	C	24.07.97	MWS COLLINGWOOD
Rowan, Nicholas Anthony, BEng,	LT CDR(FTC)	E	MESM	01.10.01	MOD (BATH)
Rowberry, Adrian Graham, BSc,	LT(IC)	X		01.01.02	MWS DRYAD
Rowe, Andrew James,	LT(FTC)	E	WE	19.02.93	FLEET HQ NWD
Rowe, Kevin Christopher,	LT(CC)	X	O	01.01.93	824 SQN
Rowe, Paula Elizabeth, MBA,	LT CDR(FTC)	E	TM	01.10.97	FOST DPORT SHORE
Rowe, Phillip James,	LT(IC)	X	HM	01.05.02	SCOTT

Name	Rank	Branch	Spec	Seniority	Where Serving
Rowe, Richard Dudley, BD,	CHAPLAIN	SF		24.09.00	FWO PORTS SEA
Rowell, Graham Edward, MSc, (Act Capt)	CDR(FTC)	E	AE	30.06.94	HARRIER IPT
Rowland, Paul Nicholas, BEng, CEng, MIMarEST,	LT CDR(FTC)	E	MESM	01.01.00	DARTMOUTH BRNC
Rowlands, Andrew Richard, BEng,	LT(FTC)	E	WE	01.06.96	RMC OF SCIENCE
Rowlands, Geoffrey Alan, BA, BSc, FRMS,	LT CDR(FTC)	X	METOC	01.09.85	FLEET HQ NWD
Rowlands, Kevin, BSc, MA,	LT CDR(FTC)	X	PWO(A)	01.10.01	NORTHUMBERLAND
Rowse, Mark Lawrence, BEng, CEng, MIMarEST,	LT CDR(FTC)	E	WE	01.07.97	T45 IPT
Rowson, Marcus Jonathan, BSc,	LT(IC)	X	P	01.05.00	846 SQN
Roy, Alexander Campbell, OBE, osc(us),	LT COL(FTC)	-		31.12.90	SACLANT USA(SEA)
Roy, Christopher,	SLT(IC)	X	P	01.01.01	RNAS CULDROSE
Roylance, Jaimie Fraser, MA,	MAJ(IC)	-	P	01.09.01	EXCHANGE USA
Royle, Nigel Alexander,	SLT(IC)	E	ME	01.05.00	SULTAN
Royston, James Lawrence, MA,	SLT(IC)	X		01.09.00	DARTMOUTH BRNC
Royston, Stuart James, pce,	LT CDR(FTC)	X	PWO(C)	01.05.98	AGRIPPA NAVSOUTH
Rucinski, Peter Gerard, BEng,	SLT(IC)	X		01.01.01	DARTMOUTH BRNC
Rudd, Timothy Gerald, LLB,	SLT(IC)	X		01.09.00	DARTMOUTH BRNC
Rudd, Vanessa Jane, BA,	LT(CC)	S		15.09.01	MWC PORTSDOWN
Ruddock, Gordon William David, n,	LT(FTC)	X		01.07.95	GRAFTON
Ruddock, Jane, MA,	LT(IC)	X		01.01.99	DARTMOUTH BRNC
Rudman, Christopher John, BSc,	LT CDR(FTC)	E	TM	15.05.90	NMA PORTSMOUTH
Runchman, Phillip Charles, BM, BCH, MA, FRCS,	SURG CDR(FCC)	-	(CGS)	30.06.85	RH HASLAR
Rundle, Anthony Littlejohns, BEng,	LT CDR(FTC)	E	WE	01.10.00	DRAKE SFM
Rundle, Robert Mark, BSc, psc(m),	LT COL(FTC)	-		30.06.87	NS OBERAMMERGAU
Rusbridger, Robert Charles, MSc, psc,	CDR(FTC)	E	ME	30.06.95	MOD (BATH)
Rushworth, Benjamin John, BSc, ARCS, n,	LT(FTC)	X		01.05.98	ILLUSTRIOUS
Russell, Bruce, BEng, CEng, MIEE,	LT CDR(FTC)	E	WESM	01.05.00	JSCSC
Russell, Colin,	LT(FTC)	E	AE	01.01.00	846 SQN
Russell, David John, rcds, pce, pce(sm), hcsc,(Commodore)	CAPT(FTC)	X	SM	31.12.93	NELSON
Russell, Gillian Spence, BEng,	LT(FTC)	S		01.08.95	MWS COLLINGWOOD
Russell, Katherine Elizabeth Filshie, BSc,	LT(IC)	X		01.05.02	MWS DRYAD
Russell, Mark James,	SLT(IC)	E	MESM	01.05.00	SULTAN
Russell, Martin Simon, BA,	LT(IC)	X	O U/T	01.01.02	849 SQN HQ
Russell, Nigel Anthony David,	LT(FTC)	X	PWO(A)	01.12.94	ARK ROYAL
Russell, Paul,	LT CDR(FTC)	X	AAWO	01.05.01	GLASGOW
Russell, Philip Robert, BTech, MSc, CEng, MIMarE,	LT CDR(FTC)	E	ME	01.02.98	WSA BRISTOL
Russell, Simon Jonathon, MSc, MInstPS, MILT, AMRAeS,psc,	CDR(FTC)	E	AE	30.06.98	JSCSC
Russell, Thomas, pce,	LT CDR(FTC)	X	MCD	01.07.93	PEMBROKE
Russell, Timothy James, BSc,	LT(CC)	X	MW	01.07.90	EXCHANGE AUSTLIA
Ruston, Mark Robert, BEng, MSc,	LT(CC)	E	WE	01.01.99	NEWCASTLE
Rutherford, Kevin John, BSc,	LT(CC)	X	P	01.10.93	848 SQN HERON
Rutherford, Timothy James, BEng,	LT CDR(FTC)	E	AE	30.12.00	RNAS YEOVILTON
Ruthven, Stuart Christopher, MB, ChB,	SURG LT(SCC)	-		01.08.01	NEPTUNE NT
Ryan, Dennis Graham, BSc,	CDR(FTC)	E	AE(P)	30.06.02	MERLIN IPT
Ryan, Jennifer Helen, BSc,	LT(IC)	X		01.03.98	CAPT IST STAFF
Ryan, John Benedict,	LT CDR(CC)	S		01.10.01	UKMARBATSTAFF
Ryan, John Peter,	LT(FTC)	E	MESM	02.05.00	TIRELESS
Ryan, Nicholas, BEng, MIMarEST,	LT(FTC)	E	ME	01.07.95	FOST SEA
Ryan, Patrick Douglas Blackwood,	SLT(IC)	X		01.09.99	YORK
Ryan, Paul Justin, BEng,	SLT(IC)	X	P U/T	01.09.99	RAF CRANWELL EFS
Ryan, Richard Michael, BSc, pcea,	LT CDR(FTC)	X	O	01.04.97	CATTISTOCK
Ryan, Sean Joseph, BA, pce(sm), SM(n),	LT CDR(FTC)	X	SM	01.04.01	SPARTAN
Rycroft, Alan Edward, pce, pcea,	CDR(FTC)	X	O	30.06.96	JSCSC
Ryder, Steven John, OBE, MB, BCh, MFOM, FRCS, FRCSEd,	SURG CDR(FCC)	-	(CO/M)	30.06.90	NBC PORTSMOUTH
Ryder, Timothy John,	LT CDR(FTC)	MS	(AD)	01.10.01	DRAKE CBS
Ryder, Tony,	SLT(IC)	X		01.01.01	DARTMOUTH BRNC
Rydiard, David Martin, BSc, AMNI, pce, psc,	LT CDR(FTC)	X	PWO(N)	01.12.81	MWS DRYAD
Rye, John Walter, MA, psc,	MAJ(FTC)	-	C	01.09.84	CTCRM
Ryland, Anthony Matthew,	MID(UCE)(IC)	E	AE	01.09.00	DARTMOUTH BRNC
Rymer, Alan Robert, BSc, CEng, MIMarEST, psc,	CAPT(FTC)	E	ME	30.06.99	FLEET HQ PORTS 2

Name	Rank	Branch	Spec	Seniority	Where Serving

S

Name	Rank	Branch	Spec	Seniority	Where Serving
Saddleton, Andrew David, psc(j)o,	MAJ(FTC)	-	LC	01.09.96	PJHQ
Salim, Muttahir, BSc,	LT(IC)	E	TM	01.09.98	RALEIGH
Salisbury, David Peter, pce, pcea,	LT CDR(FTC)	X	P	01.02.96	JSCSC
Salmon, Andrew, MA, psc,	COL(FTC)	-		30.06.00	MOD (LONDON)
Salmon, Michael Alan, pcea,	LT CDR(FTC)	X	O	01.10.96	HQ3GP HQSTC
Salt, Hedley Stephen,	LT(CC)	X	P	01.09.93	RAF CRANWELL EFS
Salter, Jeffrey Alan, BEng, AMIEE,	LT CDR(FTC)	E	WE	10.02.94	FOST SEA
Salter, Mark David, pcea,	CDR(FTC)	X	P	01.10.95	NS OBERAMMERGAU
Saltonstall, Hugh Francis Rous, LLB,	LT(IC)	X	P U/T	01.05.02	RNAS YEOVILTON
Saltonstall, Philip James Rous, BA,	LT(CC)	X	P	01.12.99	815 FLT 239
Salzano, Gerard Mark, MBE, psc,	LT COL(FTC)	-		30.06.00	COMATG SEA
Samborne, Michael David Palmer, pce, pce(sm),	CDR(FTC)	X	SM	30.06.87	MOD (LONDON)
Sambrooks, Richard John, BEng,	LT(CC)	X	P	01.08.99	FLEET AV VALLEY
Sampson, Philip Henry, psc(m),	LT COL(FTC)	-		30.06.97	MOD (LONDON)
Samuel, Christopher David Robert, BSc,	CAPT RM(IC)	-		01.05.01	FPGRM
Samuel, Katja Lilian Hamilton, BA,	LT CDR(FTC)	S	BAR	01.08.01	FOST DPORT SHORE
Samways, Michael James,	SLT(IC)	X		01.09.00	FEARLESS
Sanderson, Christopher Peter, MA,	LT(IC)	X		01.10.99	NBC PORTSMOUTH
Sanderson, Lee David, BEng,	LT(FTC)	E	WE	01.10.96	DRAKE SFM
Sanderson, Robert Christopher, BDS, FDS RCPSGlas,	SGCAPT(D)(FCC)	-	(COSM)	30.06.00	RH HASLAR
Sandle, Neil David, BEng, CEng, MIMarEST,	LT(FTC)	E	ME	01.08.95	MWS EXCELLENT
Sandover, Richard John, BSc, pce, pcea, psc, gdas,	LT CDR(FTC)	X	O	20.04.87	RNAS CULDROSE
Sangha, Randeep Singh, BEng,	LT(CC)	E	P	01.12.98	824 SQN
Sanguinetti, Hector Robert, pce, psc(j),	CDR(FTC)	X	PWO(C)	30.06.98	MOD (LONDON)
Sansford, Adrian James, BEng, MSc,	LT CDR(FTC)	E	MESM	27.05.99	TALENT
Santrian, Karl,	LT(FTC)	X	AV	01.01.97	RFANSU
Santry, Paul Matthew,	LT(FTC)	X	C	01.04.01	MOD (LONDON)
Sargent, David Reginald,	LT(IC)	S		01.01.02	848 SQN HERON
Sargent, David, BSc,	SURG SLT(SCC)	-		29.07.99	DARTMOUTH BRNC
Sargent, Kevin Stephen, MBE,	LT(FTC)	E	AE(M)	29.04.97	LOAN DARA
Sargent, Lindsay, BSc,	LT(IC)	E	TM	23.06.97	RNAS YEOVILTON
Sargent, Nicholas Matthew, BEng,	LT(CC)	E	AE	01.05.98	815 SQN HQ
Sargent, Philippa Mary, MA, n,	LT(CC)	E	TM	01.12.92	SULTAN
Sarkar, Tirthankar,	SLT(IC)	X		01.01.01	DARTMOUTH BRNC
Satterly, Robert James, BEng,	LT(IC)	E		01.09.01	MARLBOROUGH
Satterthwaite, Benjamin John, BA,	LT(CC)	X	MW	01.02.95	ATHERSTONE
Saunders, Christopher Edmund Maurice, MSc,	LT(FTC)	X		01.06.97	NEPTUNE
Saunders, Jason Mervyn, BEng,	LT(CC)	E	TM	01.09.94	RMCS SHRIVENHAM
Saunders, John Nicholas,	LT CDR(FTC)	X	N	01.10.90	MWS DRYAD
Saunders, Peter William, BEng, CEng,	LT CDR(FTC)	E	AE	01.06.00	EXCHANGE AUSTLIA
Saunders, Timothy Mark, BSc, MA, psc(j),	LT CDR(FTC)	E	TMSM	01.09.94	SULTAN
Sauze, Martin James, BEd, MSc,	LT CDR(FTC)	X	METOC	01.10.88	MWS RNHMS CULD
Savage, Daniel Liam, BEng,	SLT(IC)	E	ME U/T	01.01.00	SULTAN
Savage, Daniel McLaughlan, BSc,	LT(IC)	X	P	16.06.98	815 FLT 217
Savage, Mark Roger, pce,	LT CDR(FTC)	X	PWO(U)	01.09.98	MCM2 SEA
Savage, Nigel David, (Commodore)	CAPT(FTC)	S		30.06.95	DLO/DGDEF LOG SP
Savage, Shane, BSc,	LT CDR(FTC)	X	ATC	01.10.94	FLEET HQ PORTS
Saward, Justin Robert Ernest, BEng,	LT(CC)	E	AE	01.07.97	ES AIR MASU
Sawford, Gavin Neil,	LT(IC)	E	WE	01.01.02	WESTMINSTER
Sawyer, Trevor James, (Act Lt Col)	MAJ(FTC)	-	SO(LE)	01.10.94	FPGRM
Saxby, Christopher James, BEng, MSc, MIMarEST, MCGI,	LT CDR(FTC)	E	ME	01.11.94	FOST SEA
Saxby, Keith Alan,	LT CDR(FTC)	X	AAWO	24.02.94	FLEET CIS PORTS
Say, Russell G,	SLT(IC)	E	WE	01.01.01	MWS COLLINGWOOD
Sayer, David Julian, pce, psc,	CDR(FTC)	X	AWO(A)	31.12.88	DRAKE NBSD
Sayer, Jamie Michael, BA, BEng,	LT(CC)	E	AE	01.06.97	MERLIN IPT
Sayles, Stephen,	CDR(FTC)	E	ME	31.12.91	2SL/CNH FOTR
Saynor, Roger Michael,	LT CDR(FTC)	X	PT	01.10.96	FLEET HQ PORTS
Saywell, James Nicholas,	LT(IC)	S		01.05.02	800 SQN
Saywell-Hall, Stephen Eric,	LT(FTC)	E	AE(L)	02.09.99	FWO PORTS SEA
Scandling, Rachel Jane,	LT(FTC)	S		01.05.96	EXCHANGE AUSTLIA

Name	Rank	Branch	Spec	Seniority	Where Serving
Scanlon, Meredith Patricia, MSc,	SLT(IC)	X		01.01.01	DARTMOUTH BRNC
Scanlon, Michael Jon, BSc,	CAPT RM(IC)	-		01.05.01	40 CDO RM
Scarborough, David, (Act Lt)	SLT(IC)	MS		01.05.00	MSA
Scarlett, Christopher Joseph,	SLT(IC)	E	WESM	01.01.01	MWS COLLINGWOOD
Scarth, William, BSc, jsdc, pce, psc(j),	CDR(FTC)	X	MCD	30.06.97	JSCSC
Schillemore, Paul Colin, (Act Lt Cdr)	LT(FTC)	E	WE	18.10.85	PJHQ
Schleyer, Jonathan,	LT RM(IC)	-		01.09.00	CDO LOG REGT RM
Schmidt, James Frederick Kurt, BSc,	LT CDR(FTC)	E	MESM	01.03.91	NEPTUNE DSA
Schnadhorst, James Charles, pce,	LT CDR(FTC)	X	PWO(U)	01.05.95	FOST CSST FSLN
Schofield, Julie Claire,	SLT(IC)	X		01.09.01	CHATHAM
Schofield, Susan Ruth, MB, BS,	SURG LTCDR(MCC)	-		08.08.01	JSU NORTHWOOD
Scholes, Neil Andrew, MSc, CEng, MIMarEST,	LT(FTC)	E	MESM	02.09.99	SULTAN
Schunmann, Ceri Peter Ingo, BSc,	LT(IC)	X	MCD	01.12.93	NORTH DIVING GRP
Schwarz, Paul Michael Gunter,	CDR(FTC)	X	ATC	30.06.02	HQ3GP HQSTC
Scivier, John Stapleton, MCMI,	LT CDR(FTC)	X	ATC	01.10.01	OCEAN
Scoles, Jonathon Charles, OBE, FCMI, pce, psc, (Act Capt)	CDR(FTC)	X	PWO(U)	31.12.89	2SL/CNH
Scopes, David, BEng,	LT(FTC)	E	AE	01.12.94	ARK ROYAL
Scorer, Samuel James, jsdc, pce,	CAPT(FTC)	X	PWO(U)	30.06.00	AGRIPPA AFSOUTH
Scott, Christopher Ralph, OBE, MA, psc,	LT COL(FTC)	-		30.06.98	UKLFCSG RM
Scott, Fozeena Farida Nisha,	MID(NE)(IC)	X		01.05.01	CHATHAM
Scott, James Baxter, BEng, CEng, MIMechE,	LT CDR(FTC)	E	MESM	01.05.96	FOST CSST SEA
Scott, Jason Andrew, BA, pce,	LT CDR(FTC)	X	PWO(U)	01.04.97	NMA PORTSMOUTH
Scott, Juliet Anna, BA,	LT(IC)	X	O	01.04.00	815 FLT 229
Scott, Mark Robert, pcea,	LT(FTC)	X	P	16.12.93	702 SQN HERON
Scott, Michael, BEng,	LT(IC)	X	P	16.08.97	849 SQN A FLT
Scott, Michael, BEng, CEng, MIEE,	LT CDR(FTC)	E	WESM	01.05.99	VICTORIOUS(PORT)
Scott, Neil,	SLT(IC)	X		01.05.00	SOUTHAMPTON
Scott, Neil,	LT(IC)	X		01.09.01	SUTHERLAND
Scott, Nigel Leonard James, BEng, CEng, MIMarEST, ACGI, psc(j),	CDR(FTC)	E	WESM	30.06.02	FOST CSST SEA
Scott, Peter James Douglas Sefton, BD,	CHAPLAIN	CE		03.09.91	CTCRM
Scott, Richard Antony, BEng,	LT(FTC)	E	WE	01.08.94	RMC OF SCIENCE
Scott, Robert John, pcea,	LT CDR(FTC)	X	O	02.03.98	RNAS YEOVILTON
Scott, Samantha Leigh,	LT(IC)	X		01.08.00	GUERNSEY
Scott, Simon John, MA, psc(j),	MAJ(FTC)	-	LC	01.09.96	42 CDO RM
Scott, Stephen Charles,	CAPT RM(FTC)	-	SO(LE)	01.01.98	CDO LOG REGT RM
Scott, Timothy Edward, MB, BS,	SURG LT(SCC)	-		04.08.99	RFANSU (ARGUS)
Scott, Wendy Ann, BDS,	SGLTCDR(D)(SCC)	-		13.01.99	RALEIGH
Scott-Dickins, Charles Angus, BSc,	LT CDR(FTC)	X	METOC	01.10.94	LOAN DSTL
Scotter, Claire Marie, BSc,	LT(IC)	E		01.09.99	MWS COLLINGWOOD
Screaton, Richard Michael, BEng, CEng, MIEE,	LT(FTC)	E	ME	01.03.96	ALBION
Screech, Michael Courtney, FInstAM,	LT CDR(FTC)	S	SM	01.08.81	PJHQ
Scruton, Neil, BSc, psc,	LT CDR(FTC)	X	H CH	16.03.84	DGIA
Scutt, Martin,	SURG SLT(SCC)	-		01.07.00	DARTMOUTH BRNC
Seaborn, Adam, (Act Lt)	SLT(IC)	X	AV	01.05.99	RNAS YEOVILTON
Seager, Andrew Keith,	LT(IC)	X	ATC	08.01.01	FOST DPORT SHORE
Seagrave, Suzanna Jane, BEng,	LT(IC)	E		01.09.01	ARGYLL
Seal, Martin Richard,	MID(IC)	X		01.01.01	DARTMOUTH BRNC
Sealey, Nicholas Peter, BSc, CEng, MIMarEST, psc,	CAPT(FTC)	E	ME	30.06.02	NMA PORTSMOUTH
Seaman, Philip John,	LT(FTC)	E	WE	19.02.93	SAT IPT
Sear, Jonathan Jasper,	MAJ(FTC)	-		01.09.98	COMAMPHIBFOR
Searight, Mark Frederick Chamney, psc(j),	MAJ(FTC)	-		01.05.97	UKLFCSG RM
Searle, Edward Francis, BSc, CEng, MIEE, MIMarEST, psc,	CAPT(FTC)	E	ME	31.12.95	SA CARACAS
Seatherton, Elliot Frazer Kingston, MBE, pce, psc(j)o,	CDR(FTC)	X	PWO(N)	31.12.95	FLEET HQ PORTS
Secretan, Simon James, BEd, pce, n,	LT CDR(FTC)	X	PWO(U)	01.08.96	FLEET HQ NWD
Seddon, John Stephen Maurice,	LT CDR(FTC)	S	SM	16.10.88	DRAKE DPL
Seddon, Jonathan David,	MID(IC)	X		01.01.01	ARK ROYAL
Sedgwick, Hugo George, BSc,	SLT(IC)	X	SM	01.01.01	DARTMOUTH BRNC
Seekings, Andrew Laurence, BSc,	LT(CC)	X	METOC	01.06.89	EXCHANGE NLANDS
Segebarth, Robert Andrew,	LT(CC)	X	P	16.02.96	801 SQN
Sellar, Trevor Jefferson,	CAPT RM(FTC)	-	SO(LE)	01.01.97	RM POOLE
Sellars, Scott John, BA, MInstAM,	LT(FTC)	S	SM	01.07.94	NELSON

Name	Rank	Branch	Spec	Seniority	Where Serving
Sellers, Graham Donald, BEng, MSc, CEng, MIEE,	LT CDR(FTC)	E	WE	01.02.01	MOD (LONDON)
Selley, Dale Robert, BEng,	SLT(IC)	X	P U/T	01.01.00	DARTMOUTH BRNC
Selman, Toby Roger, BSc,	CAPT RM(FTC)	-		01.09.99	FPGRM
Selway, Mark Anthony, BEng,	LT(FTC)	E	AE	01.07.97	ES AIR MASU
Selwood, Peter, BSc,	LT(SCC)	Q		26.02.01	RH HASLAR
Semple, Brian,	SLT(IC)	X	P U/T	01.01.00	RNAS YEOVILTON
Sennitt, John William, BSc, AMIEE,	LT CDR(FTC)	E	WE	01.08.92	FLEET CIS PORTS
Sephton, John Richard, BSc, psc,	CDR(FTC)	X	METOC	30.06.00	MWS RNHMS CULD
Sergeant, Nicholas Robin, CDipAF,	LT CDR(FTC)	E	WE	01.10.99	MOD (LONDON)
Seton, James, BA,	SLT(IC)	X		01.01.01	DARTMOUTH BRNC
Seward, Stafford Allan, MBE, (Act Lt Cdr)	LT(FTC)	X	g	06.04.95	LN SIERRA LEONE
Sewed, Michael Antony, BSc,	LT CDR(FTC)	X	O	01.10.94	RNAS YEOVILTON
Sewell, Mark Anthony Philip,	LT(IC)	X	P	16.10.96	771 SQN
Sewry, Michael Ronald, BSc, CEng, MIEE, psc(a),	CDR(FTC)	E	AE	31.12.95	MOD (LONDON)
Sexton, Michael John,	CDR(FTC)	E	WE	30.06.98	AGRIPPA AFSOUTH
Seyd, Miranda, BSc,	SLT(IC)	X		01.05.00	NORTHUMBERLAND
Seymour, Kevin William, pcea,	LT CDR(FTC)	X	P	01.10.96	899 SQN HERON
Shackleton, Scott James Sinclair, BA, BD,	CHAPLAIN	SF		20.04.93	RMB STONEHOUSE
Shadbolt, Simon Edward, MBE, BSc, psc(m), psc(j),	COL(FTC)	-	C	31.12.98	PJHQ
Shaftain, Neil, BEng,	SLT(IC)	E	ME	01.09.00	CAMPBELTOWN
Shallcroft, John Edward, pcea,	LT CDR(FTC)	X	P	01.10.98	824 SQN
Shanahan, Lloyd Anthony,	SLT(IC)	X	P U/T	01.05.00	DARTMOUTH BRNC
Shand, Christopher Michael, BSc,	LT CDR(FTC)	E	WESM	01.11.82	DRAKE CBP(DLO)
Shanks, Diana Zoe, BSc,	SLT(IC)	X		01.01.00	SHOREHAM
Shanks. Graeme John, BA,	LT(IC)	X	FC	01.04.98	ARK ROYAL
Shanks, Steven Andrew, BSc,	LT(IC)	X		01.12.99	TURBULENT
Sharkey, Elton Richard, BEng, MSc,	LT(FTC)	E	MESM	01.06.95	MOD (BATH)
Sharkey, Michael,	CHAPLAIN	RC		01.10.90	OCEAN
Sharkey, Philip Joseph, BEng,	SLT(IC)	E	ME	01.09.00	SOUTHAMPTON
Sharland, Simon Patrick, BA,	MAJ(IC)	-	LC	01.09.90	NMA PORTSMOUTH
Sharman, David John Thomas, MSc, CEng, MIEE,	CDR(FTC)	E	WE	30.06.02	HQ DCSA
Sharman, Max,	2LT(IC)	-		01.09.01	CTCRM LYMPSTONE
Sharp, Andrew Peter,	LT(IC)	E	MESM	01.05.02	SOVEREIGN
Sharp, Christopher,	SLT(IC)	E	WE	01.01.01	MWS COLLINGWOOD
Sharp, John Vivian,	SLT(CC)	X	P U/T	01.01.01	DHFS
Sharp, Lee Dominic, MA,	LT(IC)	X		01.08.99	ATHERSTONE
Sharpe, Gary Anthony,	CAPT RM(FTC)	-	SO(LE)	01.01.93	RMR LONDON
Sharpe, Grantley James, pce,	LT CDR(FTC)	X	PWO(U)	01.02.88	LOAN BMATT(EC)
Sharpe, Marcus Roger,	LT RM(IC)	-	SO(LE)	01.04.00	CDO LOG REGT RM
Sharpe, Thomas Grenville,	LT(FTC)	X	FC	01.10.94	JSCSC
Sharpley, John Guy, MA, MB, BCh, MRCPsych,	SURG CDR(FCC)	-	(CN/P)	30.06.02	RH HASLAR
Sharrocks, Ian James,	LT(CC)	X	P	16.05.98	FLEET AV VALLEY
Sharrott, Christopher, BSc,	SLT(IC)	X	P U/T	01.09.00	DARTMOUTH BRNC
Shaughnessy, Sophie Louise, BEng, MIEE,	LT(FTC)	E	ME	01.05.95	FLEET HQ PORTS 2
Shaughnessy, Toby Edward,	LT(FTC)	X	FC	01.10.97	LINDISFARNE
Shaw, Andrew,	2LT(IC)	-		01.09.98	CTCRM LYMPSTONE
Shaw, Graeme Roberts, BEng, AMIEE,	LT CDR(FTC)	E	WE	01.05.00	KENT
Shaw, Ian Brian, BEng,	LT CDR(FTC)	E	WESM	15.09.91	NEPTUNE SWS
Shaw, Kevin Norman Graham, MA, PhD, CEng, MIEE, MRAeS, MRIN, psc(j),	CDR(FTC)	E	WE	30.06.02	HQ DCSA
Shaw, Michael Leslie, BEng, CEng, MRAeS,	LT CDR(FTC)	E	AE	11.02.00	DARTMOUTH BRNC
Shaw, Neil Andrew,	LT(FTC)	E	WE	01.04.01	CAMPBELTOWN
Shaw, Paul James,	LT CDR(FTC)	S		17.03.95	BULWARK
Shaw, Philip Andrew George, MBE, BSc, MA, pce, pcea, psc,	CDR(FTC)	X	P	31.12.99	MOD (LONDON)
Shaw, Steven Matthew, MA, psc(j),	CDR(FTC)	S		30.06.01	MOD (BATH)
Shaw, Stuart Lawson, MB, BS, BSc,	SURG LT(SCC)	-		06.08.97	NELSON (PAY)
Shawcross, Paul Kenneth, BSc, pcea,	LT CDR(FTC)	X	P	01.10.91	848 SQN HERON
Shearman, Alexander,	SURG SLT(SCC)	-		01.05.00	DARTMOUTH BRNC
Shearn, Matthew Arthur, BA,	LT(IC)	X		01.04.00	NORTHUMBERLAND
Shears, Gary Raymond, BSc,	SLT(IC)	X	O U/T	01.09.00	DARTMOUTH BRNC
Sheehan, Mark Andrew, pce, pcea, psc,	CDR(FTC)	X	O	30.06.01	FLEET HQ PORTS
Sheehan, Thomas John,	SLT(IC)	E		01.01.01	MWS COLLINGWOOD

Name	Rank	Branch	Spec	Seniority	Where Serving
Sheikh, Nabil, BSc, CDipAF,	LT(FTC)	S		01.11.97	2SL/CNH
Sheils, Damian Edmund Tyrie,	LT(CC)	X	P	16.07.94	849 SQN HQ
Sheldon, Mark Laurence,	LT(FTC)	E	WE	07.02.97	MWS COLLINGWOOD
Sheldrake, James Peter, BEng, SM(n),	LT(IC)	X	SM	01.08.96	FLEET HQ NWD
Sheldrake, Terence William, BSc, pce, pcea, gdas,	LT CDR(FTC)	X	O	29.04.83	MWC PORTSDOWN
Shepherd, Alan,	LT CDR(FTC)	E	WE	01.10.92	SAUDI AFPS SAUDI
Shepherd, Anya Clare, BSc,	SLT(IC)	X		01.09.99	BLYTH
Shepherd, Charles Scott, BSc, pce(sm),	LT CDR(FTC)	X	SM	01.01.97	DARTMOUTH BRNC
Shepherd, Christopher Edward,	MID(UCE)(IC)	E	WE	01.09.00	DARTMOUTH BRNC
Shepherd, Fiona Rosemary, MSc, LRPS,	LT(CC)	S		01.09.99	PJHQ
Shepherd, Iain, BSc, pce,	CDR(FTC)	X	PWO(A)	30.06.92	2SL/CNH
Shepherd, Martin Paul,	LT(FTC)	X	P	01.04.96	815 FLT 218
Shepherd, Paul Rodney, pcea,	LT CDR(FTC)	X	O	01.10.92	RNAS CULDROSE
Shepherd, Roger Guy, BEng, AMIEE,	LT CDR(FTC)	E	WESM	01.05.96	TCM IPT
Sheppard, Heidi Clare,	MID(IC)	X		01.01.01	DARTMOUTH BRNC
Shergold, Paul James,	CAPT RM(FTC)	-	SO(LE)	01.01.97	EXCH ARMY SC(G)
Sherlock, Francis Christopher Edwin, MSc, CEng, MIMarEST, psc,	CDR(FTC)	E	ME	31.12.92	T45 IPT
Sherriff, David Anthony, pce, pcea,	LT CDR(FTC)	X	P	01.01.96	MONTROSE
Sherwood, Gideon Andrew Francis,	LT(IC)	X		01.05.01	LINDISFARNE
Shield, Simon James, pce(sm), psc,	CDR(FTC)	X	SM	31.12.98	MWC SOUTHWICK
Shipperley, Ian, BSc, CEng, MIMechE,	CDR(FTC)	E	ME	30.06.98	MOD (BATH)
Shirley, Andrew John, BEng, CEng, MIMechE,	LT CDR(FTC)	E	MESM	01.08.01	MOD (LONDON)
Shirley, Wayne Peter, MA, psc(j), (Act Cdr)	LT CDR(FTC)	E	WE	12.10.93	MOD (BATH)
Shore, Elizabeth Anne, MA,	LT(IC)	X		01.01.02	LIVERPOOL
Shorland-Ball, Timothy John, BA,	LT(FTC)	X	MCD	01.04.98	PEMBROKE
Short, Gavin Conrad, BEng, MA, AMIEE, psc(j),	CDR(FTC)	E	WESM	30.06.00	JSCSC
Short, John Jeffrey, BEng,	LT CDR(FTC)	E	ME	01.06.96	EXCHANGE AUSTLIA
Shortland, Karen, BA,	SLT(IC)	S		01.01.01	DARTMOUTH BRNC
Shrestha, Shekhar, BEng,	SLT(IC)	E	ME	01.09.00	DARTMOUTH BRNC
Shrimpton, Helen Diane, MB, BCh, MRCGP, DObstRCOG, Dip FFP,	SURG LTCDR(SCC)	-	GMPP	04.02.98	RNAS YEOVILTON
Shrimpton, Matthew William, pcea,	LT(FTC)	X	P	01.04.92	815 SQN HQ
Shrives, Michael Peter, MA, pce, pcea, psc, psc(j),	CDR(FTC)	X	P	30.06.95	FLEET HQ PORTS
Shropshall, Ian James,	LT(IC)	X	O U/T	01.05.02	750 SQN SEAHAWK
Shrubsole, Steven John, BEng,	LT CDR(FTC)	E	WE	01.12.99	T45 IPT
Shuttleworth, Stephen,	LT(FTC)	E	ME	13.06.97	SFM PORTSMOUTH
Shutts, David, BEng, AMIMechE, psc(j), CEng, MIMarEST,	LT CDR(FTC)	E	ME	01.06.98	FWO PORTS SEA
Sibbit, Neil Thomas, pce, pcea, psc,	CDR(FTC)	X	O	30.06.96	FOST MPV(SEA)
Sibley, Andrew Keith,	LT(FTC)	E	ME	02.09.99	JSCSC
Sibley, Graeme Paul, BA,	MAJ(FTC)	-		27.04.02	HQ 3 CDO BDE RM
Sidebotham, Michael John, PGDip, MHCIMA,	LT(FTC)	S	CA	28.07.89	DLO/DGDEF LOG SP
Sidebotham, Simon Charles, BSc,	SLT(IC)	E	WE	01.01.00	CAMPBELTOWN
Sidoli, Giovanni Eugenio, BDS, MSc, MGDS RCS,	SGCDR(D)(FCC)	-		31.12.95	DDA HALTON
Sienkiewicz, Maryla Krystyna, LLB,	LT(IC)	X		01.09.01	CAMPBELTOWN
Siggers, Benet Richard Charles, MB, CHB, DiplMC RCSED,	SURG LTCDR(SCC)	-		02.08.00	NELSON (PAY)
Silcock, Christopher Anthony James, BA, (Commodore) rcds, pce, psc(m),	CAPT(FTC)	X	PWO(A)	31.12.95	FLEET HQ PORTS 2
Sillers, Barry, BSc, SM(n),	LT CDR(FTC)	X	SM	01.12.94	SOVEREIGN
Silver, Christina Kay,	LT CDR(FTC)	W	C	01.10.93	JSSU OAKLEY
Sim, Donald Leslie Whyte, MA, FIMgt, MNI, pce, pcea, ocds(USN),	CAPT(FTC)	X	O	30.06.02	FWO PORTS SEA
Simbeye, Martin, BEng,	LT(IC)	E	ME	01.05.02	SULTAN
Simcox, Paul Alan, MBE, MCGI, psc(j), mdtc,	MAJ(FTC)	-		19.06.99	MOD (LONDON)
Simm, Craig William, BEng,	LT(CC)	E	AE	01.07.98	SULTAN
Simmonds, Daniel Douglas Harold,	SLT(IC)	X		01.05.00	RALEIGH
Simmonds, Gary Fredrick,	LT CDR(FTC)	E	AE(L)	01.10.98	RNAS CULDROSE
Simmonds, Peter Bruce, psc(a),	MAJ(FTC)	-		01.08.83	CTCRM
Simmonds, Richard Michael, OBE, jsdc, pce, psc(a),	CDR(FTC)	X	MCD	31.12.90	LANG TRNG(UK)
Simmonite, Gavin Ian,	LT(CC)	X	P	16.11.00	EXCHANGE RAF UK
Simmons, Nigel Douglas, MSc, CEng, MIEE,	CDR(FTC)	E	WESM	30.06.99	MOD (LONDON)

Name	Rank	Branch	Spec	Seniority	Where Serving
Simmons, Robert,	2LT(IC)	-		01.09.98	CTCRM LYMPSTONE
Simms, David Martin,	LT(CC)	X	O	16.03.96	EXCHANGE RAF UK
Simpson, Alister Clive, LLB,	CAPT RM(IC)	-		01.05.98	CHFHQ
Simpson, Christopher John, BA,	SLT(IC)	X	P U/T	01.01.01	DARTMOUTH BRNC
Simpson, Colin Chisholm,	LT(FTC)	X	P	01.03.93	LYNX OEU
Simpson, David Keith, pcea,	LT(CC)	X	O	16.11.93	824 SQN
Simpson, Emma Jane, BA,	LT CDR(FTC)	W	X	01.10.01	JSSU OAKLEY
Simpson, Erin Leona,	SLT(UCE)(IC)	E	WE	01.01.02	DARTMOUTH BRNC
Simpson, Mark,	LT(IC)	E	ME	05.08.01	SULTAN
Simpson, Martin Joseph, PGDIPAN, pce,	LT CDR(FTC)	X	PWO(N)	01.07.96	FOST SEA
Simpson, Paul Emmanuel,	LT(SCC)	Q		27.10.00	RFANSU (ARGUS)
Simpson, Peter,	LT CDR(FTC)	MS	(CDO)	01.10.01	FLEET HQ PORTS 2
Simpson, Scott Forsyth,	LT(CC)	X	O	01.02.01	702 SQN HERON
Simpson, William James Stuart, BEng,	LT(IC)	E	MESM	01.01.02	SULTAN
Sims, Alexander Richard,	LT(IC)	X	O	15.06.00	815 FLT 226
Sinclair, Andrew Bruce, odc(Aus),	LT CDR(FTC)	X	P	01.02.84	DSTL CDA HLS
Sinclair, Angus Hugh, BA, jsdc,	CAPT(FTC)	S	SM	30.06.96	SA ROME
Singer, Kenneth Allan,	MID(NE)(IC)	X		01.01.02	DARTMOUTH BRNC
Singleton, Mark Donald,	LT(FTC)	X	AV	10.12.98	FLEET HQ PORTS
Sitton, John Barry, BEng,	LT(FTC)	E	MESM	01.11.95	SULTAN
Skeer, Martyn Robert, MBE, pce, pcea,	CDR(FTC)	X	P	30.06.02	RMCS SHRIVENHAM
Skelley, Alasdair Neil Murdoch, MA, n,	LT(FTC)	X		01.03.95	MWS DRYAD
Skelton, John Steven, BEng,	LT(FTC)	E	ME	01.07.94	SFM PORTSMOUTH
Skidmore, Christopher Mark, BA, FCMI, FCIPD, MILog, ACIS,	CDR(FTC)	S	SM	31.12.98	MOD (LONDON)
Skinner, John Richard, pce, psc, psc(a),	CDR(FTC)	X	P	30.06.89	FLEET AV VL
Skinsley, Terry John,	LT(IC)	X		01.05.02	LIVERPOOL
Skipper, James Alexander,	SLT(FTC)	X		01.09.00	LEDBURY
Skittrall, Steven David, BEng,	LT(FTC)	E	O	15.10.97	849 SQN B FLT
Skuse, Matthew, BSc,	MAJ(FTC)	-	MLDR	01.09.99	HQ NORTH
Slack, Jeremy Mark,	MAJ(FTC)	-	LC	01.05.97	1 ASSLT GP RM
Slade, Christopher, pcea,	LT CDR(FTC)	X	P	01.10.90	824 SQN
Slater, Dougal Gordon, BEng,	LT(IC)	E		01.09.01	OCEAN
Slater, *Sir* Jock (John Cunningham Kirkwood), GCB, LVO DL, rcds, pce	ADM	-		20.01.91	
Slattery, Damian John, BSc,	LT(IC)	X		01.01.00	MWS DRYAD
Slawson, James Mark, BSc, CEng, MIMarEST, psc,	CDR(FTC)	E	ME	31.12.97	NMA PORTSMOUTH
Slight, Oliver William Lawrence,	MID(IC)	X		01.09.00	LEEDS CASTLE
Slimmon, Kevan William, NDipM,	LT(FTC)	E	WESM	02.09.99	NEPTUNE SWS
Sloan, Graham Daniel,	SLT(IC)	X		01.04.00	INVERNESS
Sloan, Ian Alexander, BEng,	LT(CC)	X	P	01.12.99	801 SQN
Sloan, Mark Usherwood, BSc, pce, psc,	CAPT(FTC)	X	PWO(U)	31.12.99	CAMPBELTOWN
Slocombe, Christopher Alwyn, pcea,	LT CDR(FTC)	X	P	01.10.96	JSCSC
Slocombe, Nicholas Richard, (Act Lt Cdr)	LT(FTC)	X	ATC	01.11.91	RNAS YEOVILTON
Slowther, Stuart John, BEng,	LT(IC)	E	WE	01.09.01	LIVERPOOL
Small, Richard James, BSc, SM(n),	LT(FTC)	X	SM	01.03.97	TRAFALGAR
Smallman, Laurence Delaney, BSc, pce,	CDR(FTC)	X	PWO(U)	31.12.96	BDS WASHINGTON
Smallwood, Justin Patrick, MA, sq,	MAJ(FTC)	-		05.09.95	CTCRM
Smallwood, Richard Iain, pce(sm), SM(n),	LT CDR(FTC)	X	SM	12.10.01	TURBULENT
Smart, Mark James,	LT(FTC)	E	AE	02.05.00	ES AIR YEO
Smart, Steven Joe,	LT(FTC)	E	ME	23.02.90	SULTAN
Smee, Norman Lee, pce, psc,	CDR(FTC)	X	AAWO	30.06.92	MWS EXCELLENT
Smerdon, Christopher David Edward, BA,	LT CDR(FTC)	S	SM	01.07.94	FLEET HQ PORTS
Smith, Adrian Charles, BSc,	LT CDR(FTC)	E	AE	16.03.84	MOD (BATH)
Smith, Adrian Gerard, BA,	LT CDR(FTC)	E	WE	01.02.99	GRAFTON
Smith, Alexander Richard, MA,	SLT(IC)	X		01.05.00	ARK ROYAL
Smith, Andrew Paul,	LT CDR(FTC)	X	PWO(A)	01.04.98	MWC PORTSDOWN
Smith, Andrew, BA,	LT(IC)	X		01.04.99	LINDISFARNE
Smith, Andrew, BSc, psc,	CDR(FTC)	E	WE	30.06.88	MOD (LONDON)
Smith, Anthony, MEng,	LT(IC)	E	TM	09.01.99	CTCRM
Smith, Austin Bernard Dudley, (Act Lt Cdr)	LT(FTC)	X	P	01.05.96	FLEET HQ PORTS 2
Smith, Barbara Carol,	LT CDR(FCC)	Q	SCM	01.10.92	RALEIGH
Smith, Brian Joseph, AMNI, n, BA,	LT CDR(FTC)	X		01.12.99	ARK ROYAL
Smith, Brian Stephen, BDS, MGDS RCSEd,	SGCDR(D)(FCC)	-		30.06.01	NEPTUNE DLO

Name	Rank	Branch	Spec	Seniority	Where Serving
Smith, Charles John, MIMgt, (Act Lt)	SLT(IC)	X	C	01.05.00	MWS COLLINGWOOD
Smith, Christopher John Hilton, BEng, AMIEE,	LT(FTC)	E	WE	01.01.97	INVINCIBLE
Smith, Christopher Julian, MA, psc(j),	LT CDR(FTC)	S		16.03.96	JSCSC
Smith, Clive Peter, pce,	LT CDR(FTC)	X	PWO(U)	26.04.95	PEMBROKE
Smith, Clive Sherrif, OBE, MSc, CEng, MIMarEST,	CDR(FTC)	E	MESM	30.06.92	SULTAN
Smith, Daniel James, BA,	LT(CC)	X	P	01.11.93	EXCHANGE RAF UK
Smith, David Jonathan,	SLT(IC)	X		01.05.00	FWO DEVONPORT
Smith, David Leslie,	LT(FTC)	X	FC	01.03.96	MWS DRYAD
Smith, David Munro,	CAPT RM(FTC)	-	SO(LE)	01.01.99	COMAMPHIBFOR
Smith, David Thomas,	LT(CC)	X	O	16.06.91	771 SQN
Smith, Edward George Giles, BA,	LT(IC)	X		01.05.02	MWS DRYAD
Smith, Gordon Kenneth, (Act Maj)	CAPT RM(IC)	-		01.10.00	NP 1002 DIEGOGA
Smith, Graeme Douglas James, BSc,	LT CDR(FTC)	X	PWO(C)	01.01.01	JSCSC
Smith, Gregory Charles Stanley, pce, pcea,	LT CDR(FTC)	X	O	01.01.98	FLEET HQ NWD
Smith, Gregory Kenneth, BSc, CEng, MBCS, MIProdE, adp,	LT CDR(FTC)	E	IS	01.10.93	FLEET CIS PORTS
Smith, Helen Louise, BA,	LT(CC)	S		01.04.99	NORTHUMBERLAND
Smith, Jason Edward, MB, BS, MRCP,	SURG LTCDR(MCC)	-		01.08.98	NELSON (PAY)
Smith, Jason James, MB, BS,	SURG LTCDR(MCC)	-		07.08.01	RH HASLAR
Smith, Kenneth Marshall,	LT CDR(FTC)	X	TAS	16.11.88	PJHQ
Smith, Keven John, pcea,	LT CDR(FTC)	X	P	01.10.95	FLEET HQ PORTS 2
Smith, Kevin Alexander, BSc, CEng, MIMarEST,	LT CDR(FTC)	E	MESM	01.04.95	NMA PORTSMOUTH
Smith, Kevin Bernard Albert,	LT CDR(FTC)	X	AAWO	01.04.96	CINCFLEET FIMU
Smith, Kevin Donlan, MEng,	LT(CC)	E	IS	01.02.97	DRAKE CBP(DLO)
Smith, Lynnette,	LT(IC)	S		01.01.02	MOD (LONDON)
Smith, Malcolm, CDipAF,	CDR(FTC)	S	SM	30.06.96	PJHQ
Smith, Mark MacFarlane, BEng,	LT CDR(FTC)	E	AE	01.11.98	MERLIN IPT
Smith, Mark Peter,	LT(FTC)	MS		26.04.99	2SL/CNH
Smith, Mark Richard, BEng,	LT CDR(FTC)	E	ME	14.07.95	FWO DEVPT SEA
Smith, Martin Linn, MBE, BSc, psc,	LT COL(FTC)	-		31.12.99	45 CDO RM
Smith, Martin Russell Kingsley, BA, PGDip, MDA,	LT CDR(FTC)	X	METOC	01.09.93	MOD (LONDON)
Smith, Melvin Andrew, MSc, mdtc,	CDR(FTC)	E	WE	31.12.95	HQ DCSA
Smith, Michael Daren,	LT(FTC)	X	O	01.02.96	MWS DRYAD
Smith, Michael James,	LT CDR(FTC)	E	WE	01.10.00	WSA/CAPT MCTA
Smith, Michael John, BEng,	LT(FTC)	E	WESM	01.05.96	VICTORIOUS(STBD)
Smith, Neil, BSc,	SLT(IC)	X		01.01.00	SOUTHAMPTON
Smith, Neville Edward Philip, BA,	LT(IC)	X	HM	01.08.98	ALBION
Smith, Nicholas James Dominic,	LT(CC)	X	O	01.04.98	CAPT IST STAFF
Smith, Nigel John,	LT CDR(FTC)	X	PWO(U)	01.10.01	FOST SEA
Smith, Nigel Paul, BA, pce, psc,	CDR(FTC)	X	PWO(U)	31.12.89	DEF SCH OF LANG
Smith, Nigel Peter, BA, pce,	LT CDR(FTC)	X	PWO(U)	01.07.91	SULTAN
Smith, Owen John,	LT(CC)	E	ME	01.04.02	DARTMOUTH BRNC
Smith, Paul,	LT(FTC)	X	WE	01.04.01	NORTH DIVING GRP
Smith, Peter Geoffrey, BSc,	LT CDR(CC)	X	O	01.10.98	LOAN JTEG BSC DN
Smith, Richard David,	LT(FTC)	X	H2	22.07.95	DARTMOUTH BRNC
Smith, Richard William Robertson,	LT CDR(FTC)	X	PWO(U)	01.05.93	EXCHANGE NLANDS
Smith, Robert Charles Vernon,	LT CDR(FTC)	X	O	01.10.00	JSCSC
Smith, Robert Edward,	LT(FTC)	X	O	10.12.98	771 SQN
Smith, Robert James,	MID(IC)	X		01.01.01	DARTMOUTH BRNC
Smith, Rudi Adam,	LT(IC)	X		01.09.01	ATHERSTONE
Smith, Simon Ronald Frederick,	LT(IC)	X	ATC	28.07.96	RNAS CULDROSE
Smith, Stephen Frank, (Act Maj)	CAPT RM(FTC)	-	SO(LE)	01.01.95	CHFHQ
Smith, Steven Luigi, pce,	LT CDR(FTC)	X	AAWO	01.02.92	UKCEC IPT
Smith, Steven Rhodes Clifford, MB, ChB, FRCS,	SURG LTCDR(FCC)	-		01.08.95	NELSON (PAY)
Smith, Stuart Frederick,	LT CDR(FTC)	X	ATC	01.09.82	RNAS YEOVILTON
Smith-Jaynes, Ernest Royston,	CDR(FTC)	E	WESM	01.10.94	CINCFLEET FTSU
Smithson, Peter Edward, MSc, CEng, MRAeS,	CDR(FTC)	E	AE	30.06.97	JF HARROLE OFF
Smye, Malcolm Alexander, BEng,	LT(IC)	E	AE	01.01.02	SULTAN
Smyth, Catherine Roberta,	LT(SCC)	Q		12.09.99	RCDM
Smyth, Clive, (Act Lt)	SLT(IC)	S		01.05.99	CDO LOG REGT RM
Smyth, Michael James, PGDip,	LT CDR(FTC)	E	WE	01.10.94	FLEET CIS PORTS
Sneddon, Russell Neil,	LT CDR(FTC)	X	P	01.10.01	RAF SHAWBURY
Snel, Karen Elizabeth,	MID(IC)	X		01.01.01	CORNWALL

Name	Rank	Branch	Spec	Seniority	Where Serving
Snell, Andrew,	LT(IC)	S		01.05.02	MONTROSE
Snell, David Micheal,	LT(IC)	E	WE	01.01.02	CORNWALL
Snelling, Paul Douglas, BEng, MSc,	LT(FTC)	E	MESM	01.10.94	VENGEANCE(STBD)
Snelson, David George, FCMI, MNI, pce, psc, hcsc,	CAPT(FTC)	X	AWO(A)	30.06.94	ARK ROYAL
Sneyd, Eric Patrick Bartholomew, MBE, BEng, MSc,	LT CDR(FTC)	E	TM	20.06.93	ELANT/NAVNORTH
Snook, Raymond Edward, pce, pcea, psc(j),	CDR(FTC)	X	O	30.06.98	EXCHANGE USA
Snow, Christopher Allen, BA, pce,	CDRE(FTC)	X	PWO(U)	14.05.02	FLEET HQ PORTS 2
Snow, Maxwell Charles Peter, BSc, pce, pcea, psc,	CDR(FTC)	X	P	30.06.93	MOD (BATH)
Snow, Paul Frederick, BSc,	LT CDR(FTC)	E	ME	01.10.94	EDINBURGH
Snowball, Simon John, MA, psc,	CDR(FTC)	X	PWO(N)	30.06.00	1 PBS SEA
Snowden, Michael Brian Samuel, MB, ChB, DObstRCOG, Dip FFP, MRCGP,	SURG LTCDR(MCC)	-	GMPP	01.08.99	NEPTUNE DL
Soar, Gary,	LT(FTC)	X	O	16.04.93	814 SQN
Soar, Trevor Alan, OBE, pce, pce(sm), (Commodore)	CAPT(FTC)	X	SM	31.12.96	MOD (LONDON)
Sobers, Scott, BEng,	SLT(IC)	E	MESM	01.09.00	KENT
Solly, Matthew MacDonald, BSc,	LT(FTC)	E	TMSM	22.05.92	FOST CSST FSLN
Somerville, Angus James Dunmore, LLB, (Commodore) rcds, pce,	CAPT(FTC)	X	AAWO	30.06.94	STANAVFORMED
Somerville, Nigel John Powell, MA,	CAPT RM(FTC)	-		01.05.98	RM POOLE
Somerville, Stuart James,	LT(FTC)	S		01.04.01	NEPTUNE DLO
Sopinski, Gregory Francis,	LT(CC)	X	P	16.09.90	RAF CRANWELL EFS
Soul, Nicholas John, BEng,	LT(CC)	X	P	01.12.94	846 SQN
South, David John,	LT CDR(FTC)	X	AAWO	01.03.02	YORK
Southall, Emma Louise, BDS,	SG LT(D)(SCC)	-		24.09.00	NEPTUNE DLO
Southern, Mark,	2LT(IC)	-		01.09.98	RE ENTRY(RN)
Southern, Paul Jonathan, BSc, IEng, AMIMarE,	LT CDR(FTC)	E	ME	27.02.99	SOMERSET
Southern, Peter John,	LT CDR(FTC)	E	MESM	01.10.90	UPHLDER TRG TEAM
Southorn, M,	LT CDR(FTC)	X	PWO(U)	21.07.99	EXCHANGE FRANCE
Southwell, Neil Peter,	LT(FTC)	X	C	24.07.97	STRS IPT
Southwood, Shaun Christopher,	SLT(IC)	E	MESM	01.05.00	SULTAN
Southworth, Mika John, BSc,	SLT(IC)	X		01.09.00	DARTMOUTH BRNC
Sowden, Lesley Margaret, MB, ChB, DObstRCOG, Dip FFP	SURG LTCDR(MCC)	-	GMPP	02.08.00	CTCRM
Spalding, Richard Edmund Howden, BSc, CEng, MIEE, jsdc,	CDR(FTC)	E	WE	30.06.97	FWO PORTS SEA
Spalton, Gary Marcus Sean, BSc, pce,	CDR(FTC)	X	PWO(U)	31.12.92	RNU ST MAWGAN
Spanner, Paul,	MAJ(FTC)	-		01.05.01	JARIC
Spark, Stephen Michael,	SLT(IC)	X	O U/T	01.05.00	EXETER
Sparke, Philip Richard William, BA,	SLT(IC)	S		01.03.00	PORTLAND
Sparkes, Peter James, BSc, pce, n,	LT CDR(FTC)	X	PWO(C)	01.06.99	MOD (LONDON)
Sparkes, Simon Nicholas, pcea,	LT(FTC)	X	P	01.04.92	LOAN JTEG BSC DN
Sparrow, Mark Jonathan, BSc,	LT(IC)	X	P	16.04.99	801 SQN
Spayne, Nicholas John,	LT CDR(FTC)	X	PWO(U)	01.10.98	JMOTS NORTHWOOD
Speake, Jonathan, BEng,	LT(CC)	X	O	01.12.90	EXCHANGE CANADA
Spears, Andrew Graeme,	LT(CC)	X	SM	01.11.00	TORBAY
Speller, Nicholas Simon Ford, MDA, MCMI, MNI, pce(sm),	LT CDR(FTC)	X	SM	01.05.88	FLEET HQ PORTS 2
Spence, Andrei Barry, BSc,	CDR(FTC)	S	BAR	30.06.00	2SL/CNH
Spence, Nicholas Anthony, pce,	CDR(FTC)	X	PWO(U)	30.06.97	JDCC
Spence, Robert Graeme, BA,	LT(CC)	X	P	16.12.93	846 SQN
Spencer, Ashley Carver, BA,	LT(IC)	X		01.05.01	SOUTHAMPTON
Spencer, Elizabeth Anne, BEd, MA, psc(j),	CDR(FTC)	X	METOC	30.06.99	MOD (LONDON)
Spencer, Jeremy Charles,	LT(FTC)	E	ME	02.09.99	TYNE
Spencer, Richard Anthony Winchcombe, BA, psc(j)o,	LT COL(FTC)	-	C	31.12.99	PJHQ
Spencer, Steven John,	LT CDR(MCC)	Q	CC	01.10.00	2SL/CNH FOTR
Spencer, Sir Peter, KCB, ADC, MA, MSc, jsdc,	VADM	-	WE	19.01.00	2SL/CNH
Spicer, Clive Graham, BSc, CEng, MIMarEST,	CDR(FTC)	E	ME	31.12.95	RN GIBRALTAR
Spicer, Mark Nicholas, BSc, psc,	COL(FTC)	-		31.12.97	BDS WASHINGTON
Spike, Adam James, BSc,	LT(IC)	X	P U/T	01.05.02	RNAS YEOVILTON
Spillane, Paul William,	LT(CC)	X	O	01.07.96	849 SQN B FLT
Spiller, Michael Francis, BSc, psc,	CDR(FTC)	S		31.12.98	MWC SOUTHWICK
Spiller, Stephen Nicholas, BEng,	LT(FTC)	E	WE	01.08.97	MWS COLLINGWOOD
Spiller, Vanessa Jane, pce,	LT CDR(FTC)	X	PWO(U)	28.07.97	KENT
Spink, David Andrew,	LT RM(IC)	-		01.09.00	40 CDO RM

Name	Rank	Branch	Spec	Seniority	Where Serving
Spinks, David William,	LT(FTC)	X	FC	01.08.97	MWS DRYAD
Spinks, Robert John, BSc,	LT(IC)	X	P U/T	01.05.01	DHFS
Spires, Trevor Allan, BSc, CDipAF, nadc, (Commodore)	CAPT(FTC)	E	TM	31.12.94	AFPAA HQ
Spooner, Peter David,	LT CDR(FTC)	E	AE(M)	01.10.98	SULTAN
Spooner, Ross Sydney, BEng,	LT(FTC)	E	AE(P)	01.04.96	824 SQN
Spoors, Brendan Mark, BEng,	LT(CC)	X	P	01.01.98	824 SQN
Spring, Andrew Ralph James, pce, n,	LT CDR(FTC)	X	PWO(U)	01.03.98	LOAN DSTL
Spring, Jeremy Mark, BEng,	LT CDR(FTC)	E	AE	03.08.97	RNAS YEOVILTON
Springett, Julia Katherine,	LT CDR(CC)	W	C	01.10.99	RN GIBRALTAR
Springett, Simon Paul, LLB,	CHAPLAIN	CE		10.09.91	FWO PORTS SEA
Spurdle, Andrew Peter,	LT(FTC)	X	C	20.09.99	MWS DRYAD
Squibb, Clifford John, BSc, pcea, psc,	LT CDR(FTC)	X	P	16.01.84	RNAS CULDROSE
Squire, Paul Anthony, BSc, CDipAF,CEng,MIEE,MBCS, adp,	LT CDR(FTC)	E	WE	01.10.90	WSA/CAPT MCTA
St Aubyn, John David Erskine, BSc,	CDR(FTC)	E	WESM	30.06.01	FOST CSST SEA
Stace, Ivan Spencer, BA, BEng, MSc, CEng, MIEE, mdtc,	LT CDR(FTC)	E	WESM	01.07.96	JSCSC
Stacey, Andrew Michael, BSc,	LT(FTC)	X	PWO(A)	01.06.94	KENT
Stacey, Hugo Alister,	LT CDR(FTC)	X	P	01.10.93	700M MERLIN OEU
Stack, Eleanor Frances,	SLT(IC)	X		01.09.99	RAMSEY
Stackhouse, Martyn Carl,	MID(NE)(IC)	X	P U/T	01.01.02	DARTMOUTH BRNC
Stafford, Benjamin Robert, MEng,	LT(FTC)	E	MESM	01.09.00	SPARTAN
Stafford, Derek Bryan,	CAPT RM(CC)	-	P	27.04.96	848 SQN HERON
Stafford, Wayne,	LT(FTC)	E	WESM	09.01.01	TRAFALGAR
Stagg, Antony Robert, BEng,	LT(FTC)	E	AE	01.03.95	DITMTC SHRIVNHAM
Stait, Benjamin Geoffrey,	LT(CC)	X	MCD	01.04.99	MWS DRYAD
Stait, Carolyn Jane, OBE, psc,	CAPT(FTC)	W	S	31.12.98	NMA PORTSMOUTH
Staley, Simon Peter Lee, pce, pcea,	LT CDR(FTC)	X	O	01.02.99	MWS DRYAD
Stallion, Ian Michael, BA, pce, pce(sm),	CDR(FTC)	X	SM	31.12.94	RALEIGH
Stamper, Jonathan Charles Henry, BSc,	LT CDR(FTC)	E	IS	01.01.00	AFPAA(CENTURION)
Standen, Colin Anthony,	CAPT RM(FTC)	-	SO(LE)	01.01.01	UKLFCSG RM
Standen, Gary David, (Act Lt)	SLT(IC)	S		01.05.99	845 SQN
Stanesby, David Laurence, BSc, BA(OU), PGCE, psc,	CDR(FTC)	X	METOC	30.06.88	DRAKE CBP(DLO)
Stanford, Jeremy Hugh, BA, jsdc, pce,	CAPT(FTC)	X	P	30.06.01	MOD (LONDON)
Stangroom, Alastair, pce,	LT CDR(FTC)	X	MCD	24.03.95	FOST SEA
Stanham, Christopher Mark,	LT CDR(FTC)	E	AE(M)	01.10.01	815 SQN HQ
Stanhope, Mark, OBE, MA, MNI, rcds, pce, pce(sm), psc, hcsc,	VADM	X	SM	09.07.02	MOD (LONDON)
Stanley, Andrew Brian,	SLT(IC)	E	MESM	01.10.99	TALENT
Stanley, Christopher Edward, pce, psc,	CDR(FTC)	X	AAWO	30.06.94	MWC PORTSDOWN
Stanley, Nicholas James,	LT(CC)	X	O	16.09.93	815 SQN HQ
Stanley, Nicholas Paul, MPhil, pce, psc,	CAPT(FTC)	X	MCD	30.06.02	UKMARBATSTAFF
Stanley, Paul, BEd, jsdc, ODC(SWISS),	CDR(FTC)	E	TM	30.06.92	MOD (LONDON)
Stanley-Whyte, Berkeley John, BSc, MA, CEng, MIEE, psc(j),	CDR(FTC)	E	WESM	31.12.98	IMS BRUSSELS
Stannard, Adam, MB, ChB, BSc,	SURG LT(SCC)	-		02.08.00	VENGEANCE(PORT)
Stannard, Mark Philip,	LT CDR(FTC)	X		01.08.97	FEARLESS
Stanton, David Vernon, MBE, pcea,	LT CDR(FTC)	X	O	01.10.91	JSCSC
Stanton, Keith Victor,	LT RM(IC)	-	SO(LE)	01.04.00	CDO LOG REGT RM
Stanton, Paul Charles Maund, BSc, ACMA,	LT CDR(FTC)	S	CMA	16.02.97	NMA PORTSMOUTH
Stanton-Brown, Peter James, BSc, SM(n),	LT CDR(FTC)	X	SM	01.02.01	VENGEANCE(STBD)
Stanway, Charles Adrian, BSc,	LT(IC)	X		01.09.01	VICTORIOUS(PORT)
Stapley, Sarah Ann, MB, ChB, FRCS,	SURG CDR(FCC)	-		30.06.02	NELSON (PAY)
Stark, Trevor Alan, psc,	MAJ(FTC)	-		01.12.82	AST(E)
Starks, Michael Robert, BSc, MA, CEng, MRAeS, psc,	CDR(FTC)	E	AE	30.06.97	RNAS CULDROSE
Startup, Helen Jane, BSc,	LT(IC)	X		01.01.02	MWS DRYAD
Staveley, John Richard,	LT CDR(FTC)	X	MCD	01.01.87	SACLANT ITALY
Stead, Abigail, BSc,	SLT(IC)	X	P U/T	01.01.01	DARTMOUTH BRNC
Stead, Andrew Michael, BSc,	LT(IC)	E	TM	01.07.99	SULTAN
Stead, John Arthur, BSc,	LT(TC)	E	WESM	02.09.99	CLYDE MIXMAN1
Stead, Richard Alexander,	LT CDR(FTC)	MS	(AD)	01.10.01	DEF MED TRG CTR
Stead, Steven Neil,	LT(IC)	X		01.09.01	RALEIGH
Steadman, Rebecca Angharad Jane, BSc,	SLT(IC)	X	O U/T	01.09.99	750 SQN SEAHAWK
Steadman, Robert Paul, BA,	LT(FTC)	X	FC	01.05.96	JSCSC
Stearns, Rupert Paul, MA, psc, psc(j),	LT COL(FTC)	-	LC	30.06.96	JSCSC

Name	Rank	Branch	Spec	Seniority	Where Serving
Steeds, Sean Michael, pce, pcea, psc(j),	CDR(FTC)	X	P	30.06.98	RHQ AFNORTH
Steel, Christopher Michael Howard, BSc, CEng, MIEE, MCMI, jsdc,	CDR(FTC)	E	WESM	31.12.92	FLEET HQ PORTS 2
Steel, David George, BA, FCIPD, jsdc,	CAPT(FTC)	S	BAR	31.12.00	FLEET HQ PORTS
Steel, David Goodwin,	LT CDR(FTC)	MS	(CDO)	01.10.98	MODHU DERRIFORD
Steel, Peter St Clair, BSc, jsdc, pce,	CAPT(FTC)	X	P	30.06.01	MOD (LONDON)
Steel, Rodney James, BSc, CEng, MIMechE, jsdc,	CDR(FTC)	E	AE(P)	31.12.90	SULTAN
Steele, Matthew Stuart, BSc,	LT(IC)	X		01.05.02	MWS DRYAD
Steele, Richard Martin, BSc, SM,	LT(IC)	X		01.06.99	BFFI
Steele, Trevor Graeme,	LT(FTC)	X	O	11.12.92	MWC PORTSDOWN
Steen, Kieron Malcolm, BSc,	LT(CC)	X	P	01.01.98	LOAN OTHER SVCE
Steer, Andrew David,	LT(FTC)	X		01.02.98	FOSM NWOOD OPS
Steil, Cameron Wellesley Rutherford, MSc,	LT CDR(FTC)	X	PWO(A)	01.02.01	GLASGOW
Stein, Graham Kenneth, BSc,	LT(CC)	X	P	01.11.98	846 SQN
Stembridge, Daniel Patrick Trelawney,	LT(FTC)	X	P	16.04.94	899 SQN HERON
Stemp, Justin Edward, BA,	CAPT RM(FTC)	-		01.09.98	FPGRM
Stenhouse, Nicholas John, BSc, MA, CEng, MIEE, psc,	CDR(FTC)	E	WE	31.12.93	FLEET ROSYTH
Stephen, Barry Mark, BA, n,	LT CDR(FTC)	X		01.03.02	TRACKER
Stephens, Andrew William,	LT(FTC)	E	WE	09.01.01	DCSA RADIOHQ FMR
Stephens, Richard James, MBE, MA, psc(j),	MAJ(FTC)	-		01.05.97	45 CDO RM
Stephens, Richard John, BSc, PGDip,	LT(CC)	X	METOC	01.09.90	FLEET HQ NWD
Stephens, Richard Philip,	LT CDR(FTC)	X	EW	01.10.99	RNU RAF DIGBY
Stephenson, Christopher John, BSc,	LT(IC)	X		01.05.01	QUORN
Stephenson, David, BEng, MSc,	LT CDR(FTC)	E	ME	22.11.95	FOST SEA
Stephenson, Frederick, BSc, CEng, MIMechE,	LT CDR(FTC)	E	AE	16.05.80	FLEET HQ PORTS
Stephenson, Keith James MacFarlane, BA,	LT(CC)	E	TM	01.05.94	ARK ROYAL
Stephenson, Philip George, MILog, (Act Lt Cdr)	LT(FTC)	S	(S)	23.07.98	MOD (BATH)
Sterry, Jasen Edward Baxter,	LT(IC)	X		01.09.01	2SL/CNH
Stevens, Andrew John,	LT(SCC)	Q		24.09.99	RH HASLAR
Stevens, Andrew Mark Robert,	LT(IC)	X	MCD	01.10.97	MIDDLETON
Stevens, Anthony, BA,	LT(IC)	E	TM	04.12.97	CSST RNSSS
Stevens, Joseph Iain, BEng,	SLT(IC)	E	AE U/T	01.09.00	CHATHAM
Stevens, Robert Patrick, CB, pce, pce(sm),	RADM	-	SM(N)	04.08.98	AGRIPPA NAVSOUTH
Stevenson , Elizabeth,	LT(SCC)	Q		07.11.99	DRAKE CBP(CNH)
Stevenson, Charles Bernard Hilton, BSc, (Commodore)	CAPT(FTC)	X	METOC	31.12.95	MOD (LONDON)
FRMS, rcds, psc,					
Stevenson, Geoffrey Stewart, BDS,	SGLTCDR(D)(SCC)	-		14.01.99	NEPTUNE DLO
Stevenson, Julian Patrick, BEng,	LT(FTC)	E	MESM	01.11.93	SULTAN
Stevenson, Robert MacKinnon, BDS, MSc,	SGCDR(D)(FCC)	-		31.12.90	NELSON
MGDS RCS,					
Stevenson, Simon Richard,	LT(IC)	X	P U/T	01.01.02	DHFS
Stewart, Andrew Carnegie, pce,	CDR(FTC)	X	PWO(C)	30.06.00	FLEET CIS PORTS
Stewart, Benjamin Christopher,	SLT(IC)	X		01.05.00	CARDIFF
Stewart, Charles Hardie, BSc,	LT(IC)	X	PT	01.09.01	MWS DRYAD
Stewart, David James, OBE, MC, BSc, MA, psc, (Act Col)	LT COL(FTC)	-	C	30.06.95	COMSTRIKFORSTH
Stewart, James Neil, BSc, MA, psc(j),	LT CDR(FTC)	E	TMSM	01.09.93	2SL/CNH FOTR
Stewart, James, psc,	LT COL(FTC)	-	SO(LE)	01.10.97	NS OBERAMMERGAU
Stewart, Kenneth Currie, BSc,	LT CDR(FTC)	E	TM	01.09.98	FOST CSST FSLN
Stewart, Michael David, MB, ChB, MRCP,	SURG CDR(FCC)	-	(M) UT	30.06.01	NELSON (PAY)
Stewart, Robert Gordon, BSc, psc,	CDR(FTC)	X	H CH	30.06.97	MOD (LONDON)
Stewart, Rory William, BSc,	LT CDR(FTC)	E	MESM	01.07.91	DRAKE NBSD
Stickland, Charles Richard, BSc, MA, psc(j),	MAJ(FTC)	-	LC	30.04.98	MOD (LONDON)
Stidston, Ian James, BSc,	CDR(FTC)	E	TM	31.12.00	FLEET HQ PORTS
Stiles, Faye Elizabeth, BEng,	LT(IC)	E	TM	01.05.98	SULTAN
Stillwell-Cox, Andrew David Robert, MHCIMA,	LT CDR(FTC)	S	CA	01.10.00	FEARLESS
MCFA, MinstAM,					
Stilwell, James Michael, BA, SM(n),	LT(CC)	X	SM	01.01.98	EXCHANGE NLANDS
Stinton, Carol Ann,	LT CDR(FCC)	Q	OTSPEC	01.10.99	RN GIBRALTAR
Stirzaker, Mark, BSc, CEng,	LT CDR(FTC)	E	MESM	01.11.96	FLEET HQ PORTS 2
Stitson, Paul,	2LT(IC)	-		01.09.98	RE ENTRY(ARMY)
Stiven, Timothy David, MSc,	LT(FTC)	E	ME	01.03.96	STG BRISTOL
Stobie, Ian Charles Angus, MBE,	LT CDR(FTC)	S		28.07.88	SAUDI AFPS SAUDI

Name	Rank	Branch	Spec	Seniority	Where Serving
Stobie, Paul Lionel,	LT CDR(FTC)	E	AE(L)	01.10.01	700M MERLIN OEU
Stock, Christopher Mark,	LT(CC)	X	O	01.05.93	700M MERLIN OEU
Stockbridge, Antony Julian, MA,	LT(CC)	S	SM	01.03.97	VENGEANCE(STBD)
Stockings, Timothy Mark, BSc, pce, pcea,	CDR(FTC)	X	P	30.06.00	JSCSC
Stockman, Colin David, BA, MBA, pce, pce(sm), psc,	CAPT(FTC)	X	SM	30.06.02	MOD (LONDON)
Stockton, James Philip, psc,	CDR(FTC)	X	SM	01.10.98	MOD (LONDON)
Stockton, Kevin Geoffrey,	LT CDR(FTC)	X	PWO(U)	19.11.00	FOST MPV(SEA)
Stoffell, David Peter,	LT CDR(FTC)	S	SM	27.11.98	RALEIGH
Stokes, Alan William,	LT CDR(FTC)	E	WESM	01.10.98	ASM IPT
Stokes, Richard, BSc, MDA, CEng, MIEE,	CDR(FTC)	E	WESM	31.12.98	MOD (LONDON)
Stone, Colin Robert Macleod, pce,	LT CDR(FTC)	X	PWO(U)	01.05.85	FLEET HQ NWD
Stone, James William Gray, BSc,	LT(IC)	X	O U/T	01.05.02	750 SQN SEAHAWK
Stone, Nicholas Joseph John, BA,	LT(IC)	S		01.07.00	NORFOLK
Stone, Paul Christopher Julian, BSc, tp,	LT CDR(FTC)	X	P	01.10.98	801 SQN
Stone, Richard James,	LT(FTC)	E	ME	19.06.98	FOST SEA
Stoneman, Timothy John, BSc, MA, pce, psc,	CDR(FTC)	X	AAWO	31.12.91	MWC SOUTHWICK
Stonier, Paul Leslie,	CAPT RM(FTC)	-	SO(LE)	01.01.01	RMB STONEHOUSE
Stonor, Philip Francis Andrew, pce, pcea, odc(Fr),	CDR(FTC)	X	P	31.12.95	IMS BRUSSELS
Storey, Andrew Eric,	LT(IC)	X		01.05.02	ALDERNEY
Storrs-Fox, Roderick Noble, BSc,	CDR(FTC)	S		31.12.95	2SL/CNH
Stott, John Antony,	LT CDR(FTC)	E	WESM	26.05.91	FLEET HQ PORTS 2
Stovin-Bradford, Matthew,	MAJ(FTC)	-	C	01.09.99	BDS WASHINGTON
Stowell, Perry Ivan Mottram, pce, n,	LT CDR(FTC)	X	PWO(U)	01.04.98	MWS DRYAD
Stowell, Robin Barnaby Mottram, BEng, CEng,	LT(FTC)	E	ME	01.09.95	ILLUSTRIOUS
Strange, Steven Paul, BEng,	LT(FTC)	E	WESM	01.09.97	TRAFALGAR
Stratford, Peter John,	LT(CC)	X	ATC	01.04.95	GANNET SAR FLT
Strathern, Roderick James,	LT CDR(FTC)	X	PWO(U)	01.10.98	LANCASTER
Strathie, Gavin Scott,	LT(CC)	X	ATC	01.06.96	EXCHANGE RAF UK
Stratton, John Denniss, BSc, psc,	CAPT(FTC)	E	AE(P)	30.06.02	MERLIN IPT
Stratton, Matthew Paul, BEng,	LT(CC)	E	WE	01.05.99	YORK
Stratton, Nicholas Charles,	LT(CC)	X	SM	01.05.00	TIRELESS
Stratton, Stuart John,	LT(IC)	E	MESM	01.05.01	DARTMOUTH BRNC
Straughan, Christopher John, MBE, pce,	LT CDR(FTC)	X	PWO(U)	01.12.90	EXCHANGE AUSTLIA
Straughan, Harry, MSc, psc,	CDR(FTC)	E	IS	31.12.97	2SL/CNH FOTR
Straughan, Scott Richard, BEng,	LT(CC)	E	IS	01.05.97	MWS DRYAD
Straw, Andrew Nicholas, (Act Cdr)	LT CDR(FTC)	S		16.03.96	UKMARBATSTAFF
Street, Sarah Caroline,	MID(IC)	X		01.05.00	MANCHESTER
Streeten, Christopher Mark,	CDR(FTC)	E	WESM	30.06.02	NATO DEF COL
Streets, Christopher George, MB, BCh, BSc,	SURG LTCDR(MCC)	-		01.08.98	NELSON (PAY)
Stretton, Darrell George,	LT(FTC)	X	AV	03.04.97	RNAS YEOVILTON
Stride, James Alan, BSc,	LT(FTC)	X	HM	01.02.96	SCOTT
Stride, Jamieson Colin,	LT(FTC)	X	O	01.04.95	702 SQN HERON
Stringer, Graeme Ellis,	LT(FTC)	X	ATC	19.09.00	EXCHANGE RAF UK
Stringer, Karl David Paul,	LT(IC)	X	P	16.03.97	847 SQN
Stringer, Roger Andrew, pcea,	LT CDR(FTC)	X	P	01.10.97	DHFS
Stroude, Paul Addison, BEng, n,	LT(FTC)	X		01.08.96	BRECON
Strudwick, Russell,	LT(FTC)	S	(W)	24.07.97	NELSON
Strutt, Jason Fearnley, BEng, MSc,	LT CDR(FTC)	E	WE	01.05.00	LOAN DSTL
Stuart, Charles Michael Douglas,	LT CDR(FTC)	S		01.03.83	CFLT COMMAND SEC
Stuart, Euan Edward Andrew, BA, MEng,	LT(FTC)	X	FC	01.10.96	DUMBARTON CASTLE
Stubbings, Paul Richard,	CDR(FTC)	E	MESM	31.12.99	DRAKE SFM
Stubbs, Benjamin Duncan, BEng,	SLT(IC)	X	P U/T	01.09.00	DARTMOUTH BRNC
Stubbs, Gary Andrew,	LT(FTC)	X	P	16.09.94	848 SQN HERON
Stubbs, Ian,	LT(CC)	X	O	16.05.95	GANNET SAR FLT
Stubbs, Martin Andrew,	LT(FTC)	E	WESM	22.02.96	SCU LEYDENE ACNS
Stuchbury, Robert John, BEng, SM(n),	LT(CC)	X	SM	01.10.97	TIRELESS
Stuckey, Kathryn Anne,	MID(IC)	X	O U/T	01.09.00	750 SQN SEAHAWK
Studley, Steven Alan,	LT(CC)	X	MCD	01.10.97	NELSON
Sturdy, Clive Charles Markus,	LT(FTC)	X	MCD	14.06.96	MCM3 SEA
Sturgeon, David Marcus,	LT(IC)	S		01.05.02	TIRELESS
Sturgeon, Mark, BEng,	SLT(IC)	E	WE	01.09.99	MWS COLLINGWOOD
Sturman, Matthew, OBE, MPhil, FCIPD, CDipAF, psc(m), osc,	COL(FTC)	-		31.12.94	FLEET HQ PORTS 2

Name	Rank	Branch	Spec	Seniority	Where Serving
Sturman, Richard William, BSc,	LT(CC)	X	P U/T	01.01.01	DHFS
Stuttard, Mark Christopher, pce,	LT CDR(FTC)	X	PWO(A)	01.07.94	MWS DRYAD
Stuttard, Stephen Eric,	LT CDR(FTC)	X	AV	01.10.97	MOD (LONDON)
Style, Charles Rodney, MA, rcds, pce, hcsc,	RADM	-	PWO(U)	21.01.02	MOD (LONDON)
Suckling, Robin Leslie, pcea,	LT(FTC)	X	O	16.08.90	814 SQN
Suddes, Lesley Ann, BA,	LT CDR(FTC)	X	METOC	01.10.92	FLEET HQ PORTS
Suddes, Thomas,	LT CDR(FTC)	X	AV	01.10.94	CAMBRIA
Sugden, Michael Rodney, BSc, MBA,	LT CDR(FTC)	E	ME	01.10.94	ECHO
Sugden, Stephen Robert, HNC,	LT CDR(FTC)	E	WE	01.10.99	RICHMOND
Sullivan, Anne Gillian, BSc, MA, MInstP, psc(j),	CDR(FTC)	X	METOC	31.12.99	FLEET HQ NWD
Sullivan, Colin, BA, psc,	CDR(FTC)	X	METOC	31.12.96	FLEET HQ PORTS
Sullivan, Mark Nigel, BEng,	LT(FTC)	E	ME	01.12.97	JSCSC
Sullivan, Mark, BEng,	LT CDR(FTC)	E	WE	01.07.01	T45 IPT
Sullivan, Timothy, BA(OU), MIOSH, DEH,	LT(IC)	MS		29.04.01	2SL/CNH
Summerfield, David Edward, osc(us),	LT COL(FTC)	-		30.06.00	OCEAN
Summers, Alastair John,	LT(CC)	X	P	01.04.01	771 SQN
Summers, James Alexander Edward, BEd,	LT CDR(CC)	E	TM	24.05.02	FLEET HQ PORTS 2
Summerton, Duncan John, MB, ChB, BSc, FRCS, FRCSEd,	SURG CDR(FCC)	-	(CU)	30.06.02	RH HASLAR
Sumner, Michael Dennis, MIIE,	LT CDR(FTC)	E	WESM	01.10.94	FWO FASLANE
Sunderland, John Dominic, MSc, CEng, MIEE,	CDR(FTC)	E	WESM	31.12.97	IA BRISTOL
Surgey, Ian, SM,	LT CDR(FTC)	X	SM	26.10.97	TRAFALGAR
Sutcliffe, Edward Diccon, BA,	LT(IC)	S	SM	01.05.98	VICTORIOUS(PORT)
Sutcliffe, John, pce, pcea,	LT CDR(FTC)	X	O	21.12.94	MOD (LONDON)
Sutcliffe, Roy William,	LT CDR(FTC)	E	WESM	01.10.00	NEPTUNE NT
Suter, Francis Thomas,	LT(IC)	X	O U/T	01.01.02	702 SQN HERON
Sutherland, Iain,	2LT(IC)	-		01.09.01	CTCRM LYMPSTONE
Sutherland, Neil,	MAJ(FTC)	-	C	24.04.02	SCH SIG BLANDFD
Sutherland, William Murray, MA, PGCE,	CDR(FTC)	E	TM	30.06.93	DNR RCHQ NORTH
Sutton, David,	CAPT RM(IC)	-	P U/T	01.04.01	AACC MID WALLOP
Sutton, Gareth David, BSc, CEng, MIMarEST,	LT CDR(FTC)	E	ME	01.06.93	MOD (BATH)
Sutton, Gary Brian, pce,	CDR(FTC)	X	PWO(N)	30.06.98	2SL/CNH
Sutton, Richard Michael John,	LT(CC)	X	P	01.06.93	FLEET AV VL
Sutton, Stephen John,	CAPT RM(CC)	-	P	29.04.97	RNAS YEOVILTON
Swain, Andrew Vincent, pce,	LT CDR(FTC)	X	H CH	05.03.97	NP 1016 IN SURV
Swain, David Michael, BSc, MNI, pce, pcea,	CAPT(FTC)	X	O	30.06.01	SACLANT USA
Swan, Wendy,	LT(CC)	W		01.12.95	NELSON
Swann, John Ivan, (Act Lt Cdr)	LT(FTC)	X	EW	28.07.89	SCU LEYDENE ACNS
Swannick, Derek John, BSc,	CDR(FTC)	X	METOC	30.06.02	JSCSC
Swarbrick, Richard James, BA, pce, pcea, psc(j),	LT CDR(FTC)	X	P	01.12.94	PORTLAND
Sweeney, Craig, BSc,	LT(IC)	X	P	16.02.99	846 SQN
Sweeney, Keith Patrick Michael, BEng,	LT(FTC)	E	ME	01.08.95	MOD (BATH)
Sweeney, Rachel Jane, BEng,	LT(IC)	E	TM	01.01.01	DARTMOUTH BRNC
Sweeny, Brian Donald, IEng, AMIMarEST,	LT CDR(FTC)	E	HULL	01.10.93	2SL/CNH FOTR
Swift, Robin David, pce,	LT CDR(FTC)	X	PWO(U)	28.08.94	FLEET HQ NWD
Swindells, Mark, BEng,	LT(CC)	E	P	16.07.99	815 FLT 228
Sykes, Jeremy James William, MB, (Commodore) ChB, MSc, FRCP, FFOM,	SURG CAPT(FCC)	-	(CO/M)	31.12.98	FORT BLOCKHOUSE
Sykes, Malcolm, BEng, MSc, psc,	CDR(FTC)	E	MESM	30.06.02	MOD (BATH)
Sykes, Matthew John,	SLT(UCE)(FTC)	X		01.09.00	DARTMOUTH BRNC
Sykes, Robert Alan,	LT CDR(FTC)	X	O	01.10.96	702 SQN HERON
Symington, Zena Marie Alexandrea,	LT(IC)	X		01.11.97	DNR PRES TEAMS
Syrett, Matthew Edward, BSc, PGDip, PGDIPAN, n,	LT(FTC)	X	HM(AS)	01.08.95	GLEANER
Syson, Carl Frederick, MEng,	SLT(IC)	X	P U/T	01.01.01	DARTMOUTH BRNC
Syvret, Mark Edward Vibert, BSc, psc(j)o,	LT COL(FTC)	-		30.06.01	JDCC

T

Name	Rank	Branch	Spec	Seniority	Where Serving
Tabeart, George William, pce,	LT CDR(FTC)	X	HM	01.11.97	MWS DRYAD
Tacey, Richard Haydn,	LT(CC)	X		01.12.95	MWS DRYAD
Tait, Martyn David, BEng,	LT(CC)	E	MESM	01.01.00	VICTORIOUS(PORT)
Tait, Stacey Jane, BSc,	LT(IC)	E		01.01.02	MWS COLLINGWOOD
Talbot, Christopher Martin,	LT CDR(FTC)	X	C	01.10.99	ELANT/NAVNORTH

Name	Rank	Branch	Spec	Seniority	Where Serving
Talbot, Nigel Adrian, BSc, PGCE, MA(Ed),	LT CDR(CC)	E	TM	01.10.93	NELSON RNSETT
Talbot, Richard John, BSc,	LT(IC)	X		01.05.02	MWS DRYAD
Talbot, Richard Paul, MA, pce, psc(j),	CDR(FTC)	X	PWO(A)	30.06.00	NORFOLK
Talbot, Simon James,	MID(IC)	X		01.05.00	CAMPBELTOWN
Talbott, Aidan Hugh,	LT CDR(FTC)	S		01.12.99	EXCHANGE USA
Tamayo, Brando Christian Craig, MB, ChB, DiplMC RCSED,	SURG LTCDR(MCC)	-		01.08.99	NELSON (PAY)
Tamlyn, Stephen John, BSc,	CAPT RM(IC)	-		01.05.01	40 CDO RM
Tanner, Michael John, (Act Maj)	CAPT RM(FTC)	-		01.09.96	EXCHANGE USA
Tanner, Richard Carlisle, SM(n), SM,	LT(FTC)	X	SM	01.03.95	TORBAY
Tanner, Steven,	2LT(IC)	-		01.09.98	CTCRM LYMPSTONE
Tanser, Susan Jane, MB, BS, FRCA,	SURG LTCDR(FCC)	-		01.08.96	NELSON (PAY)
Tantam, Robert John Geoffrey, MEng,	SLT(IC)	E	ME U/T	01.09.00	ARK ROYAL
Tapp, Steven John,	CAPT RM(IC)	-	SO(LE)	01.01.01	CHFHQ
Tappin, Simon John, BEng,	LT(IC)	X		01.01.02	MWS DRYAD
Tapping, Kenneth, MSc,	LT CDR(FTC)	E	AE(M)	01.10.97	ES AIR BRISTOL
Tarnowski, Thomas Adam,	CAPT RM(IC)	-	LC	12.01.95	FLEET HQ PORTS
Tarr, Barry Stuart, BEng, CEng, MIMarEST,	CDR(FTC)	E	MESM	30.06.02	ASM IPT
Tarr, Michael Douglas, BSc, pce, pcea, psc(a),	CAPT(FTC)	X	AAWO	30.06.02	RN GIBRALTAR
Tarr, Richard Nicholas Vaughan, BSc,	LT CDR(FTC)	E	AE	01.08.93	FWO FASLANE
Tarrant, Robert Kenneth, pce, pce(sm),	CDR(FTC)	X	SM	30.06.97	MOD (LONDON)
Tasker, Greg, psc(m),	LT COL(FTC)	-		31.12.95	DISC
Tate, Andrew John, BSc, AMIEE, psc,	CAPT(FTC)	E	WESM	30.06.02	MOD (LONDON)
Tate, Graeme Alexander,	LT(CC)	X	P	01.02.95	824 SQN
Tate, Nicholas Mark,	LT(IC)	S		01.05.02	ILLUSTRIOUS
Tate, Simon John, BSc, CEng, MRAeS,	CDR(FTC)	E	AE	31.12.99	JSCSC
Tatham, Peter Hugh, BSc, CEng, FCIS, MBCS, MILT, OStJ,	CAPT(FTC)	S		31.12.96	MOD (BATH)
Tatham, Stephen Alan, BSc,	LT CDR(FTC)	E	TM	01.09.99	MOD (LONDON)
Tattersall, Richard Brian,	LT CDR(FTC)	X	P	01.10.01	EXCHANGE USA
Tatton-Brown, Hugh Trelawny, WE,	SLT(UCE)(IC)	E		01.09.00	DARTMOUTH BRNC
Tawse, Alistair Robert James, BSc,	LT(IC)	X	P U/T	01.09.01	RNAS YEOVILTON
Tayler, James Ralph Newton, pcea,	LT CDR(FTC)	X	P	01.10.00	814 SQN
Taylor, Andrew Ian, BSc, SM,	LT(IC)	X	SM	01.12.99	VENGEANCE(PORT)
Taylor, Andrew Lyndon, BA, MSc,	LT(CC)	E	IS	01.05.91	CTCRM
Taylor, Anna, HND, PGDip,	LT CDR(CC)	E	IS	01.10.00	RN GIBRALTAR
Taylor, Anthony Richard, BA, MA(CANTAB), SM(n),	LT CDR(FTC)	X	PWO(U)	01.11.98	UKMARBATSTAFF
Taylor, Brian David,	LT CDR(FTC)	X		01.07.96	TYNE
Taylor, Carl Richard, (Act Lt Cdr)	LT(FTC)	S		25.08.94	IRON DUKE
Taylor, Christopher Paul, BSc,	LT(IC)	X	O	16.05.98	820 SQN
Taylor, Christopher Simon, MA,	LT(CC)	E	TM	01.01.97	RALEIGH
Taylor, Gordon David, BA,	LT(IC)	X		01.01.02	GRAFTON
Taylor, Hazel Jane, BEng,	LT(CC)	E	WE	01.03.96	SCU LEYDENE ACNS
Taylor, Ian John, BEng,	LT(CC)	E	TM	05.05.96	DARTMOUTH BRNC
Taylor, Ian Kennedy,	LT CDR(FTC)	S	(S)	01.10.01	RNAS YEOVILTON
Taylor, James Edward Henry, BSc,	SLT(IC)	X		01.09.99	BROCKLESBY
Taylor, John Basil, BA,	LT(CC)	S		01.02.99	FLEET HQ PORTS 2
Taylor, John Jeremy, MSc, CEng, MIMarEST,	CDR(FTC)	E	MESM	30.06.96	MOD (BATH)
Taylor, John William, MIPM,	CDR(FTC)	X	ATC	30.06.01	FLEET HQ PORTS
Taylor, Jonathan Paul, SM(n), SM,	LT(FTC)	X	SM	24.07.97	ELANT/NAVNORTH
Taylor, Keith Milbrun, BEng,	LT(FTC)	E	WE	01.08.98	RICHMOND
Taylor, Keith, BEng,	LT CDR(FTC)	E	WESM	01.10.97	FWO FASLANE
Taylor, Kenneth Alistair, BSc, pce, pcea, psc,	CDR(FTC)	X	O	31.12.97	ARK ROYAL
Taylor, Kenneth John,	LT CDR(FTC)	E	WESM	01.10.99	RALEIGH
Taylor, Leslie, MBE,	LT CDR(FTC)	X	P	01.10.94	HQ3GP SEA
Taylor, Lisa,	LT(SCC)	Q		05.07.99	RN GIBRALTAR
Taylor, Marcus Anthony Beckett,	MAJ(FTC)	-	LC	01.09.01	539 ASSLT SQN RM
Taylor, Mark Andrew, pce,	LT CDR(FTC)	X	P	01.02.99	ARK ROYAL
Taylor, Mark Richard,	LT CDR(FTC)	X	C	01.10.00	FLEET CIS PORTS
Taylor, Martin Kenneth, OBE, osc,	LT COL(FTC)	-	C	30.06.94	RMR BRISTOL
Taylor, Nei John,	LT RM(IC)	-		01.09.00	40 CDO RM
Taylor, Neil Robert, BEng, AMIMechE, (Act Lt Cdr)	LT(FTC)	E	ME	01.06.91	CHATHAM
Taylor, Nicholas Frederick, MA, pce,	LT CDR(FTC)	X	PWO(C)	16.02.87	HQ DCSA

Name	Rank	Branch	Spec	Seniority	Where Serving
Taylor, Nigel Anthony, MIOSH, BSc, ... LT(IC)	MS			06.03.96	JSCSC
Taylor, Peter George David, BSc, MA, psc(j), ... MAJ(FTC)	-			25.04.96	EXCHANGE ARMY UK
Taylor, Peter John, MB, BS, FRCS, DA, DTM&H, ... SURG LTCDR(SCC)	-			08.01.98	NELSON (PAY)
Taylor, Robert James, ... LT(CC)	X	O	16.02.94	RNAS YEOVILTON
Taylor, Robert Paul, BSc, ... LT(IC)	X	P U/T	01.05.02	RAF CRANWELL EFS
Taylor, Robert, BEng, MSc, AMIEE, gw, ... LT CDR(FTC)	E	WE	01.09.99	FOST SEA
Taylor, Spencer Alan, MSc, CEng, MIEE, ... CDR(FTC)	E	IS	30.06.98	2SL/CNH
Taylor, Stephen Bryan, CQSW, ... LT(FS)(CAS)	FS			01.05.96	RALEIGH
Taylor, Stephen John, BA, (Act Cdr) .... LT CDR(FTC)	S	BAR	16.04.96	2SL/CNH
Taylor, Stephen John, BEng, CEng, MIEE, ... LT CDR(CC)	E	WE	01.10.01	ALBION
Taylor, Stephen Mark, ... LT CDR(FTC)	S			01.11.93	MOD (BATH)
Taylor, Stuart David, BSc, ... CAPT RM(CC)	-			01.09.97	42 CDO RM
Taylor, Terence Peter, ... LT(CC)	X	ATC	01.04.01	RNAS CULDROSE
Taylor, Timothy Jon, BSc, ... LT CDR(FTC)	X	P	01.10.00	800 SQN
Taylor, William John, osc, ... LT COL(FTC)	-			31.12.96	HQ 3 CDO BDE RM
Tazewell, Matthew Robert, BEng, ... LT(CC)	X	O	16.10.98	815 FLT 212
Teasdale, Robert Mark, BA, ... LT CDR(FTC)	S			16.01.93	RNAS CULDROSE
Tebbet, Paul Nicholas, pce, ... LT CDR(FTC)	X	PWO(U)	01.09.97	LANCASTER
Teer, David Raymond Dennis, OBE, MCMI, pce, ... CDR(FTC)	X	AAWO	30.06.88	2SL/CNH FOTR
Teideman, Ian Charles, BEng, AMIEE, ... LT CDR(FTC)	E	WE	01.03.00	MWS COLLINGWOOD
Temple, David Christopher, ... LT(FTC)	E	WE	01.04.01	NOTTINGHAM
Templeton, Thomas Appleyard Molison, HNC, IEng, MIIE, ... LT CDR(FTC)	E	WE	01.10.98	MOD (BATH)
Tennant, Michael Ian, MB, BS, ... SURG LTCDR(MCC)	-			14.09.00	NELSON (PAY)
Tennuci, Robert George, pce, ... LT CDR(FTC)	X	AAWO	01.12.99	LOAN DSTL
Terrill, Keith William, BA, pcea, gdas, (Act Cdr) .... LT CDR(FTC)	X	O	01.03.85	LOAN JTEG BSC DN
Terry, John Michael, MSc, CEng, MIMarEST, ... CDR(FTC)	E	ME	31.12.96	2SL/CNH FOTR
Terry, Judith Helen, BSc, ... LT(CC)	S			01.12.98	SCOTT
Terry, Michael Charles Gadesden, MB, BS, FRCS, ... SURG LTCDR(SCC)	-	(CGS)	15.04.94	RH HASLAR
Terry, Nigel Patrick, ... LT(CC)	X	P	01.09.96	CORNWALL FLT
Tetley, Mark, ... LT(FTC)	X	O	01.07.91	824 SQN
Tetlow, Hamish Stuart Guy, BA, ... LT CDR(FTC)	X	SM	01.07.96	BULWARK
Thain, Julie Christina, ... LT CDR(SCC)	Q			31.03.99	RN GIBRALTAR
Thatcher, Louise Frances Victoria, BA, ... LT(FTC)	X			01.02.00	ST ALBANS
Theakston, Sally Margaret, MA, ... CHAPLAIN	CE			03.06.96	JSU NORTHWOOD
Thicknesse, Philip John, MA, pce, pcea, psc, ... CDR(FTC)	X	PWO(U)	31.12.96	2SL/CNH
Thirkettle, Julian Andrew, BEng, ... LT CDR(FTC)	E	AE	01.02.02	ES AIR WYTON
Thistlethwaite, Mark Halford, BSc, psc, ... CDR(FTC)	E	AE(O)	31.12.96	DARTMOUTH BRNC
Thoburn, Ross, OBE, pce, ... CDR(FTC)	X	O	30.06.92	NMA PORTSMOUTH
Thom, Mathew Frank, BA, ... LT(IC)	X			01.01.02	MWS DRYAD
Thomas, Adam Joseph, BEng, ... SLT(IC)	E	AE U/T	01.09.00	LIVERPOOL
Thomas, Andrew Giles, ... MID(UCE)(IC)	E	ME	01.09.00	DARTMOUTH BRNC
Thomas, Ann Louise, BEng, (Act Lt Cdr) .... LT(FTC)	E	TM	01.01.91	NELSON RNSETT
Thomas, Daniel Huw, ... LT(CC)	X	P	01.07.99	815 FLT 214
Thomas, David Jonathan, ... LT(FTC)	S	(S)	10.12.98	FLEET HQ PORTS 2
Thomas, David Lynford, BDS, MSc, LDS RCS(Eng), ... SGCDR(D)(FCC)	-			30.06.87	NELSON
MGDS RCS, MGDS RCSEd,					
Thomas, David William Wallace, BA, ... CHAPLAIN	CE			18.10.88	FWO PORTS SEA
Thomas, David William, BEng, ... LT(CC)	X	P	01.10.98	820 SQN
Thomas, Francis Stephen, ... CDR(FTC)	S	(SM)	30.06.99	FOST DPORT SHORE
Thomas, Gavin Hayden, BA, ... SLT(IC)	X	O U/T	01.05.00	750 SQN SEAHAWK
Thomas, Geoffrey Charles, OBE, BSc, hcsc, pce, pce(sm), ... CAPT(FTC)	X	SM	30.06.02	MWS DRYAD
Thomas, Jeffrey Evans, ... LT CDR(FTC)	X	EW	01.10.98	MOD (LONDON)
Thomas, Jeffrey, ... 2LT(IC)	-			01.09.98	CTCRM LYMPSTONE
Thomas, Jeremy Huw, BEng, MLITT, ... LT CDR(FTC)	E	WESM	01.02.98	PJHQ
Thomas, Jeremy Hywel, psc(m), hcsc, ... BRIG(FTC)	-	WTO	17.09.01	FLEET HQ NWD
Thomas, Kevin Ian, BSc, ... LT CDR(FTC)	X	METOC	01.10.92	MWS RNHMS CULD
Thomas, Leslie, BSc, ... LT CDR(FTC)	X	C	01.10.99	HQ DCSA
Thomas, Lynn Marie, MB, BS, BSc, MRCP, ... SURG LTCDR(MCC)	-			01.08.98	NELSON (PAY)
Thomas, Mark Anthony, ... SLT(IC)	E			01.01.01	MWS COLLINGWOOD
Thomas, Mark, BSc, n, ... LT(CC)	X			01.09.98	GLASGOW
Thomas, Martyn George, IEng, AMIMarE, ... LT(FTC)	E	ME	17.02.89	SFM PORTSMOUTH
Thomas, Owen Hopkin, BSc, ... LT(CC)	X			16.10.99	PORTLAND

Name	Rank	Branch	Spec	Seniority	Where Serving
Thomas, Patrick William, sq, (Act Lt Col)	MAJ(FTC)	-	SO(LE)	01.10.96	FLEET CIS PORTS
Thomas, Paul Geraint, pce, psc(j),	CDR(FTC)	X	PWO(U)	31.12.00	SUTHERLAND
Thomas, Richard Anthony Aubrey, MBE, pce, psc(j),	CDR(FTC)	X	PWO(U)	30.06.02	GRAFTON
Thomas, Richard Kevin, BSc, pce, PSC(ONDC),	CDR(FTC)	X	PWO(U)	30.06.02	MWS DRYAD
Thomas, Richard,	SURG SLT(MDC)	-		18.10.00	DARTMOUTH BRNC
Thomas, Robert Paul, pce, pcea, psc,	CDR(FTC)	X	O	30.06.95	SA MUSCAT
Thomas, Simon Alan, MA, pce, pcea, psc(a),	CDR(FTC)	X	P	31.12.93	NMA GOSPORT
Thomas, Stephen Mark, BEng,	LT CDR(FTC)	E	ME	01.01.01	MOD (BATH)
Thomas, Stephen Michael,	LT(CC)	X	P	16.02.96	824 SQN
Thomas, William Gwynne, BSc, pce, pcea,	CDR(FTC)	X	O	31.12.00	RNAS CULDROSE
Thompson, Alastair James,	SLT(IC)	X	P U/T	01.01.01	DARTMOUTH BRNC
Thompson, Andrew Joseph, BSc, BEng,	LT(FTC)	E	AE	01.01.95	ES AIR BRISTOL
Thompson, Andrew Robert,	LT(CC)	X	O	01.02.92	815 SQN HQ
Thompson, Andrew, BSc,	CDR(FTC)	E	AE(M)	30.06.02	ES AIR WYTON
Thompson, Bernard Dominic, BA, pce,	CDR(FTC)	X	MCD	30.06.02	JSCSC
Thompson, David Anthony, BSc,	LT(IC)	X	P	16.08.99	845 SQN
Thompson, David Huw,	CAPT RM(FTC)	-		01.09.99	RM POOLE
Thompson, David William, BEng,	LT(FTC)	E	MESM	01.06.97	SOVEREIGN
Thompson, Fiona,	LT(SCC)	Q		24.09.98	NP 1067 KOSOVO
Thompson, Gary,	CDR(FTC)	X	C	30.06.00	STRS IPT
Thompson, George Christopher,	MID(NE)(IC)	X	P U/T	01.09.01	DARTMOUTH BRNC
Thompson, Graham Michael, BEM,	CAPT RM(FTC)	-	SO(LE)	01.01.97	RMR SCOTLAND
Thompson, James Peter Bibby, BSc,	CAPT RM(IC)	-	MLDR	01.05.00	45 CDO RM
Thompson, James,	SLT(IC)	X		01.05.01	MWS DRYAD
Thompson, Mark George, PGDIPAN, SM(n),	LT(FTC)	X	SM	01.03.95	MWS DRYAD
Thompson, Michael James, BEng,	LT(FTC)	E	ME	01.01.96	JSCSC
Thompson, Neil James, pcea,	LT CDR(FTC)	X	P	01.10.94	JHCHQ
Thompson, Paul L, BSc,	CAPT RM(IC)	-		01.09.01	FPGRM
Thompson, Richard Charles, BEng, psc(j),	CDR(FTC)	E	AE	30.06.02	NMA PORTSMOUTH
Thompson, Robert Anthony,	LT CDR(FTC)	X	O	01.10.98	FLEET HQ PORTS
Thompson, Robert Joseph, BSc, jsdc,	CDR(FTC)	E	ME	30.06.95	MOD (LONDON)
Thompson, Sarah Leanne,	SLT(IC)	X		01.05.00	MWS DRYAD
Thompson, Stephen John, MSc, MCGI, psc(j),	CDR(FTC)	E	ME	31.12.99	EXCHANGE USA
Thompson, William Alistair, BEng,	LT(IC)	X	P	01.09.00	702 SQN HERON
Thomsen, Lavinia Lisa, BSc,	LT(IC)	X		01.02.97	MWS COLLINGWOOD
Thomsett, Harry Fergus James, BA,	MAJ(FTC)	-	C	01.09.01	COMAMPHIBFOR
Thomson, Allan Brown, MBA, fsc, osc,	COL(FTC)	-	MLDR	30.06.01	CTCRM
Thomson, Andrew Douglas, BEng,	SLT(IC)	X	P U/T	01.09.00	DARTMOUTH BRNC
Thomson, Colin Douglas, BSc, PGDip,	LT CDR(FTC)	X	H1	01.02.01	NP 1016 IN SURV
Thomson, David Forbes,	LT(FTC)	E	AE(M)	01.04.01	JCA IPT USA
Thomson, Duncan, pce,	LT CDR(FTC)	X	PWO(U)	23.05.95	CUMBERLAND
Thomson, Iain Rodger, BSc,	LT CDR(FTC)	E	WESM	22.05.97	VICTORIOUS(STBD)
Thomson, Ian Wallace,	LT(FTC)	E	WESM	01.04.01	VANGUARD(PORT)
Thomson, James Christopher, BSc,	LT(CC)	X		01.01.99	MWS DRYAD
Thomson, Jane Margaret, BSc,	SLT(IC)	X		01.01.00	OCEAN
Thomson, Michael Lee, BEng,	LT(CC)	E	ME	01.04.99	DARTMOUTH BRNC
Thomson, Paul Damian, BSc,	LT(CC)	E	IS	24.02.97	MWS COLLINGWOOD
Thomson, Roger Geoffrey,	SURG LTCDR(SCC)	-	GMPP	05.11.93	UKSU SOUTHLANT
Thorburn, Andrew,	LT CDR(FTC)	X	AV	01.10.96	RNAS CULDROSE
Thorley, Graham,	SLT(IC)	X		01.01.01	DARTMOUTH BRNC
Thornback, John Gordon, (Act Lt Cdr)	LT(FTC)	E	WE	02.11.84	MOD (LONDON)
Thorne, Dain Jason, BEng, FRAeS,	LT(FTC)	E	AE	01.03.97	ES AIR YEO
Thornhill, Andrew Philip,	CAPT RM(FTC)	BS		01.01.00	BRNC BAND
Thornley, Jeremy George Carter, BD,	SLT(IC)	X		01.05.00	ARK ROYAL
Thornton, Charles Exley, BA, pcea, gdas,	LT CDR(FTC)	X	O	01.02.84	LOAN JTEG BSC DN
Thornton, Daniel,	2LT(IC)	-		01.09.00	CTCRM LYMPSTONE
Thornton, Michael Crawford, pce, pcea, psc,	LT CDR(FTC)	X	P	08.02.84	702 SQN HERON
Thornton, Philip John, pcea,	LT CDR(FTC)	X	P	01.10.93	RAF HANDLING SQN
Thorp, Benjamin Thomas, BEng, MSc,	LT(FTC)	E	ME	01.07.96	MOD (BATH)
Thorp, David Brian, BEng, AMIEE,	LT(FTC)	E	WE	01.03.98	CAPT IST STAFF
Thorp, Thomas Harvey, BA,	SLT(IC)	X	SM	01.01.01	DARTMOUTH BRNC
Thorpe, Christopher Robert, BSc, psc,	CDR(FTC)	E	WE	31.12.92	DRAKE CBP(DLO)

Name	Rank	Branch	Spec	Seniority	Where Serving
Thorpe, Conrad Dermot Biltcliffe, psc(j),	MAJ(FTC)	-		01.09.98	RM POOLE
Thorpe, Elaine,	LT(SCC)	Q		03.08.99	RH HASLAR
Thorpe, Robert,	2LT(IC)	-		01.09.98	CTCRM LYMPSTONE
Thrippleton, Mark Graham, BEng,	LT CDR(FTC)	E	AE	15.08.00	SULTAN
Thurstan, Richard William Farnall,	MAJ(FTC)	-	LC	01.05.97	JSCSC
Thwaites, Gerard James, BSc, CEng, MIMechE, psc,	CAPT(FTC)	E	MESM	31.12.97	FLEET HQ PORTS 2
Tibballs, Laura Rosalind, BSc,	SLT(IC)	S		01.01.01	DARTMOUTH BRNC
Tibbitt, Ian Peter Gordon, MA, CEng, MIEE, jsdc,	CDRE(FTC)	E	AE	15.04.02	ES AIR WYTON
Tidball, Ian, BEng,	LT(FTC)	X	P	01.02.92	800 SQN
Tidman, Martin David,	CAPT RM(IC)	-	SO(LE)	21.07.01	CTCRM
Tighe, John Geoffrey Hugh, OBE, (Commodore)	CAPT(FTC)	X	AWO(A)	31.12.95	UKMILREP BRUSS
nadc, jsdc, pce,					
Tighe, Simon, SM,	LT(CC)	X	SM	30.03.99	SCEPTRE
Tilden, Philip James Edward, BA, ACMI, n,	LT(FTC)	X		01.03.97	CARDIFF
Tilley, Duncan Scott Jamieson, pce,	CDR(FTC)	X	H CH	30.06.00	MOD (LONDON)
Tillion, Andrew Malcolm,	LT CDR(CC)	X	P	01.10.98	845 SQN
Tilney, Duncan Edward, BA,	LT(CC)	X	MW	01.01.97	CATTISTOCK
Timbrell, Ian Philip James, BEng,	LT(FTC)	E	ME	01.02.00	CORNWALL
Timms, Andrew Ian,	SLT(IC)	X		01.05.00	GRIMSBY
Timms, Deborah Ann, BA,	LT(IC)	X		01.05.99	ALDERNEY
Timms, Stephen John, OBE, MBA, MSc, CEng,	CAPT(FTC)	E	MESM	31.12.98	SA BRAZIL
MIMarEST, MIMechE, jsdc,					
Timson, Christopher Ian,	SLT(IC)	X	P U/T	01.09.00	DARTMOUTH BRNC
Tindal, Nicolas Henry Charles, pce, pcea,	CDR(FTC)	X	P	30.06.02	JSCSC
Tindall-Jones, Lee Douglas, BSc, MA, CEng, MIEE, psc,	CDR(FTC)	E	WESM	31.12.99	EXCHANGE AUSTLIA
Tindell, Richard William, BA,	LT(IC)	X		01.01.02	MWS DRYAD
Tinsley, Glenn Nigel, GCIS,	CDR(FTC)	S		31.12.96	SULTAN
Tinsley, Phillip,	CAPT RM(IC)	-	SO(LE)	21.07.01	CTCRM
Titcomb, Andrew Charles, BEng, MSc,	LT CDR(FTC)	E	WESM	01.06.97	SUPERB
Titcomb, Mark Richard, BSc, pce, pce(sm),	LT CDR(FTC)	X	SM	01.02.98	JSCSC
Titcombe, Adam James, BA,	LT(IC)	S		01.05.99	RALEIGH
Tite, Anthony Damian,	LT(FTC)	X	O	01.02.94	EXCHANGE USA
Titmus, Garry David, pce, psc,	CDR(FTC)	X	PWO(N)†	30.06.82	LOAN OMAN
Titmuss, Julian Francis, BA,	LT(FTC)	S	CMA	01.12.94	2SL/CNH FOTR
Titterton, Phillip James, pce, pce(sm),	CDR(FTC)	X	SM	30.06.99	CAPTAIN SM2
Todd, Donald, pce,	LT CDR(FTC)	X	AWO(A)	01.01.82	MWS DRYAD
Todd, Geoffrey Alan, (Act Lt)	SLT(IC)	MS		01.05.00	MOD (BATH)
Todd, James William, BSc,	CAPT RM(IC)	-		01.05.00	45 CDO RM
Todd, Michael Anthony,	CAPT RM(FTC)	-	SO(LE)	01.01.97	RMR BRISTOL
Todd, Oliver James, LLB,	CAPT RM(IC)	-		01.09.00	CTCRM
Toft, Michael David, BEng,	LT CDR(FTC)	E	WE	01.03.96	MOD (LONDON)
Tofts, Christopher, BEng,	LT(FTC)	E	AE	01.06.00	771 SQN
Tok, Chantelle Fen Lynne, BSc,	LT(IC)	X	ATCU/T	01.05.00	RNAS YEOVILTON
Tolley, Dominic Mark,	LT(SCC)	Q		25.07.00	RH HASLAR
Tolley, Peter Frederick Richmond, (Commodore)	SURG CAPT(FCC)	-	GMPP	31.12.95	MOD (LONDON)
MB, BCh,					
Tomes, Adrian Carl,	LT(CC)	X		01.04.00	EXCHANGE GERMANY
Tomkins, Alan Brian,	LT(FTC)	E	WE	19.02.93	WSA/CAPT MCTA
Tomlin, Ian Stephen, BEng,	SLT(IC)	E	WE	01.09.00	EXETER
Tomlinson, David Charles,	LT(FTC)	X	AV	03.04.97	RNAS CULDROSE
Tomlinson, James Henry,	LT(FTC)	X	PR	27.07.95	RALEIGH
Tong, David Keith, BA, rcds, psc(m),	LT COL(FTC)	-		31.12.90	COMSTRIKFORSTH
Tonge, Malcolm,	SLT(IC)	E	ME	01.05.00	SULTAN
Toomey, Nicholas John, BSc,	LT CDR(FTC)	S	SM	01.11.96	FOSNNI/NBC CLYDE
Toon, John Richard,	LT CDR(FTC)	E	AE(M)	01.10.92	ES AIR YEO
Toon, Paul Graham,	LT(FTC)	X	AV	26.04.99	ARK ROYAL
Toone, Stephen Anthony,	LT(FTC)	E	WE	01.04.01	CARDIFF
Toor, Jeevan Jyoti Singh, BSc, PGDip,	LT CDR(FTC)	X	METOC	01.09.98	FOST CSST SEA
Toothill, John Samuel, SM(n),	LT CDR(FTC)	X		01.04.97	AGRIPPA NAVSOUTH
Topping, James Russell,	LT(FTC)	E	AE(L)	02.09.99	ES AIR BRISTOL
Torbet, Linda, MEng,	SLT(IC)	E	AE	01.01.01	DARTMOUTH BRNC
Torney, Colin James,	LT(FTC)	E	MESM	02.09.99	NEPTUNE NT

Torvell, Matthew David Bingham, BSc, psc,	LT CDR(FTC)	E	WE	01.08.89	DRAKE CBP(DLO)
Tothill, Nicholas Michael, MSc,	CDR(FTC)	S		30.06.00	UKMARBATSTAFF
Tothill, Rachel Charlotte, MA,	LT CDR(FTC)	S		01.06.00	NELSON
Totten, Philip Mark,	CAPT RM(CC)	-		01.09.00	CTCRM
Tottenham, Timothy,	2LT(IC)	-		01.09.98	CTCRM LYMPSTONE
Tough, Iain Shand, MEng,	SLT(IC)	E	WESM	01.09.00	NEWCASTLE
Tougher, Raymond,	LT CDR(FTC)	E	AE(L)	01.10.93	ES AIR MASU
Towell, Peter James,	LT CDR(FTC)	E	ME	01.07.01	ARK ROYAL
Towler, Alison, BSc,	LT CDR(FTC)	S	BAR	14.12.97	NBC PORTSMOUTH
Towler, Perrin James Bryher, BSc, pce,	LT CDR(FTC)	X	PWO(A)	01.06.94	COMAMPHIBFOR
Towns, Andrew Richard, BSc,	LT(IC)	X	FC	01.01.99	NEWCASTLE
Townsend, David John, BEng,	LT(FTC)	E	WE	01.03.96	MWS COLLINGWOOD
Townsend, Graham Peter,	LT(CC)	X	O	01.05.94	820 SQN
Townshend, Jeremy John, BSc, MBA, (Act Cdr)	LT CDR(FTC)	X	TMSM	03.04.92	FLEET HQ PORTS
Toy, Malcolm John, BEng, CEng, MRAeS,	CDR(FTC)	E	AE	30.06.98	RNAS YEOVILTON
Tozer, Colin Vinson, (Act Cdr)	LT CDR(FTC)	X	AAWO	01.10.88	NMA PORTSMOUTH
Tracey, Alan David, BEng,	LT(FTC)	E	AE	01.05.97	ES AIR BRISTOL
Tracey, Wayne Sean, BSc,	LT(IC)	X	O U/T	01.05.02	702 SQN HERON
Trasler, Mark Farnham, MSc,	LT CDR(FTC)	MS	(LT)	01.10.00	MOD (LONDON)
Trathen, Neil Charles, BSc, pce,	LT CDR(FTC)	X	PWO(N)	01.02.92	FOST DPORT SHORE
Treanor, Martin Andrew, BSc, psc,	CDR(FTC)	E	AE	31.12.99	HARRIER IPT
Tredray, Thomas Patrick, BA,	LT CDR(FTC)	X	PWO(A)	01.02.01	CARDIFF
Tregale, Jamie, BSc,	SLT(IC)	X		01.01.01	DARTMOUTH BRNC
Tregaskis, Nicola Suzanne, BA, n,	LT(IC)	X		01.11.95	MWS DRYAD
Tregunna, Gary Andrew, SM,	LT(FTC)	X	SM	08.08.95	RNU ST MAWGAN
Treharne, Mark Adrian, BEng,	LT(CC)	E	MESM	01.08.00	SULTAN
Tremelling, Fiona Marianne, BSc,	LT(IC)	S		01.12.97	2SL/CNH
Tremelling, Paul Nicholas, BEng,	LT(CC)	X	P	07.07.98	800 SQN
Trent, Thomas, BEng,	SLT(IC)	X		01.09.00	DARTMOUTH BRNC
Tretton, Joseph Edward, BSc,	SLT(IC)	X		01.01.01	DARTMOUTH BRNC
Trevithick, Andrew Richard, BSc, MA,	CDR(FTC)	X	METOC	31.12.93	FLEET HQ PORTS 2
Trevor, Mark Gerard, pce, psc(j),	CDR(FTC)	X	PWO(C)	31.12.98	MOD (LONDON)
Trewhella, Graham Gilbey, BSc, psc,	LT CDR(FTC)	E	TM	01.05.91	2SL/CNH FOTR
Trewinnard, Robin Michael, BEng,	SLT(IC)	E	AE	01.09.99	SULTAN
Tribe, Jeremy David, BSc,	LT(IC)	X	P	16.10.87	LYNX OEU
Trinder, Stephen John,	LT(FTC)	S	CA	30.01.96	MOD (BATH)
Tritschler, Edwin Lionel, BEng, BTech, MA, CEng, MRAeS, psc(j),	LT CDR(FTC)	E	AE	01.10.98	HARRIER IPT
Trotman, Stephen Peter, IEng, MIIE,	SLT(IC)	E	WESM	01.01.00	RALEIGH
Trott, Craig Michael James, BEng,	LT(CC)	X	P	01.02.93	845 SQN
Trott, Edward Alan, BEng,	LT(FTC)	E	AE	01.12.94	CV(F) IPT
Trott, Peter Alan, HNC, MSc, AMIEE,	LT CDR(FTC)	E	WE	19.05.83	NELSON
Trotter, Steven, MSc, CEng, MIMarEST,	LT CDR(FTC)	E	ME	01.12.87	DRAKE SFM
Trubshaw, Christopher, pcea,	LT(FTC)	X	P	02.10.93	820 SQN
Trueman, Brian David,	LT(CC)	E	AE	01.05.00	DARTMOUTH BRNC
Trump, Nigel William,	LT CDR(FTC)	S		16.01.98	MOD (LONDON)
Trundle, David Jonathan William,	LT CDR(FTC)	S	SM	01.01.95	FOST CSST SEA
Trundle, Nicholas Reginald Edward, pce, pcea, psc(j),	CDR(FTC)	X	O	31.12.98	PJHQ
Tucker, Kevin Michael, (Act Lt Cdr)	LT(CC)	S		01.08.91	COMATG SEA
Tucker, Simon James William, BA,	LT RM(IC)	-		01.09.00	40 CDO RM
Tudor-Thomas, Richard James, BSc,	LT(CC)	X		01.03.98	RNAS YEOVILTON
Tuffin, Michael Graham,	SLT(IC)	X		01.01.02	DULVERTON
Tuhey, James Jonathan George,	MID(UCE)(IC)	E	WE	01.09.00	DARTMOUTH BRNC
Tulley, James Robert, BSc,	CDR(FTC)	S		31.12.99	2SL/CNH
Tulloch, Frederik Martin, BSc, CEng, MIEE,	LT CDR(FTC)	E	WE	01.04.93	WSA BRISTOL
Tulloch, Stuart William,	CAPT RM(FTC)	-	SO(LE)	01.01.97	UKLFCSG RM
Tumelty, Gerwyn Charles, BEng, MSc, AMIMechE,	LT(CC)	E	ME	01.11.97	BRNC RNSU SOTON
Tumilty, Kevin,	SLT(IC)	E	WE	01.01.01	MWS COLLINGWOOD
Tupman, Keith Campbell,	MAJ(FTC)	-	SO(LE)	01.10.99	UKLFCSG RM
Tuppen, Russell Mark, pce, pcea, psc,	CDR(FTC)	X	O	31.12.99	SACLANT USA
Tupper, Robert William,	LT CDR(FTC)	S	SM	01.10.98	NEPTUNE DLO
Turberville, Christopher Thomas Leslie, BA,	SLT(IC)	S		01.01.01	DARTMOUTH BRNC

Name	Rank	Branch	Spec	Seniority	Where Serving
Turle, Paul James, IEng, MIIE, ... LT(FTC)	E	ME	13.06.97	SCOTT
Turnbull, Graham David, pce, ... CDR(FTC)	X	H CH	30.06.02	JSCSC
Turnbull, Nicholas Robin, BDS, MSc, ... SGLTCDR(D)(MCC) FDS RCSEdin, MOrth	-		02.01.97	MODHUPORTSMOUTH
Turnbull, Paul Sands, MB, BS, AFOM, ... SURG CDR(FCC)	-	GMPP	30.06.01	NEPTUNE DLO
Turnbull, Simon Jonathan Lawson, MA, MNI, pce, psc(j), ... CDR(FTC)	X	PWO(U)	30.06.02	MOD (LONDON)
Turner, Allan James, ... LT(FTC)	E	ME	01.04.01	FEARLESS
Turner, Antony Richard, BA, ... CAPT RM(FTC)	-		01.09.00	RM POOLE
Turner, David James, LLB, PGDip, ... LT(FTC)	S		01.04.00	SCEPTRE
Turner, David Neil, ... LT(CC)	X	P	01.06.95	RAF SHAWBURY
Turner, David, pce, ... LT CDR(FTC)	X	MCD	03.06.91	FOST MPV(SEA)
Turner, Derek Bayard, MBE, BSc, ARICS, pce, ... CDR(FTC)	X	H CH	30.06.02	MWS DRYAD
Turner, Duncan Laurence, ... MID(UCE)(IC)	E	WE	01.01.01	WSA/CAPT MCTA
Turner, Gayl, ... LT(SCC)	Q		25.10.00	RCDM
Turner, Henry Charles James, BSc, ... CAPT RM(IC)	-		01.09.00	RMR LONDON
Turner, Ian, OBE, BSc, psc, ... CAPT(FTC)	X	H CH	30.06.02	IMS BRUSSELS
Turner, Jennifer Claire Belinda, BDS, BSc, ... SG LT(D)(SCC)	-		24.09.00	NELSON
Turner, Jonathan Stephen, BA, ... LT(CC)	X	O U/T	01.01.01	702 SQN HERON
Turner, Joseph Seymour Hume, MA, ... LT CDR(FTC)	S	BAR	01.04.99	NORFOLK
Turner, Kerry Ann, BEng, PGDip, ... LT CDR(CC)	X	METOC	01.10.01	FLEET HQ NWD
Turner, Matthew, BEng, ... SLT(IC)	E	ME	01.01.01	DARTMOUTH BRNC
Turner, Neil, ... SLT(IC)	E	AE	01.05.00	SULTAN
Turner, Robert Francis, BSc, ... LT CDR(FTC)	S	(W)	01.10.00	2SL/CNH
Turner, Shaun Mark, jsdc, pce, pce(sm), ... CDR(FTC)	X	SM	30.06.90	DRAKE DPL
Turner, Simon Alexander, BSc, ... CAPT RM(FTC)	-		01.09.96	COMAMPHIBFOR
Turner, Stephen Edward, pce, ... CDR(FTC)	X	PWO(U)	31.12.93	NMA GOSPORT
Turner, Vicki Mary, ... MID(UCE)(IC)	E	ME	01.09.00	DARTMOUTH BRNC
Turton, Trevor Martyn Howard, MBE, MA, psc(m), ... LT CDR(FTC)	S		16.11.79	DLO/DGDEF LOG SP
Tutchings, Andrew, ... LT(FTC)	X	PT	01.04.01	TEMERAIRE
Tweed, Christopher James, BSc, MDA, ... LT(IC)	E	WE	01.02.89	2SL/CNH
Twigg, Katherine Louise, MSc, ... LT(IC)	X	HM	01.04.99	RFANSU
Twigg, Neil Robert, BEng, ... LT(IC)	X	P U/T	01.09.01	RNAS CULDROSE
Twine, John Harold, MA, psc(j), ... LT CDR(FTC)	E	TM	01.09.99	FLEET HQ PORTS
Twiselton, Matthew James, ... SLT(IC)	E	WESM	01.05.00	DARTMOUTH BRNC
Twist, David Charles, ... LT CDR(FTC)	S	(W)	01.10.99	NORFOLK
Twist, Martin Thomas, BSc, ... MAJ(FTC)	-		01.09.01	NEPTUNE
Twitchen, Richard Christopher, pce, psc, psc(m), ... CAPT(FTC)	X	AAWO	30.06.99	MWC SOUTHWICK
Tyack, Terence James, ... LT CDR(FTC)	X	P	01.10.98	JHCHQ
Tyce, David John, (Act Maj) .... CAPT RM(FTC)	-	SO(LE)	01.01.96	CTCRM
Tyler, Jeremy Charles, ... LT(FTC)	X	FC	01.07.96	EXCHANGE FRANCE
Tyler, Peter Leslie, ... LT CDR(FTC)	S		10.07.93	ILLUSTRIOUS
Tyrrell, Richard Kim, ... MAJ(FTC)	-	LC	01.09.86	FLEET HQ PORTS

U

Name	Rank	Branch	Spec	Seniority	Where Serving
Ubhi, Wayne Gurdial, BEng, MSc, ... LT(FTC)	E	ME	01.06.96	RM POOLE
Udensi, Ernest Andrew Anene Anderson, BEng, MSc, ... LT CDR(FTC) CEng, MIEE	E	WE	01.09.93	CARDIFF
Underwood, Andrew Gavin Howard, BSc, FNI, MNI, ... CDR(FTC) MCMI, pce, pcea,	X	O	31.12.91	AGRIPPA AFSOUTH
Underwood, Nicholas John, BSc, psc(a), ... MAJ(FTC)	-		01.09.88	RM CHIVENOR
Underwood, Paul John, ... CAPT RM(FTC)	-	SO(LE)	01.01.95	RM POOLE
Underwood, Richard Alexander Howard, BA, ... SLT(FTC)	S		01.06.99	CHATHAM
Unwin, Nicholas Richard Forbes, BA, ... LT(IC)	X		01.05.02	MWS DRYAD
Upright, Stephen William, BSc, pce, pce(sm), ... CDR(FTC)	X	SM	30.06.93	MOD (LONDON)
Upton, Iain David, BSc, CEng, MIEE, ... LT CDR(FTC)	E	WE	01.02.93	WSA BRISTOL
Urry, Simon Richard, BSc, ... CAPT RM(IC)	-		01.09.98	FLEET AV SUPPORT
Urwin, Stuart James, BA, ... LT(IC)	X		01.06.00	NEWCASTLE
Usborne, Andre Christopher, BSc, FCMI, psc, ... CDR(FTC)	E	WE	31.12.92	NMA PORTSMOUTH
Usborne, Christopher Martin, BSc, CEng, MIEE, ... CDR(FTC)	E	WE	30.06.94	WSA BRISTOL
Usher, Andrew Thomas, ... CAPT RM(IC)	-	SO(LE)	01.04.02	847 SQN
Usher, Brian, ... CAPT RM(IC)	-	SO(LE)	01.04.02	UKLFCSG RM
Ussher, Jeremy Howard David, BSc, ... LT(IC)	E	TM	01.05.00	DARTMOUTH BRNC

Name	Rank	Branch	Spec	Seniority	Where Serving
Utley, Michael Keith, n,	LT CDR(FTC)	X	PWO(A)	01.10.00	NEW IPT

V

Name	Rank	Branch	Spec	Seniority	Where Serving
Vale, Andrew, (Act Surg Lt)	SURG SLT(SCC)	-		17.07.01	DARTMOUTH BRNC
Vallance, Michael Stefan, BSc,	LT(CC)	X	P	01.05.98	847 SQN
Vamplew, David,	LT CDR(FTC)	E	AE(L)	01.10.91	SULTAN
Van Beek, Dirk, BSc, CEng, MIEE, psc,	CDR(FTC)	E	WE	30.06.96	FLEET HQ PORTS 2
Van Beek, Luke, BSc, MBA, psc, psc(m),	CAPT(FTC)	E	WE	31.12.98	FLEET CIS PORTS
van der Horst, Richard Evert, BSc, psc(j),	LT COL(IC)	-		31.12.00	MOD (LONDON)
Van Duin, Martin Ivar Alexander, BSc,	LT(IC)	X	P U/T	01.01.02	DHFS
Van-Den-Bergh, William Lionel,	LT CDR(FTC)	X	FC	01.10.96	899 SQN HERON
Vanderpump, David John, BEng, psc(j),	CDR(FTC)	E	ME	30.06.00	MOD (BATH)
Vandome, Andrew Michael, BSc, AMIEE, psc(j),	CDR(FTC)	E	WE	30.06.99	LOAN DSTL
Vardy, Kevin John,	SLT(IC)	E	WE	01.01.01	MWS COLLINGWOOD
Varley, Ian Guy, BEng, pcea,	LT CDR(FTC)	X	P	01.01.01	DHFS
Varley, Peter George Sidney, BSc,	LT(IC)	X		01.06.00	CHATHAM
Vartan, Mark Richard, BSc,	LT(FTC)	X	HM	01.10.94	ENDURANCE
Varty, Jason Alan, BSc,	LT(CC)	X	HM	01.10.98	NP 1016 IN SURV
Vaughan, David Michael, BA, MNI, pce, pce(sm), MRIN,	CDR(FTC)	X	SM	31.12.90	DARTMOUTH BRNC
Vaughan, James Richard, BEng,	SLT(IC)	E	ME U/T	01.09.00	LIVERPOOL
Veal, Alan Edward, BEng,	LT(FTC)	E	WE	01.08.95	MWS COLLINGWOOD
Veal, Dominic Joseph,	LT(IC)	X		01.05.02	MWS DRYAD
Venables, Adrian Nicholas, pce,	LT CDR(FTC)	X	PWO(C)	01.12.97	MWS DRYAD
Venables, Daniel Mark,	LT RM(IC)	-		01.09.00	45 CDO RM
Ventura, Don Clark,	LT CDR(FTC)	X	H CH	01.01.94	EXCHANGE USA
Verney, Kirsty Hilary, BDS, BSc,	SG LT(D)(SCC)	-		09.07.97	NELSON
Verney, Peter Scott, pce,	LT CDR(FTC)	X	PWO(A)	01.08.99	UKMARBATSTAFF
Vernon, Sean Paul, BEng,	LT(IC)	E	ME	01.05.02	SULTAN
Verrecchia, Joseph Romano,	MID(IC)	X		01.09.00	DARTMOUTH BRNC
Vessey, Lee Matthew,	MID(IC)	X		01.01.01	MWS DRYAD
Vickers, Carl Geoffrey,	LT(FTC)	E	WESM	02.09.99	NEPTUNE NT
Vickers, John, BEng, MSc,	LT CDR(FTC)	E	AE	01.11.98	EXCHANGE USA
Vickery, Ben Robert, BA,	LT(IC)	X		01.05.01	MONTROSE
Vickery, Kay Elisabeth,	LT(IC)	X		01.07.00	TYNE
Vickery, Robert James, IEng,	LT(FTC)	E	AE(M)	02.09.99	ES AIR BRISTOL
Vickery, Timothy Kenneth, BSc,	LT CDR(FTC)	X	PWO(U)	01.11.95	LOAN DSTL
Vierow, Michael Keith,	MID(NE)(IC)	X		01.05.00	MWS DRYAD
Vincent, Adrian, BEng,MPhil,CEng,MIMechE,MRAeS,(Act Lt Cdr)	LT(CC)	E	TM	01.09.90	SULTAN
Vincent, Daniel, BSc, PhD,	LT(CC)	E	TM	01.09.95	NELSON RNSETT
Vincent, Peter Hedley,	SLT(UCE)(FTC)	X		01.09.00	DARTMOUTH BRNC
Viney, Peter Michael,	LT(IC)	S	(W)	29.04.01	FLEET HQ PORTS
Visram, Adrian Haider, BA,	SLT(IC)	X		01.01.01	DARTMOUTH BRNC
Vitali, Robert Charles, pce,	LT CDR(FTC)	X	AAWO	01.08.97	SHETLAND
Vogel, Lanning David,	LT(FTC)	S	SM	01.06.97	MOD (LONDON)
Voigt, Matthew Adam,	SLT(IC)	X		01.09.00	DARTMOUTH BRNC
Voke, Christen Alexander, BSc,	LT(IC)	X		01.05.02	MWS DRYAD
Vollentine, Lucy,	LT(FTC)	S		01.04.98	MOD (LONDON)
Vorley, Simon William, BSc,	LT(CC)	X	P	15.06.96	815 FLT 234
Vosper, Iain Attrill, BA, psc(m), MPhil,	CDR(FTC)	S		30.06.85	MOD (BATH)
Vout, Debra Kim, (Act Lt)	SLT(IC)	X	C	01.10.99	RN GIBRALTAR
Vowles, Iain Robert,	MID(UCE)(IC)	E	WE	01.09.00	DARTMOUTH BRNC
Vowles, Mitchell John,	LT(FTC)	X	PR	24.07.97	OCLC BRISTOL
Voyce, John Edington, BEng, MSc,	LT(FTC)	E	ME	01.09.94	MOD (BATH)
Voysey, Zoe,	LT(IC)	X		01.10.00	MWS DRYAD

W

Name	Rank	Branch	Spec	Seniority	Where Serving
Waddington, Andrew Kennneth, BSc, pce,	LT CDR(FTC)	X	H CH	01.12.95	NMA PORTSMOUTH
Waddington, John, BSc,	CDR(FTC)	E	WESM	30.06.02	WSA BRISTOL
Wade, Andrew,	LT(IC)	MS		01.09.01	DRAKE CBP(DLO)
Wade, Claire Victoria, BChD,	SG LT(D)(SCC)	-		29.06.00	RN GIBRALTAR
Wade, Jonathan Mark Robertson, BA,	LT(IC)	X	P	01.02.99	820 SQN

Name	Rank	Branch	Spec	Seniority	Where Serving
Wade, Nicholas Charles, BSc, (Act Cdr)	LT CDR(FTC)	X	PWO(C)	01.01.90	IMS BRUSSELS
Wadge, Guy David Ernest, BSc,	LT(IC)	E	TM	08.05.01	SULTAN
Wadham, John, psc,	CDR(FTC)	E	ME	30.06.92	2SL/CNH FOTR
Wadsworth, Richard York, BEng,	LT(CC)	E	ME	01.03.99	NORFOLK
Wagstaff, Andrew,	LT(IC)	S		01.05.02	RICHMOND
Wagstaff, Neil, (Act Lt Cdr)	LT(FTC)	MS	(LT)	10.04.95	MOD (LONDON)
Wain, Robin Nicholas, jsdc, pcea, psc, ocds(Can), psc(j),	CDR(FTC)	X	O	31.12.95	SULTAN AIB
Wainhouse, Michael James, pce,	CDR(FTC)	X	PWO(A)	30.06.02	MWS DRYAD
Wainwright, Paul Albert,	LT CDR(FTC)	X	AAWO	16.03.85	MWS DRYAD
Waite, Christopher William, pce, psc, psc(m), (Commodore)	CAPT(FTC)	X	P	30.06.95	RNAS CULDROSE
Waite, Jeremy Nicholas,	CAPT RM(CC)	-		01.05.00	40 CDO RM
Waite, Matthew T, MA,	LT RM(IC)	-		01.09.00	45 CDO RM
Waite, Tobias Gerard, BSc,	LT(IC)	X		01.05.01	RAMSEY
Wakeford, Ian Frederick, MA, MEng, NDipM,	LT(FTC)	X	FC	01.02.98	899 SQN HERON
Wakeling, Jonathan Lee, MA PGCE,	CDR(FTC)	E	TM	31.12.94	NMA PORTSMOUTH
Wakely, Stephen Argent, MC,	MAJ(FTC)	-	SO(LE)	01.10.94	RM POOLE
Waldmeyer, Edward,	2LT(IC)	-		01.09.98	CTCRM LYMPSTONE
Wales, Benjamin David, BSc,	LT(FTC)	S	CMA	01.03.95	ARK ROYAL
Walker, Alasdair James, MB, ChB, FRCS,	SURG CDR(FCC)	-	(CGS)	30.06.91	MODHU DERRIFORD
Walker, Andrew John, BA,	MAJ(FTC)	-		01.05.01	PJHQ
Walker, Carl Stephen, GCIS, psc,	CDR(FTC)	S		30.06.95	EXCHANGE AUSTLIA
Walker, Clive Leslie,	CDR(FTC)	S		31.12.00	COMAMPHIBFOR
Walker, Daniel Haydn, BSc,	SLT(IC)	X	O U/T	01.01.01	DARTMOUTH BRNC
Walker, David Edward,	MID(NE)(IC)	X	O U/T	01.09.01	DARTMOUTH BRNC
Walker, Donald William Alexander, BA,	LT CDR(FTC)	S		01.10.01	GRAFTON
Walker, Ellis George,	LT CDR(FTC)	X	REG	01.10.00	NELSON
Walker, Gavin Stewart Logan,	MAJ(FTC)	-		01.09.90	MOD (LONDON)
Walker, George,	LT(FTC)	E	WE	02.09.99	WSA BRISTOL
Walker, Ian Michael, BEng,	SLT(IC)	E	WE U/T	01.01.00	BFFI
Walker, James John,	SLT(UCE)(IC)	X		01.09.00	DARTMOUTH BRNC
Walker, Jamie, BEng,	SLT(IC)	E	ME	01.01.00	SULTAN
Walker, Louise Linda, MB, BS,	SURG LTCDR(MCC)	-		04.09.99	NELSON (PAY)
Walker, Mark Christopher, pcea,	LT CDR(FTC)	X	P	01.10.94	JHCHQ
Walker, Mark Justin, BEng,	LT(FTC)	E	TM	01.01.91	CAPT IST STAFF
Walker, Martin Denis James, BA,	SLT(IC)	S		01.01.01	DARTMOUTH BRNC
Walker, Martin, BEng, MSc, AMIEE, psc(j),	CDR(FTC)	E	WE	30.06.00	FLEET HQ PORTS 2
Walker, Michael John, (Act Lt Cdr)	LT(FTC)	X	g	04.04.94	RALEIGH
Walker, Nicholas John, MSc, psc(j),	CDR(FTC)	E	MESM	30.06.00	MOD (BATH)
Walker, Nicholas Lee, pce,	LT CDR(FTC)	X	PWO(U)	01.02.93	FEARLESS
Walker, Nicholas MacLaren, BSc,	LT CDR(FTC)	X	P	01.01.00	899 SQN HERON
Walker, Nicholas Michael Cleveland,	SLT(CC)	X	P	01.04.00	RNAS YEOVILTON
Walker, Nigel Albert,	LT CDR(FTC)	S	CA	01.10.00	JSU NORTHWOOD
Walker, Patrick John, FCMI, MNI, pce, pce(sm),	CAPT(FTC)	X	SM	31.12.93	FWO FASLANE SEA
Walker, Peter Richard, BSc, MBA,	LT CDR(FTC)	E	IS	01.05.96	MWS COLLINGWOOD
Walker, Richard Eden, MA, psc,	LT COL(FTC)	-	C	31.12.97	MOD (LONDON)
Walker, Robbie Andrew, BEng, MSc, CEng, MIEE,	LT(IC)	E	IS	01.09.90	MWS COLLINGWOOD
Walker, Robert Dixon,	LT CDR(FTC)	E	WESM	01.10.97	NEW IPT
Walker, Robin Stuart,	LT(FTC)	X		19.09.00	MWS DRYAD
Walker, Stephen James, BEng,	SLT(IC)	E	WE	01.09.99	MWS COLLINGWOOD
Walker, Stephen Paul, SM, SM(n),	LT CDR(FTC)	X	SM	09.03.02	TIRELESS
Wall, Steven Nicholas, BSc,	LT(CC)	X		01.02.99	RNAS YEOVILTON
Wallace, Allan, BSc, PGDIPAN, pce,	CDR(FTC)	X	PWO(N)	30.06.01	MOD (LONDON)
Wallace, Anthony Robert, BEng,	LT(IC)	X		01.01.02	MWS DRYAD
Wallace, David James, BSc,	LT CDR(CC)	E	TM	01.10.98	RMB STONEHOUSE
Wallace, George William Alexander, AFC, BSc, pce, pcea, ocds(Can), osc,	CDR(FTC)	X	P	30.06.94	AGRIPPA AFSOUTH
Wallace, Kirsty Gayle, MA,	LT(FTC)	S		01.09.01	814 SQN
Wallace, Michael Rupert Barry, BA, jsdc, pce,	CDR(FTC)	X	PWO(U)	30.06.95	NMA PORTSMOUTH
Wallace, Richard Stuart,	CAPT RM(IC)	-		01.04.01	FPGRM
Wallace, Richard Stuart, BSc,	SLT(IC)	X		01.09.99	CATTISTOCK
Wallace, Ryan Patrick, BSc,	SLT(IC)	X		01.09.00	DARTMOUTH BRNC
Wallace, Scott Peter, BSc,	CAPT RM(IC)	-		01.09.01	CDO LOG REGT RM

Name	Rank	Branch	Spec	Seniority	Where Serving
Wallace, Simon Jonathan,	LT CDR(FTC)	X	PWO(A)	01.03.02	SHEFFIELD
Wallace, Stewart Andrew, BSc,	LT(FTC)	X	ATC	01.12.97	ARK ROYAL
Waller, Steven Adrian, pce(sm), SM,	LT CDR(FTC)	X	SM	01.03.99	JFHQ STAFF NWOOD
Walliker, Michael John Delane, BA, pce, pce(sm),	CDR(FTC)	X	SM	31.12.99	TIRELESS
Wallis, Adrian John, pce, pcea,	CDR(FTC)	X	O	30.06.02	MOD (LONDON)
Wallis, Jonathan Spencer,	LT(FTC)	X	P	01.08.92	EXCHANGE USA
Wallis, Lee Allan, MB, CHB, FRCS(ED)A&E, DiplMC RCSED,	SURG LTCDR(MCC)	-		01.08.99	NELSON (PAY)
Walls, Kevin Finlay,	MAJ(FTC)	-	MLDR	01.05.00	UKLFCSG RM
Walmsley, Elizabeth Ann, ACIS,	LT CDR(FTC)	S		08.02.96	DLO/DGDEF LOG SP
Walpole, Peter Kenneth, BSc, pce,	CAPT(FTC)	X	PWO(C)	31.12.98	SACLANT USA(SEA)
Walsh, Andrew Harwood, BEng,	LT(IC)	E		01.12.98	RNAS CULDROSE
Walsh, David,	LT(IC)	S		01.02.01	ST ALBANS
Walsh, Dennis Gerard,	LT CDR(FTC)	E	AE(L)	01.10.01	AH IPT
Walsh, Kevin Michael, BSc, n,	LT(FTC)	X		01.11.96	LEEDS CASTLE
Walsh, Mark Anthony,	LT CDR(FTC)	S	CA	21.06.98	FLEET HQ PORTS
Walton, Andrew Paul, (Act Lt Cdr)	LT(FTC)	MS	(AD)	04.04.96	RH HASLAR
Walton, Anthony Frederick, BSc, psc,	CDR(FTC)	E	ME	30.06.91	2SL/CNH
Walton, Christopher Paul, BEng, CEng, MIMarEST,	LT CDR(FTC)	E	MESM	01.04.01	DRAKE CBS
Walton, Colin Peter, BEng,	LT CDR(FTC)	E	WE	01.09.00	FEARLESS
Walton, David,	LT CDR(FTC)	X	PWO(U)	01.09.84	MWS DRYAD
Walton, George James,	SLT(IC)	X		01.05.00	OCEAN
Walton, Jonathan Charles, MSc, AMIEE,	LT CDR(FTC)	E	WE	01.12.90	WSA BRISTOL
Walton, Simon Phillip,	LT(FTC)	X	MW	01.10.97	FOSNNI OPS DLO
Walton, Stephen David,	LT(FTC)	X		01.04.97	ILLUSTRIOUS
Walton, Stephen Paul,	LT CDR(FTC)	E	AE(L)	01.10.01	ES AIR BRISTOL
Wappner, Gary Dean, BA,	LT(CC)	X	P	10.10.98	820 SQN
Warburton, Alison Mary,	SLT(SCC)	Q		26.02.99	RH HASLAR
Ward, Alexander James, MA,	SLT(IC)	S		01.09.99	RALEIGH
Ward, Andrew James,	LT(FTC)	X	MCD	01.06.95	FOST MPV(SEA)
Ward, Andrew James, BSc,	CAPT RM(IC)	-		01.09.00	CTCRM
Ward, Colin David,	CAPT RM(FTC)	-	SO(LE)	01.01.98	539 ASSLT SQN RM
Ward, David Steven,	LT CDR(FTC)	X	PT	01.10.97	DRAKE CBP(DLO)
Ward, Douglas John, BSc,	LT(FTC)	S		01.11.98	SPARTAN
Ward, Emma Jane,	LT(IC)	X	O	01.04.01	849 SQN B FLT
Ward, Francis Stanley, (Act Cdr)	LT CDR(FTC)	X	MCD	01.03.85	MOD (LONDON)
Ward, Jason George,	MAJ(FTC)	-		01.05.99	HQ NORTH
Ward, Joanne Erien, BSc,	LT(IC)	X		01.08.98	MWS DRYAD
Ward, John Emlyn, pce, pcea,	CDR(FTC)	X	O	31.12.94	CV(F) IPT
Ward, Kristian Nigel,	LT(CC)	X	P	13.02.98	801 SQN
Ward, Michelle Therese, MA,	LT(IC)	X		01.04.99	MONTROSE
Ward, Nicholas John,	CDR(FTC)	X	PWO(A)	01.10.94	BDS WASHINGTON
Ward, Nigel Anthony, BSc, IEng, MIIE,	LT(FTC)	E	WE	02.09.99	SFM PORTSMOUTH
Ward, Rees Graham John, CB, MA, MSc, CEng, FIEE, rcds, jsdc, gw, hcsc,	RADM	-	WE	27.04.99	HQ DCSA
Ward, Simon Ira, pce,	LT CDR(FTC)	X	AAWO	01.10.98	MOD (LONDON)
Ward, Simon,	LT(FTC)	X	P	01.09.97	815 FLT 207
Ward, Stephen David, BEng,	LT CDR(FTC)	E	ME	01.01.98	BULWARK
Ward, Timothy John, BEng, CEng, MIMarEST,	LT CDR(FTC)	E	MESM	11.01.99	SOVEREIGN
Warde, Nicholas Andrew,	LT(CC)	X	O	01.04.01	771 SQN
Warden, John Mitchell, BA, MSc, MBA, CEng, MinstP, C PHYS,	CDR(FTC)	E	TMSM	30.06.02	JSCSC
Wardle, Mark,	LT(FTC)	X	C	17.12.93	PJHQ
Ware, Andrew Travis, BA,	LT(IC)	X		01.05.02	MWS DRYAD
Wareham, Michael Paul, BEng, MSc,	CDR(FTC)	E	MESM	31.12.99	MOD (LONDON)
Waring, John Robert, BSc, PhD,	LT CDR(FTC)	E	TM	01.04.99	CFPS SHORE
Warlow, Mark Richard Norman, MBA,	LT CDR(FTC)	X	MCD	01.05.93	DA SOFIA
Warn, Christopher John, SM,	LT CDR(FTC)	X	SM	09.12.98	RALEIGH
Warneken, Andrew Ellery, BEng,	LT(FTC)	E	MESM	01.10.94	VICTORIOUS(PORT)
Warnett, Derek Louis, MSc, CEng, (Commodore) MIMarEST, jsdc,	CAPT(FTC)	E	MESM	30.06.94	NP BRISTOL
Warr, Richard Frank,	LT(FTC)	E	WESM	19.02.93	WSA BRISTOL

Name		Rank	Branch	Spec	Seniority	Where Serving
Warren, Brian Howard, OBE, BSc, pce,	CDR(FTC)	X	PWO(U)	30.06.96	FEARLESS
Warren, Martin Kenneth, MSc, MIMarEST, adp, HND,	LT CDR(CC)	E	IS	01.01.96	RMCS SHRIVENHAM
Warren, Richard Alan, BSc,	SLT(IC)	X	P U/T	01.09.00	DARTMOUTH BRNC
Warren, Thomas Stephen Evrall, DEH,	MAJ(FTC)	-	SO(LE)	01.10.95	FLEET HQ PORTS
Warrender, William Jonathan, pce,	LT CDR(FTC)	X	PWO(A)	01.11.99	CORNWALL
Warrington, Paul Thomas, BEng,	LT CDR(FTC)	E	MESM	01.01.99	FLEET HQ PORTS 2
Warwick, Philip David, pce, psc(j),	CDR(FTC)	X	PWO(U)	30.06.01	IRON DUKE
Washer, Nicholas Barry John, BSc, pce,	LT CDR(FTC)	X	PWO(C)	01.01.00	ILLUSTRIOUS
Wass, Martin James, BSc,	LT CDR(FTC)	X	PWO(A)	01.08.90	WSA/CAPT MCTA
Waterer, Richard Alan, OBE, MVO, LRAM, pdm,	LT COL(FTC)	BS		29.07.94	HQ BAND SERVICE
Waterfield, Simon Jon, AMNI,	LT(FTC)	X		01.06.94	PJHQ
Waterhouse, Phillip,	LT CDR(FTC)	S		01.10.00	EDINBURGH
Waterman, David Leslie,	LT(FTC)	E	ME	10.06.94	SULTAN
Waterman, John Henry, BSc, MA, CEng, MIMarE, psc,	CDR(FTC)	E	ME	31.12.97	MOD (BATH)
Waters, Christopher David, BSc, CEng, MIEE, MCMI, nadc,	CDR(FTC)	E	WESM	31.12.87	MOD (LONDON)
Waters, Nigel Roger, BSc,	LT CDR(FTC)	S	SM	16.04.96	MOD (BATH)
Watkins, Andrew Patrick Leonard, BSc,	CAPT RM(FTC)	-		01.05.97	45 CDO RM
Watkins, Colin Francis Frederick, pce, psc,	CDR(FTC)	X	O	31.12.89	2SL/CNH FOTR
Watkins, Kevin John, BEng,	LT(FTC)	E	ME	01.01.98	FEARLESS
Watkins, Timothy Crispin, BSc, pcea,	LT CDR(FTC)	X	P	01.10.00	846 SQN
Watson, Andrew Herbert, BEng,	LT(CC)	X	O	01.06.95	RNAS CULDROSE
Watson, Anthony Peter,	LT(FTC)	E	MESM	02.09.99	SULTAN
Watson, Bradley Lawrence, BSc,	LT(IC)	X	O	01.05.01	849 SQN HQ
Watson, Brian Robert,	CAPT RM(IC)	-	SO(LE)	01.01.02	815 FLT 212
Watson, Charles Robert, HNC,	LT(FTC)	E	WE	22.02.96	MCM3 SEA
Watson, Christopher Charles, BA, pce,	LT CDR(FTC)	X	PWO(A)	16.05.86	BDS WASHINGTON
Watson, Clive Raymond, BTech,	LT(FTC)	E	WE	24.02.95	NSE NORTHWOOD
Watson, Ian, n, BA,	LT(FTC)	X		01.03.95	SHETLAND
Watson, Patrick Halfdan, pce, psc,	CAPT(FTC)	X	PWO	30.06.96	NELSON
Watson, Peter Gerald Charles, BEng, CEng, MIMarEST,	LT CDR(FTC)	E	MESM	25.10.96	SUPERB
Watson, Philip Frank,	MAJ(FTC)	BS		01.10.00	RM BAND PTSMTH
Watson, Richard Douglas,	SLT(IC)	X		01.10.99	CATTISTOCK
Watson, Richard Ian, (Act Maj)	CAPT RM(FTC)	-	SO(LE)	01.01.98	RM POOLE
Watson, Richard John, SM,	LT CDR(FTC)	X	SM	01.08.89	MOD (LONDON)
Watson, Simon Christopher,	MID(UCE)(IC)	E	WE	01.09.00	DARTMOUTH BRNC
Watson, Stuart Benedict Cooper,	LT(FTC)	S	SM	23.07.98	DCSA RADIOHQ FMR
Watt, Anthony James Landon, pce,	LT CDR(FTC)	X	PWO(U)	01.11.99	COMATG SEA
Watt, Stuart, pce, (Act Cdr)	LT CDR(FTC)	X	AAWO	29.09.88	2SL/CNH FOTR
Watts, Alexandra Jane, BA,	LT(IC)	X		01.11.94	NELSON
Watts, Alun David,	CDR(FTC)	S	SM	30.06.02	MOD (BATH)
Watts, Andrew Peter, pcea,	LT CDR(FTC)	X	O	01.10.93	GANNET SAR FLT
Watts, David John, FCIPD, MILT, ACIS,	LT CDR(FTC)	S	SM	01.10.97	2SL/CNH
Watts, Graham Michael, BSc, CEng, FIMarEST, psc,	CDR(FTC)	E	ME	31.12.95	2SL/CNH FOTR
Watts, Jason Neil, BSc,	LT(CC)	X	P	01.02.96	GANNET SAR FLT
Watts, Margaret Dora,	LT CDR(MCC)	Q	CC	01.10.99	RH HASLAR
Watts, Raymond Frederick, BSc, psc,	CAPT(FTC)	E	WE	31.12.00	RMCS SHRIVENHAM
Watts, Richard Dennis, psc(m),	LT COL(FTC)	-	C	31.12.99	HQ 3 CDO BDE RM
Watts, Robert, pce(sm),	LT CDR(FTC)	X	SM	01.07.01	TRAFALGAR
Watts, Sandra Fay,	LT(CC)	W	S	01.12.95	NELSON
Watts, Zoe Abigail, BSc,	LT(CC)	X		01.01.99	UKMARBATSTAFF
Waugh, Peter John, MA, MB, BCh, MFOM, LRCP, LRCS, DipAvMed,	SURG CDR(FCC)	-	(CO/M)	30.06.90	FLEET AV SULTAN
Waugh, Richard Peter, BEng,	SLT(IC)	X	P U/T	01.01.01	DARTMOUTH BRNC
Way, Robert Andrew,	SLT(IC)	X		01.01.01	DARTMOUTH BRNC
Weale, John Stuart, pce, pce(sm),	CDR(FTC)	X	SM	30.06.99	FLEET HQ PORTS
Weall, Elizabeth Mary, ARRC, OStJ,	CDR(FCC)	Q	OTSPEC	31.12.99	RH HASLAR
Weare, Jonathan Bran, BA, MSc,	LT(FTC)	S		01.09.99	ARK ROYAL
Wearmouth, Paul William Anthony, IEng, MIIE,	CDR(FTC)	E	WE	01.10.95	DCSA RADIOHQ FMR
Weaver, Neil,	LT(FTC)	E	MESM	13.06.97	ASM IPT
Weaver, Simon, n,	LT(CC)	X	HM	01.10.99	FEARLESS
Weaver, Thomas Henry, BA,	SLT(IC)	X		01.01.00	MWS DRYAD
Webb, Andrew James, BSc, pce, (Act Cdr)	LT CDR(FTC)	X	PWO(C)	01.05.95	MOD (LONDON)

Name	Rank	Branch	Spec	Seniority	Where Serving
Webb, Christopher McDonald, pcea,	LT CDR(FTC)	X	O	01.10.96	RNAS CULDROSE
Webb, Daniel, BEng,	LT(IC)	E	ME	01.01.02	SULTAN
Webb, Eleanor Lucy, BA,	SLT(IC)	S		01.09.99	RALEIGH
Webb, John Paul,	SLT(IC)	X		01.10.99	SULTAN
Webb, Martin Robert, BSc,	LT(IC)	X		01.09.01	MWS RNHMS CULD
Webb, Matthew David, n,	LT(FTC)	X		01.06.97	EXPLOIT
Webber, Christopher John, BEng, FRMS,	LT CDR(FTC)	X	METOC	26.08.97	RMC OF SCIENCE
Webber, Joanne Patricia, BA,	LT(CC)	X	O	01.09.94	771 SQN
Webber, Kerry Jane,	LT(CC)	X		01.11.96	JARIC
Webber, Richard James, MB, BS,	SURG LTCDR(MCC)	-		01.02.01	1 ASSLT GP RM
Webber, Shaun Anthony, MA, psc(j),	MAJ(FTC)	-	PT	01.09.96	FPGRM
Webber, Steven John Anthony Maltravers, MA, FCIS,FCMA,	LT CDR(FTC)	S	CMA	01.02.94	MOD (BATH)
Webster, Andrew Philip, BA,	LT(CC)	X		01.11.94	SHEFFIELD
Webster, Graham, pce(sm),	CDR(FTC)	X	SM	31.12.89	JHQ NORTHEAST
Webster, Richard James, BSc,	LT(IC)	X	FC	01.12.98	YORK
Webster, Richard John, BA,	LT(IC)	S		01.12.97	CAPT IST STAFF
Webster, Timothy John Cook, psc(m),	LT COL(FTC)	-	C	30.06.00	CTCRM
Weedon, Grant Antony,	SLT(UCE)(FTC)	E	ME	01.09.00	DARTMOUTH BRNC
Weeks, Deborah Clare, BEd,	LT(IC)	S		01.03.99	DRAKE DPL
Weightman, Nicholas Ellison,	LT CDR(FTC)	X	P	01.10.01	RAF AWC
Weil, Daniel Gerard,	SLT(UCE)(IC)	E	AE	01.09.01	DARTMOUTH BRNC
Weir, James Robertson,	CAPT RM(IC)	-	SO(LE)	01.04.02	JSCSC
Weir, Scott Duncan, BEng,	LT CDR(FTC)	E	WESM	01.10.99	MOD CSSE USA
Welborn, Colin George, pce, psc(m),	CDR(FTC)	X	MCD	31.12.92	STANAVFORLANT
Welbourne, Alexander Richard,	MID(NE)(IC)	X		01.09.01	DARTMOUTH BRNC
Welburn, Ross Coates,	LT(FTC)	X	EW	04.04.96	EXCHANGE USA
Welburn, Roy Stuart, BSc,	CDR(FTC)	E	AE	31.12.00	ES AIR YEO
Welch, Alan,	LT(FTC)	MS	(AD)	20.09.99	HQ 3 CDO BDE RM
Welch, Andrew Timothy, FNI, pce, (Act Capt)	CDR(FTC)	X	AWO(A)	31.12.88	SA ISLAMABAD
Welch, Andrew, MBE,	LT CDR(FTC)	X	O	13.10.95	FOST SEA
Welch, David Alexander,	LT(FTC)	X	MCD	05.07.94	SDG PORTSMOUTH
Welch, James Fleming, MB, ChB, BMS,	SURG LT(SCC)	-		05.08.98	MODHU DERRIFORD
Welch, Jonathan, BSc, jsdc, pce, (Commodore)	CAPT(FTC)	X	PWO(U)	31.12.95	SACLANT USA
Welch, Katherine Alice,	LT(IC)	S		01.07.97	2SL/CNH FOTR
Welch, Michael Edward, BSc,	LT(IC)	S		13.04.01	824 SQN
Welford, Robert Clive, BEng,	LT CDR(FTC)	X	PWO(C)	01.02.99	NP 1061
Wellesley, Richard Charles Robert, OBE, MDA, pce, pcea,	CDR(FTC)	X	O	31.12.94	MOD (LONDON)
Wellington, Stuart, HNC, BEng,	LT CDR(FTC)	E	WE	01.02.98	FLEET HQ PORTS 2
Wells, Barrie Ivor,	LT(FTC)	X	C	03.06.98	FLEET CIS PORTS
Wells, Barry Charles, BSc,	LT(FTC)	E	WESM	18.02.94	ASM IPT
Wells, Jamie Duncan, BSc,	LT(IC)	X		01.09.01	BROCKLESBY
Wells, Justin Harrington,	LT(IC)	X	P	01.04.01	771 SQN
Wells, Martin Neville,	SLT(IC)	X	O U/T	01.01.01	DARTMOUTH BRNC
Wells, Michael Peter, BSc, PGCE,	LT(FTC)	S		01.03.97	NELSON
Wells, Rebecca Jane, MSc,	SLT(IC)	X		01.01.01	DARTMOUTH BRNC
Wells, Simon Peter,	LT(FTC)	S	(W)	01.04.01	MOD (BATH)
Welsh, Georgina Louise, BA,	LT(IC)	X		01.05.02	MWS DRYAD
Welsh, John, BSc,	LT(IC)	E	TM	15.10.95	MWS COLLINGWOOD
Welsh, Richard Michael Karl,	LT(CC)	E	AE	01.03.01	DARTMOUTH BRNC
Wenger, Nicholas Andrew, BDS, MFDS,RCS,	SGLTCDR(D)(MCC)	-		23.07.01	LOAN BRUNEI
Werrey-Easterbrook, Neil,	2LT(IC)	-		01.09.98	CTCRM LYMPSTONE
West, Andrew William,	LT CDR(FTC)	S	(W)	01.10.01	FLEET HQ PORTS 2
West, Anthony Bernard,	LT CDR(FTC)	X	REG	01.10.01	DRAKE CBP(CNH)
West, Darren Colin, BSc,	LT(CC)	X	MCD	01.12.95	CHIDDINGFOLD
West, Gillian Ann,	SLT(IC)	X	ATCU/T	01.05.00	RAF SHAWBURY
West, Graham George, BEng, CEng, MIMarEST,	LT CDR(FTC)	E	ME	06.06.99	RICHMOND
West, Michael Wallace, pce,	LT CDR(FTC)	X	AAWO	05.08.92	2SL/CNH
West, Nicholas Kingsley, BA,	LT(IC)	S		01.04.00	ARK ROYAL
West, Philip James, BA,	LT(CC)	X	O	16.05.93	849 SQN A FLT
West, Rory Julian, BSc, pcea,	LT(FTC)	X	O	01.06.94	771 SQN
West, Timothy Lewis,	MID(UCE)(IC)	S		01.09.00	DARTMOUTH BRNC
West, Sir Alan, (William John,) KCB, DSC, rcds, pce, psc, hcsc,	ADM	-	AWO(A)	30.11.00	FLEET HQ NWD

Name	Rank	Branch	Spec	Seniority	Where Serving
Westbrook, Jonathan Simon, MBE, pce(sm), pce,	CAPT(FTC)	X	SM	30.06.02	FOST CSST FSLN
Westerman, Richard, MB, CHB, (Act Surg Lt)	SURG SLT(SCC)	-		02.07.01	DARTMOUTH BRNC
Westlake, Simon Richard,	CAPT RM(FTC)	-	SO(LE)	01.01.98	42 CDO RM
Westley, Alexander James Rayner,	MID(UCE)(IC)	E	WESM	01.09.01	CAMPBELTOWN
Westley, David Richard,	LT CDR(FTC)	X	P	01.10.01	COMATG SEA
Westoby, Richard Malcolm,	MAJ(FTC)	-	LC	01.09.90	EXCHANGE AUSTLIA
Weston, Graham,	MID(NE)(IC)	X		01.09.01	DARTMOUTH BRNC
Weston, Helen Louise, BSc,	SLT(IC)	X		01.09.00	DARTMOUTH BRNC
Weston, Karl Nicholas Neville, BEng,	LT(IC)	X	O	01.08.99	815 FLT 218
Weston, Mark William, BDS, MSc, MFGDP(UK),	SGCAPT(D)(FCC)	-		30.06.02	DDA PLYMOUTH
Weston, Paul Andrew, pdm,	CAPT RM(FTC)	BS		01.01.99	FLEET HQ PORTS 2
Weston, Robert,	SLT(IC)	X	P U/T	01.01.00	DARTMOUTH BRNC
Westwood, Andrew James, BEng,	SLT(IC)	X	P U/T	01.09.99	RAF CRANWELL EFS
Westwood, Mark Robin Timothy, BEng, MSc, CEng, MIMarEST, MIMechE, MCGI, psc(j), Eur Ing,	LT CDR(FTC)	E	MESM	01.07.94	VANGUARD(PORT)
Westwood, Martin William, pce, pcea, psc, psc (j)	CAPT(FTC)	X	P	30.06.02	JSCSC
Westwood, Thomas Philip,	SLT(IC)	X		01.01.01	DARTMOUTH BRNC
Whale, Victoria Alice,	LT(IC)	S		01.10.01	FLEET HQ PORTS
Whalley, Richard James,	LT CDR(FTC)	S	CMA	01.04.01	WESTMINSTER
Whalley, Simon David, psc,	CDR(FTC)	S	SM	31.12.94	MOD (BATH)
Wharrie, Craig George, BEng,	LT(CC)	E	ME	01.12.00	NOTTINGHAM
Wharrie, Ewan Killen Balnave, BSc,	LT CDR(FTC)	E	TMSM	01.10.01	CSST RNSSS
Whatling, Kevin Micheal,	LT(FTC)	X	MW	09.01.01	CHIDDINGFOLD
Whatmough, David Edward, MA, CEng, MIMechE, jsdc,	CAPT(FTC)	E	ME	30.06.96	2SL/CNH
Wheadon, Philip Charles, BEng, HNC,	LT(CC)	E	TM	01.03.96	NELSON RNSETT
Wheal, Adrian Justin, BEng,	LT CDR(FTC)	E	MESM	01.09.00	SPARTAN
Wheatley, Ian James,	CHAPLAIN	CE		08.04.94	42 CDO RM
Wheatley, Nicola Sian, BSc,	SLT(IC)	X		01.01.00	OCEAN
Wheatley, Wendy Joy, BA, PGDip,	LT CDR(FTC)	X	METOC	04.10.97	RNAS CULDROSE
Wheaton, Bowden James Stewart,	LT CDR(CC)	X	O	01.10.98	750 SQN SEAHAWK
Wheeldon, Thomas Bertram,	LT(FTC)	E	ME(L)	15.02.91	LPD(R) IPT
Wheeler, Nicholas Jules, SM(n),	LT(FTC)	X	SM	01.10.95	VICTORIOUS(PORT)
Wheen, Charles Jefferies David,	SLT(IC)	X		01.01.01	DARTMOUTH BRNC
Whetter, Richard Scott, BSc,	LT(IC)	E	TM	14.05.00	SULTAN
Whetton, Julia Barbara Dawn,	LT CDR(FTC)	W	S	01.10.96	JSCSC
Whild, Douglas James,	LT(FTC)	X	PR	24.07.97	ALDERNEY
Whitaker, Hugh Rudkin, ADC, jsdc, (Commodore)	CAPT(FTC)	S		31.12.95	FLEET HQ PORTS
Whitaker, Michael John, BSc, CEng, MIMechE, MDA,	CDR(FTC)	E	AE	30.06.97	ES AIR WYTON
Whitaker, Rachel Elizabeth,	MID(UCE)(IC)	E	AE	01.09.00	DARTMOUTH BRNC
White, Andrew Raymond, BSc, CEng, MIEE,	CDR(FTC)	E	WESM	31.12.94	MOD (LONDON)
White, David John, BSc,	LT(IC)	X	P	01.03.98	849 SQN HQ
White, David Simon Haydon, OBE, FRGS, FRIN, MNI, rcds, jsdc, pce(sm),	CAPT(FTC)	X	PWO(N)	31.12.97	FWO DEVPT SEA
White, Douglas,	SLT(IC)	E	WESM	01.01.01	MWS COLLINGWOOD
White, Haydn John,	MAJ(FTC)	-	LC	01.05.97	BDS WASHINGTON
White, Ian Frank, SM(n), SM,	LT CDR(FTC)	X	SM	01.03.02	RALEIGH
White, Jason Paul,	LT(CC)	X		01.02.01	HURWORTH
White, Jonathan Andrew Paul, pce(sm),	LT CDR(FTC)	X	SM	01.11.97	JSCSC
White, Jonathan Eric, BSc,	LT(FTC)	S		01.11.94	NEPTUNE DLO
White, Katharine Jane, BSc,	SLT(IC)	X	ATCU/T	01.01.01	DARTMOUTH BRNC
White, Kevin Frederick, BEng,	LT(FTC)	E	ME	01.07.97	MWS COLLINGWOOD
White, Mark William, BSc, MA, pce, psc,	CDR(FTC)	X	PWO(U)	31.12.98	PJHQ
White, Martin Eugene,	CDR(FTC)	X	ATC	01.10.98	SHAPE BELGIUM
White, Melvyn Andrew, MBE, BEM,	CDR(FTC)	MS	(RGN)	31.12.99	DEF MED TRG CTR
White, Paul Donald, BSc,	SLT(IC)	X	P U/T	01.05.00	DARTMOUTH BRNC
White, Peter, (Act Cdr)	LT CDR(FTC)	X	PWO(A)	01.02.87	2SL/CNH FOTR
White, Philip Alan, MSc, CEng, FIMarEST,	LT CDR(FTC)	E	MESM	16.02.92	MOD (LONDON)
White, Robert Fredrick,	LT CDR(FTC)	E	WE	01.10.97	MWS COLLINGWOOD
White, Robert Leonard,	LT(FTC)	E	AE(L)	14.10.94	FLEET AV VL
White, Sarah Michelle, MBE, n,	LT(IC)	X		01.02.98	EXCHANGE FRANCE
White, Simon Henry Wilmot, BA,	LT(CC)	X	P	16.06.93	EXCHANGE RAF UK
White, Stephen James,	LT(FTC)	X	C	09.01.01	CHATHAM

Name	Rank	Branch	Spec	Seniority	Where Serving
White, Stephen Noel, BA,	CDR(FTC)	S		31.12.97	MOD (LONDON)
White, Stephen Paul, IEng, MIIE, (Act Lt Cdr)	LT(FTC)	E	WESM	10.06.88	JSSU OAKLEY
White, Stephen, BSc,	LT(IC)	E	IS	01.01.00	WSA BRISTOL
White, Steven, BSc,	SLT(IC)	X		01.05.00	CUMBERLAND
Whitehall, Sally, BSc,	LT(IC)	X		01.02.00	ANGLESEY
Whitehead, Darryl, pcea,	LT CDR(FTC)	X	P	01.10.92	771 SQN
Whitehead, Peter James,	LT(CC)	X	O	01.12.98	849 SQN HQ
Whitehead, Steven John, BEng,	LT CDR(FTC)	E	AE	01.03.00	JF HARROLE OFF
Whitehead, Tom, BSc,	SLT(IC)	X	P U/T	01.01.01	DARTMOUTH BRNC
Whitehorn, Iain James, BSc, CEng, MIMarEST,	CDR(FTC)	E	MESM	30.06.94	SACLANT USA
Whitehouse, David Spencer, SM,	LT(IC)	X	SM	01.04.00	SUPERB
Whitehouse, Dominic Patrick, MB, ChB, MSc, DCH, DTM&H, MRCP, AFOM,	SURG LTCDR(SCC)	-	(CM)	01.05.92	NELSON (PAY)
Whitehouse, Mark Justin, BSc, MA, MEng, psc(j),	LT CDR(FTC)	E	WE	01.03.94	FLEET HQ PORTS 2
Whitehouse, Niall Robert,	LT(FTC)	E	P	01.12.96	846 SQN
Whitehouse, Simon Robert,	LT(FTC)	E	WE	01.04.01	EXETER
Whitelaw, David Andrew,	SLT(IC)	X		01.09.01	NP DNREAY
Whitelaw, Victoria Leigh, BSc,	LT(IC)	E	TM	01.09.00	MWS COLLINGWOOD
Whitfield, Joe Alexander,	LT(FTC)	X	P	16.06.91	848 SQN HERON
Whitfield, Kenneth David, BEng,	LT CDR(FTC)	E	AE	01.03.00	SULTAN
Whitfield, Philip Mark, BSc,	CAPT RM(FTC)	-	P U/T	01.09.97	847 SQN
Whitfield, Robert Matthew Patrick, BSc,	LT(FTC)	X	P	01.05.95	800 SQN
Whiting, Elizabeth Ann, MSc,	LT(CC)	E	IS	01.09.95	NMA PORTSMOUTH
Whitlam, John, pce,	LT CDR(FTC)	X	PWO(A)	01.10.00	MWS DRYAD
Whitley, Ian Derek Brake, n,	LT CDR(FTC)	X	PWO(C)	01.06.99	FOST SEA
Whitlum, Andrew Colin, BEng,	LT(CC)	X	P	16.08.96	815 FLT 226
Whitlum, Sarah, BSc, n,	LT(IC)	X		01.11.96	SOMERSET
Whitmarsh, Adam,	2LT(IC)	-		01.09.98	CTCRM LYMPSTONE
Whitson-Fay, Craig David,	LT(FTC)	X	O	15.02.01	849 SQN A FLT
Whittaker, Mark Adrian, BM, (Act Surg Cdr)	SURG LTCDR(FCC)	-	(CL)	01.08.97	RH HASLAR
Whittingham, Debra Jayne,	LT CDR(FTC)	W	X	01.10.98	EXCHANGE ARMY UK
Whitwell, Nicholas Shaun, n,	LT(CC)	X		01.07.99	CHARGER
Whitworth, Robert Maitland,	LT CDR(FTC)	X	PWO(U)	01.10.99	OCEAN
Whybourn, Lesley Ann, MB, ChB,	SURG LT(SCC)	-		28.11.97	RH HASLAR
Whyntie, Adrian, BSc, CEng, MIEE, jsdc,	CAPT(FTC)	E	WE	31.12.00	UKCEC IPT
Whyte, Iain Paul, BA, MSc,	LT CDR(FTC)	E	TM	01.04.01	NELSON RNSETT
Wick, Harry Mark Stephen,	LT(CC)	X		01.09.00	TRIUMPH
Wickett, Richard James, BEng,	SLT(IC)	E	ME	01.09.99	SULTAN
Wickham, Robert James, BEng,	LT(IC)	X		01.05.01	NOTTINGHAM
Wicking, Geoffrey Steven, BEng,	LT(FTC)	E	AE	01.05.94	LOAN JTEG BSC DN
Wielopolski, Mark Leszek Christopher Carpenter,	LT(IC)	X	P U/T	01.05.01	DHFS
Wiffin, Anthony Francis,	LT CDR(FTC)	E	AE(M)	01.10.97	RFANSU
Wightwick, Katherine Helen Torr, BA, BD,	LT(IC)	X		01.08.01	CARDIFF
Wilcocks, Philip Lawrence, DSC, ADC, BSc, (Commodore) AMRINA, pce, psc(a),	CAPT(FTC)	X	AAWO	30.06.95	MWS COLLINGWOOD
Wilcockson, Roy,	LT(CS)RM(IC)	-		07.05.99	DNR SWE 1
Wilcox, Christopher Raymond,	MID(NE)(IC)	X	O U/T	01.09.01	DARTMOUTH BRNC
Wilcox, Thomas Colin,	CAPT RM(IC)	-	SO(LE)	01.04.02	RAF SHAWBURY
Wild, Gareth, MB, BMS, CHB,	SURG LT(SCC)	-		01.08.01	CFLT MED(SEA)
Wild, Richard James, LLB,	LT(IC)	S		01.01.02	FOST CSST FSLN
Wildin, Andrew, BEng,	LT(FTC)	E	WE	01.04.97	MOD (BATH)
Wiles, Stephen John, MSc, CEng, MRAeS,	CDR(FTC)	E	AE	30.06.98	LOAN DARA
Wilkie, Neil, BDS,	SGLTCDR(D)(SCC)	-		11.06.93	CALEDONIA DLO
Wilkins, David Paul,	LT(IC)	X		01.05.01	TURBULENT
Wilkins, Richard Ronald, BEng,	LT(FTC)	E	MESM	01.06.92	VANGUARD(PORT)
Wilkins, Robert Lloyd, BEng,	SLT(IC)	E	MESM	01.05.00	DNR RCHQ SOUTH
Wilkinson, Andrew Charles,	LT(FTC)	E	WESM	09.01.01	VENGEANCE(PORT)
Wilkinson, Andrew John, MA,	LT CDR(FTC)	X		16.12.86	FLEET HQ NWD
Wilkinson, Antonio,	LT CDR(FTC)	E	AE(M)	01.10.91	FLEET AV VL
Wilkinson, David Henry, n,	LT CDR(FTC)	X	PWO(U)	01.06.00	NMA PORTSMOUTH
Wilkinson, Georgina,	LT(MCC)	Q	OTSPEC	06.10.97	RH HASLAR
Wilkinson, Jane,	LT(FTC)	X	REG	04.04.96	2SL/CNH

Name	Rank	Branch	Spec	Seniority	Where Serving
Wilkinson, John Richard,	SLT(IC)	X		01.01.01	DARTMOUTH BRNC
Wilkinson, Michael French,	LT(CC)	X	P	01.02.96	800 SQN
Wilkinson, Peter John, BA, pce, pce(sm), (Commodore)	CAPT(FTC)	X	SM	31.12.95	2SL/CNH
Wilkinson, Peter McConnell,	LT CDR(FTC)	X	P	01.10.96	EXCHANGE USA
Wilkinson, Richard Murray, BSc, PGCE, MDA, jsdc,	CAPT(FTC)	E	TM	30.06.00	SA BERLIN
Wilkinson, Robin Nicholas,	LT CDR(FTC)	X	P	01.10.98	750 SQN (HERON)
Wilkinson, Timothy Lindow, BA,	CHAPLAIN	SF		04.03.97	CDO LOG REGT RM
Will, Andrew Watt, MBE, BSc,	LT CDR(FTC)	E	WE	01.06.84	FOST CSST FSLN
Willett, Roger John, BA,	LT CDR(FTC)	X	METOC	04.01.81	FLEET HQ NWD
Williams, Andrew John, BEng,	LT CDR(FTC)	E	MESM	01.02.98	VENGEANCE(STBD)
Williams, Anthony Michael,	SLT(IC)	X		01.09.01	DARTMOUTH BRNC
Williams, Anthony Peter, DSC, MA, pce, psc(j),	CDR(FTC)	X	MCD	31.12.00	2SL/CNH
Williams, Anthony Stephen,	LT(FTC)	X	FC	01.09.98	RNAS YEOVILTON
Williams, Brett, MEng,	SLT(IC)	E	AE U/T	01.09.00	GRAFTON
Williams, Bruce Nicholas Bromley, BSc, pce, psc,	CAPT(FTC)	X	PWO(U)	30.06.01	MOD (LONDON)
Williams, Caroline Mary Alexandra, BA,	LT CDR(MCC)	Q	IC	01.10.98	RCDM
Williams, Cassandra Lyn, BEng,	SLT(IC)	E	AE	01.09.99	SULTAN
Williams, Colin Nicholas Owen, BSc,	LT CDR(FTC)	X	PWO(A)	01.06.01	NEWCASTLE
Williams, Daniel Leslie, BA,	LT(CC)	X	P	01.01.00	FLEET AV VALLEY
Williams, Darrell Anthony,	LT(FTC)	E	WE	13.06.86	MWS COLLINGWOOD
Williams, David Ian, pce,	LT CDR(FTC)	X	AAWO	29.05.92	MOD (LONDON)
Williams, David Spencer, BEng, pce, psc(j),	LT CDR(FTC)	X	PWO(U)	01.09.95	FOST SEA
Williams, David,	LT CDR(FTC)	S	SM	01.10.99	MANCHESTER
Williams, Geraint Michael Glyn, SM,	LT(FTC)	X	SM	01.10.99	TRIUMPH
Williams, James Phillip,	LT CDR(FTC)	X	PWO(A)	01.06.00	CUMBERLAND
Williams, James Robert, BSc,	LT(IC)	X	O	01.12.00	849 SQN HQ
Williams, Julian Llewelyn, BA, rcds, jsdc, (Commodore)	CAPT(FTC)	S		30.06.94	2SL/CNH FOTR
Williams, Linda Jean, BA,	LT(IC)	X		01.05.98	NEPTUNE
Williams, Malcolm Stephen, CBE, BA, pce, (Commodore)	CAPT(FTC)	X	PWO(N)	30.06.94	NMA PORTSMOUTH
Williams, Mark Adrian,	LT CDR(FTC)	X	O	01.10.00	702 SQN HERON
Williams, Mark Henry, MA, pce, pce(sm), psc(j),	CDR(FTC)	X	SM	31.12.98	MWS DRYAD
Williams, Mark Stuart, BSc,	LT CDR(FTC)	S		29.03.97	NMA PORTSMOUTH
Williams, Mark, BEng,	LT CDR(FTC)	E	MESM	01.06.01	FWO FASLANE
Williams, Martyn Jon, MA, CEng, MIEE,	CDR(FTC)	E	WESM	30.06.00	MOD (LONDON)
Williams, Matthew,	2LT(IC)	-		01.09.98	CTCRM LYMPSTONE
Williams, Nigel David Blackstone, BSc, jsdc, pce,	CDR(FTC)	X	PWO(U)	31.12.91	AGRIPPA NAVSOUTH
Williams, Nigel Lamplough, BSc, CEng, MIMarEST,	CAPT(FTC)	E	ME	30.06.00	NBC PORTSMOUTH
Williams, Oliver Charles Llewelyn,	MID(UCE)(IC)	X		01.09.01	CAMPBELTOWN
Williams, Paul Allan, BEng,	LT(IC)	E	ME	01.01.02	SULTAN
Williams, Paul Glynn, BA,	LT(IC)	X		01.05.01	INVERNESS
Williams, Peter Mark, BEng,	LT(CC)	E	TM	01.01.91	1 ASSLT GP RM
Williams, Peter,	2LT(IC)	-		01.09.98	CTCRM LYMPSTONE
Williams, Robert Evan, OBE, LLB,	CDR(FTC)	S	BAR	30.06.93	2SL/CNH
Williams, Robert John Stirling, n,	LT(CC)	X		01.09.96	MWS DRYAD
Williams, Roderick Charles, BSc,	LT CDR(FTC)	E	ME	01.10.89	2SL/CNH FOTR
Williams, Sian,	SURG SLT(SCC)	-		16.05.99	DARTMOUTH BRNC
Williams, Simon Paul, BSc, pce,	CDR(FTC)	X	PWO(C)	31.12.97	SHEFFIELD
Williams, Simon Thomas, BSc, pce, pce(sm),	CAPT(FTC)	X	SM	31.12.00	MOD (LONDON)
Williams, Stephen Wayne Leonard,	LT CDR(CC)	S		01.04.01	JHCHQ
Williams, Thomas George Edward, BA,	SLT(IC)	X		01.01.01	DARTMOUTH BRNC
Williams, Timothy Nicholas Edward, BSc, pce, pcea, psc,	CDR(FTC)	X	P	31.12.89	AGRIPPA NAVSOUTH
Williamson, Alexander Karl, MSc,	CAPT RM(FTC)	-		01.05.98	EXCHANGE ARMY UK
Williamson, Peter James,	SLT(IC)	X		01.07.00	BRECON
Williamson, Simon James, BA,	SLT(IC)	X		01.01.01	DARTMOUTH BRNC
Williamson, Stephen John, BSc,	LT(CC)	X	P	01.03.89	RAF CRANWELL EFS
Williamson, Tobias Justin Lubbock, MVO, BEng, , pce, pcea, psc(j)	CDR(FTC)	X	O	31.12.00	MOD (LONDON)
Willing, Nigel Phillip, BSc,	LT(CC)	X	P	16.08.93	815 FLT 200
Willis, Alistair James, MA, MCMI, MILT, psc(j),	LT CDR(FTC)	S		01.12.95	ALBION
Willis, Andrew Stephen,	LT(CC)	X		01.09.98	CORNWALL
Willis, Martyn Stephen,	LT CDR(FTC)	S	CA	02.05.95	DRAKE DPL
Willmett, Andrew Malcolm, BSc, pce, psc, (Commodore)	CAPT(FTC)	X	AWO(A)	31.12.93	2SL/CNH

Name	Rank	Branch	Spec	Seniority	Where Serving
Willmore, Simon,	MID(UCE)(IC)	E	WE	01.01.01	WSA/CAPT MCTA
Wills, John Robert, BSc, CEng, MIMarEST,	CAPT(FTC)	E	ME	31.12.97	NELSON
Wills, Michael Vincent,	MAJ(FTC)	-		01.09.89	CTCRM
Wills, Philip, BSc,	LT CDR(FTC)	X	O	01.01.01	YORK
Wills, Robert Hartingdon, BEng,	SLT(IC)	E	ME U/T	01.09.00	CUMBERLAND
Willson, Neil Julian, sq,	MAJ(FTC)	-		01.09.96	HQ ARRC
Wilman, David Mark, BA,	LT CDR(FTC)	S	BAR	01.10.01	2SL/CNH
Wilmott, Sarah Catherine, MB, ChB,	SURG LT(SCC)	-		01.08.01	MWS COLLINGWOOD
Wilshaw, Gary,	SLT(IC)	E	AE	01.05.00	SULTAN
Wilson, Adrian Clive, (Act Maj)	CAPT RM(FTC)	-	SO(LE)	01.01.97	FLEET HQ PORTS 2
Wilson, Alexander Charles, MA, psc, psc(j)o,	LT COL(FTC)	-	LC	31.12.95	LN BMATT SAFRICA
Wilson, Allan John, n,	LT(FTC)	X		01.08.97	BLAZER
Wilson, Andrew Stott,	LT(CC)	X	P	16.09.96	849 SQN A FLT
Wilson, Charles Dominick, OBE, BSc, jsdc, pce,	CDR(FTC)	X	MCD	30.06.95	MCM1 SEA
Wilson, Christopher Gordon Talbot, pce, pcea,	LT CDR(FTC)	X	P	01.08.85	ES AIR BRISTOL
Wilson, Christopher John, BEng, CEng, MIMarEST,	LT CDR(FTC)	E	MESM	01.12.96	VICTORIOUS(STBD)
Wilson, David Robert, pce, n,	LT CDR(FTC)	X	AAWO	01.05.00	FLEET HQ PORTS 2
Wilson, David Timothy,	LT CDR(FTC)	E	WE	01.10.98	STRS IPT
Wilson, David William Howard, psc(j),	MAJ(FTC)	-		25.04.96	EXCHANGE ARMY UK
Wilson, David, CBE, psc(m), hcsc,	MAJ GEN	-		22.11.99	PJHQ
Wilson, Gary Paul,	SLT(IC)	X		01.01.00	HURWORTH
Wilson, Geoffrey John,	LT(FTC)	X	REG	19.09.00	MCTC
Wilson, Graham John, MBE,	LT CDR(FTC)	X	MCD	01.10.01	FOST SEA
Wilson, Ian Peter, BA,	LT(IC)	X	P U/T	01.01.02	RNAS YEOVILTON
Wilson, James Andrew,	LT(FTC)	E	ME	15.06.95	SFM PORTSMOUTH
Wilson, James Robert, psc,	LT COL(FTC)	-	MLDR	30.06.87	FLEET HQ PORTS 2
Wilson, John, BEng,	LT(CC)	X	P	01.07.97	EXCHANGE ARMY UK
Wilson, Julian, BA,	CAPT RM(FTC)	-		01.09.98	45 CDO RM
Wilson, Kevin Paul, BSc, CEng, MIEE, MDA,	CDR(FTC)	E	WESM	31.12.96	HQ DCSA
Wilson, Marcus Alaric, gdas,	LT(CC)	X	O	16.07.87	LOAN JTEG BSC DN
Wilson, Michael George, BEng,	SLT(IC)	E	MESM	01.01.00	URNU NEWCASTLE
Wilson, Neil Andrew, BA,	SLT(IC)	X		01.05.00	CAMPBELTOWN
Wilson, Philip Anthony, MBE, psc,	LT COL(FTC)	-	HW	30.06.88	LN BMATT (CEE)
Wilson, Robert Paul, pcea,	LT CDR(FTC)	X	O	01.10.95	FLEET HQ PORTS 2
Wilson, Robert,	LT CDR(FTC)	X	PWO(A)	01.09.00	FEARLESS
Wilson, Robert, ARICS,	LT CDR(FTC)	X	H CH	01.07.83	LOAN HYDROG
Wilson, Simon Allistair,	SLT(IC)	X	P U/T	01.01.01	DARTMOUTH BRNC
Wilson, Stephen Gordon, MNI, pce, psc,	CDR(FTC)	X	AAWO	31.12.91	MWS DRYAD
Wilson, Stephen Richard, psc,	LT COL(FTC)	-		30.06.94	ALBION
Wilson-Chalon, Louis Michael, BSc, pcea,	LT CDR(FTC)	X	P	01.04.97	MWS DRYAD
Wiltcher, Ross Alexander,	LT CDR(FTC)	S		01.08.93	FLYING FOX
Wilton, Caroline Victoria,	SLT(IC)	X	O U/T	01.09.00	RNAS CULDROSE
Wiltshire, Graham John, MA, MSc, CEng, (Commodore)	CAPT(FTC)	E	WESM	31.12.93	BDLS AUSTRALIA
Hf, MIEE, nadc, psc,					
Winand, Francis Michael John, BA,	LT(IC)	X	SM	01.05.00	TORBAY
Winbolt, Neil, BEng,	LT(IC)	E	TM	01.04.00	MWS COLLINGWOOD
Winch, Emma Jane, BDS,	SGLTCDR(D)(MCC)	-		24.01.99	JSCSC
Windebank, Stephen John, pcea,	LT(FTC)	X	P	01.10.91	814 SQN
Window, Stephen Harvey,	LT CDR(FTC)	X	MCD	01.09.95	MWS DEF DIV SCHL
Windsar, Paul Andrew, BEng,	LT CDR(FTC)	E	WESM	27.11.98	VIGILANT(PORT)
Windsor, Mark, BSc, MA, MIMechE, psc,	CAPT(FTC)	X	METOC	31.12.00	MOD (LONDON)
Wingfield, Melissa Helen, BDS,	SGLTCDR(D)(SCC)	-		01.07.01	RNAS YEOVILTON
Wingfield, Michael James, BEng,	LT(CC)	X	O	16.07.94	849 SQN HQ
Winkle, Sean James, BA,	LT CDR(FTC)	E	TM	01.05.96	SULTAN
Winn, John Paul,	LT(CC)	X	HM	01.10.00	FWO DEVPT SEA
Winsor, James, BSc,	LT(IC)	X	SM	01.03.00	VICTORIOUS(STBD)
Winstanley, Keith, MBE, pce, hcsc,	CAPT(FTC)	X	PWO(N)	31.12.99	NMA PORTSMOUTH
Winstanley, Thomas John Horton,	MID(NE)(IC)	X		01.09.01	DARTMOUTH BRNC
Winter, Richard Jason, BEng, PGDip, adp,	LT CDR(FTC)	E	WE	01.08.01	MOD (LONDON)
Winter, Timothy McMahon, BEng, CEng, MIMarEST,	LT CDR(FTC)	E	ME	01.05.98	CHATHAM
Winterbon, Andrew Richard,	LT(IC)	X		01.05.01	NEWCASTLE
Wintle, Geoffrey Lawrence,	LT CDR(FTC)	S	SM	01.02.97	RMC OF SCIENCE

Name	Rank	Branch	Spec	Seniority	Where Serving
Wise, Graham John, BEng, MSc, CEng, MIEE,	CDR(FTC)	E	WE	30.06.02	JSCSC
Wise, Simon David, BSc, CEng, FCMI, MIEE, CDipAF,	CDR(FTC)	E	WE	31.12.96	HQ DCSA
Wiseman, George Richard,	CAPT RM(FTC)	-	SO(LE)	01.01.00	CTCRM
Wiseman, Ian Carl, n,	LT(FTC)	X		01.02.95	MWS DRYAD
Wiseman, Neil Christopher,	LT(CC)	X	O	16.06.96	815 FLT 226
Withers, James Warren, BEng, CEng, MIEE,	LT CDR(FTC)	E	WE	01.04.96	MOD (BATH)
Witt, Alister Kevin,	LT(IC)	MS		01.09.01	2SL/CNH
Witte, Richard Hugh, LLB,	LT(FTC)	X		01.12.97	EXETER
Witton, James William, pce,	LT CDR(FTC)	X	PWO(U)	01.06.93	MWS DRYAD
Witts, Christopher,	2LT(IC)	-		01.09.98	CTCRM LYMPSTONE
Woad, Jonathan Patrick Rhys, BSc,	SLT(IC)	X		01.09.99	INVERNESS
Wolfe, David Edward, pce, pcea, fsc,	CAPT(FTC)	X	O	30.06.02	FLEET HQ PORTS
Wolsey, Mark Andrew Ronald, BA, psc(m),	LT COL(FTC)	-		30.06.99	MOD (BATH)
Wombwell, John Frederick, MA, MSc, CGIA, AMIEE,	LT CDR(FTC)	E	WE	19.02.88	MOD (BATH)
Wood, Alexander, BMS, (Act Surg Lt)	SURG SLT(SCC)	-		11.07.01	DARTMOUTH BRNC
Wood, Andrew Graeme, BEng,	LT(CC)	E	AE	01.07.97	JF HARROLE OFF
Wood, Charles Andrew, MBE,	LT CDR(FTC)	X	PWO(U)	09.01.88	MOD (LONDON)
Wood, Christopher Richard,	LT(FTC)	X	P	01.01.97	820 SQN
Wood, Christopher Taylor, BEng,	LT(IC)	E	TM	01.01.00	SULTAN
Wood, Christopher,	SLT(IC)	X		01.01.02	MWS DRYAD
Wood, Craig, n,	LT CDR(FTC)	X		01.08.01	MWS DRYAD
Wood, Frank Douglas,	LT CDR(FTC)	X	AV	01.10.99	RNP TEAM
Wood, Graham Richard, BA,	LT(CC)	S		01.02.98	CHFHQ
Wood, Gregory, MB, BS, (Act Surg Cdr)	SURG LTCDR(MCC)	-	GMPP	01.08.94	NEPTUNE DLO
Wood, Iain Leslie, BA,	LT(IC)	X		01.01.99	MARLBOROUGH
Wood, Ian Derrick, IEng, AMIMarEST,	LT CDR(FTC)	E	ME	01.10.96	MOD (BATH)
Wood, Joanne Tamar, BA,	LT(IC)	X		01.01.02	LEEDS CASTLE
Wood, John Lindsay, MSc, MCGI, psc(j),	CDR(FTC)	E	ME	30.06.01	MOD (BATH)
Wood, Jonathan Richard,	SLT(UCE)(IC)	E	WE	01.09.00	DARTMOUTH BRNC
Wood, Joseph Albert,	LT(FTC)	X	PT	03.04.98	MWS COLLINGWOOD
Wood, Michael George, CBE, BSc, CEng, FIMechE, rcds, jsdc,	RADM	-	ME	09.03.99	MOD (BATH)
Wood, Michael Leslie, BSc, MPhil, n,	LT(FTC)	X		01.12.96	CAMPBELTOWN
Wood, Nicholas Robert,	LT(FTC)	X	tas	01.04.01	MWS DRYAD
Wood, Robert,	LT CDR(FTC)	S	BAR	01.03.98	FLEET HQ PORTS
Wood, Simon Andrew Hall, BEng,	LT(IC)	X	P	01.08.00	AACC MID WALLOP
Wood, Stephanie Jane,	LT(IC)	X		01.08.01	DUMBARTON CASTLE
Wood, Uvedale George Singleton,	LT CDR(FTC)	X	P	01.04.99	899 SQN HERON
Woodard, Jolyon Robert Alban, BA,	LT(IC)	X	P	01.11.92	847 SQN
Woodard, Neil Antony, BSc,	LT(CC)	S		01.04.96	2SL/CNH FOTR
Woodbridge, Graham Francis, MBE, psc,	LT CDR(FTC)	X	PWO(U)	01.11.82	MWS DRYAD
Woodbridge, Richard George, BEng,	LT(CC)	E	ME	01.08.92	ILLUSTRIOUS
Woodcock, Simon Jonathan, BSc, CEng, MIMechE, psc(j),	CDR(FTC)	E	ME	31.12.99	ARK ROYAL
Woodford, Geoffrey Ian, MBE, BEng,	LT CDR(FTC)	E	WESM	01.09.96	WSA BRISTOL
Woodham, Robert Henry, MSc, PGDip,	LT CDR(FTC)	X	METOC	01.03.99	FOST SEA
Wooding, Graham Allen,	LT(FTC)	E	WE	19.02.93	RHQ AFNORTH
Woodley, Stephen Leonard, BEng,	SLT(IC)	E		01.09.99	SULTAN
Woodman, Daniel Peter, BEng,	SLT(IC)	E	ME U/T	01.01.01	DARTMOUTH BRNC
Woodrow, Kevin, SM, (Act Lt Cdr)	LT(FTC)	X	SM	13.12.95	AGRIPPA NAVSOUTH
Woodruff, Anthony Desmond,	LT CDR(FTC)	X	PWO(U)	01.10.99	NMA GOSPORT
Woodruff, Dean Aaron, BEng, MSc,	LT CDR(FTC)	E	ME	01.12.99	PORTLAND
Woods, Jeremy Billing, pce,	LT CDR(FTC)	X	AAWO	01.07.97	BANGOR
Woods, Michael James Peter, BEng,	LT(IC)	E	WESM	01.09.01	CSST RNSSS
Woods, Roland Philip, AMIAM, pce,	CDR(FTC)	X	PWO(A)	31.12.98	MOD (LONDON)
Woods, Roland Steven, BDS,	SG LT(D)(SCC)	-		20.07.98	45 CDO RM
Woods, Timothy Christopher, MA,	LT CDR(FTC)	E	TMSM	01.02.01	FOST CSST FSLN
Woodward, Darroch John, BA, BSc,	LT CDR(FTC)	X	MCD	01.07.95	EXCHANGE CANADA
Wookey, Mark,	LT(CC)	X	O	01.02.96	702 SQN HERON
Woolfe, Kevin,	LT(IC)	E		01.05.02	815 SQN HQ
Woolhead, Andrew Lyndon, BA, n,	LT(FTC)	X	PWO(U)	01.10.94	NEWCASTLE
Woolhead, Craig Morton, BA,	LT(IC)	X		01.05.00	ALDERNEY
Woollcombe-Gosson, David James, pce,	LT CDR(FTC)	X	AAWO	01.06.97	MWS DRYAD
Wooller, Mark Adrian Hudson, BA,	LT CDR(FTC)	S	SM	01.10.01	ST ALBANS

Name	Rank	Branch	Spec	Seniority	Where Serving
Woolley, Martin James,	LT CDR(FTC)	X	MCD	01.01.93	EXCHANGE USA
Woollven, Andrew Howard, pce,	LT CDR(FTC)	X	PWO(U)	01.08.97	MWS DRYAD
Woollven, Christopher David, BSc,	LT(CC)	X	O	01.08.99	820 SQN
Woolsey, Kevin Edward Keith,	LT(CC)	X	ATC	16.05.95	RNAS YEOVILTON
Woosey, David Alan, BA,	SLT(IC)	S		01.09.00	DARTMOUTH BRNC
Workman, Rayner John,	SLT(IC)	X		01.09.00	DARTMOUTH BRNC
Worley, Thomas Frank, BA,	SLT(IC)	X		01.01.00	NBC PORTSMOUTH
Wormald, Robert Edward, MSc, CEng, FIMarEST, psc,	CDR(FTC)	E	MESM	31.12.92	DRAKE SFM
Worman, Robin, BSc,	LT CDR(CC)	X	P	01.10.98	848 SQN HERON
Wort, Roland Stephen, BA, BSc,	CHAPLAIN	SF		27.07.93	NELSON
Worthington, Jonathan Michael Francis, MA, psc(j),	LT CDR(FTC)	E	TM	01.05.96	2SL/CNH FOTR
Wotherspoon, Steven Robert, psc,	LT COL(FTC)	-		30.06.94	RMR MERSEYSIDE
Woznicki, Stanley James,	LT CDR(FTC)	X	AAWO	16.06.88	MWC SOUTHWICK
Wragg, Gareth Terence,	LT(CC)	X	SM	01.01.01	TRIUMPH
Wraith, Neil,	MAJ(FTC)	-	LC	01.09.00	COMATG SEA
Wray, Arthur Douglas,	LT CDR(FTC)	E	WESM	01.10.01	MOD (BATH)
Wrenn, Michael Reader William, FIIE, MIOSH, (Act Lt Cdr)	LT(FTC)	E	WE	18.02.94	NP 1066
Wrennall, Eric Paul,	LT(IC)	E	ME	29.04.01	CHATHAM
Wright, Bradley Lee, BEng, MSc, CEng, MIEE, gw,	LT CDR(FTC)	E	WE	01.06.99	DLO MCBU/DGMIPT
Wright, Daniel James, LLB, SM,	LT(CC)	X		01.12.98	SPLENDID
Wright, David Anthony,	LT(FTC)	X	MCD	29.07.94	EXCHANGE USA
Wright, David Ian, BEng, CEng, MIEE,	LT(FTC)	E	WE	01.09.96	WSA BRISTOL
Wright, Douglas,	SLT(IC)	E	AE	01.05.00	SULTAN
Wright, Geoffrey Neil, MBE, BSc,	CDR(FTC)	E	MESM	30.06.93	MOD (BATH)
Wright, John William Talbot, BA, pce, pcea, (Act Capt)	CDR(FTC)	X	O	30.06.87	IMS BRUSSELS
Wright, Michael John, MBE,	LT CDR(FTC)	X		01.09.85	LOAN SAUDI ARAB
Wright, Nicholas Peter, LVO, jsdc,	CAPT(FTC)	S		31.12.97	SACLANT USA
Wright, Nigel Seymour, BEng, MSc, CEng, MIMarEST,	LT CDR(FTC)	E	ME	01.02.99	FOST SEA
Wright, Stuart Hugh,	LT CDR(FTC)	S	BAR	16.07.97	2SL/CNH FOTR
Wright, Timothy Mark, BA,	LT(CC)	S		01.04.98	HQ 3 CDO BDE RM
Wright, Toby John, BSc,	LT(IC)	X	P U/T	01.01.01	RNAS CULDROSE
Wrighton, Christopher Russell, pce, psc,	LT CDR(FTC)	X	P	16.09.80	RNAS YEOVILTON
Wrightson, Hugh Mawson, BSc, MA, CEng, MIEE, psc(j),	CDR(FTC)	E	ME	31.12.97	MWS EXCELLENT
Wrigley, Bradley Stephen, ACMI,	LT(IC)	S		01.11.00	MOD (BATH)
Wrigley, Peter James,	LT CDR(FTC)	X		16.10.88	RHQ AFNORTH
Wroblewski, Jefferey Andre,	LT CDR(FTC)	E	MESM	31.10.01	SULTAN
Wunderle, Charles Albert,	CDR(FTC)	S	(W)	30.06.00	2SL/CNH
Wyatt, Christopher,	LT(FTC)	S	(S)	17.12.93	DRAKE DPL
Wyatt, David James, pce, NDipM,	LT CDR(FTC)	X	H CH	01.11.93	LOAN HYDROG
Wyatt, Julian Michael, BSc, CEng, FIMarEST, MIMechE, MDA	LT CDR(FTC)	E	MESM	01.10.90	2SL/CNH
Wyatt, Steven Patrick, BSc,	CDR(FTC)	E	WESM	31.12.95	DPA BRISTOL
Wycherley, Ian,	SLT(IC)	X	O U/T	01.01.01	DARTMOUTH BRNC
Wyld, Anthony Wallace,	LT(FTC)	E	WE	18.02.94	FOST SEA
Wylie, David Victor,	CHAPLAIN	CE		01.12.98	CTCRM
Wylie, Ian Charles Henfrey, BEng, MBA, AMIEE,	LT CDR(FTC)	E	WESM	01.11.00	NEPTUNE NT
Wylie, Robert, MB, Dip FFP, MRCGP, AFOM, CHB,	SURG LTCDR(FCC)	-	GMPP	22.11.90	RNAS CULDROSE
Wyness, Roger Simon,	LT(CC)	X	P	01.07.96	815 FLT 204
Wynn Jones, Iago, BA,	SLT(IC)	X	O U/T	01.05.99	750 SQN SEAHAWK
Wynn, Mathew Daren, BSc,	LT(IC)	X	O U/T	01.05.02	DARTMOUTH BRNC
Wynn, Simon Raymond, BSc, ME d, PGDip,	LT CDR(FTC)	X	METOC	01.09.97	MWS DRYAD
Wyper, James Robert, BSc, SM(n),	LT CDR(FTC)	X	SM	01.09.00	SCEPTRE

Y

Yardley, Andrew Philip,	LT CDR(FTC)	X	METOC	01.10.99	RNAS YEOVILTON
Yarham, Nigel Peter,	SLT(IC)	X		01.01.01	DARTMOUTH BRNC
Yarker, Daniel Lawrence, pce, NDipM,	LT CDR(FTC)	X	AAWO	01.10.97	GLASGOW
Yarnall, Nicholas John, MB, BCh, DObstRCOG, MRCGP,	SURG LTCDR(FCC)	-	GMPP	01.08.97	NELSON (PAY)
Yates, David Martin,	CHAPLAIN	RC		01.09.98	DARTMOUTH BRNC
Yates, Elizabeth Helen, MB, BS,	SURG LT(SCC)	-		01.08.01	FLEET AV SULTAN

Name	Rank	Branch	Spec	Seniority	Where Serving
Yates, Lauren Olivia, BA,	SLT(IC)	S		01.09.00	DARTMOUTH BRNC
Yates, Neal Peter, MBE, pce, pcea, psc,	LT CDR(FTC)	X	O	01.06.89	RNAS YEOVILTON
Yates, Stuart Edward, BSc, n,	LT(CC)	X		01.05.98	EXCHANGE USA
Yelland, Christopher Brian,	LT CDR(FTC)	X	O	01.10.01	815 FLT 212
Yeomans, Paul Andrew,	LT(CC)	X		01.09.93	PJHQ
York, Gideon Rufus James, BEng,	LT(FTC)	E	MESM	01.05.96	TRAFALGAR
Youldon, Louisa Jane, BSc,	LT(IC)	X		01.05.01	MWS RNHMS CULD
Young, Andrew, OBE, BSc, CEng, MIMechE,	CDR(FTC)	E	ME	31.12.90	WSA BRISTOL
Young, Angus, PGDIPAN, pce, n,	LT CDR(FTC)	X	PWO(N)	01.06.99	FOST MPV(SEA)
Young, Christopher John, BEd, HND,	LT(CC)	E	TM	18.06.92	MWS COLLINGWOOD
Young, Gavin Lee, pce,	LT CDR(FTC)	X	AAWO	01.01.98	SANDOWN
Young, Ian James, BSc, MIL, AMIEE, (Act Cdr)	LT CDR(FTC)	E	WE	16.12.80	NW IPT
Young, John Nicholas,	LT(FTC)	X	AV	24.07.97	ARK ROYAL
Young, Keith Hunter,	LT(FTC)	E	ME	23.02.90	RALEIGH
Young, Mark James,	LT(CC)	X	O	16.09.91	EXCHANGE BRAZIL
Young, Michael Stephen, MA, MSc, FCIPD, psc(j),	LT CDR(FTC)	E	TM	01.09.96	MWS COLLINGWOOD
Young, Nigel Alan, BSc,	LT(IC)	E	TM	01.01.96	MWS DRYAD
Young, Peter,	LT(FTC)	E	ME	02.05.00	DUMBARTON CASTLE
Young, Philip Charles, MB, BS, FRCA,	SURG CDR(FCC)	-	(CA)	31.12.99	RH HASLAR
Young, Rachel, BA, n,	LT(IC)	X		01.12.94	ARK ROYAL
Young, Robin,	LT CDR(FTC)	E	ME	01.10.00	MONTROSE
Young, Sally Helen, LLB,	SLT(IC)	X		01.01.01	DARTMOUTH BRNC
Young, Stephen Andrew, BEng,	LT CDR(FTC)	E	ME	01.02.00	CSST RNSSS
Young, Stephen William,	LT CDR(FTC)	S	SM	01.10.00	RALEIGH
Young, Stuart Sheldon, MEng, MSc, CEng, MIMechE, jsdc,	CDR(FTC)	E	ME	30.06.95	FLEET HQ PORTS
Youp, Allan Thomas, BSc, PGCE,	LT(CC)	E	TM	01.06.95	MWS DEF DIV SCHL
Yuill, Ian Alexander, BSc, CDipAF, adp,	CDR(FTC)	E	IS	01.10.96	2SL/CNH
Yule, Michael James, BA, n,	LT(CC)	X		01.08.95	FOST MPV(SEA)

Z

Zambellas, George Michael, DSC, BSc, pce, pcea, psc,hcsc,	CAPT(FTC)	X	P	30.06.99	FOST SEA
Zipfell, Adam James, BSc,	SLT(IC)	X	P U/T	01.09.99	RAF CRANWELL EFS

RFA OFFICERS

COMMODORE

P. J. LANNIN

COMMODORE (ENGINEERS)

M.D. NORFOLK

Captains

C.J. Fell
S.F. Hodgson psc
C.R. Knapp
D.M. Pitt
A.T. Roach
P.A. Taylor, OBE
J.P. Thompson, OBE
B.J. Waters, OBE
L.M. Coupland, OBE
N.A. Jones
J. Stones
D.J.M. Worthington

W.M. Walworth OBE
R.L. Williams
F. Brady
I.N. Pilling
R.A. Bliss
S.H. Cant
R.G. Ferris
J.P. Huxley
M.T. Jarvis
I.E. Johnson
J. Murchie
R. Robinson-Brown

R.C. Thornton
P.M. Farmer
D.I. Gough
R. H. Allan
R. Bennett
P.T. Hanton
T.J. Iles
S.P. Jones
D.P. Kehoe
P.S. Whyte
A.S. Swatridge

Captain (Engineers)

T. Adam
G.R. Axworthy
D.E. Bass
P.J. Beer, MBE
D.W. Birkett
R.J. Brewer
P.C.M. Daniels
A. Edworthy
I.W. Finlayson
I.E. Hall
K. Holder
R. Kirk
R.W. Langton

S.J. Mathews
M. Mission
D.W.G. Phasey
R. Settle
K. Smeaton
C.S. Smith
R.J. Smith
N.C. Springer
A.D. Wills
E.M. Quigley
G. T. Turner
K.R.C. Moore
A.C. Bowditch
J.E. Collins

I.M. Doolan-Phillip
A.J. Grant
B.S. Layson
J.J. Oakey
D.S.Simpson
D. Preston
I. Dunbar
P.I. Henney
A.G. Sinclair
C.L. Forrest
D.J. Moore
C.M. Brown
M.P. Cole

SENIORITY LIST

ADMIRALS OF THE FLEET

(This rank is now held in abeyance in peacetime (1996))

Edinburgh, *His Royal Highness The Prince* Philip, *Duke Of*, *KG*, *KT*, *OM*, *GBE*, *AC*, *QSO* .... 15 Jan 53

Hill-Norton, The Lord, *GCB* .... 12 Mar 71

Pollock, *Sir* Michael, (Patrick), *GCB*, *LVO*, *DSC*, *psc* .... 1 Mar 74

Ashmore, *Sir* Edward (Beckwith), *GCB*, *DSC*, *IRs*, *jssc*, *psc* .... 9 Feb 77

Leach, *Sir* Henry (Conyers), *GCB*, *DL*, *jssc*, *psc* .... 1 Dec 82

Oswald, *Sir* (John) Julian (Robertson), *GCB*, *rcds*, *psc* .... 2 Mar 93

Bathurst, *Sir* (David) Benjamin, *GCB*, *DL*, *rcds* .... 10 Jul 95

ADMIRALS

Slater, *Sir* Jock (John Cunningham Kirkwood), GCB, LVO, DL, rcds, pce .... 20 Jan 91
Former First Sea Lord (remains on the Active List)

Boyce, *Sir* Michael (Cecil) , *GCB*, *OBE*, *ADC*, *rcds*, *psc* .... 25 May 95
(CHIEF OF THE DEFENCE STAFF FEB 01)

Abbott, *Sir* Peter (Charles) *GBE, KCB, MA,rcds,pce* .... 3 Oct 95
Former Vice Chief of Defence Staff (remains on the Active List)

Essenhigh, *Sir* Nigel (Richard) , *GCB*, *ADC*, *rcds*, *pce*, *psc*, *hcsc* .... 11 Sep 98
Former First Sea Lord (remains on the Active List)

West, *Sir* Alan (William John) *KCB, DSC, rcds, pce, psc, hcsc* .... 30 Nov 00
(CHIEF OF NAVAL STAFF AND FIRST SEA LORD SEP 02)

Garnett, *Sir* Ian (David Graham), *KCB, psc,* .... 11 Sep 01
(CHIEF OF STAFF SUPREME HEADQUARTERS ALLIED POWERS EUROPE SEP 01)

Forbes, Ian Andrew, *CBE, rcds, pce, psc(a),* .... 1 Dec 01
(DEPUTY SUPREME ALLIED COMMANDER ATLANTIC JAN 02)

Band, *Sir* Jonathon , *KCB, BA, jsdc, pce, hcsc* .... 2 Aug 02
(COMMANDER IN CHIEF FLEET, COMMANDER IN CHIEF EAST ATLANTIC AND COMMANDER ALLIED NAVAL FORCES NORTH AUG 02)

VICE ADMIRALS

Haddacks, *Sir* Paul (Kenneth) , *KCB, rcds, pce, psc, hcsc* .... 24 Feb 97
(DIRECTOR OF INTERNATIONAL MILITARY STAFF MAR 01)

Blackham, *Sir* Jeremy (Joe) , *KCB, BA, rcds, pce, psc* .... 24 Jun 97
(DEPUTY CHIEF OF DEFENCE STAFF (EQUIPMENT CAPABILITY) SEP 99)

Spencer, *Sir* Peter , *KCB, ADC, MA, MSc, jsdc* .... 19 Jan 00
(SECOND SEA LORD AND COMMANDER IN CHIEF NAVAL HOME COMMAND JAN 00)

Dunt, Peter Arthur , *CB, rcds* .... 30 Apr 02
(CHIEF EXECUTIVE DEFENCE ESTATE AGENCY APR 02)

Stanhope, Mark , *OBE, MA, MNI, rcds, pce, pce(sm), psc, hcsc* .... 9 July 02
(DEPUTY COMMANDER IN CHIEF FLEET JULY 02)

REAR ADMIRALS

Lippiett, Richard John , *MBE, rcds, jsdc, pce, psc* .... 7 Jul 97
(COMMANDANT JOINT SERVICES COMMAND AND STAFF COLLEGE JAN 02)

Stevens, Robert Patrick , *CB, pce, pce(sm)* .... 4 Aug 98
(CHIEF OF STAFF TO COMMANDER ALLIED NAVAL FORCES SOUTHERN EUROPE JAN 02)

Wood, Michael George , *CBE, BSc, CEng, FIMechE, rcds, jsdc* .... 9 Mar 99
(DIRECTOR GENERAL DEFENCE LOGISTICS ORGANISATION (OPERATIONS & BUSINESS
DEVELOPMENT) OCT 01)

Ward, Rees Graham John , *MA, MSc, CEng, FIEE, rcds, jsdc, gw, hcsc* .... 27 Apr 99
(CHIEF EXECUTIVE DEFENCE COMMUNICATIONS SERVICES AGENCY JAN 02)

Meyer, Stephen Richard , *pce, psc, hcsc.* .... 1 Jul 99
(CHIEF OF STAFF, PERMANENT JOINT HEADQUARTERS MAY 01)

Backus, Alexander Kirkwood , *OBE, jsdc, pce* .... 7 Sep 99
(CHIEF OF STAFF(WARFARE) TO COMMANDER IN CHIEF FLEET FEB 02)

Burnell-Nugent, James Michael , *CBE, MA, jsdc, pce, pce(sm)* .... 6 Dec 99
(COMMANDER UNITED KINGDOM MARITIME FORCES AND COMMANDER ANTI SUBMARINE
WARFARE STRIKING FORCE MAY 01)

Guild, Nigel Charles Forbes , *BA, PhD, MIEE, AFIMA, jsdc* .... 6 Jan 00
(DEFENCE PROCUREMENT AGENCY EXECUTIVE DIRECTOR 4, CONTROLLER OF THE NAVY
MAR 00)

Dymock, Anthony Knox , *BA, pce, psc* .... 19 Jan 00
(DEPUTY COMMANDER STRIKE FORCE SOUTH JAN 00)

Reeve, Jonathon , *MA, CEng, MIEE, rcds, psc* .... 13 Mar 00
(DEPUTY CHIEF EXECUTIVE WARSHIP SUPPORT AGENCY DEC 00)

Anthony, Derek James , *MBE, jsdc, pce, pce(sm), hcsc* .... 8 Aug 00
(FLAG OFFICER SCOTLAND, NORTHERN ENGLAND AND NORTHERN IRELAND NOV 01)

Lockwood, Roger Graham , *BA, rcds, jsdc* .... 22 Aug 00
(CHIEF OF STAFF TO SECOND SEA LORD/COMMANDER IN CHIEF NAVAL HOME COMMAND
DIRECTOR GENERAL NAVAL PERSONNEL AUG 00)

Greenish, Philip Duncan , *BSc, CEng, MIEE, rcds, jsdc* .... 24 Nov 00
(CHIEF OF STAFF (SUPPORT) TO COMMANDER IN CHIEF FLEET FEB 02)

McLean, Rory Alistair Ian , *OBE, psc, hcsc* .... 9 Apr 01
(ASSISTANT CHIEF OF THE DEFENCE STAFF (PROGRAMMES) APR 01)

McClement, Timothy Pentreath , *OBE, jsdc, pce, pce(sm), hcsc* .... 23 Apr 01
(ASSISTANT CHIEF OF NAVAL STAFF APR 01)

Lidbetter, Scott, *pce,hcsc* .... 27 Jul 01
(AIR OFFICER COMMANDING 3 GROUP/FLAG OFFICER MARITIME AVIATION JUL 01)

Davies, Peter Roland, *CBE, MSc, CEng, FIEE, nadc, gw* .... 31 Jul 01
(CHIEF EXECUTIVE FLAG OFFICER TRAINING AND RECRUITING JUL 01)

Kilgour, Niall Stuart Roderick, *pce, pce(sm), psc* .... 18 Sep 01
(COMMANDER (OPERATIONS) TO COMMANDER IN CHIEF FLEET FEB 02)

Rapp, James Campsie, *pce, pcea, psc* .... 20 Nov 01
(FLAG OFFICER SEA TRAINING NOV 01)

Edleston, Hugh Anthony Harold Greswell, *MNI, AMBIM, jsdc, pce, hcsc* .... 1 Jan 02
(MILITARY ADVISOR TO THE HIGH REPRESENTATIVE IN BOSNIA AND HERZEGOVINA JAN 02)

Style, Charles Rodney, *MA, rds, pce, hcsc* .... 21 Jan 02
(CAPABILITY MANAGER STRATEGIC DEPLOYMENT JAN 02)

Kerr, Mark William Graham, *BA, pce, psc* .... 22 Jan 02
(NAVAL SECRETARY AND CHIEF EXECUTIVE NAVAL MANNING AGENCY JAN 02)

Kidner, Peter Jonathon, *BSc, CEng, FRAeS, psc, psc(m)* .... 2 April 02
(CHIEF EXECUTIVE DEFENCE MEDICAL EDUCATION AND TRAINING AGENCY APR 02)

SUBSTANTIVE COMMODORES

2002
X   Johnstone-Burt, C.A. .... 10 Jan
X   Morisetti, N. .... 26 Mar
E   Tibbitt, I.P.G. .... 15 Apr

E   Alabaster, M.B. .... 30 Apr
X   Snow, C.A. .... 15 May

MS Reed, F .... 12 Jun
X   Richards, A.D. .... 24 Jun

CAPTAINS

1991
X   Edwardes, G.H. .... 31 Dec
E   Harries, J.M.H. .... 31 Dec

1992
X   Rimington, J.A. .... 31 Dec

1993
X   Owen, N.R. .... 30 Jun
E   Cheadle, R.F. .... 30 Jun
X   Milnes, J.L. .... 31 Dec
X   Walker, P.J. .... 31 Dec
X   Massie-Taylor, C.G. .... 31 Dec
E   Goodall, S.R.J. .... 31 Dec
X   Hewitt, I.R. .... 31 Dec
X   Willmett, A.M. .... 31 Dec
E   Wiltshire, G.J. .... 31 Dec
X   Russell, D.J. .... 31 Dec

1994
X   Cosby, R.A.DE.S. .... 30 Jun
X   Cust, D.R. .... 30 Jun
E   Holmes, M.J. .... 30 Jun
X   Barton, T.J. .... 30 Jun
X   Williams, M.S. .... 30 Jun
X   Snelson, D.G. .... 30 Jun
E   Brokenshire, L.P. .... 30 Jun
E   Warnett, D.L. .... 30 Jun
S   Williams, J.L. .... 30 Jun
E   MacLean, D.J. .... 30 Jun
X   Somerville, A.J.D. .... 30 Jun
X   Boissier, R.P. .... 30 Jun
X   Johns, A.J. .... 31 Dec
E   Hurford, P.G. .... 31 Dec
X   Ainsley, R.S. .... 31 Dec
E   Spires, T.A. .... 31 Dec
E   Chittenden, T.C. .... 31 Dec
S   Preston-Jones, N.C. .... 31 Dec
E   Clark, A.I.H. .... 31 Dec
E   Finlayson, R.D. .... 31 Dec
X   Miller, A.J.G. .... 31 Dec

1995
X   Booth, M.D. .... 30 Jun
X   Bray, N.G.H. .... 30 Jun

E   Fitzgerald, M.P. .... 30 Jun
X   Waite, C.W. .... 30 Jun
X   Harris, N.H.L. .... 30 Jun
E   Raby, N.J.F. .... 30 Jun
S   Savage, N.D. .... 30 Jun
X   Clapp, R.J. .... 30 Jun
X   Auty, S.J. .... 30 Jun
E   Fairbairn, W.D.M. .... 30 Jun
X   Laurence, T.J.H. .... 30 Jun
X   Wilcocks, P.L. .... 30 Jun
E   Searle, E.F. .... 31 Dec
X   Manning, M.G.B. .... 31 Dec
X   Tighe, J.G.H. .... 31 Dec
S   Whitaker, H.R. .... 31 Dec
E   Kirkpatrick, J. .... 31 Dec
X   Batho, W.N.P. .... 31 Dec
X   Stevenson, C.B.H. .... 31 Dec
E   Dawson, E.W. .... 31 Dec
E   Richardson, I.J.W. .... 31 Dec
X   Welch, J. .... 31 Dec
X   Clayton, C.H.T. .... 31 Dec
S   Lane, M.G. .... 31 Dec
X   Cooke, D.J. .... 31 Dec
E   Melly, R.G. .... 31 Dec
X   Silcock, C.A.J. .... 31 Dec
E   Borley, K.J. .... 31 Dec
X   Wilkinson, P.J. .... 31 Dec

1996
E   Whatmough, D.E. .... 30 Jun
X   Fifield, D.J. .... 30 Jun
E   Eastley, B.R. .... 30 Jun
X   Watson, P.H. .... 30 Jun
X   Fanshawe, J.R. .... 30 Jun
X   Barritt, M.K. .... 30 Jun
E   Heselton, B.L. .... 30 Jun
X   Boyd, J.A. .... 30 Jun
X   Dickson, A.P. .... 30 Jun
S   Sinclair, A.H. .... 30 Jun
X   Massey, A.M. .... 30 Jun
X   Lambert, P. .... 30 Jun
W   Picton, A.M. .... 30 Jun
E   Latham, N.D. .... 30 Jun

S   Pennefather, W.J.R. .... 31 Dec
X   Daglish, H.B. .... 31 Dec
E   McFadyen, H. .... 31 Dec
X   Moodie, G.R. .... 31 Dec
X   Baxter, G.F. .... 31 Dec
S   Tatham, P.H. .... 31 Dec
X   Covington, W.M. .... 31 Dec
E   Jenkins, I.F. .... 31 Dec
E   Horsted, P.J. .... 31 Dec
X   Munns, C.R. .... 31 Dec
E   Palmer, R.A.N. .... 31 Dec
X   Mark, R.A. .... 31 Dec
X   Leaman, R.D. .... 31 Dec
E   Rankin, I.G. .... 31 Dec
X   Soar, T.A. .... 31 Dec

1997
X   Eberle, P.J.F. .... 30 Jun
X   Peach, C.C. .... 30 Jun
E   Jarvis, I.L. .... 30 Jun
X   Fergusson, D.C.M. .... 30 Jun
E   Kongialis, J.A. .... 30 Jun
S   Hemsworth, M.K. .... 30 Jun
X   Parry, C.J. .... 30 Jun
E   Potter, M.J. .... 30 Jun
X   Nance, A.R. .... 30 Jun
X   Gass, C.J. .... 30 Jun
E   Horrell, M.I. .... 30 Jun
X   Ibbotson, R.J. .... 30 Jun
S   Kimmons, M. .... 30 Jun
E   Bowker, M.A. .... 30 Jun
E   Henley, S.M. .... 30 Jun
X   Rix, A.J. .... 30 Jun
E   Mathews, A.D.H. .... 30 Jun
X   Goddard, I.K. .... 31 Dec
E   Wills, J.R. .... 31 Dec
E   Patrick, J. .... 31 Dec
E   Green, J.A. .... 31 Dec
S   Wright, N.P. .... 31 Dec
X   White, D.S.H. .... 31 Dec
X   Avery, M.B. .... 31 Dec
X   Jermy, S.C. .... 31 Dec
X   Montgomery, C.P.R. .... 31 Dec
X   Butler, N.A.M. .... 31 Dec

E　Thwaites, G.J. .... 31 Dec
S　Pearce, J.K.C. .... 31 Dec
E　Hussain, A.M. .... 31 Dec

1998

X　Adair, A.A.S. .... 30 Jun
X　Martin, S.C. .... 30 Jun
E　Hollidge, J.H. .... 30 Jun
X　Kirby, S.R. .... 30 Jun
X　Larmour, D.R. .... 30 Jun
X　Cameron, A.J.B. .... 30 Jun
X　Bennett, A.R.C. .... 30 Jun
E　Love, R.T. .... 30 Jun
X　Pond, D.W. .... 30 Jun
E　Graves, M.E.L. .... 30 Jun
S　Blackett, J. .... 30 Jun
X　Cooling, R.G. .... 30 Jun
X　Goodall, D.C. .... 31 Dec
E　Miklinski, A.S. .... 31 Dec
X　Docherty, P.T. .... 31 Dec
E　Little, R.M. .... 31 Dec
S　Menzies, A. .... 31 Dec
X　Harris, T.R. .... 31 Dec
E　Timms, S.J. .... 31 Dec
X　Ramm, S.C. .... 31 Dec
E　Van Beek, L. .... 31 Dec
X　Walpole, P.K. .... 31 Dec
X　Davies, P.N.M. .... 31 Dec
E　Jackman, R.W. .... 31 Dec
S　Martin, T.F.W. .... 31 Dec
W　Stait, C.J. .... 31 Dec
E　Keegan, W.J. .... 31 Dec

1999

E　Kidd, J.C. .... 30 Jun
X　Knowles, J.M. .... 30 Jun
X　Freeman, D.A.K. .... 30 Jun
S　Rayner, B.N. .... 30 Jun
E　Jaynes, P.R.W. .... 30 Jun
X　Twitchen, R.C. .... 30 Jun
E　Hyldon, C.J. .... 30 Jun
X　Harland, N.J.G. .... 30 Jun
X　Croke, A. .... 30 Jun
X　Moncrieff, I. .... 30 Jun
E　Rymer, A.R. .... 30 Jun
E　Hockley, C.J. .... 30 Jun
X　Corder, I.F. .... 30 Jun
X　Zambellas, G.M. .... 30 Jun
X　Nixon, M.C. .... 31 Dec
E　Rees, J.B.M. .... 31 Dec
E　Jarvis, D.J. .... 31 Dec
E　Ellins, S.J. .... 31 Dec

CAPTAINS

X　Mervik, C.F. .... 31 Dec
E　Hart, J. .... 31 Dec
X　Sloan, M.U. .... 31 Dec
S　Fraser, R.W. .... 31 Dec
X　Anderson, M. .... 31 Dec
X　Mathias, P.B. .... 31 Dec
E　Lister, S.R. .... 31 Dec
X　Jones, P.A. .... 31 Dec
E　Baldwin, S.F. .... 31 Dec
X　Gower, J.H.J. .... 31 Dec
X　Winstanley, K. .... 31 Dec

2000

X　Scorer, S.J. .... 30 Jun
E　Williams, N.L. .... 30 Jun
S　Quinn, P.A. .... 30 Jun
E　Leeming, R.J. .... 30 Jun
X　Mansergh, R.J. .... 30 Jun
E　Wilkinson, R.M. .... 30 Jun
X　Robinson, P.H. .... 30 Jun
S　MacDonald, G.E. .... 30 Jun
E　McFarlane, A.L. .... 30 Jun
X　Cleary, S.P. .... 30 Jun
X　Lloyd, S.J. .... 30 Jun
X　Moll, A.G. .... 30 Jun
X　Charlier, S.B. .... 30 Jun
E　Peach, G.L. .... 30 Jun
X　Lambert, N.R. .... 30 Jun
X　Halliday, D.A. .... 30 Jun
X　Potts, D.L. .... 30 Jun
X　Palmer, C.L. .... 31 Dec
X　Lye, D.J. .... 31 Dec
E　Watts, R.F. .... 31 Dec
X　Williams, S.T. .... 31 Dec
S　Crabtree, P.D. .... 31 Dec
E　Whyntie, A. .... 31 Dec
X　Mansergh, M.P. .... 31 Dec
X　Karsten, T.M. .... 31 Dec
E　Jess, I.M. .... 31 Dec
S　Steel, D.G. .... 31 Dec
X　Cunningham, T.A. .... 31 Dec
X　Penny, A.D. .... 31 Dec
X　Hudson, P.D. .... 31 Dec
E　Johns, T. .... 31 Dec
X　Windsor, M. .... 31 Dec
E　Reid, D. .... 31 Dec
X　Fraser, T.P. .... 31 Dec

2001

X　Dedman, N.J.K. .... 30 Jun
X　Steel, P.ST.C. .... 30 Jun
X　Swain, D.M. .... 30 Jun

X　Hawkins, R.C. .... 30 Jun
E　Mason, R.W. .... 30 Jun
E　Langbridge, D.C. .... 30 Jun
X　Williams, B.N.B. .... 30 Jun
E　Hart, D.J. .... 30 Jun
E　Christie, C.S. .... 30 Jun
E　Neave, C.B. .... 30 Jun
X　Stanford, J.H. .... 30 Jun
X　Best, R.R. .... 30 Jun
E　Brunton, S.B. .... 30 Jun
X　Chick, S.J. .... 30 Jun
S　Peel, G.R. .... 30 Jun

2002

X　Sim, D.L.W. .... 30 Jun
X　Stockman, C.D. .... 30 Jun
X　Morris, D.S. .... 30 Jun
S　Ross, A.A. .... 30 Jun
X　Turner, I. .... 30 Jun
S　Cornberg, M.A. .... 30 Jun
E　Tate, A.J. .... 30 Jun
X　Dickens, D.J.R. .... 30 Jun
X　Collins, P.N. .... 30 Jun
E　Hughes, R.I. .... 30 Jun
E　Stratton, J.D. .... 30 Jun
X　Tarr, M.D. .... 30 Jun
S　Albon, R. .... 30 Jun
E　Sealey, N.P. .... 30 Jun
E　Gosden, S.R. .... 30 Jun
X　Brown, R.A.M. .... 30 Jun
X　Fraser, E. .... 30 Jun
E　Powell, R.N. .... 30 Jun
E　Couch, P.J. .... 30 Jun
X　Westwood, M.W. .... 30 Jun
X　Thomas, G.C. .... 30 Jun
E　Burrell, P.M. .... 30 Jun
X　Stanley, N.P. .... 30 Jun
X　Westbrook, J.S. .... 30 Jun
W　Muxworthy, A.M.B. .... 30 Jun
E　Holloway, J.T. .... 30 Jun
X　Wolfe, D.E. .... 30 Jun
X　Cochrane, M.C.N. .... 30 Jun
E　Dearden, S.R. .... 30 Jun
X　Parr, M.J. .... 30 Jun
X　Bell, A.S. .... 30 Jun

COMMANDERS

1982
X Titmus, G.D. .... 30 Jun

1983
E Fenwick, J. .... 30 Jun
E Darch, B.N. .... 31 Dec

1984
S Abbott, C.P.G. .... 30 Jun

1985
X Hunt, G.C. .... 30 Jun
S Vosper, I.A. .... 30 Jun
E Jeffrey, I. .... 30 Jun
X Rogers, A.G. .... 31 Dec
X Harris, P.N. .... 31 Dec

1986
E Rennison, W.R. .... 31 Dec
X Bennett, S.H.G. .... 31 Dec
X Fyfe, P.M. .... 31 Dec

1987
S Farquhar, J.W. .... 30 Jun
E Moir, S. .... 30 Jun
X Baudains, D.P. .... 30 Jun
E Binns, J.B. .... 30 Jun
E Norton, A.J. .... 30 Jun
X Samborne, M.D.P. .... 30 Jun
X Wright, J.W.T. .... 30 Jun
X Johnson, G.R. .... 30 Jun
E Marley, P.S. .... 31 Dec
E Waters, C.D. .... 31 Dec
X Harrison, R.G. .... 31 Dec
X Robinson, C.P. .... 31 Dec
X Hughes, P.J. .... 31 Dec
X McKenzie, I.S. .... 31 Dec
E Bailie, D.J. .... 31 Dec

1988
X Prime, J.R.M. .... 30 Jun
E Smith, A. .... 30 Jun
X Pegg, S.M. .... 30 Jun
X Stanesby, D.L. .... 30 Jun
X Gale, H.N. .... 30 Jun
E English, C.R. .... 30 Jun
X Teer, D.R.D. .... 30 Jun
E Harbroe-Bush, R.D. .... 31 Dec
E Egerton, P.M. .... 31 Dec
E Kennaugh, A.J. .... 31 Dec
X Mitchell, R.H. .... 31 Dec
X Sayer, D.J. .... 31 Dec
X Welch, A.T. .... 31 Dec
X Meatyard, C.G.B. .... 31 Dec

E Binns, J.B.H. .... 31 Dec
X Parris, K.J. .... 31 Dec

1989
X Higham, A. .... 30 Jun
E Ewins, G.P. .... 30 Jun
X Skinner, J.R. .... 30 Jun
X Lightfoot, C.M. .... 30 Jun
X Jellyman, P.A. .... 30 Jun
X Chapman-Andrews, P.C. ..... 30 Jun
E Doxsey, R.A. .... 30 Jun
E Magill, W.J. .... 30 Jun
S Ainslie, A.A. .... 30 Jun
S Head, R.R.D'E. .... 30 Jun
X Bailey, J. .... 30 Jun
X Matthews, P. .... 30 Jun
X Jones, P.H. .... 30 Jun
X Lucey, R.N. .... 30 Jun
X Watkins, C.F.F. .... 31 Dec
S Carter, S.F. .... 31 Dec
X Webster, G. .... 31 Dec
E Meaken, J. .... 31 Dec
X Cowley, N.J. .... 31 Dec
X O'Neill, R.K. .... 31 Dec
E Douglas, F.R. .... 31 Dec
E Passingham, R.E. .... 31 Dec
E Antcliffe, G.A. .... 31 Dec
E Bell, A.D. .... 31 Dec
X Greenop, J.P.S. .... 31 Dec
X Smith, N.P. .... 31 Dec
S Knight, D.J. .... 31 Dec
X Scoles, J.C. .... 31 Dec
X Williams, T.N.E. .... 31 Dec
E Harrison, R.A. .... 31 Dec

1990
S Philpott, G.R. .... 30 Jun
X Rich, A.A. .... 30 Jun
E Broad, R.O. .... 30 Jun
X Craig, R.W.W. .... 30 Jun
E Rogers, M.S. .... 30 Jun
X Habershon, D.B. .... 30 Jun
E Murch, J.D. .... 30 Jun
E Coles, G.W.G. .... 30 Jun
E Morgan, D. .... 30 Jun
X Turner, S.M. .... 30 Jun
E Issitt, D.J. .... 30 Jun
E Geddes, W.B. .... 30 Jun
X Lamb, R. .... 31 Dec
X Dodds, M. .... 31 Dec
S Backhouse, A.W. .... 31 Dec
E Steel, R.J. .... 31 Dec

E Milton, G.J.G. .... 31 Dec
X Overington, N. .... 31 Dec
E Young, A. .... 31 Dec
E Morris, P.N. .... 31 Dec
X Hibbert, P.N. .... 31 Dec
X Bearne, J.P. .... 31 Dec
S Leatherby, J.H. .... 31 Dec
S Davis, B.J. .... 31 Dec
X Simmonds, R.M. .... 31 Dec
X Crabtree, I.M. .... 31 Dec
E Firth, S.K. .... 31 Dec
X Vaughan, D.M. .... 31 Dec

1991
E Walton, A.F. .... 30 Jun
X Clark, T.H.V. .... 30 Jun
E Hutchinson, T.J. .... 30 Jun
X Ewing, A.D. .... 30 Jun
X Chambers, N.M.C. .... 30 Jun
X Foster, G.R.N. .... 30 Jun
X Boxall-Hunt, B.P. .... 30 Jun
E Moberly, N.G.H. .... 30 Jun
X Butcher, M.W. .... 30 Jun
X Ferguson, J.N. .... 30 Jun
X MacDonald, D.H.L. .... 30 Jun
X Hudson, N.G. .... 30 Jun
X Underwood, A.G.H. .... 31 Dec
X Wilson, S.G. .... 31 Dec
X Bishop, R.J. .... 31 Dec
E Sayles, S. .... 31 Dec
E Reeder, R. .... 31 Dec
E Hume, C.B. .... 31 Dec
S Day, N.R. .... 31 Dec
X Williams, N.D.B. .... 31 Dec
E Pancott, B.M. .... 31 Dec
X De Sa, P.J. .... 31 Dec
X Stoneman, T.J. .... 31 Dec
E Knowling, P.J. .... 31 Dec
X Bramley, S. .... 31 Dec
X Fortescue, P.W. .... 31 Dec
X Armstrong, C.A. .... 31 Dec
S Jones, A. .... 31 Dec
X Johnson, G.P. .... 31 Dec
E Bailey, J.W. .... 31 Dec
E Gibb, R.W. .... 31 Dec
E King, A.M. .... 31 Dec
X Lombard, D. .... 31 Dec

1992
X Burston, R.J.K. .... 30 Jun
X Govan, R.T. .... 30 Jun
X Shepherd, I. .... 30 Jun

COMMANDERS

X Ingham, P.C. .... 30 Jun	X Upright, S.W. .... 30 Jun	S Forsyth, A.R. .... 30 Jun
E Ratcliffe, J.P. .... 30 Jun	E Sutherland, W.M. .... 30 Jun	E Whitehorn, I.J. .... 30 Jun
E Stanley, P. .... 30 Jun	E Bishop, P.R. .... 30 Jun	X Wallace, G.W.A. .... 30 Jun
X Ramsay, G.P. .... 30 Jun	X Snow, M.C.P. .... 30 Jun	S Nelson, D.T. .... 30 Jun
E Matters, A.C. .... 30 Jun	X Holihead, P.W. .... 30 Jun	X Cutt, J.J.D. .... 30 Jun
X Gregan, D.C. .... 30 Jun	E Wright, G.N. .... 30 Jun	E Molyneaux, D.G. .... 30 Jun
E Adams, R.A.S. .... 30 Jun	E Haines, S.W. .... 30 Jun	X Reid, M. .... 30 Jun
E Robb, M.C. .... 30 Jun	S Cowdrey, M.C. .... 30 Jun	X Humphreys, J.I. .... 30 Jun
X Smee, N.L. .... 30 Jun	X Hennessey, T.P.D. .... 30 Jun	E Rowell, G.E. .... 30 Jun
E Lankester, T.J. .... 30 Jun	X Harvey, K. .... 30 Jun	S Chelton, S.R.L. .... 30 Jun
E Dyer, S.J. .... 30 Jun	E Cox, P.W.S. .... 30 Jun	X Arthur, I.D. .... 30 Jun
X Durston, D.H. .... 30 Jun	E Dannatt, T.M. .... 30 Jun	X Finney, M.E. .... 30 Jun
X Lankester, P. .... 30 Jun	X Greenlees, I.W. .... 30 Jun	X Archibald, B.R. .... 30 Jun
X Donaldson, J. .... 30 Jun	X Bateman, S.J.F. .... 30 Jun	X Brown, M.K. .... 20 Sep
E Smith, C.S. .... 30 Jun	E Alexander, S.J. .... 01 Oct	X Ward, N.J. .... 01 Oct
S Hosker, T.J. .... 30 Jun	X Connell, J.A. .... 01 Oct	E Smith-Jaynes, E.R. .... 01 Oct
E Wadham, J. .... 30 Jun	E Gubbins, V.R. .... 31 Dec	E Lea, J.H.A. .... 31 Dec
X Herman, T.R. .... 30 Jun	X Turner, S.E. .... 31 Dec	X James, D.R. .... 31 Dec
X Thoburn, R. .... 30 Jun	E Coombes, D. .... 31 Dec	E Wakeling, J.L. .... 31 Dec
X Pickering, M.J. .... 01 Oct	X Goodwin, D.R. .... 31 Dec	S Whalley, S.D. .... 31 Dec
X Arnall-Culliford, N.D. ..... 01 Oct	X Thomas, S.A. .... 31 Dec	X Hosking, D.B. .... 31 Dec
X Pepper, M.R. .... 31 Dec	E Jeffcoat, S.M. .... 31 Dec	E Parry, N.T. .... 31 Dec
E Usborne, A.C. .... 31 Dec	X Bevan, S. .... 31 Dec	X Murgatroyd, A.C. .... 31 Dec
E Ayers, R.P.B. .... 31 Dec	X Pothecary, R.E. .... 31 Dec	E Faulconbridge, D. .... 31 Dec
X Marshall, R.A. .... 31 Dec	E Stenhouse, N.J. .... 31 Dec	X Fletcher, N.E. .... 31 Dec
E Cooper, J.A. .... 31 Dec	E Menlove-Platt, C.J. .... 31 Dec	X Davies, A.R. .... 31 Dec
S Peilow, B.F. .... 31 Dec	S Harbour, J.R.M. .... 31 Dec	E McElwaine, R.I. .... 31 Dec
E Thorpe, C.R. .... 31 Dec	E Lunn, J.F.C. .... 31 Dec	X Horne, T.K. .... 31 Dec
W Robbins, M.J. .... 31 Dec	X Curd, T.A. .... 31 Dec	X Evans, M.C. .... 31 Dec
X Spalton, G.M.S. .... 31 Dec	E Allwood, C. .... 31 Dec	X Stallion, I.M. .... 31 Dec
E Arnold, B.W.H. .... 31 Dec	X Trevithick, A.R. .... 31 Dec	E Peckham, D.R. .... 31 Dec
E Sherlock, F.C.E. .... 31 Dec	X Bosshardt, R.G. .... 31 Dec	X Ward, J.E. .... 31 Dec
X Brocklebank, G.P. .... 31 Dec	E Coulthard, J.K. .... 31 Dec	X Clark, K.I.M. .... 31 Dec
X Bartholomew, I.M. .... 31 Dec	X Churchill, T.C. .... 31 Dec	X Wellesley, R.C.R. .... 31 Dec
X Welborn, C.G. .... 31 Dec	E Parker, I.R. .... 31 Dec	E Holberry, A.P. .... 31 Dec
X Gibson, I.A. .... 31 Dec	X Humphrys, J.A. .... 31 Dec	X Burrows, M.J. .... 31 Dec
E Wormald, R.E. .... 31 Dec	E Edgell, J.N. .... 31 Dec	E Brough, G.A. .... 31 Dec
X Powis, J. .... 31 Dec	E Hore, R.C. .... 31 Dec	E White, A.R. .... 31 Dec
E Steel, C.M.H. .... 31 Dec	S Marsh, D.J. .... 31 Dec	S Airey, S.E. .... 31 Dec
	E Coverdale, A. .... 31 Dec	X Gillanders, F.G.R. .... 31 Dec
1993	E Costello, G.T. .... 31 Dec	
E Parsons, G. .... 30 Jun	X Riley, M.J. .... 31 Dec	**1995**
E Febbrarro, N.R. .... 30 Jun		X Carter, K. .... 30 Jun
E Lineker, R.J. .... 30 Jun	**1994**	E Podger, K.G.R. .... 30 Jun
S Williams, R.E. .... 30 Jun	X Long, P.J. .... 30 Jun	S Mullen, A.J. .... 30 Jun
X Dale, M.J. .... 30 Jun	X Hatchard, P.J. .... 30 Jun	X Phillips, D.G. .... 30 Jun
X Andrew, W.G. .... 30 Jun	E Fisher, M.A.L. .... 30 Jun	X McNair, E.A. .... 30 Jun
X Grant, A.K. .... 30 Jun	X Stanley, C.E. .... 30 Jun	X Wilson, C.D. .... 30 Jun
E Guy, T.J. .... 30 Jun	E Fox, K.A. .... 30 Jun	X Shrives, M.P. .... 30 Jun
X Bell-Davies, R.W. .... 30 Jun	E Brockwell, P.E.N. .... 30 Jun	X Norris, R.J. .... 30 Jun
X Mason, M.M.D. .... 30 Jun	X Evans, D.M. .... 30 Jun	E Evans, D.J. .... 30 Jun
X Chambers, W.J. .... 30 Jun	E Usborne, C.M. .... 30 Jun	X Thomas, R.P. .... 30 Jun

COMMANDERS

X	Gasson, N.S.C.	30 Jun	E	Heritage, L.J.	30 Jun	S	Tinsley, G.N.	31 Dec
E	Kenward, P.D.	30 Jun	X	Betteridge, J.T.	30 Jun	E	Thistlethwaite, M.H.	31 Dec
E	Pendle, M.E.J.	30 Jun	E	Middlemas, S.R.	30 Jun	X	Buckley, P.J.A.	31 Dec
S	Walker, C.S.	30 Jun	X	Langhorn, N.	30 Jun	X	Richmond, I.J.M.	31 Dec
E	Price, F.E.F.	30 Jun	X	Ayres, C.P.	30 Jun	X	Lilley, D.J.	31 Dec
E	Young, S.S.	30 Jun	E	Van Beek, D.	30 Jun	X	Hugo, I.D.	31 Dec
X	Lander, M.C.	30 Jun	E	Lovett, M.J.	30 Jun	E	Jenkin, A.M.H.	31 Dec
X	Richards, C.M.	30 Jun	X	Funnell, N.C.	30 Jun	X	Abraham, P.	31 Dec
E	Rusbridger, R.C.	30 Jun	E	Price, J.P.	30 Jun	E	Wise, S.D.	31 Dec
X	Clarke, C.M.L.	30 Jun	E	Bridger, D.W.	30 Jun	E	Farrage, M.E.	31 Dec
E	Jagger, P.R.A.	30 Jun	X	Sibbit, N.T.	30 Jun	E	King, E.M.	31 Dec
X	Wallace, M.R.B.	30 Jun	X	Drake, E.D.	30 Jun	X	Smallman, L.D.	31 Dec
E	Thompson, R.J.	30 Jun	X	Furness, S.B.	30 Jun			
X	Salter, M.D.	01 Oct	E	Haley, T.J.	30 Jun		**1997**	
X	Bull, A.J.	01 Oct	S	Smith, M.	30 Jun	X	Horne, T.G.	30 Jun
E	Wearmouth, P.W.A.	01 Oct	X	Rycroft, A.E.	30 Jun	X	Robinson, A.	30 Jun
MS	Bootland, E.G.	01 Oct	X	Warren, B.H.	30 Jun	X	Balston, D.C.W.	30 Jun
X	Wain, R.N.	31 Dec	E	Gourlay, J.S.	30 Jun	E	Spalding, R.E.H.	30 Jun
X	Holmes, R.	31 Dec	X	Perkins, M.J.	30 Jun	E	Whitaker, M.J.	30 Jun
E	Cummin, M.A.	31 Dec	X	Corrigan, N.R.	30 Jun	E	Derrick, G.G.J.	30 Jun
E	Smith, M.A.	31 Dec	E	Da Gama, J.A.J.	30 Jun	X	Moores, J.K.	30 Jun
E	Spicer, C.G.	31 Dec	S	Finlayson, A.G.	30 Jun	E	Foster, M.A.	30 Jun
X	Doyne-Ditmas, P.S.	31 Dec	E	Taylor, J.J.	30 Jun	X	Stewart, R.G.	30 Jun
S	Ireland, R.C.	31 Dec	X	Farrington, R.	30 Jun	E	Graham, G.R.	30 Jun
E	Sewry, M.R.	31 Dec	E	Erskine, P.A.	30 Jun	E	Page, D.M.	30 Jun
X	Stonor, P.F.A.	31 Dec	X	Blunden, J.J.F.	30 Jun	X	Morgan, P.T.	30 Jun
X	Seatherton, E.F.K.	31 Dec	S	King, C.E.W.	30 Jun	X	Spence, N.A.	30 Jun
E	Burton, D.S.	31 Dec	E	Beverstock, M.A.	30 Jun	E	Starks, M.R.	30 Jun
E	Beaumont, I.H.	31 Dec	E	Yuill, I.A.	01 Oct	E	Holdsworth, H.W.	30 Jun
X	Harrap, N.R.E.	31 Dec	E	Burgess, W.C.	01 Oct	X	Scarth, W.	30 Jun
S	Storrs-Fox, R.N.	31 Dec	W	Hoath, M.E.J.	01 Oct	X	Baum, S.R.	30 Jun
X	Davis-Marks, M.L.	31 Dec	S	Anderson, M.J.	01 Oct	X	Pickles, I.S.	30 Jun
E	Herridge, P.G.	31 Dec	X	Easton, R.W.	01 Oct	S	Richardson, M.P.	30 Jun
E	Powell, D.C.	31 Dec	X	Lee, D.J.	31 Dec	X	Barker, R.D.J.	30 Jun
S	Keefe, P.C.	31 Dec	E	Palmer, J.E.	31 Dec	X	Brand, S.M.	30 Jun
E	Anderson, R.G.	31 Dec	E	Grafton, M.N.	31 Dec	X	Tarrant, R.K.	30 Jun
E	Forsey, C.R.	31 Dec	X	Sullivan, C.	31 Dec	S	Crook, A.S.	30 Jun
X	O'Reilly, S.A.	31 Dec	E	Terry, J.M.	31 Dec	E	O'Neill, P.J.	30 Jun
X	Harding, R.G.	31 Dec	S	Nairn, R.	31 Dec	E	Braham, S.W.	30 Jun
X	Murphie, J.D.D.	31 Dec	X	Lambert, B.	31 Dec	X	Garratt, M.D.	30 Jun
E	Wyatt, S.P.	31 Dec	E	Lofthouse, I.	31 Dec	X	Morse, J.A.	30 Jun
E	Fulford, J.P.H.	31 Dec	X	Hamp, C.J.	31 Dec	E	Hay, J.D.	30 Jun
X	Pegg, R.M.	31 Dec	X	Handley, J.M.	31 Dec	E	Smithson, P.E.	30 Jun
X	Keble, K.W.L.	31 Dec	X	Lambourn, P.N.	31 Dec	X	Beardall, J.	01 Oct
S	Bullock, M.P.	31 Dec	S	Church, A.D.	31 Dec	MS	Baker, K.	01 Oct
E	Watts, G.M.	31 Dec	X	Wilson, K.P.	31 Dec	E	Foster, S.	01 Oct
X	Lowe, T.M.	31 Dec	X	Edney, A.R.	31 Dec	E	Brazier, F.W.T.	01 Oct
			E	Lewis, D.M.J.	31 Dec	E	Waterman, J.H.	31 Dec
	1996		X	Pearey, M.S.	31 Dec	X	Nail, V.A.	31 Dec
X	Nicholson, S.C.L.	30 Jun	X	Thicknesse, P.J.	31 Dec	S	Charlton, C.R.A.M.	31 Dec
E	Nixon, P.W.	30 Jun	X	Hughes, N.J.	31 Dec	E	Greenwood, S.	31 Dec
E	Farrington, S.P.	30 Jun				E	Wrightson, H.M.	31 Dec

COMMANDERS

E	Penniston, J.R.	31 Dec
E	Straughan, H.	31 Dec
E	Peck, I.J.	31 Dec
X	Rimmer, M.	31 Dec
X	Brooksbank, R.J.	31 Dec
X	Robinson, J.S.	31 Dec
E	Slawson, J.M.	31 Dec
X	Taylor, K.A.	31 Dec
X	Neil, S.J.	31 Dec
X	MacKay, G.A.	31 Dec
E	Newell, J.M.	31 Dec
S	White, S.N.	31 Dec
E	Sunderland, J.D.	31 Dec
X	McBarnet, T.F.	31 Dec
S	Cunningham, P.	31 Dec
X	Garrett, S.W.	31 Dec
X	Williams, S.P.	31 Dec
E	Pickthall, D.N.	31 Dec
X	Lloyd, P.R.	31 Dec
X	Ameye, C.R.	31 Dec
X	Pope, C.M.	31 Dec
X	Hawthorne, M.J.	31 Dec
X	Lemkes, P.D.	31 Dec
E	Carter, A.F.R.	31 Dec
S	Atherton, M.J.	31 Dec
X	Kenny, S.J.	31 Dec
X	Pettitt, G.W.	31 Dec
E	Beckett, K.A.	31 Dec
X	Johnstone, C.C.C.	31 Dec

1998

X	Snook, R.E.	30 Jun
E	Enticknap, K.	30 Jun
E	Clark, D.K.	30 Jun
E	Jardine, G.A.	30 Jun
X	Lade, C.J.	30 Jun
E	McLennan, R.G.	30 Jun
X	Steeds, S.M.	30 Jun
X	Jackman, A.W.	30 Jun
X	Gaunt, N.R.	30 Jun
E	Russell, S.J.	30 Jun
E	Main, E.S.	30 Jun
X	Ewence, M.W.	30 Jun
E	MacDonald, A.I.	30 Jun
E	Taylor, S.A.	30 Jun
X	Cassar, A.P.F.	30 Jun
S	Pattinson, I.H.	30 Jun
E	Quaye, D.T.G.	30 Jun
X	Robertson, K.F.	30 Jun
X	McDonnell, P.W.	30 Jun
E	Wiles, S.J.	30 Jun
X	Reynolds, T.E.	30 Jun

E	Shipperley, I.	30 Jun
X	Ingram, R.G.	30 Jun
X	Cree, M.C.	30 Jun
X	Alcock, C.	30 Jun
X	Kings, S.J.N.	30 Jun
X	Ancona, S.J.	30 Jun
E	Elford, D.G.	30 Jun
S	Litchfield, J.F.	30 Jun
E	Gulley, T.J.	30 Jun
X	Sutton, G.B.	30 Jun
E	Danbury, I.G.	30 Jun
X	Bennett, P.M.	30 Jun
X	Darlington, M.R.	30 Jun
E	Sexton, M.J.	30 Jun
E	Toy, M.J.	30 Jun
X	Sanguinetti, H.R.	30 Jun
X	Murnane, P.M.	01 Oct
X	White, M.E.	01 Oct
S	Harry, P.N.	01 Oct
X	Stockton, J.P.	01 Oct
E	Collins, R.J.	01 Oct
E	Hart, W.C.	01 Oct
MS	Holyer, R.J.	01 Oct
E	Hobbs, R.	01 Oct
X	Trundle, N.R.E.	31 Dec
E	Hawkins, I.	31 Dec
E	Dodgson, S.J.	31 Dec
E	Davies, T.G.	31 Dec
S	Spiller, M.F.	31 Dec
X	Newton, D.J.	31 Dec
X	White, M.W.	31 Dec
X	Percharde, M.R.	31 Dec
E	Mason, N.H.	31 Dec
E	Curnow, M.D.	31 Dec
E	Gray, A.J.	31 Dec
X	Woods, R.P.	31 Dec
X	Clark, A.W.C.	31 Dec
E	Stanley-Whyte, B.J.	31 Dec
S	Beard, G.T.C.	31 Dec
E	Fry, J.M.S.	31 Dec
X	Williams, M.H.	31 Dec
S	Redstone, C.	31 Dec
X	Hatch, G.W.H.	31 Dec
X	Evans, K.N.M.	31 Dec
E	Green, A.R.	31 Dec
X	McKendrick, A.M.	31 Dec
E	Chidley, T.J.	31 Dec
X	Muir, K.	31 Dec
E	Green, S.N.	31 Dec
X	McCartain, M.B.W.	31 Dec
X	Shield, S.J.	31 Dec

X	Cook, P.R.	31 Dec
S	Skidmore, C.M.	31 Dec
E	Stokes, R.	31 Dec
X	Adams, A.J.	31 Dec
X	Green, T.J.	31 Dec
E	O'Reilly, T.M.	31 Dec
X	McAlpine, P.A.	31 Dec
X	McQuaker, S.R.	31 Dec
E	Morritt, D.C.	31 Dec
S	Jameson, A.C.	31 Dec
E	Hayes, J.V.B.	31 Dec
X	Trevor, M.G.	31 Dec
S	Brown, N.L.	31 Dec

1999

E	Merriman, P.O.	30 Jun
E	Hadfield, D.	30 Jun
X	Drewett, R.E.	30 Jun
X	Haley, C.W.	30 Jun
E	Ellis, R.W.	30 Jun
E	Fear, R.K.	30 Jun
X	Alexander, R.S.	30 Jun
E	Ranson, C.D.	30 Jun
E	Darwent, A.	30 Jun
E	Pett, J.G.	30 Jun
X	Clarke, N.J.	30 Jun
X	Haworth, J.	30 Jun
E	Bisson, I.J.P.	30 Jun
E	Vandome, A.M.	30 Jun
X	Spencer, E.A.	30 Jun
X	Knibbs, M.	30 Jun
X	Jervis, N.D.	30 Jun
E	Michie, A.R.	30 Jun
S	Thomas, F.S.	30 Jun
X	Carden, P.D.	30 Jun
X	Northwood, G.R.	30 Jun
E	Ramshaw, G.W.L.	30 Jun
E	Simmons, N.D.	30 Jun
X	Ireland, A.R.	30 Jun
X	Horn, P.B.	30 Jun
S	Morton, N.P.B.	30 Jun
X	Robinson, C.E.T.	30 Jun
X	Moore, C.I.	30 Jun
E	Lewis, J.K.	30 Jun
E	Barton, P.G.	30 Jun
X	Titterton, P.J.	30 Jun
E	Daws, R.P.A.	30 Jun
X	Allen, R.M.	30 Jun
X	Clink, J.R.H.	30 Jun
X	Pollock, D.J.	30 Jun
X	Weale, J.S.	30 Jun
E	Roberts, N.S.	30 Jun

COMMANDERS

2000

S	Lavery, J.P.	30 Jun
X	Kingwell, J.M.L.	30 Jun
X	Millward, J.P.	31 Dec
E	Morley, A.D.	31 Dec
E	Tindall-Jones, L.D.	31 Dec
X	Buckland, R.J.F.	31 Dec
X	Ovens, J.J.	31 Dec
E	Treanor, M.A.	31 Dec
E	Maltby, M.R.J.	31 Dec
S	Isaac, P.	31 Dec
E	Crossley, C.C.	31 Dec
S	Tulley, J.R.	31 Dec
E	Greene, M.J.	31 Dec
X	Chalmers, D.P.	31 Dec
X	Matthews, D.N.	31 Dec
E	Mason, A.H.	31 Dec
X	Tuppen, R.M.	31 Dec
X	Johnson, A.S.	31 Dec
E	Plant, J.N.M.	31 Dec
X	Shaw, P.A.G.	31 Dec
X	Doyle, G.L.	31 Dec
E	Thompson, S.J.	31 Dec
E	Morrison, K.W.	31 Dec
E	Woodcock, S.J.	31 Dec
X	Harris, A.I.	31 Dec
S	Gray, R.S.	31 Dec
X	Reid, C.I.	31 Dec
S	Murdoch, S.J.	31 Dec
X	Race, N.J.	31 Dec
E	Hodgson, T.C.	31 Dec
E	Brown, H.S.	31 Dec
X	Hopper, S.O.	31 Dec
E	Morris, A.J.	31 Dec
X	McMichael-Phillips, S.J.	31 Dec
E	Stubbings, P.R.	31 Dec
S	Gardner, C.R.S.	31 Dec
E	Harrison, M.S.	31 Dec
E	Johnson, J.C.	31 Dec
X	Sullivan, A.G.	31 Dec
E	French, S.A.	31 Dec
E	Wareham, M.P.	31 Dec
E	Hammond, P.A.	31 Dec
X	Porter, S.P.	31 Dec
MS	White, M.A.	31 Dec
X	Healy, A.J.	31 Dec
X	Walliker, M.J.D.	31 Dec
S	Rance, M.G.W.	31 Dec
X	Bone, D.N.	31 Dec
E	Tate, S.J.	31 Dec
X	Key, B.J.	31 Dec
X	McGhie, I.A.	31 Dec

X	Daniels, S.A.	30 Jun
E	Blake, G.E.	30 Jun
E	McKenzie, D.	30 Jun
E	Moreland, M.J.	30 Jun
X	Snowball, S.J.	30 Jun
X	Stewart, A.C.	30 Jun
S	Graham, J.E.	30 Jun
X	Tilley, D.S.J.	30 Jun
X	Newton, G.A.	30 Jun
X	Sephton, J.R.	30 Jun
X	Cunningham, R.A.	30 Jun
E	Basson, A.P.	30 Jun
X	Broadley, K.J.	30 Jun
E	Atkinson, S.R.	30 Jun
E	Argent-Hall, D.	30 Jun
E	Baker, P.G.	30 Jun
E	Short, G.C.	30 Jun
X	Martin, C.J.	30 Jun
E	Morris, N.J.	30 Jun
S	Tothill, N.M.	30 Jun
S	Fergusson, H.J.	30 Jun
E	Harvey, C.A.	30 Jun
X	McNeile, R.H.	30 Jun
X	Hayes, S.J.	30 Jun
E	Vanderpump, D.J.	30 Jun
S	Wunderle, C.A.	30 Jun
X	Entwistle, S.C.	30 Jun
S	Spence, A.B.	30 Jun
E	Gilbert, S.A.	30 Jun
X	Carter, I.P.	30 Jun
X	Stockings, T.M.	30 Jun
X	Chivers, P.A.	30 Jun
E	Walker, N.J.	30 Jun
E	Walker, M.	30 Jun
X	Heley, D.N.	30 Jun
X	Pearson, S.J.	30 Jun
X	Allibon, M.C.	30 Jun
X	Thompson, G.	30 Jun
S	Bath, M.A.W.	30 Jun
E	Williams, M.J.	30 Jun
E	Little, G.T.	30 Jun
X	Talbot, R.P.	30 Jun
E	Dyer, M.D.J.	30 Jun
X	Hine, N.W.	30 Jun
E	Reason, I.M.	30 Jun
X	McKie, A.	31 Dec
E	Kerchey, S.J.V.	31 Dec
E	Welburn, R.S.	31 Dec
X	Malcolm, S.R.	31 Dec
E	Stidston, I.J.	31 Dec

X	Connolly, C.J.	31 Dec
E	Parsons, C.G.	31 Dec
E	Deaney, M.N.	31 Dec
S	Hughes, G.L.	31 Dec
E	Marmont, K.L.	31 Dec
E	Abbey, M.K.	31 Dec
X	Thomas, W.G.	31 Dec
X	Blowers, M.D.	31 Dec
E	Risley, J.	31 Dec
X	Powell, R.L.	31 Dec
E	Cargen, M.R.	31 Dec
E	Parsons, B.R.	31 Dec
S	Bond, N.D.	31 Dec
X	Durkin, M.T.G.	31 Dec
E	Martyn, A.W.	31 Dec
X	Davies, J.H.	31 Dec
MS	Jackson, S.K.	31 Dec
S	Walker, C.L.	31 Dec
X	Williams, A.P.	31 Dec
E	Glennie, A.M.G.	31 Dec
S	Buchan-Steele, M.A.	31 Dec
S	Merchant, I.C.	31 Dec
S	Rigby, J.C.	31 Dec
E	Corry, S.M.	31 Dec
E	Jones, H.A.	31 Dec
X	Reed, A.W.	31 Dec
X	Williamson, T.J.L.	31 Dec
X	Denham, N.J.	31 Dec
E	Heley, J.M.	31 Dec
X	Thomas, P.G.	31 Dec
X	Ashcroft, A.C.	31 Dec
X	Milburn, P.K.	31 Dec
X	Fulton, C.R.	31 Dec
E	Jessop, P.E.	31 Dec
E	Moore, M.N.	31 Dec
E	Frankham, P.J.	31 Dec
X	Cooper, M.A.	31 Dec
E	Clough, C.R.	31 Dec
E	Fancy, R.	31 Dec
X	Blount, K.E.	31 Dec
X	Dutton, D.	31 Dec

2001

X	Taylor, J.W.	30 Jun
E	Parker, M.N.	30 Jun
X	Faulkner, J.J.	30 Jun
X	Corbett, W.R.	30 Jun
E	Gordon, D.	30 Jun
X	Knight, D.A.	30 Jun
W	Keefe, S-A.	30 Jun
E	Martin, M.T.	30 Jun
X	Sheehan, M.A.	30 Jun

COMMANDERS

E	Grieve, S.H.	30 Jun
S	O'Grady, M.J.	30 Jun
E	Raybould, A.G.	30 Jun
X	Payne, R.C.	30 Jun
X	Greenwood, P.	30 Jun
E	Grantham, S.M.	30 Jun
X	Ashcroft, C.	30 Jun
X	Jones, M.C.	30 Jun
E	Martin, M.P.	30 Jun
X	Mitchell, H.G.M.	30 Jun
X	Cooper, S.J.	30 Jun
E	Charlesworth, G.K.	30 Jun
X	Doolan, M.	30 Jun
E	Wood, J.L.	30 Jun
S	Crozier, S.R.M.	30 Jun
E	Borland, S.A.	30 Jun
E	Podmore, A.	30 Jun
E	Haines, P.R.	30 Jun
X	Pritchard, G.S.	30 Jun
S	Shaw, S.M.	30 Jun
X	Foreman, J.L.R.	30 Jun
X	Burton, A.J.	30 Jun
X	Nolan, A.L.	30 Jun
E	St Aubyn, J.D.E.	30 Jun
X	Wallace, A.	30 Jun
E	Casson, P.R.	30 Jun
X	Barker, D.C.K.	30 Jun
E	Phenna, A.	30 Jun
X	Warwick, P.D.	30 Jun
MS	Coulton, I.C.	30 Jun
X	Hardern, S.P.	30 Jun
E	Prescott, S.	30 Jun
E	Kershaw, S.	30 Jun
S	Noyes, D.J.	30 Jun
E	Corderoy, J.R.	30 Jun

2002

X	Schwarz, P.M.G.	30 Jun
S	Bostock, C.E.	30 Jun
E	Dawson, S.L.	30 Jun
S	Faulks, D.J.	30 Jun
E	Mackay, C.R.	30 Jun
E	Dumbell, P.	30 Jun
E	Birchall, S.J.	30 Jun
X	Layland, S.	30 Jun
E	Cheesman, C.J.	30 Jun
X	Petheram, M.J.	30 Jun
E	Tarr, B.S.	30 Jun
E	Naden, A.C.K.	30 Jun
E	Warden, J.M.	30 Jun
X	King, R.W.	30 Jun
X	O'Sullivan, A.M.	30 Jun

E	Sykes, M.	30 Jun
X	Hardy, L.C.	30 Jun
X	Hodgkins, J.M.	30 Jun
X	Roberts, I.T.	30 Jun
S	Laws, P.E.A.	30 Jun
E	Jones, R.W.	30 Jun
E	Ryan, D.G.	30 Jun
X	Mair, B.	30 Jun
E	Crago, P.T.	30 Jun
X	Fitter, I.S.T.	30 Jun
X	Lacey, S.P.	30 Jun
E	Gray, A.J.	30 Jun
X	Eastaugh, T.C.	30 Jun
X	Davies, C.J.	30 Jun
X	Kelbie, E.	30 Jun
E	Moffatt, N.R.	30 Jun
X	Turnbull, S.J.L.	30 Jun
S	Watts, A.D.	30 Jun
X	Hare, N.J.	30 Jun
S	Randall, D.F.	30 Jun
X	Barrand, S.M.	30 Jun
X	Cluett-Green, S.M.	30 Jun
X	Gordon, S.R.	30 Jun
E	Shaw, K.N.G.	30 Jun
E	Sharman, D.J.T.	30 Jun
X	Gething, J.B.	30 Jun
E	Archer, G.W.	30 Jun
E	Falk, B.H.G.	30 Jun
X	Turnbull, G.D.	30 Jun
X	Skeer, M.R.	30 Jun
E	Float, R.A.	30 Jun
E	Waddington, J.	30 Jun
E	Dabell, G.L.	30 Jun
E	Grindel, D.J.S.	30 Jun
X	Thompson, B.D.	30 Jun
E	Haywood, S.A.	30 Jun
X	Evans, W.Q.F.	30 Jun
E	Magan, M.J.C.	30 Jun
X	Turner, D.B.	30 Jun
E	French, J.T.	30 Jun
E	Streeten, C.M.	30 Jun
E	Rhodes, A.G.	30 Jun
E	Thompson, A.	30 Jun
S	Renwick, J.	30 Jun
E	Clifford, T.J.	30 Jun
X	Haywood, G.	30 Jun
E	Dorricott, A.J.	30 Jun
S	Garland, N.	30 Jun
S	Lines, J.M.	30 Jun
X	Entwisle, W.N.	30 Jun
X	Tindal, N.H.C.	30 Jun

X	Burke, P.D.	30 Jun
E	Scott, N.L.J.	30 Jun
E	Wise, G.J.	30 Jun
X	Wallis, A.J.	30 Jun
E	Jarvis, L.R.	30 Jun
E	Childs, D.G.	30 Jun
S	Hall, E.C.	30 Jun
X	Thomas, R.K.	30 Jun
E	Chubb, J.J.	30 Jun
X	Reindorp, D.P.	30 Jun
E	Adams, A.M.	30 Jun
X	Swannick, D.J.	30 Jun
MS	Murphy, A.	30 Jun
X	Hodkinson, C.B.	30 Jun
X	Jackson, G.K.	30 Jun
E	Robinson, M.P.	30 Jun
X	Radakin, A.D.	30 Jun
E	Thompson, R.C.	30 Jun
E	Course, A.J.	30 Jun
E	Annett, I.G.	30 Jun
X	Robinson, G.A.	30 Jun
X	Wainhouse, M.J.	30 Jun
X	Bewick, D.J.	30 Jun

LIEUTENANT COMMANDERS

1978

E Morley-Smith, N.H. ....01 Feb

1979

X Hearnden, G.E. ....01 Apr
E Milne, D.M.F. ....16 Aug
E Mitchell, B.A. ....01 Nov
S Turton, T.M.H. ....16 Nov

1980

X Hennell, N.J. ....01 Mar
E Stephenson, F. ....16 May
X Wrighton, C.R. ....16 Sep
X Brimley, K.S. ....01 Dec
E Young, I.J. ....16 Dec
X Budd, P.R. ....16 Dec

1981

X Willett, R.J. ....04 Jan
X Brady, M.R. ....16 Jan
X Engeham, P.R. ....16 Jan
X Langrishe, J.H. ....16 Apr
S Screech, M.C. ....01 Aug
S Maguire, A.P.D. ....01 Nov
X Rydiard, D.M. ....01 Dec

1982

E Murray, R.H. ....01 Jan
X Todd, D. ....01 Jan
X Dickinson, P.N. ....01 May
E Helby, P.F.H. ....16 Jul
E Ager, R.G. ....01 Aug
X Smith, S.F. ....01 Sep
X Rothwell, J.F. ....01 Sep
E Debenham, L.A. ....20 Oct
X Woodbridge, G.F. ....01 Nov
E Shand, C.M. ....01 Nov
E Fernihough, M.R. ....08 Dec
S Austin, S.J. ....16 Dec

1983

S Hepburn, J. ....01 Feb
X Long, D.R. ....17 Feb
X Luker, G.P. ....01 Mar
S Stuart, C.W.M. ....01 Mar
X Port, L.A. ....15 Apr
X Jagger, C.E. ....16 Apr
X Sheldrake, T.W. ....29 Apr
X Felgate, H. ....01 May
X Gooder, S.P. ....01 May
E Trott, P.A. ....19 May
X Nelson, T.B. ....16 Jun
S Hutchinson, T.S. ....01 Jul

X Wilson, R. ....01 Jul
X Cook, H.C. ....10 Aug
X Davies, I.H. ....16 Oct
S Mason, C.E. ....16 Nov

1984

X Squibb, C.J. ....16 Jan
X Sinclair, A.B. ....01 Feb
X Thornton, C.E. ....01 Feb
E Robinson, D.I. ....01 Feb
X Thornton, M.C. ....08 Feb
E Noye, C.L. ....21 Feb
X Eagles, A.J. ....01 Mar
X Hoole, R.J. ....01 Mar
X Scruton, N. ....16 Mar
E Smith, A.C. ....16 Mar
E Aubrey-Rees, A.W. ....16 Apr
X Coley, A.R. ....16 Apr
X McDonald, J.J.B. ....01 May
E Will, A.W. ....01 Jun
E Dixon, R.F. ....08 Jun
X Fraser, D.K. ....01 Jul
X Fewtrell, M. ....01 Sep
X Walton, D. ....01 Sep
E Lemon, R.G.A. ....01 Sep
X Pilley, M.A. ....16 Sep
X King, N.A. ....01 Dec
X Jolly, J.E.I. ....16 Dec

1985

X Terrill, K.W. ....01 Mar
X Ward, F.S. ....01 Mar
X Harrall, P.A.R. ....03 Mar
X Archdale, P.M. ....16 Mar
X Brown, P.R. ....16 Mar
X Wainwright, P.A. ....16 Mar
X Munday, I.V. ....01 Apr
X Brown, D.J. ....01 Apr
E Fergusson, R.R. ....01 May
X Stone, C.R.M. ....01 May
X Bourn, K.E. ....09 May
X Buckley, M.J. ....16 May
E Pilsworth, D.S. ....01 Jun
S Edwards, C.C. ....01 Jul
S Gopsill, B.R. ....01 Jul
X Wilson, C.G.T. ....01 Aug
X Edmonds, G. ....02 Aug
X McKay, P.A. ....16 Aug
X Wright, M.J. ....01 Sep
X Hammond, N.J. ....01 Sep
X Rowlands, G.A. ....01 Sep
S Craven, J.A.G. ....01 Sep

E Lawton, A.C.R. ....01 Nov
X Butcher, M.C. ....16 Nov
E Franks, J.P. ....01 Dec
E Coulson, J.R. ....08 Dec

1986

E Nolton, J.R. ....01 Feb
X Grandison, J.A.S. ....01 Mar
X Robertson, F.W. ....01 Mar
S Edwards, J.M. ....01 Apr
S Hayward, P.J. ....01 Apr
S Fishlock, G.N. ....16 Apr
X Blair, S.R. ....01 May
E Evans, J.W. ....06 May
X Watson, C.C. ....16 May
X Mannion, T.S. ....01 Sep
X Osman, M.R. ....01 Sep
X Field, S.N.C. ....01 Sep
X Browning, M.L.C. ....21 Sep
E Churchill, W.J. ....01 Oct
X Lewis, P.R. ....21 Nov
X Forrester, T.R. ....01 Dec
X Wilkinson, A.J. ....16 Dec

1987

X Staveley, J.R. ....01 Jan
X Chandler, S.A. ....01 Jan
X Lewis, S.B. ....01 Jan
E Fiander, P.J. ....01 Feb
X White, P. ....01 Feb
X Taylor, N.F. ....16 Feb
S Painter, C.J. ....23 Feb
E Maidment, K.C. ....01 Mar
X Gibson, T.A. ....16 Mar
E Brook, J.G. ....21 Mar
X Creates, K.I. ....01 Apr
X Jenks, A.W.J. ....16 Apr
X Field, J.D. ....16 Apr
X Sandover, R.J. ....20 Apr
X MacNaughton, F.G. ....01 May
X Martin, N.D. ....01 Jun
E Kirk, T.L. ....01 Jun
E Hunter, K.P. ....01 Aug
X Peters, A.J.U. ....01 Aug
E Lord, A.S. ....01 Sep
X Crudgington, P. ....01 Sep
X Brown, C.D. ....01 Sep
E Newton, M.R. ....22 Sep
X Goddard, D.J.S. ....01 Oct
X Gaskin, S.E. ....01 Nov
X Holmes, G. ....01 Dec
E Trotter, S. ....01 Dec

LIEUTENANT COMMANDERS

1988

X	Wood, C.A.	09 Jan
E	Leggett, S.E.	13 Jan
E	Baker, G.R.	15 Jan
S	Billington, N.S.	01 Feb
E	Edwards, A.D.P.	01 Feb
X	Sharpe, G.J.	01 Feb
E	Wombwell, J.F.	19 Feb
X	Pamphilon, M.J.	01 Mar
E	Honey, J.P.	01 Mar
E	Cross, M.G.	01 Apr
X	Nelson, D.E.	01 Apr
X	Malin, M.J.	01 Apr
E	O'Brien, P.C.	23 Apr
X	MacKett, D.G.	01 May
X	Johnson, B.	01 May
X	Speller, N.S.F.	01 May
E	Nurse, M.T.	01 Jun
X	Appleyard, T.P.	05 Jun
X	Woznicki, S.J.	16 Jun
S	Clark, R.W.	01 Jul
X	Davis, M.P.	01 Jul
S	Stobie, I.C.A.	28 Jul
E	Boyes, N.	11 Aug
X	Hirst, R.T.	01 Sep
X	Watt, S.	29 Sep
X	Bristow, G.D.	01 Oct
X	Sauze, M.J.	01 Oct
X	Tozer, C.V.	01 Oct
X	Abbey, M.P.	01 Oct
E	Dinham, A.C.	01 Oct
X	Chambers, T.G.	01 Oct
X	Holt, A.F.	01 Oct
X	Wrigley, P.J.	16 Oct
S	Seddon, J.S.M.	16 Oct
X	Smith, K.M.	16 Nov
E	Quine, N.J.	01 Dec
E	Gabriel, C.J.	01 Dec
E	Gillam, R.L.	01 Dec

1989

S	Dwane, C.M.R.	01 Jan
X	Newlands, G.A.	01 Feb
E	Tweed, C.J.	01 Feb
X	Gibbs, P.N.C.	01 Feb
E	Denison, A.R.V.T.	01 Feb
E	Jackson, S.M.	09 Feb
S	Cass, P.S.	11 Feb
X	O'Riordan, M.P.	01 Apr
X	Pollitt, D.N.A.	01 Apr
X	Baudains, T.J.	01 Apr
X	Foale, S.J.	01 Apr

S	Ramsey, J.S.	16 Apr
E	Cooper, P.F.	21 Apr
X	Newman, P.H.	01 May
E	Carver, A.G.	01 May
X	Joyner, A.	01 May
X	Kent, M.D.	01 May
E	Davey, P.J.	01 Jun
X	Yates, N.P.	01 Jun
S	Almond, D.E.M.	01 Jul
E	Jackson, S.H.	01 Jul
X	Palmer, P.A.	01 Jul
E	Faulkner, R.I.	01 Aug
E	Torvell, M.D.B.	01 Aug
X	Watson, R.J.	01 Aug
S	Lewis, G.D.	01 Sep
X	Boast, M.T.	01 Sep
X	Milton, G.B.M.	01 Oct
E	Clement, C.J.	01 Oct
X	Jennings, M.P.	01 Oct
E	Rawlings, G.C.	01 Oct
E	Eastaugh, A.C.	01 Oct
X	Murray, S.J.	01 Oct
X	Rich, J.G.	01 Oct
X	Hipsey, S.J.	01 Oct
X	Booker, G.R.	01 Oct
X	Gill, C.M.	01 Oct
X	Carr, D.L.	01 Oct
X	Dawson, P.J.	01 Oct
E	Williams, R.C.	01 Oct
E	Mant, J.N.	01 Oct
X	Carroll, P.W.M.	01 Oct
X	Carlton, I.P.	01 Oct
X	Grimley, D.M.J.	01 Nov
X	Baileff, R.I.	01 Dec

1990

X	Wade, N.C.	01 Jan
S	Large, J.L.	17 Jan
X	Croome-Carroll, M.P.J.	27 Jan
X	Knight, A.W.	01 Feb
X	Little, C.S.A.	01 Feb
X	Beats, K.A.	16 Feb
X	Leaney, M.J.	01 Mar
X	Kerr, W.M.M.	09 Mar
X	Currie, D.W.	01 Apr
X	Britton, N.J.	01 Apr
E	Fowler, P.J.S.	01 Apr
X	Kirkwood, J.A.D.	01 Apr
E	Dickinson, R.J.	01 Apr
X	Griffiths, D.T.	01 Apr
E	Boraston, P.J.	01 Apr
X	Chapple, C.P.	01 May

E	Menzies, A.J.	01 May
X	Barker, N.J.	01 May
X	Chapman, N.J.	01 May
E	Rudman, C.J.	15 May
S	Cropper, M.A.K.	16 May
X	Howarth, D.W.	01 Jun
X	Clegg, M.L.	01 Jun
E	Howard, K.A.	01 Jul
X	Chatwin, N.J.	01 Jul
E	Plant, I.R.	01 Jul
X	Pringle, A.	01 Jul
X	Lightfoot, C.D.	01 Jul
X	Finnemore, R.A.	09 Jul
X	Wass, M.J.	01 Aug
X	Mayhew, N.M.	16 Aug
X	Davies, C.S.	01 Sep
X	Mathias-Jones, P.D.	01 Sep
E	Carpenter, C.J.	01 Sep
X	Murphy, N.	01 Sep
X	Hall, D.W.	01 Oct
X	Burgess, S.	01 Oct
E	Howells, G.R.	01 Oct
X	Riches, I.C.	01 Oct
X	Saunders, J.N.	01 Oct
X	Buckett, E.J.	01 Oct
X	Slade, C.	01 Oct
E	Southern, P.J.	01 Oct
MS	Hayes, D.J.	01 Oct
E	Squire, P.A.	01 Oct
E	Robertson, D.C.	01 Oct
X	Bell, R.P.W.	01 Oct
X	Chichester, M.A.R.	01 Oct
E	Wyatt, J.M.	01 Oct
E	Elliott, T.F.	01 Oct
E	Perry, R.	01 Nov
X	Roper, M.	01 Nov
X	Straughan, C.J.	01 Dec
X	Corner, G.C.	01 Dec
X	Evans, G.R.	01 Dec
E	Maw, M.J.	01 Dec
E	Walton, J.C.	01 Dec
X	Ferguson, R.G.	12 Dec

1991

W	Hawes, G.E.	01 Jan
S	Kingsbury, J.A.T.	01 Feb
X	Marchant, T.A.C.	01 Feb
S	Radcliffe, N.	16 Feb
S	Pike, M.S.	01 Mar
E	Schmidt, J.F.K.	01 Mar
X	Eedle, R.J.	01 Mar
S	Lynch, M.	24 Mar

X	Crowther, K.W.	29 Mar
E	Martin, E.J.	01 Apr
X	Henderson, T.M.P.	01 Apr
X	Dobson, R.A.	01 Apr
X	Dunlop, P.F.	01 Apr
X	Roberts, D.H.W.	01 Apr
X	Kelly, R.	03 Apr
S	Barnwell, K.L.	23 Apr
X	Naismith, D.H.	01 May
E	Trewhella, G.G.	01 May
E	Barclay, J.H.B.	01 May
E	Long, N.A.	01 May
X	MacDonald, G.D.	01 May
E	Quick, N.H.	01 May
E	Stott, J.A.	26 May
E	Griffiths, D.M.	01 Jun
E	Gibson, D.T.	01 Jun
X	Gomm, K.	01 Jun
E	James, C.	01 Jun
X	Turner, D.	03 Jun
E	Gibson, A.	08 Jun
E	Plant, M.G.	13 Jun
E	Lacey, I.N.	16 Jun
E	Stewart, R.W.	01 Jul
X	Smith, N.P.	01 Jul
E	Cochrane, M.D.	09 Aug
X	Greenwood, M.J.	01 Sep
E	Canty, N.R.	01 Sep
E	Lawson, S.J.	01 Sep
E	Ball, M.P.	01 Sep
S	Lloyd, D.P.J.	01 Sep
X	Donaldson, S.B.	01 Sep
X	Leaning, M.V.	01 Sep
E	Clark, A.N.	01 Sep
E	Shaw, I.B.	15 Sep
X	Lee, M.M.	01 Oct
X	Owen, P.C.	01 Oct
X	Harvey, P.A.	01 Oct
E	Hanslip, M.R.	01 Oct
E	Wilkinson, A.	01 Oct
X	Hawkins, R.H.	01 Oct
X	Stanton, D.V.	01 Oct
X	Bunn, M.E.	01 Oct
X	Carrington-Wood, C.G.	01 Oct
E	Cowton, E.N.	01 Oct
X	Shawcross, P.K.	01 Oct
X	Graham, D.E.	01 Oct
E	Vamplew, D.	01 Oct
X	Burden, J.C.	01 Nov
X	Key, D.F.	01 Nov
X	Bernau, J.C.	01 Nov

LIEUTENANT COMMANDERS

X	Metcalfe, A.P.W.	01 Dec
X	McHale, G.J.	01 Dec

1992

E	Masters, R.H.	01 Jan
X	Morse, A.C.	01 Jan
X	Price, T.W.	01 Jan
X	Drylie, A.J.	01 Feb
X	Potts, K.M.	01 Feb
X	Smith, S.L.	01 Feb
X	Trathen, N.C.	01 Feb
E	Morgan, A.K.G.	06 Feb
E	White, P.A.	16 Feb
X	Moss, P.	18 Feb
X	Blakey, A.L.	01 Mar
E	Mundin, A.J.	01 Apr
E	Townshend, J.J.	03 Apr
X	Powell, S.	16 Apr
X	Jenkin, J.R.S.L.	01 May
X	Deighton, D.S.	01 May
E	Kennedy, N.H.	01 May
X	Roberts, D.A.	01 May
X	Giles, K.D.L.	01 May
E	Bone, C.J.	01 May
X	Bromige, T.R.J.	19 May
E	Clarke, R.D.	27 May
X	Williams, D.I.	29 May
X	Abbott, S.S.C.	01 Jun
E	Burdett, R.W.	01 Jun
E	Peacock, S.	01 Jun
X	Bridger, R.J.	01 Jun
X	Emmerson, G.J.	01 Jun
S	Murphy, J.	01 Jun
X	Morris, P.J.	10 Jun
X	Jones, P.	01 Jul
X	Barnes-Yallowley, J.J.H.	16 Jul
S	Giles, A.R.	21 Jul
E	Randall, R.D.	01 Aug
E	Sennitt, J.W.	01 Aug
X	West, M.W.	05 Aug
E	John, G.D.	01 Sep
E	King, P.C.	01 Sep
X	Mardon, K.F.	02 Sep
X	Thomas, K.I.	01 Oct
X	Richford, T.F.	01 Oct
X	Murton, W.M.	01 Oct
X	Shepherd, P.R.	01 Oct
X	Austin, J.D.	01 Oct
W	Price, T.L.	01 Oct
X	Fox, R.G.	01 Oct
X	Nelson, D.L.	01 Oct
X	Dunn, N.G.	01 Oct

E	Toon, J.R.	01 Oct
X	Maude, C.P.	01 Oct
S	Chapman, N.P.	01 Oct
X	Needham, P.D.	01 Oct
X	Suddes, L.A.	01 Oct
X	Whitehead, D.	01 Oct
S	Davies, J.P.	01 Oct
E	Shepherd, A.	01 Oct
X	Crumplin, C.A.	01 Oct
E	Coppin, P.D.	01 Oct
E	Dalton, D.J.	01 Oct
X	Howorth, K.	01 Dec

1993

X	Bilson, J.M.F.	01 Jan
X	Woolley, M.J.	01 Jan
S	Teasdale, R.M.	16 Jan
X	Walker, N.L.	01 Feb
X	Chesterman, G.J.	01 Feb
X	Langley, E.S.	01 Feb
E	Upton, I.D.	01 Feb
E	Claxton, M.G.	18 Feb
E	Dustan, A.J.	19 Feb
X	Fortescue, R.C.	01 Mar
X	Hall, N.J.	01 Mar
X	Hall, A.P.	01 Mar
E	Loring, A.	01 Mar
E	Pratt, I.H.	01 Mar
X	Hobbs, A.R.	01 Apr
S	Lister, S.R.	01 Apr
X	Osbourn, S.E.J.	01 Apr
X	Price, D.J.	01 Apr
E	Tulloch, F.M.	01 Apr
E	Fogg, D.S.	01 Apr
X	Edwards, P.J.	01 May
X	Dodds, R.S.	01 May
X	Smith, R.W.R.	01 May
X	Warlow, M.R.N.	01 May
X	Hall, R.L.	01 May
E	McTear, K.	16 May
S	Mellor, B.J.	16 May
E	Sutton, G.D.	01 Jun
E	Collier, A.S.	01 Jun
E	Murdoch, A.W.	01 Jun
X	Witton, J.W.	01 Jun
E	Sneyd, E.P.B.	20 Jun
X	Bennett, G.L.N.	01 Jul
X	Aiken, S.R.	01 Jul
E	Giles, D.W.	01 Jul
E	McNaughton, J.A.	01 Jul
X	Russell, T.	01 Jul
X	French, K.L.	09 Jul

S	Tyler, P.L.	10 Jul
E	Burnip, J.M.	01 Aug
E	Tarr, R.N.V.	01 Aug
S	Wiltcher, R.A.	01 Aug
X	Green, D.P.	13 Aug
X	Godfrey, K.R.	01 Sep
X	Smith, M.R.K.	01 Sep
E	Stewart, J.N.	01 Sep
E	Knight, P.R.	01 Sep
X	Landrock, G.J.	01 Sep
E	Udensi, E.A.A.A.	01 Sep
E	Anderson, F.B.	01 Oct
X	Burgess, J.D.A.	01 Oct
X	Chartres, D.I.	01 Oct
X	Thornton, P.J.	01 Oct
X	Bate, C.	01 Oct
X	Doherty, K.	01 Oct
E	Mills, T.C.	01 Oct
E	Talbot, N.A.	01 Oct
E	Lawrence, S.P.	01 Oct
X	Bradburn, S.J.	01 Oct
E	Smith, G.K.	01 Oct
X	Drury, M.H.	01 Oct
E	Ford, N.P.	01 Oct
E	Franks, P.D.	01 Oct
X	Stacey, H.A.	01 Oct
E	Hamilton, R.A.	01 Oct
E	Tougher, R.	01 Oct
E	Robertson, D.M.	01 Oct
X	Bowker, G.N.	01 Oct
E	Pitcher, J.	01 Oct
X	Bird, D.E.	01 Oct
E	Sweeny, B.D.	01 Oct
X	Clark, P.M.C.	01 Oct
W	Silver, C.K.	01 Oct
E	Janaway, P.	01 Oct
S	McKnight, N.W.	01 Oct
X	Watts, A.P.	01 Oct
X	Acland, D.D.	01 Oct
E	Goodrich, D.L.	01 Oct
E	Muscroft, P.J.V.	01 Oct
X	Hinch, N.E.	01 Oct
E	Gray, D.	01 Oct
E	Greenfield, K.	01 Oct
S	Burt, P.R.	01 Oct
S	Howell, M.	01 Oct
S	Nowosielski, F.	01 Oct
E	Shirley, W.P.	12 Oct
X	James, C.W.	27 Oct
X	Conway, J.J.	01 Nov
X	Raisbeck, P.T.	01 Nov

LIEUTENANT COMMANDERS

S	Taylor, S.M.	01 Nov
X	Wyatt, D.J.	01 Nov
S	Flynn, M.T.	01 Nov
X	Howell, S.B.	01 Nov
X	Elvin, A.J.	06 Nov
X	Gladwell, T.J.	01 Dec
X	Cunningham, J.G.	01 Dec

1994

E	Adams, P.	01 Jan
X	Brown, W.C.	01 Jan
X	McGrenary, A.	01 Jan
X	Ventura, D.C.	01 Jan
E	Blackman, N.T.	01 Jan
E	Denovan, P.A.	01 Jan
E	Horton, P.A.	01 Jan
X	Hunter, N.M.	01 Jan
E	Brads, W.	14 Jan
S	Webber, S.J.A.M.	01 Feb
E	Salter, J.A.	10 Feb
X	Neve, P.C.	11 Feb
X	Saxby, K.A.	24 Feb
X	Newall, J.A.	01 Mar
E	Kirkup, J.P.	01 Mar
X	Moorey, C.G.	01 Mar
X	Harrison, C.A.	01 Mar
E	Cattroll, I.M.	01 Mar
X	Deller, M.G.	01 Mar
E	Whitehouse, M.J.	01 Mar
E	Depledge, I.G.	01 Apr
X	Meredith, N.	01 Apr
X	Poole, J.L.	01 Apr
X	Robertson, M.G.	01 Apr
E	Blount, D.R.	01 Apr
X	Crispin, T.A.B.	01 Apr
X	Hailstone, J.H.S.	16 May
X	Eaton, P.G.	01 Jun
E	Bolam, A.G.	01 Jun
X	Andrews, P.N.	01 Jun
E	Duncan, I.S.	01 Jun
X	Fields, D.G.	01 Jun
X	Lunn, A.C.	01 Jun
X	Hardacre, P.V.	01 Jun
X	Haycock, T.P.	01 Jun
X	Towler, P.J.B.	01 Jun
E	Pryde, C.S.	01 Jul
X	Horsley, A.M.R.	01 Jul
X	Houghton, P.J.	01 Jul
S	Smerdon, C.D.E.	01 Jul
X	Stuttard, M.C.	01 Jul
E	Westwood, M.R.T.	01 Jul
X	Abernethy, L.J.F.	11 Jul

E	Griffiths, A.J.	26 Jul
X	Horner, P.A.	01 Aug
E	Dowell, P.H.N.	01 Aug
X	Denholm, I.G.	13 Aug
X	Swift, R.D.	28 Aug
E	Cropley, A.	01 Sep
E	Saunders, T.M.	01 Sep
X	Glass, J.E.	01 Sep
X	Robin, C.C.E.	01 Sep
X	Fleming, S.A.	30 Sep
X	Rawson, C.	01 Oct
E	Day, T.M.	01 Oct
E	Bryce, C.G.	01 Oct
X	Hands, A.P.	01 Oct
E	Alison, L.A.	01 Oct
E	Haskell, E.T.	01 Oct
X	Monger, P.D.	01 Oct
X	Scott-Dickins, C.A.	01 Oct
X	Davison, A.P.	01 Oct
X	Taylor, L.	01 Oct
X	Hicking, N.	01 Oct
X	Sewed, M.A.	01 Oct
X	Porter, C.W.	01 Oct
X	Walker, M.C.	01 Oct
X	Dowdell, R.E.J.	01 Oct
E	Smyth, M.J.	01 Oct
E	Franks, D.I.	01 Oct
E	Hammersley, J.M.	01 Oct
E	Naden, J.R.	01 Oct
X	Burrows, M.J.	01 Oct
X	Fraser, P.T.	01 Oct
X	Thompson, N.J.	01 Oct
X	Madge, A.W.J.	01 Oct
E	Sugden, M.R.	01 Oct
X	Savage, S.	01 Oct
X	Suddes, T.	01 Oct
X	Lee, J.C.	01 Oct
X	Elliman, S.M.	01 Oct
E	Hyde, T.	01 Oct
X	Dane, R.M.H.	01 Oct
E	Snow, P.F.	01 Oct
S	De La Mare, R.M.	01 Oct
X	Hamilton, G.R.	01 Oct
X	Disney, P.W.	01 Oct
E	Gilbert, L.G.	01 Oct
E	Sumner, M.D.	01 Oct
X	Bryant, D.J.	01 Oct
E	De Jonghe, P.T.	01 Oct
X	Francis, J.	01 Oct
S	David, S.E.J.	16 Oct
E	Howard, N.	31 Oct

LIEUTENANT COMMANDERS

X	Gunn, W.J.S.	01 Nov
E	Clark, K.C.	01 Nov
X	Hurry, A.P.	01 Nov
E	Bull, G.C.	01 Nov
E	Saxby, C.J.	01 Nov
E	Clark, I.D.	01 Nov
E	Harding, G.A.	01 Dec
X	Hills, A.A.	01 Dec
X	Swarbrick, R.J.	01 Dec
X	Hart, M.A.	01 Dec
X	Sutcliffe, J.	21 Dec

1995

X	Lydiate, G.	01 Jan
S	Trundle, D.J.W.	01 Jan
X	George, A.P.	16 Jan
X	Hutchison, G.B.	01 Feb
E	Campbell, R.D.H.	01 Feb
X	Ovenden, N.S.P.	01 Feb
X	Hunt, J.S.P.	05 Feb
X	Lewis, T.J.	05 Feb
X	Baldwin, C.M.	01 Mar
E	Boyd, N.	01 Mar
E	Dathan, T.J.	01 Mar
X	Pillar, C.D.	01 Mar
X	Firth, N.R.	01 Mar
X	Jones, M.	01 Mar
E	Gillham, P.R.	02 Mar
S	Shaw, P.J.	17 Mar
X	Stangroom, A.	24 Mar
X	Law, J.	27 Mar
E	Gray, D.K.	01 Apr
E	Munro, K.	01 Apr
X	Egeland-Jensen, F.A.	01 Apr
E	Gill, M.R.	01 Apr
E	Gillan, G.M.	01 Apr
E	Holmes, R.W.	01 Apr
E	Reed, J.H.	01 Apr
E	Smith, K.A.	01 Apr
X	Greenland, M.R.	16 Apr
X	Smith, C.P.	26 Apr
E	Reynolds, T.P.	30 Apr
X	Birley, J.H.	01 May
X	Amphlett, N.G.	01 May
E	Mills, A.	01 May
E	Harding, D.M.	01 May
X	Hawkins, M.A.J.	01 May
X	Marshall, R.G.C.	01 May
X	Goldsmith, S.V.W.	01 May
X	Webb, A.J.	01 May
E	Green, D.P.S.	01 May
X	Schnadhorst, J.C.	01 May
S	Willis, M.S.	02 May
X	Gurmin, S.J.A.	18 May
X	Thomson, D.	23 May
E	Hewitt, A.	01 Jun
E	Brown, P.S.J.	01 Jun
E	Grenfell-Shaw, M.C.	01 Jun
X	Johnston, T.A.	01 Jun
E	McInnes, J.G.K.	01 Jun
X	Mannion, R.V.	01 Jun
X	Woodward, D.J.	01 Jul
X	Cornish, M.C.	01 Jul
X	Foster, D.G.S.	01 Jul
E	Gibbs, N.D.	01 Jul
X	Lochrane, A.E.R.	01 Jul
X	Pollock, M.P.	01 Jul
X	Nisbet, J.H.T.	01 Jul
E	Roberts, T.J.	01 Jul
E	Smith, M.R.	14 Jul
X	Coomber, M.A.	18 Jul
E	Rawlings, D.P.	01 Aug
X	Greenaway, N.M.	01 Aug
E	Kennedy, I.J.A.	01 Aug
X	Juckes, M.A.	16 Aug
E	Collins, P.R.	01 Sep
X	Harper, C.H.	01 Sep
X	Jones, G.R.	01 Sep
X	Beardall, M.J.D.	01 Sep
X	Burke, M.C.	01 Sep
X	Hill, R.A.	01 Sep
E	Jenkins, G.W.	01 Sep
X	Williams, D.S.	01 Sep
X	Window, S.H.	01 Sep
X	Fitzsimmons, M.B.	01 Sep
X	Martin, R.G.	01 Sep
E	Murphy, P.W.	01 Sep
X	Evans, M.J.	01 Sep
X	Evans, A.W.	01 Oct
X	Gobey, C.G.	01 Oct
X	Moffatt, R.	01 Oct
E	Oldfield, P.H.	01 Oct
E	Macaulay, N.	01 Oct
X	Dean, W.M.H.	01 Oct
X	Daniels, I.J.R.	01 Oct
E	Nunn, G.E.	01 Oct
E	Goble, I.J.	01 Oct
X	Holley, A.J.	01 Oct
E	Chapman, G.J.D.	01 Oct
X	Wilson, R.P.	01 Oct
X	Carter, R.I.	01 Oct
E	Edwards, R.A.	01 Oct
X	Smith, K.J.	01 Oct
X	Callister, D.R.	01 Oct
E	Cunningham, C.	01 Oct
E	Hassall, H.	01 Oct
X	Pipkin, S.C.	01 Oct
X	Lawler, J.A.	01 Oct
X	Mathieson, K.R.	01 Oct
X	Brundle, P.R.	01 Oct
X	Carretta, M.V.	01 Oct
X	Collins, D.A.	01 Oct
E	Nelson, A.	01 Oct
X	Daniell, C.J.	01 Oct
E	Rippingale, S.N.	01 Oct
X	Cox, J.P.	01 Oct
X	Fincher, K.J.	01 Oct
X	Bate, D.I.G.	01 Oct
E	Andrews, I.	01 Oct
E	Roberts, E.W.	01 Oct
E	Pickbourne, M.	01 Oct
E	Peerman, S.J.	01 Oct
S	Dobson, B.J.	01 Oct
E	Maidment, P.C.	01 Oct
X	Daniel, A.G.	01 Oct
X	Jenrick, M.F.	01 Oct
X	Welch, A.	13 Oct
X	Davis, A.R.	18 Oct
X	MacKenzie, M.D.	01 Nov
E	Lipscomb, P.	01 Nov
X	Vickery, T.K.	01 Nov
E	Burlingham, B.L.	01 Nov
X	Hutton, S.J.	01 Nov
X	Allen, D.R.	01 Nov
S	Porrett, J.A.	14 Nov
E	Stephenson, D.	22 Nov
S	Willis, A.J.	01 Dec
X	Aspden, A.M.	01 Dec
X	Waddington, A.K.	01 Dec
X	Pentreath, J.P.	01 Dec
X	Cunningham, D.A.	15 Dec
X	Boddington, J.D.L.	16 Dec
X	Meeds, K.	16 Dec
X	Bath, E.G.	27 Dec

1996

E	Warren, M.K.	01 Jan
X	Cramp, A.M.	01 Jan
X	Rogers, I.A.	01 Jan
X	Sherriff, D.A.	01 Jan
E	Munns, A.R.	01 Jan
X	Craig, P.D.	01 Feb
X	Dyke, C.L.	01 Feb
X	Atkinson, M.	01 Feb
S	Carter, S.N.	01 Feb

E	Metcalfe, P.G.	01 Feb
X	Salisbury, D.P.	01 Feb
E	Mace, S.B.	01 Feb
S	Walmsley, E.A.	08 Feb
X	Bankier, S.	19 Feb
X	Draper, S.P.	26 Feb
E	Fieldsend, M.A.	01 Mar
X	Furlong, K.	01 Mar
E	Toft, M.D.	01 Mar
S	Notley, L.P.	01 Mar
E	Gilbert, P.D.	01 Mar
S	Smith, C.J.	16 Mar
S	Straw, A.N.	16 Mar
X	Harry, A.D.	01 Apr
S	Hayle, J.K.	01 Apr
E	Jackson, I.A.	01 Apr
X	Lindsay, I.G.	01 Apr
X	Smith, K.B.A.	01 Apr
E	Withers, J.W.	01 Apr
X	Chrishop, T.I.	01 Apr
X	Kilby, S.E.	01 Apr
E	Kingsbury, S.H.	01 Apr
E	Pear, I.K.	01 Apr
X	Collins, G.J.S.	07 Apr
S	Waters, N.R.	16 Apr
S	Marston, P.A.	16 Apr
S	McConochie, A.D.	16 Apr
S	Taylor, S.J.	16 Apr
X	Mahony, D.G.	16 Apr
E	Walker, P.R.	01 May
E	Worthington, J.M.F.	01 May
E	Winkle, S.J.	01 May
E	Fitzjohn, D.	01 May
E	Merritt, J.J.	01 May
E	Harrop, I.	01 May
X	Masters, J.C.	01 May
E	Scott, J.B.	01 May
E	Shepherd, R.G.	01 May
X	Maher, M.P.	16 May
E	Carter, J.M.	01 Jun
X	Moore, P.H.G.	01 Jun
X	Gazzard, J.H.	01 Jun
E	Hill, P.J.	01 Jun
X	Corbett, A.S.	01 Jun
E	Freeman, D.R.	01 Jun
X	Hayward, C.E.W.	01 Jun
E	Hutchins, T.P.	01 Jun
E	Short, J.J.	01 Jun
E	Prior, G.M.	02 Jun
S	Goldthorpe, M.	06 Jun
X	Hill, M.R.	22 Jun

LIEUTENANT COMMANDERS

E	Kempsell, I.D.	26 Jun
X	Clayton, S.	01 Jul
X	Taylor, B.D.	01 Jul
X	Bellfield, R.J.A.	01 Jul
E	Buckle, I.L.	01 Jul
X	McDonough, A.G.	01 Jul
X	Simpson, M.J.	01 Jul
X	Tetlow, H.S.G.	01 Jul
X	Green, P.J.	01 Jul
S	Jewitt, C.J.B.	01 Jul
X	McCall, I.R.	01 Jul
E	Pooley, S.W.	01 Jul
E	Stace, I.S.	01 Jul
E	Rimmer, H.E.	22 Jul
S	Hibbert, N.J.	29 Jul
E	Geary, T.W.	01 Aug
X	Coles, A.L.	01 Aug
X	Secretan, S.J.	01 Aug
X	Abernethy, J.R.G.	01 Aug
X	Howard, P.M.	16 Aug
E	Hope, K.	01 Sep
X	Benton, A.M.	01 Sep
E	Young, M.S.	01 Sep
E	Geddis, R.D.	01 Sep
X	Brady, S.E.	01 Sep
X	Bark, J.S.	01 Sep
E	Woodford, G.I.	01 Sep
E	Coles, C.J.	01 Sep
E	Harrison, P.G.	12 Sep
E	Goodings, G.J.	01 Oct
X	Corbett, G.J.	01 Oct
X	Meakin, B.R.	01 Oct
X	Hibbert, M.C.	01 Oct
X	Creech, R.D.	01 Oct
X	Jefferson, P.M.	01 Oct
E	Gratton, S.W.	01 Oct
E	Hartley, S.W.	01 Oct
E	Johns, S.A.B.	01 Oct
X	Sykes, R.A.	01 Oct
X	Dickson, J.P.E.	01 Oct
X	Munro-Lott, P.R.J.	01 Oct
X	Hoper, P.R.	01 Oct
X	Biggs, D.M.	01 Oct
X	Webb, C.M.	01 Oct
E	O'Brien, P.M.C.	01 Oct
X	Wilkinson, P.M.	01 Oct
E	Ashton Jones, G.	01 Oct
X	Armstrong, N.P.B.	01 Oct
W	Whetton, J.B.D.	01 Oct
E	Clarke, R.	01 Oct
W	Kent, I.M.	01 Oct

X	Slocombe, C.A.	01 Oct
E	Lias, C.D.	01 Oct
X	Salmon, M.A.	01 Oct
E	Ashton, R.D.	01 Oct
E	Bracher, H.	01 Oct
E	Rook, D.J.	01 Oct
X	Hudson, P.T.	01 Oct
MS	Lloyd, C.J.	01 Oct
S	Olliver, A.J.	01 Oct
E	Lovegrove, R.A.	01 Oct
X	Newland, M.I.	01 Oct
E	Foster, G.J.	01 Oct
X	Seymour, K.W.	01 Oct
X	Leitch, I.R.	01 Oct
E	Myerscough, A.P.	01 Oct
E	Peacock, M.R.	01 Oct
E	Dobbin, V.W.	01 Oct
X	Evans, D.J.	01 Oct
X	Saynor, R.M.	01 Oct
E	Wood, I.D.	01 Oct
E	Galvin, D.	01 Oct
E	Rodgers, S.	01 Oct
S	Aitken, K.M.	01 Oct
X	Mitchinson, L.	01 Oct
X	Thorburn, A.	01 Oct
X	Van-Den-Bergh, W.L.	01 Oct
E	Mockford, J.A.	01 Oct
S	Ewen, R.J.	01 Oct
E	Cooper, K.P.	01 Oct
E	Fraser, W.C.	01 Oct
S	McGarel, D.F.	01 Oct
E	Marson, G.M.	14 Oct
X	Edgley, A.D.	15 Oct
E	Watson, P.G.C.	25 Oct
E	Burwin, H.L.	01 Nov
S	Toomey, N.J.	01 Nov
X	Gale, S.P.	01 Nov
E	Stirzaker, M.	01 Nov
X	Bowen, N.T.	01 Nov
X	Briers, M.P.	01 Nov
S	Philpott, N.E.	01 Nov
E	Higgins, G.N.	01 Nov
X	Dible, J.H.	16 Nov
E	Wilson, C.J.	01 Dec
S	Blackwell, R.E.	01 Dec
E	Cran, B.C.	01 Dec
S	Hollins, R.P.	01 Dec
X	Barnbrook, J.C.	16 Dec
S	Kyte, A.J.	16 Dec

1997

X	Shepherd, C.S.	01 Jan

LIEUTENANTCOMMANDERS

X	Lister, M.	01 Jan	X	Pethybridge, R.A.	01 May	X	Daw, S.J.	01 Oct
X	Adam, I.K.	01 Jan	E	Carrick, R.J.	01 May	W	Cobb, J.E.	01 Oct
X	Carson, N.D.E.	01 Jan	E	King, N.W.	01 May	X	Mickleburgh, A.	01 Oct
E	Jackson, A.S.	01 Jan	E	Martin, B.A.	01 May	X	Lambourne, D.J.	01 Oct
E	Harrison, D.	05 Jan	S	Mearns, C.M.	01 May	E	Cooper, N.P.	01 Oct
E	Irwin, M.A.	09 Jan	X	Rich, D.C.	20 May	X	Clucas, M.R.	01 Oct
X	Noyce, N.R.	15 Jan	E	Thomson, I.R.	22 May	E	Morris, S.T.	01 Oct
X	Davies, M.B.	24 Jan	E	Read, J.M.	23 May	X	James, A.J.	01 Oct
S	Wintle, G.L.	01 Feb	X	Robertson, D.C.	01 Jun	E	Morgan, S.A.	01 Oct
X	Drysdale, S.R.	01 Feb	E	Titcomb, A.C.	01 Jun	X	Moys, A.J.	01 Oct
E	Gillies, R.R.	01 Feb	X	Woollcombe-Gosson, D.J.	01 Jun	X	Fleming, K.P.	01 Oct
E	Parvin, P.S.	01 Feb	S	Edge, J.H.	01 Jun	X	Brooks, M.L.	01 Oct
S	Hill, R.K.J.	16 Feb	X	Breckenridge, I.G.	01 Jul	E	Monk, C.D.	01 Oct
S	Stanton, P.C.M.	16 Feb	X	Irons, P.A.	01 Jul	E	Lawrence, S.R.	01 Oct
X	Hulme, T.M.	01 Mar	E	Rowse, M.L.	01 Jul	X	Dawkins, M.W.	01 Oct
X	Ireland, P.C.	01 Mar	X	Woods, J.B.	01 Jul	X	Cook, D.J.	01 Oct
X	Bell, R.D.	01 Mar	E	MacDonald, J.R.	01 Jul	E	Price, T.P.	01 Oct
E	Bartlett, D.S.G.	01 Mar	E	Mather, G.P.	01 Jul	X	Cornick, R.M.	01 Oct
X	Chandler, N.J.	01 Mar	E	Peace, R.W.	02 Jul	X	Harmer, J.N.J.	01 Oct
S	Chapell, A.	01 Mar	X	Wright, S.H.	16 Jul	X	Hunt, C.J.	01 Oct
X	Cummings, A.T.	01 Mar	X	Ellis, N.M.	18 Jul	X	Hargreaves, N.	01 Oct
X	Hogg, C.W.	01 Mar	X	Forester-Bennett, R.M.W.	24 Jul	E	Leonard, M.	01 Oct
E	Mallinson, R.	01 Mar	X	Spiller, V.J.	28 Jul	E	Rowe, P.E.	01 Oct
S	Murrison, R.A.	01 Mar	E	Pearson, N.	01 Aug	W	Campbell, K.L.	01 Oct
E	Bull, C.M.S.	01 Mar	X	Woollven, A.H.	01 Aug	E	Davies, T.M.	01 Oct
X	Harvey, R.M.M.J.	01 Mar	X	Stannard, M.P.	01 Aug	S	Watts, D.J.	01 Oct
X	Swain, A.V.	05 Mar	E	Graham, D.W.S.	01 Aug	E	Wiffin, A.F.	01 Oct
S	Williams, M.S.	29 Mar	S	Horswill, M.N.	01 Aug	E	Taylor, K.	01 Oct
X	Cowley, R.M.	01 Apr	X	Vitali, R.C.	01 Aug	X	Randall, N.J.	01 Oct
X	New, C.M.	01 Apr	X	Kyd, J.P.	01 Aug	E	Cole, S.P.	01 Oct
X	Scott, J.A.	01 Apr	E	Reynolds, A.G.	01 Aug	E	Downie, A.J.	01 Oct
X	Morris, R.J.	01 Apr	E	Spring, J.M.	03 Aug	X	Harper, J.A.	01 Oct
E	Patterson-Hollis, C.	01 Apr	S	Evans, E.M.	16 Aug	MS	Kenney, R.P.	01 Oct
X	Toothill, J.S.	01 Apr	X	Bourne, C.M.	16 Aug	X	Yarker, D.L.	01 Oct
X	Barker, P.T.	01 Apr	X	Ovens, M.J.	20 Aug	X	Stuttard, S.E.	01 Oct
X	Bowbrick, R.C.	01 Apr	X	Webber, C.J.	26 Aug	E	Tapping, K.	01 Oct
X	Bower, N.S.	01 Apr	X	Hare, J.H.	01 Sep	S	Bennett, A.J.	01 Oct
X	Holt, S.	01 Apr	E	Richardson, M.A.	01 Sep	S	Finch, T.S.A.	01 Oct
E	Kissane, R.E.T.	01 Apr	E	Cree, A.M.	01 Sep	X	Morris, P.J.	01 Oct
X	Lane, R.N.	01 Apr	X	Wynn, S.R.	01 Sep	E	Graham, R.	01 Oct
X	Lowson, R.M.	01 Apr	X	Petheram, A.J.	01 Sep	E	Moss, T.E.	01 Oct
E	Dailey, P.G.J.	01 Apr	X	Tebbet, P.N.	01 Sep	E	Hellyn, D.R.	01 Oct
X	Ryan, R.M.	01 Apr	X	Hutchinson, O.J.P.	01 Sep	E	McHale, K.	01 Oct
X	Wilson-Chalon, L.M.	01 Apr	X	Llewelyn, K.	01 Oct	X	Ward, D.S.	01 Oct
X	Davison, J.E.	06 Apr	E	Evans, S.J.	01 Oct	E	Morrison, R.W.	01 Oct
S	Nicholson, H.	06 Apr	E	Mann, G.D.	01 Oct	X	Griffiths, A.	01 Oct
E	Harris, A.G.	12 Apr	E	Granger, C.R.	01 Oct	E	Walker, R.D.	01 Oct
E	Finch, R.L.	01 May	X	Broster, P.T.	01 Oct	E	White, R.F.	01 Oct
E	Feeney, M.L.	01 May	X	Edwards, J.P.T.	01 Oct	S	Knill, R.L.	01 Oct
E	Clark, S.R.	01 May	X	Stringer, R.A.	01 Oct	E	Oflaherty, J.S.	03 Oct
E	Knight, P.J.	01 May	E	Heneghan, J.F.	01 Oct	X	Wheatley, W.J.	04 Oct

X	Surgey, I.C.	26 Oct
X	Tabeart, G.W.	01 Nov
X	Hibberd, N.J.	01 Nov
X	Jones, A.D.	01 Nov
E	Morgan, F.S.	01 Nov
X	White, J.A.P.	01 Nov
X	Houlberg, K.M.T.	01 Nov
S	Gibson, A.D.	16 Nov
S	Asbridge, J.I.	16 Nov
X	Rolph, A.P.M.	16 Nov
S	Hewitt, L.R.	16 Nov
E	Faulkner, D.W.	29 Nov
X	Allen, S.M.	01 Dec
X	Dale-Smith, G.	01 Dec
X	Ince, D.P.	01 Dec
X	Montgomery, M.H.	01 Dec
X	Venables, A.N.	01 Dec
X	Halton, P.V.	01 Dec
E	Coulson, P.	01 Dec
S	Towler, A.	14 Dec
X	Prentice, D.C.	22 Dec

1998

X	Carroll, P.J.	01 Jan
X	Peacock, T.J.	01 Jan
E	Bartlett, I.D.	01 Jan
S	Burningham, M.R.	01 Jan
E	Kitchen, S.A.	01 Jan
X	Lea, J.	01 Jan
E	Matthews, D.W.	01 Jan
X	Romney, P.D.	01 Jan
X	Smith, G.C.S.	01 Jan
E	Ward, S.D.	01 Jan
X	Young, G.L.	01 Jan
E	Hemsworth, K.J.	01 Jan
E	Hill, G.F.	01 Jan
X	Dunn, R.P.	02 Jan
S	Trump, N.W.	16 Jan
S	Hood, K.C.	16 Jan
X	Haseldine, S.G.	01 Feb
X	Allen, A.D.	01 Feb
E	Williams, A.J.	01 Feb
E	Beadsmoore, J.E.	01 Feb
X	Bence, D.E.	01 Feb
X	Carroll, B.J.	01 Feb
E	Hughesdon, M.D.	01 Feb
X	MacIver, G.	01 Feb
X	Mugridge, D.R.	01 Feb
S	Parry, A.K.I.	01 Feb
E	Petitt, S.R.	01 Feb
E	Rogers, A.G.	01 Feb
E	Russell, P.R.	01 Feb

LIEUTENANT COMMANDERS

E	Thomas, J.H.	01 Feb
X	Titcomb, M.R.	01 Feb
E	Wellington, S.	01 Feb
E	Franks, C.S.	01 Feb
E	Blackburn, S.A.	01 Mar
X	Hatcher, R.S.	01 Mar
X	Goodman, A.T.	01 Mar
X	Mules, A.J.	01 Mar
E	Powell, M.A.	01 Mar
X	Spring, A.R.J.	01 Mar
S	Wood, R.	01 Mar
X	Dainton, S.	01 Mar
X	Scott, R.J.	02 Mar
X	McKenzie, M.	03 Mar
X	Stowell, Pl.M.	01 Apr
E	Hamilton, A.J.B.	01 Apr
E	Lynn, S.R.	01 Apr
X	MacDonald-Robinson,NUS.	01 Apr
E	Petherick, J.S.	01 Apr
E	Roberts, S.D.	01 Apr
E	Rook, G.I.	01 Apr
X	Smith, A.P.	01 Apr
X	Chapman, S.J.	01 Apr
E	Hood, K.M.	01 Apr
E	MacGillivray, I.	01 Apr
E	Biggs, W.P.L.	01 Apr
E	Ferris, D.P.S.	01 Apr
E	Paris, W.	15 Apr
E	Bone, R.C.	01 May
E	Green, A.J.	01 May
E	Fawcett, F.P.	01 May
E	Hepworth, A.W.D.	01 May
X	Merewether, H.A.H.	01 May
X	Goodacre, I.R.	01 May
E	Helliwell, M.A.	01 May
E	Hutchison, P.G.	01 May
E	Winter, T.M.	01 May
X	Burns, D.I.	01 May
E	Dunn, G.R.	01 May
X	Royston, S.J.	01 May
X	Anstey, R.J.	01 May
E	Christian, D.	01 May
E	Morshead, C.H.	14 May
E	Millar, G.C.	15 May
S	Evans, M.D.	16 May
X	Long, A.D.	16 May
E	Harvey, G.	25 May
E	Philo, J.Q.	01 Jun
E	Murray, G.M.	01 Jun
E	Baker, M.J.	01 Jun
E	Bosustow, A.M.	01 Jun

X	Davidson, A.M.	01 Jun
E	Evans, G.	01 Jun
X	Green, J.	01 Jun
X	Payne, J.D.	01 Jun
E	Shutts, D.	01 Jun
X	Deacon, S.	01 Jun
E	Hanson, N.A.	01 Jun
S	Walsh, M.A.	21 Jun
X	Kimberley, R.	01 Jul
X	Lowther, J.M.	01 Jul
X	Powell, S.R.	01 Jul
X	Beech, C.M.	01 Jul
X	Price, T.A.	01 Jul
X	Axon, D.B.	01 Jul
X	Bird, R.A.J.	01 Jul
E	O'Shea, E.P.	01 Jul
X	Hurrell, P.R.	01 Jul
X	Badrock, B.	05 Jul
E	Roots, S.	01 Aug
E	Hall, A.J.	01 Aug
X	Cryar, T.M.C.	01 Aug
X	Graham, I.E.	01 Aug
X	Ford, M.J.	05 Aug
X	Albon, M.	12 Aug
X	Hawkins, J.S.	16 Aug
E	Hinks, K.J.	25 Aug
X	McGuire, M.J.	31 Aug
B	Band, J.W.	01 Sep
E	Stewart, K.C.	01 Sep
X	Toor, J.J.S.	01 Sep
X	Cartwright, D.	01 Sep
X	Murphy, S.R.A.	01 Sep
X	Savage, M.R.	01 Sep
X	May, N.P.	01 Sep
E	Manson, T.E.	07 Sep
E	Bowden, M.N.	01 Oct
E	Forer, D.A.	01 Oct
E	Wallace, D.J.	01 Oct
E	Hart, P.A.	01 Oct
X	Cooper, C.J.	01 Oct
E	Spooner, P.D.	01 Oct
W	Hayle, E.A.	01 Oct
X	Manson, C.R.	01 Oct
X	Reed, M.	01 Oct
X	Worman, R.	01 Oct
E	Carr, M.P.	01 Oct
E	Wilson, D.T.	01 Oct
E	Biggs, C.R.	01 Oct
X	Haynes, J.W.	01 Oct
E	Davies, L.J.	01 Oct
X	Stone, P.C.J.	01 Oct

LIEUTENANT COMMANDERS

E	Krosnar-Clarke, S.M.	01 Oct
E	Norman, S.L.	01 Oct
X	Tyack, T.J.	01 Oct
E	Darling, J.I.	01 Oct
E	Mills, G.W.	01 Oct
E	Templeton, T.A.M.	01 Oct
MS	Steel, D.G.	01 Oct
W	Whittingham, D.J.	01 Oct
X	Neave, A.M.	01 Oct
X	Thompson, R.A.	01 Oct
E	Bourne, D.S.	01 Oct
X	Wilkinson, R.N.	01 Oct
X	Shallcroft, J.E.	01 Oct
X	Spayne, N.J.	01 Oct
E	Dawson, S.N.	01 Oct
X	Smith, P.G.	01 Oct
S	Cunane, J.R.	01 Oct
X	Chapman, D.A.	01 Oct
X	Franklin, B.J.	01 Oct
X	Tillion, A.M.	01 Oct
X	Wheaton, B.J.S.	01 Oct
E	Hill, G.A.	01 Oct
E	Lord, M.	01 Oct
X	Lewis, D.J.	01 Oct
X	Barrick, P.V.	01 Oct
X	Dann, A.S.	01 Oct
W	Eastlake, A.C.	01 Oct
E	Foster, J.S.	01 Oct
E	Tritschler, E.L.	01 Oct
X	Haslam, P.J.	01 Oct
S	MacDougall, G.R.	01 Oct
X	Strathern, R.J.	01 Oct
X	Ward, S.I.	01 Oct
E	McCue, D.	01 Oct
S	Oliphant, W.	01 Oct
E	Simmonds, G.F.	01 Oct
X	Price, D.W.	01 Oct
S	Tupper, R.W.	01 Oct
MS	McAuslin, T.M.	01 Oct
MS	Derby, P.J.	01 Oct
E	Clarke, J.	01 Oct
E	Grace, T.P.	01 Oct
E	Jordan, N.S.	01 Oct
X	Thomas, J.E.	01 Oct
X	Huntington, S.P.	01 Oct
X	Meadows, B.	01 Oct
E	Birbeck, K.	01 Oct
E	Rimmer, R.	01 Oct
E	Stokes, A.W.	01 Oct
E	Arnell, S.J.	01 Oct
E	Ferguson, G.H.	01 Oct

E	McCaffery, G.F.	01 Oct
S	Case, P.	01 Oct
S	Laggan, P.J.	01 Oct
S	Pye, P.M.	01 Oct
X	Hughes, G.G.H.	01 Oct
E	Pomeroy, M.A.	01 Oct
S	Fisher, C.R.A.	06 Oct
X	Dawson, W.	01 Nov
X	Davison, J.C.	01 Nov
S	McNally, N.J.	01 Nov
E	Reidy, P.A.	01 Nov
S	Clark, M.T.	01 Nov
E	Hall, B.J.	01 Nov
X	Olive, P.N.	01 Nov
E	Smith, M.M.	01 Nov
X	Taylor, A.R.	01 Nov
E	Vickers, J.	01 Nov
E	Davey, G.S.	01 Nov
X	Bark, A.M.	01 Nov
E	Guy, M.A.	13 Nov
E	Boulton, N.A.	20 Nov
E	Donnelly, J.S.	22 Nov
X	Redman, C.J.R.	23 Nov
S	Stoffell, D.P.	27 Nov
E	Windsar, P.A.	27 Nov
X	Davies, I.E.	01 Dec
E	MacKay, P.	01 Dec
S	Clark, S.M.	01 Dec
X	Rogers, T.H.G.	04 Dec
E	Foster, B.M.T.	07 Dec
X	Warn, C.J.	09 Dec
X	Powell, W.G.	16 Dec
E	Makepeace, P.A.	24 Dec

1999

X	Millard, A.R.	01 Jan
E	Twine, J.H.	01 Jan
X	Hancock, A.P.	01 Jan
X	Manfield, M.D.	01 Jan
E	Greatwood, I.M.	01 Jan
E	Warrington, P.T.	01 Jan
X	Ponsford, P.K.	01 Jan
E	Roberts, K.E.	01 Jan
E	Ward, T.J.	11 Jan
X	Orchard, A.P.	16 Jan
X	Lees, E.C.	01 Feb
X	Osborn, R.M.	01 Feb
X	Staley, S.P.L.	01 Feb
E	Copeland, S.N.	01 Feb
X	Godwin, C.A.	01 Feb
X	Goodsell, C.D.	01 Feb
E	Hancox, M.J.	01 Feb

E	Jackson, P.N.	01 Feb
X	Jones, N.P.	01 Feb
X	Kerslake, R.W.	01 Feb
S	Nairn, A.B.	01 Feb
E	Osmond, J.B.	01 Feb
E	Smith, A.G.	01 Feb
X	Taylor, M.A.	01 Feb
X	Welford, R.C.	01 Feb
E	Wright, N.S.	01 Feb
X	Betton, A.	01 Feb
E	Fergusson, N.A.	01 Feb
E	Crofts, D.J.	01 Feb
X	Holmes, J.D.	04 Feb
X	Pitt, J.M.	17 Feb
E	Southern, P.J.	27 Feb
X	London, M.R.	01 Mar
X	Lee, N.F.	01 Mar
E	Lauste, W.E.	01 Mar
E	Casson, N.P.	01 Mar
X	Hussain, S.	01 Mar
X	Woodham, R.H.	01 Mar
X	Burns, R.D.J.	01 Mar
X	McDonnell, D.S.	01 Mar
X	Bingham, D.S.	01 Mar
E	Hill, D.	01 Mar
X	Waller, S.A.	01 Mar
E	Currass, T.D.	01 Mar
E	Douglass, M.C.M.	01 Mar
E	Gray, R.	01 Mar
E	Groom, I.S.	01 Mar
E	Henderson, S.P.	01 Mar
E	Mackie, D.F.S.	01 Mar
E	Rawlinson, S.J.	01 Mar
X	Moss, R.A.	01 Mar
X	O'Flaherty, C.P.J.	01 Mar
E	Bywater, R.L.	01 Mar
X	Hogben, A.L.	01 Mar
E	Mould, T.P.	16 Mar
S	Turner, J.S.H.	01 Apr
X	Brooks, G.L.	01 Apr
X	Beck, S.K.	01 Apr
X	Collighan, G.T.	01 Apr
X	Dodd, K.M.	01 Apr
E	Goldman, P.H.L.	01 Apr
S	Mardlin, S.A.	01 Apr
E	Marriott, M.N.	01 Apr
X	Mimpriss, G.D.	01 Apr
E	Roscoe, R.D.	01 Apr
S	Dodd, N.C.	01 Apr
E	Foster, S.J.H.	01 Apr
X	Harris, K.J.	01 Apr

X	Wood, U.G.S.	01 Apr
E	Waring, J.R.	01 Apr
X	Groves, C.K.	01 Apr
X	Mahony, C.D.C.	03 Apr
S	Athayde Banazol, C.V.N.	04 Apr
E	Roberts, D.	04 Apr
X	Foster, D.H.	01 May
E	Bowhay, S.	01 May
X	Burstow, R.S.	01 May
E	Scott, M.	01 May
X	Bravery, M.A.E.	01 May
E	Cooper, S.S.	01 May
X	Duffy, H.	01 May
X	Garratt, J.K.	01 May
E	Lison, A.C.	01 May
E	Sansford, A.J.	27 May
X	Golden, D.S.C.	01 Jun
X	Bush, A.J.T.	01 Jun
X	Allen, P.L.	01 Jun
S	Ferns, T.D.	01 Jun
X	Mackey, M.C.	01 Jun
X	Sparkes, P.J.	01 Jun
X	Whitley, I.D.B.	01 Jun
E	Wright, B.L.	01 Jun
X	Young, A.	01 Jun
E	West, G.G.	06 Jun
E	Proud, A.D.	11 Jun
S	Rees, J.P.	29 Jun
X	Hewitt, D.L.	01 Jul
E	Jones, D.B.	01 Jul
E	Parkin, M.I.	01 Jul
S	Percival, M.C.	01 Jul
X	Honnoraty, M.R.	01 Jul
X	Bushell, G.R.	09 Jul
S	Perry, A.J.	16 Jul
X	Allen, R.	20 Jul
X	Southorn, M.D.	21 Jul
E	Richardson, P.S.M.	01 Aug
E	Lee, P.A.	01 Aug
X	Churcher, J.E.	01 Aug
E	Collis, M.J.	01 Aug
E	Currie, S.M.	01 Aug
X	Dreelan, M.J.	01 Aug
E	Owens, D.T.	01 Aug
E	Quekett, I.P.S.	01 Aug
X	Verney, P.S.	01 Aug
X	Brown, P.A.E.	01 Aug
E	Lowe, J.C.	01 Aug
X	Paterson, F.J.B.	01 Aug
X	Barnes, J.R.	01 Aug
X	Morley, J.D.	01 Aug

LIEUTENANT COMMANDERS

E	Dyer, J.D.T.	01 Sep
E	Grears, J.	01 Sep
E	McLarnon, C.P.C.	01 Sep
E	Tatham, S.A.	01 Sep
E	Bolton, J.P	01 Sep
X	Cameron, I.	01 Sep
X	Goode, A.N.	01 Sep
X	Beard, H.D.	01 Sep
E	Greener, C.	01 Sep
E	Taylor, R.	01 Sep
E	Punton, I.M.	01 Sep
W	Springett, J.K.	01 Oct
X	Whitworth, R.M.	01 Oct
X	Luscombe, M.D.	01 Oct
X	Johns, M.G.	01 Oct
X	King, R.J.	01 Oct
X	Marsh, B.H.	01 Oct
X	Hartley, J.L.	01 Oct
X	Callaghan, P.F.	01 Oct
X	Hayde, P.J.	01 Oct
E	Morris, P.	01 Oct
X	Howard, D.G.	01 Oct
E	Sergeant, N.R.	01 Oct
E	Barrett, S.J.	01 Oct
X	Rae, A.J.W.	01 Oct
X	Goldsmith, D.	01 Oct
X	Anderson, S.C.	01 Oct
W	Edge, P.A.	01 Oct
X	Cooke, G.J.	01 Oct
X	Wood, F.D.	01 Oct
E	Preston, M.R.	01 Oct
X	Holden, R.J.	01 Oct
E	Weir, S.D.	01 Oct
E	Ford, A.	01 Oct
X	Yardley, A.P.	01 Oct
X	Dolby, M.J.	01 Oct
E	O'Shaughnessy, P.J.	01 Oct
X	Barker, J.W.	01 Oct
E	Mason, M.	01 Oct
E	Robertson, M.N.	01 Oct
X	Pegrum, T.A.	01 Oct
X	Cowie, K.M.	01 Oct
E	Linderman, I.R.	01 Oct
E	Matthews, P.B.	01 Oct
X	Avison, M.J.	01 Oct
E	Burnett, G.A.	01 Oct
E	Roberts, S.C.	01 Oct
X	Murray, A.S.	01 Oct
X	Miller, C.R.	01 Oct
E	Gunther, P.T.	01 Oct
E	Nicholls, G.A.	01 Oct

X	Ash, T.C.V.	01 Oct
S	Moore, D.D.V.	01 Oct
E	Milsom, J.	01 Oct
E	Appelquist, P.	01 Oct
X	Blythe, P.C.	01 Oct
E	Bougourd, M.A.	01 Oct
X	Chalmers, P.	01 Oct
X	Lower, I.S.	01 Oct
E	McDermott, O.D.	01 Oct
E	Gazard, P.N.	01 Oct
E	Hoyle, J.J.	01 Oct
S	Bryant, G.D.	01 Oct
X	Talbot, C.M.	01 Oct
E	Payne, D.	01 Oct
E	Dutton, P.J.	01 Oct
E	Glennie, B.W.	01 Oct
E	Lowes, C.	01 Oct
S	Freegard, I.P.	01 Oct
MS	Griffiths, D.A.	01 Oct
S	Williams, D.	01 Oct
E	Maude, D.H.	01 Oct
X	Edwards, R.	01 Oct
S	Twist, D.C.	01 Oct
X	Woodruff, A.D.	01 Oct
E	Bassett, N.E.	01 Oct
MS	Durning, W.M.	01 Oct
X	Thomas, L.	01 Oct
E	Jones, D.A.	01 Oct
X	Knights, R.	01 Oct
X	Stephens, R.P.	01 Oct
X	Horne, A.	01 Oct
E	Norman, P.D.	01 Oct
E	Sugden, S.R.	01 Oct
E	Taylor, K.J.	01 Oct
S	Harris, M.T.	01 Oct
S	Holland, N.R.	01 Oct
X	Millen, I.S.	01 Oct
W	Graham, P.J.	22 Oct
X	Jones, C.A.	01 Nov
X	Necker, C.D.	01 Nov
X	Baker, A.P.	01 Nov
X	Joyce, T.J.	01 Nov
E	Edmonds, R.M.	01 Nov
X	Watt, A.J.L.	01 Nov
S	Ackland, H.K.	01 Nov
E	Methven, P.	01 Nov
X	Warrender, W.J.	01 Nov
E	Chapman, C.L.	29 Nov
X	Smith, B.J.	01 Dec
E	Easterbrook, K.I.E.	01 Dec
E	McRae, P.C.	01 Dec

E	Shrubsole, S.J.	01 Dec
X	Tennuci, R.G.	01 Dec
E	Woodruff, D.A.	01 Dec
X	Boynton, S.J.	01 Dec
X	Hunkin, D.J.	01 Dec
E	Gayfer, M.E.	01 Dec
S	Talbott, A.H.	01 Dec
X	Moore, C.R.	05 Dec
E	Rose, M.F.	28 Dec

2000

E	Campbell, M.A.	01 Jan
X	Harcourt, R.J.	01 Jan
E	Stamper, J.C.H.	01 Jan
E	Nickolls, K.P.	01 Jan
E	Baxter, I.M.	01 Jan
X	Bryan, R.J.L.	01 Jan
X	Parsons, A.D.	01 Jan
E	Rowland, P.N.	01 Jan
X	Walker, N.M.	01 Jan
X	Washer, N.B.J.	01 Jan
X	Connell, M.J.	01 Jan
E	Higham, J.G.	01 Jan
S	Dunthorne, J.A.	04 Jan
X	Griffiths, M.O.J.	16 Jan
X	Aylott, P.R.F.D.	29 Jan
E	Young, S.A.	01 Feb
X	Crosbie, D.E.F.	01 Feb
X	Pierce, A.K.M.	01 Feb
E	Burgess, G.T.M.	01 Feb
E	Gale, M.A.	01 Feb
E	Greenway, S.A.	01 Feb
E	Kelly, J.A.	01 Feb
E	Martin, S.J.	01 Feb
E	O'Brien, K.J.	01 Feb
S	Rae, S.G.	01 Feb
S	Cole, A.C.	01 Feb
E	Dinsdale, A.M.	01 Feb
S	Pomeroy, P.M.	01 Feb
E	Lewis, G.D.	03 Feb
E	Bolton, M.T.W.	06 Feb
E	Shaw, M.L.	11 Feb
S	Brenchley, N.G.	17 Feb
S	Ashman, R.G.	28 Feb
S	Sparke, P.R.W.	01 Mar
E	Cotterill, B.M.	01 Mar
E	Balhetchet, A.S.	01 Mar
X	Dominy, D.J.D.	01 Mar
E	Halliwell, D.C.	01 Mar
S	Murphy, P.A.	01 Mar
E	Reece, N.D.	01 Mar
E	Teideman, I.C.	01 Mar

LIEUTENANT COMMANDERS

E	Whitehead, S.J.	01 Mar
E	Jackson, D.J.	01 Mar
X	Johnson, L.S.	01 Mar
E	Whitfield, K.D.	01 Mar
E	Macleod, J.N.	01 Mar
E	Hartley, A.P.	02 Mar
E	Pugh, J.	08 Mar
S	Fletcher, R.J.	16 Mar
E	Cameron, M.J.	01 Apr
E	Bedding, S.W.E.	01 Apr
E	Bignell, S.	01 Apr
X	Bruford, R.M.C.	01 Apr
X	Buck, J.E.	01 Apr
E	Curlewis, A.J.	01 Apr
E	Long, A.M.	01 Apr
X	Burns, A.P.	01 Apr
X	Firth, R.J.G.	08 Apr
S	Knowles, M.M.	15 Apr
X	Lindsey, R.J.	30 Apr
X	Gurr, A.W.G.	01 May
X	Guy, T.J.	01 May
X	Parry, J.D.F.	01 May
E	Russell, B.	01 May
E	Strutt, J.F.	01 May
X	Wilson, D.R.	01 May
E	Bye, M.D.	01 May
E	Chambers, I.R.	01 May
E	Shaw, G.R.	01 May
E	Reah, S.	02 May
E	Prinsep, T.J.	01 Jun
X	Gray, J.A.	01 Jun
E	Bradley, P.M.	01 Jun
E	Helps, A.R.	01 Jun
E	Howard, N.H.	01 Jun
E	Rogers, C.M.	01 Jun
E	Fleisher, S.M.	01 Jun
X	Moore, M.	01 Jun
E	Mulvaney, P.A.	01 Jun
E	Nicklas, C.J.	01 Jun
E	Saunders, P.W.	01 Jun
S	Tothill, R.C.	01 Jun
X	Wilkinson, D.H.	01 Jun
X	Williams, J.P.	01 Jun
X	Gregory, A.S.	01 Jun
E	Bond, A.J.	09 Jun
X	Campbell, L.M.	01 Jul
X	Gardner, J.E.	01 Jul
E	Barton, M.A.	01 Jul
E	Crundell, R.J.	01 Jul
E	Lunn, M.H.B.	01 Jul
E	Moody, D.C.	01 Jul

E	Panther, A.M.	01 Jul
E	Atkins, I.	01 Jul
E	Ewen, A.P.	01 Jul
E	Etchells, S.B.	03 Jul
E	Philpot, D.J.	18 Jul
E	Bulcock, M.	28 Jul
E	Lauchlan, R.A.	01 Aug
X	Dando, J.N.	01 Aug
X	Ley, J.A.	01 Aug
E	Ross, I.	01 Aug
E	Miles, G.J.	07 Aug
E	Thrippleton, M.G.	15 Aug
X	Hutchinson, C.J.	01 Sep
E	Richter, A.S.B.	01 Sep
X	Duff, A.P.	01 Sep
X	Oulds, K.A.	01 Sep
E	Walton, C.P.	01 Sep
E	Wheal, A.J.	01 Sep
X	Wyper, J.R.	01 Sep
X	Wilson, R.	01 Sep
X	Perks, J.I.E.S.	01 Sep
E	Marshall, P.	01 Sep
E	Hendy, L.S.	28 Sep
X	Taylor, T.J.	01 Oct
E	Taylor, A.	01 Oct
X	Watkins, T.C.	01 Oct
X	Cook, G.E.	01 Oct
X	Bithell, I.S.	01 Oct
X	Hogan, T.	01 Oct
X	Tayler, J.R.N.	01 Oct
X	Clarke, A.P.	01 Oct
X	Williams, M.A.	01 Oct
E	Picksley, M.R.	01 Oct
E	Sutcliffe, R.W.	01 Oct
E	Ford, J.A.	01 Oct
X	Higgs, R.J.	01 Oct
S	Walker, N.A.	01 Oct
X	Oddy, D.M.	01 Oct
X	Gardiner, P.F.D.	01 Oct
X	Robertson, P.N.	01 Oct
X	O'Sullivan, B.O.	01 Oct
E	Pears, I.J.	01 Oct
X	Grindon, M.G.	01 Oct
X	Phillips, J.P.	01 Oct
X	Smith, R.C.V.	01 Oct
E	Cook, C.B.	01 Oct
E	Orton, D.M.	01 Oct
E	Lacey, C.M.	01 Oct
E	Low, M.E.	01 Oct
E	Moss, P.J.	01 Oct
E	Smith, M.J.	01 Oct

E	Richman, P.J.	01 Oct
X	Hinch, D.G.W.	01 Oct
X	Hart, T.G.DE.B.	01 Oct
W	Armstrong, S.	01 Oct
X	Bennett, W.D.	01 Oct
X	Garlick, E.C.	01 Oct
X	Lynch, S.	01 Oct
X	Howell, H.R.G.	01 Oct
E	Bissett, I.M.	01 Oct
E	Bissett, P.K.	01 Oct
S	Plaice, G.C.	01 Oct
E	Young, R.	01 Oct
MS	O'Callaghan, S.T.	01 Oct
MS	Trasler, M.F.	01 Oct
X	Finn, G.J.	01 Oct
S	Bell, M.	01 Oct
E	Dyke, K.A.	01 Oct
S	Adlam, G.M.	01 Oct
E	Dunn, A.J.P.	01 Oct
E	Hutchings, J.S.	01 Oct
E	Parrett, J.W.	01 Oct
X	Curtis, R.J.	01 Oct
E	Joyce, D.A.	01 Oct
S	Turner, R.F.	01 Oct
E	Burge, R.G.	01 Oct
E	Hatcher, T.R.	01 Oct
E	Rundle, A.L.	01 Oct
S	Waterhouse, P.	01 Oct
X	Barron, P.J.	01 Oct
X	Billington, T.J.	01 Oct
S	Hall, D.A.	01 Oct
W	Gale, S.L.	01 Oct
X	Utley, M.K.	01 Oct
E	Aniyi, C.B.J.	01 Oct
E	Ralphson, M.D.	01 Oct
E	Jordan, L.	01 Oct
E	Love, T.S.N.	01 Oct
X	Lett, J.D.	01 Oct
E	Prince, M.E.	01 Oct
MS	Richards, B.R.	01 Oct
E	Pearson, C.P.B.	01 Oct
X	Henry, T.M.	01 Oct
X	Jordan, A.A.	01 Oct
S	Pheasant, J.C.S.	01 Oct
E	Bell, D.P.	01 Oct
E	Phesse, J.P.L.	01 Oct
S	Stillwell-Cox, A.D.R.	01 Oct
X	Walker, E.G.	01 Oct
E	Game, P.G.	01 Oct
E	Hobson, I.S.	01 Oct
E	Finn, I.R.	01 Oct

LIEUTENANT COMMANDERS

MS	Gerrell, F.J.	01 Oct
S	Grocott, P.C.	01 Oct
MS	McLaughlan, C.J.	01 Oct
X	Pugh, M.R.	01 Oct
E	Cowper, I.R.	01 Oct
X	Taylor, M.R.	01 Oct
X	Dufosee, S.W.	01 Oct
X	Ahlgren, E.G.	01 Oct
X	Beaumont, S.J.	01 Oct
X	Whitlam, J.	01 Oct
S	Young, S.W.	01 Oct
S	Bunt, K.J.	01 Oct
E	Berry, P.	01 Oct
X	Elsom, G.K.	01 Oct
S	Pocock, D.	16 Oct
X	Fedorowicz, R.	16 Oct
E	Evans, C.H.	01 Nov
E	Norris, J.G.	01 Nov
X	Ramsey, R.T.	01 Nov
X	O'Byrne, P.B.M.	01 Nov
E	Wylie, I.C.H.	01 Nov
S	Hally, P.J.	01 Nov
X	Stockton, K.G.	19 Nov
E	Ballard, M.L.	01 Dec
E	Daly, A.	01 Dec
E	Lowe, S.M.	01 Dec
X	Broadhurst, M.R.	01 Dec
X	Douglas, P.J.	01 Dec
X	Knight, D.W.	01 Dec
X	Douglas, P.G.	03 Dec
E	Reeves, K.	04 Dec
S	Beresford-Green, P.M.	16 Dec
S	Gale, C.V.	24 Dec
E	Rutherford, T.J.	30 Dec

2001

E	Cogdell, P.C.	01 Jan
E	McMullan, N.L.	01 Jan
E	Kerr, A.N.	01 Jan
E	Malley, M.P.	01 Jan
X	Smith, G.D.J.	01 Jan
X	Thomas, S.M.	01 Jan
S	Donovan, R.J.	01 Jan
X	MacKinnon, D.J.	01 Jan
X	Varley, I.G.	01 Jan
X	Wills, P.J.	01 Jan
E	Clarke, A.R.	03 Jan
X	Brown, S.H.	15 Jan
E	Sellers, G.D.	01 Feb
X	Stanton-Brown, P.J.	01 Feb
X	Steil, C.W.R.	01 Feb
X	Black, J.J.M.	01 Feb

E	Harrison, A.	01 Feb
X	Hopper, S.M.	01 Feb
X	Knott, M.B.	01 Feb
X	Miller, P.D.	01 Feb
X	Thomson, C.D.	01 Feb
X	Tredray, T.P.	01 Feb
E	Woods, T.C.	01 Feb
E	Bowker, I.C.	13 Feb
X	Chaston, S.P.	01 Mar
X	Cox, R.J.	01 Mar
S	Hallett, S.J.	01 Mar
E	Head, S.A.	01 Mar
X	Nelson, C.S.	01 Mar
X	Pearson, M.F.	01 Mar
X	Bristowe, P.A.	01 Mar
X	Giles, R.K.	01 Mar
X	Robinson, M.S.	04 Mar
X	George, D.M.	13 Mar
S	Williams, S.W.L.	01 Apr
X	Holden, N.	01 Apr
E	Whyte, I.P.	01 Apr
E	Adams, G.H.	01 Apr
X	Parnell, A.D.	01 Apr
X	Ryan, S.J.	01 Apr
X	Walton, C.P.	01 Apr
E	Drywood, T.	01 Apr
E	Reid, J.C.J.	01 Apr
S	Whalley, R.J.	01 Apr
E	Holland, S.M.W.	01 May
E	Rand, M.J.	01 May
X	Russell, P.	01 May
E	Davies, J.W.	11 May
X	Bessell, D.A.	01 Jun
X	Paterson, M.P.	01 Jun
X	Williams, C.N.O.	01 Jun
E	Baller, C.R.	01 Jun
E	Bonnar, J.A.	01 Jun
E	Hutchins, R.F.	01 Jun
E	Keen, N.	01 Jun
X	Newell, P.R.	01 Jun
E	Williams, M.	01 Jun
E	Cropper, F.B.N.	24 Jun
X	Norgan, D.J.	01 Jul
X	Watts, R.	01 Jul
X	Dunn, P.E.	01 Jul
S	Richardson, G.N.	01 Jul
E	Green, A.M.	01 Jul
E	Napier, G.A.	01 Jul
E	Sullivan, M.	01 Jul
E	Towell, P.J.	01 Jul
X	McHugh, T.P.	01 Aug

LIEUTENANT COMMANDERS

E	Shirley, A.J.	01 Aug
X	Bower, A.J.	01 Aug
S	Finch, B.A.	01 Aug
X	O'Sullivan, M.L.J.	01 Aug
X	Coyle, G.J.	01 Aug
E	Graham, A.N.S.	01 Aug
S	Preece, D.G.	01 Aug
E	Winter, R.J.	01 Aug
X	Wood, C.	01 Aug
X	Markey, A.P.	01 Aug
S	Samuel, K.L.H.	01 Aug
E	Campbell, J.C.	01 Sep
E	Lewis, D.J.	01 Sep
E	Laing, I.	01 Sep
X	Dowsett, P.G.	01 Sep
E	Chapman, P.	01 Sep
X	Downes, C.H.	01 Sep
X	Yelland, C.B.	01 Oct
X	Reid, P.F.	01 Oct
X	Eatwell, R.A.	01 Oct
X	Hanrahan, M.W.	01 Oct
X	Liggins, M.P.	01 Oct
W	Simpson, E.J.	01 Oct
X	Nicholas, B.J.	01 Oct
S	Ryan, J.B.	01 Oct
E	Hutton, K.D.	01 Oct
X	Turner, K.A.	01 Oct
X	Deverson, R.T.M.	01 Oct
X	Graham, M.A.	01 Oct
X	Knight, A.R.	01 Oct
E	Taylor, S.J.	01 Oct
S	Cottis, M.C.	01 Oct
X	Hannigan, P.F.	01 Oct
X	Scivier, J.S.	01 Oct
E	Lake, P.H.	01 Oct
X	Bowers, J.P.	01 Oct
X	Duncan, J.	01 Oct
MS	Simpson, P.	01 Oct
X	Forster, R.A.	01 Oct
E	Horwell, B.B.	01 Oct
X	Tattersall, R.B.	01 Oct
X	Westley, D.R.	01 Oct
X	Noblett, P.G.A.	01 Oct
X	Dunn, P.E.	01 Oct
X	Roberts, S.	01 Oct
E	Baines, D.M.L.	01 Oct
E	Morgan-Hosey, J.N.	01 Oct
X	Rowlands, K.	01 Oct
X	Richardson, G.A.	01 Oct
X	Gough, S.R.	01 Oct
X	Rogers, A.	01 Oct

X	Brunsden-Brown, S.E.	01 Oct
E	Davies, S.P.	01 Oct
E	Mountjoy, B.J.	01 Oct
E	Wray, A.D.	01 Oct
X	Sneddon, R.N.	01 Oct
E	Mills, I.	01 Oct
E	Procter, J.E.	01 Oct
E	Wharrie, E.K.B.	01 Oct
S	Wooller, M.A.H.	01 Oct
E	Stobie, P.L.	01 Oct
S	West, A.W.	01 Oct
E	Bannister, A.N.	01 Oct
E	Johnson, M.J.	01 Oct
X	Griffin, N.R.	01 Oct
E	Langrill, M.P.	01 Oct
MS	Ryder, T.J.	01 Oct
X	Beattie, P.S.	01 Oct
X	Dennis, M.J.	01 Oct
S	Knock, G.P.	01 Oct
X	Houston, D.J.M.	01 Oct
S	Joll, S.M.	01 Oct
X	Cooke, G.S.	01 Oct
E	Barrett, D.L.	01 Oct
E	Leaning, D.J.	01 Oct
E	Rowan, N.A.	01 Oct
E	Crawford, L.	01 Oct
X	Kerr, J.	01 Oct
E	Hancock, R.T.A.	01 Oct
E	Baggaley, J.A.L.	01 Oct
E	Farrington, J.L.	01 Oct
S	Wilman, D.M.	01 Oct
X	Weightman, N.E.	01 Oct
E	Dewsnap, M.D.	01 Oct
E	Hooper, G.P.	01 Oct
E	Cunnane, K.J.	01 Oct
E	Green, T.C.	01 Oct
S	Melville-Brown, M.G.	01 Oct
X	Howe, J.P.	01 Oct
S	Walker, D.W.A.	01 Oct
X	Clark, J.L.	01 Oct
E	Cox, D.J.	01 Oct
E	Metcalf, R.	01 Oct
X	Clink, A.D.	01 Oct
X	Nugent, C.J.	01 Oct
MS	Phillips, I.M.	01 Oct
X	West, A.B.	01 Oct
X	Gritt, L.A.	01 Oct
X	Lintern, R.D.	01 Oct
E	Walton, S.P.	01 Oct
X	Jaggers, G.G.	01 Oct
S	Taylor, I.K.	01 Oct

E	Evans, S.	01 Oct
X	Kerr, A.T.F.	01 Oct
MS	Stead, R.A.	01 Oct
E	Dunsby, N.B.	01 Oct
E	Mitchell, S.D.	01 Oct
X	Clarke, I.B.	01 Oct
X	McKernan, J.	01 Oct
X	Wilson, G.J.	01 Oct
E	Phillips, A.R.	01 Oct
E	Walsh, D.G.	01 Oct
X	Roberts, P.S.	01 Oct
S	Fearnley, A.T.	01 Oct
S	Jackson, P.A.	01 Oct
X	Metcalfe, M.P.	01 Oct
X	Smith, N.J.	01 Oct
E	Stanham, C.M.	01 Oct
X	Smallwood, R.I.	12 Oct
E	Wroblewski, J.A.	31 Oct
X	Moore, S.K.	01 Nov
X	Noyce, V.R.A.	01 Nov
E	Palmer, M.E.	01 Nov
X	Curry, R.E.	01 Nov
E	Chamberlain, N.R.L.	01 Nov
X	Castle, A.S.	01 Dec
X	Buckingham, G.	01 Dec
E	Ford, J.D.	01 Dec
X	Edey, M.J.	01 Dec
X	Currie, D.G.	16 Dec

2002

E	Browning, R.S.	01 Jan
E	Davies, L.	01 Jan
E	Onyike, C.E.	01 Jan
X	Pink, S.E.	01 Jan
E	Goldsmith, D.T.	01 Jan
E	Lang, A.J.N.	01 Feb
E	Thirkettle, J.A.	01 Feb
E	Barnett, A.C.	01 Feb
X	Fryer, A.C.	01 Feb
S	Higgs, T.A.	01 Feb
E	Macleod, M.S.	01 Feb
E	Prendergast, S.A.	26 Feb
X	Hesling, G.	28 Feb
E	Carroll, P.C.	01 Mar
E	Clarke, R.W.	01 Mar
E	Jose, S.	01 Mar
E	Meek, C.S.	01 Mar
E	Proctor, W.J.G.	01 Mar
X	Stephen, B.M.	01 Mar
X	Wallace, S.J.	01 Mar
E	Humphrey, I.J.	01 Mar
X	White, I.F.	01 Mar

LIEUTENANTCOMMANDERS

S	Brock, R.F.	01 Mar
E	Bugg, K.J.	01 Mar
X	South, D.J.	01 Mar
S	Lawrence, S.P.	01 Mar
E	Broadbent, P.S.	01 Mar
E	Corps, S.D.	01 Mar
S	Burns, A.C.	04 Mar
X	Walker, S.P.	09 Mar
E	Arthur, A.W.	15 Mar
X	Ritchie, J.N.	01 Apr
E	Derby, B.D.	01 Apr
X	Kohler, A.P.	01 Apr
E	Cubbage, J.	01 Apr
S	Goudge, S.D.P.	01 Apr
E	Johnson, C.C.B.	01 Apr
E	Kelly, H.C.	01 Apr
X	Offord, M.R.	01 Apr
X	Childs, J.R.	01 Apr
X	Dineen, J.M.G.	01 Apr
S	Moore, S.B.	01 Apr
X	Hopper, I.M.	09 Apr
X	Chan-A-Sue, S.S.	15 Apr
X	Lynch, R.D.F.	16 Apr
X	Brotherton, J.D.	16 Apr
E	Blacow, C.	24 Apr
E	Flint, H.A.	01 May
E	Mandley, P.J.	01 May
X	Cull, I.	01 May
X	Blackburn, S.J.	01 May
X	Hygate, A.M.	01 May
X	Maxwell, R.	01 May
X	Bradley, M.T.	01 May
X	Craig, J.A.	01 May
E	Noakes, K.M.	01 May
S	Porter, T.B.	01 May
E	Summers, J.A.E.	24 May
E	Rose, C.M.	07 Jun

LIEUTENANTS

1982
E Moore, M.R. .... 29 Oct

1984
E Maskell-Bott, J.M. .... 16 Feb
X Ellett, K.G. .... 01 Jun
X Read, A.J. .... 01 Sep
E Gamble, J. .... 02 Nov
E Thornback, J.G. .... 02 Nov

1985
X Bentley, D.A. .... 06 Sep
X Gorrod, P.C.A. .... 06 Sep
E Curtis, P.A. .... 18 Oct
E Halls, B.C. .... 18 Oct
E Ranger, J.L. .... 18 Oct
E Schillemore, P.C. .... 18 Oct

1986
E Davison, T.J. .... 13 Jun
E Longstaff, R. .... 13 Jun
E Williams, D.A. .... 13 Jun
E Miller, J.C. .... 17 Oct

1987
X Carne, R.J.P. .... 16 May
E Foubister, R. .... 18 Jun
X Wilson, M.A. .... 16 Jul
X Tribe, J.D. .... 16 Oct

1988
E Lane, R.M. .... 18 Feb
E Fisher, R. .... 10 Jun
E Gamble, R. .... 10 Jun
E Nicholson, P.J. .... 10 Jun
E White, S.P. .... 10 Jun
E Collins, S.J. .... 27 Jun
X Dearling, P.C. .... 29 Jul
X Roberts, M. .... 01 Oct

1989
X Bance, N.D. .... 16 Feb
E Thomas, M.G. .... 17 Feb
X Williamson, S.J. .... 01 Mar
X Boyes, R.A. .... 01 Mar
X Seekings, A.L. .... 01 Jun
E Griffiths, A.R. .... 09 Jun
X Swann, J.I. .... 28 Jul
S Sidebotham, M.J. .... 28 Jul
E Lusted, R.P. .... 13 Oct
E Mason, L.C. .... 01 Nov

1990
X McDermott, M. .... 01 Jan

E Smart, S.J. .... 23 Feb
E Young, K.H. .... 23 Feb
X Cobbett, J.F. .... 16 May
E Allen, D.P. .... 15 Jun
E Davies, G.P. .... 15 Jun
X Bhattacharya, D. .... 16 Jun
X Booker, S.R. .... 16 Jun
E Cook, M.C. .... 01 Jul
E Fraser, I.D. .... 01 Jul
X Russell, T.J. .... 01 Jul
X Davies, A.J.A. .... 01 Aug
X Suckling, R.L. .... 16 Aug
X D'Arcy, P.A. .... 16 Aug
X Crockatt, S.R.J. .... 01 Sep
E Marratt, R.J. .... 01 Sep
X Stephens, R.J. .... 01 Sep
E Vincent, A. .... 01 Sep
E Walker, R.A. .... 01 Sep
E Choules, B. .... 01 Sep
S Church, C.R. .... 01 Sep
X Sopinski, G.F. .... 16 Sep
X Harrison, P.D. .... 01 Oct
E Forward, D.J. .... 19 Oct
X Adams, I. .... 01 Nov
X Speake, J. .... 01 Dec
X Imrie, P.B. .... 14 Dec
E Gutteridge, J.D.J. .... 20 Dec

1991
E Diver, P.H. .... 01 Jan
E Frost, M.A. .... 01 Jan
E Thomas, A.L. .... 01 Jan
E Walker, M.J. .... 01 Jan
E Williams, P.M. .... 01 Jan
E Bosustow, B.F. .... 01 Feb
E Wheeldon, T.B. .... 15 Feb
X Crimmen, D.J. .... 01 Mar
X Rogers, J.C.E. .... 01 Mar
X Davison, G.J. .... 01 Apr
X Eldridge, T.J. .... 01 Apr
X Herriman, J.A. .... 01 Apr
S Atkinson, I.N. .... 01 Apr
X Davidson, N.R. .... 01 Apr
X Clucas, P.R. .... 04 Apr
W Ambler, K.K. .... 04 Apr
X May-Clingo, M.S. .... 04 Apr
X Carr, R.A. .... 13 Apr
X Oliver, G. .... 01 May
E Taylor, A.L. .... 01 May
X McDonald, I.G. .... 01 May
X Allen, P.M. .... 01 May
E Coulthard, A.J. .... 11 May

X Adams, B.M. .... 16 May
E Taylor, N.R. .... 01 Jun
X Beirne, S. .... 01 Jun
X Brunskill, J.E.T. .... 01 Jun
E Gilliland, S.S. .... 13 Jun
X Whitfield, J.A. .... 16 Jun
X Smith, D.T. .... 16 Jun
X Gladston, S.A. .... 01 Jul
X Leaver, C.E.L. .... 01 Jul
X Tetley, M. .... 01 Jul
X McKnight, D.J.S. .... 01 Jul
X Hayward, G. .... 16 Jul
S Kerwood, R.J. .... 25 Jul
X McIntyre, A.W. .... 25 Jul
X Morrell, A.J. .... 25 Jul
X Ellwood, P.G. .... 29 Jul
S Tucker, K.M. .... 01 Aug
X Gray, P.R. .... 01 Aug
X Lindsay, D.J. .... 01 Aug
X Richardson, G.L. .... 01 Aug
X Christmas, S.P. .... 16 Aug
E Jones, A.F. .... 28 Aug
E Jones, G.D. .... 01 Sep
X Carnell, G.J. .... 01 Sep
E Moores, C.P. .... 01 Sep
X Young, M.J. .... 16 Sep
X Milne, P.B. .... 16 Sep
X Logan, J.M. .... 01 Oct
X Hilson, S.M. .... 01 Oct
X Roberts, I.G. .... 01 Oct
X Windebank, S.J. .... 01 Oct
E Bissett, R.W. .... 17 Oct
X Lea, S.A.P. .... 01 Nov
E Donovan, P. .... 01 Nov
X Slocombe, N.R. .... 01 Nov
X Hutton, G. .... 01 Nov
X Finch, C.R. .... 16 Nov
X Hamilton, I.J. .... 16 Nov
S Gill, S.C. .... 12 Dec

1992
E Beadnell, R.M. .... 01 Jan
E Millman, D.J. .... 01 Jan
E Ritsperis, A. .... 01 Jan
E Rostron, D.W. .... 01 Jan
X Moulton, S.J. .... 01 Jan
X Richardson, P. .... 16 Jan
X Neal, S.M. .... 16 Jan
X Poole, T.J. .... 16 Jan
S Quinn, M.E. .... 01 Feb
X Thompson, A.R. .... 01 Feb
X Brown, A.P. .... 01 Feb

LIEUTENANTS

X	Atkinson, G.C.	01 Feb
X	Tidball, I.C.	01 Feb
E	Ball, S.J.	13 Feb
X	Dale, A.	23 Feb
X	King, A.R.	01 Mar
X	Canning, C.P.	01 Mar
X	Hatchard, J.P.	04 Mar
X	Sparkes, S.N.	01 Apr
X	Murphy, D.A.	01 Apr
X	Shrimpton, M.W.	01 Apr
X	Milligan, R.J.C.	16 Apr
X	Birse, G.J.	01 May
E	Plackett, A.J.	01 May
X	Bird, J.M.	01 May
X	Foreman, S.L.	01 May
X	Quinn, S.A.	16 May
X	Lawrance, G.M.	16 May
X	Read, C.T.	16 May
E	Solly, M.M.	22 May
E	Wilkins, R.R.	01 Jun
X	Radford, A.J.	01 Jun
X	Reilly, T.G.	03 Jun
E	Craib, A.G.	05 Jun
E	Dyer, G.R.	05 Jun
E	Hunt, P.E.R.D.	05 Jun
E	Mitchell, P.	05 Jun
E	Radbourne, N.I.	05 Jun
X	King, S.J.	16 Jun
E	Young, C.J.	18 Jun
X	Rasor, A.M.	01 Jul
E	Ellis, D.F.	09 Jul
W	Mayell, J.A.	14 Jul
X	Jameson, R.M.	16 Jul
X	Wallis, J.S.	01 Aug
X	Brian, N.	01 Aug
E	Woodbridge, R.G.	01 Aug
X	Lambert, A.	09 Aug
X	Jaques, D.A.	16 Aug
E	Harding, C.S.	01 Sep
X	Langrish, G.J.	01 Oct
X	Allen, L.B.	01 Oct
X	Gibbons, N.P.	01 Oct
E	Cheseldine, D.	16 Oct
E	Cooke, M.J.	16 Oct
E	Parry, R.J.	16 Oct
E	Dickens, D.S.	01 Nov
E	Gordon, N.L.	01 Nov
S	Cogan, R.E.C.	01 Nov
S	Fogell, A.D.	01 Nov
X	Woodard, J.R.A.	01 Nov
X	Julian, T.M.	16 Nov

X	Patterson, A.J.	16 Nov
X	Fitzgerald, N.J.	01 Dec
X	Haigh, A.J.	01 Dec
E	Sargent, P.M.	01 Dec
W	Elborn, T.K.	11 Dec
W	Green, J.L.	11 Dec
S	MacAskill, C.H.	11 Dec
W	McBain, M.S.	11 Dec
X	McTear, N.J.	11 Dec
X	Mitchell, M.	11 Dec
X	Steele, T.G.	11 Dec

1993

E	Boston, J.	01 Jan
E	Lewis, S.J.	01 Jan
X	Rowe, K.C.	01 Jan
E	Higson, B.L.	01 Jan
E	Daly, J.M.	04 Jan
X	Mercer, D.C.	16 Jan
X	Binstead, K.N.	01 Feb
E	Cleminson, M.D.	01 Feb
E	Trott, C.M.J.	01 Feb
E	Batten, A.J.	19 Feb
E	Bedelle, S.J.	19 Feb
E	MacDougall, S.J.	19 Feb
E	McCabe, D.S.	19 Feb
E	Rowe, A.J.	19 Feb
E	Seaman, P.J.	19 Feb
E	Tomkins, A.B.	19 Feb
E	Warr, R.F.	19 Feb
E	Wooding, G.A.	19 Feb
E	Lavin, G.J.	01 Mar
E	McCaughey, V.J.	01 Mar
X	MacNeil, S.W.	01 Mar
X	Simpson, C.C.	01 Mar
X	Darwent, S.A.	01 Mar
X	Gates, N.S.	16 Mar
X	Bramwell, J.G.	01 Apr
X	Millen, S.C.W.	01 Apr
MS	Chilcott, P.L.H.	02 Apr
X	Clements, S.J.	02 Apr
X	Moreby, M.F.	02 Apr
X	Soar, G.	16 Apr
X	Milton, G.P.	01 May
X	Harlow, S.R.	01 May
X	Mould, P.	01 May
X	Payne, M.J.	01 May
X	Stock, C.M.	01 May
X	Gamble, P.	15 May
X	Crossley, G.A.	16 May
X	West, P.J.	16 May
X	Loane, M.M.	01 Jun

X	Jacques, N.A.	01 Jun
X	Sutton, R.M.J.	01 Jun
X	White, S.H.W.	16 Jun
E	Byrne, A.C.	18 Jun
E	McLachlan, M.P.	18 Jun
E	Elliott, S.	01 Jul
X	Morris, A.M.	01 Jul
X	Mudge, A.M.	01 Jul
X	Rodgers, D.	01 Jul
E	McQueen, J.B.	01 Jul
X	Brosnan, M.A.	16 Jul
X	Norris, G.P.	16 Jul
X	Crascall, S.J.	23 Jul
MS	Dell, I.M.	23 Jul
X	Harper, I.L.	23 Jul
X	Hawkes, J.D.	23 Jul
X	Massey, P.	23 Jul
X	Cox, S.A.J.	16 Aug
X	Choat, J.H.	16 Aug
X	Willing, N.P.	16 Aug
E	Ellis, J.P.	01 Sep
X	Salt, H.S.	01 Sep
X	Yeomans, P.A.	01 Sep
X	Duncan, C.J.	01 Sep
X	Lees, S.N.	02 Sep
X	Elwell-Deighton, D.C.	16 Sep
X	Stanley, N.J.	16 Sep
X	Rutherford, K.J.	01 Oct
X	Trubshaw, C.	02 Oct
E	Bowness, P.	15 Oct
E	Burrows, J.C.	15 Oct
E	Butler, L.P.	15 Oct
E	Ireland, J.M.	15 Oct
X	Bolton, S.J.	16 Oct
X	May, P.J.	29 Oct
X	Perry, R.J.	01 Nov
X	Gamble, N.	01 Nov
E	Stevenson, J.P.	01 Nov
X	MacFarlane, I.S.D.	01 Nov
X	Polding, M.	01 Nov
X	Smith, D.J.	01 Nov
X	Simpson, D.K.	16 Nov
E	Price, T.E.	01 Dec
X	Marquis, A.C.	01 Dec
X	Schunmann, C.P.I.	01 Dec
X	Scott, M.R.	16 Dec
X	Bing, N.A.	16 Dec
X	Spence, R.G.	16 Dec
S	Arnold, A.S.	17 Dec
X	Coyne, J.D.	17 Dec
X	Doyle, N.P.	17 Dec

LIEUTENANTS

S	Johnson, M.D.	17 Dec	X	Hempsell, A.M.	01 Jun	X	Aitken, A.J.	01 Sep
X	Miller, G.	17 Dec	X	Hurley, C.	01 Jun	E	Beautyman, A.J.	01 Sep
X	Wardle, M.	17 Dec	X	McGlory, S.J.	01 Jun	E	MacDonald, A.J.	01 Sep
S	Wyatt, C.	17 Dec	S	Park, B.C.	01 Jun	X	Mutch, J.R.	01 Sep
			S	Roberts, S.M.	01 Jun	E	Ajala, A.A.	01 Sep
	1994		X	Stacey, A.M.	01 Jun	E	Balcombe, J.S.	01 Sep
X	Campbell, P.R.	01 Jan	X	Waterfield, S.J.	01 Jun	E	Voyce, J.E.	01 Sep
E	Kies, L.N.	01 Jan	E	Dunningham, S.	10 Jun	S	Goldsworthy, P.J.	01 Sep
X	Haywood, P.J.	01 Jan	E	Grant, B.G.	10 Jun	X	Reese, D.M.	01 Sep
X	Hitchings, D.L.	01 Jan	E	Page, T.A.	10 Jun	X	Webber, J.P.	01 Sep
X	Allen, D.J.K.	16 Jan	E	Waterman, D.L.	10 Jun	X	Downing, I.M.	16 Sep
X	Gotke, C.T.	16 Jan	X	Naylor, A.J.	16 Jun	X	Stubbs, G.A.	16 Sep
X	Buckley, D.D.G.	01 Feb	X	Oakes, I.J.	16 Jun	X	Ling, J.W.L.	16 Sep
X	Tite, A.D.	01 Feb	X	Hunt, S.C.	01 Jul	E	Warneken, A.E.	01 Oct
X	Phipps, T.A.	01 Feb	E	Campbell-Balcombe, A.A.	01 Jul	X	Drodge, A.P.F.	01 Oct
X	Bunney, G.J.	01 Feb	E	Doran, S.E.	01 Jul	X	Lee, P.M.	01 Oct
E	Cheshire, T.E.	01 Feb	X	O'Nyons, Y.I.	01 Jul	X	Mullen, J.J.	01 Oct
X	Taylor, R.J.	16 Feb	X	Raeburn, M.	01 Jul	X	Penprase, J.M.	01 Oct
E	Bradshaw, K.T.	18 Feb	X	Jacques, M.J.	01 Jul	E	Richardson, D.	01 Oct
E	Brothers, A.H.G.	18 Feb	E	Block, A.W.G.	01 Jul	E	Snelling, P.D.	01 Oct
E	Buckeridge, V.W.	18 Feb	X	Gill, M.H.	01 Jul	E	Boyle, J.B.	01 Oct
E	Dymond, N.R.J.	18 Feb	E	Hamilton, S.M.	01 Jul	S	Bryant, D.J.G.	01 Oct
E	Penfold, M.J.	18 Feb	E	Mincher, D.J.F.	01 Jul	S	Goodman, P.R.	01 Oct
E	Wells, B.C.	18 Feb	X	Mollard, M.J.	01 Jul	X	Lord, R.J.	01 Oct
E	Wrenn, M.R.W.	18 Feb	X	Payne, P.J.	01 Jul	X	Morgan, D.H.	01 Oct
E	Wyld, A.W.	18 Feb	S	Sellars, S.J.	01 Jul	X	Sharpe, T.G.	01 Oct
X	Chadfield, L.J.	01 Mar	E	Skelton, J.S.	01 Jul	X	Vartan, M.R.	01 Oct
X	Bryson, S.A.	01 Mar	X	Welch, D.A.	05 Jul	X	Woolhead, A.L.	01 Oct
X	Hinchcliffe, A.	01 Mar	X	Hopkins, S.D.	16 Jul	X	Lamont, N.J.	06 Oct
X	Knight, A.C.F.	01 Mar	X	Sheils, D.E.T.	16 Jul	X	Barry, J.P.	11 Oct
X	Clarke, D.	16 Mar	X	Oatley, T.P.	16 Jul	E	Bryce, N.A.	14 Oct
X	Corbett, T.J.	01 Apr	X	Wingfield, M.J.	16 Jul	E	Ford, G.R.	14 Oct
X	Barnes, P.A.L.	01 Apr	X	Laycock, A.	16 Jul	E	Midmore, M.J.	14 Oct
E	Hindson, C.L.	01 Apr	X	Carter, K.S.	29 Jul	E	White, R.L.	14 Oct
E	Nicholas, S.P.	01 Apr	MS	Howells, M.J.	29 Jul	X	Brayson, M.	16 Oct
X	Manser, D.N.	01 Apr	X	Wright, D.A.	29 Jul	X	Ellerton, P.	16 Oct
X	Page, L.	01 Apr	X	Garner, S.M.	01 Aug	X	Jones, A.E.	01 Nov
S	Austen, R.M.	08 Apr	E	Bonner, N.	01 Aug	X	Pitcher, P.P.	01 Nov
S	Lewins, G.	08 Apr	E	Combe, G.R.	01 Aug	X	Roberts, M.A.	01 Nov
X	Lister, S.	08 Apr	X	Goldstone, R.S.	01 Aug	X	Brown, S.D.	01 Nov
X	Mailes, I.R.A.	16 Apr	X	Mortimer, R.P.	01 Aug	E	Cummings, D.J.	01 Nov
X	Stembridge, D.P.T.	16 Apr	S	Nicholson, K.J.	01 Aug	X	Webster, A.P.	01 Nov
X	Townsend, G.P.	01 May	E	Scott, R.A.	01 Aug	E	Bird, M.G.J.	01 Nov
E	Wicking, G.S.	01 May	S	Dickson, J.I.	01 Aug	X	Peachey, R.M.	01 Nov
S	Hart, N.L.W.	01 May	X	Kirkham, S.P.	16 Aug	X	Ripley, B.E.	01 Nov
X	Hoare, P.J.E.	01 May	S	Taylor, C.R.	25 Aug	S	White, J.E.	01 Nov
E	Stephenson, K.J.M.	01 May	E	Dawson, N.J.F.	01 Sep	E	Doull, D.J.M.	01 Nov
X	Kennington, L.A.	01 May	E	Saunders, J.M.	01 Sep	X	Kirkwood, T.A.H.	01 Nov
X	Matthews, J.	16 May	X	Cottee, B.R.J.	01 Sep	S	Murdoch, A.P.	01 Nov
X	West, R.J.	01 Jun	E	Hodge, C.M.	01 Sep	S	Watts, A.J.	01 Nov
X	Osborn, C.G.	01 Jun	X	McDonald, N.	01 Sep	X	Allison, G.	16 Nov
X	Hedworth, A.J.	01 Jun						

LIEUTENANTS

X Roster, S.P. ...... 16 Nov	X Wiseman, I.C. ...... 01 Feb	MS Wagstaff, N. ...... 10 Apr
X Bratby, S.P. ...... 16 Nov	X Barber, C.J.H. ...... 01 Feb	E Panic, A. ...... 15 Apr
X Nicholson, S.R. ...... 22 Nov	X Borbone, N. ...... 06 Feb	X Kelynack, M.T. ...... 16 Apr
X Russell, N.A.D. ...... 01 Dec	X Johnson, A.R. ...... 16 Feb	S Jones, C.J. ...... 28 Apr
S Birse, B.L. ...... 01 Dec	X Cooke, J.E. ...... 18 Feb	E Hardiman, N.A. ...... 01 May
X Lamb, A.G. ...... 01 Dec	E Abbott, D.A. ...... 24 Feb	X Cooke-Priest, N.C.R. ...... 01 May
X Sillers, B. ...... 01 Dec	E Dawson, A.J. ...... 24 Feb	S Hall, E.L. ...... 01 May
X Brodie, R.W.J. ...... 01 Dec	E Eddie, A.G.W. ...... 24 Feb	X Whitfield, R.M.P. ...... 01 May
X Young, R. ...... 01 Dec	E Fallowfield, J.P. ...... 24 Feb	X Inge, D.J. ...... 01 May
E Patterson, D. ...... 01 Dec	E Harwood, C.G. ...... 24 Feb	X Byron, J.D. ...... 01 May
E Craggs, S. ...... 01 Dec	E Henderson, P.P. ...... 24 Feb	E Malkin, S.L. ...... 01 May
E Ronaldson, G.I. ...... 01 Dec	E Jones, D.L. ...... 24 Feb	X Murison, L.C. ...... 01 May
E Scopes, D. ...... 01 Dec	E Knight, K.J. ...... 24 Feb	E Shaughnessy, S.L. ...... 01 May
X Soul, N.J. ...... 01 Dec	E O'Brien, I.P. ...... 24 Feb	X Hynett, W.A. ...... 16 May
S Titmuss, J.F. ...... 01 Dec	E Watson, C.R. ...... 24 Feb	X Stubbs, I. ...... 16 May
E Trott, E.A. ...... 01 Dec	E Adams, R.J. ...... 01 Mar	X Woolsey, K.E.K. ...... 16 May
X Elston, A.J. ...... 16 Dec	E Carlisle, C.R. ...... 01 Mar	E Durham, P.C.L. ...... 18 May
X Hardy, L.B. ...... 16 Dec	X Foulis, N.D.A. ...... 01 Mar	E Youp, A.T. ...... 01 Jun
X Pledger, D. ...... 16 Dec	S Gennard, A. ...... 01 Mar	X Noyce, R.G. ...... 01 Jun
X Dembrey, M.N.S. ...... 16 Dec	S Malins, D.J.H. ...... 01 Mar	X Peppe, A.G. ...... 01 Jun
	X Tanner, R.C. ...... 01 Mar	X Monk, S.R. ...... 01 Jun
1995	X Bainbridge, S.D. ...... 01 Mar	X Asquith, S.P. ...... 01 Jun
E Carpenter, B.H. ...... 01 Jan	E Burvill, J.P. ...... 01 Mar	X Euden, C.P. ...... 01 Jun
E Deakin, J. ...... 01 Jan	E Coope, P.J. ...... 01 Mar	X Jarrett, M.T.J. ...... 01 Jun
E Jordan, C. ...... 01 Jan	E Fisher, P.C. ...... 01 Mar	E Barrows, D.M. ...... 01 Jun
E Lovering, T.T.A. ...... 01 Jan	X Goulding, J.P. ...... 01 Mar	E Sharkey, E.R. ...... 01 Jun
E Roberts, A.M. ...... 01 Jan	E Harms, J.G. ...... 01 Mar	X Turner, D.N. ...... 01 Jun
E Rogers, P.S. ...... 01 Jan	E Holmes, R.A.G. ...... 01 Mar	X Ward, A.J. ...... 01 Jun
E Thompson, A.J. ...... 01 Jan	E Jennings, W. ...... 01 Mar	X Watson, A.H. ...... 01 Jun
X Braithwaite, J.S. ...... 01 Jan	E Large, S.A. ...... 01 Mar	E Keeley, S.P. ...... 15 Jun
X Lunn, T.R. ...... 01 Jan	E Phillips, J.N. ...... 01 Mar	E Knight, R.H. ...... 15 Jun
X Mills, S.D.G. ...... 01 Jan	E Stagg, A.R. ...... 01 Mar	E Wilson, J.A. ...... 15 Jun
X Allfree, J. ...... 01 Jan	X Thompson, M.G. ...... 01 Mar	X Day, M.K. ...... 15 Jun
E Cragg, R.D. ...... 01 Jan	S Wales, B.D. ...... 01 Mar	X McCowan, D.J. ...... 16 Jun
X Jones, M.D. ...... 01 Jan	X Watson, I. ...... 01 Mar	X Lee, N.D. ...... 16 Jun
E McCarthy, S.J. ...... 01 Jan	X Skelley, A.N.M. ...... 01 Mar	X Lynn, I.H. ...... 30 Jun
E Nelson, L.M. ...... 01 Jan	X Rawlinson, D. ...... 16 Mar	S Cowan, C.J. ...... 01 Jul
E Benn, S.W. ...... 01 Jan	X Gray, J.N.S. ...... 01 Apr	X May, J.W. ...... 01 Jul
X Jones, M.D. ...... 16 Jan	X Marten, A.D. ...... 01 Apr	E May, S.C. ...... 01 Jul
X Laverty, R.E. ...... 01 Feb	E Rawson, S.M. ...... 01 Apr	X Parrock, N.G. ...... 01 Jul
X Tate, G.A. ...... 01 Feb	X Humphries, J.E. ...... 01 Apr	X Beacham, P.R. ...... 01 Jul
E Kellett, A. ...... 01 Feb	X Foster, T.G. ...... 01 Apr	E Dalton, F.J. ...... 01 Jul
X Satterthwaite, B.J. ...... 01 Feb	X Stratford, P.J. ...... 01 Apr	X Deavin, M.J. ...... 01 Jul
X Gray, Y.M. ...... 01 Feb	X Lovatt, G.J. ...... 01 Apr	X Doran, I.A.G. ...... 01 Jul
E Bowden, M.T.E. ...... 01 Feb	X Reid, M.R. ...... 01 Apr	E Edward, G.J. ...... 01 Jul
E Boyes, M.R. ...... 01 Feb	X Stride, J.C. ...... 01 Apr	E Lincoln, K.J. ...... 01 Jul
S Dutton, A.C. ...... 01 Feb	X McLennan, A. ...... 01 Apr	X Mitchell, J.R. ...... 01 Jul
X Franklin, G.D. ...... 01 Feb	X Atkinson, C.P. ...... 01 Apr	X Ruddock, G.W.D. ...... 01 Jul
E Gair, S.D.H. ...... 01 Feb	E Bowman, R.J. ...... 01 Apr	E Ryan, N. ...... 01 Jul
X Langrill, T.J. ...... 01 Feb	X Gold, J.W. ...... 06 Apr	E Palmer, J. ...... 01 Jul
X Maynard, C.I. ...... 01 Feb	X Seward, S.A. ...... 06 Apr	X Smith, R.D. ...... 22 Jul
X McCutcheon, G. ...... 01 Feb		

LIEUTENANTS

X	Bishop, G.C.	27 Jul	S	Matthews, P.K.	01 Oct	X	Wookey, M.	01 Feb
X	Cunningham, N.J.W.	27 Jul	X	Wheeler, N.J.	01 Oct	X	Wilkinson, M.F.	01 Feb
X	Tomlinson, J.H.	27 Jul	E	Welsh, J.	15 Oct	S	MacKay, A.C.	01 Feb
S	Goldsworthy, E.T.	01 Aug	E	Sitton, J.B.	01 Nov	X	Moorhouse, S.M.R.	01 Feb
X	Higgins, A.J.	01 Aug	X	Jardine, D.S.	01 Nov	E	Read, M.R.	01 Feb
E	Paulson, R.B.	01 Aug	X	Jones, P.D.	01 Nov	X	Rimington, A.K.	01 Feb
E	Harrington, J.B.H.	01 Aug	X	Ley, A.B.	01 Nov	X	Stride, J.A.	01 Feb
E	Sandle, N.D.	01 Aug	E	Parker, T.S.	01 Nov	X	Watts, J.N.	01 Feb
X	Syrett, M.E.	01 Aug	X	Bassett, D.A.	01 Nov	X	Smith, M.D.	01 Feb
X	Yule, M.J.C.	01 Aug	X	Neild, T.	01 Nov	X	Segebarth, R.A.	16 Feb
X	Cahill, K.A.	01 Aug	X	Tregaskis, N.S.	01 Nov	X	Thomas, S.M.	16 Feb
E	Hickson, M.S.H.	01 Aug	X	Rackham, A.D.H.	01 Nov	E	Edson, M.A.	22 Feb
E	Letts, A.J.	01 Aug	X	Chick, N.S.	16 Nov	E	Hyland, R.A.	22 Feb
X	Lucocq, N.J.	01 Aug	E	Lee, S.Y.L.	01 Dec	E	Stubbs, M.A.	22 Feb
S	Russell, G.S.	01 Aug	W	Swan, W.	01 Dec	E	Watson, C.R.	22 Feb
E	Sweeney, K.P.M.	01 Aug	W	Watts, S.F.	01 Dec	E	Wheadon, P.C.	01 Mar
E	Veal, A.E.	01 Aug	E	Mallen, D.J.	01 Dec	X	Smith, D.L.	01 Mar
X	Nash, P.D.	01 Aug	X	Marriott, N.K.	01 Dec	X	Hunt, F.B.G.	01 Mar
X	Tregunna, G.A.	08 Aug	X	Tacey, R.H.	01 Dec	X	Peters, W.R.	01 Mar
X	Brooman, M.J.	16 Aug	X	West, D.C.	01 Dec	X	Packham, C.N.R.	01 Mar
X	Armstrong, S.T.	16 Aug	X	Craig, C.L.	01 Dec	X	Clark, M.H.	01 Mar
X	Phillips, M.B.	16 Aug	E	Hughes, N.D.	01 Dec	X	Clay, J.C.	01 Mar
E	Blow, P.T.	01 Sep	X	Ingram, G.J.	01 Dec	S	Hanson, M.N.	01 Mar
E	Hunter, N.J.	01 Sep	X	Rees, R.T.	01 Dec	E	Ling, C.	01 Mar
E	Le Gassick, P.J.	01 Sep	X	Byrne, T.M.	13 Dec	S	Nelson, V.	01 Mar
E	Mehta, K.L.	01 Sep	X	Knight, J.D.	13 Dec	X	Philpott, A.M.	01 Mar
E	Proffitt Burnham, J.M.	01 Sep	X	Lawson, G.J.	13 Dec	E	Punch, G.K.	01 Mar
E	Vincent, D.	01 Sep	X	Marsh, M.P.A.	13 Dec	X	Rae, D.G.	01 Mar
X	Brennan, A.J.	01 Sep	X	Morrison, P.	13 Dec	E	Screaton, R.M.	01 Mar
E	Edwards, A.G.	01 Sep	X	Woodrow, K.J.	13 Dec	E	Stiven, T.D.	01 Mar
E	Foster, P.J.	01 Sep	X	Evans, D.A.	20 Dec	E	Taylor, H.J.	01 Mar
E	Hambly, B.J.	01 Sep				E	Townsend, D.J.	01 Mar
X	Rhodes, M.J.	01 Sep		**1996**		X	Backus, R.I.K.	01 Mar
E	Cullen, N.L.	01 Sep	E	Collins, T.L.	01 Jan	E	Lewis, A.J.	01 Mar
X	Lanni, M.N.	01 Sep	E	Harrison, T.I.	01 Jan	MS	Taylor, N.A.	06 Mar
E	McWilliams, J.E.	01 Sep	E	Heighway, M.R.	01 Jan	X	Simms, D.M.	16 Mar
E	Stowell, R.B.M.	01 Sep	E	Young, N.A.	01 Jan	X	Flintham, J.E.	16 Mar
E	Whiting, E.A.	01 Sep	S	Bollen, J.M.	01 Jan	X	Long, M.S.	01 Apr
X	Hayton, S.R.C.	05 Sep	X	Okukenu, D.	01 Jan	X	Lockett, D.J.	01 Apr
E	Brown, P.A.	07 Sep	E	Pakes, D.T.	01 Jan	S	Barber, R.W.	01 Apr
E	Holden, P.A.	07 Sep	E	Hendrickx, C.J.	01 Jan	X	Capes, S.G.	01 Apr
E	Reed, J.C.	07 Sep	X	Bratt, A.R.	01 Jan	X	Readwin, R.R.	01 Apr
X	Harrison, R.S.	15 Sep	E	Field, C.R.H.	01 Jan	X	Shepherd, M.P.	01 Apr
X	Newton, J.L.	16 Sep	X	Gibson, J.B.	01 Jan	S	Woodard, N.A.	01 Apr
X	Baxter, J.C.	27 Sep	X	Johnston, J.A.	01 Jan	E	Barrows, S.M.	01 Apr
E	O'Neill, P.J.	01 Oct	E	Perkins, R.J.	01 Jan	X	Battrick, R.R.	01 Apr
X	Horne, J.R.	01 Oct	E	Thompson, M.J.	01 Jan	X	Crabb, A.J.	01 Apr
X	Bosley, B.D.	01 Oct	E	Bailey, J.J.	01 Jan	X	Hains, J.	01 Apr
S	Dean, J.R.	01 Oct	S	Trinder, S.J.	30 Jan	X	Laughton, P.	01 Apr
X	Hanneman, M.N.	01 Oct	E	Pinder, C.D.	01 Feb	E	Robertshaw, I.W.	01 Apr
X	Irons, R.C.S.	01 Oct	X	Officer, R.L.	01 Feb	E	Spooner, R.S.	01 Apr
			E	Powles, D.A.	01 Feb			

LIEUTENANTS

MS Blocke, A.D. ...... 04 Apr	E King, G.C. ...... 14 Jun	X Terry, N.P. ...... 01 Sep
MS Bradford, T.H.C. ...... 04 Apr	E Rendell, D.J. ...... 14 Jun	E McCombe, J. ...... 01 Sep
X Brailey, I.S.F. ...... 04 Apr	E Riley, G.A. ...... 14 Jun	X Enever, S.A. ...... 01 Sep
S Carter, S.P. ...... 04 Apr	X Vorley, S.W. ...... 15 Jun	X Williams, R.J.S. ...... 01 Sep
X Easton, D.W. ...... 04 Apr	X Hourigan, M.P. ...... 16 Jun	E Wright, D.I. ...... 01 Sep
X Ford, A.J. ...... 04 Apr	X Wiseman, N.C. ...... 16 Jun	X Campbell, M.A.M. ...... 01 Sep
X Walker, M.J. ...... 04 Apr	X Hutchins, T.S. ...... 16 Jun	S Harris, R.P. ...... 01 Sep
MS Walton, A.P. ...... 04 Apr	X Platt, J.H. ...... 16 Jun	X Hindmarch, S.A. ...... 01 Sep
X Welburn, R.C. ...... 04 Apr	E Clare, K. ...... 29 Jun	S Percival, F. ...... 01 Sep
X Wilkinson, J. ...... 04 Apr	X Adams, P.N.E. ...... 01 Jul	E Puxley, M.E. ...... 01 Sep
X Campbell, I.A. ...... 16 Apr	X Fox, T.M. ...... 01 Jul	X Raeburn, C. ...... 01 Sep
X Fraser, I.E. ...... 16 Apr	X Spillane, P.W. ...... 01 Jul	E Bottomley, S. ...... 06 Sep
E Evans, P.C. ...... 01 May	X Wyness, R.S. ...... 01 Jul	X Wilson, A.S. ...... 16 Sep
X MacColl, A.A.J. ...... 01 May	X Atkinson, R.J. ...... 01 Jul	E Donnelly, S. ...... 17 Sep
E Marjoram, G.K. ...... 01 May	E Fraser, H.L. ...... 01 Jul	X Clifford, C.T. ...... 25 Sep
E Hiscock, S.R.B. ...... 01 May	E Hope, M.R. ...... 01 Jul	X McGuire, J. ...... 01 Oct
X Smith, A.B.D. ...... 01 May	E Jones, D.M. ...... 01 Jul	E Sanderson, L.D. ...... 01 Oct
E Fraser, P. ...... 01 May	E Leach, S.J. ...... 01 Jul	X Jaini, A. ...... 01 Oct
X Hammond, P.J. ...... 01 May	X Parrott, J.P. ...... 01 Jul	X McEwan, A.M. ...... 01 Oct
X Riggall, A.D. ...... 01 May	X Pickering, I.J. ...... 01 Jul	X Parr, M.J.E. ...... 01 Oct
S Scandling, R.J. ...... 01 May	X Davies, H.G.A. ...... 01 Jul	X Donegan, C.L. ...... 01 Oct
E Bell, J.M. ...... 01 May	X Armstrong, N.S. ...... 01 Jul	E Haworth, J.H.T. ...... 01 Oct
E Blair, G.J.L. ...... 01 May	X Burke, D.E. ...... 01 Jul	X Hill, A.J. ...... 01 Oct
E Howells, S.L. ...... 01 May	X May, C. ...... 01 Jul	E Day, S.N. ...... 01 Oct
E Parry, M.R.R. ...... 01 May	E Thorp, B.T. ...... 01 Jul	X Stuart, E.E.A. ...... 01 Oct
E Smith, M.J. ...... 01 May	X Tyler, J.C. ...... 01 Jul	E Purvis, D.M. ...... 16 Oct
E York, G.R.J. ...... 01 May	S Bagworth, J.F. ...... 01 Jul	X Sewell, M.A.P. ...... 16 Oct
E Flynn, A. ...... 01 May	X Dennis, P.E. ...... 01 Jul	X Bonnar, S.M. ...... 01 Nov
X Mowatt, P. ...... 01 May	X Church, S.C. ...... 16 Jul	E Davis, S.R. ...... 01 Nov
X Steadman, R.P. ...... 01 May	X Forbes, P.T. ...... 16 Jul	E Gothard, A.M. ...... 01 Nov
E Taylor, I.J. ...... 05 May	X Brember, P.B. ...... 25 Jul	X Balletta, R.J. ...... 01 Nov
X Robley, W.F. ...... 01 Jun	X Dale, N.R. ...... 25 Jul	X McBratney, J.A.G. ...... 01 Nov
E Nimmons, P. ...... 01 Jun	MS Miller, D.E. ...... 25 Jul	X Walsh, K.M. ...... 01 Nov
X Strathie, G.S. ...... 01 Jun	X Richards, F.C. ...... 25 Jul	X Webber, K.J. ...... 01 Nov
X Griffiths, R.H. ...... 01 Jun	X Smith, S.R.F. ...... 28 Jul	X Bradley, R.L. ...... 01 Nov
E Potts, G. ...... 01 Jun	E McNamara, I.M. ...... 01 Aug	X Dickins, B.R. ...... 01 Nov
S Evans, C.A. ...... 01 Jun	X Stroude, P.A. ...... 01 Aug	X Essenhigh, A.N.P. ...... 01 Nov
E Ubhi, W.G. ...... 01 Jun	E Murphy, S.M. ...... 01 Aug	X Whitlum, S. ...... 01 Nov
X Criddle, G.D.J. ...... 01 Jun	X Patterson, J.D. ...... 01 Aug	X Ollerton, J.C. ...... 16 Nov
X Fisher, R.J. ...... 01 Jun	X Moules, C.E. ...... 01 Aug	E Mullins, A.D. ...... 01 Dec
X Gilmore, M.P. ...... 01 Jun	X Moules, M.A.J. ...... 01 Aug	X Wood, M.L. ...... 01 Dec
E Hedgecox, D.C. ...... 01 Jun	X Sheldrake, J.P. ...... 01 Aug	X Donworth, D.M.J. ...... 01 Dec
E Lyons, M.J. ...... 01 Jun	X Abel, N.P. ...... 16 Aug	X Mitchell, C.D. ...... 01 Dec
E McCloskey, I.M. ...... 01 Jun	X Clarke, R.J. ...... 16 Aug	E Ankah, G.K.E. ...... 01 Dec
X Monk, C.R. ...... 01 Jun	X Hall, D. ...... 16 Aug	E Brooks, K.M.L. ...... 01 Dec
X Rowlands, A.R. ...... 01 Jun	X Whitlum, A.C. ...... 16 Aug	X Hayden, T.W. ...... 01 Dec
X Lindsay, I.B. ...... 01 Jun	X Everitt, T.W. ...... 19 Aug	E Ashworth, H.J. ...... 01 Dec
X Sturdy, C.C.M. ...... 14 Jun	E Drummond, H. ...... 01 Sep	E Brown, A.M. ...... 01 Dec
E Grant, D.J. ...... 14 Jun	E Edwards, J. ...... 01 Sep	X Lacy, L.H. ...... 01 Dec
E Hutchinson, P. ...... 14 Jun	E Kelly, G.J. ...... 01 Sep	S Reed, D.K. ...... 01 Dec
E Jones, R.V. ...... 14 Jun	W Dobie, F.E. ...... 01 Sep	E Whitehouse, N.R. ...... 01 Dec

LIEUTENANTS

1997

E	Collins, D.R.	01 Jan
E	Dennis, M.J.	01 Jan
E	Dick, C.M.	01 Jan
E	Nelson, P.M.	01 Jan
E	Smith, C.J.H.	01 Jan
E	Taylor, C.S.	01 Jan
X	Santrian, K.	01 Jan
S	Dow, C.S.	01 Jan
E	Hunwicks, S.E.	01 Jan
X	Miles, R.L.	01 Jan
X	Ottewell, P.S.	01 Jan
X	Tilney, D.E.	01 Jan
X	Wood, C.R.	01 Jan
X	Clague, J.J.	15 Jan
X	Johnson, S.R.D.	16 Jan
E	Smith, K.D.	01 Feb
X	Caldicott-Barr, V.A.	01 Feb
X	Harper, P.R.	01 Feb
X	Codd, J.S.	01 Feb
E	Jefferson, T.S.	01 Feb
X	Foster, N.P.	01 Feb
S	Gullett, H.R.	01 Feb
E	Kendrick, A.M.	01 Feb
E	Kingdom, M.A.	01 Feb
E	Miller, M.C.	01 Feb
S	Nathanson, H.	01 Feb
X	Robertson Gopffarth,A.A.J.	01 Feb
X	Thomsen, L.L.	01 Feb
E	Cain, C.W.	07 Feb
E	Collins, S.A.	07 Feb
E	Eardley, J.M.	07 Feb
E	Fulford, R.N.	07 Feb
E	McTaggart, D.A.	07 Feb
E	Ridge, M.H.	07 Feb
E	Sheldon, M.L.	07 Feb
X	Owen, G.	16 Feb
E	Thomson, P.D.	24 Feb
X	Barlow, M.J.	01 Mar
E	Haddow, T.R.	01 Mar
E	Read, P.S.	01 Mar
X	Butterworth, P.G.	01 Mar
S	Hefford, C.J.	01 Mar
X	Jackson, I.	01 Mar
X	Mason, D.J.	01 Mar
X	McHugh, R.H.	01 Mar
X	Philip, A.D.	01 Mar
S	Quantrill, S.W.	01 Mar
S	Stockbridge, A.J.	01 Mar
E	Thorne, D.J.	01 Mar
X	Tilden, P.J.E.	01 Mar
S	Wells, M.P.	01 Mar
X	Rackham, K.L.M.	01 Mar
X	Small, R.J.	01 Mar
X	Stringer, K.D.P.	16 Mar
X	Cook, C.M.	01 Apr
E	Rae, A.L.	01 Apr
E	Cumming, R.A.	01 Apr
E	Foreman, S.M.	01 Apr
E	Wildin, A.	01 Apr
X	Walton, S.D.	01 Apr
E	Bernard, A.R.	01 Apr
E	Boxall, P.	01 Apr
X	Brooks, G.C.G.	01 Apr
X	Green, I.A.	01 Apr
E	Harding, H.R.	01 Apr
X	Hounsom, T.R.	01 Apr
X	Lumsden, P.I.	01 Apr
E	Mealing, D.W.	01 Apr
E	Nicoll, A.J.	01 Apr
X	Cole, D.J.	01 Apr
X	Alcindor, D.J.	01 Apr
S	Barratt, S.M.	03 Apr
X	Bennetts, N.	03 Apr
X	Clark, A.S.	03 Apr
X	Conway, M.J.	03 Apr
S	Darlow, P.R.	03 Apr
X	Dunne, M.G.	03 Apr
MS	Finn, D.W.	03 Apr
X	Guiver, P.	03 Apr
X	Lewis, K.A.	03 Apr
X	McGrane, R.J.	03 Apr
MS	McGunigall, R.J.	03 Apr
S	Moores, J.	03 Apr
X	Norford, M.A.	03 Apr
X	Stretton, D.G.	03 Apr
X	Tomlinson, D.C.	03 Apr
X	Heaney, M.J.	16 Apr
X	Hooton, D.R.	16 Apr
E	Sargent, K.S.	29 Apr
E	Bennett, D.P.	01 May
E	McGinley, C.T.	01 May
E	Adams, G.	01 May
E	Straughan, S.R.	01 May
E	Marr, J.	01 May
E	Tracey, A.D.	01 May
X	Hibberd, K.M.	01 May
X	Oakley, S.E.	01 May
X	Jones, J.	01 May
E	Kirk, A.C.	01 May
E	Murchie, A.D.	01 May
X	Pavey, E.L.	01 May
X	Frean, J.P.	16 May
X	Lewis, B.C.	16 May
S	Berisford, A.W.	01 Jun
E	Briggs, M.D.	01 Jun
E	Thompson, D.W.	01 Jun
E	Pannett, L.W.	01 Jun
S	Dobbins, S.J.	01 Jun
S	Exworthy, D.A.G.	01 Jun
E	Lee, W.	01 Jun
E	McCallum, N.R.	01 Jun
E	Sayer, J.M.	01 Jun
X	Webb, M.D.	01 Jun
E	Burley, M.R.	01 Jun
E	Edwards, J.E.	01 Jun
X	Ellison, T.G.	01 Jun
X	Gamble, S.B.	01 Jun
E	Harvey, B.	01 Jun
X	Leighton, M.R.	01 Jun
E	O'Shaughnessy, D.J.	01 Jun
S	Porter, D.L.	01 Jun
X	Saunders, C.E.M.	01 Jun
S	Vogel, L.D.	01 Jun
E	Cattroll, D.	13 Jun
E	Finnie, H.M.	13 Jun
E	Jones, M.A.	13 Jun
E	Shuttleworth, S.	13 Jun
E	Turle, P.J.	13 Jun
E	Weaver, N.	13 Jun
E	Sargent, L.M.	23 Jun
X	Donovan, S.J.	01 Jul
E	Boyes, G.A.	01 Jul
S	Welch, K.A.	01 Jul
E	White, K.F.	01 Jul
X	Arden, V.G.	01 Jul
X	Fitzpatrick, J.A.J.	01 Jul
X	Baines, A.R.	01 Jul
X	Crookes, W.A.	01 Jul
E	Kennedy, I.	01 Jul
X	McKee, H.M.	01 Jul
E	Patterson, S.D.	01 Jul
X	Pedler, M.D.	01 Jul
E	Richards, J.I.H.	01 Jul
E	Saward, J.R.E.	01 Jul
E	Selway, M.A.	01 Jul
X	Wilson, J.	01 Jul
E	Wood, A.G.	01 Jul
X	Boughton, T.F.	01 Jul
X	Birrell, G.C.	01 Jul
X	Canale, A.J.	01 Jul
S	Cox, M.B.	03 Jul
X	Hughes, S.M.	16 Jul

LIEUTENANTS

E Driscoll, R. .... 22 Jul	E Haggerty, S.M. .... 01 Oct	E Chambers, P.D. .... 01 Dec
X Barraclough, C.D. .... 24 Jul	X Stevens, A.M.R. .... 01 Oct	E Mealing, S.P. .... 01 Dec
S Bower, J.W. .... 24 Jul	X Holloway, S.A. .... 01 Oct	S Tremelling, F.M. .... 01 Dec
X Collins, M.C. .... 24 Jul	X Daveney, D.A. .... 01 Oct	E Stevens, A.J. .... 04 Dec
X Corkett, K.S. .... 24 Jul	E O'Toole, M.C. .... 01 Oct	X Rose, A.D. .... 16 Dec
X Magill, T.E. .... 24 Jul	E Quade, N.A.C. .... 01 Oct	
X McDermott, P.A. .... 24 Jul	X Livesey, J.E. .... 01 Oct	**1998**
X McEvoy, L.P. .... 24 Jul	X Shaughnessy, T.E. .... 01 Oct	E Auld, D.M. .... 01 Jan
S Morris, K.I. .... 24 Jul	X Studley, S.A. .... 01 Oct	E Watkins, K.J. .... 01 Jan
X Potter, D.J. .... 24 Jul	X Walton, S.P. .... 01 Oct	E Darkins, C.R. .... 01 Jan
X Rowan, M.E. .... 24 Jul	X Denton, A.M. .... 01 Oct	X Pickering-Wheeler, C.W. .... 01 Jan
X Southwell, N.P. .... 24 Jul	S Jenking-Rees, D. .... 01 Oct	X Stilwell, J.M. .... 01 Jan
S Strudwick, R. .... 24 Jul	X Mansfield, J.A. .... 01 Oct	E Ablett, S.D. .... 01 Jan
X Taylor, J.P. .... 24 Jul	S Ray, M.W. .... 01 Oct	S Carrigan, J.A. .... 01 Jan
X Vowles, M.J. .... 24 Jul	X Stuchbury, R.J. .... 01 Oct	E Chestnutt, J.M. .... 01 Jan
X Whild, D.J. .... 24 Jul	X Bramall, K.S. .... 01 Oct	S Gillies, E.M. .... 01 Jan
X Young, J.N. .... 24 Jul	X Davey, T.J. .... 01 Oct	X McMichael, J.S. .... 01 Jan
E Mallabone, J.J.K. .... 01 Aug	X Pedre, R.G. .... 01 Oct	X Spoors, B.M. .... 01 Jan
E Edwards, J. .... 01 Aug	E Skittrall, S.D. .... 15 Oct	X Steen, K.M. .... 01 Jan
X Chawira, D.N. .... 01 Aug	X Green, P.D. .... 16 Oct	X Willis, A.S. .... 01 Jan
E Evans, M.E. .... 01 Aug	X Alexander, O.D.D. .... 01 Nov	E Goodship, M.T. .... 01 Jan
X Spinks, D.W. .... 01 Aug	X Symington, Z.M.A. .... 01 Nov	E Murray, S.C. .... 01 Jan
X Jappy, G.W.G. .... 01 Aug	X Brockington, G.C. .... 01 Nov	S Kennedy, A. .... 08 Jan
X Northover, A.F. .... 01 Aug	E Tumelty, G.C. .... 01 Nov	X Blackwell, J.M. .... 16 Jan
E Spiller, S.N. .... 01 Aug	S Bull, C.V.R. .... 01 Nov	X Maley, C.E. .... 16 Jan
E Brutton, J.H. .... 01 Aug	S Goulder, J.D. .... 01 Nov	X Wakeford, I.F. .... 01 Feb
S Burnham, J.A.I. .... 01 Aug	X Howe, T. .... 01 Nov	S Haigh, J.J. .... 01 Feb
X Clemson, A.J. .... 01 Aug	X Leadbetter, A.J. .... 01 Nov	X Steer, A.D. .... 01 Feb
X Holder, J.M. .... 01 Aug	E McLellan, J.D. .... 01 Nov	X Curry, J.H. .... 01 Feb
X Johnson, A.D. .... 01 Aug	E Morley, J.I. .... 01 Nov	E D'Silva, D.M. .... 01 Feb
S Robb, M.E. .... 01 Aug	S Sheikh, N. .... 01 Nov	S Drake, C.L. .... 01 Feb
X Wilson, A.J. .... 01 Aug	E Harrison, M.A. .... 01 Nov	X Gibbs, D.J.E. .... 01 Feb
S Pring, S.J. .... 14 Aug	S Rickard, J. .... 12 Nov	E Jacobs, M.P. .... 01 Feb
X Fuller, C.E. .... 16 Aug	X Richman, P.G. .... 16 Nov	E Millard, J.R. .... 01 Feb
X Scott, M. .... 16 Aug	S Ashby, M.K. .... 01 Dec	X White, S.M. .... 01 Feb
E Clark, S.R. .... 01 Sep	E Hawkins, S.R. .... 01 Dec	S Wood, G.R. .... 01 Feb
E Pettigrew, T.R. .... 01 Sep	E Hassall, I. .... 01 Dec	X Roberts, N.D. .... 10 Feb
E Ashby, K.J. .... 01 Sep	E Sullivan, M.N. .... 01 Dec	X Ward, K.N. .... 13 Feb
E Griffiths, D.P. .... 01 Sep	E Banham, A.W.D.B. .... 01 Dec	X Eastwood, R.N. .... 15 Feb
E Strange, S.P. .... 01 Sep	X Davies, G.W.T. .... 01 Dec	X Priest, J.E. .... 15 Feb
E Elsey, D.J. .... 01 Sep	X Witte, R.H. .... 01 Dec	X Holroyd, J.E.J. .... 16 Feb
E MacKinnon, A. .... 01 Sep	S Allsford, K.M. .... 01 Dec	E McCleary, S.P. .... 01 Mar
X Ward, S. .... 01 Sep	X Carrick, J.P. .... 01 Dec	X Guy, C.R. .... 01 Mar
S Hayes, C.L. .... 01 Sep	X Collen, S.J. .... 01 Dec	S Haggard, A. .... 01 Mar
S Hills, I.E. .... 01 Sep	X Wallace, S.A. .... 01 Dec	E Hay, M. .... 01 Mar
X Palethorpe, N. .... 01 Sep	X Anderson, M.E.J. .... 01 Dec	X Johns, A.W. .... 01 Mar
E Butler, I.A. .... 12 Sep	E Bamforth, C.J.M. .... 01 Dec	X Richardson, P.C. .... 01 Mar
E Fitzgerald, C. .... 12 Sep	X Doig, B.J. .... 01 Dec	X Ryan, J.H. .... 01 Mar
X Prole, N.M. .... 16 Sep	X Hutchings, R.P.H. .... 01 Dec	E Thorp, D.B. .... 01 Mar
E Jenner, A.C. .... 16 Sep	X Palin, G.R. .... 01 Dec	X Tudor-Thomas, R.J. .... 01 Mar
S Hendy, R. .... 23 Sep	S Webster, R.J. .... 01 Dec	X White, D.J. .... 01 Mar
		X Gray, J.A. .... 01 Mar

LIEUTENANTS

E	Harrington, L.B.	01 Mar	X	Denham, D.J.	01 Jun	S	Park, I.D.	01 Aug
X	Calhaem, R.T.	15 Mar	S	Gilbert, R.G.	01 Jun	X	Pollard, A.E.	01 Aug
X	McCormick, P.E.	15 Mar	X	Hicks, N.J.I.	01 Jun	X	Hammock, S.G.	16 Aug
X	Beech, D.J.	16 Mar	X	Wells, B.I.	03 Jun	X	McTeer, I.J.	16 Aug
X	Compain, C.H.	21 Mar	X	Coulton, J.R.S.	16 Jun	E	Bird, T.S.V.	01 Sep
E	Griffiths, L.	01 Apr	X	Savage, D.M.	16 Jun	E	Bristow, P.C.	01 Sep
X	Lippitt, S.T.	01 Apr	X	Jenkins, A.R.	16 Jun	E	Coles, S.P.	01 Sep
E	Benstead, N.W.J.	01 Apr	E	Jones, R.K.	19 Jun	E	Jameson, A.J.	01 Sep
X	Brotton, P.J.	01 Apr	E	Norgate, P.R.E.	19 Jun	E	MacCorquodale, M.A.	01 Sep
E	Mountford, P.C.	01 Apr	E	Paton, A.J.M.	19 Jun	E	Rees, A.M.	01 Sep
X	Shorland-Ball, T.J.	01 Apr	E	Rankine, I.M.	19 Jun	E	Salim, M.	01 Sep
S	Vollentine, L.	01 Apr	E	Stone, R.J.	19 Jun	S	Hardwick, M.J.	01 Sep
X	Smith, N.J.D.	01 Apr	X	Bainbridge, J.R.	30 Jun	X	Allan, C.R.	01 Sep
S	Cox, G.F.	01 Apr	E	Simm, C.W.	01 Jul	X	Amey, J.M.	01 Sep
X	Shanks, G.J.	01 Apr	E	Cross, A.L.	01 Jul	X	Bagshaw, J.R.W.	01 Sep
S	Wright, T.M.	01 Apr	X	Johnson, M.R.E.	01 Jul	X	Birchall, J.C.	01 Sep
S	Goodwin, L.B.	03 Apr	X	Tremelling, P.N.	01 Jul	X	Davies, N.M.S.	01 Sep
X	Hayes, B.J.	03 Apr	X	Howe, C.M.	01 Jul	X	Berry, T.J.	01 Sep
X	Peak, M.	03 Apr	X	Mason, A.C.	01 Jul	X	Griffiths, N.	01 Sep
S	Platt, N.	03 Apr	X	Pressdee, S.J.	01 Jul	X	Howard, N.A.	01 Sep
X	Wood, J.A.	03 Apr	E	Chilton, J.	01 Jul	X	Hutchins, I.D.M.	01 Sep
X	Bates, A.J.	16 Apr	X	Rogers, S.J.P.	01 Jul	E	McDonald, D.J.	01 Sep
X	Blackmore, J.	16 Apr	E	Lewis, D.	19 Jul	X	Thomas, M.	01 Sep
X	Haggo, J.R.	16 Apr	X	Beale, M.D.	23 Jul	X	Williams, A.S.	01 Sep
E	Cameron, F.	24 Apr	X	Clelland, G.	23 Jul	X	Burbidge, K.	01 Sep
E	Buck, S.R.	01 May	X	Deam, P.A.V.	23 Jul	X	Colin-Thome, N.J.	01 Sep
E	Goward, R.J.	01 May	MS	Follington, D.C.	23 Jul	X	Ingham, A.R.	01 Sep
E	Hartley, J.H.D.	01 May	X	Johns, L.E.	23 Jul	X	Parkin, J.M.B.	01 Sep
E	Stiles, F.E.	01 May	X	Louden, C.A.	23 Jul	E	Brodier, M.I.	04 Sep
X	Rushworth, B.J.	01 May	S	Noon, D.	23 Jul	E	Curtis, D.	04 Sep
X	McWilliams, A.R.	01 May	X	Parkinson, A.P.	23 Jul	E	Henderson, R.J.	04 Sep
E	Clarke, M.D.	01 May	S	Stephenson, P.G.	23 Jul	E	Metcalfe, R.J.	04 Sep
X	Clay, T.C.D.C.	01 May	S	Watson, S.B.C.	23 Jul	E	Raynor, S.D.	04 Sep
X	Williams, L.J.	01 May	X	Kewley, I.D.	01 Aug	X	Raynes, C.	16 Sep
E	Bartlett, M.J.	01 May	E	Love, R.J.	01 Aug	X	Ashlin, J.M.	16 Sep
E	Beaver, R.M.S.	01 May	E	Taylor, K.M.	01 Aug	X	Osbaldestin, R.A.	01 Oct
E	Grennan, E.F.	01 May	X	Ward, J.E.	01 Aug	E	Lyons, A.G.	01 Oct
X	Marshall, M.	01 May	E	Burns, E.P.	01 Aug	X	Anderson, G.S.	01 Oct
X	Mason, M.J.	01 May	X	Carolan, K.S.	01 Aug	X	Crane, O.R.	01 Oct
X	Vallance, M.S.	01 May	E	Cartwright, J.A.	01 Aug	X	Fletcher, I.J.	01 Oct
E	Goodall, M.A.	01 May	X	Morgan, F.A.	01 Aug	X	Gould, J.D.	01 Oct
X	Heap, J.T.	01 May	S	Cooper, A.	01 Aug	X	Griffiths, G.H.	01 Oct
X	Higham, S.W.J.	01 May	X	Craven, M.W.	01 Aug	X	Thomas, D.W.	01 Oct
S	Sutcliffe, E.D.	01 May	X	Dale, W.D.J.	01 Aug	X	Varty, J.A.	01 Oct
X	Yates, S.E.	01 May	X	Ellis, N.J.	01 Aug	X	Benzie, N.J.E.	01 Oct
E	Sargent, N.M.	01 May	X	Heirs, G.G.	01 Aug	X	Densham, M.P.J.	01 Oct
X	Sharrocks, I.J.	16 May	X	MacLaughlin, R.A.	01 Aug	X	Drodge, K.N.	01 Oct
X	Taylor, C.P.	16 May	X	Muirhead, B.G.	01 Aug	X	Lamb, C.J.	01 Oct
X	Kurth, R.P.E.	18 May	X	Perry, E.M.	01 Aug	X	Wappner, G.D.	10 Oct
X	Full, R.J.	01 Jun	X	Smith, N.E.P.	01 Aug	X	Gaskell, H.D.	16 Oct
E	Humphery, D.	01 Jun	S	Miles, P.J.	01 Aug	X	Tazewell, M.R.	16 Oct

LIEUTENANTS

X	Doubleday, S.	16 Oct	X	Conlin, J.A.	01 Jan	E	Wadsworth, R.Y.	01 Mar
S	Atwill, J.W.O.	22 Oct	X	Wood, I.L.	01 Jan	S	Weeks, D.C.	01 Mar
X	Gillett, D.A.	01 Nov	X	Brazier, L.F.	01 Jan	E	Barton, K.J.A.	01 Mar
X	Downing, S.J.	01 Nov	X	Cox, M.J.	01 Jan	X	Mains, G.	18 Mar
X	Instone, M.J.	01 Nov	X	Monachello, P.G.	01 Jan	X	Tighe, S.	30 Mar
X	Chacksfield, E.N.	01 Nov	E	Newman, D.J.	01 Jan	X	Dodds, M.L.	01 Apr
X	Cowin, T.J.	01 Nov	E	Ruston, M.R.	01 Jan	X	Dann, A.	01 Apr
S	Curwood, J.E.	01 Nov	X	Towns, A.R.	01 Jan	X	Rawles, J.R.	01 Apr
E	Greig, J.A.	01 Nov	X	Ansell, C.N.	01 Jan	X	Twigg, K.L.	01 Apr
X	McCall, G.	01 Nov	S	Arend, F.M.	01 Jan	X	Ward, M.T.	01 Apr
E	McCoy, M.	01 Nov	X	Bradburn, J.A.	01 Jan	X	Arkle, N.J.	01 Apr
X	Norgate, A.T.	01 Nov	X	Carrington, V.L.	01 Jan	X	Hanks, P.E.	01 Apr
X	Stein, G.K.	01 Nov	X	Croft, D.F.	01 Jan	X	Smith, A.	01 Apr
S	Ward, D.J.	01 Nov	E	Hunt, P.S.	01 Jan	X	Stait, B.G.	01 Apr
X	Iliffe, D.I.	16 Nov	X	Johnson, A.D.	01 Jan	E	Thomson, M.L.	01 Apr
X	Nelson, M.R.	16 Nov	X	Munro, N.F.H.	01 Jan	X	Beavis, J.A.	01 Apr
E	McLaughlin, S.	01 Dec	E	O'Shaughnessy, P.C.	01 Jan	S	Finn, E.J.	01 Apr
E	Whitehead, P.J.	01 Dec	X	Ruddock, J.	01 Jan	X	Hilton, S.T.	01 Apr
X	Howe, T.A.I.O.	01 Dec	X	Thomson, J.C.	01 Jan	X	James, A.W.	01 Apr
E	Sangha, R.S.	01 Dec	X	Watts, Z.A.	01 Jan	X	Hutchings, J.R.	01 Apr
E	Walsh, A.H.	01 Dec	E	Smith, A.	09 Jan	X	Manoy, S.	01 Apr
X	Hartley, B.Pl.	01 Dec	E	Dry, I.	31 Jan	X	Percy, N.A.	01 Apr
X	Johnston, G.S.	01 Dec	E	Burns, J.E.	01 Feb	S	Smith, H.L.	01 Apr
X	Alsop, S.H.	01 Dec	X	Dempsey, S.P.	01 Feb	E	Grey, E.J.W.	03 Apr
X	Astle, D.S.	01 Dec	E	Downing, P.L.	01 Feb	X	Sparrow, M.J.	16 Apr
E	Blackburn, A.R.J.	01 Dec	X	Greenwood, A.W.	01 Feb	X	Blacklock, J.F.	26 Apr
E	Crabbe, R.J.	01 Dec	S	Haines, R.J.	01 Feb	X	Calter, M.	26 Apr
S	Hawthorn, E.M.	01 Dec	X	Khan, L.A.	01 Feb	S	Case, A.	26 Apr
E	McCann, T.	01 Dec	X	Wade, J.M.R.	01 Feb	X	Dunkley, S.C.	26 Apr
X	Meyer, A.J.	01 Dec	X	Bell, C.M.	01 Feb	X	Harriman, P.	26 Apr
S	Terry, J.H.	01 Dec	X	Benson, R.A.	01 Feb	X	Lovett, S.A.	26 Apr
X	Webster, R.J.	01 Dec	X	Denney, J.R.	01 Feb	MS	Manwaring, R.G.	26 Apr
X	Wright, D.J.	01 Dec	X	Hirons, F.D.	01 Feb	X	Pearch, S.M.	26 Apr
E	Pine, P.M.	06 Dec	E	Johnson, P.R.	01 Feb	S	Reed, N.	26 Apr
X	Beard, R.G.	10 Dec	E	Kilmartin, A.	01 Feb	MS	Smith, M.P.	26 Apr
X	Egerton, S.B.	10 Dec	X	Mullowney, P.	01 Feb	X	Toon, P.G.	26 Apr
S	Jones, M.A.	10 Dec	S	Taylor, J.B.	01 Feb	X	Ellis, A.C.	01 May
X	Martin, A.J.	10 Dec	X	Wall, S.N.	01 Feb	X	Baldie, S.A.H.	01 May
X	Routledge, W.D.	10 Dec	E	Jones, L.H.	14 Feb	S	Clements, E.J.	01 May
X	Singleton, M.D.	10 Dec	X	Sweeney, C.	16 Feb	X	Felters, A.W.	01 May
X	Smith, R.E.	10 Dec	E	Northcott, M.K.	01 Mar	X	Timms, D.A.	01 May
S	Thomas, D.J.	10 Dec	X	Barton, J.E.	01 Mar	S	Titcombe, A.J.	01 May
S	Prest, N.A.	10 Dec	S	Collacott, J.S.	01 Mar	X	Daly, P.	01 May
	1999		X	Gibbs, A.M.	01 Mar	S	Downing-Waite, J.A.	01 May
E	Gibson, S.J.	01 Jan	X	Boswell, D.J.	01 Mar	X	Dransfield, J.A.J.	01 May
E	Ray, P.	01 Jan	X	Brewin, D.J.	01 Mar	X	Nethercott, E.R.	01 May
X	Ball, A.D.	01 Jan	S	Carcone, S.H.	01 Mar	E	Stratton, M.P.	01 May
X	Davis, R.	01 Jan	X	Hume, K.J.	01 Mar	X	Flatman, T.D.	16 May
X	Harold, R.S.J.	01 Jan	S	Pickard, D.M.	01 Mar	X	Mann, D.M.	01 Jun
E	Carroll, S.L.	01 Jan	X	Richards, A.V.	01 Mar	X	Pittard, D.C.	01 Jun
X	Clarke, D.	01 Jan	S	Robertson, S.T.	01 Mar	E	Deal, C.	01 Jun

LIEUTENANTS

X	Hughes, C.B.	01 Jun	X	Fisher, S.J.	01 Sep	X	Spurdle, A.P.	20 Sep
X	Moran, R.J.	01 Jun	X	Hinton, L.	01 Sep	MS	Welch, A.	20 Sep
X	Redmayne, M.E.	01 Jun	X	Livsey, A.E.J.	01 Sep	X	Martin, N.	20 Sep
X	Steele, R.M.	01 Jun	E	McClement, D.L.	01 Sep	S	Coyle, P.J.	24 Sep
E	Stead, A.M.	01 Jul	E	Kitt, R.G.	01 Sep	E	Osborne, J.M.	01 Oct
X	Kennedy, R.J.	01 Jul	E	Redgrove, M.A.	01 Sep	S	Ames, K.M.M.	01 Oct
S	MacKenzie, J.E.	01 Jul	X	Murphy, R.J.	01 Sep	S	Black, S.B.	01 Oct
X	Butler, R.	01 Jul	X	Buchan, J.A.	01 Sep	X	Bowen, C.N.	01 Oct
X	Fennell, C.B.	01 Jul	X	Green, J.H.	01 Sep	E	Buckenham, P.J.	01 Oct
E	Ford, J.S.	01 Jul	E	Hepplewhite, M.B.	01 Sep	S	Cutler, T.P.	01 Oct
X	Gillard, V.A.	01 Jul	X	Johnson, S.	01 Sep	X	Hammon, M.A.	01 Oct
E	Hamilton-Bruce, E.C.	01 Jul	E	Leivers, A.J.	01 Sep	E	Healey, M.J.	01 Oct
S	Hooper, J.	01 Jul	E	MacRae, K.L.	01 Sep	X	Hudson, P.J.	01 Oct
S	Relf, K.M.	01 Jul	S	Matthew, M.J.	01 Sep	X	Nitsch, K.D.	01 Oct
X	Thomas, D.H.	01 Jul	S	Weare, J.B.	01 Sep	X	Rex, C.A.	01 Oct
S	Caple, J.N.	01 Jul	S	Curtis, S.E.H.	01 Sep	X	Sanderson, C.P.	01 Oct
X	Kelly, S.P.	01 Jul	X	Knight, D.S.	01 Sep	X	Weaver, S.	01 Oct
X	Whitwell, N.S.	01 Jul	S	Shepherd, F.R.	01 Sep	X	Williams, G.M.G.	01 Oct
X	Swindells, M.	16 Jul	E	Booth, W.N.	02 Sep	X	Duncan, K.C.L.	01 Oct
E	Epps, M.P.	17 Jul	E	Brennan, P.A.	02 Sep	X	Hardman, M.J.	01 Oct
E	Bailey, S.	01 Aug	E	Brunell, P.J.	02 Sep	S	Knox, G.P.	01 Oct
X	Bewley, N.J.	01 Aug	E	Flatt, L.D.	02 Sep	X	Thomas, O.H.	16 Oct
S	Burchell, H.E.	01 Aug	E	Forshaw, D.R.	02 Sep	X	Greenwood, P.A.	16 Oct
X	Hughes, J.J.	01 Aug	E	Leaver, A.M.	02 Sep	X	Barker, T.J.	16 Oct
X	Lilly, D.M.	01 Aug	E	MacLean, M.T.	02 Sep	X	Ackerley, R.S.J.	01 Nov
X	Neofytou, A.G.K.	01 Aug	E	Millar, K.I.	02 Sep	E	Clear, N.J.	01 Nov
X	Sambrooks, R.J.	01 Aug	E	Nicholson, J.C.	02 Sep	X	Finch, I.R.	01 Nov
X	Clark, R.A.	01 Aug	E	Nursey, A.P.	02 Sep	X	Cable, P.M.	01 Nov
X	Crowe, D.M.	01 Aug	E	Penketh, M.G.	02 Sep	X	Hayashi, L.R.	01 Nov
X	Hannam, D.B.	01 Aug	E	Quirk, A.T.	02 Sep	E	Hubschmid, S.R.	01 Nov
X	Harborth, J.A.	01 Aug	E	Rom, S.P.	02 Sep	X	Richards, C.D.	01 Nov
E	Holmwood, M.A.G.	01 Aug	E	Saywell-Hall, S.E.	02 Sep	X	Aldous, B.W.	01 Nov
E	Martin, S.W.	01 Aug	E	Scholes, N.A.	02 Sep	S	Clarke, A.G.	01 Nov
X	Weston, K.N.N.	01 Aug	E	Sibley, A.K.	02 Sep	E	Jones, I.M.	01 Nov
X	Woollven, C.D.	01 Aug	E	Slimmon, K.W.	02 Sep	E	Lee, S.E.	01 Nov
X	Frazer, H.F.	01 Aug	E	Spencer, J.C.	02 Sep	X	Oneill, J.	22 Nov
E	Molyneux, I.T.	01 Aug	E	Stead, J.A.	02 Sep	X	Gates, D.A.	01 Dec
X	Sharp, L.D.	01 Aug	E	Topping, J.R.	02 Sep	X	Alderwick, J.R.C.	01 Dec
X	Thompson, D.A.	16 Aug	E	Torney, C.J.	02 Sep	E	Cessford, R.I.	01 Dec
X	Currie, M.J.	16 Aug	E	Vickers, C.G.	02 Sep	E	Derrick, M.J.G.	01 Dec
E	Scotter, C.M.	01 Sep	E	Vickery, R.J.	02 Sep	X	Marshall, A.J.	01 Dec
X	Bussey, E.L.	01 Sep	E	Walker, G.	02 Sep	X	Chambers, C.P.	01 Dec
E	Hoather, M.S.	01 Sep	E	Ward, N.A.	02 Sep	X	Dunn, R.A.P.	01 Dec
X	Jordan, A.F.	01 Sep	E	Watson, A.P.	02 Sep	X	Gray, N.J.	01 Dec
X	Knight, S.D.	01 Sep	X	Bull, M.A.J.	11 Sep	X	Jenkins, R.C.	01 Dec
E	Alexander, A.L.	01 Sep	X	Netherwood, L.D.	15 Sep	S	Oliver, G.J.	01 Dec
X	Barr, S.P.	01 Sep	X	Lawrence, L.J.	16 Sep	X	Saltonstall, P.J.R.	01 Dec
X	Birleson, P.D.	01 Sep	MS	Goodrum, S.E.	19 Sep	X	Sloan, I.A.	01 Dec
X	Carnie, M.J.	01 Sep	S	Baker, N.J.	20 Sep	E	Ball, M.P.	01 Dec
X	Cobban, M.J.	01 Sep	S	Burns, R.J.	20 Sep	S	Carcone, P.N.	01 Dec
X	Deighton, A.W.G.	01 Sep	X	Llewellyn, J.G.	20 Sep	X	Holden, J.L.	01 Dec

LIEUTENANTS

S	Horne, C.A.	01 Dec
E	Orr, K.J.	01 Dec
E	Pollard, J.R.	01 Dec
E	Hamilton, M.I.	01 Dec
X	Jones, R.J.	01 Dec
X	Shanks, S.A.	01 Dec
X	Taylor, A.I.	01 Dec
X	Bevan, J.R.	16 Dec

2000

E	Beattie, K.E.	01 Jan
E	Blethyn, H.P.	01 Jan
E	Gill, P.S.	01 Jan
E	Hemingway, D.G.	01 Jan
E	Muyambo, N.N.	01 Jan
E	Perryman, I.T.C.	01 Jan
E	White, S.P.	01 Jan
E	Wood, C.T.	01 Jan
E	Aston, J.A.	01 Jan
E	Corderoy, R.I.	01 Jan
X	Kitteridge, D.J.	01 Jan
X	Mason, M.J.	01 Jan
X	Brewer, C.E.	01 Jan
X	Crew, J.M.	01 Jan
X	Deakin, D.J.	01 Jan
S	Gulliford, K.A.	01 Jan
E	Jackson, S.N.	01 Jan
E	Moody, A.C.	01 Jan
E	Tait, M.D.	01 Jan
X	Williams, D.L.	01 Jan
X	Bloska, R.M.	01 Jan
E	Andrew, P.	01 Jan
E	Mortlock, P.A.	01 Jan
X	Rant, O.J.	01 Jan
E	Russell, C.M.L.	01 Jan
E	Slattery, D.J.	01 Jan
X	Gill, C.D.	01 Jan
E	Law, R.	01 Jan
X	Mabbott, K.I.	01 Jan
X	McIntyre, L.	01 Jan
E	Nicklin, G.J.E.	01 Jan
X	Phillips, R.M.	01 Jan
X	Pollock, C.J.	01 Jan
E	Robinson, P.	01 Jan
E	Boeckx, T.J.F.	01 Jan
E	Green, R.R.	08 Jan
X	Francis, D.E.	10 Jan
X	Irving, D.	10 Jan
X	Lester, R.L.	10 Jan
X	Moran, C.A.	10 Jan
E	Priestley, C.	14 Jan
S	Brimacombe, L.M.	01 Feb

S	Pritchard, I.J.	01 Feb
X	Harford Cross, P.J.	01 Feb
X	Harwood, L.B.	01 Feb
X	Jackson, P.	01 Feb
X	Marjoram, J.W.	01 Feb
E	Martin, R.J.	01 Feb
X	McAulay, P.J.	01 Feb
X	Thatcher, L.F.V.	01 Feb
E	Timbrell, I.P.J.	01 Feb
X	Whitehall, S.	01 Feb
X	Conyers, W.L.	01 Feb
X	Adams, E.S.	16 Feb
X	Coverdale, P.	01 Mar
X	Hodgson, R.S.	01 Mar
X	Winsor, J.	01 Mar
E	Ellis, C.R.	01 Mar
X	Heyworth, J.E.	01 Mar
X	Lanning, R.M.	01 Mar
E	Mathieson, N.B.	01 Mar
E	McDonald, A.W.	01 Mar
X	Richardson, I.H.	01 Mar
E	Risley, J.G.	01 Mar
X	Madigan, L.	01 Mar
X	Brown, A.R.A.	01 Mar
X	McGannity, C.S.	16 Mar
X	Bagshaw, E.F.	01 Apr
X	Barritt, O.D.	01 Apr
E	Pipkin, P.J.	01 Apr
E	Winbolt, N.I.	01 Apr
X	Cornford, M.	01 Apr
X	Griffiths, C.S.H.	01 Apr
X	Lloyd, B.J.	01 Apr
X	Moore, N.J.	01 Apr
X	Murgatroyd, K.J.	01 Apr
X	Scott, J.A.	01 Apr
E	Barker, P.D.	01 Apr
X	Bates, N.S.	01 Apr
X	Chambers, R.	01 Apr
X	Feeney, M.B.	01 Apr
E	Gilmore, S.J.	01 Apr
X	Hinxman, M.A.	01 Apr
X	Tomes, A.C.	01 Apr
X	Whitehouse, D.S.	01 Apr
X	Bodman, S.A.	01 Apr
X	England, P.M.	01 Apr
X	Griffen, D.J.	01 Apr
X	Headley, M.J.	01 Apr
S	McLocklan, L.M.	01 Apr
X	Rae, F.	01 Apr
X	Shearn, M.A.	01 Apr
S	Turner, D.J.	01 Apr

S	West, N.K.	01 Apr
X	Davies, T.C.	16 Apr
X	Morse, J.	16 Apr
E	Bartholomew, D.J.	01 May
E	Free, A.S.	01 May
E	Goodall, J.C.	01 May
E	Hollyfield, P.R.	01 May
E	Holt, J.D.	01 May
E	Ussher, J.H.D.	01 May
E	Andrews, C.	01 May
X	Andrews, C.J.	01 May
E	Baillie, R.W.	01 May
X	Cannell, G.M.	01 May
X	Firth, J.S.	01 May
S	Forge, S.M.	01 May
X	Gardner, M.P.	01 May
E	Newth, C.S.	01 May
X	Page, M.R.	01 May
X	Rowson, M.J.	01 May
X	Tok, C.F.L.	01 May
E	Austin, S.T.	01 May
E	Coles, C.P.	01 May
X	Keith, B.C.	01 May
S	Lane, N.	01 May
X	Woolhead, C.M.	01 May
X	Stratton, N.C.	01 May
X	Leason, N.C.	01 May
X	Banks, M.C.	01 May
X	Brearley, R.L.	01 May
X	Brown, J.A.	01 May
X	Cromie, J.M.	01 May
X	Daulby, D.J.	01 May
X	Hember, M.J.C.	01 May
X	Pritchard, A.M.	01 May
X	Reid, J.L.	01 May
X	Winand, F.M.J.	01 May
S	Ashley, P.D.	01 May
E	Jones, M.R.	01 May
E	Trueman, B.D.	01 May
S	Benfell, N.A.	02 May
E	Bowser, N.J.	02 May
E	Burton, P.R.	02 May
E	Collins, D.A.	02 May
E	Edwins, M.R.	02 May
X	Evans, B.D.	02 May
X	Fairnie, D.W.	02 May
E	Hodgson, J.R.	02 May
E	Liddell, M.L.	02 May
E	Lowe, C.	02 May
E	McNair, J.	02 May
E	Moy, D.K.	02 May

LIEUTENANTS

X	Paget, S.J.	02 May
E	Ryan, J.P.	02 May
E	Smart, M.J.	02 May
E	Young, P.	02 May
E	Pearmain, S.R.	14 May
E	Whetter, R.S.	14 May
X	O'Kane, R.J.	16 May
E	Mantri, A.H.	22 May
E	George, S.D.	01 Jun
S	Carter, G.R.	01 Jun
X	Beanland, P.L.	01 Jun
X	Bedding, D.	01 Jun
X	Campbell, T.R.	01 Jun
E	Tofts, C.	01 Jun
E	Grant, W.G.	01 Jun
X	Higginson, N.J.	01 Jun
X	Ives, D.J.	01 Jun
X	Money, C.J.	01 Jun
X	Mount, J.B.	01 Jun
X	Randles, S.	01 Jun
X	Urwin, S.J.	01 Jun
X	Varley, P.G.S.	01 Jun
X	Irwin, S.G.	01 Jun
X	Sims, A.R.	15 Jun
X	Vickery, K.E.	01 Jul
E	Dickinson, P.H.	01 Jul
X	Gare, C.J.	01 Jul
X	Humphries, M.	01 Jul
S	Hynde, C.L.	01 Jul
E	Kitchen, B.	01 Jul
X	Mullen, M.L.	01 Jul
X	Retter, R.L.	01 Jul
X	Bull, L.P.	01 Jul
X	Davies, M.C.	01 Jul
X	Jacob, A.W.	01 Jul
S	Stone, N.J.J.	01 Jul
E	Elliott, J.A.	01 Jul
S	Jones, N.S.	01 Jul
X	Kohn, P.A.	01 Jul
E	Lovett, A.R.	01 Jul
X	Rea, S.D.	01 Jul
E	Rooney, M.	01 Jul
X	Holmes, A.M.	16 Jul
X	Bennett, C.D.	01 Aug
X	Considine, K.J.	01 Aug
E	Treharne, M.A.	01 Aug
X	Wood, S.A.H.	01 Aug
S	Fleming, R.E.	01 Aug
X	Hewitson, J.G.A.	01 Aug
X	Scott, S.L.	01 Aug
X	Ainsley, A.M.J.	01 Aug

X	Anderson, S.R.	01 Aug
S	May, C.L.	01 Aug
S	Middleton, W.T.	01 Aug
X	Barnes, P.I.	01 Aug
E	Foote, A.S.	01 Aug
X	Mc Currach, R.H.	01 Aug
E	Reeves, P.K.	01 Aug
X	Brown, S.G.	04 Aug
X	Hammond, M.M.V.	16 Aug
E	Collins, L.J.	01 Sep
E	Rogers, S.M.	01 Sep
E	Stafford, B.R.	01 Sep
X	Harcombe, A.	01 Sep
X	Armstrong, S.M.	01 Sep
E	Bennett, W.E.	01 Sep
E	Blackburn, L.R.	01 Sep
X	Dawson, G.A.E.	01 Sep
E	Dixon, A.K.	01 Sep
X	Gadsden, A.C.	01 Sep
X	Keeping, D.J.	01 Sep
S	Lear, S.F.	01 Sep
X	Liddle, R.D.	01 Sep
X	Menzies, B.	01 Sep
E	Miller, I.	01 Sep
E	Milne, W.J.C.	01 Sep
X	Nimmo-Scott, S.J.	01 Sep
X	Phillips, C.J.	01 Sep
X	Thompson, W.A.	01 Sep
E	Whitelaw, V.L.	01 Sep
X	Bailes, K.P.	01 Sep
X	Bullock, R.A.	01 Sep
X	Hearn, S.P.	01 Sep
X	Lynas, J.F.A.	01 Sep
X	Parker, S.A.M.	01 Sep
X	Armstrong, C.D.	01 Sep
S	Johnson, A.C.	01 Sep
S	Peyman, T.A.	01 Sep
S	Ransom, B.R.J.	01 Sep
X	Wick, H.M.S.	01 Sep
E	Casson, R.F.	01 Sep
X	Boon, G.J.	19 Sep
X	Castle, C.D.	19 Sep
X	Cowan, A.R.	19 Sep
X	Griffin, P.J.	19 Sep
X	Howells, S.M.	19 Sep
S	Longstaff, T.W.	19 Sep
S	Love, J.D.	19 Sep
X	Lynn, H.W.	19 Sep
X	Mills, G.A.	19 Sep
X	Parton, A.	19 Sep
X	Pirrie, J.A.	19 Sep

X	Stringer, G.E.	19 Sep
X	Walker, R.S.	19 Sep
X	Wilson, G.J.	19 Sep
X	Hancock, J.H.	01 Oct
S	Henderson, S.C.	01 Oct
X	Fyfe, K.S.	01 Oct
X	Hadland, G.V.	01 Oct
X	Hampshire, T.	01 Oct
S	Richards, A.J.	01 Oct
X	Robey, J.C.	01 Oct
X	Winn, J.P.	01 Oct
X	Dodd, S.E.	01 Oct
E	Pickard, S.R.	01 Oct
X	Voysey, Z.	01 Oct
E	Gould, A.A.	01 Oct
X	Parsons, R.J.	01 Nov
X	Collins, A.C.	01 Nov
X	Crompton, P.J.	01 Nov
X	Owen, S.T.L.	01 Nov
S	Rollason, C.A.	01 Nov
S	Wrigley, B.S.	01 Nov
X	Burton, A.	01 Nov
S	Mac Donald, S.B.	01 Nov
X	Spears, A.G.	01 Nov
X	Guilfoyle, V.M.	15 Nov
X	Simmonite, G.I.	16 Nov
X	Hall, C.J.	01 Dec
X	Partridge, S.C.	01 Dec
E	Wharrie, C.G.	01 Dec
X	Williams, J.R.	01 Dec
X	Barlow, B.M.	01 Dec
X	Dermody, R.T.	01 Dec
X	Jones, D.J.	01 Dec
X	Pearson, J.C.	01 Dec
X	Fillmore, R.J.	01 Dec
X	Northcote, M.R.	01 Dec

2001

E	Blackler, S.	01 Jan
E	Oakley, A.J.	01 Jan
E	Sweeney, R.J.	01 Jan
S	Halsey, K.E.	01 Jan
X	Aitken, S.R.	01 Jan
E	Alexander, P.M.D.	01 Jan
X	Bane, N.S.J.	01 Jan
X	Bradbury, J.E.D.	01 Jan
X	Butler, P.M.	01 Jan
X	Finn, J.S.	01 Jan
X	Gladwin, M.D.	01 Jan
X	Holmes, A.N.	01 Jan
X	Lander, D.T.J.	01 Jan
E	Lutman, C.R.	01 Jan

LIEUTENANTS

X Milles, O.K. ...... 01 Jan	X Lightfoot, R.A. ...... 16 Feb	E Prowse, D.G. ...... 01 Apr
E Morphet, K. ...... 01 Jan	X Gallimore, R.M.C. ...... 16 Feb	E Rawlings, G.A. ...... 01 Apr
X Sturman, R.W. ...... 01 Jan	E Welsh, R.M.K. ...... 01 Mar	E Rhodes, A.W. ...... 01 Apr
X Turner, J.S. ...... 01 Jan	X Price, J.C. ...... 05 Mar	MS Robinson, A. ...... 01 Apr
X Wright, T.J. ...... 01 Jan	E Alberts, P.W. ...... 01 Apr	E Robinson, D.P. ...... 01 Apr
X Chapman, S.J. ...... 01 Jan	X Bartram, R.J. ...... 01 Apr	X Robinson, R.J. ...... 01 Apr
X Dallamore, R.A. ...... 01 Jan	S Bell, S.W. ...... 01 Apr	X Ross, A.D. ...... 01 Apr
X Dingley, P.A. ...... 01 Jan	E Blois, S.D. ...... 01 Apr	X Santry, P.M. ...... 01 Apr
X Dixon, R.A. ...... 01 Jan	X Bouyac, D.R.L. ...... 01 Apr	E Shaw, N.A. ...... 01 Apr
X Pickles, D.R. ...... 01 Jan	S Brady, T.W. ...... 01 Apr	X Smith, P.A. ...... 01 Apr
X Wragg, G.T. ...... 01 Jan	E Carter, P. ...... 01 Apr	S Somerville, S.J. ...... 01 Apr
X Robins, M.D. ...... 01 Jan	S Challis, S.E. ...... 01 Apr	X Summers, A.J. ...... 01 Apr
S Grigg, S.K. ...... 08 Jan	S Chilton, D.J. ...... 01 Apr	X Taylor, T.P. ...... 01 Apr
S Harvey, P.J. ...... 08 Jan	X Clarke, M. ...... 01 Apr	E Temple, D.C. ...... 01 Apr
X Lewis, P.L. ...... 08 Jan	S Cotton, E.L. ...... 01 Apr	E Thomson, D.F. ...... 01 Apr
S McGrath, W.J. ...... 08 Jan	E Crawley, D.A. ...... 01 Apr	E Thomson, I.W. ...... 01 Apr
X Naldrett, G.C. ...... 08 Jan	X Daniels, S.P. ...... 01 Apr	E Toone, S.A. ...... 01 Apr
X Seager, A.K. ...... 08 Jan	E Dawson, P. ...... 01 Apr	E Turner, A.J. ...... 01 Apr
E Austin, P.N. ...... 09 Jan	E Dumbleton, D.W. ...... 01 Apr	X Tutchings, A. ...... 01 Apr
E Collins, D. ...... 09 Jan	X Dunn, A. ...... 01 Apr	X Ward, E.J. ...... 01 Apr
E Collins, M.A. ...... 09 Jan	X Edmondson, J.A. ...... 01 Apr	X Warde, N.A. ...... 01 Apr
E Conneely, S.A. ...... 09 Jan	X Farr, I.R. ...... 01 Apr	X Wells, J.H. ...... 01 Apr
E Cope, M.A. ...... 09 Jan	E Freeman, M.J. ...... 01 Apr	S Wells, S.P. ...... 01 Apr
E Donaldson, A.M. ...... 09 Jan	X Gallimore, J.M. ...... 01 Apr	E Whitehouse, S.R. ...... 01 Apr
E Emms, S.M. ...... 09 Jan	E Gibson, M.J.S. ...... 01 Apr	X Wood, N.R. ...... 01 Apr
X Flynn, S.J. ...... 09 Jan	S Gosling, D.J. ...... 01 Apr	X Godfrey, S.D.W. ...... 01 Apr
X Gray, M.J.H. ...... 09 Jan	MS Haughey, J.P. ...... 01 Apr	X Meikle, K.E.J. ...... 01 Apr
X Hayman, P.S. ...... 09 Jan	E Havron, P.R. ...... 01 Apr	X Cooksley, R.E.C. ...... 08 Apr
E Hoare, D.W. ...... 09 Jan	E Hocking, M.J.E. ...... 01 Apr	X Gibbs, A.E. ...... 08 Apr
S Hubbarde, S.D. ...... 09 Jan	E Holvey, P.J. ...... 01 Apr	S Welch, M.E. ...... 13 Apr
S Johnson, K. ...... 09 Jan	E Hughes, T. ...... 01 Apr	E Anderson, C.J. ...... 13 Apr
E Jones, P.A. ...... 09 Jan	E James, M. ...... 01 Apr	E Baxter, F.J. ...... 29 Apr
E Murphy, A. ...... 09 Jan	X Jayes, N.J. ...... 01 Apr	S Brint, I. ...... 29 Apr
X Riley, J. ...... 09 Jan	X Jones, S.S. ...... 01 Apr	X Carter, N.R. ...... 29 Apr
E Stafford, W. ...... 09 Jan	MS Jones, T.M. ...... 01 Apr	S Christie, A.B. ...... 29 Apr
E Stephens, A.W. ...... 09 Jan	X Jones-Thompson, M.J. ...... 01 Apr	E Cooke, R.N. ...... 29 Apr
E Whatling, K.M. ...... 09 Jan	X Kay, P.S. ...... 01 Apr	X Dainty, R.C. ...... 29 Apr
X White, S.J. ...... 09 Jan	S Latham, L.B. ...... 01 Apr	E Finch, S. ...... 29 Apr
E Wilkinson, A.C. ...... 09 Jan	S Ledward, K.L. ...... 01 Apr	E Griffiths, C.J.J. ...... 29 Apr
X Laurence, S.T. ...... 16 Jan	E Matthews, P.R. ...... 01 Apr	X Gwatkin, N.J. ...... 29 Apr
X Hudson, A.I. ...... 01 Feb	X Meikle, R.B. ...... 01 Apr	E Hamilton, G.D. ...... 29 Apr
S New, R.A. ...... 01 Feb	E Meikle, S.A. ...... 01 Apr	E Hardy, R.J. ...... 29 Apr
X Paulet, M.R. ...... 01 Feb	E Metcalf, S.W. ...... 01 Apr	E Harrison, A.D. ...... 29 Apr
X Simpson, S.F. ...... 01 Feb	MS Milburn, V. ...... 01 Apr	X Hattle, P.M. ...... 29 Apr
E Richardson, A.P. ...... 01 Feb	X Molnar, R.M. ...... 01 Apr	E Hewitt, M.J. ...... 29 Apr
E White, J.P. ...... 01 Feb	X Moore, M.J. ...... 01 Apr	E Loughrey, N.C. ...... 29 Apr
X Hurst, C.N.S. ...... 01 Feb	S Northeast, P. ...... 01 Apr	E Newell, G.D. ...... 29 Apr
E Melville, A.C. ...... 01 Feb	E Nottley, S.M. ...... 01 Apr	E Nicholson, B.H. ...... 29 Apr
E Roberts, S.R. ...... 01 Feb	E Parmenter, A.J. ...... 01 Apr	E Richards, P. ...... 29 Apr
S Walsh, D. ...... 01 Feb	E Pollard, A.J. ...... 01 Apr	E Robert, I.A. ...... 29 Apr
X Whitson-Fay, C.D. ...... 15 Feb	E Prior, I.A. ...... 01 Apr	MS Sullivan, T.E. ...... 29 Apr

LIEUTENANTS

S	Viney, P.M.	29 Apr
E	Wrennall, E.P.	29 Apr
X	Reynolds, M.J.	01 May
X	Wilkins, D.P.	01 May
X	Aldridge, D.	01 May
E	Barron, J.M.	01 May
X	Binns, J.F.	01 May
X	Broster, M.	01 May
E	Buchanan, R.M.	01 May
S	Carthew, R.J.	01 May
X	Cave, J.H.J.	01 May
X	Corbett, M.T.	01 May
X	Crouch, M.	01 May
X	Duce, M.	01 May
X	Evans, L.S.	01 May
X	Fabik, A.N.	01 May
X	Garreta, C.E.	01 May
X	Gordon, D.I.	01 May
X	Hackland, A.S.	01 May
X	Hall, K.J.D.	01 May
E	Holford, S.J.	01 May
X	Hopkins, C.	01 May
X	Humphries, G.D.	01 May
X	Jackson, H.C.	01 May
X	Jones, R.J.	01 May
E	Jordan, M.D.	01 May
E	Kent, M.J.	01 May
S	Kenyon, C.M.	01 May
X	Klidjian, M.J.	01 May
X	Lawrence, M.A.	01 May
E	Layton, C.	01 May
X	Little, M.I.G.	01 May
X	Martyn, D.	01 May
X	McCauley, L.J.	01 May
S	McCowen, P.A.C.	01 May
E	Miller, K.R.	01 May
E	Moon, I.L.	01 May
X	Noonan, C.D.	01 May
X	Nunnen, C.R.	01 May
X	Oakley, C.M.	01 May
S	Ollis, V.	01 May
S	Pearson, S.	01 May
X	Pickles, M.R.	01 May
X	Quick, S.J.	01 May
X	Sherwood, G.A.F.	01 May
X	Spencer, A.C.	01 May
X	Spinks, R.J.	01 May
X	Stephenson, C.J.	01 May
E	Stratton, S.J.	01 May
X	Vickery, B.R.	01 May
X	Waite, T.G.	01 May
X	Watson, B.L.	01 May
X	Wickham, R.J.	01 May
X	Wielopolski, M.L.C.C.	01 May
X	Williams, P.G.	01 May
X	Winterbon, A.R.	01 May
X	Youldon, L.J.	01 May
E	Wadge, G.D.E.	08 May
X	Goodman, D.F.	09 May
E	Prest, S.F.	01 Jun
X	Hayes, S.	01 Jul
X	Henaghen, S.J.	13 Jul
X	Malone, J.M.	29 Jul
X	Wightwick, K.H.T.	01 Aug
X	Gamble, M.J.	01 Aug
X	Prosser, M.J.	01 Aug
X	Burghall, R.C.	01 Aug
X	Huxford, S.	01 Aug
X	Perryment, C.P.	01 Aug
X	Wood, S.J.	01 Aug
X	Antrobus, S.R.	05 Aug
E	Simpson, M.G.	05 Aug
X	Sienkiewicz, M.K.	01 Sep
X	Abbott, R.J.	01 Sep
X	Agnew, R.L.P.	01 Sep
X	Andrews, I.S.	01 Sep
E	Beadling, D.J.	01 Sep
E	Billington, S.	01 Sep
E	Bland, C.D.	01 Sep
X	Boullin, J.P.	01 Sep
E	Breen, J.E.	01 Sep
E	Brooks, N.R.	01 Sep
X	Brown, A.S.	01 Sep
E	Bulter, D.B.	01 Sep
E	Buxton, D.A.	01 Sep
E	Cantellow, S.J.	01 Sep
S	Chapman, M.S.	01 Sep
E	Cheyne, R.D.	01 Sep
X	Clapham, G.T.	01 Sep
S	Cole, B.B.	01 Sep
X	Collins, S.J.P.	01 Sep
X	Crawford, K.	01 Sep
MS	Davies, J.L.	01 Sep
S	De La Rue, A.N.	01 Sep
E	Dodd, L.	01 Sep
X	Doran, K.E.	01 Sep
X	Dowling, A.J.	01 Sep
X	Filtness, D.M.	01 Sep
E	Finley, P.M.	01 Sep
X	Finn, S.A.	01 Sep
E	Flegg, M.J.	01 Sep
X	Fraser, M.J.S.	01 Sep
S	Gray, E.J.	01 Sep
X	Greenwood, B.C.J.	01 Sep
E	Heal, T.S.	01 Sep
X	Hirstwood, J.L.	01 Sep
X	Horton, J.R.	01 Sep
X	Hulston, L.M.	01 Sep
X	Jackson-Smith, S.P.	01 Sep
X	Jenkins, D.G.	01 Sep
X	King, W.R.C.	01 Sep
E	King, W.T.P.	01 Sep
X	Knowles, C.J.	01 Sep
E	Leyland, E.M.	01 Sep
S	Manning, G.P.	01 Sep
X	Martin, D.C.S.	01 Sep
X	McGowan, A.B.	01 Sep
X	Mitchell, J.D.	01 Sep
S	Monday, J.E.	01 Sep
X	Monnox, J.	01 Sep
X	Montague, R.J.	01 Sep
X	Morris, P.J.	01 Sep
MS	Murray, A.	01 Sep
E	Palmer, C.R.	01 Sep
X	Penson, J.G.	01 Sep
X	Pepper, P.M.	01 Sep
E	Perkins, B.	01 Sep
X	Punch, J.M.	01 Sep
X	Rankin, G.J.	01 Sep
E	Ritchie, D.B.	01 Sep
E	Robinson, S.L.	01 Sep
E	Satterly, R.J.	01 Sep
X	Scott, N.	01 Sep
E	Seagrave, S.J.	01 Sep
E	Slater, D.G.	01 Sep
E	Slowther, S.J.	01 Sep
X	Smith, R.A.	01 Sep
X	Stanway, C.A.	01 Sep
X	Stead, S.N.	01 Sep
X	Sterry, J.E.B.	01 Sep
X	Stewart, C.H.	01 Sep
X	Tawse, A.R.J.	01 Sep
X	Twigg, N.R.	01 Sep
MS	Wade, A.	01 Sep
S	Wallace, K.G.	01 Sep
X	Webb, M.R.	01 Sep
X	Wells, J.D.	01 Sep
MS	Witt, A.K.	01 Sep
E	Woods, M.J.P.	01 Sep
X	Colley, R.	01 Sep
X	Ingham, L.E.	01 Sep
E	Cunningham, D.B.	01 Sep
X	Griffin, S.	01 Sep

LIEUTENANTS

S	Rudd, V.J.	15 Sep	S	Holmes, H.J.	01 Jan	X	Tappin, S.J.	01 Jan
E	Grinnell, J.	01 Oct	X	Hopkins, A.E.T.	01 Jan	X	Taylor, G.D.	01 Jan
S	Whale, V.A.	01 Oct	S	Horwood, N.A.	01 Jan	X	Thom, M.F.	01 Jan
X	Renaud, G.A.R.	16 Oct	E	Hughes, G.D.	01 Jan	X	Tindell, R.W.	01 Jan
X	Goddard, I.A.	16 Nov	X	Hutchinson, N.J.	01 Jan	X	Van Duin, M.I.A.	01 Jan
X	Horton, S.	01 Dec	X	Inglis, D.J.	01 Jan	X	Wallace, A.R.	01 Jan
X	Humphrey, I.R.	01 Dec	X	Issitt, B.D.	01 Jan	E	Webb, D.	01 Jan
X	Bush, N.	01 Dec	E	Jarman, P.R.	01 Jan	S	Wild, R.J.	01 Jan
S	Jackson, A.	21 Dec	E	Jones, C.D.	01 Jan	E	Williams, P.A.	01 Jan
			X	Jones, M.R.	01 Jan	X	Wilson, I.P.	01 Jan
	2002		S	Kingdon, S.C.	01 Jan	X	Wood, J.T.	01 Jan
E	Priddle, A.C.	01 Jan	X	Ladislaus, C.J.	01 Jan	X	Davis, G.R.	01 Jan
E	Kierstan, S.J.J.	01 Jan	X	Latus, S.H.	01 Jan	X	Ludlow, J.A.	01 Jan
X	Barnard, T.J.	01 Jan	E	Louw, L.	01 Jan	S	Huynh, C.C.	01 Mar
X	Barrow, C.M.	01 Jan	E	MacIntyre, I.D.	01 Jan	X	Fuller, J.E.	01 Mar
X	Beegan, C.F.	01 Jan	E	Mann, A.W.	01 Jan	S	Parry, S.D.	05 Mar
E	Berry, S.M.	01 Jan	S	Marland, E.E.	01 Jan	E	Barr, D.D.	01 Apr
E	Binns, J.R.	01 Jan	E	Marshall, G.P.	01 Jan	E	Smith, O.J.	01 Apr
X	Black, E.J.	01 Jan	X	Mc Allister, S.E.	01 Jan	S	Kirwan, J.A.	07 Apr
S	Blick, S.L.	01 Jan	E	McCamphill, P.J.	01 Jan	X	Campbell, A.L.	12 Apr
S	Boardman, S.J.	01 Jan	X	McKay, T.W.	01 Jan	X	Adams, W.J.	01 May
X	Boulind, M.A.	01 Jan	X	Mitchell, J.M.	01 Jan	X	Adamson, S.E.	01 May
X	Brock, M.J.	01 Jan	X	Moran, B.M.	01 Jan	E	Ainscow, A.J.	01 May
E	Brodie, D.J.	01 Jan	X	Morgan, B.P.	01 Jan	E	Andrews, J.P.	01 May
E	Bukhory, H.	01 Jan	E	Morris, D.W.	01 Jan	X	Atkinson, L.V.	01 May
X	Burgon, R.	01 Jan	X	Mountney, G.A.	01 Jan	X	Ballantyne, C.	01 May
E	Carbery, S.J.	01 Jan	X	Nash, R.D.C.	01 Jan	E	Bartram, G.J.	01 May
S	Chadwick, K.	01 Jan	X	Nash, R.P.	01 Jan	E	Bastiaens, P.A.	01 May
X	Chandler, P.J.	01 Jan	X	Nicholson, D.A.G.	01 Jan	E	Baxter, A.C.	01 May
X	Chapman, J.L.J.	01 Jan	X	O'Neill, T.J.	01 Jan	S	Bell, L.J.	01 May
X	Clarke, M.	01 Jan	X	Parsons, R.M.J.	01 Jan	X	Biggs, P.	01 May
X	Cooke, S.N.	01 Jan	X	Pearce, R.J.	01 Jan	E	Boakes, P.J.	01 May
E	Cowie, A.D.	01 Jan	MS	Pinhey, A.D.	01 Jan	X	Bond, J.E.	01 May
X	Crawford, V.E.	01 Jan	X	Quinn, M.G.	01 Jan	E	Bowie, R.	01 May
E	Creek, S.B.	01 Jan	E	Rand, M.A.	01 Jan	E	Bradley, T.A.	01 May
E	Dawson, P.M.D.	01 Jan	E	Richards, S.C.A.	01 Jan	E	Brooking, R.R.	01 May
X	Day, B.T.	01 Jan	X	Rider, J.C.R.	01 Jan	X	Buggins, B.	01 May
X	Dowie, M.E.	01 Jan	X	Rimmer, O.F.	01 Jan	E	Burdett, V.C.	01 May
X	Eaton, D.C.	01 Jan	X	Rowberry, A.G.	01 Jan	X	Burgess, D.J.	01 May
MS	Edwards, D.	01 Jan	X	Russell, M.S.	01 Jan	E	Carey, T.J.	01 May
X	Evans, I.C.	01 Jan	S	Sargent, D.R.	01 Jan	X	Clee, J.S.	01 May
X	Filshie, S.J.	01 Jan	E	Sawford, G.N.	01 Jan	X	Coleman, H.L.	01 May
E	Fitzgerald, G.S.	01 Jan	X	Shore, E.A.	01 Jan	E	Collins, D.A.	01 May
X	French, J.H.	01 Jan	E	Simpson, W.J.S.	01 Jan	S	Cook, N.J.H.	01 May
E	Fry, T.G.	01 Jan	S	Smith, L.	01 Jan	X	Cooke, D.C.J.	01 May
E	Gaytano, R.T.M.	01 Jan	E	Smye, M.A.	01 Jan	E	Coyle, R.D.	01 May
E	Gibson, T.A.	01 Jan	E	Snell, D.M.	01 Jan	X	Donovan, S.J.	01 May
E	Godley, D.J.	01 Jan	X	Startup, H.J.	01 Jan	E	Eaglestone, S.	01 May
X	Grey, C.S.	01 Jan	X	Stevenson, S.R.	01 Jan	S	Elkins, S.S	01 May
E	Hawkins, S.	01 Jan	X	Suter, F.T.	01 Jan	X	Ellis-Morgan, R.T.	01 May
X	Henry, G.P.	01 Jan	E	Tait, S.J.	01 Jan	X	Fergusson, I.B.	01 May
X	Holliehead, C.L.	01 Jan						

LIEUTENANTS

X	Flaherty, C.L.	01 May
X	Fosbury, C.F.	01 May
X	Fraser, A.G.	01 May
E	Fulton, D.M.	01 May
E	Goddard, P.	01 May
X	Hall, S.L.	01 May
X	Hamiduddin, I.	01 May
X	Harrison, J.A.G.	01 May
X	Hart, S.J.	01 May
X	Heaton, H.G.	01 May
S	Holland, C.C.	01 May
X	Holmes, P.J.M.	01 May
X	Hughes, G.E.	01 May
S	Johnston, D.R.	01 May
E	Kestle, M.E.	01 May
X	Kiernan, C.G.	01 May
X	Leeder, T.R.	01 May
E	Leese, J.F.	01 May
X	Lewis, E.J.	01 May
X	Lindeyer, M.J.	01 May
E	Livingston, M.P.J.	01 May
X	Lock, W.J.	01 May
X	Long, A.B.M.	01 May
X	Loveridge, P.J.	01 May
E	Lucas, D.P.	01 May
X	Luxford, C.A.	01 May
E	MacCormick, J.	01 May
E	MacQuarrie, G.A.	01 May
X	Marsh, S.D.	01 May
X	Masson, N.G.	01 May
X	Minall, M.L.	01 May
X	Morgan, C.W.	01 May
X	Newman, C.R.S.	01 May
X	O'Callaghan, P.F.	01 May
S	O'Rourke, R.M.	01 May
X	Oakes, M.C.	01 May
X	Olivey, T.D.	01 May
X	Orme, W.B.	01 May
X	Owen, V.F.	01 May
X	Paston, W.A.	01 May
S	Peattie, I.W.	01 May
E	Plummer, R.W.J.	01 May
E	Porritt, C.J.	01 May
E	Powne, S.P.W.	01 May
X	Ritchie, I.D.	01 May
E	Roberts, A.P.	01 May
X	Round, M.J.	01 May
X	Rowe, P.J.	01 May
X	Russell, K.E.F.	01 May
X	Saltonstall, H.F.R.	01 May
S	Saywell, J.N.	01 May
E	Sharp, A.P.	01 May
X	Shropshall, I.J.	01 May
E	Simbeye, M.	01 May
X	Skinsley, T.J.	01 May
X	Smith, E.G.G.	01 May
S	Snell, A.J.	01 May
X	Spike, A.J.	01 May
X	Steele, M.S.	01 May
X	Stone, J.W.G.	01 May
X	Storey, A.E.	01 May
S	Sturgeon, D.M	01 May
X	Talbot, R.J.	01 May
S	Tate, N.M.	01 May
X	Taylor, R.P.	01 May
X	Tracey, W.S.	01 May
X	Unwin, N.R.F.	01 May
X	Veal, D.J.	01 May
E	Vernon, S.P.	01 May
X	Voke, C.A.	01 May
S	Wagstaff, A.	01 May
X	Ware, A.T.	01 May
X	Welsh, G.L.	01 May
E	Woolfe, K.D.	01 May
X	Wynn, M.D.	01 May

SUB LIEUTENANTS

1998

X	Powell, R.J.	01 Apr
X	Day, C.P.	01 May
S	Chesters, D.M.B.	01 Sep
X	Morey, K.N.	01 Sep
X	Parkinson, J.H.G.	01 Sep

1999

S	Briggs, H.C.	01 Jan
X	Leeper, J.S.	01 Jan
S	Cleary, C.M.	16 Jan
X	Blythe, J.	01 Apr
X	Rawlins, S.T.	01 Apr
E	Fuller, S.P.	01 May
X	Jones, M.A.	01 May
X	Morgan, D.	01 May
MS	Mundy, A.R.	01 May
MS	Patton, R.R.	01 May
X	Seaborn, A.	01 May
S	Smyth, C.R.	01 May
S	Standen, G.D.	01 May
X	Wynn Jones, I.	01 May
S	Kennan, N.P	01 Jun
S	Underwood, R.A.H.	01 Jun
X	Dadwal, R.K.	01 Aug
E	Abbotts, M.C.	01 Sep
X	Anderson, L.A.	01 Sep
E	Ashton, J.	01 Sep
X	Ayrton, R.E.	01 Sep
E	Best, R.M.	01 Sep
X	Botting, N.A.	01 Sep
X	Bradford, G.J.	01 Sep
E	Brierley, S.P.J.	01 Sep
X	Briggs, C.E.	01 Sep
E	Bromwell, M.S.	01 Sep
X	Budge, D.J.	01 Sep
X	Burrell, D.J.	01 Sep
E	Callis, G.J.	01 Sep
E	Canty, T.A.	01 Sep
E	Carvosso-White, A.L.	01 Sep
X	Causton, J.F.	01 Sep
E	Chatterjee, S.	01 Sep
E	Cripps, M.J.	01 Sep
X	Crompton, A.P.J.	01 Sep
E	Douglas, E.E.	01 Sep
E	Edge, H.R.	01 Sep
X	Eling, R.J.	01 Sep
X	Elliot-Smith, T.J.	01 Sep
E	Ellis, D.R.	01 Sep
X	Evans, L.J.	01 Sep
X	Farrell, J.A.	01 Sep
X	Feasey, I.D.	01 Sep

X	Fullman, G.	01 Sep
X	Garner, M.E.	01 Sep
E	Gibbs, M.P.	01 Sep
E	Gooch, M.D.	01 Sep
E	Goodenough, R.H.	01 Sep
X	Gorman, D.A.	01 Sep
E	Gubby, A.W.	01 Sep
X	Gulliver, J.W.	01 Sep
E	Hall, C.L.	01 Sep
E	Handoll, G.N.G.	01 Sep
E	Harding, D.V.	01 Sep
S	Harman, S.J.	01 Sep
E	Heath, S.P.R.	01 Sep
X	Hesketh, J.J.	01 Sep
X	Higgins, P.M.	01 Sep
E	Horsted, J.A.	01 Sep
S	Hunt, R.J.C.	01 Sep
E	Hyde, J.W.	01 Sep
E	Iyamu, O.B.	01 Sep
E	James, A.G.	01 Sep
X	James, R.M.	01 Sep
X	Johnson, M.W.	01 Sep
E	Johnston, A.G.	01 Sep
E	Keenan, B.F.	01 Sep
X	King, I.A.	01 Sep
X	Kingston, E.A.	01 Sep
X	Laidler, P.J.	01 Sep
S	Lawrence, R.G.	01 Sep
X	Lee-Gallon, T.J.	01 Sep
E	Leonard, T.P.	01 Sep
E	Lewis, M.D.	01 Sep
S	Lloyd, M.R.	01 Sep
X	Malcolm, P.S.	01 Sep
E	Marden, T.	01 Sep
X	Marriott, M.J.	01 Sep
X	Masterman, A.P	01 Sep
S	Mawdsley, G.R.	01 Sep
E	McCarthy, D.J.	01 Sep
E	McClurg, R.J.	01 Sep
E	McEwan, R.D.	01 Sep
X	Molloy, L.	01 Sep
S	Morris, H.S.	01 Sep
X	Moseley, S.H.	01 Sep
X	Murray, G.M.	01 Sep
E	Newall, P.J.	01 Sep
E	Nguyo, D.N.	01 Sep
E	Northcott, P.J.	01 Sep
E	Norton, A.L.E.	01 Sep
X	Owen, D.P.C.	01 Sep
E	Peck, S.R.	01 Sep
X	Pollock, S.	01 Sep

X	Rees, D.S.J.	01 Sep
E	Reynolds, A.C.J.	01 Sep
E	Reynolds, H.F.	01 Sep
X	Riddett, A.O.	01 Sep
E	Rose, A.	01 Sep
X	Ryan, P.D.B.	01 Sep
X	Ryan, P.J.	01 Sep
X	Shepherd, A.C.	01 Sep
X	Stack, E.F.	01 Sep
X	Steadman, R.A.J.	01 Sep
E	Sturgeon, M.	01 Sep
X	Taylor, J.E.H.	01 Sep
E	Trewinnard, R.M.	01 Sep
E	Walker, S.J.	01 Sep
X	Wallace, R.S.	01 Sep
S	Ward, A.J.	01 Sep
S	Webb, E.L.	01 Sep
S	Westwood, A.J.	01 Sep
E	Wickett, R.J.	01 Sep
E	Williams, C.L.	01 Sep
X	Woad, J.P.R.	01 Sep
E	Woodley, S.L.	01 Sep
X	Zipfell, A.J.	01 Sep
X	Baverstock, A.P	01 Oct
E	Burt, D.J.	01 Oct
X	Corbett, P.	01 Oct
MS	Green, P.G.	01 Oct
S	Harding, E.L.	01 Oct
X	Harrison, I.	01 Oct
X	Little, C.M.	01 Oct
X	May, D.M.	01 Oct
X	Monk, K.N.	01 Oct
S	Robinson, D.	01 Oct
E	Stanley, A.B.	01 Oct
X	Vout, D.K.	01 Oct
X	Watson, R.D.	01 Oct
X	Webb, J.P.	01 Oct
E	Ford, B.E.	08 Oct

2000

E	Alderton, P.A.	01 Jan
X	Armstrong, R.J.	01 Jan
E	Bailey, T.D.	01 Jan
E	Bass, P.W.	01 Jan
S	Beales, N.S.	01 Jan
X	Bickley, G.N.	01 Jan
X	Birch, P.L.	01 Jan
X	Black, J.M.	01 Jan
X	Bosley, S.N.	01 Jan
E	Brindley, M.W.	01 Jan
E	Brooks, P.N.	01 Jan
E	Brown, J.A.	01 Jan

SUB LIEUTENANTS

X	Bullock, J.R.	01 Jan	X	Norman, T.B.	01 Jan	S	Barnes, N.J.	01 May
S	Bulmer, W.E.	01 Jan	X	Notley, E.J.	01 Jan	X	Barnwell, N.A.M.	01 May
X	Burns, A.J.	01 Jan	E	O'Connor, D.P.	01 Jan	S	Barrett, S.J.	01 May
X	Cantellow, R.B.	01 Jan	X	O'Neill, H.L.	01 Jan	X	Bass, A.S.	01 May
X	Chang, H.W.	01 Jan	S	Pallett, A.J.	01 Jan	X	Bayntun, D.A.	01 May
E	Clarkson, A.M.	01 Jan	X	Palmer, M.D.	01 Jan	X	Becker, R.K.	01 May
S	Conran, N.W.D.	01 Jan	S	Pitman, L.J.	01 Jan	MS	Bennett, G.C.	01 May
S	Coppin, N.J.	01 Jan	X	Pitt, W.T.	01 Jan	X	Bennett, I.D.	01 May
E	Craven, D.	01 Jan	E	Prodger, A.P.	01 Jan	E	Bingham, A.A.J.	01 May
S	Cunnell, R.L.	01 Jan	X	Quaite, D.G.	01 Jan	X	Botterill, H.W.S.	01 May
X	Day, A.	01 Jan	X	Reaves, C.E.	01 Jan	X	Bowker, A.M.	01 May
S	Di Maio, M.D.	01 Jan	X	Redmayne, M.J.	01 Jan	E	Briscoe, J.W.A.	01 May
X	Duffy, M.L.	01 Jan	X	Reynolds, J.	01 Jan	E	Buchanan, D.C.	01 May
X	Gascoigne, J.	01 Jan	E	Rostron, J.H.	01 Jan	MS	Burnett, P.H.	01 May
X	Gater, J.C.	01 Jan	S	Roue, J.L.	01 Jan	X	Campbell-Baldwin, J.W.	01 May
X	George, C.A.	01 Jan	E	Savage, D.L.	01 Jan	S	Chang, C.J.	01 May
E	Goodsell, D.L.	01 Jan	X	Selley, D.R.	01 Jan	X	Chudley, I.V.	01 May
X	Green, J.	01 Jan	X	Semple, B.	01 Jan	E	Courtney, T.P.	01 May
E	Griffiths, N.C.	01 Jan	X	Shanks, D.Z.	01 Jan	X	Craig, M.J.	01 May
X	Hall, G.W.R.	01 Jan	E	Sidebotham, S.C.	01 Jan	X	Dray, J.M.	01 May
X	Harrison, L.E.	01 Jan	X	Smith, N.	01 Jan	X	Edwards, T.H.H.	01 May
E	Harvey, G.A.	01 Jan	X	Thomson, J.M.	01 Jan	E	Emery, C.S.	01 May
X	Hayes, M.A.	01 Jan	E	Trotman, S.P.	01 Jan	X	Evans, C.A.	01 May
S	Hughes, B.F.M.	01 Jan	E	Walker, I.M.	01 Jan	X	Evelyn, R.H.	01 May
E	Hughes, F.C.	01 Jan	E	Walker, J.	01 Jan	X	Fairclough-Kay, M.	01 May
X	Hunt, R.E.	01 Jan	X	Weaver, T.H.	01 Jan	E	Fanshawe, E.L.	01 May
E	Inness, M.J.	01 Jan	X	Weston, R.	01 Jan	X	Felfel, S.I.	01 May
X	Jackson, D.J.	01 Jan	X	Wheatley, N.S.	01 Jan	X	Ferran, S.H.M.	01 May
X	Johnston, J.J.	01 Jan	X	Wilson, G.P.	01 Jan	X	Fitzpatrick, N.J.	01 May
X	Jones, E.N.L.	01 Jan	E	Wilson, M.G.	01 Jan	E	Foster, A.J.	01 May
X	Kelly, S.	01 Jan	X	Worley, T.F.	01 Jan	X	Gamble, I.W.	01 May
E	Keogh, S.D.	01 Jan	E	Griffiths, G.	28 Jan	X	Geneux, N.S.	01 May
E	Kiff, I.W.	01 Jan	X	Bannister, J.	01 Apr	X	Glendinning, C.J.A.	01 May
X	Kilbane, D.K.J.	01 Jan	E	Braithwaite, G.C.	01 Apr	X	Gordon, J.	01 May
X	Kitson, R.H.	01 Jan	X	Dobson, A.C.	01 Apr	S	Gott, S.B.	01 May
X	L'Amie, C.A.	01 Jan	X	Ewer, J.E.	01 Apr	E	Gould, I.	01 May
X	Lancaster, J.H.D.	01 Jan	X	Farmer, P.A.	01 Apr	E	Grange, A.B.	01 May
X	Lansdale, T.J.	01 Jan	X	Hart, S.D.	01 Apr	E	Green, L.D.	01 May
S	Lawson, A.F.	01 Jan	E	Holgate, J.A.	01 Apr	X	Hall, J.E.	01 May
E	Liebnitz, A.D.	01 Jan	X	Holmes, M.D.	01 Apr	X	Hill, T.E.	01 May
X	Ligale, E.	01 Jan	X	Howorth, G.M.R.	01 Apr	X	Hogg, A.J.	01 May
X	Lovell, J.E.C.	01 Jan	S	Lanigan, B.R.	01 Apr	E	Holland, C.J.R.	01 May
X	MacPherson, C.A.C.	01 Jan	X	Leeson, A.R.	01 Apr	S	Irving, T.C.	01 May
X	MacSephney, T.L.H.	01 Jan	X	Morris, D.R.	01 Apr	S	James, G.C.M.	01 May
X	Malone, R.W.	01 Jan	X	Sloan, G.D.	01 Apr	S	Jemmeson, S.H.	01 May
X	McGreal, B.	01 Jan	X	Walker, N.M.C.	01 Apr	X	Jones, D.K.	01 May
X	McMaster, G.T.	01 Jan	X	Alexander, E.J.	01 May	X	Jones, O.C.	01 May
E	McQuire, D.E.A.	01 Jan	X	Anderson, A.E.	01 May	E	Jones, S.	01 May
X	Meacher, P.G.	01 Jan	E	Andrews, D.M.	01 May	E	Keane, B.M.	01 May
S	Mowat, A.D.J.	01 Jan	E	Atkins, P.R.	01 May	X	Kerley, B.J.	01 May
X	Nolan, G.J.	01 Jan	E	Ball, W.J.E.	01 May	E	Law, J.S.	01 May

SUB LIEUTENANTS

X	Leggett, S.J.	01 May	S	Lai-Hung, J.J.P.	01 Jul	S	Imrie, S.J.	01 Sep
X	Leslie, B.D.	01 May	X	Williamson, P.J.	01 Jul	E	Jerrold, W.H.	01 Sep
E	Love, J.J.	01 May	X	Abbot, R.L.	01 Sep	X	Jones, G.J.L.	01 Sep
MS	MacPhail, N.M.	01 May	X	Abel, L.	01 Sep	X	Jones, N.T.E.	01 Sep
S	Mallinson, L.J.	01 May	X	Baird, G.M.	01 Sep	X	Kirkby, S.J.	01 Sep
S	Malone, M.T.	01 May	X	Baker, J.E.G.	01 Sep	S	Law, S.J.	01 Sep
X	Markwick, K.W.	01 May	X	Barber, M.	01 Sep	X	Lewis, W.D.	01 Sep
X	McCallum, M.D.	01 May	X	Barfoot, P.M.	01 Sep	X	Lupini, J.M.	01 Sep
X	Miall, M.C.	01 May	E	Barr, C.A.	01 Sep	X	Lynn, S.L.	01 Sep
X	Mitchell, P.J.	01 May	X	Berry, J.T.	01 Sep	X	MacDonald, K.L.	01 Sep
X	Mittins, S.	01 May	X	Bettles, J.	01 Sep	X	MacLean, G.F.	01 Sep
X	Molyneux, M.E.	01 May	S	Boon, S.E.	01 Sep	E	Maddison, H.R.	01 Sep
E	Nicholls, L.R.	01 May	E	Boughton, J.A.L.	01 Sep	X	Marjoribanks, C.	01 Sep
X	Ottaway, T.A.	01 May	X	Bowman, S.K.J.	01 Sep	E	Maude, C.D.	01 Sep
X	Payne, W.D.	01 May	X	Briggs, A.D.	01 Sep	X	McCallum, G.P.	01 Sep
E	Pond, R.J.	01 May	E	Butler, J.E.	01 Sep	X	McLeod, K.Y.L.	01 Sep
S	Proctor, N.S.	01 May	S	Byron, D.C.	01 Sep	S	Mettam, S.R.	01 Sep
X	Pugh, G.N.J.	01 May	E	Caddick, A.	01 Sep	E	Mole, A.J.	01 Sep
X	Riches, A.I.	01 May	X	Carnew, S.F.	01 Sep	X	Nixon, S.E.K.	01 Sep
E	Robertson, I.W.	01 May	X	Cassidy, S.M.	01 Sep	E	O'Sullivan, P.B.	01 Sep
S	Rose, S.	01 May	X	Cloney, J.W.J.	01 Sep	E	Parker, J.D.	01 Sep
X	Ross, G.D.A.	01 May	E	Coates, A.J.	01 Sep	E	Peskett, D.M.	01 Sep
E	Royle, N.A.	01 May	X	Cook, S.G.	01 Sep	E	Petch, A.N.	01 Sep
E	Russell, M.J.	01 May	X	Cooper, A.	01 Sep	E	Peterson, K.A.	01 Sep
MS	Scarborough, D.C.	01 May	X	Coughlan, S.	01 Sep	X	Phillips, R.E.	01 Sep
X	Scott, N.	01 May	E	Cowell, R.J.	01 Sep	X	Plenty, A.J.	01 Sep
X	Seyd, M.	01 May	X	Cumming, F.S.	01 Sep	X	Reeves, A.P.	01 Sep
X	Shanahan, L.A.	01 May	X	De-Yoxall, J.	01 Sep	X	Reynolds, Z.A.	01 Sep
X	Simmonds, D.D.H.	01 May	X	Delvin, S.L.	01 Sep	S	Roberts, B.	01 Sep
X	Smith, A.R.	01 May	E	Dillon, B.	01 Sep	X	Royston, J.L.	01 Sep
X	Smith, C.J.	01 May	X	Doe, J.R.	01 Sep	X	Rudd, T.G.	01 Sep
X	Smith, D.J.	01 May	E	Dymond, J.R.M.	01 Sep	X	Samways, M.J.	01 Sep
E	Southwood, S.C.	01 May	E	Earle-Payne, G.E.	01 Sep	E	Shaftain, N.	01 Sep
X	Spark, S.M.	01 May	E	Fearon, D.J.	01 Sep	E	Sharkey, P.J.	01 Sep
X	Stewart, B.C.	01 May	E	Fiddock, M.L.	01 Sep	X	Sharrott, C.	01 Sep
X	Thomas, G.H.	01 May	X	Fox, J.P.	01 Sep	X	Shears, G.R.	01 Sep
X	Thompson, S.L.	01 May	X	Fraser, J.M.	01 Sep	E	Shrestha, S.	01 Sep
X	Thornley, J.G.C.	01 May	X	Gaskin, D.E.	01 Sep	X	Skipper, J.A.	01 Sep
X	Timms, A.I.	01 May	X	Gilmore, J.E.	01 Sep	E	Sobers, S.	01 Sep
MS	Todd, G.A.	01 May	X	Gorman, G.K.	01 Sep	X	Southworth, M.J.	01 Sep
E	Tonge, M.S.	01 May	E	Gray, J.M.	01 Sep	E	Stevens, J.I.	01 Sep
E	Turner, N.B.	01 May	X	Gray, R.L.	01 Sep	X	Stubbs, B.D.	01 Sep
E	Twiselton, M.J.	01 May	E	Grice, M.G.	01 Sep	E	Tantam, R.J.G.	01 Sep
X	Walton, G.J.	01 May	E	Hale, A.D.	01 Sep	E	Thomas, A.J.	01 Sep
X	West, G.A.	01 May	E	Hale, B.W.	01 Sep	X	Thomson, A.D.	01 Sep
X	White, P.D.	01 May	X	Hansen, C.J.	01 Sep	X	Timson, C.I.	01 Sep
X	White, S.	01 May	E	Hetherington, T.A.	01 Sep	E	Tomlin, I.S.	01 Sep
E	Wilkins, R.L.	01 May	X	Hodder, P.J.	01 Sep	E	Tough, I.S.	01 Sep
E	Wilshaw, G.I.	01 May	S	Hughes, G.A.	01 Sep	X	Trent, T.	01 Sep
X	Wilson, N.A.	01 May	X	Hulse, R.M.	01 Sep	E	Vaughan, J.R.	01 Sep
E	Wright, D.W.	01 May	X	Hunt, B.P.	01 Sep	X	Voigt, M.A.	01 Sep

SUB LIEUTENANTS

X	Wallace, R.P.	01 Sep	X	Greenhill, M.C.	01 Jan	E	Sheehan, T.J.	01 Jan
X	Warren, R.A.	01 Sep	X	Griffiths, N.M.	01 Jan	S	Shortland, K.	01 Jan
X	Weston, H.L.	01 Sep	E	Harvey, P.G.	01 Jan	X	Simpson, C.J.	01 Jan
E	Williams, B.	01 Sep	X	Hayward, J.A.D.	01 Jan	X	Stead, A.	01 Jan
E	Wills, R.H.	01 Sep	X	Heward, M.G.	01 Jan	X	Syson, C.F.	01 Jan
S	Woosey, D.A.	01 Sep	X	Hewitt, R.P.	01 Jan	E	Thomas, M.A.	01 Jan
X	Workman, R.J.	01 Sep	X	Hill, C.J.	01 Jan	X	Thompson, A.J.	01 Jan
S	Yates, L.O.	01 Sep	E	Hopper, G.	01 Jan	X	Thorley, G.	01 Jan
			X	Hounsome, J.R.	01 Jan	X	Thorp, T.H.	01 Jan
	2001		E	Hughes, T.W.	01 Jan	S	Tibballs, L.R.	01 Jan
X	Aldous, R.J.	01 Jan	X	Hunt, P.R.	01 Jan	E	Torbet, L.	01 Jan
S	Allan, N.S.J.	01 Jan	X	Ingamells, S.D.	01 Jan	X	Tregale, J.	01 Jan
X	Armstrong, D.M.	01 Jan	X	Jackson, R.A.	01 Jan	X	Tretton, J.E.	01 Jan
S	Ball, U.E.	01 Jan	S	Jennings, C.R.	01 Jan	E	Tumilty, K.	01 Jan
X	Banks, M.J.	01 Jan	X	Koheeallee, M.C.R.C.	01 Jan	S	Turberville, C.T.L.	01 Jan
X	Barrett, S.	01 Jan	X	Lee, C.J.	01 Jan	E	Turner, M.	01 Jan
X	Barron, P.R.	01 Jan	E	Lee, R.A.	01 Jan	E	Vardy, K.J.	01 Jan
X	Baxendale, A.G.	01 Jan	X	Lindley, J.	01 Jan	X	Visram, A.H.	01 Jan
X	Beard, S.A.	01 Jan	S	Marsh, D.R.	01 Jan	X	Walker, D.H.	01 Jan
X	Beattie, M.R.	01 Jan	S	Marsh, S.W.	01 Jan	S	Walker, M.D.J.	01 Jan
X	Benbow, J.A.K.	01 Jan	X	Marshall, J.M.	01 Jan	X	Waugh, R.P.	01 Jan
E	Bennett, M.A.	01 Jan	X	McKenna, D.R.	01 Jan	X	Way, R.A.	01 Jan
X	Benson, M.M.	01 Jan	X	McMahon, D.S.	01 Jan	X	Wells, M.N.	01 Jan
MS	Birkin, K.	01 Jan	X	McParland, J.M.	01 Jan	X	Wells, R.J.	01 Jan
X	Brace, A.F.	01 Jan	E	Mortimer, P.R.	01 Jan	X	Westwood, T.P.	01 Jan
X	Brazenall, B.C.	01 Jan	X	Munday, S.W.	01 Jan	X	Wheen, C.J.D.	01 Jan
E	Ciaravella, T.J.	01 Jan	E	Nash, R.F.R.	01 Jan	E	White, D.	01 Jan
S	Clark, S.M.	01 Jan	X	Nekrews, A.N.L.M.	01 Jan	X	White, K.J.	01 Jan
X	Claxton, A.G.D.	01 Jan	X	Norwood, J.K.	01 Jan	X	Whitehead, T.	01 Jan
E	Cox, M.D.	01 Jan	E	O'Brien, T.P.	01 Jan	X	Wilkinson, J.R.	01 Jan
E	Crosland, S.A.	01 Jan	X	Parker, M.J.	01 Jan	X	Williams, T.G.E.	01 Jan
X	Culshaw, J.	01 Jan	X	Pate, C.M.	01 Jan	X	Williamson, S.J.	01 Jan
E	Cunningham, R.A.	01 Jan	E	Pearce, J.	01 Jan	X	Wilson, S.A.	01 Jan
E	Daly, M.P.	01 Jan	X	Penalver, W.C.	01 Jan	E	Woodman, D.P.	01 Jan
X	Daniel, B.J.E.	01 Jan	E	Pike, R.T.	01 Jan	X	Wycherley, I.	01 Jan
X	Davey, C.S.	01 Jan	E	Quince, A.G.	01 Jan	X	Yarham, N.P.	01 Jan
X	Dewar, M.J.	01 Jan	X	Reehal, T.G.	01 Jan	X	Young, S.H.	01 Jan
E	Dixon, M.E.	01 Jan	S	Richards, G.B.	01 Jan	E	Gibson, A.	27 Jan
X	Dodd, P.M.	01 Jan	S	Riggs, M.G.W.	01 Jan	MS	Hazard, L.	27 Jan
E	Dooley, M.E.	01 Jan	X	Riley, R.A.	01 Jan	X	Leightley, S.M.	01 Apr
E	Elliott, S.P.	01 Jan	X	Roy, C.A.	01 Jan	X	Bligh, S.L.	01 May
X	Evans, B.G.	01 Jan	X	Rucinski, P.G.	01 Jan	X	Bunn, T.J.	01 May
X	Evans, R.P.	01 Jan	X	Ryder, T.	01 Jan	X	Coles, A.J.	01 May
X	Fisher, C.E.D.	01 Jan	X	Sarkar, T.	01 Jan	X	Devine, A.R.	01 May
X	Fisher, M.R.	01 Jan	E	Say, R.G.	01 Jan	X	Dicker, N.M.	01 May
X	Fisher, R.V.	01 Jan	X	Scanlon, M.P.	01 Jan	X	Dixon, S.P.	01 May
S	Flannagan, D.L.	01 Jan	E	Scarlett, C.J.	01 Jan	X	Goosen, R.D.	01 May
X	Fox, D.J.	01 Jan	X	Sedgwick, H.G.	01 Jan	X	Greaves, M.R.	01 May
X	Gardner, L.P.	01 Jan	X	Seton, J.	01 Jan	X	Mason, R.J.	01 May
S	Gershater, S.C.	01 Jan	E	Sharp, C.	01 Jan	X	McPhail, T.C.	01 May
X	Gillett, N.D.	01 Jan	X	Sharp, J.V.	01 Jan	X	Robinson, M.S.	01 May
S	Goscomb, P.A.	01 Jan						

SUB LIEUTENANTS

X	Ronald, E.T.	01 May
X	Thompson, J.	01 May
X	Ballard, A.P.V.	01 Sep
X	Blackburn, C.J.	01 Sep
X	Bond, R.D.A.	01 Sep
X	Dale, N.A.	01 Sep
X	Dart, D.J.	01 Sep
S	Deacon, P.R.	01 Sep
X	Fooks-Bale, M.E.	01 Sep
X	Hewit, S.	01 Sep
X	Ingham, N.H.	01 Sep
X	Keillor, S.J.	01 Sep
X	Knowles, D.	01 Sep
X	Lewis, J.M.	01 Sep
X	MacLean, S.M.	01 Sep
X	McMillan, N.	01 Sep
X	Morgan, G.L.	01 Sep
X	Phillips, L.C.	01 Sep
X	Schofield, J.C.	01 Sep
X	Whitelaw, D.A.	01 Sep
X	Williams, A.M.	01 Sep
X	Wilton, C.V.	01 Sep
X	Mason-Matthews, A.	01 Dec

2002

X	Aitken, L.	01 Jan
X	Dawe, C.J.	01 Jan
X	Dixon, R.J.	01 Jan
X	Emerson, M.J.	01 Jan
X	Hampson, A.G.	01 Jan
X	Hutchinson, M.R.	01 Jan
X	Mattock, N.J.	01 Jan
X	Mifflin, M.J.	01 Jan
X	Norriss, M.W.	01 Jan
X	Pittock, S.J.	01 Jan
X	Tuffin, M.G.	01 Jan
X	Wood, C.	01 Jan

SUB LIEUTENANTS (UCE)

1999
X	Carpenter, G.E.	01 Sep
E	Dyter, R.C.	01 Sep
E	Mann, C.A.	01 Sep

2000
E	Anderson, L.C.	01 Sep
E	Bailey, I.J.	01 Sep
X	Benarr, C.M.	01 Sep
S	Farrant, J.D.	01 Sep
E	Faulkner, S.G.	01 Sep
E	Gordon, A.J.	01 Sep
E	Kadinopoulos, B.A.	01 Sep
X	Louis, D.R.A.	01 Sep
E	Marshall, C.G.	01 Sep
E	McCormack, G.	01 Sep
E	Parkinson, H.M.L.	01 Sep
E	Reynolds, M.E.	01 Sep
S	Richardson, S.C.	01 Sep
X	Sykes, M.J.	01 Sep
E	Tatton-Brown, H.T.	01 Sep
X	Vincent, P.H.	01 Sep
X	Walker, J.J.	01 Sep
E	Weedon, G.A.	01 Sep
E	Wood, J.R.	01 Sep

2001
E	Amorosi, R.G.F.L.	01 Sep
E	Bell, F.J.	01 Sep
E	Bowen, R.J.	01 Sep
E	Colley, I.P.	01 Sep
X	Dacombe, C.A.	01 Sep
E	Dalglish, K.M.	01 Sep
X	Elliott, T.D.	01 Sep
E	Fisher, N.D.	01 Sep
E	Golden, C.A.	01 Sep
E	Gosden, D.R.	01 Sep
E	Hobbs, T.P.	01 Sep
E	Huggett, C.L.	01 Sep
X	O'Neill, C.M.	01 Sep
E	Piaggesi, G.F.	01 Sep
E	Purdy, R.J.	01 Sep
E	Reed, P.K.	01 Sep
E	Weil, D.G.	01 Sep

2002
E	Chaudhary, R.	01 Jan
E	Simpson, E.L.	01 Jan

2000

X	Blake, M.G.	01 May
S	Brooksbank, R.	01 May
X	Cleeve, K.A.	01 May
X	Herridge, D.J.	01 May
X	Hucker, O.C.	01 May
X	Macaulay, S.C.	01 May
X	Malster, D.A.	01 May
X	McCallum, N.	01 May
X	Neil, D.A.	01 May
X	Purchase, L.O.	01 May
X	Purvis, S.G.	01 May
X	Street, S.C.	01 May
X	Talbot, S.J.	01 May
X	Vierow, M.K.	01 May
X	Barr, D.J.	01 Sep
X	Brown, A.P.	01 Sep
E	Byers, H.R.	01 Sep
E	Cheater, C.J.	01 Sep
X	Coatalen-Hodgson, R.	01 Sep
X	Coxon, H.E.M.	01 Sep
X	Craven, O.E.	01 Sep
E	Errington, R.J.B.	01 Sep
X	Fletcher, A.S.	01 Sep
X	Hougham, T.N.	01 Sep
X	Hurman, R.N.	01 Sep
X	Jenkins, T.R.	01 Sep
E	Kendall-Torry, G.C.	01 Sep
E	King, M.A.	01 Sep
E	Magzoub, M.M.M.	01 Sep
E	Mourant, R.E.	01 Sep
X	Newport, D.J.	01 Sep
X	Pearce, S.L.	01 Sep
X	Rees, S.G.	01 Sep
E	Robertson, A.J.	01 Sep
E	Ryland, A.M.	01 Sep
E	Shepherd, C.E.	01 Sep
X	Slight, O.W.L.	01 Sep
X	Stuckey, K.A.	01 Sep
E	Thomas, A.G.	01 Sep
E	Tuhey, J.J.G.	01 Sep
E	Turner, V.M.	01 Sep
X	Verrecchia, J.R.	01 Sep
E	Vowles, I.R.	01 Sep
E	Watson, S.C.	01 Sep
S	West, T.L.	01 Sep
E	Whitaker, R.E.	01 Sep

2001

X	Akers, S.J.	01 Jan
X	Allan, R.W.	01 Jan
X	Beedle, J.D.S.	01 Jan

MIDSHIPMEN

X	Bretten, N.J.	01 Jan
X	Dickson, A.M.	01 Jan
X	Haynes, J.G.	01 Jan
X	Jacobs, B.	01 Jan
X	Jamieson, P.A.	01 Jan
X	Knight, J.M.	01 Jan
X	Lamb, R.J.F.	01 Jan
X	Powell, B.M.E.	01 Jan
X	Seal, M.R.	01 Jan
X	Seddon, J.D.	01 Jan
X	Sheppard, H.C.	01 Jan
X	Smith, R.J.	01 Jan
X	Snel, K.E.	01 Jan
E	Turner, D.L.	01 Jan
X	Vessey, L.M.	01 Jan
E	Willmore, S.	01 Jan
X	Cackett, T.E.R.	01 May
X	Harper, K.J.	01 May
X	Leigh, C.J.	01 May
X	Piper, B.J.	01 May
X	Scott, F.F.N.	01 May
X	Austin, S.A.	01 Sep
E	Betts, A.T.J.	01 Sep
X	Blackett, W.P.H.	01 Sep
X	Dale, J.R.	01 Sep
X	Davison, L.M.	01 Sep
X	Dyer, S.D.	01 Sep
E	Griffiths, F.M.	01 Sep
X	Martin, D.L.	01 Sep
X	Munns, E.N.	01 Sep
X	Nokes, O.	01 Sep
E	Riordan, S.P.	01 Sep
E	Roberts, D.L.	01 Sep
X	Thompson, G.C.	01 Sep
X	Walker, D.E.	01 Sep
X	Welbourne, A.R.	01 Sep
E	Westley, A.J.R.	01 Sep
X	Weston, G.	01 Sep
X	Wilcox, C.R.	01 Sep
X	Williams, O.C.L.	01 Sep
X	Winstanley, T.J.H.	01 Sep

2002

X	Cook, J.S.	01 Jan
X	Gillingham, G.	01 Jan
X	Gooding, D.C.	01 Jan
X	Guy, F.L.	01 Jan
X	Lenehan, D.J.	01 Jan
X	Powell, G.M.J.	01 Jan
X	Singer, K.A.	01 Jan
X	Stackhouse, M.C.	01 Jan

MEDICAL OFFICERS

SURGEON VICE ADMIRALS

Jenkins, Ian Lawrence , *CVO, QHS, MB, BCh, FRCS, OStJ* .... 21 Oct 02
(SURGEON GENERAL OCT 02)

SURGEON REAR ADMIRALS

Curr, Ralph Donaldson, MB, BS, DObstRCOG, FRCGP, AKC .... 3 Oct 02
(MEDICAL DIRECTOR GENERAL (NAVAL) OCT 02)

SURGEON CAPTAINS
(Full Career Commission)

1989		1996		2000	
- Evans,C.W.	30 Jun	- Edmondstone,W.M.	30 Jun	- Morgan,N.V.	30 Jun
1992		- Douglas-Riley,T.R.	31 Dec	- Gabb,J.H.	31 Dec
- Baldock,N.E.	31 Dec	1997		- Johnston,C.G.	31 Dec
- McMillan,G.H.G.	31 Dec	- Churcher-Brown,C.J.	31 Dec	2001	
1993		1998		- Barker,C.PG.	30 Jun
- Farquharson-Roberts,M.A.	30 Jun	- Mugridge,A.R.	30 Jun	2002	
1994		- Sykes,J.J.W.	31 Dec	- Brown, D.C.	30 Jun
- Cunningham,D.A.	30 Jun	- Raffaelli,P.I.	31 Dec	- Campbell, J.K.	30 Jun
- Howard,O.M.	31 Dec	1999		- McArthur, C.J.G.	30 Jun
1995		- Bevan,N.S.	31 Dec		
- Tolley,P.F.R.	31 Dec	- Jarvis,L.J.	31 Dec		

SURGEON COMMANDERS
(Full Career Commission)

1985		1995		2000	
- Kershaw,C.R.	30 Jun	- Hughes,A.S.	31 Dec	- Groom,M.R.	30 Jun
- Runchman,P.C.	30 Jun	- Buxton,P.J.	31 Dec	- Bree,S.E.P.	30 Jun
- Ashton,R.E.	31 Dec	1996		- Dashfield,A.K.	30 Jun
1990		- Burgess,A.J.	30 Jun	- Hill,G.A.	31 Dec
- Ryder,S.J.	30 Jun	- Neal,A.J.D.	30 Jun	- Nicholson,G.	31 Dec
- Waugh,P.J.	30 Jun	- McNeill Love,R.M.C.	30 Jun	- Glover,M.A.	31 Dec
1991		- Perry,J.N.	31 Dec	- Foster,C.R.M.	31 Dec
- Lunn,D.V.	30 Jun	1997		- Nichols,E.A.	31 Dec
- Allison,A.S.C.	30 Jun	- Johnston,R.P.	30 Jun	2001	
- Walker,A.J.	30 Jun	- Edwards,C.J.A.	31 Dec	- Turnbull,P.S.	30 Jun
1992		1998		- Stewart,M.D.	30 Jun
- Butterfield,N.P.	31 Dec	- Howell,G.E.D.	30 Jun	- Guy,R.J.	30 Jun
1993		- Hughes,P.A.	30 Jun	- Birt,D.J.	30 Jun
- Dean,M.R.	30 Jun	- Crawford,P.I.	31 Dec	2002	
- Balmer,A.V.	31 Dec	- Midwinter,M.J.	31 Dec	- Pearson, C.R.	30 Jun
- Benton,P.J.	31 Dec	- Risdall,J.E.	31 Dec	- Campbell, D.J.	30 Jun
- Hett,D.A.	31 Dec	1999		- Summerton, D.J.	30 Jun
1994		- Lambert,A.W.	30 Jun	- Clarke, J.M.	30 Jun
- Nicol,P.J.S.	30 Jun	- Howell,M.A.	30 Jun	- Parker, S.J.	30 Jun
- Baker,A.B.	30 Jun	- Ross, S J	14 Oct	- Stapley, S.A.	30 Jun
- Pipkin,C.	30 Jun	- Low,C.D.T.	31 Dec	- Sharpley, J.G.	30 Jun
		- Ross,R.A.	31 Dec	- Millar, S.W.S.	30 Jun
		- Young,P.C.	31 Dec		
		- Gent,R.P.ST.J.	31 Dec		

SURGEON LIEUTENANT COMMANDERS
(Full Career & Medium Career Commission)

1987	- Chaudhry,K.A. .... 01 Aug	- Bateman,R.M. .... 02 Aug
- Haddon,R.W.J. .... 19 Oct	- Craner,M.J. .... 01 Aug	- Sowden,L.M. .... 02 Aug
1990	- Matthews,G.A. .... 01 Aug	- Dickson,S.J. .... 02 Aug
- Wylie,R.D.S. .... 22 Nov	- Thomas,L.M. .... 01 Aug	- Mercer,S.J. .... 03 Aug
1994	- Streets,C.G. .... 01 Aug	- Ayers,D.E.B. .... 03 Aug
- Wood,G. .... 01 Aug	- Smith,J.E. .... 01 Aug	- McLachlan,J.K. .... 17 Aug
1995	- Rickard,R.F. .... 03 Aug	- Lew-Gor,S.T.W. .... 05 Sep
- Hand,C.J. .... 04 Jan	- Freshwater,D.A. .... 09 Aug	- Tennant,M.I. .... 14 Sep
- Smith,S.R.C. .... 01 Aug	**1999**	- Kehoe,A.D. .... 01 Dec
- Edwards,P.D. .... 21 Dec	- Bowie,A.N. .... 11 Mar	**2001**
1996	- Dekker,B.J. .... 01 Aug	- Webber,R.J. .... 01 Feb
- Miles,R. .... 01 Aug	- Heames,R.M. .... 01 Aug	- Atkinson,P.A. .... 01 Aug
- Tanser,S.J. .... 01 Aug	- Counter,P.R. .... 01 Aug	- Matthews, J.J. .... 01 Aug
- Mellor,A.J. .... 06 Sep	- Snowden,M.B.S. .... 01 Aug	- Porter, S. .... 01 Aug
- Rawal,K.M. .... 01 Nov	- Brinsden,M.D. .... 01 Aug	- Mantle, M. .... 07 Aug
- Leigh-Smith,S.J. .... 01 Dec	- Tamayo,B.C.C. .... 01 Aug	- Marshall, F.T. .... 07 Aug
1997	- Houlberg,K.A.N. .... 01 Aug	- Denholm, J.L. .... 07 Aug
- Palmer,A.C. .... 01 Mar	- Wallis,L.A. .... 01 Aug	- Smith, J.J. .... 07 Aug
- Whittaker,M.A. .... 01 Aug	- Gibson,A.R. .... 01 Aug	- Reston, S.C. .... 07 Aug
- Blair,D.G.S. .... 01 Aug	- Hughes,D.J. .... 01 Aug	- Milner, R.A. .... 07 Aug
- Yarnall,N.J. .... 01 Aug	- Parry,C.A. .... 12 Aug	- Schofield, S.R. .... 08 Aug
- Cannon,L.B. .... 01 Aug	- Greenberg,N. .... 01 Sept	- Mackie, S.J. .... 12 Aug
- Fisher,N.G. .... 01 Aug	- Walker, L.L. .... 01 Sep	**2002**
- Connor,D.J. .... 01 Aug	**2000**	- Armstrong, E.M. .... 05 Feb
1998	- Coltman, T.P. .... 01 Aug	- Norris, W.D. .... 20 May
- Every,M. .... 03 Feb	- McCabe,S.E.T. .... 01 Aug	

SURGEON LIEUTENANT COMMANDERS
(Short Career Commission)

1992	- Taylor,P.J. .... 08 Jan	**2001**
- Whitehouse,D.P. .... 01 May	- Masilamani,N.S. .... 14 Jan	- Clarkson, S.J. .... 01 Aug
1993	- Shrimpton,H.D. .... 04 Feb	- Bland, S.A. .... 07 Aug
- Thomson, R.G. .... 05 Nov	- Daramola, O .... 01 Dec	- Mather, R.H. .... 07 Aug
1994	**2000**	**2002**
- Terry,M.C.G. .... 15 Apr	- Siggers,B.R.C. .... 02 Aug	- Dewar, J.C. .... 30 Apr
1998	- Hudson,J.D.P. .... 02 Aug	
- Pimpalnerkar,A.L. .... 04 Jan		

SURGEON LIEUTENANTS
(Full Career & Medium Career Commission)

1997	**1998**	**1999**
- Prior,K.R.E.J. .... 06 Aug	- Brown, A. .... 05 Aug	- Barton, S.J. .... 04 Aug
- Hutchings,S.D. .... 06 Aug	- Gay, D.A.T. .... 05 Aug	- Keogh, J.M.E. .... 04 Aug
- Beadsmoore, E.J. .... 06 Aug	- Brims, F.J.H. .... 05 Aug	- Coates, P.J.B. .... 04 Aug
- Henry, M.F. .... 06 Aug	- Allsop, A.R.L. .... 05 Aug	
- Dow, W.A.M. .... 06 Aug	- Evans, G.C. .... 05 Aug	
- Rees, P.S.C. .... 06 Aug	- Cormack, A.J.R. .... 05 Aug	
- McIntosh, J.D. .... 26 Aug		

SURGEON LIEUTENANTS
(Short Career Commission)

1997
- Shaw, S.L. .... 06 Aug
- Rahman, J. .... 06 Aug
- Whybourn, L.A. .... 28 Nov

1998
- Carty, J. .... 05 Aug
- Welch, J.F. .... 05 Aug
- Knight, E.M. .... 05 Aug
- Collett, S.M. .... 05 Aug
- Fitzsimons, D.E. .... 05 Aug

1999
- Nelstrop, A.M. .... 10 Feb
- Prendergast, M.P. .... 04 Aug
- Price, V.J. .... 04 Aug
- Franklyn-Miller, A.D. .... 04 Aug
- Martin, N. .... 04 Aug
- Scott, T.E. .... 04 Aug

- Grainge, C.L. .... 04 Aug
- Brodribb, T.J. .... 04 Aug
- Read, J.A.J.M. .... 04 Aug
- Martin, N.P. .... 26 Aug

2000
- Cooke, J.M. .... 02 Aug
- Gardner, C.B. .... 02 Aug
- Gregory, J.R.C. .... 02 Aug
- Hayton, J.C. .... 02 Aug
- Harrison, J.C. .... 02 Aug
- Stannard, A. .... 02 Aug
- Dew, A.M. .... 02 Aug
- Lamont, S.N.J. .... 02 Aug
- Baden, J.M. .... 02 Aug
- Mercer, S.J. .... 02 Aug
- Robin, J.I. .... 02 Aug
- Guyver, P.M. .... 04 Aug

2001
- Patel, D.R. .... 01 Aug
- Bennett, S.A.F.J. .... 01 Aug
- Wild, G. .... 01 Aug
- Hicks, A.R. .... 01 Aug
- Yates, E.H. .... 01 Aug
- Khan, M.A. .... 01 Aug
- Bray, K.E. .... 01 Aug
- Wilmott, S.C. .... 01 Aug
- Ruthven, S.C. .... 01 Aug
- Beard, D.J. .... 01 Aug
- Mercer, A.J. .... 01 Aug
- Maples, A.T. .... 01 Aug
- Bains, B.S. .... 01 Aug
- Arthur, C.H.C. .... 01 Aug
- Bonner, T.J. .... 09 Aug

ACTING SURGEON LIEUTENANTS

2001
- Edward, A.M. .... 02 Jul
- Westerman, R.W. .... 02 Jul
- Kershaw, R.J. .... 06 Jul
- Evans, T.E. .... 09 Jul

- Picken, C.R. .... 09 Jul
- Allcock, E.C. .... 10 Jul
- Barker, V.S. .... 11 Jul
- Cordner, M.A. .... 11 Jul
- Hemingway, R. .... 11 Jul
- Mears, K.P. .... 11 Jul

- Wood, A.M. .... 11 Jul
- Ambrose, R.E.F. .... 15 Jul
- Hunter, C.R. .... 15 Jul
- Vale, A.J. .... 17 Jul
- Phillips, J.C. .... 19 Jul

MEDICAL CADETS SURGEON
SUB LIEUTENANTS RN

1999
- Middleton, S.W.F. .... 30 Apr
- Pengelly, S.P. .... 16 May
- Williams, S.W. .... 16 May
- O'Shea, M.K. .... 17 May
- Gardiner, D.R.C. .... 24 Jun
- Sargent, D.S. .... 29 Jul
- Isbister, E.J. .... 01 Aug
- Pardoe, E.R. .... 12 Sep
- McMenamin, D.M. .... 01 Oct
- Gilmartin, K.P. .... 04 Oct

2000
- Newton, N.J.P. .... 11 Jan
- Penn-Barwell, J.G. .... 11 Jan
- Lindsay, M.H. .... 14 Apr
- Shearman, A.J. .... 01 May
- Boddy, K.L. .... 01 Jul
- Gokhale, S.G. .... 01 Jul
- Morris, L.E. .... 01 Jul
- Potter, D.L. .... 01 Jul
- Roscoe, D. .... 01 Jul
- Scutt, M.J. .... 01 Jul
- Bradley, H.E. .... 03 Jul
- Kingsbury-Smith, R.E. ...... 14 Aug
- Longmore, D. .... 14 Aug
- Hillman, C.M. .... 18 Oct
- Jaques, S.C.D. .... 18 Oct
- Thomas, R.P. .... 18 Oct
- Jones, A.L. .... 30 Nov

- Fries, C.A. .... 01 Dec
- McKinlay, J.A.C. .... 01 Dec

2001
- Miles, S.A. .... 01 May
- Barker, R.J. .... 01 Jul
- Durkin, J.L. .... 01 Jul
- Halpin, A.C. .... 01 Jul
- Herbert, L.J. .... 01 Jul
- Martin, L.C. .... 01 Jul
- Robinson, T.G. .... 01 Jul
- Minshall, D.M. .... 27 Nov

DENTAL OFFICERS

SURGEON CAPTAINS(D)
(Full Career Commission)

1994		1996		2000	
- Myers,G.W. .... 31 Dec		- Morrison,G.L. .... 31 Dec		- Sanderson,R.C. .... 30 Jun	
1995		1997		2002	
- Lambert-Humble,S. .... 31 Dec		- Lock,W.R. .... 30 Jun		- Weston, M.W. .... 30 Jun	

SURGEON COMMANDERS(D)
(Full Career & Medium Career)

1987	1997	2000
- Thomas, D.L. .... 30 Jun	- Aston, M.W. .... 30 Jun	- McJarrow, D.J. .... 30 Jun
1990	- Liggins, S.J. .... 31 Dec	- Redman, C.D.J. .... 31 Dec
- Stevenson, R.M. .... 31 Dec	1998	2001
1995	- Howe, S.E. .... 31 Dec	- Smith, B.S. .... 30 Jun
- Gall, M.R.C. .... 30 Jun	- Jordan, A.M. .... 31 Dec	2002
- Sidoli, G.E. .... 31 Dec	1999	- Riden, D.K. .... 30 Jun
1996	- Hall, D.J. .... 31 Dec	- Elmer, T.B. .... 30 Jun
- Norris, R.E. .... 30 Jun		
- Culwick, P.F. .... 31 Dec		

SURGEON LIEUTENANT COMMANDERS(D)
(Full Career & Medium Career Commission)

1995	1998	2001
- McMeekin, N.S. .... 15 Jul	- Moore, P.G. .... 31 Dec	- Wenger, N.A. .... 23 Jul
- Fenwick, J.C. .... 03 Sep	1999	- Madgwick, E.C.C. .... 23 Jul
1997	- James, I. .... 09 Jan	
- Turnbull, N.R. .... 02 Jan	- Winch, E.J. .... 24 Jan	
- Davenport, N.J. .... 16 Jan		
- Everitt, C.J. .... 11 Mar		

SURGEON LIEUTENANT COMMANDERS(D)
(Short Career Commission)

1993	1999	2000
- Wilkie, N. .... 11 Jun	- Leyshon, R.J. .... 09 Jan	- Nurton, K.E. .... 09 Aug
	- Scott, W.A. .... 13 Jan	2001
	- Stevenson, G.S. .... 14 Jan	- Wingfield, M.H. .... 01 Jul

SURGEON LIEUTENANTS(D)
(Medium Career Commission)

1997	1998	1999
- Hands, A.J. .... 26 Jun	- Drummond, K.B. .... 13 Jul	- Foulger, T.E. .... 11 Jun
- Chittick, W.B.O. .... 10 Jul	- Murdoch, G.A. .... 20 Jul	

SURGEON LIEUTENANTS(D)
(Short Career Commission)

1997
- Jessiman, S.I. .... 20 Jun
- Verney, K.H. .... 09 Jul
- Dean, T.C. .... 22 Jul
- Huxtable, B.J. .... 22 Jul

1998
- McGill, E.J. .... 17 Jun
- McDicken, I.N. .... 25 Jun
- Holmes, P.S. .... 20 Jul
- Woods, R.S. .... 20 Jul

2001
- McNab, G.J. .... 01 Jan

1999
- Grosse, S.E.K. .... 25 Jun
- Burton, T.J. .... 05 Jul
- Anderton, S.W. .... 06 Sep

2000
- Wade, C.V. .... 29 Jun
- Bryce, G.E. .... 29 Jun
- Southall, E.L. .... 24 Sep
- Turner, J.C.B. .... 24 Sep

2001
- Hamilton, M.S. .... 26 Jun
- Kershaw, S.H.C. .... 18 Jul

SURGEON SUB
LIEUTENANTS(D)

CHAPLAINS

DIRECTOR GENERAL NAVAL CHAPLAINCY SERVICE AND THE CHAPLAIN OF THE FLEET

Hammett, Barry Keith, *QHC* .... 01 Jun 02
(DIRECTOR GENERAL NAVAL CHAPLAINCY SERVICE.JUN 02)

PRINCIPAL ANGLICAN CHAPLAIN

Hammett, Barry Keith , *QHC* .... 01 Jun 02
(DIRECTOR GENERAL NAVAL CHAPLAINCY SERVICE. JUN 02)

CHAPLAINS

1975		1987		1993	
CE Ames,J.P.	19 Jun	CE Eglin,I.	27 Jan	CE Beveridge,S.A.R.	28 Apr
1978		CE Luckraft,C.J.	05 Aug	**1994**	
CE Barlow,D.	04 Apr	**1988**		CE Hill,J.	17 Jan
1979		CE Thomas,D.W.W.	18 Oct	**1996**	
CE Harman,M.J.	20 Sep	**1989**		CE Petzer,G.S.	09 Jan
1980		CE Franklin,W.H.	10 Jan	CE Theakston,S.M.	03 Jun
CE Hilliard,R.G.	01 Aug	**1990**		**1997**	
1981		CE Pyne,R.L.	23 Jan	CE Wheatley,I.J.	08 Apr
CE Clarke,B.R.	30 Jun	CE Callon,A.M.	05 Jun	**1998**	
1982		CE Poll,M.G.	14 Jun	CE Hills,M.J.	21 Apr
CE Howard,C.W.W.	28 Sep	**1991**		CE Catherall,M.L.	01 Sep
1983		CE Green,J.	04 Jun	CE Evans,M.L.	01 Sep
CE Jackson,M.H.	19 Apr	CE Fairbank,B.D.S.	03 Sep	CE Gough,M.J.	01 Sep
CE Baxendale,R.D.	14 Jul	CE Scott,P.J.D.S.	03 Sep	CE Wylie,D.V.	01 Dec
1984		CE Springett,S.P.	10 Sep	**2000**	
CE Brotherton,M.	04 Sep	**1992**		CE Phillips,A.G.	14 Feb
1986		CE Kelly,N.J.	26 May	CE Heycocks,C.J.	24 Sep
CE Naylor,I.F.	16 Sep	CE Bromage,K.C.	02 Aug	**2002**	
CE Elmore,G.M.	30 Sep	CE Morris,J.O.	06 Oct	CE Hallam, S P.	05 May

PRINCIPAL CHURCH OF SCOTLAND AND FREE CHURCHES CHAPLAIN

Maze, Andrew Terence, *QHC*, *BSc* .... 11 Sep 79
(DIRECTOR NAVAL CHAPLAINCY SERVICE(TRAINING AND PROGRAMMES), MAY 00)

CHAPLAINS

1981		1990		1993	
SF Rae,S.M.	02 Feb	SF Eglin,C.A.	10 Sep	SF Brown,S.J.	20 Apr
1984		**1992**		SF Shackleton,S.J.S.	20 Apr
SF Keith,D.	15 May	SF Britchfield,A.E.P.	01 Oct	SF Wort,R.S.	27 Jul

1995
SF Beadle,J.T. .... 30 Mar

1996
SF Martin,R.C.J.R. .... 03 Sep

1997
SF Wilkinson,T.L. .... 04 Mar
SF Meachin,M.C. .... 07 Jul

1998
SF Macleod,R.A.R. .... 20 Feb

1999
SF McFadzean,I. .... 01 Jul

2000
SF Ellingham,R.E. .... 17 Apr
SF Grimshaw,E. .... 02 May

SF Kennon,S. .... 24 Sep
SF Rowe,R.D. .... 24 Sep

2002
SF Goodwin,T .... 05 May

PRINCIPAL ROMAN CATHOLIC CHAPLAIN

Burns, Thomas Matthew, *SM, QHC, VG, BA, BD, MBIM* .... 04 Jan 94
(DIRECTOR NAVAL CHAPLAINCY SERVICE (MANNING) MAY 00)

CHAPLAINS

1985
RC Donovan,P.A. .... 22 Apr
RC Madders,B.R. .... 09 Sep

1990
RC Sharkey,M. .... 01 Oct

1992
RC Couch,P.H.R.B. .... 05 May

1994
RC Forster,S. .... 08 Aug

1996
RC Bradbury,S. .... 18 Sep
RC McLean,D. .... 18 Sep

1998
RC McFadden,A. .... 01 Sep
RC Yates,D.M. .... 01 Sep

2000
RC Cassidy,M.J. .... 24 Sep
RC Conroy,D.A. .... 24 Sep

NAVAL CAREERS SERVICE OFFICERS (RN)

LIEUTENANTS (CS)

1990	1994	1998
- Breslin,M.J. .... 07 Jan	- McDonald,J. .... 06 Feb	- Newport,J.D.M. .... 09 Jan
1991	1997	- Drewett,C.E. .... 19 Sep
- Kirkbright,K.L.M. .... 17 Feb	- Connolly,M.H. .... 19 Sep	- Jones, C.R. .... 08 Jan
	- Hall,J. .... 19 Sep	- Concarr,D.T. .... 19 Sep

NAVAL CAREERS SERVICE OFFICERS (RM)

LIEUTENANTS (C.S.)

1997	1998	1999
- Maxwell,A.M. .... 10 Jan	- Barker,J.E. .... 01 May	- Wilcockson,R. .... 07 May
- Nickisson,D.J. .... 02 May	- Rennie,J.G. .... 18 Sep	

FAMILY SERVICE

LIEUTENANTS F.S.

1989	1997	1999
FS Knox, M.M. .... 17 Apr	FS Buckley, N.C. .... 19 Sep	FS Millington, I.R. .... 08 Jan
1996		FS Butterworth, L. .... 16 Jan
FS Taylor, S.B. .... 01 May		

ROYAL MARINES

CREST.- The Globe surrounded by a Laurel wreath and surmounted by the Crowned Lion and Crown with 'Gibraltar' on a scroll. The Fouled Anchor imposed on the wreath below the Globe. Motto - 'Per Mare Per Terram'.

THE QUEEN'S COLOUR. - The Union. In the centre the Fouled Anchor with the Royal Cypher interlaced ensigned with the St Edward's Crown and 'Gibraltar' above; in base the Globe surrounded by a Laurel wreath. Motto - 'Per Mare Per Terram'. In the case of Royal Marines Commando units the distinguishing colour of the units is interwoven in the gold cords and tassles.

THE REGIMENTAL COLOUR. - Blue. In the centre the Fouled Anchor interlaced with the Royal Cypher 'G.R.IV' ensigned with the St Edward's Crown and 'Gibraltar' above, in base the Globe surrounded by a Laurel wreath. Motto - 'Per Mare Per Terram'. In the dexter canton the Union in the remaining three corners the Royal Cypher. In the case of Royal Marines Commando units the numerical designation of the unit is shown immediately below the insignia. The distinguishing colour of the unit is interwoven in the gold cords and tassles.

ROYAL MARINES SECRETARY. - Whale Island, Portsmouth Hants PO2 8ER.

CORPS JOURNAL.- 'The Globe and Laurel,' Whale Island Portsmouth, Hants PO2 8ER

ROYAL MARINES ASSOCIATION. - General Secretary, Southsea, Hants, PO4 9PX.

ROYAL MARINES MUSEUM. - Southsea, Hants, PO4 9PX.

THE ROYAL MARINES

CAPTAIN GENERAL

His Royal Highness The Prince Philip Duke of Edinburgh, KG, KT, OM, GBE, AC, QSO

HONORARY COLONEL

His Majesty King Harald V of Norway, GCVO

COLONELS COMMANDANT

Major General A M Keeling, CB, CBE .... 6 Nov 98
    (REPRESENTATIVE COLONEL COMMANDANT ROYAL MARINES)

Major General P T Stevenson , *OBE*... 8 Aug 89
    (COLONEL COMMANDANT ROYAL MARINES)

MAJOR GENERALS

Fulton, Robert Henry Gervase , *BA*, *rcds*, *psc(m)*, *hcsc* .... 23 Oct 98
    (CAPABILITY MANAGER (INFORMATION SUPERIORITY) JAN 01)

Milton, Anthony Arthur , *CB, OBE*, *MPhil*, *rcds*, *jsdc*, *psc(m)* .... 01 Apr 99
    (COMMANDER UK AMPHIBIOUS FORCES AND COMMANDANT GENERAL ROYAL MARINES
    MAY 02)

Wilson, David , *CBE*, *MID*, *psc(m)*, *hcsc* .... 22 Nov 99
    (SENIOR BRITISH MILITARY ADVISOR US CENTRAL COMMAND MAY 02)

Fry, Robert Allan , *CBE, BSc, MA, psc(m)* .... 16 Mar 01
    (CHIEF OF STAFF PERMANENT JOINT HEADQUARTERS MAY 02)

BRIGADIERS

1998		1999		2000	
- Pillar, A.R.*	30 Jun	- Lane, R.G.T.*	30 Jun	- Rose, J.G	30 Jun
- Dutton, J.B.*	31 Dec	- Pounds, N.E.	31 Dec	- Gregory, T.M	31 Dec

2001					
- Thomas	30 Jun				

*Colonels OF6 (Seniority before Jul 99) holding Brigadier Appointments

COLONELS

1994
- Mason,A.M.* .... 30 Jun
- Sturman,M. .... 31 Dec

1995
- MacCormick,A.W. .... 31 Dec

1996
- Heaver,D.G.V. .... 30 Jun
- Hopley,D.A. .... 31 Dec

1997
- Reynolds,P.A. .... 30 Jun
- Spicer,M.N. .... 31 Dec

1998
- Hartnell,S.T. .... 30 Jun
- Robison,G.S. .... 31 Dec
- Hobson,C.W.P. .... 31 Dec
- Shadbolt,S.E. .... 31 Dec

1999
- Cox,S.J. .... 30 Jun
- Robbins,J.M.F. .... 30 Jun
- Capewell,D.A. .... 31 Dec
- Heal,J.P.C. .... 31 Dec
- Noble,M.J.D. .... 31 Dec

2000
- Haddow,F. .... 30 Jun
- Salmon,A. .... 30 Jun
- Bibbey,M.W. .... 31 Dec
- Chicken,S.T. .... 31 Dec

2001
- Thomson,A.B. .... 30 Jun
- Mason,J.S. .... 30 Jun

2002
- Howes, F.H.R. .... 30 Jun
- Dunham, M.W. .... 30 Jun
- Huntley, I.P. .... 30 Jun
- Messenger, G.K. .... 30 Jun

*Colonel OF6 (Seniority before Jun 99)

LIEUTENANT COLONELS

1986
- Babbington, P.M. .... 30 Jun
- de Val, K.L. .... 31 Dec
- Bush, S.J.D. .... 31 Dec

1987
- Wilson, J.R. .... 30 Jun
- Rundle, R.M. .... 30 Jun

1988
- Wilson, P.A. .... 30 Jun
- Nunn, C.J. .... 30 Jun

1990
- Grant, R.S. .... 30 Jun
- Hunter, T.C.G. .... 30 Jun
- Tong, D.K. .... 31 Dec
- Roy, A.C. .... 31 Dec

1991
- Cooke, M.Y. .... 30 Jun
- Grant, I.W. .... 30 Jun
- House, N.P.J. .... 31 Dec
- de Jager, H. .... 31 Dec

1992
- Parker, J.V.V. .... 30 Jun
- Balm, S.V. .... 30 Jun
- Parsons, P.H. .... 31 Dec
- McCabe, J. .... 31 Dec
- Armstrong, R.I. .... 31 Dec

1993
- Crosby, J.P. .... 30 Jun
- Canning, W.A. .... 30 Jun
- Gelder, G.A. .... 31 Dec
- Martin, P.J. .... 31 Dec

1994
- Beadon, C.J.A. .... 30 Jun
- Hughes, S.J. .... 30 Jun
- Lovelock, R.B. .... 30 Jun
- Wilson, S.R. .... 30 Jun
- Wotherspoon, S.R. .... 30 Jun
- Taylor, M.K. .... 30 Jun
- BS Waterer, R.A. .... 29 Jul

1995
- Guyer, S.T.G. .... 30 Jun
- Getgood, J.A. .... 30 Jun
- Stewart, D.J. .... 30 Jun
- Wilson, A.C. .... 31 Dec
- Tasker, G. .... 31 Dec
- Heatly, R.J. .... 31 Dec

1996
- Bruce, S.L. .... 30 Jun
- Stearns, R.P. .... 30 Jun
- Leigh, J. .... 31 Dec
- Musto, E.C. .... 31 Dec

- Taylor, W.J. .... 31 Dec
- Denning, P.R. .... 31 Dec

1997
- Conway, S.A. .... 30 Jun
- Sampson, P.H. .... 30 Jun
- Hutton, J.K. .... 30 Jun
- Stewart, J. .... 01 Oct
- Foster, G.R. .... 31 Dec
- Pickup, R.A. .... 31 Dec
- Walker, R.E. .... 31 Dec
- Hook, D.A. .... 31 Dec

1998
- Herring, J.J.A. .... 30 Jun
- Arding, N.M.B. .... 30 Jun
- Brown, N.P. .... 30 Jun
- Newing, S.G. .... 30 Jun
- Scott, C.R. .... 30 Jun
- Marino, D.J. .... 01 Oct
- Ellis, M.P. .... 31 Dec
- Davies, J.R. .... 31 Dec
- Price, M.J. .... 31 Dec
- Davis, E.G.M. .... 31 Dec
- Mallalieu, A.J. .... 31 Dec
- Bevis, T.J. .... 31 Dec

1999
- Cusack, N.J. .... 30 Jun
- Mudford, H.C. .... 30 Jun
- Page, M.C. .... 30 Jun
- Wolsey, M.A.R. .... 30 Jun
- Dechow, W.E. .... 30 Jun
- Smith, M.L. .... 31 Dec
- Hall, S.J. .... 31 Dec
- Watts, R.D. .... 31 Dec
- Lindley, N.P. .... 31 Dec
- Spencer, R.A.W. .... 31 Dec
- Clark, D.M.J. .... 31 Dec
- Summerfield, D.E. .... 30 Jun

2000
- Webster, T.J.C. .... 30 Jun
- Cawthorne, M.W.S. .... 30 Jun
- Salzano, G.M. .... 30 Jun
- Middleton, T.P.W. .... 21 Nov
- Burnell, J.R.J. .... 31 Dec
- Barnes, R.W. .... 31 Dec
- Bruce-Jones, N.W. .... 31 Dec
- van der Horst, R.E. .... 31 Dec
- Matthews, G. .... 31 Dec

2001
- Paul, R.W.F. .... 30 Jun
- Syvret, M.E.V. .... 30 Jun
- Evans, D.M.M. .... 30 Jun

- Anthony, N.M.K. .... 30 Jun
- King, D.C.M. .... 30 Jun

2002
- McCardle, J.A. .... 30 Jun
- Hudson, J.D. .... 30 Jun
- Copinger-Symes, R.S. .... 30 Jun
- Harradine, P.A. .... 30 Jun
- Marok, J. .... 30 Jun
- Maddick, M.J. .... 30 Jun
- Cameron, P.S. .... 30 Jun
- Ross, J.H. .... 30 Jun
- Manger, G.S.C. .... 30 Jun
- Curry, B.R. .... 30 Jun
- Gray, M.N. .... 30 Jun
- Maynard, A.T.W. .... 30 Jun
- BS Davis, C.J. .... 30 Jun

MAJORS

1979
- Craven-Phillips, T.C.D. ...... 01 Feb

1981
- Cailes, M.J. .... 10 Feb

1982
- Bailey, A.M.S. .... 01 Aug
- Stark, T.A. .... 01 Dec

1983
- Simmonds, P.B. .... 01 Aug
- Corner, I.L.F. .... 01 Nov

1984
- Rye, J.W. .... 01 Sep

1985
- Clapson, K. .... 01 Jul
- Pritchard, R.C. .... 01 Aug

1986
- Tyrrell, R.K. .... 01 Sep

1987
- Ebbens, A.J. .... 01 Sep

1988
- Underwood, N.J. .... 01 Sep
- Gidney, N. .... 01 Sep

1989
- Milne, A.R. .... 01 Sep
- Milner, H.C. .... 01 Sep
- Wills, M.V. .... 01 Sep

1990
- Walker, G.S.L. .... 01 Sep
- Gittoes, M.A.W. .... 01 Sep
- Hall, R.M. .... 01 Sep
- Parks, E.P. .... 01 Sep
- Phillips, S.J. .... 01 Sep
- Westoby, R.M. .... 01 Sep
- Grixoni, M.R.R. .... 01 Sep
- Sharland, S.P. .... 01 Sep

1992
- Cook, P.W.J. .... 01 May
- Corrin, C.ST.J. .... 01 Sep
- Bentham-Green, N.R.H. .... 01 Sep
- Glaze, J.W. .... 01 Oct
- Brown, R.J. .... 01 Oct

1993
- MacDonald, I.R. .... 08 Feb
- Daniels, T.N. .... 01 Sep
- Evans, M.A. .... 01 Sep
- Gwillim, V.G. .... 01 Sep

1994
- Pritchard, S.A. .... 18 Apr
- Howe, P.A. .... 01 May
- Forster, R.M. .... 01 Sep
- Wakely, S.A. .... 01 Oct

- Sawyer, T.J. .... 01 Oct

1995
- Green, M.G.H. .... 01 Sep
- Smallwood, J.P. .... 05 Sep
- Warren, T.S.E. .... 01 Oct

1996
- Allison, K.R. .... 25 Apr
- Hood, M.J. .... 25 Apr
- Pelly, G.R. .... 25 Apr
- Taylor, P.G.D. .... 25 Apr
- Wilson, D.W.H. .... 25 Apr
- Cullis, C.J. .... 25 Apr
- Francis, S.J. .... 25 Apr
- Ross, A.C.P. .... 25 Apr
- Scott, S.J. .... 01 Sep
- Freeman, M.E. .... 01 Sep
- Cundy, R.G. .... 01 Sep
- Webber, S.A. .... 01 Sep
- Saddleton, A.D. .... 01 Sep
- Willson, N.J. .... 01 Sep
- Moore, C.B. .... 01 Sep
- James, S.A. .... 01 Sep
- Bennett, N.M. .... 01 Sep
- Birrell, S.M. .... 01 Sep
- Holmes, M.J. .... 01 Sep
- Cooper, R.T. .... 01 Oct
- Anderson, S.T. .... 01 Oct
- Collins, P.R. .... 01 Oct
- Greedus, D.A. .... 01 Oct
- Thomas, P.W. .... 01 Oct

1997
- Bell, D.W.A. .... 26 Apr
- Pulvertaft, R.J. .... 01 May
- Coldrick, S.A. .... 01 May
- Gadie, P.A. .... 01 May
- Maybery, J.E. .... 01 May
- Thurstan, R.W.F. .... 01 May
- McKinney, M.D. .... 01 May
- Morris, P.E.M. .... 01 May
- Price, A.M. .... 01 May
- Searight, M.F.C. .... 01 May
- Slack, J.M. .... 01 May
- Stephens, R.J. .... 01 May
- White, H.J. .... 01 May
- Johnson, A.D. .... 29 May
- Livingstone, A.J. .... 01 Sep
- Hughes, J-P.H. .... 01 Sep
- Magowan, R.A. .... 01 Sep
- Cook, T.A. .... 01 Sep
- Kassapian, D.L. .... 01 Sep
- Oliver, K.B. .... 01 Sep

- McKeown, J.R. .... 01 Sep
- Hembrow, T. .... 01 Oct
- Maese, P.A. .... 01 Oct
- Ritchie, W.J. .... 01 Oct
- Corbidge, S.J. .... 01 Oct
- O'Donnell, I.M. .... 01 Oct

1998
- Pressly, J.W. .... 25 Apr
- Joyce, P. .... 25 Apr
- McCormack, C.P. .... 30 Apr
- Stickland, C.R. .... 30 Apr
- Kenworthy, R.A. .... 30 Apr
- Mc Laren, J.P. .... 30 Apr
- Porter, M.E. .... 01 May
- Chandler, M.F.H. .... 01 May
- Holmes, C.J. .... 01 May
- Litster, A. .... 01 Sep
- Morris, J.A.J. .... 01 Sep
- Kemp, P.J. .... 01 Sep
- Sear, J.J. .... 01 Sep
- Amos, J.H.J. .... 01 Sep
- Thorpe, C.D.B. .... 01 Sep
- Gilding, D.R. .... 01 Sep
- Green, G.M. .... 01 Sep
- Chapman, S. .... 01 Sep
- Jones, M.R. .... 01 Sep
- Fitzgerald, B. .... 01 Oct
- Cunningham, J.S. .... 01 Oct
- Potter, S. .... 01 Oct
- Crouden, S.F. .... 01 Oct
- Everritt, R. .... 01 Oct

1999
- Dewar, D.A. .... 01 Mar
- Case, A.C. .... 24 Apr
- Kettle, R.A. .... 24 Apr
- Fergusson, A.C. .... 01 May
- Cunningham, J.T. .... 01 May
- Hills, R.B. .... 01 May
- Armour, G.A. .... 01 May
- Ward, J.G. .... 01 May
- Simcox, P.A. .... 19 Jun
- Holt, J.S. .... 27 Aug
- Ashby, P.J.C. .... 01 Sep
- Manson, P.D. .... 01 Sep
- Pierson, M.F. .... 01 Sep
- Evans, P.J. .... 01 Sep
- McInerney, A.J. .... 01 Sep
- Baxendale, R.F. .... 01 Sep
- Hussey, S.J. .... 01 Sep

-	Skuse, M.	01 Sep
-	Stovin-Bradford, M.	01 Sep
-	Green, M.R.	01 Oct
BS	Mills, B.	01 Oct
-	Tupman, K.C.	01 Oct
-	Richards, S.W.	01 Oct
-	Beazley, P.	01 Oct
-	Reed, J.W.	01 Oct

2000

-	Murray, A.B.	26 Apr
-	Robertson, N.B.	01 May
-	Mattin, P.R.	01 May
-	Bucknall, R.J.W.	01 May
-	Cooper-Simpson, R.J.	01 May
-	Hammond, M.C.	01 May
-	Walls, K.F.	01 May
-	May, D.P.	01 May
-	Chattin, A.P.	01 May
-	Congreve, S.C.	01 May
-	Cook, M.F.	01 May
-	Murchison, E.A.	01 Sep
-	Blythe, T.S.	01 Sep
-	Wraith, N.	01 Sep
-	Kern, A.S.	01 Sep
-	Bakewell, T.D.	01 Sep
-	Jermyn, N.C.	01 Sep
-	Hickman, S.M.	01 Sep
-	Bailey, J.J.	01 Sep
-	Davies, H.C.A.	01 Sep
-	Devlin, H.F.G.	01 Oct
-	Bain, D.I.	01 Oct
-	Bulmer, R.J.	01 Oct
-	Perry, R.W.	01 Oct
BS	Watson, P.F.	01 Oct

2001

-	Geldard, M.A.	01 May
-	Bestwick, M.C.	01 May
-	Bray, M.R.	01 May
-	Walker, A.J.	01 May
-	Craig, K.M.	01 May
-	King, R.J.	01 May
-	Spanner, P.	01 May
-	Page, D.C.M.	01 Sep
-	Daukes, N.M.	01 Sep
-	Dowd, J.W.	01 Sep
-	Hedges, J.W.	01 Sep
-	Liddle, S.J.	01 Sep
-	Murray, W.R.C.	01 Sep
-	Hermer, J.P.	01 Sep
-	Hughes, M.J.	01 Sep
-	Jenkins, G.	01 Sep

MAJORS

-	Taylor, M.A.B.	01 Sep
-	James, P.M.	01 Sep
-	Coomber, J.M.	01 Sep
-	De Reya, A.L.	01 Sep
-	Harris, C.C.	01 Sep
-	Roylance, J.F.	01 Sep
-	Thomsett, H.F.J.	01 Sep
-	Twist, M.T.	01 Sep
-	Fuller, S.R.	01 Sep
-	Fraser, G.W.	01 Oct
-	Green, G.E.	01 Oct
-	Hannah, W.F.	01 Oct
-	Kelly, A.P.	01 Oct

2002

-	Brighouse, N.G.	24 Apr
-	Dresner, R.J.	24 Apr
-	Moorhouse, E.J.	24 Apr
-	Balmer, G.A.	24 Apr
-	Sutherland, N.	24 Apr
-	Hardy, D.M.	24 Apr
-	Kearney, P.L.	27 Apr
-	Hale, J.N.	27 Apr
-	Plewes, A.B.	27 Apr
-	Sibley, G.P.	27 Apr
-	Roddy, M.P.	27 Apr

CAPTAINS

1993
- Sharpe, G.A. .... 01 Jan
- Goodridge, T.J. .... 01 Jan
- BS Henderson, A.D. .... 01 Jan
1995
- Ginn, R.N. .... 01 Jan
- Heward, A.F. .... 01 Jan
- Nicholls, B.A. .... 01 Jan
- Richardson, M.C. .... 01 Jan
- Smith, S.F. .... 01 Jan
- Underwood, P.J. .... 01 Jan
- Tarnowski, T.A. .... 12 Jan
- Ethell, D.R. .... 28 Apr
- Hall, S.B. .... 28 Apr
1996
- Nicoll, S.K. .... 01 Jan
- Bourne, P.J. .... 01 Jan
- Rearden, R.J. .... 01 Jan
- Tyce, D.J. .... 01 Jan
- Everett, E.J. .... 24 Apr
- Lee, S.P. .... 27 Apr
- Stafford, D.B. .... 27 Apr
- Parry, J.A. .... 27 Apr
- Pilkington, A.G.H. .... 01 Jul
- Tanner, M.J. .... 01 Sep
- Blanchford, D. .... 01 Sep
- Read, R.J. .... 01 Sep
- Turner, S.A. .... 01 Sep
- Bailey, D.S. .... 01 Sep
- Harris, T. .... 01 Sep
- Hammond, D.E. .... 01 Sep
- Ballard, S.A. .... 01 Sep
- Cunningham, A.N. .... 01 Sep
- Jackson, M.J.A. .... 01 Sep
- Kelly, P.M. .... 01 Sep
- McGhee, C. .... 01 Sep
- Paton, C.M. .... 01 Sep
- Preston, R.W. .... 01 Sep
- Oherlihy, S.I. .... 01 Sep
1997
- Wilson, A.C. .... 01 Jan
- Shergold, P.J. .... 01 Jan
- Thompson, G.M. .... 01 Jan
- Todd, M.A. .... 01 Jan
- Sellar, T.J. .... 01 Jan
- Jones, G.J. .... 01 Jan
- Tulloch, S.W. .... 01 Jan
- Clark, P.A. .... 01 Jan
- Kilmartin, S.N. .... 04 Apr
- Gray, J.A. .... 29 Apr
- Maltby, R.J. .... 29 Apr

- Morley, A. .... 29 Apr
- Sutton, S.J. .... 29 Apr
- Parvin, R.A. .... 01 May
- Revens, C.A. .... 01 May
- Fenwick, R.J. .... 01 May
- Watkins, A.P.L. .... 01 May
- Brown, L.A. .... 01 Sep
- O'Hara, G.C. .... 01 Sep
- Jepson, N.H.M. .... 01 Sep
- Muddiman, A.R. .... 01 Sep
- Raitt, J.E. .... 01 Sep
- Whitfield, P.M. .... 01 Sep
- Manning, D. .... 01 Sep
- Atherton, B.W. .... 01 Sep
- Bowra, M.A. .... 01 Sep
- Brady, S.P. .... 01 Sep
- Clayton, M.J. .... 01 Sep
- Combe, S.A.N. .... 01 Sep
- Devereux, M.E. .... 01 Sep
- Guy, P.S. .... 01 Sep
- Lancashire, A.C. .... 01 Sep
- McCabe, G.P. .... 01 Sep
- Taylor, S.D. .... 01 Sep
1998
- BS Best, P. .... 01 Jan
- Holloway, N. .... 01 Jan
- Lugg, J.C. .... 01 Jan
- Maddison, J.D. .... 01 Jan
- Merchant, J.M. .... 01 Jan
- Scott, S.C. .... 01 Jan
- Ward, C.D. .... 01 Jan
- Watson, R.I. .... 01 Jan
- Westlake, S.R. .... 01 Jan
- Burrell, A.M.G. .... 28 Apr
- Collin, M. .... 28 Apr
- Lock, A.G.D. .... 28 Apr
- Lee, O.A. .... 01 May
- Alderson, R.J. .... 01 May
- Churchward, M.J. .... 01 May
- Crawford, A.T.S. .... 01 May
- Duncan, G.S. .... 01 May
- Haw, C.E. .... 01 May
- Lynch, P.P. .... 01 May
- Pruden, I. .... 01 May
- Simpson, A.C. .... 01 May
- Somerville, N.J.P. .... 01 May
- Murphy, K.S. .... 01 May
- Williamson, A.K. .... 01 May
- Houvenaghel, I.M. .... 01 Sep
- Cheesman, D.J.E. .... 01 Sep
- Wilson, J.G. .... 01 Sep

- Baker, M.B. .... 01 Sep
- Cantrill, R.J. .... 01 Sep
- Coats, D.S. .... 01 Sep
- Fisher, A.G. .... 01 Sep
- Jess, A.E.K. .... 01 Sep
- Lonsdale, R.J. .... 01 Sep
- Mantella, D.N. .... 01 Sep
- Masters, N.N.J. .... 01 Sep
- McMulkin, J.P. .... 01 Sep
- Middleton, C.S. .... 01 Sep
- Pearson, G.D. .... 01 Sep
- Penkman, W.A.V. .... 01 Sep
- Stemp, J.E. .... 01 Sep
- Urry, S.R. .... 01 Sep
1999
- Lawton, P. .... 01 Jan
- Hadlow, D.K. .... 01 Jan
- Clare, J.F. .... 01 Jan
- Smith, D.M. .... 01 Jan
- Pickard, D.M. .... 01 Jan
- Ross, G. .... 01 Jan
- Phillips, M.C. .... 01 Jan
- Gosney, C.J. .... 01 Jan
- BS Weston, P.A. .... 01 Jan
- Cowan, K.G. .... 23 Apr
- Moffat, J.W. .... 23 Apr
- Cleaver, J.P. .... 24 Apr
- Moran, J.T. .... 28 Apr
- Blyth, M. .... 28 Apr
- Davies, C.R. .... 01 May
- Alexander, G.D. .... 01 May
- Bubb, J.D. .... 01 May
- Edmondson, S.P. .... 01 May
- Garnham, S.W. .... 01 May
- Hasted, D. .... 01 May
- Hill, J.P. .... 01 May
- Mawson, J.R. .... 01 May
- Pirie, S.K. .... 01 May
- Nicholson, D.P. .... 01 Sep
- Bird, G.M. .... 01 Sep
- Boschi, P.H. .... 01 Sep
- Dennis, J.A. .... 01 Sep
- Fuller, J.B. .... 01 Sep
- Hart, S.J.E. .... 01 Sep
- Johnson, M. .... 01 Sep
- Oden, M. .... 01 Sep
- Selman, T.R. .... 01 Sep
- Cambridge, G.A. .... 01 Sep
- Hopkins, R.M.E. .... 01 Sep
- Leyden, T.N. .... 01 Sep
- Ordway, C.N.M.P. .... 01 Sep

CAPTAINS

-	Thompson, D.H.	01 Sep
-	Howarth, S.J.	01 Sep

2000

-	Price, D.G.	01 Jan
-	Hazelwood, C.D.	01 Jan
-	Wiseman, G.R.	01 Jan
-	Garland, A.N.	01 Jan
-	Howarth, J.	01 Jan
-	Cooper, N.	01 Jan
-	Kenneally, S.J.	01 Jan
BS	Thornhill, A.P.	01 Jan
-	Read, C.D.	01 May
-	Atkinson, N.C.	01 May
-	Edye, R.F.	01 May
-	Foster, N.P.	01 May
-	Gray, K.D.	01 May
-	Howard, R.D.	01 May
-	Mears, R.J.	01 May
-	Thompson, J.P.B.	01 May
-	Todd, J.W.	01 May
-	Waite, J.N.	01 May
-	Bowyer, R.J.	01 May
-	Griffiths, N.A.	01 May
-	Oura, A.N.	01 Sep
-	Turner, A.R.	01 Sep
-	Hardie, M.J.	01 Sep
-	Totten, P.M.	01 Sep
-	Foster, B.	01 Sep
-	Brain, W.J.	01 Sep
-	Durup, J.M.S.	01 Sep
-	Huntingford, D.J.	01 Sep
-	Kelly, T.J.	01 Sep
-	MacOwan, A.S.	01 Sep
-	Muncer, R.A.	01 Sep
-	Todd, O.J.	01 Sep
-	Turner, H.C.J.	01 Sep
-	Ward, A.J.	01 Sep
-	Smith, G.K.	01 Oct

2001

-	Stonier, P.L.	01 Jan
-	Baines, G.A.	01 Jan
-	Adcock, G.E.	01 Jan
-	Collins, J.	01 Jan
-	Fitzpatrick, P.S.	01 Jan
-	Standen, C.A.	01 Jan
-	Lucas, S.U.	01 Jan
-	Giles, G.J.	01 Jan
BS	Grace, N.J.	01 Jan
-	Tapp, S.J.	01 Jan
-	Frost, M.J.	01 Jan
-	Hunt, D.	01 Jan

BS	Kelly, J.A.	01 Jan
-	Gibson, A.J.	01 Jan
-	Sutton, D.	01 Apr
-	Hulse, A.W.	01 Apr
-	Hall, C.M.I.	01 Apr
-	McCulley, S.C.	01 Apr
-	Howe, S.	01 Apr
-	Wallace, R.S.	01 Apr
-	Fomes, C.J.H.	01 Apr
-	Cavill, N.R.D.	01 May
-	Hanson, S.C.	01 May
-	Hart, A.P.W.	01 May
-	Lindsay, J.M.	01 May
-	Roskilly, M.	01 May
-	Samuel, C.D.R.	01 May
-	Scanlon, M.J.	01 May
-	Tamlyn, S.J.	01 May
-	Hoare, P.F.	21 Jul
-	Rhodes, P.E.	21 Jul
-	Tinsley, P.	21 Jul
-	Barnwell, A.F.	21 Jul
-	Tidman, M.D.	21 Jul
-	Perrin, M.S.	01 Sep
-	Bonney, J.E.	01 Sep
-	Darley, M.E.	01 Sep
-	Forbes, D.G.	01 Sep
-	Francis, T.D.H.	01 Sep
-	Halsted, B.E.	01 Sep
-	Hester, J.F.W.	01 Sep
-	Hopkins, R.	01 Sep
-	Thompson, P.L.	01 Sep
-	Mansergh, A.C.	01 Sep
-	Maynard, P.A.	01 Sep
-	Morgan, H.L.	01 Sep
-	Pennington, C.E.	01 Sep
-	Robinson, P.J.O.	01 Sep
-	Wallace, S.P.	01 Sep
-	Liva, A.J.	01 Sep

2002

-	Clarke, P.M.	01 Jan
-	Cross, E.J.	01 Jan
-	Robbins, H.V.	01 Jan
-	Watson, B.R.	01 Jan
-	Kemp, A.C.	01 Apr
-	May, D.J.	01 Apr
-	Nolan, P.E.	01 Apr
-	Cross, A.G.	01 Apr
-	MacPherson, W.G.C.	01 Apr
-	McLelland, P.H.	01 Apr
-	Mewes, D.B.	01 Apr
-	Morton, J.C.	01 Apr

-	Orr, S.D.	01 Apr
-	Paterson, T.J.	01 Apr
-	Price, R.T.	01 Apr
-	Usher, A.T.	01 Apr
-	Usher, B.	01 Apr
-	Weir, J.R.	01 Apr
-	Wilcox, T.C.	01 Apr

LIEUTENANTS

1999
- MacRae, J.R. .... 05 Sep

2000
- Dawson, A. .... 30 Mar
- Gibb, A.K.B. .... 30 Mar
- Bryars, P.M. .... 01 Apr
- Butcher, D. .... 01 Apr
- Hembury, L. .... 01 Apr
- Nicholas, J.R. .... 01 Apr
- Peters, A.D. .... 01 Apr
- Phillips, D.G. .... 01 Apr
- Sharpe, M.R. .... 01 Apr
- Stanton, K.V. .... 01 Apr
- Flinn, J.A. .... 01 Apr
- Abbott, D. .... 01 Apr
- Burgess, M.J. .... 01 Apr
- Flower, N.P. .... 01 Apr

BS Burcham, J.R. .... 01 Apr
BS Dowrick, M.P. .... 01 Apr
- Gordon, R.S. .... 01 Apr
- Noble, K.L. .... 01 Apr
- Abbott, G.P. .... 01 Sep
- Alston, R. .... 01 Sep
- Axcell, M.F. .... 01 Sep
- Bartley, D.J. .... 01 Sep
- Brocklehurst, K.P. .... 01 Sep
- Butler, S. .... 01 Sep
- Dean, S.I.R. .... 01 Sep
- Delahay, J.E. .... 01 Sep
- Fidler, J.Q. .... 01 Sep
- Flannery, J. .... 01 Sep
- Gray, S.A.N. .... 01 Sep
- Hecks, I.J. .... 01 Sep
- Menzies, G.M. .... 01 Sep
- Norman, J.M. .... 01 Sep
- Parker, M.C. .... 01 Sep
- Pascoe, J.R.M. .... 01 Sep
- Preston, T.E. .... 01 Sep
- Price, J.E.O. .... 01 Sep
- Rochester, A.D. .... 01 Sep
- Rogers, S.M. .... 01 Sep
- Schleyer, J. .... 01 Sep
- Spink, D.A. .... 01 Sep
- Taylor, N.J. .... 01 Sep
- Tucker, S.J.W. .... 01 Sep
- Waite, M.T. .... 01 Sep
- Venables, D.M. .... 01 Sep

2001
- Brading, R.D. .... 01 Mar
- O'Sullivan, M.R.J. .... 01 Sep

SECOND LIEUTENANTS

1997

- Norton, T.C.H. .... 01 Sep

1998

- Payne, M.T. .... 01 May
- Allan, F.S. .... 01 Sep
- Tanner, S.J. .... 01 Sep
- Archer, T.W.K. .... 01 Sep
- Arwynck, L.R. .... 01 Sep
- Bennet, G.C. .... 01 Sep
- Buczkiewicz, M.J. .... 01 Sep
- Caldwell, D.J. .... 01 Sep
- Conroy, T.J. .... 01 Sep
- Copsey, N.R.B. .... 01 Sep
- Coryton, O.C.W.S. .... 01 Sep
- Eve, L. .... 01 Sep
- Ferrey, R.M. .... 01 Sep
- Galbraith, L.A. .... 01 Sep
- Guest, S.J. .... 01 Sep
- Hillier, C.A. .... 01 Sep
- Hubbard, C.E.S. .... 01 Sep
- Southern, M.J. .... 01 Sep
- Whitmarsh, A.T. .... 01 Sep
- Johnston, K.G. .... 01 Sep
- McKeating, P.M. .... 01 Sep
- Metcalfe, L.M. .... 01 Sep
- Morris, R.C. .... 01 Sep
- Newton, R.W. .... 01 Sep
- Norris, E.J. .... 01 Sep
- Owen, A.R. .... 01 Sep
- Shaw, A.T. .... 01 Sep
- Simmons, R.L. .... 01 Sep
- Stitson, P. .... 01 Sep
- Thomas, J.G. .... 01 Sep
- Thorpe, R.M. .... 01 Sep
- Tottenham, T.W. .... 01 Sep
- Waldmeyer, E.T. .... 01 Sep
- Werrey-Easterbrook, N.J. .. 01 Sep
- Williams, M.C. .... 01 Sep
- Williams, P.M. .... 01 Sep
- Witts, C.I. .... 01 Sep

1999

- Pinckney, M.R.N. .... 01 Sep
- Clark, D.J. .... 01 Sep

2000

- Carty, M.G. .... 01 Sep
- Dow, A.J.R. .... 01 Sep
- Postgate, M.O. .... 01 Sep
- MacLean, R.G. .... 01 Sep
- O'Keefe, T.D. .... 01 Sep
- Thornton, D.M. .... 01 Sep

2001

- Jones, R.P.M. .... 01 Sep
- Denney, A. .... 01 Sep
- Eldridge, G.E. .... 01 Sep
- Elliott, M.F. .... 01 Sep
- Ginn, R.O. .... 01 Sep
- Glancy, J.A.G. .... 01 Sep
- Hayler, B.V. .... 01 Sep
- Moffatt, D. .... 01 Sep
- Sharman, M.C. .... 01 Sep
- Sutherland, I.D. .... 01 Sep
- Hilton, J.N. .... 01 Oct

QUEEN ALEXANDRA'S ROYAL NAVAL NURSING SERVICE

CAPTAINS

2001
Bowen, M. .... 27 Mar

COMMANDERS

1999
Weall, E.M. .... 31 Dec

2000
Gibbon, L. .... 31 Dec

2002
Onions, J.M. .... 30 Jun

LIEUTENANT COMMANDERS

1988
Butcher, L.J. .... 08 Jan

1992
Smith, B.C. .... 01 Oct

1996
Duke, R.M. .... 31 Dec

1997
Allkins, H.L. .... 31 Dec

1999
Howes, N.J. .... 01 Oct
Broom, N.J. .... 01 Oct
Stinton, C.A. .... 01 Oct

LIEUTENANT COMMANDERS
(Medium Career Commission)

1998
Williams, C.M. .... 01 Oct

1999
Watts, M.D. .... 01 Oct

2000
Robson, C.J. .... 01 Oct
Spencer, S.J. .... 01 Oct

2001
Aldwinckle, T.W. .... 01 Oct
Knight, D.J. .... 01 Oct

LIEUTENANT COMMANDERS
(Short Career Commission)

1997
Kennedy, I.J. .... 31 Mar

1999
Thain, J.C. .... 31 Mar

LIEUTENANTS
(Medium Career Commission)

1986
McKillop, H.E.L. .... 14 Feb

1991
England, L. .... 11 Jan

1995
Ferguson, V.S. .... 21 Jan
Piper, N.D. .... 23 Nov

1996
Rankin, S.J. .... 15 Aug
James, K.J. .... 26 Nov

1997
Wilkinson, G. .... 06 Oct

LIEUTENANTS
(Short Career Commission)

1995
Munden, C.S. .... 07 Jul

1996
Johnson, V. .... 25 Jan
Harriman, S.J. .... 20 Feb
Linton, P.J. .... 30 Mar
Bagnall, S.A.E. .... 28 May
Logan, J.G. .... 27 Jul
Dilloway, P.J. .... 07 Dec

1997
Ouvry, J.E.D. .... 25 Mar
Armstrong, M.A. .... 28 Apr
Newman, S.A. .... 18 Aug
Beare, A.L. .... 10 Oct

1998
Kennedy, C.H. .... 07 May
Thompson, F. .... 24 Sep
Lang, J.S. .... 30 Sep

Hofman, A.J. .... 26 Oct
Gardner, S.L. .... 05 Nov
Carnell, R.P. .... 06 Nov
Blakeley, A.L. .... 17 Nov

1999
McFarland, N. .... 14 Jan
Kenworthy, L.K. .... 01 Apr
Hurley, K.A. .... 26 May
Taylor, L.M. .... 05 Jul
Thorpe, E. .... 03 Aug
Newby Stubbs, R.L. .... 15 Aug
France, S.C. .... 25 Aug
Morgan, R.S. .... 06 Sep
Smyth, C.R. .... 12 Sep
Stevens, A.J. .... 24 Sep
Stevenson, E. .... 07 Nov
Chilvers, L.D. .... 14 Nov

2000
Charlton, K.W. .... 14 Jan
McConville, C.W. .... 28 Mar
Brown, B.C. .... 11 Jun
Hyde, D.M. .... 22 Jun
Tolley, D.M. .... 25 Jul
Geraghty, F. .... 01 Sep
Lokai, D.S. .... 14 Sep
Turner, G. .... 25 Oct
Simpson, P.E. .... 27 Oct
Fletcher, H.M. .... 24 Dec

2001
Procter, K.J. .... 15 Jan
Selwood, P.J. .... 26 Feb
Middleton, J.E. .... 26 Apr
McFarlane, R.W.A. .... 02 Jul
Bryce-Johnston, F.L.S. .... 16 Jul
Penney, L.M. .... 16 Sep
Lloyd-West, C. .... 21 Sep
Haslam, C.L. .... 24 Oct

SUB LIEUTENANTS

1998
Despres, J.P. .... 19 Nov
Quemby, S.E. .... 20 Feb

Warburton, A.M. .... 26 Feb
Johnson, S.V. .... 26 Sep

KEY ROYAL NAVAL PERSONNEL, ATTACHES AND ADVISERS

(See Sec. 1 for Admiralty Board Members and Defence Council Members)

MOD/CENTRAL STAFF

CDS	Admiral Sir Michael Boyce GCB OBE ADC
1SL/CNS	Admiral Sir Alan West KCB DSC ADC
CE DEA	Vice Admiral P A Dunt CB
ACNS	Rear Admiral T P McClement OBE
CM (SD)	Rear Admiral C R Style
CM(IS)	Major General R H G Fulton
DCJO(OPS)	Major General R A Fry CBE
SBMA CENTCOM	Major General D Wilson CBE
CMDT JSCSC	Rear Admiral R J Lippiet MBE
ACDS(RP)	Rear Admiral R A I McLean OBE

CINCFLEET

CINCFLEET	Admiral Sir Jonathon Band KCB
DCINC	Vice Admiral M Stanhope OBE
COS(W)	Rear Admiral A K Backus OBE
COM(OPS)	Rear Admiral N S R Kilgour
AOC 3 GROUP/FOMA	Rear Admiral S Lidbetter
COMUKMARFOR	Rear Admiral Burnell-Nugent CBE
FOST	Rear Admiral J C Rapp
COS(SPT)	Admiral P D Greenish
CGRM/COMUKAMPHIBFOR	Major General A A Milton CB OBE

SECOND SEA LORD

2SL/CNH	Vice Admiral Sir Peter Spencer KCB ADC
COS/2SL	Rear Admiral R F Cheadle ADC
NAVSEC/CE NMA	Rear Admiral M W G Kerr
FOTR/CE NRTA	Rear Admiral P R Davies CBE
DGNCS	The Venerable B K Hammett QHC

DLO

DG Def Log (Ops & Bus Dev)	Rear Admiral M G Wood CBE
FOSNNI	Rear Admiral D J Anthony MBE
DCE WSA	Rear Admiral J Reeve
DCE DCSA	Rear Admiral R G J Ward CB

PROCUREMENT EXECUTIVE

DPA XD4/CofN	Rear Admiral N C F Guild

NATO

DEPSACLANT	Admiral I A Forbes CBE
COS SHAPE	Admiral Sir Ian Garnett KCB
DIMS	Vice Admiral Sir Paul Haddacks KCB
COS/COMNAVSOUTH	Rear Admiral R P Stevens CB
DEP COMSTRIKFORSTH	Rear Admiral R P Boissier
MA HIGH REP	Rear Admiral H A H G Edleston

MEDICAL

MDG(NAVY)	Surgeon Rear Admiral R D Curr
CE DMTO	Rear Admiral P J Kidner
SURGEON GENERAL	Vice Admiral I L Jenkins CVO

ATTACHES AND ADVISERS

NAVAL ATTACHES IN FOREIGN COUNTRIES

Service Mail
All official service mail is to be forwarded in accordance with current instructions.

OFFICERS PROVIDING A NAVAL SERVICE IN FOREIGN COUNTRIES

Albania
    Defence Attaché
    Tirana

Angola
    Defence Attaché
    Luanda

Argentina
    Defence Attaché
    Buenos Aires

Austria
    Defence Attaché
    Vienna

Bahrain
    Defence Attaché
    Manama

Belgium
    Defence Attaché
    Brussels

Brazil
    Naval Attaché
    Brasilia

Bulgaria
    Defence Attaché
    Sofia

Chile
    Defence Attaché
    Santiago

China
    Naval Attaché
    Peking

Colombia
    Defence Attaché
    Bogota

Congo (Democratic Republic)
    Defence Attaché
    Kinshasa

Croatia
    Defence Attaché
    Zagreb

Czech Republic
    Defence Attaché
    Prague

Denmark
    Defence Attaché
    Copenhagen

Egypt
    Naval & Air Attaché
    Cairo

Finland
    Defence Attaché
    Helsinki

France
    Naval Attaché
    Paris

Georgia
    Defence Attaché
    Tbilisi

Germany
    Naval Attaché
    Bonn

Greece
  Defence Attaché
  Athens

Guatemala
  Defence Attaché
  Guatemala City

Hungary
  Defence Attaché
  Budapest

Indonesia
  Defence Attaché
  Jakarta

Ireland
  Defence Attaché
  Dublin

Israel
  Naval & Air Attaché
  Tel Aviv

Italy
  Naval Attaché
  Rome

Japan
  Defence Attaché
  Tokyo

Jordan
  Defence Attaché
  Amman

Kazakhstan
  Defence Attaché
  Almaty

Korea
  Naval & Air Attaché
  Seoul

Kuwait
  Defence Attaché
  Kuwait City

Latvia
  Defence Attaché
  Riga

Lebanon
  Defence Attaché
  Beirut

Lithuania
  Defence Attaché
  Vilnius

Macedonia
  Defence Attaché
  Skopje

Morocco
  Defence Attaché
  Rabat

Nepal
  Defence Attaché
  Kathmandu

Netherlands
  Defence Attaché
  The Hague

Norway
  Defence Attaché
  Oslo

Oman
  Naval & Air Attaché
  Muscat

Philippines
  Defence Attaché
  Manila

Poland
  Naval & Military Attaché
  Warsaw

Portugal
  Defence Attaché
  Lisbon

Qatar
  Defence Attaché
  Doha

Romania
  Defence Attaché
  Bucharest

Russia
    Naval Attaché
    Assistant Naval Attaché
    Moscow

Saudi Arabia
    Naval Attaché
    Riyadh

Slovakia
    Defence Attaché
    BratislSlovakia

Slovakia
    Defence Attaché
    Ljubljana

Spain
    Defence Attaché
    Madrid

Sweden
    Defence Attaché
    Stockholm

Switzerland
    Defence Attaché
    Berne

Syria
    Defence Attaché
    Damascus

Thailand
    Defence Attaché
    Bangkok

Turkey
    Naval & Air Attaché
    Ankara

Ukraine
    Defence Attaché
    Kiev

United Arab Emirates
    Defence Attaché
    Abu Dhabi

United States of America
    Naval Attaché
    Assistant Naval Attaché
    Washington DC

Uzbekistan
    Defence Attaché
    Tashkent

Venezuela
    Defence Attaché
    Caracas

Yugoslavia (Federal Republic)
    Defence Attaché
    Belgrade

OFFICERS PROVIDING A NAVAL SERVICE IN COMMONWEALTH COUNTRIES

Australia
    Defence & Naval Adviser
    Canberra

Barbados
    Defence Adviser
    Bridgetown

Brunei
    Defence Adviser
    Bandar Seri Begawan

Canada
    Naval & Air Adviser
    Ottawa

Cyprus
    Defence Adviser
    Nicosia

Ghana
    Defence Adviser
    Accra

India
    Naval and Air Adviser
    New Delhi

Jamaica
    Defence Adviser
    Kingston

Kenya
    Defence Adviser
    Nairobi

Malaysia
    Defence Adviser
    Kuala Lumpur

New Zealand
    Defence Adviser
    Wellington

Nigeria
    Defence Adviser
    Abuja

Pakistan
    Naval & Air Adviser
    Islamabad

Singapore
    Assistant Defence Adviser & Royal Navy
    Liaison Officer
    Singapore

South Africa
    Naval & Air Adviser
    Pretoria

Sri Lanka
    Defence Adviser
    Colombo

Uganda
    Defence Adviser
    Kampala

Zimbabwe
    Defence Adviser
    Harare

NON-RESIDENTIAL ACCREDITATIONS

Attaches accredited to the following countries are non-residential

Algeria
    (Is resident London (DOMA))

Anguilla
    (Is resident Barbados)

Antigua & Barbuda
    (Is resident Barbados)

Armenia
    (Is resident Georgia)

Azerbaijan
    (Is resident Georgia)

Bahamas
    (Is resident Jamaica)

Bangladesh
    (Is resident India)

Belarus
    (Is resident Russia)

Belize
    (Is resident Jamaica)

Bermuda
    (Is resident USA)

Bolivia
    (Is resident Chile)

Botswana
    (Is resident Zimbabwe)

British Virgin Islands
    (Is resident Barbados)

Burundi
    (Is resident Uganda)

Cayman Islands
    (Is resident Jamaica)

Cuba
    (Is resident Venezuela)

Curacao
    (Is resident Barbados)

Dominica
    (Is resident Barbados)

Ecuador
(Is resident Venezuela)

El Salvador
(Is resident Guatemala)

Eritrea
(Is resident Kenya)

Estonia
(Is resident Finland)

Ethiopia
(Is resident Kenya)

Fiji
(Is resident New Zealand)

Gabon
(Is resident Congo DR)

Granada
(Is resident Barbados)

Guadeloupe
(Is resident Barbados)

Guinea
(Is resident Sierra Leone)

Guyana
(Is resident Barbados)

Honduras
(Is resident Guatemala)

Ivory Coast
(Is resident Ghana)

Kyrgyzstan
(Is resident Russia)

Lesotho
(Is resident South Africa)

Luxembourg
(Is resident Belgium)

Madagascar
(Is resident London (DOMA))

Malawi
(Is resident Zimbabwe)

Maldives
(Is resident Sri Lanka)

Mauritania
(Is resident Morocco)

Mauritius
(Is resident Kenya)

Mexico
(Is resident Guatemala

Moldova
(Is resident Romania)

Mongolia
(Is resident China)

Montserrat
(Is resident Barbados)

Mozambique
(Is resident Zimbabwe)

Namibia
(Is resident South Africa)

Nicaragua
(Is resident Guatemala)

Panama
(Is resident Venezuela)

Papua New Guinea
(Is resident Australia)

Paraguay
(Is resident Argentina)

Peru
(Is resident Colombia)

Rwanda
(Is resident Uganda)

St Kitts & Nevis
(Is resident Barbados)

St Lucia
(Is resident Barbabos)

St Vincent
(Is resident Barbados)

Senegal
(Is resident Morocco)

Seychelles
(Is resident Kenya)

Suriname
(Is resident Barbados)

Swaziland
(Is resident South Africa)

Tajikistan
(Is resident Kazakhstan)

Tanzania
(Is resident Kenya)

The Gambia
(Is resident Morocco)

Togo
(Is resident Ghana)

Tonga
(Is resident New Zealand)

Trinidad & Tobago
(Is resident Barbados)

Tunisia
(Is resident London (DOMA))

Turkmenistan
(Is resident Russia)

Turks & Caicos Islands
(Is resident Jamaica)

Uruguay
(Is resident Argentina)

Vietnam
(Is resident Malaysia)

Yemen
(Is resident Saudi Arabia)

Zambia
(Is resident London (DOMA))

INTERPRETERS

Name	Rank	Date Of Qualifying or Re-qualifying
ARABIC		
Pearce, J.K.C.	CAPT	Mar 90
Vosper, I.A.	CDR	Feb 73
CHINESE		
Gopsill, B.R.	LT CDR	Sep 84
Rayner, B.N.	CAPT	Dec 83
White, S.N.	CDR	Sep 90
DUTCH		
Davies, A.R.	CDR	Mar 84
Ewence, M.W.	CDR	Mar 88
Shipperley, I.	CDR	Oct 93
FRENCH		
Adair, A.A.S	CAPT	Dec 99
Airey, S.E.	CDR	Mar 80
Braithwaite, G.C.	SLT	Jul 00
Bussey, E.L.	LT	Apr 99
Cook, T.A.	MAJ	Jun 01
Craven, J.A.G.	LT CDR	Mar 90
Cree, M.C.	CDR	Feb 95
Dermody, R.T.	LT	Mar 98
Ewence, M.W.	CDR	Mar 98
Fieldsend, M.A.	LT CDR	May 95
Gubbins, V.R.	CDR	Jul 96
Harlow, S.R.	LT	Jun 01
Hollins, R.P.	LT CDR	Apr 99
Irwin, S.G.	LT	Mar 02
Jeffrey, I.	A/CAPT	Sep 72
Keefe, S-A.	CDR	Mar 89
Kettle, R.A.	MAJ	Jun 98
Mansergh, M.P.	CAPT	Mar 91
Newell, J.M.	CDR	Mar 89
Stonor, P.F.A.	CDR	Mar 88
Stride, J.A.	LT	Apr 99
Turner, J.S.H.	LT CDR	Mar 94
Young, I.J.	A/CDR	Jul 01
GERMAN		
Airey, S.E.	CDR	Apr 81
Dashfield, A.K.	SURG CDR	Mar 90
Durston, D.H.	CDR	Mar 83
Eberle, P.J.F.	CDRE	Mar 77
Finch, B.A.	LT CDR	Mar 96
Hill, D.	LT CDR	Mar 98

Name	Rank	Date Of Qualifying or Re-qualifying
Hollins, R.P.	LT CDR	Mar 98
Howard, D.G.	LT CDR	Apr 00
Knight, P.J.	LT CDR	Apr 97
Marjoram, J.W.	LT	Mar 01
Massey, A.M.	CAPT	Mar 80
Nurse, M.T.	LT CDR	Mar 86
Pitcher, P.P	LT	Nov 97
Robertson Gopffarth, A.A.J.	LT	Mar 95
Robin, C.C.E.	LT CDR	Mar 98
Sparke, P.R.W.	LT CDR	Mar 92
Tregaskis, N.S.	LT	Jul 96
Williams, N.L.	CAPT	Mar 85
GREEK		
Ritsperis, A.	LT	Sep 00
ITALIAN		
Amorosi, R.G.F.L.	SLT(UCE)	Sep 00
Jeffrey, I.	A/CAPT	Oct 97
Young, I.J .	A/CDR	Dec 01
JAPANESE		
Chelton, S.R.L.	CDR	Oct 88
Taylor, G.D.	LT	Aug 01
NORWEGIAN		
Stallion, I.M.	CDR	Mar 79
Taylor, W.J.	LT COL	Mar 91
POLISH		
Tarnowski, T.A.	CAPT RM	Mar 99
PORTUGUESE		
Harrison, R.A.	CDR	Mar 83
McGlory, S.J.	LT	Jul 96
Pannett, L.W.	LT	Jul 96
RUSSIAN		
Airey, S.E.	CDR	Mar 94
Connolly, C.J.	CDR	Mar 89
Davies, A.R.	CDR	Mar 89
Devlin, H.F.G.	MAJ	Oct 96
Drewett, R.E., *MBE*	A/CAPT	Mar 91
Fields, D.G.	LT CDR	Mar 90
Foreman, J.L.R.	CDR	Mar 92
Green, T.J.	CDR	Mar 89

Name	Rank	Date Of Qualifying or Re-qualifying	Name	Rank	Date Of Qualifying or Re-qualifying
Gwillim, V.G.	MAJ	Mar 94	Curry, B.R., *MBE*	LT COL	Mar 98
Hodgson, T.C., *MBE*	CDR	Mar 94	Dedman, N.J.K.	CAPT	Mar 86
Lister, S.R, *OBE*	CAPT	Mar 90	Eedle, R.J.	LT CDR	Sep 98
McTear, K.	LT CDR	Mar 91	Graham, J.E.	CDR	Jun 99
Newton, G.A.	CDR	Mar 94	Harrison, C.A.	LT CDR	Mar 89
Peters, W.R.	LT	Mar 00	Humphrys, J.A.	CDR	Mar 98
Ross, A.D.	SLT	Nov 99	Lynch, R.D.F.	LT CDR	Mar 91
Simpson, E.J.	LT	Mar 91	McGlory, S.J.	LT	Mar 94
Tarnowski, T.A.	CAPT RM	Mar 00	McLennan, R.G.	CDR	Mar 94
Watson, C.C.	LT CDR	Mar 88	Sanguinetti, H.R.	CDR	Mar 90
			Turner, J.S.H.	LT CDR	Nov 94
SPANISH			Wolfe, D.E.	CAPT	Mar 95
Adam, I.K.	LT CDR	Mar 91			
Bussey, E.L.	LT	Mar 98	**SWEDISH**		
Croome-Carroll, M.P.J, *MBE*.	LT CDR	Dec 01	Rigby, J.C.	CDR	Mar 86

OFFICERS OF THE SUPPLY AND SECRETARIAT SPECIALISATION QUALIFIED AS BARRISTERS AND CALLED TO THE BAR

COMMODORES

Blackett, J. (Chief Naval Judge Advocate)

CAPTAINS

Martin, T F W
Fraser, R W
Crabtree, P D, OBE
Steel, D G
Albon, R

COMMANDERS

Davis, B J, OBE
Williams, R E, OBE
Jameson, A C
Brown, N L
Gray, R S
Spence, A B
Crozier, S R M
Anderson, H A

LIEUTENANT COMMANDERS

Kingsbury, J A T (Act Cdr)
Taylor, S J
Hollins, R P
Wright, S H
Towler, A
Wood, R
Turner, J S H
Cole, A C
Pheasant, J C S
Adlam, G M
Samuel K L H
Goldsworthy, P J
Wilman, D M
Moore, S B

LIEUTENANTS

Murdoch, A P
Dow, C S
Atwill, J W O

HM SHORE ESTABLISHMENTS

AFPAA (CENTURION)
CENTURION BUILDING
Grange Road
GOSPORT
Hants
PO13 9XA

CALEDONIA
HMS CALEDONIA
ROSYTH
FIFE
SCOTLAND
KY11 2XH

MARITIME WARFARE SCHOOL
HMS COLLINGWOOD
Newgate Lane
FAREHAM
Hants
PO14 1AS

DARTMOUTH BRNC
Britannia Royal Naval College
DARTMOUTH
Devon
TQ6 0HJ

DRAKE SFM
HMS DRAKE
HM Naval Base
PLYMOUTH
Devon
PL2 2BG

MARITIME WARFARE SCHOOL
HMS DRYAD
Southwick
FAREHAM
Hants
PO17 6EJ

EXCELLENT
HMS EXCELLENT
Whale Island
PORTSMOUTH
Hants
PO2 8ER

FOREST MOOR
HMS FOREST MOOR
Menwith Hill Road
Darley
HARROGATE
HG3 2RE

GANNET
GANNET SEARCH AND RESCUE DETACHMENT
Greensite
MONKTON
Ayrshire
KA9 2RZ

HERON
RNAS YEOVILTON
Ilchester
Nr YEOVIL
Somerset
BA22 8HT

NELSON
HMS NELSON
PORTSMOUTH
Hants
PO1 3HH

NEPTUNE DLO
HMS NEPTUNE
HM Naval Base Clyde
FASLANE
Argyll and Bute
Scotland
G84 8HL

JSU NORTHWOOD
JOINT SUPPORT UNIT
NORTHWOOD
Middlesex
HA6 3HP

RALEIGH
HMS RALEIGH
TORPOINT
Cornwall
PL11 2PD

SEAHAWK
RNAS CULDROSE
HELSTON
Cornwall
TR12 7RH

SULTAN
HMS SULTAN
GOSPORT
Hants
PO12 3BY

SULTAN AIB
Admiralty Interview Board
HMS SULTAN
GOSPORT
Hants
PO12 3BY

TEMERAIRE
HMS TEMERAIRE
Burnaby Road
PORTSMOUTH
Hants
PO1 2HB

VICTORY
HMS VICTORY
HM Naval Base
PORTSMOUTH
Hants
PO1 3PZ

HM SHIPS

ALDERNEY (Island)
BFPO 203
LT CDR X   D Cartwright

ANGLESEY (Island)
BFPO 207
LT CDR X   D G Mahony

ARCHER (Archer P2000)
BFPO 208
LT X   P J Hammond

ARGYLL (Type 23)
BFPO 210
CDR X   J M L Kingwell

ARK ROYAL (Invincible)
BFPO 212
CAPT X   D G Snelson

ATHERSTONE (Hunt)
BFPO 215
LT CDR X   M Atkinson

BANGOR (Sandown)
BFPO 222
LT CDR X   J B Woods

BITER (Archer P2000)
BFPO 229
LT X   M T J Jarrett

BLAZER (Archer P2000)
BFPO 231
LT X   A J Wilson

BLYTH (Hunt)
BFPO 221
LT CDR X   G J Landrock

BRECON (Hunt)
BFPO 235
LT CDR X   A A Jordan

BRIDPORT (Sandown)
BFPO 236
LT CDR X   P D Craig

BROCKLESBY (Hunt)
BFPO 241
LT CDR X   P C Ireland

CAMPBELTOWN (Type 22)
BFPO 248
CAPT X   M U Sloan

CARDIFF (Type 42)
BFPO 249
CAPT X   T P Fraser

CATTISTOCK (Hunt)
BFPO 251
LT CDR X   R M Ryan

CHARGER (Archer P2000)
BFPO 252
LT X   N S Whitwell

CHATHAM (Type 22)
BFPO 253
CAPT X   A G Moll

CHIDDINGFOLD (Hunt)
BFPO 254
LT CDR X   M Lister

CORNWALL (Type 22)
BFPO 256
CAPT X   S R Kirby

COTTESMORE (Hunt)
BFPO 257
LT X   T G Ellison

CUMBERLAND (Type 22)
BFPO 261
CAPT X   I F Corder

DASHER (Archer P2000)
BFPO 271
LT X   C P Euden

DULVERTON (Hunt)
BFPO 273
LT X   S G Capes

DUMBARTON CASTLE (Castle)
BFPO 274
LT CDR X   T I Chrishop

ECHO (ECHO)
BFPO 275
CDR X   M C Jones

EDINBURGH (Type 42)
BFPO 277
CDR X   G A Robinson

ENDURANCE (Ice patrol)
BFPO 279
CAPT X   I Moncrieff

EXAMPLE (Archer P2000)
BFPO 281
LT X   J C Clay

EXETER (Type 42)
BFPO 278
CDR X   M T G Durkin

EXPLOIT (Archer P2000)
BFPO 285
LT X   M D Webb

EXPLORER (Archer P2000)
BFPO 280
LT X   L H Lacy

EXPRESS (Archer P2000)
BFPO 282
LT X   T Neild

FEARLESS (Fearless)
BFPO 283
CDR X   B H Warren OBE

GLASGOW (Type 42)
BFPO 287
CDR X   D Dutton

GLEANER (Gleaner)
BFPO 288
LT X   G Hesling

GLOUCESTER (Type 42)
BFPO 289
CDR X   A M Panther

GRAFTON (Type 23)
BFPO 291
CDR X   R A A Thomas MBE

GRIMSBY (Sandown)
BFPO 292
LT CDR X   K Furlong

GUERNSEY (Island)
BFPO 290
LT CDR X   J H Dible

HURWORTH (Hunt)
BFPO 300
LT CDR X   J S Petherick

ILLUSTRIOUS (Invincible)
BFPO 305
CDR X   J A Morse

INVERNESS (Sandown)
BFPO 307
LT CDR X   H A H Merewether

INVINCIBLE (Invincible)
BFPO 308
CDR X   J M S Fry

IRON DUKE (Type 23)
BFPO 309
CDR X   P D Warwick

KENT (Type 23)
BFPO 318
CDR X   S P Hardern

LANCASTER (Type 23)
BFPO 323
CDR X   B J Key

LEDBURY (Hunt)
BFPO 324
LT CDR X   P N Olive

LEEDS CASTLE (Castle)
BFPO 325
LT CDR X   J C Masters

LINDISFARNE (Island)
BFPO 326
LT CDR X   C M Bourne

LIVERPOOL (Type 42)
BFPO 327
CDR X   M W Ewence

MANCHESTER (Type 42)
BFPO 331
CDR .... E   A C Ashcroft

MARLBOROUGH (Type 23)
BFPO 333
CAPT X   D L Potts

MIDDLETON (Hunt)
BFPO 335
LT CDR X   M A Hart

MONMOUTH (Type 23)
BFPO 338
LT CDR X   D Pocock

MONTROSE (Type 23)
BFPO 339
CAPT X   M J Parr

NEWCASTLE (Type 42)
BFPO 343
CDR X   J J F Blunden LVO

NORFOLK (Type 23)
BFPO 344
CDR X   R P Talbot

NORTHUMBERLAND (Type 23)
BFPO 345
CDR X   A J Burton

NOTTINGHAM (Type 42)
BFPO 346
CDR X   R Farrington OBE

OCEAN (Ocean)
BFPO 350
CAPT X   A J Johns CBE

ORWELL (River)
BFPO 355
LT X   I B Clarke

PEMBROKE (Sandown)
BFPO 357
LT CDR X   T Russell

PENZANCE (Sandown)
BFPO 358
CDR X   R S Hatcher

PORTLAND (Type 23)
BFPO 361
CDR X   J M Handley

PUNCHER (Archer P2000)
BFPO 362
LT X   W R Peters

PURSUER (Archer P2000)
BFPO 363
LT X   J D Byron

QUORN (Hunt)
BFPO 366
LT CDR X   M I Newland

RAIDER (Archer P2000)
BFPO 377
LT X   B R Dickens

RAMSEY (Sandown)
BFPO 368
LT CDR X   D B Axon

RANGER (Archer P2000)
BFPO 369
LT CDR X   C D Pillar

RICHMOND (Type 23)
BFPO 375
CDR X   K W L Keble

ROEBUCK (Roebuck)
BFPO 376
LT CDR X   A J James

SANDOWN (Sandown)
BFPO 379
LT CDR X   G L Young

SCEPTRE (Swiftsure)
BFPO 380
LT CDR X   J S Bark

SCOTT (Scott)
BFPO 381
CDR X   S J McMichael-Phillips

SHEFFIELD (Type 22)
BFPO 383
CDR X   S P Williams

SHETLAND (Island)
BFPO 385
LT CDR X   R C Vitali

SHOREHAM (Sandown)
BFPO 386
LT CDR X   T J Guy

SMITER (Archer P2000)
BFPO 387
LT X   C I Maynard

SOMERSET (Type 23)
BFPO 395
CDR X   K E Blount

SOUTHAMPTON (Type 42)
BFPO 389
CDR X   G L Doyle

SOVEREIGN (Swiftsure)
BFPO 390
CDR X   C R Fulton

SPARTAN (Swiftsure)
BFPO 391
LT CDR .... E   I S Pickles

SPLENDID (Swiftsure)
BFPO 393
CDR X   P D Burke

ST ALBANS (Type 23)
BFPO 399
CDR X   D C K Barker

SUPERB (Swiftsure)
BFPO 396
CDR X   N J Hughes

SUTHERLAND (Type 23)
BFPO 398
CDR X   P G Thomas

TALENT (Trafalgar)
BFPO 401
CDR X   N W Hine

TIRELESS (Trafalgar)
BFPO 402
CDR X   M J D Walliker

TORBAY (Trafalgar)
BFPO 403
CDR .... E   M A Cooper

TRACKER (Archer P2000)
BFPO 409
LT X   A N P Essenhigh

TRAFALGAR (Trafalgar)
BFPO 404
CDR X   R Fancy

TRENCHANT (Trafalgar)
BFPO 405
CDR .... E   M E Prince

TRIUMPH (Trafalgar)
BFPO 406
CDR X   I T Roberts

TRUMPETER (Archer P2000)
BFPO 407
LT X   A G Lamb

TURBULENT (Trafalgar)
BFPO 408
LT CDR X   A M McKendrick

VANGUARD(PORT) (Trident)
BFPO 418
CDR X   P W Nixon

VENGEANCE(PORT) (Trident)
BFPO 421
CDR X   D C W Balston

VENGEANCE(STBD) (Trident)
BFPO 421
CDR .... XJ N Ferguson

VICTORIOUS(PORT) (Trident)
BFPO 419
CDR X   J I Humphreys

VICTORIOUS(STBD) (Trident)
BFPO 419
CDR X   C I Reid

VIGILANT(PORT) (Trident)
BFPO 420
CDR X   G A Newton

WALNEY (Sandown)
BFPO 423
LT CDR X   A T Cummings

WESTMINSTER (Type 23)
BFPO 426
CDR X   D P Reindorp

YORK (Type 42)
BFPO 430
CDR X   R L Powell

RN FISHERY PROTECTION & MINE COUNTERMEASURES SQUADRONS

FIRST MCM SQN
CDR X   C D Wilson OBE

SECOND MCM SQN
CDR X   P N Lambourn

THIRD MCM SQN
CDR X   D J Bewick

FISHERY PROTECTION SQN
CDR X   D N Matthews MBE

FIRST PATROL BOAT SQUADRON
CDR X   S J Snowball

ROYAL NAVAL AIR SQUADRONS

CHFHQ
LT COL .... RM   M P Ellis

700M SQN CULDROSE
LT CDR X   C P Maude

702 SQN HERON
LT CDR..............X   S E Kilby

705 SQN RAF SHAWBURY
LT CDR X   A P Hands

727 SQN PLYMOUTH
LT CDR X   W M Murton

750 SQN CULDROSE (Jetsteam)
LT CDR X   S Powell

771 SQN CULDROSE (Sea King)
LT CDR X   D Whitehead

800 SQN HERON (Sea Harrier)
BFPO 200
CDR X   R C Payne

801 SQN HERON (Sea Harrier)
BFPO 200
A/CDR X   J A Lawler MBE

814 SQN CULDROSE (Sea King Mk6)
BFPO 200
LT CDR X   S J Murray

815 SQN HERON (Lynx)
LT CDR X   A M Cramp

820 SQN CULDROSE (Sea King Mk6)
BFPO 200
CDR X   I S T Fitter

824 SQN CULDROSE (Merlin)
LT CDR X   S J Bradburn

845 SQN HERON(Sea King Mk4)
LT CDR X   J P Pentreath

846 SQN CULDROSE (Sea King Mk4)
LT CDR X   J D A Burgess

847 SQN HERON (Lynx AN7 and Gazelle)
LT COL .... RM   J A McCardle

848 SQN HERON (Sea King Mk 4)
LT CDR X   P K Shawcross

849 SQN HQ CULDROSE
LT CDR X   G B Hutchison

849 SQN A FLT (Sea King AEW)
BFPO 200
LT CDR X   M McKenzie

849 SQN B FLT (Sea King AEW)
BFPO 200
LT CDR X   I J R Daniels

899 SQN HERON (Sea Harrier)
CDR X   T C Eastaugh

RESERVE TRAINING CENTRES

HMS CALLIOPE
South Shore Road
GATESHEAD
Tyne & Wear
NE8 2BE

HMS CAMBRIA
Hayes Lane
Sully
SOUTH GLAMORGAN
CF64 2XU

HMS CAROLINE
BFPO 806

HMS DALRIADA(MOB)
Navy Buildings
Eldon Street
GREENOCK
Strathclyde
PA16 7SL

HMS EAGLET
RNHQ Merseyside
East Brunswick Dock
LIVERPOOL
L3 4DZ

HMS FERRET
Chicksands
SHEFFORD
Beds
SG17 5PR

HMS FLYING FOX
Winterstoke Road
BRISTOL
BS3 2NS

HMS FORWARD
42 Tilton Road
BIRMINGHAM
B9 4PP

HMS KING ALFRED
Fraser Building
Whale Island
PORTSMOUTH
Hants
PO2 8ER

HMS PRESIDENT
72 St Katharine's Way
LONDON
E1W 9UQ

HMS SCOTIA
C/O RNSE Caledonia
Hilton Road
ROSYTH
Fife
KY11 2X

HMS SHERWOOD
Chalfont Drive
NOTTINGHAM
NG8 3LT

HMS VIVID
Mount Wise Court
DEVONPORT
Devon
PL1 4JJ

HMS WILDFIRE
Brakenhill House
The Woods
NORTHWOOD
HA6 3EX

ROYAL MARINES ESTABLISHMENTS AND UNITS

FLEET HQ PORTSMOUTH 2
Headquarters Royal Marines
West Battery
Whale Island
PORTSMOUTH
Hants
PO2 8DX

40 CDO RM
40 Commando Royal Marines
Norton Manor Camp
TAUNTON
Somerset
TA2 6PF

42 CDO RM
42 Commando Royal Marines
Bickleigh Barracks
Shaugh Prior
nr PLYMOUTH
Devon
PL6 7AJ

45 CDO RM
45 Commando Royal Marines
RM CONDOR
ARBROATH
Angus
Scotland
DD11 3SJ

CDO LOG REGT RM
Commando Logistics Regiment
Royal Marines
RMB Chivenor
BARNSTAPLE
Devon
EX31 1AZ

HQ 3 CDO BDE RM
Headquarters 3 Commando Brigade
Royal Marines
RM Barracks
Stonehouse
PLYMOUTH
Devon
PL1 3QS

29 CDO REGT RA
29 Commando Regiment Royal
Artillery
The Royal Citadel
PLYMOUTH
Devon
PL1 2PD

RM STONEHOUSE
Royal Marines Stonehouse
RM Barracks
Stonehouse
PLYMOUTH
Devon
PL1 3QS

1 ASSAULT GROUP RM
RM POOLE
Royal Marines Poole
Hamworthy
POOLE
Dorset
BH15 4NQ

CTCRM
Commando Training Centre Royal Marines
Lympstone
EXMOUTH
Devon
EX8 5AR

ATTURM
Amphibious Trials & Training Unit
Instow
BIDEFORD
Devon
EX39 4JH

RM CONDOR
Royal Marines Condor
ARBROATH
Angus
Scotland
DD11 3SJ

UKLFCSG
United Kingdom Landing Force Command
Support Group
Royal Marines Barracks
Stonehouse
PLYMOUTH
Devon
PL1 3QS

148 FOU BTY RA
148(MEIKTILA) Commando Forward Observation
Battery Royal Artillery
Royal Marines Poole
HAMWORTHY
Dorset
BH15 4NQ

HQ BAND SERVICE RM
Headquarters Band Service Royal Marines
Eastney Block
HMS NELSON
Queen Street
PORTSMOUTH
Hants
PO1 3HH

RM BAND PORTSMOUTH
Royal Marines Band Portsmouth
Eastney Block
HMS NELSON
Queen Street
PORTSMOUTH
Hants
PO1 3HH

RM BAND SCOTLAND
Royal Marines Band Scotland
HMS CALEDONIA
ROSYTH
Fife
Scotland
KY11 2XH

RM BAND BRNC
Royal Marines Band BRNC
BRNC
DARTMOUTH
Devon
TQ6 0HJ

RMSM
Royal Marines School of Music
Gibraltar Block
HMS NELSON
Queen Street
PORTSMOUTH
Hants
PO1 3HH

RM BAND PLYMOUTH
Royal Marines Band Plymouth
HMS RALEIGH
TORPOINT
East Cornwall
PL11 2PD

RM BAND CTCRM
Royal Marines Band CTCRM
CTCRM
Lympstone
EXMOUTH
Devon
EX8 5AR

ROYAL MARINES RESERVE UNITS

RMR BRISTOL
Royal Marines Reserve Bristol
Dorset House
Litfield Place
BRISTOL
BS8 3NA

RMR LONDON
Royal Marines Reserve
City of London
2 Old Jamaica Road
Bermondsey
LONDON
SE16 4AN

RMR MERSEYSIDE
Royal Marines Reserve Merseyside
RNHQ Merseyside
East Brunswick Dock
LIVERPOOL
Merseyside
L3 4DZ

RMR SCOTLAND
Royal Marines Reserve Scotland
37-51 Birkmyre Road
Govan
GLASGOW
G51 3JH

RMR TYNE
Royal Marines Reserve Tyne
Anzio House
Quayside
NEWCASTLE-UPON-TYNE
NE6 1BU

ROYAL FLEET AUXILIARY SERVICE

ARGUS,   *Aviation Training Ship (AG)*

BAYLEAF,   *Support Tanker, (AO)*

BLACK ROVER,   *Small Fleet Tanker, (AORL)*

BRAMBLELEAF,   *Support Tanker, (AO)*

DILIGENCE,   *Forward Repair Ship, (AR)*

FORT AUSTIN,   *Solid Support Ship (AFS)*

FORT ROSALIE,   *Solid Support Ship, (AFS)*

FORT VICTORIA,   *Auxiliary Oiler Replenishment, (AOR)*

FORT GEORGE,   *Auxiliary Oiler Replenishment, (AOR)*

GOLD ROVER,   *Small Fleet Tanker, (AORL)*

GREY ROVER,   *Small Fleet Tanker, (AORL)*

OAKLEAF,   *Support Tanker, ((AO)*

ORANGELEAF,   *Support Tanker, (AO)*

SIR BEDIVERE,   *Landing Ship Logistics, (LSL)*

SIR GALAHAD,   *Landing Ship Logistics, (LSL)*

SIR GERAINT,   *Landing Ship Logistics, (LSL)*

SIR PERCIVALE,   *Landing Ship Logistics, (LSL)*

SIR TRISTRAM,   *Landing Ship Logistics, (LSL)*

SEA CRUSADER,   *RO RO*

SEA CENTURION,   *RO RO*

KEY ADDRESSES

ARMED FORCES PERSONNEL ADMINISTRATION AGENCY HEADQUARTERS (AFPAA HQ)

AFPAA (Central Office)
Building 182
RAF Innsworth
GLOUCESTER
Gloucestershire
GL3 1EZ

AFPAA (Centurion)
Centurion Building
Grange Road
GOSPORT
Hants
PO13 9XA

COMBINED CADET FORCE

Director of Naval Reserves
South Terrace
HM Naval Base
PORTSMOUTH
Hants
PO1 3LS

COMMITTEES

UNITED KINGDOM COMMANDERS IN CHIEF COMMITTEE (UKCICC)(H)

Erskine Barracks
Wilton
SALISBURY
Wiltshire
SP2 0AG
(01722 433208)

COMMONWEALTH LIAISON OFFICES

AUSTRALIA
Australia House
Strand
London
WC2B 4LA

BANGLADESH
28 Queens Gate
LONDON
SW7 5JA

CANADA
Macdonald House
Grosvenor Square
LONDON
W1K 4AB

GHANA
13 Belgrave Square
LONDON
SW1X 8PN

INDIA
India House
Aldwych
LONDON
WC2B 4NA

MALAYSIA
45 Belgrave Square
LONDON
SW1X 8QT

NEW ZEALAND
New Zealand House
Haymarket
LONDON
SW1Y 4TQ

NIGERIA
Nigeria House
9 Northumberland Avenue
LONDON
WC2N 5BX

EDUCATIONAL ESTABLISHMENTS

THE ROYAL COLLEGE OF DEFENCE STUDIES
Seaford House
37 Belgrave Square
LONDON
SW1 X8NS
(020 7915 4804)

THE JOINT SERVICES COMMAND AND STAFF TRAINING COLLEGE
BRACKNELL
Berkshire
RG12 9DD
(01344 457271)

JSCSC SHRIVENHAM
Faringdon Road
Watchfield
Swindon
Wiltshire
SN6 8TS
(01793 788001)

MEDICAL SERVICES

The Medical Director General (Naval)
Victory Building
HM Naval Base
PORTSMOUTH
PO1 3LS

Ministry of Defence Hospital Unit Portsmouth
Royal Hospital Haslar
Haslar Road
GOSPORT
Hants
PO12 2AA

Ministry of Defence Hospital Unit Derriford
Derriford Hospital
PLYMOUTH
Devon
PL6 8DH

Institute of Naval Medicine
ALVERSTOKE
Hants
PO12 2DL

MINISTRY OF DEFENCE POLICE HEADQUARTERS

Ministry of Defence Police Headquarters
MDP Wethersfield
BRAINTREE
Essex
CM7 4AZ
(01371 854000)

NAVAL BASES AND SUPPLY AGENCY

CHIEF EXECUTIVE, WARSHIP SUPPORT AGENCY
Management Suite
Block B
FOXHILL
Bath
BA1 5AB

NAVAL BASE COMMANDER CLYDE
HM Naval Base
Clyde
Dunbartonshire
G84 8HL

BEITH(RN Armament Depot)
Ayrshire
KA15 1JT

CAMBELTOWN(NATO POL Depot)
Argyll
PA28 6RD

COULPORT (RN Armament Depot)
PO Box 1
Cove
Helensburgh
Dunbartonshire
G84 0PD

CROMBIE (RN Armament Depot)
Dunfermline
Fife
KY12 8LA

FASLANE (RN Store Depot)
HM Naval Base
Faslane
G84 8HL

GLEN DOUGLAS (NATO Ammunition Depot)
PO Box 1
Arrochar
Dunbartonshire
G83 7BA

LOCH EWE (NATO POL Depot)
Aulbea
Achnasheen
Ross Shire
IV22 2HU

LOCH STRIVEN (NATO POL Depot)
Toward
Argyll
PA23 7UL

ROSYTH (RN Store Depot)
Fife
KY11 2XP

NAVAL BASE COMMANDER DEVONPORT
HM Naval Base
Devonport
Plymouth
PL1 4SL

Devonport (RN Store Depot)
HM Naval Base
DEVON PORT
Plymouth
PL1 4SL

Ernesettle (RN Armament Depot)
Ernesettle Lane
PLYMOUTH
PL5 2TX

Exeter (Support Engineering Facility)
Topsham
EXETER
Devon

NAVAL BASE COMMANDER PORTSMOUTH
HM Naval Base
PORTSMOUTH
Hants
PO1 3LT

DIRECTOR SUPPLY (SOUTH)
South Office Block
HM Naval Base
PORTSMOUTH
PO1 3LU

Colerne (RN Store Depot)
Nr CHPPENHAM
Wiltshire
SN14 8QR

Dean Hill (RN Armament Depot)
West Dean
SALISBURY
Wiltshire
SP5 1EY

GOSPORT (RN Armament Depot)
Hants
PO13 0AH

PORTSMOUTH(RN Armament Depot)
Hants
PO1 3LU

MARINE SERVICES SUPPORT

Deputy Director Marine Services Support
Room 92A
Block E
ENSLEIGH
Bath
BA1 5AB

General Manager
HM Mooring Depot
Pembroke Dock
Pembrokeshire
SA72 6TB

Singapore (OFD Senko)
RNSTO Singapore
NP1022
BFPO 489
LONDON

NAVY, ARMY AND AIR FORCE INSTITUTES

NAAFI HQ
LONDON Road
Amesbury
SALISBURY
Wiltshire
SP4 7EN
(01980 627000)

NATO HEADQUARTERS-MILITARY COMMITTEE (UKMILREP)

UKMILREP
NATO Headquarters
BFPO 49

ALLIED COMMAND ATLANTIC (ACLANT)

HEADQUARTERS, SUPREME ALLIED
COMMANDER ATLANTIC (SACLANT)
Naval Party 1964
(Saclant)
BFPO 493

REGIONAL HEADQUARTERS
EAST ATLANTIC
(RHQ EASTLANT)
Eastbury Park
Northwood
Middlesex
HA6 3HP

REGIONAL HEADQUARTERS
SOUTH ATLANTIC
(RHQ SOUTHLANT)
BFPO 6

SUBMARINE FORCES EASTERN ATLANTIC
(SUBEASTLANT)
Eastbury Park
NORTHWOOD
Middlesex
HA6 3HP

ANTI-SUBMARINE WARFARE STRIKING FORCE
Office of COMUKMARFOR
7-8 The Parade
HM Naval Base
PORTSMOUTH
Hants
PO1 3NA

SACLANT UNDERSEA RESEARCH CENTRE
Viale San Bartolomeo 400
I-19026 San Bartolomeo
Italy

ALLIED COMMAND EUROPE (ACE)

SUPREME HEADQUARTERS ALLIED POWERS
EUROPE (SHAPE)
BFPO 26

NATO SCHOOL (SHAPE)
Oberammergau
Box 2003
BFPO 105

REGIONAL HEADQUARTERS
AFSOUTH
BFPO 8

STRIKFORSOUTH
RHQ AFSOUTH
BFPO 8

HQ ALLIED NAVAL FORCES SOUTHERN
EUROPE
(HQ NAVSOUTH)
BFPO 8

JOINT HQ SOUTHEAST
Sirinyer
Izmir
Turkey

FRENCH COMMANDER-IN-
CHIEF MEDITERRANEAN
(CECMED)
Prefecture Maritime
83800 Toulon Naval
France

REGIONAL HEADQUARTERS AFNORTH
BPFO 28

JHQ NORTHEAST
BFPO 150

NAVAL PERSONAL AND FAMILY SERVICE (NPFS)

Area Office (NPFS) Eastern
Swiftsure Block
HMS Nelson
H M Naval Base
PORTSMOUTH
Hants
PO1 3HH
(02392 722712)

Area Office (NPFS) Western
Fenner Block
H M Naval Base Devonport
HMS DRAKE
PLYMOUTH
Devon
PL2 2BG
(01752 555041)

Area Office (NPFS) Northern
Triton House
1-5 Churchill Square
HELENSBURGH
Argyll and Bute
G84 9HL
(01436 672798)

NAVAL REGIONAL OFFICES

SCOTLAND & NORTHERN IRELAND REGIONS
HMS CALEDONIA
ROSYTH
Fife
KY11 2XH
(01383 425532)

NORTHERN ENGLAND REGION
Royal Naval Headquarters Merseyside
Brunswick Dock
LIVERPOOL
L3 4DZ
(0151 707 3400)

Naval Regional Sub-Office
HMS CALLIOPE
South Shore Road
GATESHEAD
Tyne & Wear
NE8 2BE
(0191 477 2536)

WALES & WESTERN REGIONS
Naval Regional Management Centre
HMS FLYING FOX
Winterstoke Road
BRISTOL
BS3 2NS
(0117 953 0996)

EASTERN ENGLAND REGION
HMS PRESIDENT
72 St Katharine's Way
LONDON
E1W 1UQ
(020 7481 7324)

REGULAR FORCES EMPLOYMENT ASSOCIATION

(NATIONAL ASSOCIATION FOR EMPLOYMENT OF REGULAR SAILORS SOLDIERS AND AIRMEN)
49 Pall Mall
LONDON
SW1Y 5JG
(020 7321 2011)

ABERDEEN
46A Union Street
ABERDEEN
AB10 1BD

BEDFORD
TA Centre
28 Bedford Road
KEMPSTON
Beds
MK42 8AJ

BELFAST
Northern Ireland War Memorial Building
Waring Street
BELFAST
BT1 2EU

BIRMINGHAM
2nd Floor, City Gate
25 Moat Lane
BIRMINGHAM
B5 6BH

BRISTOL
Borough Park Business Centre
Borough Park
Romney Avenue
BRISTOL
BS7 9ST

BURY ST. EDMUNDS
Room 4
90 Guildhall Street
BURY ST EDMUNDS
IP33 1PR

CARDIFF
Maindy Barracks
CARDIFF
CF4 3YE

CHELMSFORD
The Gate House
AMT Centre
Upper Chase
Writtle Road
CHELMSFORD
CM2 0BN

CHELTENHAM
Potter House
St Annes Road
CHELTENHAM
Glos
GL52 2SS

CHESTER
156 Percival Road
The Dale
CHESTER
Cheshire
CH2 4AN

DARLINGTON
67 Duke Street
Darlington
Co. Durham
DL3 7SD

DERBY
The College Business Centre
Uttoxeter New Road
DERBY
DE22 3WZ

EDINBURGH
New Haig House
Logie Green Road
EDINBURGH
EH7 4HQ

EXETER
Wyvern Barracks
EXETER
Devon
EX2 6AF

GLASGOW
Haig House
1 Fitzroy Place
GLASGOW
G3 7RJ

LEEDS
Carlton Barracks
Carlton Gate
LEEDS
LS7 1HE

LINCOLN
Cobb Hall Centre
St. Pauls Lane
Bailgate
LINCOLN
Ln1 3AX

LIVERPOOL
Suite 43 Oriel Chambers
14 Water Street
LIVERPOOL
L2 8TD

LONDON
49 Pall Mall
LONDON
SW1Y 5JG

MAIDSTONE
Royal British Legion Industries
Royal British Legion Village
Aylesford
Nr MAIDSTONE
Kent
ME20 7NL

MANCHESTER
TA Centre
Belle Vue Street
MANCHESTER
M12 5PW

NEWCASTLE-ON-TYNE
4th Floor, MEA House
Ellison Place
NEWCASTLE-UPON-TYNE
NE1 8XS

NORTHAMPTON
TA Centre
28 Bedford Road
KEMPSTON
Beds
MK42 8AJ

NORWICH
TA Centre
Britannia House
325 Aylsham Road
NORWICH
NR3 2AB

PLYMOUTH
Raglan Cottage
MOD Mt Wise Business Park
Devonport
PLYMOUTH
PL1 4JH

PORTSMOUTH
2B Tipner Road
Stamshaw
PORTSMOUTH
PO2 8QP

PRESTON
Fulwood Barracks
Fulwood
PRESTON
Lancs
PR2 8AA

READING
Watlington House
Watlington Street
READING
RG1 4RJ

SALISBURY
27 Castle Street
SALISBURY
Wilts
SP1 1TT

SHEFFIELD
2nd Floor
9 Paradise Square
SHEFFIELD
S1 2DE

SHREWSBURY
Building 4
Copthorne Barracks
Copthorne Road
SHREWSBURY
SY3 7LT

SWANSEA
TA Centre
The Grange
West Cross
SWANSEA
SA3 5LB

QINETIQ, FORMERLY DERA (DEFENCE EVALUATION AND RESEARCH AGENCY) MAJOR ESTABLISMENTS

From 2 Jul 01, on privatisation, DERA separates into Qinetiq, a plc, and DSTL (Defence Science and Technology Laboratory). DSTL is the MOD-retained part of DERA.

HEAD OFFICE
QINETIQ
Ively Road
FARNBOROUGH
Hampshire
GU14 0LX

DSTL Portsdown West
Portsdown Hill Road
FAREHAM
Hampshire
PO17 6AD

QINETIQ
Winfrith Technology Centre
Newburgh
DORCHESTER
Dorset
DT2 8XJ

DSTL Porton Down
SALISBURY
Wiltshire
SP4 0JQ

QINETIQ
St Andrews Road
MALVERN
Worcs
WR14 3PS

DSTL Fort Halstead
SEVENOAKS
Kent
TN14 7BP

QINETIQ
SALISBURY
Wilts
SP4 0JF

DEFENCE AVIATION REPAIR AGENCY

HEAD OFFICE
DARA St Athan
St Athan
BARRY
Vale of Glamorgan
CF62 4WA

DARA Almondbank
Almondbank
PERTH
PH1 3NQ

DARA Fleetlands
Fareham Road
GOSPORT
Hampshire
PO13 0AA

DARA Sealand
Welsh Road
DEESIDE
Flintshire
CH5 2LS

DIRECTORATE OF NAVAL RECRUITING REGIONAL CAREERS HEADQUARTERS (RCHQS) AND ARMED FORCE CAREERS OFFICES (AFCOs)

RCHQ NORTH
RN Support Establishment
HMS Caledonia
ROSYTH
KY11 2XH
(01383 425516)

AFCOs NORTH REGION
63 Belmont Street
ABERDEEN
AB10 1JS
(01224 639999)

Palace Barracks
Holywood
BELFAST
Co. Down
BT18 9RA
(02890 423832)

94-96 English Street
CARLISLE
CA3 8ND
(01228 523958)

148 Northgate
DARLINGTON
DL1 1QT
(01325 461850)

29/31 Bank Street
PO BOX 81
DUNDEE
DD1 1RW
(01463-233668)

32-34 East Port
DUNFERMLINE
KY12 7GB
01383 625283

67-83 Shandwick Place
EDINBURGH
EH2 4SN
(0131 221 1111)

Charlotte House
78 Queen Street
GLASGOW
G1 3DN
(0141 221 6110/9)

Britannia Suite
Norwich House
Savile Street
KINGSTON-UPON-HULL
HU1 3ES
(01482 325902)

3 Bridge Street
INVERNESS
IV1 1HG
(01463 233668)

10 - 14 Bond Street
LEEDS
LS1 2JY
0113 2458195

15 James Street
LIVERPOOL
L2 7NX
(0151 236 1566)

Petersfield House
29-31 Peters Street
MANCHESTER
M2 5QJ
(0161 835 8220)

67 Borough Road
MIDDLESBROUGH
Cleveland
TS1 3AE
(01642 211749/230677)

New England House
20 Ridley Place
NEWCASTLE UPON TYNE
NE1 8JW
(0191 2327048)

63 College Street
St Helens
MERSEYSIDE
WA10 1TN
(01744 753560)

83A Fishergate
PRESTON
PR1 2NJ
(01772 555675)

Central Buildings
1A Church Street
SHEFFIELD
S1 2GJ
(0114 272 1476)

Halkyn House
21 Rhosddu Road
WREXHAM
LL11 1NF
(01978 263334)

RCHQ SOUTH
Ladywood House
45/46 Stephenson Street
BIRMINGHAM
B2 4DY
(0121 606 5102)

AFCOs SOUTH REGION
Unit 46
The Pallasades
BIRMINGHAM
B2 4XD
(0121 633 4995)

244 Holdenhurst Road
BOURNEMOUTH
BH8 8AZ
(01202 311224)

120 Queen's Road
BRIGHTON
BN1 3WB
(01273 325386)

4 Colston Avenue
BRISTOL
BS1 4TY
(0117 9260233)

82-88 Hills Road
CAMBRIDGE
CB2 1LQ
(01223 315118)

17 St Peters Street
CANTERBURY
Kent
CT1 2BQ
(01227 457848)

South Gate House
Wood Street
CARDIFF
CF1 1GR
(02920 726810)

1-3 Dock Road
CHATHAM
ME4 4JR
(01634 826206)

1 - 3 Dorset House
CHELMSFORD
Essex
CM1 1HQ
(01245 355134)

60 Hertford Street
COVENTRY
CV1 1LB
(02476 226513)

35 - 36 Castlefield
Main Centre
DERBY
DE1 2PE
(01332 348120)

Fountain House
Western Way
EXETER
EX1 2DQ
(01392 274040)

4th Floor
Britannia Warehouse
The Docks
GLOUCESTER
GL1 2EH
(01452 521676)

Stanford House
91 Woodbridge Road
GUILDFORD
GU1 4QE
(01483 302304)

180A Cranbrook Road
ILFORD
Essex
IG1 4LR
(020 851 858855)

37 Silent Street
IPSWICH
IP1 1TP
(01473 254450)

St George's House
6 St George's Way
LEICESTER
LE1 1SH
(01162 543233)

Sibthorpe House
350/352 High Street
LINCOLN
LN5 7BN
(01522 525661)

1A Iverna Gardens
Kensington
LONDON
W8 6TN
(020 7937 3493/0749)

453/454 Strand
LONDON
WC2R 0RG
(020 7839 4643)

Dunstable House
Dunstable Road
LUTON
LU1 1EA
(01582 721501)

22 Unthank Road
NORWICH
NR2 1AH
(01603 620033)

70 Milton Road
Victoria Centre
NOTTINGHAM
NG1 3QX
(0115 9419503)

35 St Giles
OXFORD
OX1 3LJ
(01865 553431)

21 - 23 Hereward Centre
PETERBOROUGH
PE1 1TB
(01733 568833)

Mount Wise
Devonport
PLYMOUTH
PL1 4JH
(01752 501750)

Cambridge Road
PORTSMOUTH
PO1 2EN
(023 9282 6536)

Oak House
Chapel Street
REDRUTH
TR15 2BY
(01209 314143)

2nd Floor
Princess House
The Square
SHREWSBURY
Shropshire
SY1 1JZ
(01743 232541)

152 High Street
Lower Bar
SOUTHAMPTON
Hants
SO14 2BT
(023 8063 0486)

36 - 38 Old Hall Street
Hanley
STOKE-ON-TRENT
ST1 3AP
(01782 214688)

Llanfair Buildings
19 Castle Street
SWANSEA
SA1 1JF
(01792 654208/642516)

35 East Street
TAUNTON
Somerset
TA1 3LS
(01823 354430)

43A Queens Street
WOLVERHAMPTON
WV1 3BL
(01902 420340/423892)

OFFICER CAREERS LIAISON CENTRES (OCLCs)

OCLCs NORTH REGION

RN Support Establishment
HMS CALEDONIA
ROSYTH
KY11 2XH
(01383 425522)

Petersfield House
29-31 St Peter's Street
MANCHESTER
M2 5QN
(0161 8352916

OCLCs SOUTH REGION

Ladywood House
45/46 Stephenson Street
BIRMINGHAM
B2 4DY
(0121 6065099)

1A Iverna Gardens
Kensington
LONDON
W8 6TN
(020 7938 4646)

HMS FLYING FOX
Winterstoke Road
BRISTOL
BS3 2NS
(0117 9664246)

ROYAL NAVAL FILM CHARITY

Registered Office
HM Naval Base (PP23)
PORTSMOUTH
PO1 3NH
(023 927 23108)

SEA CADET CORPS

HEADQUARTERS
202 Lambeth Road
LONDON
SE1 7JF
(020 7928 8978)

NORTHERN AREA
HMS CALEDONIA
ROSYTH
Fife
KY11 2XH
(01383 416300)

NORTH WEST AREA
Royal Naval Headquarters Merseyside
East Bruswick Dock
LIVERPOOL
L3 4DZ
(0151 707 3440)

SOUTH WEST AREA
HMS FLYING FOX
Winterstoke Road
BRISTOL
Avon
BS3 2NS
(0117 953 1991)

EASTERN AREA
The Drill Hall
Ropery Road
GAINSBOROUGH
Lincolnshire
DN21 2NS
(01427 614441)

LONDON AREA
HMS PRESIDENT
72 St. Katharine's Way
LONDON
E1W 1UQ
(020 7481 7372)

SOUTHERN AREA
HMS NELSON
PORTSMOUTH
Hants
PO1 3HH
(023 927 24263)

SHIPPING POLICY DIVISION (DEFENCE PLANNING AND EMERGENCIES BRANCH)

Department for Transport, Local Government and
the Regions
Zone 4/21
Great Minster House
76 Marsham Street
LONDON
SW1P 4DR
(020 7944 5148)

SHIPYARD OVERSEEING SERVICE

CLYDE
c/o BAE Systems Marine (YSL) Ltd
South Street
Scotstoun
GLASGOW
G14 0XN
(0141 4355200)

SOUTHAMPTON
c/o Vosper Thornycroft (UK) Ltd
Victoria Road
Woolston
SOUTHAMPTON
SO19 9RR
(023 804 26000)

BARROW
c/o BAE Systems Marine Ltd
BARROW-IN-FURNESS
Cumbria
LA14 1AF
(01229 876235)

YACHT CLUBS USING A SPECIAL ENSIGN

Yachts belonging to members of the following Yacht Clubs may, subject to certain conditions, obtain a Warrant to wear a Special Ensign.

Club	Address

WHITE ENSIGN

Club	Address
Royal Yacht Squadron	Royal Yacht Squadron, Castle Cowes, PO31 7QT

BLUE ENSIGN

Club	Address
Royal Albert Yacht Club	17 Pembroke Road, Portsmouth, PO1 2NT
Royal Brighton Yacht Club	253 St Kilda Street,Middle Brighton, 3186 Victoria,Australia
Royal Cinque Ports Yacht Club	4-5 Waterloo Crescent, Dover, CT6 1LA
Royal Cruising Club	Bywaters, Taylors Lane, Bosham, West Susex, PO18 8QQ
Royal Dorset Yacht Club	11 Custom House Quay, Weymouth, Dorset, DT4 8BG
Royal Engineer Yacht Club	86 Training Squadron, Army Apprentice College, Chepstow, Gwent, NP6 7YG
Royal Geelong Yacht Club	PO Box 156, Geelong, 3220 Victoria, Australia
Royal Gourock Yacht Club	Ashton Gourock PA19 1DA
Royal Highland Yacht Club	Westmanse House, Lichrenan Tanyuilt, Argyl, PH35 1HG
Royal Marines Sailing Club	Poole, Dorset, BH15 4NQ
Royal Melbourne Yacht Club	Lower Esplanade, St Kilda, 3182
Royal Motor Yacht Club	Panorama Road, Sandbanks, Poole, Dorset, BH13 7RN
Royal Naval Sailing Association	Royal Naval Club, 10 Haslar Marina, Haslar Road, Gosport, PO12 1NU
Royal Naval Volunteer Reserve Yacht Club	The Naval Club, 38 Hill Street, London, W1X 8DB
Royal New Zealand Yacht Squadron	Squadron Rooms, Westhaven, PO Box 46128 Herne Bay, Auckland, New Zealand
Royal Northern and Clyde Yacht Club	The Club House, Rhu, Dumbartonshire, G84 8NG
Royal Perth Yacht Club of Western Australia	PO Box 5, Nedlands, West Australia 6009
Royal Port Nicholas Yacht Club	Clyde Quay Boat Harbour, PO Box 9674, Wellington,New Zealand
Royal Queensland Yacht Club	PO Box 21, Manly, Queensland 4179, Australia
Royal Scottish Motor Yacht Club	5 St Vincent Place, Glasgow, G1 2DJ
Royal Solent Yacht Club	Yarmouth, Isle of Wight, PO41 0NS

Royal South Australia Yacht Club .... North Haven 5018, South Australia
Royal Southern Yacht Club .... Hamble, Southampton, SO3 5HB
Sussex Motor Yacht Club .... 7 Ship Street, Brighton, East Sussex, BN1 1AD
Royal Sydney Yacht Squadron .... PO Box 484, Milsons' Point, NSW 2061,
.... Australia
Royal Temple Yacht Club .... 6 West Cliff Mansions, Ramsgate, Kent,
.... CT11 9WY
Royal Thames Yacht Club .... 60 Knightsbridge, London, SW1X 7LF
Royal Western Yacht Club of England .... West Hoe, Plymouth, PL1 3DG
Royal Western Yacht Club of Scotland .... Lochabar, 20 Barclay Drive, Helensburgh,
.... Dunbartonshire, G84 9RB
Royal Yacht Club of Tasmania .... Marieville Esplanade, Sandy Bay, Tasmania 7005
Royal Yacht Club of Victoria .... 120 Nelson Place, Williamstown, 3016, Australia

BLUE ENSIGN DEFACED BY BADGE OF CLUB

Aldburgh Yacht Club .... Aldebrugh, Suffolk
Army Sailing Association .... c/o MOD (ASCB), M Block, Clayton Barracks,
.... Aldershot, Hants
Bar Yacht Club .... 1 Mitre Court Buildings, Temple, London,
.... EC4Y 7BS
City Livery Yacht Club .... Shortlands, Bromley, Kent BR2 0LG
Cruising Yacht Club of Australia .... New Beach Road, Darling Point, New South
.... Wales 2027
Royal Air Force .... Yacht Club Riverside House, Hamble,
.... Southampton,SO3 5HD
Royal Akrana Yacht Club .... PO Box 42004, Orakei, Auckland 5,
.... New Zealand
Royal Anglesey Yacht Club .... 3 Cadnant Court, Rating Row, Beaumaris,
.... Anglesey, Gwynnedd, LL58 8AL
Royal Armoured Corps Yacht Club .... Bovington Camp, Wareham, Dorset, BH20 6ND
Royal Artillery Yacht Club .... Tamberton, Upton Lovell, Warminster, Wilts,
.... BA12 0JP
Royal Australian Navy Sailing Association .... New Beach Road, Edgecliffe, New South
.... Wales 2027, Australia
Royal Bermuda Yacht Club .... PO Box 894, Hamilton HM DX, Bermuda
Royal Bombay Yacht Club .... PO Box 206, Apollo Bunder, Fort Bombay
.... 400039
Royal Burnham Yacht Club .... The Quay, Burnham-on-Crouch, Essex,
.... CM0 8AO
Royal Channel Islands Yacht Club .... Le Boulevard, Bulwark, St Aubin, Jersey,
.... Channel Islands, JE5 8AD
Conway Club Cruising Association .... 5 Furlong Lane, Totternhoe, Nr Dunstable,
.... Beds
Royal Corinthian Yacht Club .... Burnham-on-Crouch, Essex
Royal Cornwall Yacht Club .... Greenbank, Falmouth, Cornwall
Royal Dee Yacht Club .... 16 Holford Crescent, Knutsford, Cheshire,
.... WA16 8DZ
Royal Forth Yacht Club .... Middle Pier, Granton Harbour, Edinburgh

Royal Freshwater Bay Yacht Club of Western Australia ... Keane's Point, Peppermint Grove, Western Australia 6011

Royal Gibraltar Yacht Club .... Queensway, Gibraltar

Royal Harwich Yacht Club .... Woolverstone, Ipswich, IP9 1AT

Royal Hong Kong Yacht Club .... Kellet Island, Hong Kong

Household Division Yacht Club .... HQ Welsh Guards, Wellington Barracks, Birdcage Walk, London SW1E 6HQ

Royal Irish Yacht Club .... Dun Loaghaire, Co Dublin

Royal Jamaica Yacht Club .... Kingston, Jamaica

Little Ship Club .... Bell Wharfe Lane, Upper Thames Street, London EC4R 3TB

Little Ship Club (Queensland Squadron) .... 119 Bank Street, Newmarket, Queensland 4051, Australia

Royal London Yacht Club .... The Parade, Cowes, Isle of Wight, PO31 7QS

Medway Cruising Club .... Boyses Hill Farm, Newington, Sittingbourne, Kent, ME9 7JF

Royal Malta Yacht Club .... Couvre Port, Fort Manoel, Manoel Island, Gzira, Malta

Royal Mersey Yacht Club .... Bedford Road East, Rockferry, Birkenhead, Merseyside, L42 1LS

Royal Motor Yacht Club of New South Wales .... Wunulla Road, Point Piper, New South Wales 2027

Royal Nassau Sailing Club .... PO Box SS 6891, Nassau, Bahamas

Royal North of Ireland Yacht Club .... Cultra, 7 Seaford Road, Co Down, Ireland

Royal Northumberland Yacht Club .... 36 Longridge Drive, Whitley Bay, Tyne & Wear

Royal Ocean Racing Club .... 20 St James's Place SW1A 1NN

Parkstone Yacht Club .... Pearce Avenue, Parkstone, Poole, Dorset, BH14 8EN

Royal Plymouth Corinthian Yacht Club .... Madeira Road, Plymouth, PL1 2NY

Poole Yacht Club .... New Harbour Road West, Hamworthy, Poole, Dorset

Royal Prince Alfred Yacht Club .... PO Box 99, Newport Beach, New South Wales 2106, Australia

Royal Prince Edward Yacht Club .... 160 Wolseley Road, Point Piper, 2027 New South Wales, Australia

Severn Motor Yacht Club .... Bath Road, Broomhall, Worcester, WR5 3HR

Royal Southampton Yacht Club .... 1 Channel Way, Ocean Village, Southampton, SO1 1XE

Sussex Yacht Club .... 85-89 Brighton Road, Shoreham by Sea, Sussex

Royal Suva Yacht Club .... PO Box 335, Suva, Fiji

The Cruising Association .... Ivory House, St Katherine's Dock, London E1 9AT

The House of Lords Yacht Club .... House of Lords, London, SW1A 0PW

The Medway Yacht Club .... Upnor, Rochester, Kent

The Poole Harbour Yacht Club .... 38 Salterns Way, Lilliput, Poole, Dorset, BH14 8JR

Thames Motor Yacht Club .... The Green, Hampton Court, East Molesey,Surrey

Royal Torbay Yacht Club .... Beacon Hill, Torquay, Devon

Royal Ulster Yacht Club .... 101 Clifton Road, Bangor, Co Down

Royal Welsh Yacht Club .... Porth yr Aur, Caernarvon, Gwynedd

Royal Yorkshire Yacht Club .... 1 Windsor Crescent, Bridlington, YO15 3HY
Old Worcesters Yacht Club .... Les Heches, St Peter in the Wood, Guernsey,
.... Channel Islands

RED ENSIGN DEFACED BY BADGE OF CLUB

Brixham Yacht Club .... Overgang, Brixham, Devon, TQ5 8AR
Royal Dart Yacht Club .... Kingswear, South Devon, TQ6 0AB
Royal Fowey Yacht Club .... Fowey, Cornwall, PL23 8IH
House of Commons Yacht Club .... RYA House, Romsey Road, Eastleigh, Hants,
.... SO5 4YA
Lloyd's Yacht Club .... London, SW6 5DP
Royal Hamilton Amateur Dinghy Club .... PO Box 298, Paget PG BX, Bermuda
Royal Lymington Yacht Club .... Bath Road, Lymington, Hants, S41 9SE
Royal Norfolk and Suffolk Yacht Club .... Royal Plain, Lowestoft, Suffolk, NR33 0AQ
Royal St George Yacht Club .... Dun Laoghaire, Co Dublin
St Helier Yacht Club .... South Pier, St Helier, Jersey
Royal Victoria Yacht Club .... Fishbourne, Isle of Wight, PO33 4EU
Royal Windermere Yacht Club .... Fallbarrow Road, Bowness in Windermere,
.... Cumbria, LA33 3DJ
Royal Yachting Association .... RYA House, Romsey Road, Eastleigh, Hants,
.... SO5 4YA
West Mersea Yacht Club .... 116 Coast Road, West Mersea, Colchester,
.... Essex

HONORARY OFFICERS OF
THE ROYAL NAVAL RESERVE

Honorary Commodore HRH The Prince Michael of Kent, KCVO .... 01 Apr 94

Honorary Captain The Right Honourable The Lord Sterling of Plaistow, Kt CBE .... 15 Jan 91

Honorary Captain Mrs Mary Fagan JP. .... 17 Nov 00

Honorary Captain Mr Eric Dancer CBE JP. .... 09 Jan 01

Honorary Captain (Supernumerary) The Duke of Buccleugh and Queensberry Kt VRD JP. ... 02 Feb 88

Honorary Captain (Supernumerary) Sir Donald Gosling Kt .... 27 Jun 93

Honorary Commander E J Billington

Honorary Commander F A Mason MBE

Honorary Commander P R Moore RD*

Honorary Commander (Supernumerary) R D P Gilbert

Honorary Chaplain (Supernumerary) The Right Reverend D G Hawker, MA, (CofE)

Honorary Chaplain (Supernumerary) The Right Reverend M A P Woods, DSc, MA, (CofE)

HONORARY OFFICERS OF
THE ROYAL MARINES RESERVE

Honorary Colonel E P R Cautley .... 01 Jul 99

Honorary Colonel G M Simmers, CBE, CA .... 01 Apr 00

Honorary Colonel J N Tidmarsh, MBE, JP .... 01 Jan 98

Honorary Colonel Sir David Trippier RD JP DL .... 01 Jan 96

Honorary Colonel Sir Neville Trotter, FCA, JP, DL .... 01 Sep 98

OFFICERS OF THE ACTIVE LIST
OF THE ROYAL NAVAL RESERVE,
ROYAL MARINES RESERVE, THE QUEEN ALEXANDRA'S
ROYAL NAVAL NURSING RESERVE,
SEA CADET CORPS AND COMBINED
CADET FORCE

ROYAL NAVAL RESERVE

Name	Rank	Branch	Unit	Seniority
A				
Abdel-Khalek, Adham Ahmad,	PSG SLT		PRESIDENT	29.11.01
Ackerman, Richard,	LT	SM	CAMBRIA	09.05.99
Ackland, Simon Robert,	LT	NCS	CAMBRIA	14.10.00
Adair, Jonathan,	HON MID	URNU	U/A	11.10.01
Adams, A C, RD	CAPT	AW	PRESIDENT	30.09.99
Adams, David,	LT	NCAGS	WILDFIRE	23.02.81
Adams, Kelly,	HONCADET	URNU	U/A	20.10.00
Adeoye, Ibukunolu,	HONCADET	URNU	U/A	12.10.00
Adeyeye, Ayodeji Olabode,	HON MID	URNU	U/A	24.10.00
Ahmed, Iftikhar,	LT	LOGS	FORWARD	19.03.93
Ainsworth, Jeffery,	LT CDR	AIR	RNR AIR BR VL	31.03.01
Aitchison, Ian,	LT	MR	PRESIDENT	02.06.94
Aitken, Rebecca,	HONCADET	URNU	U/A	08.10.98
Alcock, Charles Edward Hayes,	LT CDR	AW	PRESIDENT	31.03.00
Alcock, David John, RD	LT CDR	MW	KING ALFRED	18.02.87
Alderson, Victoria,	HONCADET	URNU	U/A	06.11.00
Allan, Richard Michael,	LT	INTR	FERRET (RNR)	20.05.94
Allan, Sophie,	HONCADET	URNU	U/A	08.10.98
Allan, William, RD	LT CDR	HQ	SCOTIA	02.09.88
Allaway, Edward,	HON MID	URNU	U/A	21.10.99
Allen, Clare,	HONCADET	URNU	U/A	07.10.01
Allen, Caroline,	HONCADET	URNU	U/A	20.10.99
Allen, Elinor Jane,	LT CDR	HQ	VIVID	30.09.91
Allen, Ian James, RD	LT CDR	MW	CAROLINE	31.03.97
Allinson, Graeme,	HON MID	URNU	U/A	11.10.01
Almond, Nicholas,	HON MID	URNU	U/A	07.10.99
Altoft, Kerry,	HONCADET	URNU	U/A	21.10.99
Anderson, Adrian,	LT CDR	AIR	RNR AIR BR VL	31.03.00
Anderson, Graeme,	HON MID	URNU	U/A	27.09.01

Name	Rank	Branch	Unit	Seniority
Anderson, Isobel,	HONCADET	URNU	U/A	12.10.00
Anderson, John Christopher,	LT	MW	DALRIADA	06.03.99
Anderson, James,	HON MID	URNU	U/A	08.02.01
Anderson, Kerry McGowan, BSC	LT CDR	HQ	CAROLINE	31.03.99
Andersson, James,	HON MID	URNU	U/A	14.10.99
Andreou, Alexander,	HON MID	URNU	U/A	12.10.00
Andrews, Mark David,	LT	LOGS	FLYING FOX	03.11.00
Arbeid, Mark Leon,	SLT	CEW	PRESIDENT	19.11.96
Armstrong, Michael,	LT	AIR	RNR AIR BR VL	14.03.96
Arnold, Christopher,	HON MID	URNU	U/A	19.10.00
Ashpole, Richard David,	SG LTCDR		SHERWOOD	01.08.90
Ashton, Jonathan Richard,	SG CDR		CALLIOPE	11.11.00
Ashworth, Lorna Elizabeth, BSC, RD	LT CDR	HQ	SCOTIA	31.03.99
Aslam, Zabeada,	HONCADET	URNU	U/A	22.10.98
Aspden, Mark Charles,	LT	AWNIS	WILDFIRE	01.10.95
Aspinell, Charles, RD*	CDR	NCAGS	KING ALFRED	30.09.97
Aspinell, Pamela Ann, RD	LT CDR	Q	KING ALFRED	31.03.96
Aston, Christopher,	HON MID	URNU	U/A	20.10.98
Aston, Dora Ann,	LT	CEW	FLYING FOX	05.07.99
Athol, Stuart Charles,	ASL	NE	PRESIDENT	20.11.01
Attwood, Keith,	HON MID	URNU	U/A	14.10.99
Auld, David,	HON MID	URNU	U/A	05.11.01
Austin, Kevin,	LT CDR	AW	SHERWOOD	31.03.98
Avery, Philip,	LT CDR	AIR	RNR AIR BR VL	31.03.97
Avis, Robert Graeme, RD*	CDR	AW	PRESIDENT	30.09.97
Awenat, William,	LT CDR	AIR	RNR AIR BR VL	31.03.95

B

Name	Rank	Branch	Unit	Seniority
Backhouse, Jonathan,	LT CDR	AIR	RNR AIR BR VL	01.03.91
Bailey, Stuart,	HON MID	URNU	U/A	12.10.99
Baines, Mark,	LT CDR	AIR	RNR AIR BR VL	01.02.93
Baird, Andrew,	LT	HQ	CAROLINE	17.11.97
Baird, Elaine,	LT CDR	Q	KING ALFRED	31.03.96
Baker, Henrietta,	HONCADET	URNU	U/A	11.10.01
Baker, Peter Alan,	ACDR	NCAGS	PRESIDENT	01.08.01
Balchin, Trevor,	HON MID	URNU	U/A	17.10.01
Balmain, Stephen Service,	LT	SEA	DALRIADA	01.07.94
Bancroft, David Gideon,	LT	AW	CALLIOPE	20.12.94
Bankhead, Maurice, RD	LT CDR	NCAGS	CAROLINE	31.03.95
Banks, Iain,	LT CDR	AIR	RNR AIR BR VL	31.03.01
Barbour, Abigail,	ASL	NE	CAROLINE	02.12.98
Barclay, Nicholas,	HON MID	URNU	U/A	12.10.00
Barfield, Kevin Lloyd, RD	LT CDR	CEW	FORWARD	31.01.96
Barham, Edward,	HON MID	URNU	U/A	19.10.00
Barker, Amy,	HONCADET	URNU	U/A	26.09.99
Barker, Elizabeth Charlotte,	SLT	NCAGS	PRESIDENT	13.10.96
Barker, Peter,	HON MID	URNU	U/A	11.10.01
Barnes, David,	HON MID	URNU	U/A	07.10.99
Barnes, Judith Margaret,	SLT	CEW	EAGLET	05.10.97
Barnwell, Andrew,	ACAPT	AIR	RNR AIR BR VL	05.03.02
Barraclough, Ross,	HON MID	URNU	U/A	24.10.01
Barrand, William,	HON MID	URNU	U/A	07.10.98
Barratt, Stephen,	ASL	NE	FORWARD RNR	23.02.02
Barrett, Mark,	LT CDR	AIR	RNR AIR BR VL	31.03.01
Barter, Emma,	HONCADET	URNU	U/A	10.09.01
Bartlett, David Christopher,	ASG LT		VIVID	27.07.01
Bartlett, David,	HON MID	URNU	U/A	10.09.01
Barton, Christopher James, RD	LT CDR	HQ	CAMBRIA	30.09.87
Basis, Rawi,	HON MID	URNU	U/A	11.10.01
Bassett, Nigel Peter, RD	LT CDR	AW	KING ALFRED	31.03.97
Bate, Rohan,	HON MID	URNU	U/A	18.10.00
Bates, Jodie,	HONCADET	URNU	U/A	07.10.99

Name	Rank	Branch	Unit	Seniority
Bates, Jocelyn,	HONCADET	URNU	U/A	20.10.00
Baughan, Philip John, RD	LT CDR	HQ	SHERWOOD	01.11.89
Baxter, Ross John, RD	LT	NCAGS	FORWARD	01.09.91
Baylis, Clive,	LT CDR	AIR	RNR AIR BR VL	01.10.90
Bazley, John Charles,	LT CDR	AW	KING ALFRED	01.09.97
Bean, Maurice,	LT CDR	SEA	FLYING FOX	15.02.93
Beaton, Iain William,	ASL	NE	DALRIADA	24.03.99
Beattie, Jane Elizabeth,	LT CDR	Q	WILDFIRE	31.03.93
Beauchamp, Martyn,	HON MID	URNU	U/A	01.10.98
Beaumont, Andrew John, RD	LT	MW	EAGLET	31.07.95
Beaumont, Richard,	HON MID	URNU	U/A	10.09.01
Bedford, Helena,	HONCADET	URNU	U/A	21.10.00
Bedford, Johnathon,	SG CDR		SCOTIA	30.09.00
Beech, Eric Edward, RD	LT CDR	DIS	FERRET (RNR)	03.06.87
Beedall, Richard Anthony,	LT	HQ	SHERWOOD	24.03.95
Bell, Charlotte,	HONCADET	URNU	U/A	04.10.01
Bell, Charlotte,	HONCADET	URNU	U/A	25.10.01
Bellamy, Simon,	LT	URNU	U/A	01.10.97
Benn, Peter Quentin,	LT	MR	PRESIDENT	28.02.98
Benson, Carol Ann,	ASL	NE	FORWARD	15.09.01
Bentall, Estelle,	HONCADET	URNU	U/A	07.10.98
Bentley, David Scott Arthur,	ASL	NE	VIVID	09.05.00
Benton, Simon,	HON MID	URNU	U/A	09.10.00
Bereznyckyj, Susan Dorothy, RD	LT CDR	Q	SHERWOOD	31.03.94
Bernays, Annie,	HONCADET	URNU	U/A	08.10.98
Berry, Dominic,	HON MID	URNU	U/A	17.10.01
Berry, Ian, RD	LT CDR	MW	CALLIOPE	31.03.96
Betts, Peter,	HON MID	URNU	U/A	10.09.01
Bewley, Geoffrey, RD	LT CDR	MW	KING ALFRED	31.03.99
Bhimjiani, Ronak,	HON MID	URNU	U/A	12.10.00
Bickerton, Lisa,	HONCADET	URNU	U/A	14.10.99
Bicknell, Richard Anthony,	LT CDR	MW	KING ALFRED	31.03.01
Biddlecombe, Amy,	HONCADET	URNU	U/A	14.10.99
Biggerstaff, Adam Graham, RD	LT CDR	HQ	DALRIADA	03.04.85
Biggerstaff, Fiona Joyce,	SLT	SM	SCOTIA	10.10.96
Biggs, Nigel,	LT	SEA	PRESIDENT	31.07.95
Billson, Rachel,	HONCADET	URNU	U/A	12.10.00
Binns, James,	HON MID	URNU	U/A	10.09.01
Birch, Anthony,	LT CDR	AIR	RNR AIR BR VL	31.03.99
Bird, Amy,	HONCADET	URNU	U/A	07.10.99
Bird, Graham,	HON MID	URNU	U/A	30.09.99
Bird, Michael,	HON MID	URNU	U/A	09.10.00
Birdsey, Nicola,	HONCADET	URNU	U/A	25.10.01
Bishop, Jonathan,	LT CDR	AIR	RNR AIR BR VL	31.03.96
Bissett, Leigh Robert,	ASL	NE	SCOTIA	25.10.01
Black, Karen,	HONCADET	URNU	U/A	24.10.01
Black, Simon Mitchell, RD	LT CDR	HQ	SCOTIA	30.06.83
Blackburn, Claire,	HONCADET	URNU	U/A	18.10.01
Blackburn, John Adam Francis,	ASL	NE	EAGLET	12.06.01
Bloom, Michael,	SLT	URNU	U/A	25.03.99
Blyth, Anne Scotland,	SG LTCDR	MEDF	PRESIDENT	14.08.83
Blythe, Wendy Elizabeth,	LT	LOGS	KING ALFRED	29.01.96
Boag, Kyle Ian,	LT	SEA	PRESIDENT	12.01.96
Boal, Michael,	LT	MW	CAROLINE	23.02.98
Boardman, Andrew,	HON MID	URNU	U/A	10.09.01
Boardman, Sarah,	HONCADET	URNU	U/A	16.10.97
Boath, Gerard,	HON MID	URNU	U/A	21.10.99
Bomby, David,	LT CDR	AIR	RNR AIR BR VL	26.03.90
Bonham-Smith, Rupert,	HON MID	URNU	U/A	05.11.98
Booth, Rachael,	HONCADET	URNU	U/A	11.10.01
Boothroyd, Susan Elizabeth,	ASL	NE	CALLIOPE	02.06.99
Boulton, Jeremy Charles,	LT CDR	SM	PRESIDENT	31.03.01
Bowen, Michael Leslie,	ASGLTCDR		PRESIDENT	30.09.98

Name	Rank	Branch	Unit	Seniority
Bowles, William,	LT CDR	AW	SCOTIA	31.03.98
Bown, Anthony Mark,	LT CDR	HQ	CAMBRIA	08.03.91
Bown, Carol Diane, BA, RD	LT	HQ	CAMBRIA	30.01.96
Boyd, Edward Russell,	LT	AWNIS	KING ALFRED	13.03.96
Boyle, Abigail Elder,	ASL	NE	KING ALFRED	12.12.00
Boyle, Kirk,	LT	DIS	FERRET (RNR)	11.05.96
Boyle, Lucy,	HONCADET	URNU	U/A	22.02.01
Brabner, Susan,	LT CDR	DIS	FERRET (RNR)	28.07.99
Bracewell, Anna,	HONCADET	URNU	U/A	09.10.00
Bradburn, James,	HON MID	URNU	U/A	24.10.00
Bradbury, Miles,	ASL	URNU	U/A	29.09.98
Bradford, Christine Mary Patricia,	LT CDR	NCAGS	EAGLET	31.03.93
Bradford, Michelle,	HONCADET	URNU	U/A	21.10.99
Bradford, Nigel Stuart,	LT	SM	EAGLET	18.12.87
Bradley, Bradley,	HON MID	URNU	U/A	11.11.99
Bradshaw, Francis John C, LVO	CDR	NA	EAGLET	01.02.82
Brady, Matthew`,	HON MID	URNU	U/A	14.10.99
Braine, David,	LT CDR	AIR	RNR AIR BR VL	31.03.98
Brampton, Susan,	LT	Q	PRESIDENT	08.01.97
Branyan, Lawrence,	LT	SEA	EAGLET	06.09.89
Brayfield, Rosalind Marion,	LT CDR	MR	WILDFIRE	26.12.84
Breyley, Nigel,	LT CDR	AIR	RNR AIR BR VL	31.03.98
Bridge, Benedict Lenthall,	LT	INTR	FERRET (RNR)	01.10.96
Bridgen, Andrew Urquhart,	LT	INTR	FERRET (RNR)	23.07.92
Brierley, Rachel,	HONCADET	URNU	U/A	06.11.00
Brigden, Kevin,	LT CDR	AIR	RNR AIR BR VL	16.04.92
Bright, James,	HON MID	URNU	U/A	18.10.01
Britton, Jonathan,	HON MID	URNU	U/A	19.10.00
Broadwith, Joanna,	HONCADET	URNU	U/A	11.10.01
Brockie, Brian,	CDR	MS(M)	SCOTIA	30.09.01
Brodie, Hazel,	HONCADET	URNU	U/A	08.10.98
Brogan, Gary Edward,	SLT	NCAGS	EAGLET	29.09.97
Brokenshire, Sarah,	ASL	NE	VIVID RNR	06.02.02
Brook, Roger,	LT	AIR	RNR AIR BR VL	22.02.97
Brooking, Stephen,	LT CDR	AIR	RNR AIR BR VL	11.05.87
Brooks, Alexandra,	ASL	NE	FLYING FOX	03.02.99
Brooks, Richard,	HON MID	URNU	U/A	14.10.99
Broom, Karen,	HONCADET	URNU	U/A	20.10.00
Brothwood, Michael,	LT CDR	AIR	RNR AIR BR VL	03.04.99
Browett, Jon,	ASL	URNU	U/A	16.10.01
Brown, Alastair,	HON MID	URNU	U/A	30.09.99
Brown, Andrew,	HON MID	URNU	U/A	08.10.98
Brown, Andrew,	HON MID	URNU	U/A	18.10.00
Brown, Andrew,	LT CDR	AIR	RNR AIR BR VL	01.10.90
Brown, Colin,	LT CDR	AIR	RNR AIR BR VL	30.04.97
Brown, Gillian,	HONCADET	URNU	U/A	02.10.00
Brown, John Erskine,	LT CDR	AWNIS	WILDFIRE	31.03.96
Brown, Katharine Jane,	LT CDR	MR	WILDFIRE	12.03.86
Brown, Karl,	LT CDR	AIR	RNR AIR BR VL	31.03.98
Brown, Sabrina,	HONCADET	URNU	U/A	15.10.98
Brown, Timothy,	LT CDR	AIR	RNR AIR BR VL	19.03.93
Brown, Wendy,	HONCADET	URNU	U/A	11.10.01
Browne, Kiera,	HONCADET	URNU	U/A	28.09.00
Browne, Thomas,	HON MID	URNU	U/A	14.10.99
Browning, James,	ASL	NE	PRESIDENT RNR	16.01.02
Brownsword, Lee,	HON MID	URNU	U/A	02.10.00
Bryning, Christopher,	LT CDR	AIR	RNR AIR BR VL	01.03.85
Buchanan, Craig,	HON MID	URNU	U/A	06.12.01
Buckley, Jonathan Mark,	LT	MW	CAMBRIA	08.11.97
Bucknell, David Ian,	LT CDR	SEA	FLYING FOX	01.07.96
Budd, Christopher,	HON MID	URNU	U/A	20.10.00
Bugg, Jennifer,	HONCADET	URNU	U/A	17.10.01
Bugler, Martin,	LT CDR	AIR	RNR AIR BR VL	31.03.97

Name	Rank	Branch	Unit	Seniority
Bull, Elizabeth,	HONCADET	URNU	U/A	18.10.00
Burchett, Rupert,	HON MID	URNU	U/A	30.11.01
Burchinshaw, Philip,	HON MID	URNU	U/A	07.10.99
Burden, Fraser,	LT	AIR	RNR AIR BR VL	01.04.88
Burgess, Philip,	HON MID	URNU	U/A	06.09.99
Burne, Penelope Jane, RD	CDR	INTR	VIVID	30.09.01
Burnet, Alexander,	HON MID	URNU	U/A	30.09.99
Burns, Katherine,	HONCADET	URNU	U/A	19.10.00
Burrow, Adele,	HONCADET	URNU	U/A	22.10.01
Butterworth, James,	HON MID	URNU	U/A	08.10.98
Button, Edward,	HON MID	URNU	U/A	21.10.99
Byers, Penelope,	HONCADET	URNU	U/A	18.10.01
Byrte, James,	HON MID	URNU	U/A	17.10.01

C

Name	Rank	Branch	Unit	Seniority
Cadden, Edward,	ALT	URNU	U/A	01.03.00
Caddock, Matthew,	HON MID	URNU	U/A	09.10.97
Cadman, Mark,	ASL	Q	CAMBRIA	12.09.01
Cain, Neal,	LT CDR	AIR	RNR AIR BR VL	31.03.01
Callahan, David Robert,	LT	LOGS	SCOTIA	13.07.01
Cambridge, Aaron Russell,	LT CDR	MR	KING ALFRED	20.02.89
Cameron, Anne Louise, RD	LT CDR	NCAGS	KING ALFRED	31.03.01
Cameron, Christopher,	ASL	URNU	U/A	08.12.95
Campbell, Graham John,	LT	CEW	FORWARD	24.01.97
Campbell, Jonathan,	HON MID	URNU	U/A	25.10.01
Campbell, Mairi,	HONCADET	URNU	U/A	08.10.98
Campbell, William,	LT CDR	AIR	RNR AIR BR VL	01.04.92
Camwell, Barry,	HON MID	URNU	U/A	07.10.98
Canham, Wendy Jacqueline, RD	LT CDR	CEW	SHERWOOD	31.03.98
Capper, Huw,	HON MID	URNU	U/A	07.10.01
Carder, Dorian,	HON MID	URNU	U/A	27.09.01
Carey, Andrew William,	ASL	NE	WILDFIRE	13.06.01
Carey-Jones, Kathryn,	HONCADET	URNU	U/A	11.10.01
Carman, Felix,	HON MID	URNU	U/A	08.10.98
Carnegie, Rebecca,	HONCADET	URNU	U/A	12.10.00
Carpenter, David, RD	LT CDR	MR	SCOTIA	05.06.85
Carruthers, Calum,	HON MID	URNU	U/A	02.11.00
Carss, George Alexander,	SG CDR		KING ALFRED	30.09.01
Carter, David,	ALT	AW	EAGLET	22.03.99
Carter, Richard,	LT	AIR	RNR AIR BR VL	06.01.87
Cartwright, James,	HON MID	URNU	U/A	07.10.01
Carty, David,	HON MID	URNU	U/A	17.10.01
Carty, Jonathan,	HON MID	URNU	U/A	04.10.01
Carvasso-White, Helen,	HONCADET	URNU	U/A	21.10.99
Carver, Andrew,	LT CDR	AIR	RNR AIR BR VL	31.03.98
Casey, Graham Peter,	LT CDR	DIS	FERRET (RNR)	31.03.00
Casey, Neil,	LT CDR	AIR	RNR AIR BR VL	31.03.00
Caskie, Iain Neil,	LT CDR	SM	SCOTIA	16.05.92
Cassells, Jason Bern Costello,	ASL	NE	CAROLINE	12.04.00
Casson, Hilary Patricia, RD	LT CDR	NCAGS	VIVID	31.03.96
Castrinoyannakis, Timothy,	HON MID	URNU	U/A	15.02.01
Caulfield, Lee,	HONCADET	URNU	U/A	01.10.99
Challis, Harriet,	HONCADET	URNU	U/A	15.11.01
Chalmers, Amalia Lourdes, RD	LT CDR	INTR	FERRET (RNR)	31.03.95
Chamberlain, Moira,	SLT	Q	KING ALFRED	31.05.01
Chambers, Catherine Louise,	ASG LT	MEDF	VIVID	17.11.99
Chapman, Anthony,	LT	MW	PRESIDENT	31.07.95
Chapman, David Ralph,	LT CDR	AW	CALLIOPE	31.03.01
Chapman, Graham Philip,	LT	AW	PRESIDENT	14.11.92
Chapman, John,	HON MID	URNU	U/A	11.10.01
Chapman, Kate,	HONCADET	URNU	U/A	12.10.99
Chapman, David Quentin,	LT CDR	X	RNR AIR BR VL	01.10.90

Name	Rank	Branch	Unit	Seniority
Charters, Emma,	HONCADET	URNU	U/A	28.10.00
Chatterton, Robert Martin,	LT CDR	AW	FLYING FOX	31.03.95
Chauvelin, David Coulson Wyllie,	LT	MW	SCOTIA	26.11.98
Cheang, Tia,	HONCADET	URNU	U/A	26.10.99
Cheyne, Steven,	LT CDR	AIR	RNR AIR BR VL	01.04.93
Chisholm, David,	HON MID	URNU	U/A	11.09.00
Chua, Jimmy,	HON MID	URNU	U/A	26.10.99
Church, Elizabeth Ann, RD	LT	SM	PRESIDENT	16.11.88
Church, Jonathan,	HON MID	URNU	U/A	15.11.01
Churchley, Richard,	LT CDR	AIR	RNR AIR BR VL	26.04.98
Citrine, Harry,	HON MID	URNU	U/A	11.10.01
Clark, Angela Catherine,	LT	LOGS	VIVID	06.10.92
Clark, Philip,	HON MID	URNU	U/A	30.11.00
Clark, Suzanne,	LT CDR	AIR	RNR AIR BR VL	31.03.97
Clarke, Amanda Lesley,	LT	MR	PRESIDENT	23.07.90
Clarke, Peter,	LT CDR	AIR	RNR AIR BR VL	01.10.90
Clarke, Roger Derek, RD	LT CDR	NCAGS	VIVID	31.03.96
Clarke, Steven David,	LT	AW	CALLIOPE	09.06.90
Clarke, William Stephen, RD	LT CDR	MW	CAROLINE	31.03.00
Cleary, Deidre,	LT CDR	MR	PRESIDENT	31.03.99
Cleary, Sonia,	HONCADET	URNU	U/A	12.10.00
Cleeve, Felicity,	ASL	NE	FORWARD RNR	30.01.02
Cliffe, Daniela Maria,	LT	Q	VIVID	18.05.01
Clifford, Martin,	LT CDR	AIR	RNR AIR BR VL	09.05.98
Coad, Ivan Harry, RD	LT CDR	AW	FLYING FOX	13.03.88
Coady, Catherine,	HONCADET	URNU	U/A	15.02.01
Cobbold, Andrew Reginald, MA	LT	INTR	FERRET (RNR)	12.11.95
Cochrane, Christopher,	HON MID	URNU	U/A	26.10.99
Cochrane, Mark,	HON MID	URNU	U/A	12.10.00
Cockburn, Frank,	LT CDR	MR	CALLIOPE	31.12.94
Cockram, Alice,	HONCADET	URNU	U/A	12.10.00
Cody, William Jonathan Kinsborough,	LT CDR	DIS	FERRET (RNR)	01.07.97
Coe, Morgan,	ASL	NE	PRESIDENT	02.06.99
Coffey, Ralph,	HON MID	URNU	U/A	15.10.98
Cohen, James Seymour Lionel, BSC, RD	LT CDR	NCAGS	PRESIDENT	31.03.97
Cohen, Rachel,	HONCADET	URNU	U/A	22.10.97
Colborne, Raymond,	LT CDR	AIR	U/A	01.01.89
Coldham, David,	HON MID	URNU	U/A	21.10.99
Cole, James,	LT CDR	AIR	RNR AIR BR VL	01.09.84
Coles, Victoria,	HONCADET	URNU	U/A	21.10.99
Colley, Derek,	LT CDR	AW	FORWARD	01.04.94
Collie, James,	HON MID	URNU	U/A	07.10.99
Collier, David,	HON MID	URNU	U/A	04.10.01
Collins, Charles,	HON MID	URNU	U/A	14.10.99
Collins, David,	HON MID	URNU	U/A	12.10.99
Collins, Paul Andrew Peter,	ALT	Q	WILDFIRE	27.09.00
Collins, Steven Mark,	CDR	AW	FORWARD	30.09.01
Collinson, James,	ASL	NE	KING ALFRED	02.12.99
Colquhoun, Rodger,	LT CDR	AIR	RNR AIR BR VL	31.03.01
Colton, Ian,	LT CDR	AIR	RNR AIR BR VL	22.11.92
Colyer, Michael Andrew James,	LT	SEA	CALLIOPE	22.06.94
Comins, Amy,	HONCADET	URNU	U/A	27.09.01
Condick, Jodie,	HONCADET	URNU	U/A	19.10.00
Condy, Sallie Louise,	LT	DIS	FERRET (RNR)	30.09.89
Conlon, Rebecca,	HONCADET	URNU	U/A	07.10.01
Connell, John,	LT CDR	AIR	RNR AIR BR VL	01.10.91
Connelly, Shirley,	HONCADET	URNU	U/A	15.11.01
Constable, Thomas,	HON MID	URNU	U/A	04.10.01
Constant, David,	LT	AIR	RNR AIR BR VL	27.03.97
Conway, Keith Alexander,	LT CDR	MW	SCOTIA	31.03.99
Cook, Simon Hugh Home,	LT	MW	PRESIDENT	31.03.98
Cook, William John,	LT CDR	AW	SCOTIA	01.03.85
Coombes, Kirsty,	HONCADET	URNU	U/A	28.06.99

Name	Rank	Branch	Unit	Seniority
Coombes, Stewart,	LT CDR	AIR	RNR AIR BR VL	31.03.95
Cooper, David John,	LT CDR	HQ	PRESIDENT	31.03.99
Cooper, Susan, BSC	LT CDR	HQ	PRESIDENT	31.03.01
Copeland-Davis, Terence,	LT	AIR	RNR AIR BR VL	01.05.88
Copleston, Charlotte,	HONCADET	URNU	U/A	11.10.01
Corbett, Edward,	HON MID	URNU	U/A	11.10.01
Corbin, Matthew,	HON MID	URNU	U/A	09.10.00
Corcoran, Robert,	HON MID	URNU	U/A	21.10.99
Cornell, Patricia Jane,	LT CDR	Q	KING ALFRED	31.03.01
Cornes, John,	LT	URNU	U/A	01.01.92
Corrigan, Paul,	HON MID	URNU	U/A	12.10.00
Corson, Robert John,	SG LTCDR		CALLIOPE	13.10.98
Cottam, Simon Roscoe,	LT CDR	AWNIS	FLYING FOX	31.03.97
Cotterell, Roger Creswell,	ALT	LOGS	KING ALFRED	31.01.01
Cottingham, Neil,	LT CDR	AIR	RNR AIR BR VL	01.10.98
Cotton, Michael,	HON MID	URNU	U/A	14.10.99
Coulson, James Robert Bradley,	LT	LOGS	SHERWOOD	02.05.92
Council, Robert,	HON MID	URNU	U/A	18.11.99
Couper, Donald,	SG LTCDR		EAGLET	01.02.99
Courtney, Kurt David,	ASL	NE	CAROLINE	10.02.00
Cowan, Andrew Stuart, RD	LT CDR	MW	DALRIADA	31.03.97
Cowan Gray, Duncan,	HON MID	URNU	U/A	11.10.01
Cowen, Alexander,	HON MID	URNU	U/A	04.10.00
Cox, Hugh Jeremy,	SG CDR		KING ALFRED	30.05.94
Cox, Rhoderick,	LT CDR	AIR	RNR AIR BR VL	01.12.88
Coyle, Mark Francis,	LT	SEA	CALLIOPE	14.09.01
Coyle, Stephen,	ASL	NE	SCOTIA	16.10.01
Craig, Caroline Alexandra,	ASL	NE	PRESIDENT	08.02.00
Craig, Graeme,	ALT	URNU	U/A	29.04.98
Craik, Lorna,	HONCADET	URNU	U/A	10.10.97
Crawford, Andrew John, RD	CDR	AW	VIVID	30.09.01
Crawford, Judith,	HONCADET	URNU	U/A	01.10.98
Cribley, Michael,	LT CDR	AIR	RNR AIR BR VL	01.10.91
Crockett, Victor Andrew, RD	LT CDR	DIS	FERRET (RNR)	31.03.95
Crombie, Nicholas,	LT	AIR	RNR AIR BR VL	01.02.93
Crombie, Stuart,	HON MID	URNU	U/A	19.10.00
Crone, David James Edward, RD	ACDR	MW	CAROLINE	02.07.99
Crossley, Samuel Neil Thomas,	ASL	NE	PRESIDENT	07.01.99
Crump, Peter Charles, RD*	CDR	AW	KING ALFRED	30.09.97
Crumpton, Peter,	HON MID	URNU	U/A	19.10.00
Culshaw, Joanne,	ASL	NE	EAGLET	16.08.01
Cumming, Alastair,	HON MID	URNU	U/A	28.09.00
Cummings, Angela Lynn,	ASL	NE	KING ALFRED	11.12.01
Cunnold, Anne-Marie,	HONCADET	URNU	U/A	12.10.00
Curley, Ronald Robertson,	LT	MW	SCOTIA	17.10.90
Curnock, Timothy,	HON MID	URNU	U/A	07.10.01
Curran, Stuart,	HON MID	URNU	U/A	04.10.00
Currie, Katherine,	HONCADET	URNU	U/A	15.10.97
Curry, Victoria Jane,	HONCADET	URNU	U/A	12.10.00
Curtis, Andrew,	HON MID	URNU	U/A	19.10.00
Curtis, Roger Stafford,	LT	SEA	SCOTIA	26.01.94

D

Name	Rank	Branch	Unit	Seniority
Dace, Katherine Elizabeth, RD	LT CDR	DIS	FERRET (RNR)	31.03.95
Dady, Simon James,	ASL	NE	PRESIDENT	29.09.98
Dale, Marcus,	HON MID	URNU	U/A	12.10.99
Dale, Rebecca,	HONCADET	URNU	U/A	13.10.98
Dalgliesh, Chrstopher,	HON MID	URNU	U/A	24.10.01
Dalton, Neil Jarvis,	LT CDR	MR	PRESIDENT	31.03.01
Daly, Paul,	LT CDR	AIR	RNR AIR BR VL	31.03.95
Dalziel, Simon Anthony Cannon,	LT CDR	MR	KING ALFRED	16.02.89
Dann, Nicola,	ASG LT	MEDF	EAGLET	22.06.01

Name	Rank	Branch	Unit	Seniority
Daros, Aloysia,	HONCADET	URNU	U/A	12.10.99
Darragh, Peter Edward John,	ASL	NE	CAROLINE	05.04.00
Davidson, Serena,	ASL	NE	CAROLINE	05.02.02
Davies, George,	LT	AIR	RNR AIR BR VL	01.07.91
Davies, Jennifer,	HONCADET	URNU	U/A	24.10.01
Davies, James,	HON MID	URNU	U/A	11.09.00
Davies, Kimberley,	HONCADET	URNU	U/A	18.10.00
Davies, Luke,	HON MID	URNU	U/A	12.10.00
Davies, Nicola,	HONCADET	URNU	U/A	25.10.01
Davies, Robert Michael,	LT CDR	SEA	SHERWOOD	31.03.00
Davies, Richard Myall,	SLT	MW	PRESIDENT	23.08.95
Davies, Sarah Elizabeth,	LT	AWNIS	FLYING FOX	19.02.99
Davies, Sarah Jane,	ASL	NE	PRESIDENT	06.01.00
Davies, William,	SLT	URNU	U/A	31.07.95
Davis, Peter,	HON MID	URNU	U/A	12.10.99
Davy, Martin,	HON MID	URNU	U/A	06.11.00
Dawe, Nicholas,	HON MID	URNU	U/A	12.10.00
Dawes, Emma,	HONCADET	URNU	U/A	19.10.00
Dawes, Gawaine,	HON MID	URNU	U/A	14.10.99
Dawes, Helyne,	HONCADET	URNU	U/A	19.10.00
Dawson, Alexander,	HON MID	URNU	U/A	12.10.00
Day, Andrew,	HON MID	URNU	U/A	17.10.01
Day, Henry,	ASL	NE	PRESIDENT RNR	22.01.02
Daye, Angela,	HONCADET	URNU	U/A	22.10.98
De Labat, Victoria,	HONCADET	URNU	U/A	11.10.01
De Silva, Oliver,	HON MID	URNU	U/A	11.10.01
Dean, Georgina,	ASL	URNU	U/A	30.10.01
Dear, Joanna,	HONCADET	URNU	U/A	07.10.99
Dedman, Kirstin,	HONCADET	URNU	U/A	11.10.01
Delf, Jeannie,	HONCADET	URNU	U/A	14.10.99
Delleur, Laura,	HONCADET	URNU	U/A	07.10.01
Denholm, Margaret,	LT	Q	VIVID	07.02.95
Denison-Davies, Edward,	HON MID	URNU	U/A	12.10.99
Denman, Rachel,	HONCADET	URNU	U/A	14.10.99
Dennard, Kieron,	HON MID	URNU	U/A	14.10.99
Dennis, James,	HON MID	URNU	U/A	18.10.01
Derrick, Malcom, RD	LT CDR	AIR	RNR AIR BR VL	10.12.91
Devereaux, James,	LT CDR	AIR	RNR AIR BR VL	31.03.98
Dick, Steven,	HON MID	URNU	U/A	11.10.01
Dickin, Arnie,	HON MID	URNU	U/A	11.10.01
Dickinson, Carolyn,	HONCADET	URNU	U/A	25.10.01
Dickinson, Dorothy Emily,	ALT	Q	CALLIOPE	06.06.00
Dilks, Paul David Peter, RD	LT CDR	AW	KING ALFRED	05.04.87
Dilmahomed, Soraya,	HONCADET	URNU	U/A	18.10.01
Dingwall, Donald,	HON MID	URNU	U/A	08.10.98
Dinsmore, Simon,	HON MID	URNU	U/A	01.02.01
Dismore, Oliver,	LT CDR	AIR	RNR AIR BR VL	01.01.88
Ditton, Nathan,	ASL	NE	KING ALFRED	29.01.02
Divers, Barry,	HON MID	URNU	U/A	30.09.99
Dix, Caroline,	HONCADET	URNU	U/A	17.10.01
Dobson, Serena,	HONCADET	URNU	U/A	11.10.01
Dodds, Nicholas,	HON MID	URNU	U/A	26.10.99
Donaldson, John Richard,	LT CDR	SM	FLYING FOX	12.08.94
Donkin, Martin,	HON MID	URNU	U/A	18.10.01
Doran, Catherine Margaret Campbell,	PSG LT	MEDF	DALRIADA	12.10.00
Dorman, Nicholas Roger Vause,	LT CDR	MW	SCOTIA	31.03.97
Douglas, Fiona,	HONCADET	URNU	U/A	24.10.01
Douglas, Norman, RD	LT	MW	CALLIOPE	19.01.96
Downie, Anne Louise, RD	LT	SEA	SCOTIA	01.12.95
Downing, Carl,	LT CDR	AIR	RNR AIR BR VL	16.11.92
Downing, Neil Edmond,	LT CDR	MW	CAROLINE	31.03.00
Downing, Rebecca,	HONCADET	URNU	U/A	28.10.00
Doyle, Lucie,	HONCADET	URNU	U/A	14.10.99

Name	Rank	Branch	Unit	Seniority
Doyle, Rebecca,	HONCADET	URNU	U/A	25.10.01
Drake, Roderick Allan, RD	LT CDR	NCAGS	FLYING FOX	31.03.98
Driscoll, Mark,	HON MID	URNU	U/A	01.12.99
Drummond, Andrew Duprose,	PSG LT		EAGLET	10.01.02
Dudill, Louise,	ASL	NE	SHERWOOD	27.09.00
Duffey-Price, James,	HON MID	URNU	U/A	07.10.01
Duffield, Gary,	LT CDR	AIR	RNR AIR BR VL	01.02.90
Duggan, Emily,	HONCADET	URNU	U/A	09.10.00
Duggua, Rodney, RD	LT CDR	CEW	KING ALFRED	31.03.93
Dukes, Nicholas,	LT CDR	AIR	RNR AIR BR VL	01.10.93
Duncan, Barbara Mary,	LT	AWNIS	EAGLET	31.03.92
Duncan, Euan Maver,	MID	NE	SCOTIA	22.11.01
Duncan, Keith Julian, RD	LT CDR	AW	EAGLET	31.03.94
Dunford, Victoria,	HONCADET	URNU	U/A	14.10.99
Dunn, Jonathan,	HON MID	URNU	U/A	14.10.99
Dunn, Josephine,	SLT	URNU	U/A	11.11.98
Dunn, Matthew John,	SG LTCDR		FORWARD	24.11.99
Dunne, James,	HON MID	URNU	U/A	07.10.99
Dunne, Lawrence John,	LT	SEA	FORWARD	01.12.95
Duthie, David James Ralph,	SG CDR		SHERWOOD	30.09.00
Duthie, Ruth Mary Mitchell,	LT	AWNIS	KING ALFRED	16.04.94
Dutt, Trevor Peter, RD	SG CDR		PRESIDENT	30.09.89

E

Name	Rank	Branch	Unit	Seniority
Eacott, Jonathan,	HON MID	URNU	U/A	19.10.00
Eagles, Susan Jane,	CDR	MR	FLYING FOX	30.09.95
Eaglesham, Phillip,	ASL	NE	CAROLINE	16.01.02
Ealey, Nicholas,	HON MID	URNU	U/A	12.10.99
Earl, Nicholas,	LT	AIR	RNR AIR BR VL	01.12.94
Easen, Sam,	HON MID	URNU	U/A	06.11.00
Easterbrook, Christopher,	HON MID	URNU	U/A	19.10.00
Eastham, Allam, BSC, RD	LT CDR	NCAGS	FORWARD	01.04.94
Ebdy, Carina,	HONCADET	URNU	U/A	27.09.01
Edmonds, Paul,	ASL	NE	KING ALFRED	22.01.02
Edwards, Michael Steven De La Warr,	ASGLTCDR		SHERWOOD	07.09.98
Edwards, Tracy,	HONCADET	URNU	U/A	11.10.01
Eldridge, James,	HON MID	URNU	U/A	10.09.01
Ellender, Tony,	LT	URNU	U/A	06.02.92
Elliott, James,	HON MID	URNU	U/A	20.10.00
Elliott, Robin,	LT CDR	AIR	RNR AIR BR VL	01.04.97
Ellis, Barry,	HON MID	URNU	U/A	02.10.00
Ellis, John Anthony, RD	CDRE	MW	FLYING FOX	08.11.01
Ellis, Richard Alwyn, RD	LT	HQ	PRESIDENT	18.08.90
Ellis, Simon Christopher,	PSG SLT		SCOTIA	19.03.02
Elmquist, Anne,	HONCADET	URNU	U/A	12.10.00
England, Robert Frederick Charles,	LT	Q	KING ALFRED	30.08.96
Esfahani, Shahrokh,	LT	HQ	WILDFIRE	27.01.95
Etti, Kehinde,	HONCADET	URNU	U/A	11.10.01
Evans, Ann, RD	LT CDR	INT	FORWARD	31.03.94
Evans, Alex,	LT CDR	AIR	RNR AIR BR VL	31.03.99
Evans, Carol,	LT	MR	VIVID	12.01.92
Evans, Christian,	ASL	NE	VIVID RNR	05.02.02
Evans, Charlotte,	HONCADET	URNU	U/A	18.10.01
Evans, Dominique,	HONCADET	URNU	U/A	11.10.01
Evans, Ewan,	HON MID	URNU	U/A	01.10.98
Evans, Geraint William Lewis,	SG LTCDR		CAMBRIA	04.09.01
Evans, Keith,	HON MID	URNU	U/A	11.10.01
Evans, Louisa,	HONCADET	URNU	U/A	09.10.00
Evans, Michael,	LT CDR	AIR	RNR AIR BR VL	17.05.88
Evans, Paul,	HON MID	URNU	U/A	18.10.01
Evans, Rebecca,	HONCADET	URNU	U/A	19.10.00
Everest, Jonathan,	HON MID	URNU	U/A	27.09.01

Name	Rank	Branch	Unit	Seniority
Eyre, Caroline,	HONCADET	URNU	U/A	11.09.00

F

Name	Rank	Branch	Unit	Seniority
Falconer, Alistair James,	LT	MR	KING ALFRED	16.04.95
Farmer, Gary Gordon,	LT	HQ	SCOTIA	28.06.92
Farrand, Rachel, RD*	LT CDR	NCAGS	SHERWOOD	30.09.89
Farrant, Sam,	HON MID	URNU	U/A	19.10.00
Farrington, Mark,	HON MID	URNU	U/A	07.10.01
Faulkner, Keith Michael,	LT CDR	LOGS	WILDFIRE	26.05.90
Faulks, Robert,	LT CDR	AIR	RNR AIR BR VL	17.06.84
Fearnley, David George, B.ED, RD*	LT CDR	MW	EAGLET	31.03.89
Fearon, John,	S/LT	MW	EAGLET	12.07.98
Fellows, Christopher,	HON MID	URNU	U/A	17.10.01
Ferens, Samantha,	HONCADET	URNU	U/A	18.10.00
Ferguson, Alistair,	HON MID	URNU	U/A	19.10.00
Ferguson, Neil,	LT	HQ	CAROLINE	20.08.89
Ferguson, Nicholas Alistair Malcolm,	LT CDR	HQ	VIVID	31.03.99
Fickling, James,	HON MID	URNU	U/A	06.09.99
Filtness, Rosemary Jane, RD	LT CDR	DIS	FERRET (RNR)	31.03.93
Findlay, Alan,	LT CDR	AIR	RNR AIR BR VL	31.03.01
Fisher, Nigel,	HON MID	URNU	U/A	18.10.00
Fisher, Simon,	HON MID	URNU	U/A	25.10.01
Fitchsampson, Steven R,	SLT	SEA	FLYING FOX	16.11.94
Fittes, Mark,	HON MID	URNU	U/A	10.09.01
Fitzgerald, Elizabeth,	HONCADET	URNU	U/A	10.05.00
Fitzgibbon, John,	HON MID	URNU	U/A	07.10.01
Flanagan, Martin,	LT CDR	AIR	RNR AIR BR VL	01.02.92
Flannigan, Aiden,	HON MID	URNU	U/A	24.10.01
Flatt, Liam,	HON MID	URNU	U/A	20.10.00
Fleming, Samuel,	LT CDR	HQ	SHERWOOD	31.03.02
Fletcher, Leigh,	HON MID	URNU	U/A	12.10.00
Fletcher, Richard Paul,	SLT	SM	EAGLET	04.07.97
Flexer, Richard,	HON MID	URNU	U/A	19.10.00
Flint, Grahame,	HON MID	URNU	U/A	18.10.01
Flower, Clare,	HONCADET	URNU	U/A	12.10.99
Floyd, Robert,	HON MID	URNU	U/A	26.10.99
Flynn, Joanna,	HONCADET	URNU	U/A	12.10.99
Flynn, Nicola Jane,	LT	MR	VIVID	06.12.01
Foote, Clive,	HON MID	URNU	U/A	18.10.01
Forbes, Matthew,	ASL	AW	EAGLET	17.05.00
Ford, Suzanne,	HONCADET	URNU	U/A	10.09.01
Fordham, Christopher,	HON MID	URNU	U/A	11.10.01
Foreman, Timothy,	LT	AIR	RNR AIR BR VL	04.08.94
Forrest, David,	HON MID	URNU	U/A	11.10.01
Fortey, Louise,	HONCADET	URNU	U/A	20.10.98
Fortey, Melissa,	HONCADET	URNU	U/A	02.10.00
Forward, Kirsty,	HONCADET	URNU	U/A	26.10.99
Foster, Stephen, RD	CDR	NCAGS	FORWARD	03.06.97
Fouracre, Andrew Mark George,	ASL	NE	CAMBRIA	22.09.99
Fowler, Alan,	LT CDR	AIR	RNR AIR BR VL	01.06.78
Fowler, Darren Joseph,	PSG LT		PRESIDENT	04.09.96
Fox, Gemma,	HONCADET	URNU	U/A	04.10.01
Fox-Roberts, Patrick,	HON MID	URNU	U/A	04.10.01
Foxon, James,	HON MID	URNU	U/A	20.10.00
Franks, James,	HON MID	URNU	U/A	22.10.98
Fraser, Emma,	ASL	NE	SCOTIA RNR	10.01.02
Fraser, Simon,	HON MID	URNU	U/A	12.10.00
Fry, Christopher Wesley,	LT	HQ	FORWARD	28.07.95
Fry, Stephen Michael,	LT	NCAGS	CAMBRIA	15.06.95
Fulford, Spike,	HON MID	URNU	U/A	05.10.00
Fuller, Anna,	HONCADET	URNU	U/A	20.10.00
Fuller, Jonathan Peter,	LT	SEA	SHERWOOD	01.06.94

Name	Rank	Branch	Unit	Seniority

G

Name	Rank	Branch	Unit	Seniority
Gadsby, Helen,	HONCADET	URNU	U/A	19.10.00
Galloway, Gareth,	HON MID	URNU	U/A	06.11.00
Galloway, Richard,	HON MID	URNU	U/A	03.12.99
Gardiner, George David,	SG LTCDR		CAROLINE	31.03.97
Garlick, Alexander,	HON MID	URNU	U/A	17.10.01
Garrod, Michael,	HON MID	URNU	U/A	06.09.98
Gaskin, Matthew,	HON MID	URNU	U/A	11.10.01
Gaskin, Sarah,	HONCADET	URNU	U/A	21.10.00
Gatenby, Chrisopher,	LT	AW	EAGLET RNR	01.10.97
Gausden, Christine,	LT CDR	SM	PRESIDENT	31.03.00
Gavey, Stephen John, RD	LT CDR	HQ	VIVID	01.08.88
Gearing, Richard,	HON MID	URNU	U/A	19.10.00
Geary, Michael,	LT	AIR	RNR AIR BR VL	01.07.93
Gee, Michael,	ASL	NE	EAGLET	18.07.00
Geeson, Andrea,	HONCADET	URNU	U/A	22.10.01
Georgeson, Ian,	LT CDR	AIR	RNR AIR BR VL	01.06.91
Georghiou, Marie,	HONCADET	URNU	U/A	22.10.01
Ghaibi, Adam,	HON MID	URNU	U/A	14.10.99
Giaro, Annelyn,	HONCADET	URNU	U/A	18.10.01
Gibb, Peter,	LT CDR	AIR	RNR AIR BR VL	24.01.98
Giblin, Matthew,	HON MID	URNU	U/A	12.02.01
Gibson, Stephen,	LT CDR	AIR	RNR AIR BR VL	31.03.94
Gilbert, Geoffrey,	HON MID	URNU	U/A	11.10.01
Gilbertson, Cheryl,	MID	NE	SCOTIA RNR	22.01.02
Giles, Simon,	HON MID	URNU	U/A	15.10.00
Gilligan, James,	HON MID	URNU	U/A	01.10.99
Gleave, Anthony,	HON MID	URNU	U/A	07.10.01
Gleave, James, RD	LT	CEW	DALRIADA	17.11.97
Glover, David,	HON MID	URNU	U/A	06.11.97
Glover, Martyn Richard Timothy, RD, MA	LT CDR	NCAGS	PRESIDENT	31.03.01
Goldenberg, Alick,	HON MID	URNU	U/A	20.10.00
Goldthorpe, Sally Louise,	LT CDR	MR	PRESIDENT	31.03.95
Gooch, Christopher,	HON MID	URNU	U/A	18.10.00
Goodall, Tracey, :	ASL	NE	KING ALFRED	03.05.00
Goodes, Simon Newbury, RD	LT CDR	NCAGS	WILDFIRE	31.03.97
Goodwin, Jonathan Paul Ker,	LT CDR	SM	PRESIDENT	31.03.97
Gopaul, Raul,	HON MID	URNU	U/A	07.10.01
Goram, Malcolm,	LT	AIR	RNR AIR BR VL	05.05.87
Gordon, Kirsten,	HONCADET	URNU	U/A	04.04.01
Gorrod, Richard George,	PSG LTCDR		PRESIDENT	28.09.00
Gould, Andrew Edward, RD	CDR	LOGS	SCOTIA	30.09.97
Gouldson, Elizabeth J,	ASL	NE	SHERWOOD	15.03.00
Govier, Hannah,	HONCADET	URNU	U/A	12.10.00
Gow, Neil Henry Keefe,	LT	SM	CALLIOPE	21.03.94
Grace, Jonathan,	LT CDR	AIR	RNR AIR BR VL	31.03.00
Graham, Adrian William, RD	LT CDR	DIS	FERRET (RNR)	19.02.89
Graham, Finnbarr,	HON MID	URNU	U/A	19.10.00
Grainger, Julia Catherine Ishbel,	ASL	NE	KING ALFRED	05.10.00
Grainger, Serena Jane,	ASL	NE	PRESIDENT	01.05.01
Grant, David,	HON MID	URNU	U/A	05.10.00
Graves, Malcolm Harold, RD*	LT CDR	AW	CAMBRIA	19.07.82
Graveson, Allan,	LT CDR	AW	PRESIDENT	09.07.92
Gray, Andrew Crispian,	LT CDR	AW	PRESIDENT	31.03.99
Gray, Susan Kathryn,	LT CDR	MR	SCOTIA	01.10.93
Gray, William,	HON MID	URNU	U/A	04.10.01
Greaves, Christopher,	LT CDR	AIR	RNR AIR BR VL	01.10.95
Greaves, Jeremy Justin,	LT	MR	FLYING FOX	13.06.95
Greaves, Michael,	LT CDR	AIR	RNR AIR BR VL	01.04.94
Greenacre, Richard Paul, RD	LT CDR	AWNIS	VIVID	31.03.97
Greene, Alistair Michael Iyan,	ASL	NE	PRESIDENT	13.12.00

Name	Rank	Branch	Unit	Seniority
Greenhough, Helen,	HONCADET	URNU	U/A	18.10.01
Greenshields, Thomas James,	ASL	NE	KING ALFRED	08.10.01
Greenwood, Elizabeth Jane,	LT CDR	MR	PRESIDENT	31.03.99
Greenwood, Jeanette,	LT	LOGS	EAGLET	30.03.01
Greenwood, Lauren,	HONCADET	URNU	U/A	16.10.01
Greenwood, Stephen,	HON MID	URNU	U/A	14.10.99
Gregory, Anthony Edward,	ASL	NE	EAGLET	10.05.01
Gregory, Jonathan,	HON MID	URNU	U/A	17.10.01
Gregory, Simon,	LT CDR	AIR	RNR AIR BR VL	31.03.01
Grierson, Andrew,	ASL	URNU	U/A	29.10.99
Griffin, Alexandra,	HONCADET	URNU	U/A	21.10.99
Griffin, Danielle,	HONCADET	URNU	U/A	08.10.98
Griffiths, Andrew Derek,	LT	AW	FLYING FOX	26.02.94
Griffiths, Charlotte Mary,	SLT	LOGS	PRESIDENT	24.09.96
Griffiths, Helen,	HONCADET	URNU	U/A	19.10.00
Griffiths, Michael Edward, BSC, RD	LT CDR	SM	CAMBRIA	31.03.02
Griffiths, Sara Louise,	LT CDR	Q	KING ALFRED	31.03.02
Grist, David Francis Neil,	LT	MS(M)	KING ALFRED	05.07.00
Groves, Clare Julia,	SG LT	MEDF	EAGLET	31.03.92
Guild, Ian,	HON MID	URNU	U/A	16.01.01
Guild, Malcolm Donald,	SG LTCDR		SCOTIA	12.07.87
Guilfoyle, Daniel,	HON MID	URNU	U/A	25.10.01
Gunn, Debra Ann, RD	LT CDR	HQ	SCOTIA	31.03.94
Gurney, Henry,	HON MID	URNU	U/A	18.10.00

H

Name	Rank	Branch	Unit	Seniority
Hadden, James,	HON MID	URNU	U/A	20.10.00
Hadfield, Marc,	HON MID	URNU	U/A	22.10.01
Hadnett, Edmund Robert,	LT CDR	AW	PRESIDENT	29.01.93
Haffenden, Simon, BSC, MIEE, C.ENG	LT	SM	FLYING FOX	26.04.96
Hagger, Michael,	HON MID	URNU	U/A	01.02.01
Haikin, Peter Harry, BSC	LT	DIS	FERRET (RNR)	02.02.96
Halblander, Craig James Michael, RD, BA, LLB, LLM	LT	MW	KING ALFRED	06.05.94
Hall, Euan James Armstrong, RD	LT CDR	LOGS	EAGLET	16.11.92
Hall, Gareth,	HON MID	URNU	U/A	19.10.00
Hall, Stephen Scott,	ASL	NE	SCOTIA	16.04.02
Haller, Pauline Mary, RD	LT CDR	NCAGS	WILDFIRE	31.03.93
Halliday, Ian,	LT CDR	AIR	RNR AIR BR VL	01.09.90
Hamilton, Andrew Robert,	SG LTCDR		SCOTIA	01.08.86
Hamilton, Adam,	HON MID	URNU	U/A	28.10.00
Hamilton, Benjamin,	HON MID	URNU	U/A	11.10.01
Hamilton, Ronald, RD	LT	LOGS	DALRIADA	14.10.95
Hamilton, Stuart,	HON MID	URNU	U/A	19.10.00
Hammond, Christopher,	HON MID	URNU	U/A	06.11.00
Hamnett, Richard,	HON MID	URNU	U/A	09.10.00
Hancock, Angela,	LT	MR	VIVID	10.10.90
Handley, Dane,	LT CDR	AIR	RNR AIR BR VL	31.03.96
Hands, Carolyn, RD	LT CDR	NCAGS	FLYING FOX	30.09.85
Hankey, Mark Harold,	LT	MR	PRESIDENT	31.07.95
Hankin, Robert,	HON MID	URNU	U/A	30.09.99
Hansom, Edward John,	LT	MR	PRESIDENT	25.11.91
Harbour, Karen,	HONCADET	URNU	U/A	19.10.00
Harding, David,	HON MID	URNU	U/A	12.10.00
Harding, Janet Elizabeth, RD*	LT CDR	HQ	WILDFIRE	31.03.93
Hardinge, Christopher Harry, MBE	LT CDR	SM	KING ALFRED	31.03.98
Hardy, Gareth,	HON MID	URNU	U/A	07.10.01
Hargreaves, Simon,	LT CDR	AIR	RNR AIR BR VL	01.10.89
Harker, Rebecca,	HONCADET	URNU	U/A	19.10.00
Harkin, James,	ASL	NE	SCOTIA RNR	05.02.02
Harper, Kate,	HONCADET	URNU	U/A	11.10.01
Harper, Robert Simon, RD	LT	HQ	CAROLINE	27.01.95
Harper, Stephen,	HON MID	URNU	U/A	11.10.01

Name	Rank	Branch	Unit	Seniority
Harrington, Anthony Christopher Robert,	LT CDR	INTR	FERRET (RNR)	31.03.97
Harris, Adrian James,	LT	SM	WILDFIRE	30.07.95
Harris, Hugh,	HON MID	URNU	U/A	18.10.01
Harris, Mark Edward,	LT	MR	FLYING FOX	15.05.95
Harris, Richard,	HON MID	URNU	U/A	06.09.99
Harris, Raymond Leo, RD	LT CDR	MR	U/A	23.10.80
Harris, Rafe,	HON MID	URNU	U/A	19.10.00
Harrison, Mark Alastair Timothy,	ASL	NE	FLYING FOX	12.04.00
Harrison, Peter,	LT CDR	SEA	KING ALFRED	30.05.90
Harrison, Richard William,	SG LTCDR		SHERWOOD	30.09.96
Hart, Daniel,	HON MID	URNU	U/A	07.10.99
Hart, Keith, RD	CDR	AWNIS	WILDFIRE	30.09.01
Hartley, Ann Theresa, RD	LT CDR	DIS	FERRET (RNR)	30.09.87
Hartley, David,	LT CDR	SM	WILDFIRE	01.06.91
Hartley, Philip Terence,	LT CDR	SM	FERRET (RNR)	16.12.88
Hartley, Sheila Ann, RD	LT	HQ	VIVID	20.01.89
Hartley, Sarah Boyt,	LT	NCAGS	PRESIDENT	06.12.96
Harvey, Paul,	HON MID	URNU	U/A	01.10.98
Harwood, Steven,	LT CDR	MR	EAGLET	31.03.96
Haslam, David,	HON MID	URNU	U/A	01.10.98
Hatch, Lucy,	HONCADET	URNU	U/A	22.10.01
Hathway, Steven,	LT CDR	AIR	RNR AIR BR VL	31.03.98
Hawes, Alison Linda,	LT CDR	MR	KING ALFRED	31.03.98
Hawkins, Duncan,	SLT	URNU	U/A	01.03.00
Hawkins, James,	HON MID	URNU	U/A	14.10.99
Hawkins, Laura,	HONCADET	URNU	U/A	07.10.01
Hawkins, Mitchell,	HON MID	URNU	U/A	18.10.00
Hawksley, Alex,	HON MID	URNU	U/A	20.10.00
Hawthorne, Gillian Louise,	ASL	Q	CAROLINE	23.04.02
Haydock, Lynsay,	HONCADET	URNU	U/A	28.09.00
Haynes, Zoe,	HONCADET	URNU	U/A	08.10.98
Hayton, Carrie Jane,	LT CDR	MR	WILDFIRE	30.09.91
Hayton, Philip,	ASL	NE	PRESIDENT RNR	23.01.02
Hayward, James Douglas, MA, B.ENG	LT CDR	LOGS	FORWARD	31.03.00
Haywood, Andrew,	HON MID	URNU	U/A	21.10.00
Haywood, Paul,	LT CDR	AIR	RNR AIR BR VL	28.08.93
Healey, Philip,	HON MID	URNU	U/A	08.01.02
Healy, Pamela Joyce, BSC	LT CDR	MR	KING ALFRED	30.09.90
Heap, Matthew James,	SLT	NCAGS	PRESIDENT	03.11.98
Hearn, Victoria,	HONCADET	URNU	U/A	18.10.01
Heathcote, Paul,	LT CDR	AIR	RNR AIR BR VL	31.03.96
Heffron, Kirsty,	HONCADET	URNU	U/A	14.11.95
Helsby, Edward,	LT CDR	AIR	RNR AIR BR VL	31.03.96
Henderson, Andrew,	HON MID	URNU	U/A	21.10.99
Henderson, Elizabeth,	LT CDR	AIR	RNR AIR BR VL	01.07.00
Henwood, A, RD	CDR	AW	PRESIDENT	30.09.98
Hetherington, Simon David Francis,	ASL	NE	PRESIDENT	30.01.01
Hewins, Clive William,	LT CDR	AW	SHERWOOD	20.05.91
Hewitt, Shirley Angela,	LT CDR	MR	WILDFIRE	21.07.94
Hewlett, Philip,	HON MID	URNU	U/A	18.10.00
Hick, David,	LT	AIR	RNR AIR BR VL	20.11.91
Hickey, Gurney,	LT CDR	AIR	RNR AIR BR VL	31.03.99
Hickey, Ruth,	HONCADET	URNU	U/A	05.10.00
Hicks, John David,	ALT CDR	HQ	EAGLET	31.03.00
Hickson, Craig,	LT	AIR	RNR AIR BR VL	27.06.89
Higgins, Rebecca,	HONCADET	URNU	U/A	19.10.00
Higgs, Jane Ann,	LT	Q	EAGLET	25.01.98
Highett, David Francis Trevor,	LT CDR	LOGS	KING ALFRED	02.08.83
Higson, Rennie Malcolm,	ASL	NE	SHERWOOD	10.01.02
Hill, Andrew,	HON MID	URNU	U/A	07.10.01
Hill, Christine,	HONCADET	URNU	U/A	18.10.01
Hill, Douglas,	ASL	NE	PRESIDENT RNR	22.11.01
Hill, Matthew Charles,	LT	SEA	PRESIDENT	25.01.91

Name	Rank	Branch	Unit	Seniority
Hill, Paul Terence,	LT CDR	SM	PRESIDENT	31.03.00
Hill, Sarah Lyness Dane,	ASL	NE	SHERWOOD	13.04.00
Hill, Stuart John Moody,	LT	SM	PRESIDENT	09.05.93
Hiller, Timothy,	HON MID	URNU	U/A	07.10.01
Hilliard, John Stephen,	ASGLTCDR		CAMBRIA	15.03.00
Hills, Emma,	HONCADET	URNU	U/A	15.11.01
Hills, Stephen John,	ALT	AW	VIVID	08.04.99
Hilton, Caroline,	HONCADET	URNU	U/A	27.01.00
Hindle, Sean,	LT	SM	EAGLET	18.09.91
Hines, Richard,	HON MID	URNU	U/A	22.11.99
Hines, Stephen Frederic, RD	LT CDR	AW	KING ALFRED	01.08.86
Hitchings, Michael,	HON MID	URNU	U/A	18.10.00
Hodges, Philip,	HON MID	URNU	U/A	10.09.01
Hodgson, Jane Lee,	LT	MR	PRESIDENT	04.04.90
Hodkinson, Alice Clare,	PSG LT		PRESIDENT	26.09.01
Hogan, Ambrose Dominic,	ASL	NE	PRESIDENT	15.05.01
Hogan, Francis John, RD*	LT CDR	MW	EAGLET	31.03.01
Hogg, Michael,	HON MID	URNU	U/A	21.10.99
Holborn, Carl,	LT	AIR	RNR AIR BR VL	16.09.90
Holbrook, Bryony,	HONCADET	URNU	U/A	21.01.00
Holley, Steven,	ASL	URNU	U/A	15.11.01
Holliday, Pamela,	HONCADET	URNU	U/A	12.10.00
Hollins, Timothy,	HON MID	URNU	U/A	24.10.00
Hollis, Robert Leslie Graham,	LT CDR	AWNIS	EAGLET	31.03.02
Holloway, Stephen Leslie,	LT	AW	EAGLET	17.09.88
Holman, Emma,	HONCADET	URNU	U/A	08.10.01
Holman, Jonathan,	HON MID	URNU	U/A	20.10.00
Holmes, David Grindall, RD	ACDR	NCAGS	FLYING FOX	03.04.01
Holmes, Rachel,	ASL	NE	WILDFIRE	27.09.00
Honey, Victoria,	HONCADET	URNU	U/A	17.10.01
Hook, Samantha Elisabeth,	PSG LT		FLYING FOX	23.10.01
Hooper, Nicholas Robert Joseph, RD	SG CAPT		FLYING FOX	30.09.98
Hooton, Karen,	HONCADET	URNU	U/A	12.10.00
Hope, Nigel Charles Dawson, RD	CDR	AW	SCOTIA	30.09.96
Hopper, Timothy,	HON MID	URNU	U/A	11.09.00
Hopps, Francis,	LT CDR	AIR	RNR AIR BR VL	31.03.98
Horne, Martin,	LT	SEA	PRESIDENT	23.05.97
Horner, Benjamin Brian Harold,	LT	SM	PRESIDENT	13.05.02
Horner, Ian David,	LT CDR	DIS	FERRET (RNR)	01.11.83
Horrell, Stephen Peter,	LT	CEW	VIVID	01.12.97
Hough, Peter,	HON MID	URNU	U/A	05.10.00
Hounsell, Andrew,	HON MID	URNU	U/A	25.10.00
Hounsham, Thomas,	HON MID	URNU	U/A	11.10.01
Howard, Alexander, The Hon	LT CDR	AIR	RNR AIR BR VL	31.03.94
Howard, William Jonathon, RD*	CDR	AW	KING ALFRED	30.09.92
Howe, Jonathan,	HON MID	URNU	U/A	09.10.00
Howell, Colin, RD	LT CDR	HQ	KING ALFRED	31.03.99
Howes, Simon Tee, RD	LT CDR	DIS	FERRET (RNR)	28.03.84
Howorth, Charles,	HON MID	URNU	U/A	18.10.00
Hoyle, Stephen,	LT	SM	EAGLET	20.11.95
Hubbard, Paul,	LT CDR	LOGS	SCOTIA RNR	22.05.98
Hubber, Keith Michael,	LT CDR	AW	FLYING FOX	31.03.96
Hubbert, Sherard,	HON MID	URNU	U/A	30.09.99
Hubble, Robert,	LT CDR	AIR	RNR AIR BR VL	01.10.97
Huddleston, Eleanor,	HONCADET	URNU	U/A	06.11.00
Huey, Joanne,	HONCADET	URNU	U/A	01.12.00
Hughes, Clare Yvonne, RD*	LT CDR	CEW	PRESIDENT	30.09.90
Hughes, John Fraser,	LT CDR	MR	KING ALFRED	14.05.92
Hughes, Jill Elizabeth,	LT CDR	NCAGS	CAROLINE	31.03.95
Hughes, Josephine,	HONCADET	URNU	U/A	12.10.99
Hughes, Kai,	LT CDR	DIS	FERRET (RNR)	01.05.92
Hughes, Paul James, RD	SG CDR		KING ALFRED	30.09.95
Hulse, Rebecca,	HONCADET	URNU	U/A	21.10.99

Name	Rank	Branch	Unit	Seniority
Humphreys, John Martyn, PHD	LT CDR	MW	KING ALFRED	31.03.01
Hunot, Michael,	HON MID	URNU	U/A	18.10.00
Hunt, Phillippa,	HONCADET	URNU	U/A	26.10.99
Hunt, Stephen Neil,	LT	MR	VIVID	20.02.93
Huntly, Victoria,	HONCADET	URNU	U/A	14.10.99
Hurndall, Dominic Christopher Lake,	LT	MR	CALLIOPE	31.08.94
Hutchings, Carol,	HONCADET	URNU	U/A	07.10.99
Hutchings, Stuart,	LT	URNU	U/A	25.05.00
Hutchinson, Janice Elizabeth,	LT CDR	NCAGS	EAGLET	31.03.93
Hyre, Stephanie,	HONCADET	URNU	U/A	12.10.99

I

Name	Rank	Branch	Unit	Seniority
Inkpin, Julie Anne,	ALT	Q	KING ALFRED	18.05.01
Insley, Andrew,	HON MID	URNU	U/A	20.10.99
Inwood, John Maxwell,	SG CDR		SCOTIA	30.09.98
Irvine, Morag Mary,	ALT	MR	DALRIADA	08.01.02
Irving, Paul,	HON MID	URNU	U/A	11.10.01
Isted, Lee,	HON MID	URNU	U/A	27.09.01
Ivory, Thomas,	HON MID	URNU	U/A	11.09.00

J

Name	Rank	Branch	Unit	Seniority
Jachnik, Clive Vincent, RD	LT CDR	INTR	FERRET (RNR)	31.03.99
Jackson, Graham,	LT CDR	AIR	RNR AIR BR VL	01.10.88
Jackson, Trevor,	LT CDR	AIR	RNR AIR BR VL	01.10.94
Jacobs, Sarah,	HONCADET	URNU	U/A	17.10.01
Jacques, Charlotte,	HONCADET	URNU	U/A	04.10.00
Jaffier, Robert Gary,	SLT	CEW	FORWARD	13.04.97
James, Nichola,	HONCADET	URNU	U/A	25.10.01
James, Roy Arthur, BSC	CDR	SM	FORWARD	30.09.00
Jameson, Susan Catherine,	LT CDR	HQ	FLYING FOX	31.03.00
Jardine, Corriene Marie,	LT	AWNIS	WILDFIRE	12.10.93
Jarrett, Catherine,	HONCADET	URNU	U/A	26.01.00
Jarvis, Alan R,	LT CDR	NCAGS	PRESIDENT	10.12.80
Jasper, Mark Jonathan,	LT	MW	SHERWOOD	01.01.96
Jaundrill, Simon,	HON MID	URNU	U/A	07.10.01
Jeffcoate, Richard,	HON MID	URNU	U/A	22.10.01
Jeffery, Samuel,	HON MID	URNU	U/A	18.10.01
Jeffries, Felicity,	HONCADET	URNU	U/A	19.10.00
Jeffries, Rebecca,	HONCADET	URNU	U/A	11.10.01
Jenkins, Andrew,	HON MID	URNU	U/A	19.10.00
Jenkins, Clare,	HONCADET	URNU	U/A	06.11.00
Jenkins, Kathryn Louise,	PSG LT	MEDF	WILDFIRE	15.07.01
Jenner, Alexander,	HON MID	URNU	U/A	20.10.98
Jepson, Zara,	HONCADET	URNU	U/A	25.10.01
Jermy, Richard Alexander,	LT	INTR	FERRET (RNR)	13.12.91
John, Peter Martin,	LT CDR	AW	CAMBRIA	11.06.92
Johnson, Catherine,	HONCADET	URNU	U/A	14.10.99
Johnson, David G,	ASL	NE	EAGLET	05.10.00
Johnson, Edward,	HON MID	URNU	U/A	20.10.99
Johnson, Jill Ena, RD	LT CDR	Q	CAMBRIA	31.03.01
Johnson, Symon,	LT	AIR	RNR AIR BR VL	01.07.96
Johnston, Michael,	HON MID	URNU	U/A	14.10.99
Johnstone, James Oliver,	LT	SEA	PRESIDENT	18.04.00
Johnstone, Peter Hughes, RD	LT CDR	LOGS	PRESIDENT	31.03.97
Jones, Anna,	HONCADET	URNU	U/A	11.10.01
Jones, Andrew David,	ASL	NE	KING ALFRED	30.04.02
Jones, Christopher, RD	LT CDR	AW	PRESIDENT	01.05.88
Jones, Charles David, RD	LT CDR	SM	DALRIADA	31.03.00
Jones, Geoffrey Mark,	LT CDR	AW	EAGLET	31.03.02
Jones, Helen,	PSG LT	MEDF	EAGLET	17.05.00
Jones, Hayley,	HONCADET	URNU	U/A	10.09.01

Name	Rank	Branch	Unit	Seniority
Jones, Kristoffer,	HON MID	URNU	U/A	01.03.01
Jones, Keith Williams,	SLT	LOGS	FORWARD	22.04.99
Jones, Leslie,	LT CDR	INTR	FERRET (RNR)	08.11.00
Jones, Pauline, RD	LT CDR	LOGS	CALLIOPE	31.03.98
Joshi, Tejas,	HON MID	URNU	U/A	26.01.00
Journeaux, Simon Francis,	ASGLTCDR		EAGLET	28.09.99
Joyce, David,	HON MID	URNU	U/A	06.09.99
Juby, Amy,	HONCADET	URNU	U/A	11.10.01
Judd, Simon,	LT CDR	AIR	RNR AIR BR VL	01.10.96

K

Kadera, Stephen John,	LT CDR	MR	FLYING FOX	31.03.02
Kay, David,	LT CDR	LOGS	FLYING FOX	31.03.97
Kay, Ivan Charles Michael,	LT	SEA	KING ALFRED	12.11.88
Kay, Victoria,	HONCADET	URNU	U/A	14.10.99
Kaye, Sophie,	HONCADET	URNU	U/A	22.10.01
Kearney, Melian Jane, RD	LT CDR	HQ	VIVID	31.03.97
Keating, Fergus Stephen Jonathon,	PSG LTCDR		PRESIDENT	10.01.02
Keating, Guy,	HON MID	URNU	U/A	12.10.00
Kedge, Jennifer,	HONCADET	URNU	U/A	12.10.00
Keevan, Nina,	HONCADET	URNU	U/A	25.10.01
Keith, Rory,	HON MID	URNU	U/A	07.10.99
Kelley, Victoria,	HONCADET	URNU	U/A	18.10.01
Kelly, Sarah Louise,	ASL	NE	SCOTIA	01.05.01
Kelly, Timothy,	LT CDR	X	RNR AIR BR VL	04.07.92
Kembery, Simon John,	LT	AW	CAMBRIA	11.06.93
Kemp, Paul,	HON MID	URNU	U/A	30.05.01
Kemp, Richard,	HON MID	URNU	U/A	07.10.99
Kemp, Simon,	LT CDR	DIS	FERRET (RNR)	31.03.99
Kendall, Martyn, M, J	ASL	NE	EAGLET	31.05.01
Kendall-Torry, Kiri,	HONCADET	URNU	U/A	18.10.01
Kenney, Dawn Elizabeth,	CDR	Q	VIVID	30.09.99
Kent, Alan,	LT	AIR	RNR AIR BR VL	15.06.94
Kent, Thomas William Henry, RD	CDR	AW	SHERWOOD	30.09.99
Kenyon, Christopher,	LT CDR	HQ	PRESIDENT	17.11.97
Kerby, Robert,	HON MID	URNU	U/A	19.10.00
Kernick, Jillian,	ALT	AW	EAGLET	26.06.00
Kesteven, Ralph,	ASL	NE	EAGLET	24.01.02
Keyte, Lauren,	HONCADET	URNU	U/A	27.09.01
Khan, Sophia,	HONCADET	URNU	U/A	06.11.00
Kidd, Alex,	HON MID	URNU	U/A	05.10.00
Kidd, Madeleine,	HONCADET	URNU	U/A	18.10.01
Kilbride, Paul,	HON MID	URNU	U/A	27.09.01
King, Andrew Stephen, RD	LT CDR	MW	KING ALFRED	31.03.99
King, Charles Guy Hall,	LT CDR	SEA	KING ALFRED	31.03.02
King, David,	HON MID	URNU	U/A	14.10.99
King, Hannah,	HONCADET	URNU	U/A	27.11.01
King, Ian,	LT	HQ	EAGLET	05.12.97
King, Ian,	HON MID	URNU	U/A	11.09.00
King, Lindsay,	ASL	URNU	U/A	15.10.01
Kinsella, Kevin John, QVRM, RD*	CDR	MW	KING ALFRED	30.09.96
Kirk, William Walter,	LT	NCAGS	SHERWOOD	31.03.96
Kirkham, Anna,	HONCADET	URNU	U/A	07.10.99
Kirkpatrick, Alasdair MacLaren,	ASL	NE	WILDFIRE	18.11.99
Kirkpatrick, Robin,	HON MID	URNU	U/A	08.10.98
Kirwin, Ciara,	HONCADET	URNU	U/A	12.10.00
Kisler, Jonathan Daniel,	PSG LT		CALLIOPE	17.05.00
Kistruck, David,	LT CDR	AIR	RNR AIR BR VL	31.03.00
Kitchen, Catherine Anne,	LT	HQ	WILDFIRE	12.12.92
Knight, David,	ACDR	AIR	RNR AIR BR VL	05.03.02
Knight, Stephen,	HON MID	URNU	U/A	11.09.00
Knopp, Jonathon,	HON MID	URNU	U/A	28.10.00

Name	Rank	Branch	Unit	Seniority
Knott, Clive,	LT CDR	AIR	RNR AIR BR VL	31.03.98
Knott, Robert,	HON MID	URNU	U/A	10.09.01
Knotts, George William,	LT CDR	CEW	CALLIOPE	31.03.02
Knowles, Donna Maureen,	LT CDR	MW	CAROLINE	31.03.01
Knowles, Thomas,	HON MID	URNU	U/A	14.10.99
Knupffer, Alexander,	HON MID	URNU	U/A	18.10.01
Kordowski, Nicholas,	ASL	NE	PRESIDENT	01.11.00
Krasun, Charles Robert,	ASL	NE	SCOTIA	30.10.01
Kyme, Michael John,	LT	SM	KING ALFRED	30.11.93
Kyriakidis, Evangelos,	HON MID	URNU	U/A	12.10.00

L

Name	Rank	Branch	Unit	Seniority
Lai, Patrick,	HON MID	URNU	U/A	12.10.00
Laird, William,	HON MID	URNU	U/A	26.10.99
Lamont, Claire,	HONCADET	URNU	U/A	11.10.01
Govan, Leonie,	LT	SEA	SCOTIA	23.05.97
Lanchbery, Alexandra,	HONCADET	URNU	U/A	11.10.01
Lane, Timothy,	HON MID	URNU	U/A	23.11.01
Lang, Tracey,	HONCADET	URNU	U/A	18.10.00
Langdon, Simon,	HON MID	URNU	U/A	12.10.99
Langmead, Clive Francis, RD	LT CDR	AW	FORWARD	01.07.90
Lapage-Norris, Thomas Richard William,	LT	LOGS	FLYING FOX	19.01.98
Larsen, Thomas,	HON MID	URNU	U/A	11.10.01
Last, Nick, AFC	LT CDR	AIR	RNR AIR BR VL	01.10.91
Lathrope, Jennifer,	HONCADET	URNU	U/A	30.09.99
Laundy, Nicholas,	PSG LT		EAGLET	23.05.00
Lauretani, Andrew Stephen David,	LT	MR	VIVID	05.10.90
Laverick, Helen Tanya,	SLT	LOGS	PRESIDENT	02.08.98
Law, Debbie,	HONCADET	URNU	U/A	18.10.01
Lawrence, Ian Martin,	ASL	AW	KING ALFRED	03.06.01
Lawrence, Jenna,	HONCADET	URNU	U/A	30.05.01
Le Roux, Gordon,	HON MID	URNU	U/A	19.10.00
Leach, Simon,	LT	AIR	RNR AIR BR VL	22.09.93
Leather, Roger James,	LT CDR	AW	EAGLET	01.06.87
Ledwidge, Francis Andrew,	LT	INTR	FERRET (RNR)	15.01.95
Lee, David Antony,	LT CDR	SM	DALRIADA	31.03.98
Lee, Daren,	HON MID	URNU	U/A	07.10.99
Lee, John,	ACDR	NCAGS	CALLIOPE	13.12.99
Lee, Robert,	LT	AIR	RNR AIR BR VL	01.10.91
Lee, Thomas William Robert,	LT	INTR	FERRET (RNR)	03.09.95
Legge, Fiona,	HONCADET	URNU	U/A	14.09.99
Leigh, Daniel,	HON MID	URNU	U/A	12.10.00
Lemon, John,	ALT	X	U/A	09.02.88
Lentell, Heather,	LT	Q	EAGLET	03.05.01
Leonard, John Francis,	SG CDR		KING ALFRED	30.09.01
Leonard, Maria,	HONCADET	URNU	U/A	20.10.99
Leong, Melvin,	HON MID	URNU	U/A	11.10.01
Leslie, Sarah,	HONCADET	URNU	U/A	30.09.99
Lewis, Elizabeth,	HONCADET	URNU	U/A	19.10.00
Lewis, John Charles, RD	LT CDR	MR	PRESIDENT	31.03.02
Lewis, Jennifer,	HONCADET	URNU	U/A	11.10.01
Lewis, Justine,	HONCADET	URNU	U/A	26.10.99
Lewis, Kathryn Elizabeth,	LT	MW	PRESIDENT	31.07.95
Lewis, Richard,	LT CDR	AIR	RNR AIR BR VL	31.03.01
Lewis, Simon, RD	LT	LOGS	EAGLET	17.11.97
Lewis, Shannon,	LT	MW	CALLIOPE RNR	30.01.02
Leyshon, Sally Louise,	LT CDR	AWNIS	FLYING FOX	31.03.93
Linden, Roy Stephen,	ASL	NE	FLYING FOX	01.11.00
Lindsley, Michael James,	LT CDR	AW	CALLIOPE	31.03.99
Lindvall, Kate,	HONCADET	URNU	U/A	04.10.01
Lineham, Samuel,	HON MID	URNU	U/A	11.10.01
Lines, Jessica,	HONCADET	URNU	U/A	07.10.99

Name	Rank	Branch	Unit	Seniority
Lipczynski, Benjamin,	HON MID	URNU	U/A	11.09.00
Lippell, Sabrina Rose, RD, BSC	LT CDR	MR	WILDFIRE	30.09.89
Lister, Andrew,	LT	AIR	RNR AIR BR VL	16.06.93
Lister, Matthew,	HON MID	URNU	U/A	10.09.01
Little, Julia,	HONCADET	URNU	U/A	18.10.00
Livingstone, Martin Jeremy,	LT	MW	EAGLET	26.12.89
Lloyd, David Vernon,	LT CDR	AW	KING ALFRED	31.03.99
Lloyd, Douglas,	HON MID	URNU	U/A	21.10.00
Lloyd, Gareth, RD	LT CDR	HQ	EAGLET	31.03.98
Lloyd, Peter John,	LT CDR	AW	KING ALFRED	31.03.00
Lloyd, Susan,	LT	MR	PRESIDENT RNR	01.09.90
Loates, Mark,	SLT	URNU	U/A	22.01.98
Lock, Alan,	HON MID	URNU	U/A	18.10.01
Lockett, Alex,	HON MID	URNU	U/A	17.10.01
Lockwood, Neville Antony,	ASL	NE	VIVID RNR	06.05.02
Lokrantz-Bernitz, Gudmund,	HON MID	URNU	U/A	11.10.01
London, Nicholas,	HON MID	URNU	U/A	18.10.00
Longman, Matthew,	HON MID	URNU	U/A	10.09.01
Lord, Richard,	HON MID	URNU	U/A	30.09.99
Lort, Timothy,	LT CDR	AIR	RNR AIR BR VL	01.10.95
Loughran, Cedric Grenville, RD	CDR	AW	EAGLET	30.09.98
Lovegrove, Richard Edward,	PSG LT		WILDFIRE	05.06.01
Low, Simeon,	HON MID	URNU	U/A	01.02.01
Lowry, Claire,	HONCADET	URNU	U/A	15.10.98
Luke, Warren Munro, RD	SG CDR		SCOTIA	30.09.99
Lyall, Kenneth Alexander,	LT CDR	HQ	SCOTIA	31.03.97
Lydon, Michael,	LT	LOGS	CALLIOPE	30.09.96
Lyman, David,	HON MID	URNU	U/A	18.10.01
Lynch, Suzanne Marie,	SLT	LOGS	CAMBRIA	31.10.95
Lyne, James,	HON MID	URNU	U/A	28.09.00

M

Name	Rank	Branch	Unit	Seniority
MacBeth, Jonathan,	HON MID	URNU	U/A	11.10.01
MacDonald, Alastair,	HON MID	URNU	U/A	07.10.99
MacDonald, Colin,	ASL	NE	SCOTIA	07.01.98
MacDonald, Fiona,	HONCADET	URNU	U/A	14.10.99
MacHell, Louise,	HONCADET	URNU	U/A	09.10.00
Machin, Peter Charles Clive, RD*	CDR	HQ	CAMBRIA	30.09.00
MacKay, Evan George,	PALT	AW	DALRIADA	06.12.96
MacKenzie-Philps, Linda,	LT CDR	MR	KING ALFRED	31.03.99
Mackie, Robert Charles Gordon,	SLT	SEA	FORWARD	19.11.97
MacLean, Nicholas Peter, RD	LT CDR	SM	PRESIDENT	31.03.97
Macleod, Alistair David, RD*	SG LTCDR		SCOTIA	17.10.78
Macleod, Alanna,	HONCADET	URNU	U/A	08.11.01
MacMillan, Alasdair Iain Macaulay,	SG LTCDR		SCOTIA	04.03.97
MacRae, Kirk,	HON MID	URNU	U/A	14.10.99
MacTaggart, Alasdair Donald, RD	ACDR	CEW	DALRIADA	01.09.99
Maddison, Simon,	LT	MCDO	FLYING FOX	19.07.96
Magnay, Claire Georgina,	SLT	SM	FLYING FOX	16.07.94
Mainwaring, Luke,	HON MID	URNU	U/A	25.10.01
Malik, Alia,	HONCADET	URNU	U/A	18.10.01
Malik, Ussamah,	HON MID	URNU	U/A	18.10.01
Malkin, Emma Mary, BA	LT	SEA	PRESIDENT	14.09.95
Malkin, Roy Vyvian,	LT	AW	PRESIDENT	03.07.01
Mallinson, Ian,	HON MID	URNU	U/A	21.10.99
Mallinson, Stuart Jeffry, MSC	LT	MW	PRESIDENT	31.03.96
Malloy, Richard,	HON MID	URNU	U/A	14.10.00
Malone, Keith,	ASGLTCDR		EAGLET	07.01.00
Malpas, Peter,	LT CDR	NCAGS	KING ALFRED	31.03.02
Manley, John Preston,	LT	AW	VIVID	02.06.01
Mann, Barbara Louise,	LT CDR	MR	VIVID	31.03.01
Manning, Jacqueline Vera,	LT CDR	SM	PRESIDENT	31.03.02

Name	Rank	Branch	Unit	Seniority
Marandola, Stefan,	LT	AIR	RNR AIR BR VL	17.01.96
Markham, Paul Anthony,	LT	SM	PRESIDENT	28.07.92
Markwell, Jonathan,	HON MID	URNU	U/A	22.10.01
Marland, Helen,	HONCADET	URNU	U/A	14.12.99
Marlor, Andrew,	HON MID	URNU	U/A	11.09.00
Marlow, Stephen, QGM	LT CDR	AIR	RNR AIR BR VL	31.03.97
Marple, Natalie,	HONCADET	URNU	U/A	19.10.00
Marr, David,	LT CDR	AIR	RNR AIR BR VL	01.10.94
Marsh, Timothy,	LT	AIR	RNR AIR BR VL	06.07.87
Marshall, Henry,	HON MID	URNU	U/A	19.10.00
Marshall, Stephen Michael,	LT	MCDO	CINCNAVHOME	17.04.88
Martin, Darren Hinna,	LT CDR	AW	PRESIDENT	31.03.01
Martin, Dion,	HON MID	URNU	U/A	18.10.01
Martin, Nicholas John, RD	LT CDR	MW	CALLIOPE	31.03.95
Maryon, Karen Anne, RD	LT	Q	SHERWOOD	24.12.87
Mason, Andrew Robert,	ASL	NE	PRESIDENT	11.06.99
Mason, Andrew,	HON MID	URNU	U/A	12.10.00
Mason, Ann, RD	LT CDR	LOGS	EAGLET	01.04.99
Mason, David,	HON MID	URNU	U/A	12.10.00
Mason, Grace Victoria,	ASL	NE	PRESIDENT	25.09.01
Mason, Thomas,	LT CDR	AIR	RNR AIR BR VL	01.10.88
Massey, Steven,	LT	AIR	RNR AIR BR VL	01.02.91
Mattos, Alexander,	HON MID	URNU	U/A	11.09.00
Mawdsley, Katherine,	HONCADET	URNU	U/A	18.10.01
Mawer, Kieren,	HON MID	URNU	U/A	06.09.99
Maxey, Anna,	HONCADET	URNU	U/A	19.10.00
Maxwell, Andrew Alistair, RD	LT CDR	INTR	FERRET (RNR)	05.08.88
May, Oliver,	HON MID	URNU	U/A	24.10.00
May, Sarah,	HONCADET	URNU	U/A	06.09.99
Mayo, Guy,	HON MID	URNU	U/A	20.10.00
Mc Alear, Stuart Douglas,	LT CDR	MW	KING ALFRED	25.10.95
McArdell, Steven,	LT	AIR	RNR AIR BR VL	01.04.90
McBride, Andrew,	HON MID	URNU	U/A	27.09.01
McCabe, Jeremy Charles,	LT CDR	AW	VIVID	31.03.02
McCartney, William Robert,	SLT	LOGS	PRESIDENT	10.03.96
McCleary, Christopher James,	ASL	NE	EAGLET	06.09.00
McClelland, Matthew,	HON MID	URNU	U/A	22.02.01
McConn-Finch, Dervla,	ASL	NE	KING ALFRED	23.07.98
McCormack, Patrick, RD	LT CDR	NCAGS	DALRIADA	15.07.92
McCormick, Alana,	HONCADET	URNU	U/A	12.12.01
McCormick, Damion Kevin,	ASL	NE	SHERWOOD	20.04.99
McCreery, Robert George,	LT	SEA	CAROLINE	20.06.89
McDermott Evans, Rachel,	HONCADET	URNU	U/A	29.10.98
McDonald, Roger,	LT CDR	AIR	RNR AIR BR VL	01.09.87
McEwan, Craig,	HON MID	URNU	U/A	24.10.01
McGee, Alexander,	HON MID	URNU	U/A	25.10.01
McGhee, Stephen James,	ALT	HQ	DALRIADA	18.12.01
McGrath, Gerard Francis,	LT	SEA	PRESIDENT	08.06.01
McGrath, Owen Micheal,	ASL	NE	CAROLINE	29.03.00
McGuire, Dee,	HONCADET	URNU	U/A	08.10.01
McHardy-Roberts, Jaqueline Carole,	ASL	NE	EAGLET	10.10.01
McInnes, Vivian,	LT	Q	DALRIADA	14.12.92
McKeating, John Brendan,	SG CDR		SHERWOOD	31.12.99
McKeever, Kevin,	HON MID	URNU	U/A	11.10.01
McKenzie, Alexander,	HON MID	URNU	U/A	14.10.99
McKenzie-Boyle, Thomas,	HON MID	URNU	U/A	10.09.01
McKetty, Paul,	HON MID	URNU	U/A	30.09.99
McKinley, Mairi Catriona,	ASL	NE	DALRIADA	19.10.00
McKinnon, Laura,	HONCADET	URNU	U/A	08.10.98
McKittrick, Lucinda,	HONCADET	URNU	U/A	18.10.01
McKnight, Christopher,	HON MID	URNU	U/A	18.10.01
McKnight, Edward,	ASL	X	U/A	17.10.90
McLaughlin, Vincent,	HON MID	URNU	U/A	06.09.99

Name	Rank	Branch	Unit	Seniority
McLaverty, Karen Anne,	LT	NCAGS	CAROLINE	17.03.99
McLeod, Charles,	HON MID	URNU	U/A	06.10.00
McLeod, Thomas,	HON MID	URNU	U/A	05.10.00
McLintock, Mark William,	LT	SM	DALRIADA	01.12.94
McManus, Peter,	LT CDR	AIR	RNR AIR BR VL	01.10.89
McMaster, Isaac,	HON MID	URNU	U/A	07.10.01
McMinn, Sandra,	ASL	URNU	U/A	01.10.98
McMorkine, Sarah,	HONCADET	URNU	U/A	11.10.01
McMurran, Robert Campbell,	LT CDR	HQ	CAROLINE	31.03.97
McNair, Erin,	HONCADET	URNU	U/A	24.10.01
McNaught, Edward William Gordon,	LT CDR	MW	CALLIOPE	31.03.97
McPherson, Emma,	LT	Q	CAROLINE	15.06.00
McQueen, Patrick,	HON MID	URNU	U/A	01.10.98
Mdoe, Charlotte,	HONCADET	URNU	U/A	07.10.01
Meakin, Matthew,	HON MID	URNU	U/A	18.10.00
Medland, Elizabeth Ellen,	ASL	NE	VIVID	20.02.01
Meerza, Andrew,	LT	AW	VIVID	16.04.93
Meharg, Neil,	LT	MW	CAROLINE	11.08.96
Meldram, Sheryl Christine Anne,	LT	Q	PRESIDENT	30.10.93
Mellor, Richard,	HON MID	URNU	U/A	11.10.01
Mellor, Daniel,	HON MID	URNU	U/A	11.09.00
Melson, Janet,	LT	LOGS	KING ALFRED	25.02.96
Mercer, Ian S,	LT	INTR	FERRET (RNR)	18.02.00
Mercer, Lara,	HONCADET	URNU	U/A	07.10.99
Merrington, Matthew,	HON MID	URNU	U/A	12.10.99
Millar, Caroline,	HONCADET	URNU	U/A	14.11.00
Miller, Charles,	HON MID	URNU	U/A	22.10.98
Miller, David,	LT CDR	AIR	RNR AIR BR VL	01.04.95
Miller, Gary,	HON MID	URNU	U/A	01.10.98
Milligan, Kevin,	HON MID	URNU	U/A	14.10.99
Mills, Mary Kathleen,	LT CDR	CEW	FLYING FOX	31.03.93
Millward, Jonathan,	LT CDR	SM	KING ALFRED	01.09.91
Milne-Home, Elizabeth Mary,	LT	DIS	FERRET (RNR)	23.05.97
Minter, Louise Inglis Hood,	LT CDR	Q	DALRIADA	01.08.83
Minto, Paul,	HON MID	URNU	U/A	21.10.00
Minty, Darren,	HON MID	URNU	U/A	18.10.00
Mitchell, Colin Roderick,	LT	INTR	FERRET (RNR)	05.08.94
Mitchell, Natalie,	ASL	NE	WILDFIRE	19.09.01
Mitchell, Robert,	LT CDR	AIR	RNR AIR BR VL	31.03.93
Mitchell, Samantha,	HONCADET	URNU	U/A	09.11.00
Mitchell, Shouna,	HONCADET	URNU	U/A	07.10.99
Mochar, Melanie,	HONCADET	URNU	U/A	30.09.99
Moghraby, Chetal,	HONCADET	URNU	U/A	20.10.98
Mohyud Din, Nayef,	HON MID	URNU	U/A	09.10.00
Molina, Alexandra,	HONCADET	URNU	U/A	11.10.01
Monkhouse, Joanna,	HONCADET	URNU	U/A	20.10.00
Montgomery, William George,	LT CDR	SEA	FLYING FOX	31.03.00
Mooney, Ryan,	HON MID	URNU	U/A	18.10.01
Moore, Ian,	HON MID	URNU	U/A	18.10.01
Moore, William Ian,	ASL	NE	CAROLINE	06.12.00
Moorthy, Roham Michael,	LT	SM	PRESIDENT	02.03.02
Moran, Simon,	LT	AIR	RNR AIR BR VL	18.02.94
Morden, Hayley,	HONCADET	URNU	U/A	30.09.99
Morgan, Eugene Peter,	LT	MW	PRESIDENT	31.07.95
Morgan, Gareth William,	LT CDR	LOGS	CAMBRIA	31.03.01
Morgan, Linda Frances,	LT	Q	WILDFIRE	26.09.96
Morgan, Nicola,	HONCADET	URNU	U/A	18.10.00
Morgan, Richard,	HON MID	URNU	U/A	17.10.01
Morgans, Daniel James,	LT	MW	PRESIDENT	09.05.99
Moriarty, Helen Jean,	ALT	Q	PRESIDENT	03.09.01
Morison, Julian Ronald,	ASL	NE	KING ALFRED	17.11.99
Morley, Dietmar Allen,	LT	NCAGS	SHERWOOD	20.10.98
Morris, Alan Philip,	LT CDR	MR	DALRIADA	01.10.95

Name	Rank	Branch	Unit	Seniority
Morris, David John,	CDR	SM	WILDFIRE	30.09.01
Morris, Jessica,	HONCADET	URNU	U/A	14.10.99
Morris, Rachel,	HONCADET	URNU	U/A	11.10.01
Morris, William Alexander,	LT	MW	SCOTIA	19.07.89
Morrison, Susan Ellen,	ASL	NE	DALRIADA	24.11.99
Moseley, Allison,	ASL	NE	CALLIOPE	10.03.98
Mostyn, Isabel,	HONCADET	URNU	U/A	07.11.01
Mouatt, David,	HON MID	URNU	U/A	18.10.00
Mowbray, Roger, QCVSA	LT CDR	AIR	RNR AIR BR VL	01.10.88
Moyes, Peter,	ASL	URNU	U/A	24.03.99
Mullins, Natalie,	HONCADET	URNU	U/A	06.09.99
Mundy, Ross,	HON MID	URNU	U/A	22.10.01
Munn, Claudia,	HONCADET	URNU	U/A	25.10.01
Munson, Eileen Patricia,	LT	Q	CAMBRIA	23.09.95
Munt, Marcus,	HON MID	URNU	U/A	08.10.98
Murphy, Christian,	HON MID	URNU	U/A	09.10.00
Murphy, Samantha,	ASL	URNU	U/A	16.06.99
Murray, Anita May,	ASL	NE	VIVID	09.05.00
Murray, Abigail,	HONCADET	URNU	U/A	08.10.98
Murray, Christine,	HONCADET	URNU	U/A	15.11.99
Murray, Edward Charles, RD	LT CDR	INTR	FERRET (RNR)	31.03.99
Murrison, Andrew William,	SG CDR		KING ALFRED	31.12.97
Murrison, M P, RD	LT CDR	AW	PRESIDENT	31.03.99
Myers, Margaret Cynthia, RD*	LT CDR	CEW	VIVID	31.03.93
Myers, Paul,	LT	AIR	RNR AIR BR VL	01.08.84

N

Name	Rank	Branch	Unit	Seniority
Naaz, Amina,	HONCADET	URNU	U/A	07.12.00
Nadin, Robert,	LT CDR	AIR	RNR AIR BR VL	01.09.95
Nasmyth, James,	HON MID	URNU	U/A	11.10.01
Neale, Andrea,	HONCADET	URNU	U/A	28.10.00
Neale, Daniel,	HON MID	URNU	U/A	19.10.00
Neale, Kirsty A,	LT	NCAGS	EAGLET	30.11.94
Neate, Benjamin Louis,	PSG LT		PRESIDENT	15.07.01
Nelson, Victoria,	HONCADET	URNU	U/A	08.10.98
Nettleton, Philip,	LT	MR	WILDFIRE	23.08.88
Newby, Christopher,	HON MID	URNU	U/A	11.09.00
Newby-Grant, William, MBE, RD	LT CDR	INTR	FERRET (RNR)	26.03.80
Newell, Gary Douglas,	LT	MR	FLYING FOX	13.07.91
Newland, Anthony D,	SG LTCDR		DALRIADA	23.11.97
Newton, David Jason,	LT	MR	PRESIDENT	28.03.96
Newton, Ingrid Catherine,	LT CDR	LOGS	EAGLET	31.03.99
Newton, Mark,	LT CDR	AIR	RNR AIR BR VL	31.03.01
Newton, Russell Scott Henry,	ASL	NE	PRESIDENT	22.05.01
Newton, Rebecca,	HONCADET	URNU	U/A	06.11.00
Niblock, Gareth Leigh Charles,	ASL	NE	EAGLET	05.06.01
Nichol, R C F,	LT CDR	MR	PRESIDENT	18.09.75
Nicholson, Emma Sarah,	ASL	NE	DALRIADA	22.01.98
Nicholson, Jeremy David, RD*	LT CDR	AW	FLYING FOX	01.10.84
Nicholson, Peter Adrian, RD	LT CDR	INTR	FERRET (RNR)	19.02.87
Nicolson, Vernon,	ASL	NE	DALRIADA	22.02.00
Nightingale, Samuel,	HON MID	URNU	U/A	09.10.00
Nisbet, James,	ASL	NE	PRESIDENT RNR	24.01.02
Noakes, David Anthony,	ALT	LOGS	EAGLET	06.10.00
Noble, Alexander Peter,	ASL	NE	KING ALFRED	09.01.02
Noble, Robert Howard, BSC, RD	LT CDR	NCAGS	FORWARD	31.03.97
Norris, Andrew,	ALT	NCAGS	KING ALFRED	01.10.90
North, Adam,	HON MID	URNU	U/A	11.09.00
Northcott, John,	LT CDR	LOGS	CALLIOPE	31.03.98
Norton, Rachel,	LT CDR	Q	WILDFIRE	31.03.02
Norwood, Jeffrey Michael,	SG CDR		FORWARD	30.09.97
Nudd, Kathryn Louise,	PSG LT	MEDF	PRESIDENT	04.04.00

Name	Rank	Branch	Unit	Seniority
Nugent, Helen,	MID	NE	EAGLET	26.10.01
Nunn, James,	LT CDR	AIR	RNR AIR BR VL	31.03.99

O

O`neill, Emily,	HONCADET	URNU	U/A	18.10.00
O'Callaghan, Penelope Jane,	LT CDR	Q	KING ALFRED	31.03.96
O'Connor, Sarah Elizabeth Rowland, RD	LT	NCAGS	PRESIDENT	09.06.83
O'Donohue, Ian,	HON MID	URNU	U/A	09.10.00
O'Driscoll, Edward Hugh,	SLT	SEA	PRESIDENT	10.03.98
O'Hara, Katherine,	HONCADET	URNU	U/A	11.10.01
O'Neill, George Paul,	LT	INTR	FERRET (RNR)	08.08.93
O'Sullivan, Kathryn Winifred, RD	LT	SEA	VIVID	26.07.96
Oag, Denis Cairns,	LT CDR	MW	SCOTIA	31.03.00
Oakley, Richard,	ALT	AW	PRESIDENT	29.09.98
Oaten, Timothy John, RD	LT	NCAGS	SHERWOOD	03.06.87
Oates, Edward,	LT CDR	AIR	RNR AIR BR VL	16.02.93
Offords, Stephen,	HON MID	URNU	U/A	01.12.00
Ogden, Braddan,	LT	AIR	RNR AIR BR VL	01.04.95
Oldfield, Christian,	HON MID	URNU	U/A	11.09.00
Olivant, David Francis,	LT CDR	CEW	SHERWOOD	31.03.99
Omope, Sylvester,	HON MID	URNU	U/A	18.10.01
Ormshaw, Andrew,	LT CDR	AIR	RNR AIR BR VL	23.06.87
Otto, Lucy,	HONCADET	URNU	U/A	18.10.01
Overson, Lauien,	HONCADET	URNU	U/A	11.10.01
Owen, Sarah Elizabeth,	ASL	NE	SHERWOOD	29.09.98

P

Paddock, Lee David,	LT	SM	FORWARD	01.03.94
Padget, Joanna Louise,	LT	NCAGS	KING ALFRED	18.05.00
Padgham, Philip,	ALT	URNU	U/A	30.06.97
Paffey, Darren,	HON MID	URNU	U/A	05.01.01
Pain, Sarah Louise,	ASL	NE	KING ALFRED	30.01.02
Palmer, Alon, RD	LT CDR	AW	SCOTIA	09.05.91
Palmer, Andrew,	HON MID	URNU	U/A	28.09.00
Palmer, Helen,	ASL	URNU	U/A	01.10.90
Palmer, Helen,	SLT	URNU	U/A	18.04.98
Palmer, James,	HON MID	URNU	U/A	14.10.99
Papaioannou, Theodore,	HON MID	URNU	U/A	07.10.99
Pardoe, Christopher Richard,	LT CDR	MR	VIVID	13.09.86
Park, Lindsay,	HONCADET	URNU	U/A	08.02.01
Park, Susanne,	HONCADET	URNU	U/A	24.10.01
Parkins, Jennifer,	HONCADET	URNU	U/A	20.10.98
Parkinson, Amy,	HONCADET	URNU	U/A	18.10.01
Parris, John Stewart, RD	MR	FLYING FOX		30.09.01
Parry, Christopher John,	ASL	NE	WILDFIRE	10.10.01
Parsonage, Neil David, LLM	ALT CDR	NCAGS	EAGLET	31.03.00
Parsons, Laura Elizabeth,	ASL	NE	KING ALFRED	15.01.02
Passmore, Susan Margaret, QVRM, RD	CDR	HQ	FLYING FOX	30.09.97
Paterson, Charlotte,	HONCADET	URNU	U/A	18.10.01
Paterson, Gordon Laird,	LT CDR	AWNIS	KING ALFRED	02.11.84
Paterson, Jamie,	HON MID	URNU	U/A	28.09.00
Paterson, Stuart,	HON MID	URNU	U/A	08.10.01
Patten, Michelle,	MID	NE	FORWARD RNR	07.09.01
Patten, Mark Thomas,	ASG LT		PRESIDENT	12.02.02
Patten, Nicholas William,	LT CDR	NCAGS	FORWARD	31.03.00
Patterson, Jarrod Lee,	LT CDR	MR	PRESIDENT	31.03.01
Paxton, Alan,	HON MID	URNU	U/A	14.10.99
Payne, Gareth,	HON MID	URNU	U/A	14.10.99
Payne, Joseph,	HON MID	URNU	U/A	11.10.01
Payne, Robert,	HON MID	URNU	U/A	28.10.00
Payton, Philip John,	CDR	MR	VIVID	30.09.00

Name	Rank	Branch	Unit	Seniority
Pearce, Alexandra,	HONCADET	URNU	U/A	12.11.01
Pearce, Desmond,	ALT	URNU	U/A	12.05.80
Pearson, Craig Antony,	ASL	AW	KING ALFRED	25.10.01
Pearson, Ian,	HON MID	URNU	U/A	01.04.99
Pearson, Paul Austin Kevin,	LT CDR	SM	FLYING FOX	31.03.00
Peart, James,	HON MID	URNU	U/A	10.09.01
Peasley, Helen Susan,	ASL	NE	SHERWOOD	13.11.01
Pedley, Michael,	ASL	NE	FORWARD RNR	16.01.02
Pellatt, Alison,	HONCADET	URNU	U/A	22.10.01
Percival, Victoria,	HONCADET	URNU	U/A	26.10.99
Perkins, Lucy,	HONCADET	URNU	U/A	14.10.99
Perks, Edward,	HON MID	URNU	U/A	14.10.99
Perry, Daniel,	HON MID	URNU	U/A	12.10.00
Peter, Kathleen Elizabeth,	ASL	NE	SCOTIA	04.04.01
Pethick, Ian,	LT	LOGS	VIVID	17.11.97
Pethick, Louise,	ASL	NE	VIVID	01.08.00
Petrie, Melville,	LT CDR	LOGS	FLYING FOX	09.01.87
Phillips, Katie,	HONCADET	URNU	U/A	19.10.00
Phillips, Nicholas James,	ASL	NE	PRESIDENT	23.04.02
Phillips, Matthew,	HON MID	URNU	U/A	14.10.99
Phillips, Sophia,	ASL	NE	PRESIDENT	13.11.01
Philpott, Sally Anne,	ASL	NE	KING ALFRED	04.01.95
Pickard, Amanda,	HONCADET	URNU	U/A	06.11.00
Pickup, David Julian,	LT CDR	MR	WILDFIRE	17.09.75
Piddington, Charlotte,	HONCADET	URNU	U/A	22.10.01
Pike, Christine Margaret,	LT CDR	DIS	FERRET (RNR)	31.03.95
Pike, Daniella,	HONCADET	URNU	U/A	20.10.98
Pike, Stuart,	LT	AIR	RNR AIR BR VL	12.02.95
Pimm, Anthony,	HON MID	URNU	U/A	14.10.99
Pimm, Michael,	HON MID	URNU	U/A	18.10.01
Pirie, Katherine,	LT	AIR	RNR AIR BR VL	15.12.89
Pittaway, Ernest,	HON MID	URNU	U/A	21.10.97
Plant, James,	HON MID	URNU	U/A	10.09.01
Platt, Timothy Samuel,	LT CDR	MCDO	PRESIDENT	01.04.00
Plummer, Ian,	HON MID	URNU	U/A	11.09.00
Pocock, James,	HON MID	URNU	U/A	11.10.01
Poole, Daniel,	HON MID	URNU	U/A	12.10.00
Porter, Jonathan Mitchell Alexander,	ASL	NE	EAGLET	22.02.00
Posnett, Dickon,	LT	AIR	RNR AIR BR VL	01.08.88
Poulton-Watt, Andrew Ritchie,	LT	CEW	SCOTIA	03.03.00
Powell, Stephen,	LT CDR	AIR	RNR AIR BR VL	01.10.93
Powell, William,	LT CDR	AIR	RNR AIR BR VL	31.03.99
Powis, Megan,	HONCADET	URNU	U/A	11.09.00
Powley, Simon Owen Maxwell, RD	LT CDR	INTR	FERRET (RNR)	31.03.98
Poynton, Claire,	HONCADET	URNU	U/A	06.12.01
Pratt, Angela Susan,	LT	Q	SHERWOOD	09.05.95
Preece, Adam,	HON MID	URNU	U/A	01.02.00
Pressagh, John Patterson, RD	LT CDR	INTR	FERRET (RNR)	02.04.78
Price, Julian,	LT	AIR	RNR AIR BR VL	16.11.94
Price, Naomi,	HONCADET	URNU	U/A	30.09.99
Price, Susan,	LT CDR	NCAGS	KING ALFRED	07.07.98
Prichard, Robert Edward,	LT CDR	CEW	PRESIDENT	05.01.96
Prichard, Robert Edward, RD*	LT CDR	CEW	PRESIDENT	14.10.92
Pryce, Helen,	HONCADET	URNU	U/A	01.12.00
Pryce, Simon,	LT	AIR	RNR AIR BR VL	05.10.88
Pugh, Hywel Jones,	ALT	AW	PRESIDENT	10.06.90
Pugh, Neil,	LT	LOGS	CAMBRIA	15.05.91
Pugsley, Andrew,	HON MID	URNU	U/A	12.10.99
Puplett, Michael,	ASL	URNU	U/A	06.11.00
Purdy, Helen,	HONCADET	URNU	U/A	25.11.99
Pye, Steven,	ALT	URNU	U/A	21.10.97

Name	Rank	Branch	Unit	Seniority

Q

| Quelch, Matthew, | HON MID | URNU | U/A | 12.02.01 |

R

Name	Rank	Branch	Unit	Seniority
Rainey, Owen Hamilton,	ASL	NE	CAROLINE	03.12.00
Ramsay, Brian, MA, ACMA	LT CDR	SM	PRESIDENT	31.03.01
Ramsdale, Timothy,	LT	AIR	RNR AIR BR VL	16.04.89
Ramshaw, Colin,	HON MID	URNU	U/A	02.11.00
Randles, Philip Neil,	ASL	NE	KING ALFRED	03.10.00
Ratzer, Edward,	HON MID	URNU	U/A	28.11.00
Ray, Louise Barbara,	ASL	NE	CAMBRIA	20.02.02
Rayne, Jeremy,	HON MID	URNU	U/A	02.11.99
Razaq, Sohail,	HON MID	URNU	U/A	07.10.01
Read, David Arthur, BSC	LT CDR	HQ	PRESIDENT	31.03.97
Read, Edward,	HON MID	URNU	U/A	19.10.00
Redmond, Robert,	LT CDR	AW	PRESIDENT	31.03.00
Reen, Stephen,	LT	AIR	RNR AIR BR VL	01.10.92
Rees, Nicola,	ASL	NE	KING ALFRED	07.01.00
Reid, Iain,	LT	AIR	RNR AIR BR VL	01.06.88
Reid, Joseph,	HON MID	URNU	U/A	21.10.98
Reilly, Paul,	HON MID	URNU	U/A	22.11.01
Relf, Elizabeth,	HONCADET	URNU	U/A	10.09.01
Rennell, Ian Joseph,	LT	NCAGS	EAGLET	19.11.96
Rentoul, Donald,	HON MID	URNU	U/A	08.11.00
Reubens, Edwin George Oliver,	CDR	NCAGS	VIVID	30.09.82
Reynolds, Edward,	HON MID	URNU	U/A	07.10.01
Reynolds, Louisa,	HONCADET	URNU	U/A	09.10.97
Reynolds, Nelson James Elliott, RD	CAPT	MW	CAROLINE	30.09.99
Reynoldson, Howard, QVRM	LT CDR	AIR	RNR AIR BR VL	02.11.85
Rhodes, Davina,	HONCADET	URNU	U/A	09.10.00
Richard-Dit-Leschery, Stanley Ernest, RD	LT CDR	AW	VIVID	22.11.92
Richardson, Mark,	HON MID	URNU	U/A	07.10.99
Richards, Anna-Rose,	HONCADET	URNU	U/A	07.10.01
Richards, Guy,	LT CDR	SEA	CAMBRIA	31.03.02
Richards, Simon,	LT	AIR	RNR AIR BR VL	10.06.96
Richardson, Ian John,	LT CDR	INTR	FERRET (RNR)	15.01.91
Richardson, John,	HON MID	URNU	U/A	14.10.99
Richardson, Margaret Lynda Maither, RD	LT CDR	Q	DALRIADA	31.03.98
Richardson, Nicholas,	LT CDR	AIR	RNR AIR BR VL	01.10.96
Richmond, Alan,	HON MID	URNU	U/A	18.10.01
Rickard, Margaret Mary,	LT	MS(F)	KING ALFRED	15.05.94
Riley, Peter John,	LT CDR	AW	CALLIOPE	31.03.98
Rimay-Muranyi, Gary,	LT	INTR	FERRET (RNR)	18.02.00
Ritchie, David,	LT CDR	AIR	RNR AIR BR VL	01.10.00
Roberts, Emma,	HONCADET	URNU	U/A	22.10.01
Roberts, Suzi,	SLT	LOGS	FLYING FOX	28.04.98
Roberts, Sophie,	HONCADET	URNU	U/A	18.10.01
Robertson, Jennifer Louise,	ASL	NE	WILDFIRE	10.05.01
Robertson, Lorne, RD	LT CDR	MW	DALRIADA	17.11.97
Robertson-Nicol, Henry,	HON MID	URNU	U/A	11.10.01
Robinson, Anthony Michael, RD	LT CDR	AW	CAMBRIA	16.06.92
Robinson, Andrew Ronald,	ASL	NE	KING ALFRED	29.01.02
Robinson, Ian Michael, RD	CAPT	NA	SHERWOOD	30.09.01
Robinson, James Brian,	LT	AW	EAGLET	24.02.90
Robinson, Jonathon Charles King,	LT CDR	AIR	RNR AIR BR VL	01.11.91
Robinson, Lloyd Charles,	LT	SEA	FORWARD	01.04.97
Robinson, Martyn Shaun,	LT	SM	WILDFIRE	30.10.97
Robinson, Nigel,	LT CDR	AIR	RNR AIR BR VL	31.03.94
Robinson, Paul,	HON MID	URNU	U/A	09.10.00
Robinson, William,	HON MID	URNU	U/A	12.10.00
Robson, Nicholas,	HON MID	URNU	U/A	18.10.01

Name	Rank	Branch	Unit	Seniority
Rodgers, Beth,	HONCADET	URNU	U/A	14.10.99
Roe, Robert,	ASG LT		EAGLET	23.01.01
Rollings, David Jonathan, RD	LT CDR	HQ	CAMBRIA	30.10.87
Romito, Charles,	HON MID	URNU	U/A	01.03.00
Rooke, Adam,	HON MID	URNU	U/A	06.09.99
Rooke, Zoe,	HONCADET	URNU	U/A	14.01.99
Rose, Norman, RD	LT CDR	URNU	U/A	23.02.90
Rose, Simon,	HON MID	URNU	U/A	25.10.01
Rosindale, Philip Michael, RD	LT	SEA	VIVID	19.05.97
Ross, Bruce James,	LT CDR	AW	KING ALFRED	05.05.90
Ross, Jonathan Anthony Duncan, RD	LT CDR	MW	DALRIADA	31.03.98
Ross, Nicholas,	HON MID	URNU	U/A	12.10.00
Roth, Charlotte,	HONCADET	URNU	U/A	04.10.01
Roue, Kathryn,	HONCADET	URNU	U/A	19.10.00
Rowe, Susan Margaret,	ALT CDR	NCAGS	VIVID	31.03.01
Rowell, Nina,	HONCADET	URNU	U/A	20.10.99
Rowles, Joanne,	LT	CEW	CAMBRIA	21.07.96
Rowley, Andrew,	ASL	URNU	U/A	10.08.00
Rowley, Alexandra,	HONCADET	URNU	U/A	11.10.01
Rowntree, Paul,	HON MID	URNU	U/A	18.10.01
Rudkin, Adam,	HON MID	URNU	U/A	26.10.99
Ruglys, Matthew,	LT	AIR	RNR AIR BR VL	16.11.86
Russ, Philip John,	LT CDR	MW	EAGLET	31.03.96
Russell, David Robert,	LT CDR	MR	KING ALFRED	19.03.89
Rutherford, Lesley Ann,	SLT	LOGS	DALRIADA	06.11.95
Ryan, Amy Jemima,	ASL	NE	FLYING FOX	04.08.00
Ryan, Peter,	PALT	AW	PRESIDENT	18.01.01
Ryan, Simon John D Arcy, RD	LT CDR	HQ	EAGLET	31.03.99
Ryder, Lucy,	HONCADET	URNU	U/A	25.10.01

S

Name	Rank	Branch	Unit	Seniority
Saffell, Thomas,	HON MID	URNU	U/A	15.10.98
Samwell, Michael,	HON MID	URNU	U/A	21.10.99
San, Howald Kin Loong,	LT	SM	PRESIDENT	15.12.90
Sandeman, Lillian,	HONCADET	URNU	U/A	30.09.99
Sanders, Ella,	HONCADET	URNU	U/A	08.02.01
Sanders, Kate,	HONCADET	URNU	U/A	11.09.00
Sanderson, Jennifer Patricia,	LT	HQ	KING ALFRED	08.07.96
Satchell, Peter James,	LT CDR	MW	PRESIDENT	31.03.00
Saunders, David James, RD	LT CDR	MW	PRESIDENT	31.03.95
Saunders, Duncan,	ASL	URNU	U/A	10.10.96
Scanlan, Oliver,	HON MID	URNU	U/A	11.10.01
Scanlon, Michael Stephen,	SLT	INTR	FERRET (RNR)	13.08.98
Scarth, Martin Richard,	LT	SM	PRESIDENT	18.05.01
Schwab, Robert,	LT CDR	AIR	RNR AIR BR VL	01.10.97
Scott, J G,	LT CDR	AW	PRESIDENT	31.03.99
Scott-Foxwell, Julian, RD	LT CDR	NA	U/A	15.03.98
Scribbins, Christopher John, RD	LT CDR	HQ	CALLIOPE	11.10.91
Seakins, Patrick Edward,	LT CDR	INTR	FERRET (RNR)	31.03.00
Sealy, Douglas Edward,	LT CDR	DIS	FERRET (RNR)	01.10.94
Searle, Geoffrey Derek,	LT CDR	MW	KING ALFRED	31.03.00
Seaton, Christopher Shaun Tudor,	LT CDR	AW	FLYING FOX	01.11.91
Seaton, Judith Ann,	SG LT	MEDF	VIVID	15.10.98
Seldon, John,	HON MID	URNU	U/A	22.10.97
Sellar, Susan,	HONCADET	URNU	U/A	14.10.99
Service, Brian,	LT CDR	AIR	RNR AIR BR VL	31.03.99
Shah, Tanvi,	HONCADET	URNU	U/A	18.10.01
Shakespeare, Christopher,	HON MID	URNU	U/A	04.11.99
Shakespeare, Martin, RD	LT CDR	DIS	FERRET (RNR)	31.03.97
Shannon, Tom, RD	LT CDR	URNU	U/A	01.11.95
Sharples, Derek,	ACDR	AIR	RNR AIR BR VL	05.03.02
Shaw, James Elliot, RD*	CDR	AW	PRESIDENT	30.09.97

Name	Rank	Branch	Unit	Seniority
Shaw, Katherine,	HONCADET	URNU	U/A	04.10.01
Shaw, Stuart,	HON MID	URNU	U/A	06.11.00
Shaw, Simon,	HON MID	URNU	U/A	06.10.00
Shawcross, Jayne,	LT CDR	AIR	RNR AIR BR VL	03.01.95
Shears, Stephen,	LT CDR	AIR	RNR AIR BR VL	31.03.00
Sheffield, Raphael,	HON MID	URNU	U/A	17.03.99
Shelley, James Charles,	PSG LT		PRESIDENT	12.06.01
Shepherd, David,	HON MID	URNU	U/A	11.10.01
Shepherd, Sarah Louise,	SLT	LOGS	VIVID	10.03.01
Shepherd, William James,	LT	DIS	FERRET (RNR)	25.04.95
Sheppard, Adam James,	ASL	NE	CAMBRIA	01.03.00
Sherman, Christopher James,	LT CDR	HQ	KING ALFRED	24.11.91
Sherwin, Anthony,	HON MID	URNU	U/A	14.10.99
Shilson, Stuart James,	ASL	NE	PRESIDENT	17.01.02
Shiner, David,	LT	DIS	FERRET (RNR)	02.11.99
Shinner, Patrick Anthony,	LT CDR	SM	PRESIDENT	31.03.99
Shinner, Stephanie Katherine Fleur,	LT CDR	NCAGS	WILDFIRE	31.03.00
Shirtcliffe, Kevin,	HON MID	URNU	U/A	04.10.01
Short, Matthew,	HON MID	URNU	U/A	04.10.01
Shouler, Martin Clifford,	ASL	NE	PRESIDENT	27.09.00
Shrives, Jonathan,	HON MID	URNU	U/A	11.10.01
Sibcy, James Robert William,	ASL	NE	PRESIDENT	03.08.01
Siddiqi, Omar,	HON MID	URNU	U/A	07.10.01
Sides, Susan C.,	LT CDR	HQ	FORWARD	30.09.91
Sigley, Arthur David Martin,	ASL	AW	SCOTIA	04.08.98
Simcock, Julia,	LT	NCAGS	CAMBRIA	02.02.01
Simmonds, Richard Charles Kenneth,	LT CDR	AWNIS	WILDFIRE	31.03.02
Simmonds, Timothy Paul,	LT	MW	PRESIDENT	23.05.97
Simmons, Annelie,	HONCADET	URNU	U/A	11.10.01
Simons, David,	HON MID	URNU	U/A	09.10.00
Simpson, Alex,	ASL	URNU	U/A	10.01.02
Simpson, James,	HON MID	URNU	U/A	28.09.00
Simpson, Paul John Caesar, RD	LT CDR	CEW	SHERWOOD	04.07.88
Sims, Richmal Jane,	LT	SM	KING ALFRED	16.08.98
Sinclair, James,	HON MID	URNU	U/A	30.09.99
Sinnott, Luke,	HON MID	URNU	U/A	24.10.00
Sivagnanam, Piriyah,	HONCADET	URNU	U/A	09.10.00
Skelton, Richard,	HON MID	URNU	U/A	11.10.01
Skidmore, Paul,	ALT	URNU	U/A	01.01.98
Skinner, Christopher,	HON MID	URNU	U/A	28.09.00
Skinner, Nigel Guy, BSC, M.ENG	LT	NCAGS	SHERWOOD	15.11.99
Skuriat, Olenka,	HONCADET	URNU	U/A	23.10.97
Slater, Elizabeth,	HONCADET	URNU	U/A	11.10.01
Slonecki, Adam,	HON MID	URNU	U/A	11.10.01
Small, Peter Kenneth,	SG CDR		CALLIOPE	30.09.97
Small, Pauline,	ALT	Q	SCOTIA	15.03.00
Smalldridge, Lindsay,	HONCADET	URNU	U/A	18.10.01
Smith, Andrew,	HON MID	URNU	U/A	06.10.00
Smith, Blair Hamilton,	PSG LTCDR		SCOTIA	13.12.00
Smith, Craig,	HON MID	URNU	U/A	05.10.00
Smith, David,	LT CDR	AIR	RNR AIR BR VL	31.03.00
Smith, David,	ALT	LOGS	EAGLET	03.07.01
Smith, Dominic,	HON MID	URNU	U/A	14.10.99
Smith, Gordon,	LT CDR	AIR	RNR AIR BR VL	31.03.01
Smith, Hannah,	HONCADET	URNU	U/A	01.10.98
Smith, Jennifer,	HONCADET	URNU	U/A	06.11.00
Smith, Jillian,	HONCADET	URNU	U/A	12.10.99
Smith, Jane Marion,	ASL	Q	VIVID	16.04.02
Smith, Kenneth,	HON MID	URNU	U/A	28.09.00
Smith, Lesley Gay Isabel, RD*	CDR	LOGS	VIVID	30.09.96
Smith, Michael,	LT	URNU	U/A	08.02.95
Smith, Neil L, RD*	LT CDR	AWNIS	DALRIADA	31.03.81
Smith, Paul,	HON MID	URNU	U/A	17.10.01

Name	Rank	Branch	Unit	Seniority
Smith, Rebecca,	HONCADET	URNU	U/A	18.10.01
Smith, Stephen,	ALT	CEW	WILDFIRE	03.05.00
Smith, William Charles,	ASL	NE	SCOTIA	02.12.99
Smith, Wilfred Donald Fitzroy, RD	SG CDR		EAGLET	30.09.99
Smyth, Kiaran,	ASL	URNU	U/A	06.10.98
Smyth, Michael Paul,	LT	MW	PRESIDENT	05.06.89
Snoddon, Robert,	LT CDR	CEW	CALLIOPE	31.03.01
Snow, Emma,	HONCADET	URNU	U/A	18.10.01
Souter, Michael David, RD	LT CDR	MR	WILDFIRE	01.01.84
Southall, Nicholas,	HON MID	URNU	U/A	18.10.01
Spacey, Craig,	HON MID	URNU	U/A	10.09.01
Spaine, Victor,	HON MID	URNU	U/A	14.10.99
Spencer, Gary,	LT CDR	AIR	RNR AIR BR VL	21.10.94
Spencer, Michael David,	ASL	NE	PRESIDENT	18.01.01
Spencer, Philip,	HON MID	URNU	U/A	01.12.00
Spray, Alison, RD	LT CDR	NCAGS	VIVID	31.03.93
Spring, Avril Ann,	SLT	LOGS	KING ALFRED	04.12.96
Sprowles, K J, RD	LT CDR	NCAGS	PRESIDENT	04.11.90
Squire, Elizabeth,	LT	INTR	FERRET (RNR)	17.06.96
Squire, Robert James, RD	LT CDR	CEW	FORWARD	12.05.01
Stacpoole, Sybil,	HONCADET	URNU	U/A	15.10.98
Stafford-Smith, Karen Julie, RD	LT CDR	SM	CAMBRIA	31.03.98
Staniforth, Claire,	HONCADET	URNU	U/A	19.10.00
Stanley, Dermot Alan, RD	LT	SEA	CALLIOPE	12.01.96
Staples, David Richard,	PSG LT		WILDFIRE	28.11.01
Staples, Karl James,	ASL	NE	PRESIDENT	25.04.01
Steer, Rebecca,	HONCADET	URNU	U/A	09.10.00
Stephen, Cameron,	HON MID	URNU	U/A	11.09.00
Stephenson, Michael Edward,	ASL	NE	CALLIOPE	19.11.98
Stephenson, Richard, RD	LT CDR	AIR	RNR AIR BR VL	01.03.80
Stevenson, Adam,	HON MID	URNU	U/A	20.10.99
Stevenson, Paul,	HON MID	URNU	U/A	08.09.99
Stewart, Allan,	LT CDR	SM	EAGLET	31.03.02
Stewart, Iain, RD	LT CDR	LOGS	SCOTIA	21.03.87
Stewart, William Roderick,	LT CDR	NA	SCOTIA	06.12.86
Stickland, Anthony Charles Robert, RD	LT CDR	AW	KING ALFRED	31.03.98
Stidston, David,	LT CDR	AIR	RNR AIR BR VL	01.10.94
Stocker, Jeremy Richard,	LT CDR	HQ	CALLIOPE	01.06.89
Stocker, John,	HON MID	URNU	U/A	11.10.01
Stones, Nicholas,	LT	SEA	FORWARD	01.04.95
Stopford, Jeremy,	HON MID	URNU	U/A	18.10.01
Stopps, Claire,	HONCADET	URNU	U/A	14.10.99
Storey, David,	HON MID	URNU	U/A	25.10.01
Story, Ruth,	HONCADET	URNU	U/A	12.10.00
Strachan, Robin Kinnear,	SG CDR		PRESIDENT	30.09.95
Strain, Justin Damian Russell,	LT	MW	KING ALFRED	01.05.98
Strawbridge, Chantal,	HONCADET	URNU	U/A	07.10.99
Strawbridge, Rona,	HONCADET	URNU	U/A	19.10.00
Streeter, Pamela,	HONCADET	URNU	U/A	04.02.99
Strike, Peter,	LT	URNU	U/A	30.09.92
Strong, Tobias,	LT	SEA	FLYING FOX	01.11.94
Strudwick, Peggy Barbara,	LT	LOGS	VIVID	17.12.96
Styles, Sarah Jane,	ASL	NE	PRESIDENT	09.05.00
Sutcliff, Jonathon,	HON MID	URNU	U/A	11.10.01
Sutton, Gareth,	HON MID	URNU	U/A	18.10.01
Swabey, Matthew,	HON MID	URNU	U/A	06.09.98
Swaby, James,	HON MID	URNU	U/A	18.10.00
Swann, Adam,	HON MID	URNU	U/A	21.10.99
Swann, Judith Helen, QVRM, RD*, JP	CDR	N/A	SHERWOOD	03.09.90
Sweenie, John Fraser,	SG LTCDR		DALRIADA	13.02.90
Sweetman, David,	HON MID	URNU	U/A	18.10.00
Sweetnam, Meriel,	HONCADET	URNU	U/A	24.10.01

Name	Rank	Branch	Unit	Seniority
Sykes, Andrew,	HON MID	URNU	U/A	18.10.00
Sykes, Karen Dawn,	SLT	MS(F)	VIVID	04.05.99
Syme, Allan, RD*	LT CDR	HQ	DALRIADA	11.02.83

T

Name	Rank	Branch	Unit	Seniority
Tabner, Reuben,	HON MID	URNU	U/A	30.09.99
Tall, Louisa,	HONCADET	URNU	U/A	20.10.98
Tall, Richard Edward,	LT	SM	FLYING FOX	14.12.97
Tarmey, Sarah,	HONCADET	URNU	U/A	08.10.98
Tarrant, David Charles,	LT CDR	AW	KING ALFRED	30.11.93
Taylor, Dale,	HON MID	URNU	U/A	21.10.99
Taylor, Louise Elizabeth,	LT CDR	NCAGS	EAGLET	31.03.00
Taylor, Nicholas Robert,	PSG LT		FORWARD	14.04.99
Taylor, Neville,	LT CDR	HQ	CALLIOPE RNR	01.04.89
Taylor, Nicholas,	HON MID	URNU	U/A	20.10.98
Taylor, Rupert James, RD	LT CDR	AW	KING ALFRED	31.03.99
Taylor, Stephen,	HON MID	URNU	U/A	25.10.01
Taylor, Thomas,	HON MID	URNU	U/A	04.10.01
Teasdale, David Andrew,	LT	SM	FLYING FOX	01.12.93
Teasdale, James,	HON MID	URNU	U/A	11.09.00
Telfer, Alison, RD	LT CDR	NCAGS	EAGLET	30.09.91
Temple, Miles,	LT	SEA	WILDFIRE	01.11.94
Templeton, Susan,	LT CDR	LOGS	FLYING FOX	31.03.96
Tetchner, David,	HON MID	URNU	U/A	30.11.00
Thomas, David Graham,	SLT	CEW	KING ALFRED	21.07.96
Thomas, David James,	ASL	NE	CAMBRIA	27.02.02
Thomas, Emma Margaret,	LT CDR	MR	WILDFIRE	31.03.01
Thomas, Jeffrey,	LT CDR	AIR	RNR AIR BR VL	01.09.92
Thomas, Neil,	HON MID	URNU	U/A	25.11.99
Thomas, Peter Glyn, RD	LT CDR	MW	EAGLET	31.03.99
Thomas, Philip,	HON MID	URNU	U/A	17.10.01
Thomas, Stephen,	LT	MW	CAMBRIA	26.01.97
Thomas, Tenny,	HON MID	URNU	U/A	20.10.99
Thomason, Michael,	LT	LOGS	EAGLET	09.11.97
Thompson, Andrew John, RD	CDR	NCAGS	VIVID	30.09.01
Thompson, Elizabeth,	HONCADET	URNU	U/A	06.09.98
Thompson, Glenn,	LT CDR	AIR	RNR AIR BR VL	31.03.99
Thompson, Huw,	HON MID	URNU	U/A	04.10.01
Thomson, Paul,	HON MID	URNU	U/A	07.10.99
Thomson, Sheena Rosemary, BA	LT CDR	MR	DALRIADA	31.03.00
Thomson, Susie Jane,	LT CDR	MR	FLYING FOX	31.03.99
Thorne, Brian John, RD	CDR	CEW	CAMBRIA	30.09.97
Thorne, Lee James,	LT CDR	SEA	SHERWOOD	31.03.02
Thorne, Stephen Paul, RD	CDR	CEW	KING ALFRED	30.09.98
Tiffen, Jonathan,	HON MID	URNU	U/A	11.10.01
Tighe, Christopher,	HON MID	URNU	U/A	21.10.99
Tighe, Gary,	LT CDR	AIR	RNR AIR BR VL	01.02.91
Till, Alexander,	HON MID	URNU	U/A	01.11.01
Tindall-Jones, Julia Mary, BA	CDR	LOGS	VIVID	30.09.01
Titterton, Jody,	HONCADET	URNU	U/A	02.10.00
Todd, Andrew Harry Campbell,	LT CDR	NCAGS	SCOTIA	31.03.98
Todd, Susan,	ASL	URNU	U/A	05.03.96
Tonkin, Neil,	LT CDR	AIR	RNR AIR BR VL	01.10.90
Topping, Mark,	LT CDR	HQ	CAMBRIA	31.03.97
Tornambe, Richard,	HON MID	URNU	U/A	07.10.99
Townsend, John Stafford,	SG LTCDR		SHERWOOD	11.02.85
Townsend-Rose, Christopher,	SG LTCDR		CALLIOPE	13.12.00
Toy, James, RD	LT CDR	NA	CAROLINE	03.07.80
Trafford, Rebecca Jane,	ASL	NE	VIVID	16.05.01
Trangmar, Paul,	LT	LOGS	WILDFIRE	22.11.93
Trelawny, Christopher Charles, RD	LT	SEA	PRESIDENT	14.12.89
Trelinska, Victoria Jane,	ACDR	NA	SHERWOOD	18.12.01

Name	Rank		Establishment	Date
Treloar, Philip,	LT CDR	MR	WILDFIRE	16.09.88
Tribe, David,	LT CDR	AIR	RNR AIR BR VL	31.03.99
Trimmer, Patrick David Mark,	LT CDR	HQ	CALLIOPE	31.03.96
Trosh, Nicholas,	HON MID	URNU	U/A	30.09.99
Truscott, Rena Julie,	LT	HQ	VIVID	12.09.96
Tubb, Anna,	HONCADET	URNU	U/A	12.10.00
Tudor, Simon,	HON MID	URNU	U/A	12.10.00
Tulloch, Alan,	SLT	X	U/A	08.04.87
Tunstall, Sarah,	HONCADET	URNU	U/A	06.03.00
Tuppen, Heather Jill,	LT	MR	WILDFIRE	24.10.94
Turner, Christopher,	LT	URNU	U/A	01.11.96
Turner, Jonathan Andrew McMahon, RD	SG CDR		KING ALFRED	30.09.99
Turner, Ryan,	HON MID	URNU	U/A	25.10.01
Turner, Simon John,	LT CDR	AWNIS	VIVID	31.03.99
Turtill, Lisa Helen,	ASL	NE	DALRIADA	07.10.99
Tutton, Amanda,	HONCADET	URNU	U/A	14.10.99
Tweed, S, JP, RD*	CDR	NCAGS	VIVID	30.09.99
Tyrell, Carol Marguerite,	LT CDR	DIS	FERRET (RNR)	11.04.90

U

Name	Rank		Establishment	Date
Upton, Vivienne,	HONCADET	URNU	U/A	22.10.01
Ure, Fiona, RD	LT	Q	SHERWOOD	04.03.99
Utting, Penelope Anne,	LT CDR	MR	KING ALFRED	31.03.01

V

Name	Rank		Establishment	Date
Valentine, Robert Innes,	LT CDR	SEA	SCOTIA	31.03.99
Van Asch, Alexandra,	HONCADET	URNU	U/A	12.10.99
Van Den Bergh, Mark	LT	HQ	WILDFIRE	16.12.92
Vardy, Emma,	HONCADET	URNU	U/A	12.10.00
Varley, Peter,	ACDR	AIR	RNR AIR BR VL	05.03.02
Veale, Bryony,	HONCADET	URNU	U/A	19.10.00
Vernon, Michael A, RD	LT CDR	CEW	VIVID	27.08.90
Vincent, Claire Elaine,	LT	AWNIS	KING ALFRED	23.04.92
Vitali, Julie Elizabeth,	LT	DIS	FERRET (RNR)	08.06.96
Vora, Nina,	HONCADET	URNU	U/A	18.10.01

W

Name	Rank		Establishment	Date
Wain, Alexis,	HON MID	URNU	U/A	05.07.99
Wainwright, Barnaby,	LT CDR	AIR	RNR AIR BR VL	01.09.89
Waite, Stephen,	LT	Q	VIVID	18.05.01
Wake, Thomas Baldwin, RD	LT CDR	CEW	SHERWOOD	31.03.00
Wakefield, Gary,	LT CDR	AIR	RNR AIR BR VL	01.03.93
Wakeford, Mark Warren,	LT CDR	MR	KING ALFRED	31.03.02
Walden, Geoffery Gerald,	LT	SM	SHERWOOD	10.12.90
Wale, Martin Charles Johnson, Dr	LT CDR	DIS	FERRET (RNR)	01.08.86
Wales, Frederick Anthony, RD	LT CDR	AW	KING ALFRED	31.03.98
Walker, David,	LT CDR	LOGS	PRESIDENT	31.03.97
Walker, Graeme,	HON MID	URNU	U/A	10.09.01
Walker, Gail,	HONCADET	URNU	U/A	14.10.99
Walker, Paul MacKenzie,	ALT	SM	CALLIOPE	11.02.02
Walker-Spicer, Ian Edward,	LT CDR	AW	PRESIDENT	12.11.84
Wallace, Stuart Iain,	LT	AW	EAGLET	23.07.99
Wallace, Simon John,	ASL	AW	SHERWOOD	08.06.00
Waller, James,	ASL	NE	FORWARD	14.11.00
Waller, Vincent Francis, RD	LT CDR	AW	CALLIOPE	01.09.88
Wallom, Anne,	LT	MR	SCOTIA	13.09.92
Walmsley, Stephen Graham,	LT	HQ	CAROLINE	01.10.97
Walsh, Richard Michael,	ASL	NE	FORWARD	12.12.00
Walters, Richard John,	LT	MR	PRESIDENT	06.08.93
Walthall, Fiona Elizabeth,	LT CDR	NCAGS	SCOTIA	31.03.02

Name	Rank	Branch	Ship	Date
Walworth, William Michael,	CDR	AW	PRESIDENT	30.09.95
Ward, Suzanne,	HONCADET	URNU	U/A	30.09.97
Warne, Mark,	LT	SEA	VIVID	19.10.01
Warner, Adrian,	HON MID	URNU	U/A	11.10.01
Warnock, Gavin,	LT CDR	AIR	RNR AIR BR VL	01.10.95
Warren, Julian,	HON MID	URNU	U/A	28.09.00
Warrick, Mark,	HON MID	URNU	U/A	06.09.99
Wartlier, Lee,	HON MID	URNU	U/A	19.10.00
Waterhouse, Guy,	HON MID	URNU	U/A	22.10.01
Waters, Anna,	HONCADET	URNU	U/A	11.10.01
Waters, Christopher Martin,	LT CDR	NCAGS	KING ALFRED	01.05.86
Waters, Michael,	HON MID	URNU	U/A	14.10.99
Waterworth, Stephen Norman,	LT	CEW	WILDFIRE	01.04.93
Watkin, Melissa Clare,	ASL	NE	SCOTIA	26.06.00
Watson, Catherine, RD	LT CDR	HQ	EAGLET	31.03.98
Watson, David,	HON MID	URNU	U/A	06.11.00
Watson, Karen Marie,	LT CDR	INTR	FERRET (RNR)	31.03.99
Watson, Lloyd,	LT CDR	AIR	RNR AIR BR VL	01.10.94
Watts, Alexandra,	HONCADET	URNU	U/A	18.10.01
Watts, Nicholas,	HON MID	URNU	U/A	11.10.01
Waugh, Gillian,	HONCADET	URNU	U/A	11.10.01
Way, Katherine,	HONCADET	URNU	U/A	07.10.99
Weaver, Peter,	ALT	HQ	VIVID RNR	23.10.01
Webber, Christina,	HONCADET	URNU	U/A	11.10.01
Webborn, Elizabeth,	HONCADET	URNU	U/A	17.10.01
Webster, Mark,	MID	NE	DALRIADA	26.02.02
Wedgewood, Jonathon James,	PSG LTCDR		SCOTIA	26.11.98
Weeden, Alexandra Louise,	ASL	NE	PRESIDENT	09.12.97
Weedon, Matthew,	HON MID	URNU	U/A	02.10.00
Weldon, Helen Wright,	LT	HQ	DALRIADA	16.03.89
Wells, Christopher Michael,	LT CDR	AW	KING ALFRED	31.03.94
Wells, Jonathan,	LT CDR	AIR	RNR AIR BR VL	01.12.91
Welsh, Audrey,	LT	CEW	WILDFIRE	17.02.97
Welsh, Nicholas Paul,	ASL	NE	PRESIDENT	17.10.01
Wesley, John R,	LT CDR	HQ	PRESIDENT	12.11.89
West, Nicholas,	LT CDR	AIR	RNR AIR BR VL	31.03.99
West, Susan Elizabeth,	SG CDR	MEDF	PRESIDENT	30.09.01
Westwood, Steve,	LT CDR	AIR	RNR AIR BR VL	01.10.92
Whawell, Peter Gerald Maber,	LT	MW	PRESIDENT	06.11.98
Wheeldon, Matthew,	HON MID	URNU	U/A	26.10.99
Wheeler, Joanne Natalie,	ASL	NE	PRESIDENT	01.05.01
Wheeler, Robert Alec,	SG CDR		KING ALFRED	30.09.98
Wheeler, Sophia Rebecca Frances,	SLT	SM	PRESIDENT	29.11.96
Whitby, David John, RD*	CDR	AW	PRESIDENT	30.09.84
Whitby, Philip,	LT CDR	SM	VIVID	26.12.90
Whitby, Stephen,	LT CDR	HQ	SCOTIA	01.01.92
White, Andrew,	HON MID	URNU	U/A	19.10.00
White, Ian Roy,	LT CDR	HQ	CALLIOPE	31.03.96
White, Olivia,	HONCADET	URNU	U/A	19.10.00
Whitehead, Andrea,	HONCADET	URNU	U/A	18.10.00
Whitehead, Keith Stuart, BSC, RD	LT CDR	HQ	KING ALFRED	31.03.00
Whitehead, Lucy,	HONCADET	URNU	U/A	04.10.01
Whitehouse, Andrew,	HON MID	URNU	U/A	25.11.99
Whitehouse, Marie,	HONCADET	URNU	U/A	21.10.99
Whitlock, Michael Anthony,	LT	SEA	KING ALFRED	27.01.92
Whitney, Camilla,	HONCADET	URNU	U/A	07.10.01
Whittaker, Maime,	HON MID	URNU	U/A	17.10.01
Whittall, Andrew,	LT	AIR	RNR AIR BR VL	15.10.90
Wickens, Ian,	LT CDR	AIR	RNR AIR BR VL	31.03.00
Widdick, David,	HON MID	URNU	U/A	07.10.01
Wilcockson, Alastair Quentin,	SG LTCDR		KING ALFRED	24.07.01
Wilkie, Suzanne Ellen,	LT CDR	HQ	SCOTIA	26.06.01

Name	Rank			
Wilkinson, Lynn,	LT	Q	EAGLET	11.01.92
Wilkinson, Sarah,	HONCADET	URNU	U/A	01.12.00
Willcox, Joanna,	HONCADET	URNU	U/A	18.10.01
Williams, Alex,	HON MID	URNU	U/A	22.10.01
Williams, Gemma,	HONCADET	URNU	U/A	09.10.00
Williams, Kate,	HONCADET	URNU	U/A	28.09.00
Williams, Kristian,	HON MID	URNU	U/A	07.10.01
Williams, Mark Jeremy,	LT	NCAGS	EAGLET	27.10.92
Williams, Owain,	HON MID	URNU	U/A	08.10.98
Williams, Peter Lunt, RD	LT CDR	CEW	EAGLET	11.05.90
Williams, Paul David,	LT CDR	AW	CALLIOPE	05.08.86
Williams, Rudolph Stephen,	ASL	NE	VIVID	01.05.02
Williams, Scott,	HON MID	URNU	U/A	11.10.01
Williams, Thomas,	HON MID	URNU	U/A	11.10.01
Williams, Timothy Paul,	LT	MW	WILDFIRE	22.09.95
Williamson, Helen,	HONCADET	URNU	U/A	12.10.00
Wilson, Gary,	LT CDR	URNU	U/A	10.10.95
Wilson, Garth,	HON MID	URNU	U/A	24.10.01
Wilson, Jonathan,	ASL	NE	SCOTIA	30.11.00
Wilson, Jennifer Maureen,	LT CDR	Q	KING ALFRED	31.03.95
Wilson, Karyn, RD	LT	NCAGS	FLYING FOX	19.07.90
Wilson, Paul,	HON MID	URNU	U/A	19.10.00
Wilson, Peter,	LT CDR	AIR	RNR AIR BR VL	07.09.99
Wilson, Scott McDonald,	ASL	NE	SCOTIA	11.04.02
Wilson, Stephen John,	SG LTCDR		WILDFIRE	30.09.96
Winder, Nicholas,	ASL	NE	U/A	03.05.00
Winfield, Adrian,	LT CDR	AIR	RNR AIR BR VL	31.03.99
Wingrove, Catherine Barbara,	LT	Q	CALLIOPE	30.03.98
Winn, Alexander,	HON MID	URNU	U/A	12.10.00
Winser, Charlotte,	HONCADET	URNU	U/A	11.10.01
Winstanley, Nichola Ann, VRSM	LT CDR	MR	VIVID	31.03.95
Winterton, James,	HON MID	URNU	U/A	04.10.01
Wiseman, Anee-Marie,	HONCADET	URNU	U/A	04.10.01
Wiseman, Jane,	LT CDR	AIR	RNR AIR BR VL	31.03.01
Wolstenholme, Clare,	HONCADET	URNU	U/A	25.10.01
Wolstenholme, David,	LT CDR	AIR	RNR AIR BR VL	01.10.93
Wolstenholme, Fiona,	HONCADET	URNU	U/A	18.10.01
Wood, Clare,	HONCADET	URNU	U/A	27.11.01
Wood, Daniel James,	ASL	NE	EAGLET	23.10.96
Wood, Graham,	HON MID	URNU	U/A	19.10.00
Wood, John,	LT CDR	CEW	CALLIOPE	31.03.01
Wood, Justin,	LT CDR	AIR	RNR AIR BR VL	01.03.90
Wood, Matthew,	HON MID	URNU	U/A	18.10.01
Wood, Richard,	HON MID	URNU	U/A	20.10.99
Wood, Suzanne,	LT	HQ	PRESIDENT	05.04.93
Woodham, Jeremy,	LT CDR	AIR	RNR AIR BR VL	02.07.92
Woodman, Clive Andrew,	LT CDR	MR	VIVID	01.09.87
Woods, Fergus,	LT CDR	AIR	RNR AIR BR VL	01.10.88
Woods, Martin John,	ASL	NE	PRESIDENT	15.08.01
Wordie, Andrew George Lyon, RD	LT CDR	CEW	SHERWOOD	31.03.95
Worral, Andrew,	HON MID	URNU	U/A	09.10.00
Worsley, Alistair Louis, RD	LT CDR	MR	WILDFIRE	31.03.96
Wray, Ronald Maurice,	LT CDR	NCAGS	CAROLINE	31.03.99
Wreford, Katrine Patricia,	LT CDR	MR	SCOTIA	31.03.93
Wrigglesworth, Peter John,	SG LTCDR		SHERWOOD	02.08.88
Wright, Alan Howard,	LT CDR	AW	EAGLET	01.11.91
Wright, Antony,	LT CDR	AIR	RNR AIR BR VL	01.10.97
Wright, Douglas John,	LT	DIS	FERRET (RNR)	26.01.96
Wright, Gordon, RD	LT CDR	AIR	RNR AIR BR VL	17.04.86
Wright, Gabriel,	HON MID	URNU	U/A	11.10.01
Wright, Iain Alistair MacKay,	LT CDR	DIS	FERRET (RNR)	18.08.97
Wright, Stephen,	LT CDR	CEW	KING ALFRED	31.03.00

Wright, Stephen, GM	LT CDR	AIR	RNR AIR BR VL	31.03.01
Wrightson, Ian,	LT	AIR	RNR AIR BR VL	01.04.93
Wring, Matthew Anthony,	LT	MW	FLYING FOX	25.01.95
Wuidart Gray, Spencer Richard,	LT CDR	SEA	KING ALFRED	31.03.02
Wyatt, Mark Edward, RD	CDR	MW	KING ALFRED	30.09.99
Wyglendacz, Jan Andrew,	LT	LOGS	CAMBRIA	28.01.90
Wyness, Sharon,	LT	AIR	RNR AIR BR VL	01.09.96

X

Xu, Hui,	HONCADET	URNU	U/A	24.10.01

Y

Yates, Steven,	LT CDR	MW	FLYING FOX	31.03.00
Yeo, Sophie,	HONCADET	URNU	U/A	18.10.01
Yetman, Philip John, RD	CDR	NCAGS	KING ALFRED	30.09.98
Yibowei, Christophe Amaebi,	ASL	NE	PRESIDENT	06.12.00
Yong, Andrew,	HON MID	URNU	U/A	19.10.98
Young, Carl,	LT CDR	AIR	RNR AIR BR VL	31.03.98
Young, Duncan, RD	LT CDR	MW	CALLIOPE	31.03.98
Young, Gregory Christian,	SLT	MW	PRESIDENT	29.10.95
Young, William David,	LT	LOGS	KING ALFRED	11.05.93
Yule Vt, Victoria,	ASL	URNU	U/A	21.03.96

ROYAL NAVAL RESERVE INTERPRETERS

Name	Rank	Date Of Qualifying or Re-qualifying
FRENCH		
Nicholson, P.A.	LT CDR	1980
Pressagh, J.P.	LT CDR	1994
GERMAN		
Cobbold, A.R.	LT	2001
Pressagh, J.P.	LT CDR	1983
ITALIAN		
Pressagh, J.P.	LT CDR	1999
Alcock, M.L.	LT	2001
JAPANESE		
Nicholson, P.A.	LT CDR	1995
PERSIAN		
Cobbold, A.R.	LT	1982

Name	Rank	Date Of Qualifying or Re-qualifying
POLISH		
Pressagh, J.P.	LT CDR	1989
RUSSIAN		
Cobbold, A.R.	LT	1989
Pressagh, J.P.	LT CDR	1995
Seakins, P.E.	LT	1995
Jones, L.	LT CDR	1989
SPANISH		
Alcock, M.L.	LT	1995
Nicholson, P.A.	LT CDR	1997
Pressagh, J.P.	LT CDR	1993

ROYAL MARINES RESERVE

Name	Rank	Branch	Unit	Seniority

B

Name	Rank	Branch	Unit	Seniority
Baker, AMair,	Lt	M1	LONDON	08.03.00
Barnwell, Barry, RD	Lt Col	M1	SCOTLAND	01.12.90
Billington, Ed,	Capt	M1	MERSEYSIDE	07.06.92
Brooker-Gillespie, Robin,	Loc Maj	M1	LONDON	04.01.95
Brown, Roger,	Capt	M1	MERSEYSIDE	15.07.90
Bruce, Rory,	Lt Col	M1	BRISTOL	30.06.98
Brunskill, Michael,	Lt	M1	MERSEYSIDE	21.05.00

C

Name	Rank	Branch	Unit	Seniority
Campbell, Mike,	Act Maj	M1	TYNE	01.04.95
Chamberlain, Henry,	Capt	M1	BRISTOL	28.04.94
Churchill, Colin,	2lt	M2	SCOTLAND	19.04.99
Coard, Thomas, RD	Maj	M1	SCOTLAND	30.06.98
Crichton, Dayle,	2lt	M1	SCOTLAND	11.01.02

D

Name	Rank	Branch	Unit	Seniority
Day, Jason,	Lt	M1	LONDON	25.06.99
Doubleday, Iain,	Capt	M1	LONDON	01.04.97

F

Name	Rank	Branch	Unit	Seniority
Fielder, David,	Maj	M1	BRISTOL	01.04.99
Figgins, Phil,	Maj	M2	LONDON	01.04.91
Finn, Tristan,	2lt	M1	BRISTOL	11.01.02
Fothergill, Nicholas,	Capt	M1	LONDON	02.11.00

G

Name	Rank	Branch	Unit	Seniority
Gardiner, Andrew,	Capt	M1	BRISTOL	03.08.96
Gardner, Andrew,	Lt	M1	MERSEYSIDE	04.04.00
Gibson, Mark,	Capt	M1	MERSEYSIDE	01.02.95
Ginnever, Mark,	Capt	M1	BRISTOL	01.09.01
Guest, Simon,	Capt	M1	LONDON	29.04.93

H

Name	Rank	Branch	Unit	Seniority
Halls, Monty,	Capt	M2	BRISTOL	09.11.99
Harker, Andrew,	Capt	M1	TYNE	11.11.01
Hayes, G.M.,	2lt	M1	MERSEYSIDE	09.08.98
Hebron, Bryan,	Capt	M1	TYNE	22.05.90
Hillman, David,	Capt	M1	SCOTLAND	07.01.00
Holt, Andy,	Lt Col	M1	MERSEYSIDE	31.12.93
Hough, Brian, RD	Col	M1	MERSEYSIDE	01.06.97
Hunter, Ben,	Capt	M2	LONDON	15.01.98
Hutchinson, Philip,	Capt	M1	RNR AIR BR VL	

I

Name	Rank	Branch	Unit	Seniority
Ilng, John,	Maj	M1	LONDON	01.09.94

J

Name	Rank	Branch	Unit	Seniority
Jackson, Fraser,	Capt	M1	SCOTLAND	01.10.92
Jobbins, Paul, OBE, RD* ADC	Col	M2	BRISTOL	28.01.94

Name	Rank	Branch	Unit	Seniority

K

Name	Rank	Branch	Unit	Seniority
Kinninmonth, Craig,	Lt	M1	SCOTLAND	14.09.99
Knox, David,	Maj	M2	TYNE	01.07.99

L

Name	Rank	Branch	Unit	Seniority
Lacy, Robert,	Act Maj	M1	MERSEYSIDE	01.04.91
Lang, Tom,	Brig	M1	BRISTOL	28.02.95
Langford, Haj,	2lt	M1	LONDON	25.01.00
Lewis, James,	2lt	M1	BRISTOL	07.01.02
Lewis, Robbie,	Capt	M1	BRISTOL	01.07.98
Lindfield, Barry, RD	Maj	M1	MERSEYSIDE	25.10.91
Love, Gavin,	2lt	M1	SCOTLAND	01.07.99
Loynes, Phillip,	Lt Col	M1	MERSEYSIDE	31.12.94

M

Name	Rank	Branch	Unit	Seniority
Mannion, Steve,	Maj	M2	LONDON	26.03.96
Martin, Simon,	Capt	M1	LONDON	01.09.01
Mason, Andrew,	Capt	M1	BRISTOL	16.12.96
Mawhood, Christopher,	Maj	M1	MERSEYSIDE	01.09.87
May, Philip,	Act Maj	M1	MERSEYSIDE	02.10.01
McGovern, James,	Lt	M1	SCOTLAND	14.05.01
McLaughlin, Stephen,	Capt	M1	SCOTLAND	18.09.91
Mirtle, Frank, RD	Lt Col	M1	LONDON	01.06.99
Moulton, Frederick,	Maj	M1	BRISTOL	27.04.99

P

Name	Rank	Branch	Unit	Seniority
Paul, Thomas, RD	Maj	M1	SCOTLAND	01.06.91
Phillips, Andy,	Capt	M1	BRISTOL	01.09.95
Pike, Andrew,	Lt	M1	TYNE	30.07.95
Pollock, Andrew,	Capt	M1	LONDON	27.03.00

R

Name	Rank	Branch	Unit	Seniority
Radford, Barry, MBE	Col	M1	BRISTOL	30.06.94
Reed, Jerry,	Maj	M1	TYNE	01.07.01
Reynolds, Stephen,	Maj		RNR AIR BR VL	01.05.98
Richards, Gavin, RD	Maj	M1	LONDON	16.09.93
Richards, Stephen,	Maj		RNR AIR BR VL	28.04.94
Roberts, John,	Capt	M1	SCOTLAND	22.08.92
Robinson, David, BEM	Maj	M1	TYNE	14.11.95
Rochester, Richard,	Capt	M1	BRISTOL	01.07.95
Rowland, Johnny,	Maj	M1	BRISTOL	25.06.96
Rowlstone, David,	Maj	M1	MERSEYSIDE	01.04.97

S

Name	Rank	Branch	Unit	Seniority
Scott, John,	Maj	M1	BRISTOL	01.03.96
Sharp, Gordon,	Maj	M1	LONDON	30.06.98
Smith, Anthony, RD*	Col	M2	BRISTOL	18.07.96
Smith, Fraser,	Act Maj	M1	LONDON	03.08.96
Storrie, Richard,	Capt	M1	BRISTOL	24.04.91

T

Name	Rank	Branch	Unit	Seniority
Tayler, Harry,	Act Maj	M1	LONDON	01.07.94
Terry, Stuart,	Maj	M1	BRISTOL	01.02.93
Thompson, Joseph,	Capt	M1	TYNE	07.12.98
Tomkins, Richard,	Maj	M2	BRISTOL	30.06.98
Tonner, Raymond,	Maj	M1	BRISTOL	03.05.95
Travis, Adrian, RD	Maj	M1	LONDON	01.05.96

Name	Rank	Branch	Unit	Seniority

W

Name	Rank	Branch	Unit	Seniority
Waddell, Ian, RD	Capt	M1	SCOTLAND	01.08.91
Watkinson, Neil,	Maj	M1	LONDON	02.09.99
Watt, David,	Maj	M1	BRISTOL	01.08.00
Whitehead, Andrew,	2lt	M1	MERSEYSIDE	01.08.99

X

Name	Rank	Branch	Unit	Seniority
Xiberras, Maurice,	2lt	M1	MERSEYSIDE	24.05.00

SEA CADET CORPS

Name	Rank	Seniority	Name	Rank	Seniority

A

Adams, Thomas	Lt	07.09.83
Agar, Andrew	Lt	22.03.91
Agnew, Anthony	Capt RMR	05.06.98
Allam, John	Lt	31.08.87
Allam, Vicki	Slt	14.05.00
Allen, Karen	Lt	08.10.88
Allen, Leslie	Lt Cdr	01.01.99
Allo, David	Lt Cdr	06.05.72
Andersen, Kim	Lt RMR	01.07.99
Anderson, Alex	Lt	20.03.00
Anderson, Robert	Lt	01.04.99
Appleby, Keith	Lt	21.02.98
Archbold, Dennis	Lt Cdr	11.08.99
Archbold, Theresa	Lt	20.11.97
Archer, Barry	Lt	08.03.94
Archer, Lynn	Lt	14.11.96
Argo, James	Slt	11.12.00
Atherton, John	Slt	02.06.96
Atkin, Andrew	Slt	06.05.01
Atkins, Doreen	Lt	08.04.92
Attwood, Anthony	Lt	22.02.87
Avill, Susan	Lt	01.11.89
Ayers, William	Lt	04.01.02

B

Baddley, Stephen	Lt	28.11.95
Bailey, Robert	Lt	12.03.91
Bailey, Terence	Lt	01.12.95
Bainbridge, Patricia	Lt	03.11.98
Baker, Michael	Lt RMR	24.05.95
Baker, Roy	Maj RMR	18.05.82
Banks, Michael	Lt Cdr	06.09.88
Banks, Paul	Lt	06.06.96
Banner, Peter	Slt	30.03.92
Barber, Anthony	Lt	12.03.91

Barker, David	Lt	21.06.99
Barker, Sandra	Lt	07.10.98
Barons, Simon	Lt	28.04.99
Barr, William	Lt	15.02.00
Barras, Hugh	Lt	30.10.98
Barritt, Richard	Lt Cdr	05.03.89
Barron, Edward	Capt RMR	15.10.91
Barron, Valery	Lt Cdr	01.11.92
Barrow, Joan	Lt	05.11.97
Bartlett, Jonathan	Lt	21.09.96
Bartlett, Peter	Lt Cdr	05.01.78
Bartlweman, Alexander	Lt	25.11.72
Bassett, Gary	Lt	28.10.96
Bayley, George	Lt	24.03.99
Bayliss, John	Lt Cdr	18.02.87
Bayly, Peter	Slt	23.03.91
Bayton, Trevor	Lt	25.02.00
Beal, Peter	Lt	26.03.85
Beck, Roger	Slt	27.02.00
Bedford, Michael	Lt	01.04.86
Bell, Brian	Lt	25.02.00
Bell, Joseph	Lt	13.09.01
Bell, Veronica	Lt	29.01.98
Bennett, Stephen	Slt	01.12.00
Benton, Anthony	Capt RMR	01.08.99
Benton, Ruth	Lt	08.10.91
Bereznyckyj, Nicholas	Capt RMR	03.11.94
Bickle, Margaret	SLt	05.05.96
Billinghay, Sandra	Lt	01.07.85
Bilverstone, Brian	Lt Cdr	01.01.01
Bingham, Keith	Lt Cdr	01.01.01
Bingham, Maurice	Lt	01.01.88
Bird, Sarah	Slt	23.09.01
Birkwood, Geoffrey	Capt RMR	15.10.87
Bishop, Peter	Lt	01.11.95
Black, Magdalene	Lt Cdr	01.01.96
Blackburn, Alan	Slt	03.03.91

Name	Rank	Seniority	Name	Rank	Seniority
Blackwood, Alan	Lt	09.01.92	Burton, Craig	Lt	01.02.02
Blaker, Malcolm	Lt Cdr	03.01.80	Busby, Roger	Lt	19.02.99
Bloor, John	Capt RMR	15.01.97	Butcher, Colin	Slt	26.11.00
Board, Brian	Lt	15.11.91	Butler, Colin	Lt	05.12.01
Boardman, Richard	Lt Cdr	27.04.86	Butler, John	Lt	20.11.97
Bolton, David	Slt	05.02.99	Butterworth, John	Lt	23.03.87
Bond, Paul	Lt Cdr	01.01.02			
Bonfield, Christopher	Lt	06.11.96	**C**		
Bonjour, Andre	Lt	27.05.92			
Boorman, Nicholas	Lt	12.11.86	Cadman, Julie	Lt	07.10.89
Booth, Christina	Lt	03.12.91	Cadman, John	Lt Cdr	29.04.70
Bowen, Terrence	Lt	03.03.82	Cadman, Leslie	Lt Cdr	30.06.99
Bowman, Thomas	Lt Cdr	21.11.98	Callow, Lorna	Lt	10.11.95
Bowskill, Michael	Lt	10.11.85	Calvert, Martin	Lt	18.08.92
Boyes, Stephen	Lt	25.02.99	Campbell, William	Lt	01.01.88
Boyne, John	Slt	16.03.94	Carney, Robert	Lt	08.08.97
Bradbury, David	Lt	01.01.88	Carr, Barry	Slt	01.12.00
Bradbury, Jason	Lt	05.05.98	Carr, Leonard	Lt Cdr	19.02.76
Bradbury, Scott	Lt	05.12.01	Carroll, Paul	Capt RMR	02.05.87
Bradford, David	Lt Cdr	01.11.00	Carter, David	Lt	04.03.92
Bradford, William	Lt	21.10.99	Caslaw, Paul	Lt	01.08.94
Bradley, John	Lt	10.09.91	Catterall, Susan	Lt	20.01.87
Brady, Philip	Lt	05.06.94	Cea, Franklin	Lt Cdr	01.01.02
Bratley, Charles	Lt	09.10.90	Challacombe, Jonathan	Lt Cdr	27.06.90
Bratley, Norma	Lt	11.06.88	Chalmers, John	Lt Cdr	12.12.95
Bray, John	Lt	07.12.99	Chambers, John	Lt Cdr	01.01.88
Brayford, John	Lt Cdr	02.02.83	Chantler, Michael	Lt	01.01.02
Brazier, Colin	Lt	29.09.82	Charlton, Adrian	Lt	08.09.86
Brentnall, Charles	Slt	24.09.94	Chesworth, Howard	Lt	03.12.91
Bridle, Stephen	Lt	12.11.94	Childs, Paul	Slt	28.09.98
Briggs, Donald	Lt Cdr	01.09.77	Chinn, John	Lt Cdr	01.01.83
Brimelow, Michael	Lt	15.02.01	Chittock, Michael	Lt	25.03.94
Briscoe, Robert	Lt	14.11.96	Chitty, Rosemary	Lt	14.04.98
Britto, Elizabeth	Slt	31.10.00	Chritchlow, Julian	Lt	08.09.95
Broadbent, Graham	Lt Cdr	01.01.88	Church, Elizabeth	Lt	01.01.02
Brockwell, Graham	Lt	21.09.90	Cioma, Antoni	Lt Cdr	01.07.90
Brooks, Henry	Lt Cdr	02.05.87	Clark, Anne	Lt	05.11.97
Brotherton, Stephen	Lt	03.07.97	Clark, Ian	Lt Cdr	01.03.92
Broughton, Carol	Lt	16.11.01	Clarke, Judith	Lt	06.07.87
Brown, Alexander	Lt	22.09.86	Clarke, Leonard	Slt	09.06.94
Brown, Anthony	Lt	04.02.87	Clarke, Mark	Lt	03.11.98
Brown, Damien	Lt	26.03.02	Clarke, Reuben	Lt	30.12.89
Brown, David	Lt Cdr	30.03.80	Clay, John	Lt Cdr	01.04.99
Brown, David	Lt Cdr	02.06.86	Cleworth, Dean	Slt	26.03.00
Brown, Jeremy	Slt	04.02.00	Clifford, Ian	Lt	11.02.99
Brown, John	Lt Cdr	04.07.78	Clissold, Mark	Lt	01.04.93
Brown, Keith	Lt	26.10.84	Coast, Philip	Lt Cdr	09.07.90
Brown, Norman	Lt	01.06.91	Coates, Margaret	Slt	21.01.01
Brown, Sylvia	Lt	01.09.88	Cockell, Richard	Lt Cdr	04.12.96
Browning, Martin	Slt	01.09.98	Cole, Ain	Slt	08.06.95
Browning, Sharon	Slt	21.05.00	Coleman, Keith	Lt	26.11.98
Browning, Tony	Lt	19.12.93	Coles, Thomas	Lt Cdr	19.12.87
Broxham, Roy	Lt	21.09.90	Collier, David	Alt	01.09.88
Bryant, Charles	Lt	19.02.87	Collins, Ann	Lt	25.01.91
Bullock, Lynn	Lt	01.12.84	Collins, David	Lt Cdr	01.01.88
Burbridge, Lee	Lt	08.11.00	Collins, Raymond	Slt	31.08.94
Burdeyron-Dyster, Ian	Lt Cdr	01.01.88	Collins, Timothy	Slt	27.01.02
Burns, Clifford	Lt	01.11.93	Constable, David	Lt	01.03.81
Burns, Desmond	Lt	18.02.78	Cook, Hayden	Slt	11.11.01
Burns, Lisa	Slt	21.01.01	Coombes, Paul	Lt	25.01.94
Burns, Philip	Lt	27.06.80	Cope, Derek	Lt Cdr	16.02.82
Burrage, Richard	Lt	25.06.90	Copelin, Maureen	Lt	05.10.87
Burt, Christopher	Lt	20.08.99	Corbett, Sandra	Lt	23.04.99

Name	Rank	Seniority	Name	Rank	Seniority
Cormack, Raymond	Lt	20.11.97	Eaton, Trevor	Lt	01.09.96
Cornish, Michael	Lt	15.09.89	Edmondson, Denis	Lt	28.03.01
Costerd, David	Lt	08.08.94	Edwards, Stuart	Slt	04.06.95
Cowell, Christopher	Lt	06.05.87	Elbrow, Kevin	Lt	14.04.99
Cowell, Ian	Lt Cdr	01.01.92	Ellis, Henry	Lt	22.06.95
Cowell, John	Lt	01.04.91	Ellis, Kenneth	Slt	24.03.97
Coxon, John	Lt	14.11.00	Ellis, Wininfred	Lt	21.04.93
Craig, Neil	Lt	01.04.86	Ellison, Michael	Lt Cdr	01.01.88
Craighead, Roderick	Lt	08.03.93	English, Michael	Lt Cdr	01.04.88
Crawley, Stephen	Capt RMR	04.06.95	Evans, Ivor	Slt	17.07.97
Creighton, Edward William	Lt	26.11.92	Evans, Janet	Lt Cdr	01.07.94
Crick, Kenneth	Lt	20.10.92	Evans, John	Lt	28.09.00
Critchlow, Jonathan	Lt	05.02.87	Evans, Richard	Lt Cdr	16.09.96
Cross, Stuart	Lt	05.12.97	Evans, Wendy	Lt Cdr	01.04.90
Crowley, Derek	Lt	01.07.90	Everard, Gordon	Lt	11.08.89
Cruse, Gillian	Lt	16.10.98	Every, Paul David	Lt	17.04.92
Cruse, Malcolm	Lt Cdr	17.10.89			
Cummins, Sheila	Lt	01.11.86	**F**		
Cumper, Alan	Lt	01.12.98			
Curran, Paul	Lt	01.02.88	Fairbairn, Rachel	Slt	22.11.00
Curtis, Owen	Lt	25.06.85	Farrant, Paul	Lt	01.06.96
			Fazey, Kate	Slt	06.05.01
D			Feist, Ivor	Lt Cdr	12.07.80
			Fenn, Paul	Slt	29.11.99
Dale, Philip	Slt	01.03.99	Fifield, Mark	Lt	14.06.97
Daly, Martin	Lt	19.11.91	Finister, Anthony	Capt RMR	15.08.95
Daniels, Roger	Lt Cdr	14.01.91	Finlay, David	Lt	21.02.98
Dann, John	Lt	09.07.95	Finley, Martin	Capt RMR	27.04.96
Davies, Bruno	Lt Cdr	15.04.86	Fisher, Hazel	Lt	26.01.92
Davies, Colin	Lt	18.09.97	Fitch, Michael	Slt	16.01.00
Davies, Richard	Lt Cdr	07.12.81	Fitzgerald, Terence	Lt RMR	19.06.01
Davies, William	Lt	09.04.70	Fleet, Gordon	Capt RMR	21.03.97
Davison, Henry	Lt	30.01.00	Fleming, Alan	Lt	10.07.93
Daw, Clifford	Lt Cdr	01.01.88	Fleming, Andrea	Slt	22.11.00
Deacon, Maureen	Lt	06.09.00	Fletcher, Carol	Lt Cdr	01.04.80
Delderfield, Robin	Slt	01.12.00	Fletcher, David	Lt	01.03.99
Delin, Roual	Lt RMR	01.07.99	Fletcher, John	Lt Cdr	01.08.87
Demellweek, Gilbert	Lt	01.01.92	Fletcher, Malcolm	Lt	20.02.84
Derbyshire, David	Lt	03.06.92	Flett, William	Capt RMR	17.11.96
Devenish, Ian	Capt RMR	12.02.02	Flynn, John	Lt Cdr	09.11.75
Devereux, Edwin	Lt Cdr	31.07.72	Forbes, John	Lt	18.09.89
Dibben, Michael	Lt	03.11.86	Ford, Stuart	Lt	02.09.96
Dibben, Nigel	Lt Cdr	19.10.98	Foreman, Waleria	Lt	20.10.95
Dibnah, Robert	Lt	05.03.00	Forrester, Michael	Lt	01.02.79
Dickinson, Keith	Lt	10.11.85	Fortune, Colin	Lt	01.10.99
Dixie, Colin	Lt	15.10.00	Foster, Andrew	Lt	19.11.91
Doggart, James	Lt	09.03.01	Foster, Alexandra	Lt	04.10.96
Doggart, Norman	Lt	01.07.88	Foster, David	Lt	05.11.97
Donovan, Terence	Lt	06.11.96	Foster, Ian	Lt	05.08.85
Dorricott, Peter	Lt	26.10.85	Fowler, Alison	Lt	16.01.97
Dougal, Alexander	Lt	02.10.81	Fox, Jane	Slt	27.03.92
Dowdeswell, Robin	Lt	12.07.86	Franklin, Patrick	Slt	07.12.00
Draper, Philip	Lt	20.12.99	Fraser, Garry	Lt	01.05.93
Dryden, Graeme	Lt	26.03.02	Freeman, Brian	Lt	16.06.95
Dryden, Stephen	Lt	19.01.81	Freestone, Andrew	Lt	07.11.95
Dunkeld, Brian	Lt	04.06.97	Fry, Brian	Lt	25.09.78
Dyer, Geoffrey	Maj RMR	01.05.99	Fulcher, Diane	Lt	06.09.94
Dyer, Gillian	Lt	21.06.94	Fulcher, Graham	Slt	24.04.94
Dyer, Roger	Lt	07.06.97	Fuller, Andrew	Lt RMR	20.06.00
			Fuller, Keith Duncan	Lt Cdr	01.10.01
E			Fulton, Karen	Lt	20.03.02
			Fussell, Christopher	Lt	01.10.90
Eagles, Alan	Lt	05.02.94			

Name	Rank	Seniority	Name	Rank	Seniority

G

			Hale, Carol	Lt	21.01.99
Gale, Ronnie	Lt	01.11.90	Hale, Ronald	Lt Cdr	23.02.77
Gallagher, Eamon	Lt	23.06.92	Hall, Derek	Lt Cdr	19.01.98
Gambell, Mark	Lt	14.12.96	Halliday, Angela	Lt	20.03.95
Gardner, Keith	Lt	01.05.94	Hamilton, Kerry	Lt	01.05.92
Gardner, Robert	Lt	06.03.82	Hammond, Stephen	Lt	30.05.97
Garner, James	Lt Cdr	01.07.01	Hankey, Carolyne	Lt	29.09.99
Garrett, John	Lt Cdr	01.01.02	Hanley, David	Lt	18.11.93
Garrett, Robert	Slt	06.11.94	Hanna, June	Slt	21.06.96
Gathergood, John	Lt	17.04.98	Hanson, David	Lt Cdr	26.07.88
Gearing, Robert	Lt Cdr	01.09.77	Hanson, Neil	Slt	11.11.01
Gell, Dorothy	Lt	16.10.87	Harman, Robert	Lt	04.08.90
George, Brian	Lt	01.09.85	Harmer, Robert	Lt	28.10.99
Gerald, Anthony	Lt	01.09.98	Harries, Mark	Slt	05.06.94
Gerrard, David	Lt Cdr	01.12.88	Harris, Brian Stanley	Lt Cdr	01.01.02
Gerrard, Mary	Lt Cdr	01.09.98	Harris, Stephen	Lt	01.10.91
Gilbert, John	Lt Cdr	31.12.75	Harris, Trevor	Lt	05.12.01
Gilbert, Robin	Maj RMR	01.06.99	Hartley, Jacqueline	Lt Cdr	27.03.87
Giles, Roger	Lt Cdr	30.06.94	Hartwell, Neil	Lt	26.03.02
Gill, Jacqueline	Lt	28.02.95	Harvey, Brian	Slt	01.11.94
Gillard, Terence	Lt Cdr	01.01.95	Hatchett, Robin	Lt	27.09.86
Gillert, Valerie	Lt	19.10.91	Hatrick, James	Lt	29.07.93
Gilliam, Kevin	Lt	01.07.93	Hawes, Sandra	Lt	06.11.95
Gillott, Peter	Slt	23.05.99	Hawkins, Leslie	Slt	08.11.99
Gittens, Adrian	Slt	05.02.99	Hayes, Stephen	Slt	01.11.92
Gittens, Susan	Slt	07.12.00	Hayton, Alan	Lt	20.07.89
Glanfield, Mark	Lt	06.02.82	Hazeldon, Donald	Slt	28.04.93
Glanville, Barry	Lt Cdr	14.07.00	Hazzard, Keith	Lt	02.06.98
Glanville, Debra	Lt	23.05.01	Headen, Geoffrey	Lt	28.09.00
Glendinning, Michael	Lt	07.07.99	Healen, Stephen	Lt	05.05.82
Goode, Eric	Lt	13.12.97	Hearl, James	Lt	21.12.89
Goode, Victoria	Lt	18.11.00	Hebbes, Margaret	Lt	05.06.96
Gooding, Peter	Lt Cdr	01.01.81	Hebbes, Peter	Slt	01.09.91
Goodwin, Michael	Lt	08.12.01	Helkin, Margaret	Lt Cdr	01.01.01
Gordon, Andrew	Lt	19.02.89	Henderson, Ian	Lt RMR	10.09.00
Govier, Adrian Terry	Lt Cdr	27.09.99	Henwood, Martin	Lt Cdr	21.10.80
Grace, Roger	Lt Cdr	13.07.76	Herbert, Michael	Lt Cdr	01.01.00
Grainge, Andrew	Lt	09.09.00	Hercock, Norman	Lt	03.11.93
Grant, Malcolm	Lt	28.02.95	Hewitt, Graham	Lt Cdr	07.04.92
Gray, Brian	Lt	24.12.87	Hide, Brenda	Lt	17.05.84
Green, Cecilia	Slt	02.12.87	Hill, Anthony	Slt	26.06.85
Green, Malcom	Lt	16.08.97	Hill, Ian	Alt	15.03.89
Green, Paul	Lt	01.09.86	Hill, Monica	Lt	18.11.93
Greenfield, Stephen	Lt	23.05.01	Hill, Reginald	Lt Cdr	01.03.88
Greenhalgh, Peter	Lt	30.04.86	Hillier, Barbara	Slt	07.12.00
Greer, John	Lt Cdr	01.01.88	Hinds, Michael	Lt	10.11.95
Gresty, Stephen	Lt	07.10.98	Hiscock, Andrew	Lt	01.03.83
Grice, Robert	Lt Cdr	05.07.73	Hithersay, John	Lt	28.10.78
Griffin, Paul	Lt	24.10.86	Hoey, David	Lt	10.11.94
Griffiths, Meirion	Lt Cdr	04.11.88	Holland, Donald	Lt	15.09.84
Grocott, Alan	Lt	22.05.97	Holliday, Anthony	Lt Cdr	01.01.01
Grogan, Kenneth	Lt	16.09.78	Hollywell, Gary	Lt Cdr	01.05.99
Guiver, Carl	Maj RMR	01.01.96	Holmes, Kevin	Lt	09.11.90
Guppy, Graham	Maj RMR	20.06.84	Holt, Martin	Lt Cdr	01.01.01
			Holt, Wendy	Lt	29.11.97
			Horne, Allan	Lt	16.09.89

H

			Horner, John	Lt Cdr	16.09.92
Hackett, Clive	Lt Cdr	12.10.90	Houlden, Wendy	Lt	30.09.01
Hadfield, Philip	Capt RMR	09.04.91	Howie, Thomas	Lt Cdr	01.11.88
Hagan, George	Slt	29.11.92	Hoyle, Keith	Slt	01.10.86
Hailwood, Paul	Lt Cdr	01.12.92	Hudson, Christopher	Slt	29.11.95
Haines, Linda	Lt	01.11.89	Hughes, Thomas	Lt Cdr	14.09.83
			Hulonce, Michael	Lt Cdr	12.03.82

Name	Rank	Seniority
Hunt, Claire	Lt	14.06.97
Hunter, Lesley	Lt	05.05.98
Hunter, Phillip	Slt	01.12.00
Hurst, Paul	Slt	29.09.93
Hurst, Thomas	Lt Cdr	12.07.85
Hurst, Walter	Lt	30.09.91
Hutchings, Andrew	Lt	25.11.00
Huttley, Kenneth	Lt	13.11.87
Huyton, Gillian	Lt	07.10.98

I

Name	Rank	Seniority
Iggo, David	Lt	26.01.96
Ingahm, Mark	Slt	22.11.00
Ingham, Anthony	Slt	24.02.99
Ingham, David	Lt Cdr	28.04.98
Izzard, Michael	Lt	25.06.98

J

Name	Rank	Seniority
Jackson, Graeme	Lt	18.09.94
Jaconelli, Nicholas	Lt	12.09.00
James, George	Lt	22.08.78
James, Robert	Lt Cdr	01.01.95
Janner-Burgess, Mark	Slt	21.01.01
Jardine, Roderick	Lt	05.10.95
Jeffrey, Andrew	Slt	30.08.94
Jehan, Paula	Slt	19.05.91
Jenkins, Ian	Capt RMR	01.09.91
Jennings, William	Lt	19.10.84
Jepson, Mary	Lt	21.03.96
Jezzard, Kevin	Lt Cdr	01.01.01
Johns, Bevan	Lt Cdr	21.05.91
Johns, Emma	Slt	21.01.01
Johns, Nicholas	Lt	08.04.92
Johnson, Andrew	Lt	17.02.96
Johnson, Laurence	Lt Cdr	02.08.87
Johnson-Paul, David	Lt	18.04.92
Johnston, Peter	Lt	02.11.84
Jones, Antony	Slt	19.05.87
Jones, Christopher	Lt Cdr	11.08.99
Jones, Dorothy Edwina	Lt	22.10.94
Jones, Kelvin	Lt	06.05.92
Jones, Lily	Lt	09.04.91
Jones, Margaret	Lt	05.11.97
Jones, Mark	Lt	06.11.96
Jones, Neil	Lt	24.03.94
Jones, Neil	Lt	03.01.96
Jones, Philip	Slt	23.09.01
Jones, Peter	Lt	16.06.89
Jones, Trevor	Lt	10.03.00
Jordan, Robert	Lt Cdr	01.01.95
Jordan, Roger	Lt	22.06.87
Jordan, Sheila	Lt	26.07.90
Juniper, Stephanie	Slt	11.11.01
Jupe, Paul	Slt	02.03.86
Justice, David	Lt	07.02.84

K

Name	Rank	Seniority
Kay, Anne	Slt	29.05.01
Kaye, Malcolm	Lt	01.11.89
Keenan, Robert	Lt Cdr	01.04.91
Keery, Neil	Lt	18.05.01
Keery, William	Lt Cdr	01.01.83
Kenna, Bryan	Lt Cdr	22.10.84
Kennedy, Ivan	Lt	16.05.87
Kenrick, Peter	Lt	23.11.94
Kerwin, James	Lt	09.05.97
Killick, Peter	Lt	09.10.85
King, Leslie	Lt Cdr	15.03.98
Kinghorn, Jason	Lt	14.04.98
Knight, Nicholas	Lt Cdr	22.01.01
Knight, Robert	Lt	15.02.00
Knill, Colin	Lt	01.05.89
Kyle, Raymond	Slt	01.11.90

L

Name	Rank	Seniority
Lamb, Maureen	Lt Cdr	15.03.95
Lamkin, John	Lt	15.02.96
Lampert, Brian	Lt Cdr	11.01.85
Lampert, Susan	Lt	01.11.89
Lamport, John	Slt	01.07.98
Lane, John	Lt	31.05.91
Larsen, Colin	Lt	09.05.97
Lawes, Sonia	Lt	08.03.94
Lawrence, Barrie	Lt	04.10.92
Lawrence, Kevin	Lt	01.05.01
Lawrence, Marion	Slt	20.03.94
Lea, Garry	Slt	05.05.99
Leatherbarrow, Ronald	Lt	29.03.95
Ledgeton, Anthony	Capt RMR	24.01.91
Lee, David	Lt Cdr	31.03.79
Lees, Martin	Slt	19.09.92
Leet, James	Lt	26.03.02
Lentell, Heather	Lt	31.07.01
Lentle, Robert	Lt	01.11.90
Leslie, Harry	Slt	03.03.91
Lewis, Clifford Bruce	Lt	04.11.92
Lewis, David	Lt	14.04.98
Lewis, Eleanor	Lt	23.11.94
Lewis, John	Capt RMR	17.11.98
Lewis, Peter	Lt	31.10.90
Lewis, Walter	Lt	06.05.79
Lincoln, David	Lt	01.01.96
Lister, Richard	Slt	27.01.02
Lock, Keith	Slt	01.12.92
Locke, David	Lt	10.09.88
Login, Brenda	Lt	10.11.89
Login, Derek	Lt Cdr	12.12.88
Long, Adam	Lt	01.04.97
Lonsdale, Bryan	Lt Cdr	01.09.90
Lorimer, Deirdre	Lt	24.06.98
Louden, Elizabeth Jane	Slt	01.07.90
Loveridge, Anthony	Lt Cdr	01.12.89
Low, William	Slt	05.04.94
Lowe, David	Lt	23.07.77
Lowe, Stuart	Capt	21.04.02
Lucas, Peter	Lt	24.03.99
Luckman, Bruce Innes	Lt	01.10.92
Lumley, Margaret	Lt	14.06.97
Luxton, Phillip	Lt	05.11.00
Luxton, Peter	Lt Cdr	20.05.69

Name	Rank	Seniority	Name	Rank	Seniority
			Mitchell, Ray	Lt	20.07.86
			Mohammed, Barbara	Lt	07.12.83

M

Name	Rank	Seniority
Mac Iver, Lynn	Lt	19.04.96
MacAusland, Iain	Lt Cdr	01.09.98
MacCallum, James	Lt	18.01.98
MacDonald, Peter	Lt	07.11.91
Macey, Mark	Lt	13.11.93
Machin, Ian	Maj RMR	01.08.96
MacKay, Charles	Slt	01.12.97
MacKay, David	Lt	01.07.84
MacKinlay, Colin	Lt	08.04.92
MacKinlay, Sherie	Lt	01.09.93
MacLean, Donald	Lt	28.03.90
Madden, Brian	Lt Cdr	01.11.88
Mahoney, Jane	Lt Cdr	01.01.01
Maiden, Philip	Slt	27.01.02
Main, Paul	Lt	12.03.91
Mair, Brian	Lt Cdr	01.01.02
Mannough, John	Lt	14.05.90
Marson, Victoria	Lt	07.11.92
Martin, John	Lt Cdr	01.01.87
Martin, Kevin	Lt	14.03.94
Mason, Edward	Lt Cdr	18.11.69
Mathers, David	Lt	15.02.96
Matson, Christopher	Lt	16.11.97
Mattey, Barry John	Lt Cdr	04.02.91
Matthews, Christopher	Lt	26.01.95
Matthews, John	Lt	19.06.95
Matthews,Philip Kenneth, MBE	Lt Cdr	01.02.89
Matthews, Ronald	Lt	14.01.97
Maynard, Robert	Lt Cdr	21.03.76
McAvady, Andrew	Lt	12.06.98
McAvennie, John	Lt	03.02.90
McAvoy, William	Lt	17.12.79
McClements, George	Capt RMR	01.01.86
McCune, Barry	Lt	04.06.88
McDonald, Peter	Lt	29.06.92
McGarry, George	Lt	03.09.80
McGuire, Gerald	Slt	12.11.97
McIntyre, Rosamund	Lt Cdr	11.01.80
McKaig, Alexander	Lt	08.01.87
McKee, David	Lt Cdr	01.04.88
McKenna, John	Lt Cdr	19.12.01
McKenna, Paul	Lt	14.03.96
McKeown, Glenda	Lt	24.04.96
McLaren, George	Slt	02.12.95
McMaster, George	Lt	06.10.88
McRobb, Brian	Lt	06.04.85
McVinnie, Elizabeth	Lt	06.11.00
Meek, Caroline	Slt	06.05.01
Meikle, John	Lt RMR	06.05.01
Meldon, Michael	Lt Cdr	01.03.92
Menhams, Angela	Lt	02.12.90
Meyer, Jonathan	Lt	16.11.90
Milby, Stuart	Lt Cdr	27.07.93
Milligan, Kevin	Lt	10.06.00
Milligan, Victoria	Lt	01.05.98
Mills, William	Lt	23.06.93
Milner, Anna	Lt Cdr	01.03.85
Minett, Clive	Lt RMR	07.12.00
Mitchell, David	Lt	15.05.98
Mitchell, Jane	Lt	01.06.00

Name	Rank	Seniority
Mitchell, Ray	Lt	20.07.86
Mohammed, Barbara	Lt	07.12.83
Mohammed, John	Lt Cdr	09.09.87
Moir, Brian	Lt	18.09.95
Money, Alan	Lt	25.03.94
Monkcom, Susan	Lt	01.01.98
Mons-White, Margaret	Lt	01.09.92
Montrose, Keith	Lt RMR	31.10.01
Moody, Roger	Lt Cdr	01.04.74
Moore, Antony	Lt	07.12.85
Moore, Robert	Lt Cdr	01.01.01
Morgan, John	Lt	10.02.90
Morgan, Norman	Lt	01.01.95
Morgan, Stephen	Lt	13.04.96
Morley, Andrew	Lt	07.10.98
Morley, Michael	Lt	16.03.88
Morrin, Kevin	Lt	05.04.97
Morton, Rita	Lt	13.05.98
Mould, Peter	Lt Cdr	01.08.78
Moulton, Nicholas	Lt Cdr	21.11.98
Mountier, Peter	Lt	19.11.90
Muggeridge, Edwin	Lt	06.05.84
Mugridge, Toni	Lt	15.02.02
Mulholland, Ross	Lt Cdr	01.06.87
Mullin, Margaret	Lt	01.06.84
Mullin, William	Lt	15.11.86
Murchison, Donald	Lt Cdr	12.12.67
Murdock, Gordon	Lt Cdr	11.02.76
Murphy, William	Slt	24.05.99
Murray, Donald	Lt	01.05.93
Musselwhite, Ruth	Slt	11.12.00
Musson, Paul	Lt RMR	04.04.00

N

Name	Rank	Seniority
Newman, Raymond	Lt	24.10.82
Nice, David	Lt	01.01.88
Nicholls, David	Lt	11.09.98
Nichols, David	Slt	15.07.99
Nixon, Joseph	Lt	30.06.84
Norman, David	Lt	01.04.86
Norman, John	Lt Cdr	01.08.87
Norris, Norman Terence	Lt	01.04.92

O

Name	Rank	Seniority
O Brien, Gary	Lt	30.01.96
O Neill, Dawn	Lt	02.12.94
O'Connor, Brian	Lt	30.07.85
O'Connor, Roy	Maj RMR	14.05.01
O'Donnell, Adrian	Lt	06.11.90
O'Donnell, Dominic	Lt	01.12.83
O'Hagan, William	Lt	19.05.86
O'Keefe, Richard	Lt	28.04.89
O'Shaughnessy, Helen	Slt	22.05.95
Oglesby, Simon	Slt	08.12.00
Orfila, Andrew	Slt	11.10.00
Orr, Robert	Lt	26.03.02
Orton, Adrian	Capt RMR	01.07.99
Osborne, Brian	Lt	26.10.83
Osborne, Dawn	Lt	20.04.83
Osborne, James	Lt Cdr	01.10.74
Owen, William	Lt	05.06.96

Name	Rank	Seniority	Name	Rank	Seniority
Owens, Christopher	Lt	30.05.97	Pritchard, David	Lt Cdr	01.01.95
			Pugh, Heather	Lt Cdr	28.04.98
P			Pugh, John	Lt	30.04.96
			Pusill, David	Lt	07.02.92
Packwood, Shelagh	Lt Cdr	01.12.86			
Page, Helen	Lt	01.10.90	**R**		
Painter, Lorretta	Lt	10.06.92			
Painting, Peter	Lt	18.03.79	Radcliffe, Brian	Lt Cdr	15.01.89
Paling, John	Lt Cdr	01.10.96	Rawcliffe, Michael	Lt	17.04.98
Palmer, Alan	Lt RMR	20.11.99	Rawlinson, Martin	Lt	01.03.98
Palmer, Robert	Lt	18.11.93	Rayson, Trevor	Lt Cdr	01.01.01
Palmer, Richard	Lt	23.09.97	Read, Christopher	Slt	21.01.01
Parker, Derek	Lt Cdr	01.06.90	Reddecliffe, Phillip	Lt	13.04.91
Parker, Ian	Lt	20.09.97	Redhead, Gavin	Lt	28.09.00
Parker, Simon	Lt	01.03.90	Redhead, Julie	Slt	28.03.99
Parks, Edwin	Lt	02.12.95	Redmond, Lee	Lt	01.12.96
Parr, Geoffrey Lawrence	Lt	28.11.92	Rees, Andrew	Lt	14.07.86
Parris, Stephen	Capt RMR	30.01.99	Rees, Celia	Lt Cdr	01.01.94
Parry, Michael	Lt	01.06.84	Rees, Susan	Lt	05.04.97
Pascoe, William	Lt	26.07.84	Reeve, John	Lt	19.11.91
Paterson, Gordon	Lt Cdr	01.12.99	Reeves, Angela	Lt Cdr	01.01.01
Patterson, Phillip	Lt	21.01.99	Reeves, Mark	Lt	11.05.01
Patterson, Paul	Lt	01.07.00	Regan, Paul	Maj RMR	01.10.96
Paul, Patrick	Slt	12.08.99	Regler, Stanley	Lt	07.12.82
Payne, David	Lt	26.11.98	Reid, Jeffery	Slt	04.11.98
Payne, Derek	Lt Cdr	01.01.01	Reid, Morag	Slt	21.03.99
Payne, David	Lt	18.03.00	Rhind, Robert	Lt	22.03.90
Pearce, Peter	Lt	01.06.98	Richards, Philip	Lt	12.04.01
Pearson, James	Lt	09.03.93	Richings, David	Lt	15.04.99
Peck, John	Lt	23.04.96	Richmond, Peter	Lt	01.01.00
Penny, Carl	Lt RMR	04.05.00	Ridgway, Paul	Lt Cdr	21.02.00
Perkins, Jonathon	Slt	14.08.86	Rimmer, Kevin	Lt	30.03.94
Perkins, Kevin	Lt	05.11.97	Roaf, Alistair	Slt	07.06.96
Perrins, John	Lt Cdr	26.11.86	Robbins, Allan	Lt Cdr	01.10.01
Perry, Paul	Lt Cdr	04.02.94	Roberts, Evphemia	Lt	03.11.98
Peters, Kenneth	Lt	15.06.00	Roberts, Ronald	Lt Cdr	06.01.86
Pether, Phillip	Lt	07.07.65	Robins, William	Lt	01.09.74
Pettit, Nicholas	Lt	09.03.99	Robinson, Eric	Lt	18.03.99
Phelps, Joanne	Lt	02.04.99	Robinson, Paul	Lt	01.02.99
Phillips, Pamela	Lt	01.06.00	Rock, William	Slt	12.11.98
Pickering, Jean	Lt	03.07.90	Rockey, David	Slt	11.03.98
Picton, Janet	Lt Cdr	18.09.87	Roden, John	Lt RMR	01.07.99
Piercy, Peter	Lt Cdr	25.10.86	Rogan, Christopher	Slt	23.03.00
Pike, John	Lt	31.05.96	Rogers, Neil	Lt	30.09.00
Pilbeam, Linda	Slt	04.05.00	Rogers, Sallyanne	Lt	22.11.97
Plummer, Thomas	Lt	25.04.91	Rollins, Linda	Lt	03.11.98
Pocock, Stewart	Lt Cdr	01.07.88	Rooney, Frederick	Slt	14.11.96
Pogson, Godfrey	Lt Cdr	11.12.85	Roots, Joseph	Lt	21.09.01
Poke, David	Capt RMR	01.07.99	Ross, David	Lt	13.10.90
Pool, Adam	Slt	08.06.94	Ross, Malcoln	Lt	09.05.95
Pope, Darren	Lt	22.04.93	Rowe, Raymond	Lt	02.04.99
Porter, John	Lt Cdr	01.01.02	Rowles, David	Lt Cdr	01.01.88
Postill, John	Lt RMR	19.01.99	Rummins, Ann	Lt	01.01.88
Poth, Anthony	Lt Cdr	17.03.86	Rundle, Trevor	Lt	26.12.87
Pow, David John	Lt	06.10.92	Rushton, Steven	Lt	15.03.95
Powell, Denise	Lt Cdr	19.01.94	Rusiecki, Lawrence Joseph	Capt RMR	10.12.93
Powell, Robert	Lt RMR	13.05.96	Russell, Audrey	Lt	01.03.99
Power, Fiona	Lt	05.03.99	Russell, John	Lt	01.11.89
Pratt, Alison	Slt	05.07.00	Russell-Brown, Eric	Slt	06.06.00
Preston, Frank	Slt	01.06.94	Rutter, Thomas	Lt	30.10.87
Priestley, Gary	Slt	18.09.94	Rycroft, Paul	Lt Cdr	08.09.89
Prince, Ramon	Slt	13.04.97	Ryder, Ruth	Lt	03.11.93
Pritchard, Carol	Lt	06.09.94			

Name	Rank	Seniority	Name	Rank	Seniority

S

Salisbury, Linda	Lt	02.04.99
Salveson, Anthony	Lt Cdr	01.03.79
Saunders, Donald	Lt	28.08.94
Saupe, Peter	Lt	01.01.88
Sawford, Michael	Lt	09.02.85
Scanlan, John	Lt	31.03.89
Scarratt, Leslie	Lt RMR	02.09.98
Schembri, Winifred	Lt Cdr	07.02.97
Schofield, George	Lt	01.04.91
Scholes, David	Capt RMR	13.03.91
Scholes, Stephen	Capt RMR	01.07.01
Scott, Francis	Lt Cdr	01.04.92
Scott, Gordon	Lt Cdr	01.12.98
Scourfield, Royston	Lt	01.06.91
Scrivens, Stuart	Lt	03.12.91
Seabury, Paul	Lt	16.08.97
Searles, Andrew	Lt	09.11.96
Sedgwick, Mark	Lt	03.06.00
Servis, Thomas	Lt	20.08.85
Shakespeare, William	Lt Cdr	01.04.99
Sharp, Terence	Lt Cdr	08.09.80
Shaw, David	Lt	01.03.88
Shaw, Geoff	Lt	12.06.98
Shaw, Gail	Lt	26.10.83
Shelton, Clive	Lt Cdr	24.04.98
Sherwin, Peter	Lt Cdr	01.10.77
Shiel, Garry	Lt	18.03.90
Shiels, Robert	Lt Cdr	08.09.86
Shone, Michael	Lt	15.06.00
Short, Keith	Lt Cdr	06.04.86
Shuttleworth, Tye	Slt	19.10.01
Sickelmore, Barry	Lt Cdr	05.04.99
Sidney, Gerald	Maj RMR	01.01.96
Sigley, Dermid	Lt	01.05.89
Silverthorne, Robert	Lt	31.10.91
Simmons, Melvyn	Lt	10.04.93
Simpson, Alfred	Lt Cdr	08.04.92
Simpson, Leonard	Slt	01.05.93
Simpson, Timothy	Lt	01.02.95
Sinden, Daniel	Lt	26.03.02
Skingle, Stephen	Slt	14.07.96
Skinner, Angela	Lt	08.11.00
Skinner, John	Lt	14.07.98
Smales, Geoffrey	Lt Cdr	01.01.97
Smart, Claude	Lt Cdr	26.04.79
Smith, Adrian	Lt	21.08.92
Smith, Deborah	Lt	29.03.95
Smith, Graham	Lt	05.04.97
Smith, John	Slt	12.11.98
Smith, James	Lt	05.10.98
Smith, James	Lt	09.05.94
Smith, Robin	Lt	06.07.89
Smith, Victoria	Lt Cdr	01.04.80
Soilleux, Peter	Slt	12.04.99
Speariett, Gail	Lt Cdr	16.11.91
Spencer, Allan	Lt	15.10.93
Spencer, Edward	Lt	09.09.76
Spicer, Janice	Lt	01.07.87
Spink, James	Lt	02.03.88
Sprogis, Alfred	Lt	22.04.94

Squires, John	Lt	06.12.86
Squirrell, Daren	Slt	21.01.01
Stacey, Stephen	Lt	16.02.87
Standen, Roy	Lt Cdr	31.12.67
Stanier, Tina	Slt	23.09.01
Stanley, Trevor	Slt	22.01.01
Steele, Tommy	Lt	23.11.98
Steggall, Mark	Lt	19.11.91
Steggall, Stephen	Lt	19.05.87
Stevens, Alan	Lt	01.07.00
Stevenson, Ian	Lt	31.03.87
Steward, Karen	Lt	14.02.98
Stewart, James	Lt	22.05.79
Stewart, Patrick	Lt Cdr	27.07.83
Stewart, Rosaleen	Slt	01.10.90
Stone, Terrence	Lt	25.05.86
Storey, Hugh	Lt RMR	27.10.01
Stott, Barry	Lt	19.01.96
Straderick, Barbara	Lt	10.11.95
Street, Steven	Lt	14.04.99
Strutt, Dupre	Lt Cdr	28.01.98
Stubbs, Edward	Lt	18.11.93
Sturt, Lisa	Lt	20.03.96
Sumner, Robert	Lt	06.12.99
Sutherland, Shane	Lt	01.07.94
Sutton, Philippa	Slt	01.12.00
Svendsen, Peter	Lt Cdr	01.05.02
Swan, Gordon	Lt	11.03.96
Swarbrick, David	Lt	16.06.83
Sydes, Daniel	Capt	21.09.01

T

Tait, Graham	Lt	12.05.97
Tait, Kevin	Slt	21.03.00
Tanner, Roland	Lt Cdr	21.07.87
Tannock, Andrew	Capt RMR	30.01.99
Tapp, Maria	Lt	23.10.95
Taylor, Brian	Capt RMR	01.07.91
Taylor, Duncan	Lt	22.11.97
Taylor, Fay	Slt	21.01.01
Taylor, John	Lt	01.08.00
Taylor, Pauline	Lt Cdr	01.03.81
Teare, Glenys	Lt	26.08.88
Tebby, Alan	Slt	23.05.99
Tebby, Christine	Lt	05.09.89
Temple, Edward	Lt Cdr	01.01.88
Thackery, Richard	Lt	02.03.96
Theobald, Robert	Lt	10.11.87
Theobald, Wendy Margaret	Lt Cdr	01.01.96
Thomas, Alan	Lt	14.04.98
Thomas, Adrian	Capt RMR	09.07.85
Thomas, Derek	Lt	10.10.94
Thomas, Jacqueline	Lt	31.05.93
Thomas, Michael	Lt	19.07.80
Thomas, Roderick Leslie	Lt	26.11.92
Thomas, Valerie	Lt	22.11.97
Thomas, William	Lt	01.01.82
Thompson, Robert	Slt	05.05.98
Thompson, Andrew	Slt	15.10.99
Thompson, John	Lt	23.02.84
Thomson, Andrew	Lt	07.04.95
Thomson, Rose	Lt	12.10.01

Name	Rank	Seniority	Name	Rank	Seniority
Thomson, Robert	Lt	21.10.85	Warwick, Stephen	Lt	12.03.98
Thorne, Christopher	Lt	13.07.90	Waters, Alan	Lt Cdr	01.01.81
Thornton, Peter	Lt	24.11.79	Waters, Scott	Lt	21.04.94
Thwaites, Carol	Lt	25.03.93	Watson, Adrian	Slt	06.05.01
Thwaites, David	Lt Cdr	01.01.95	Watson, Sheila	Lt	04.02.00
Tilley, Lorna	Lt	09.06.93	Watts, Reginald	Lt Cdr	27.10.91
Timothy, Emile	Maj RMR	20.04.92	Waugh, John	Lt	06.09.78
Titley, John	Lt	04.07.93	Waylett, Graham	Lt Cdr	01.04.01
Tomlinson, Alan	Lt	27.10.00	Webb, Colin	Lt	17.11.95
Totty, Paul	Capt RMR	11.10.96	Webb, John	Lt Cdr	09.11.85
Touhey, Martin	Lt	15.07.87	Webb, John	Lt Cdr	21.04.99
Townsend, Graham	Lt	01.05.98	Webb, Martin	Lt	07.06.96
Townshend, Shella	Lt	03.11.98	Webster, John	Lt Cdr	14.12.90
Trahair, Estelle	Lt	24.04.96	Weightman, Eric	Lt Cdr	01.07.00
Tranter, Gary	Lt Cdr	01.03.87	Welsh, John	Lt	07.11.93
Trojan, Margaret	Lt	30.11.99	Welsh, Michelle	Lt	07.11.95
Trott, Peter	Lt Cdr	02.06.83	Weobley, Malcolm	Maj RMR	28.08.86
Truelove, Gary	Lt	20.11.89	Weston, Mark	Lt	07.11.95
Truscott, Gary	Lt Cdr	01.01.96	Westover, Robert	Lt	01.04.74
Tubbs, Sean	Slt	16.10.96	Wheatley, Noel	Lt Cdr	01.01.95
Tubman, Vernon	Slt	18.10.91	Wheeler, Michael	Lt	22.03.75
Tucker, Neil	Lt	03.11.95	White, David	Slt	02.12.95
Turner, Ian	Lt	04.11.97	White, Robert	Lt	29.10.99
Tuson, Barry	Slt	24.03.97	White, William	Slt	08.12.00
Tuson, Denise	Lt	30.03.94	Whitehead, William	Capt	05.12.99
Tweed, Alan Campbell	Lt	06.01.93	Whiteman, Mark	Lt	01.01.88
Tyrrell, Richard	Lt Cdr	19.06.91	Whitley, Glenda	Lt	08.05.85
Tyson, Michael	Lt	22.03.83	Whitley, Roger	Lt	14.04.99
			Whorwood, Julia	Lt	07.05.97

U

Name	Rank	Seniority	Name	Rank	Seniority
Ulrich, Geoffrey	Lt Cdr	27.11.82	Whyte, Lawrence	Lt Cdr	01.03.98
Ulrich, Jacquelyn	Lt	12.03.91	Wickenden, Frances	Lt	01.09.98
Unwin, Mark	Lt	24.02.01	Wigley, Grahame	Lt	12.04.01
Urquhart, John	Lt	05.05.97	Wilde, James	Slt	01.03.93
Utting, Joseph	Lt	21.09.01	Wilkinson, Christopher	Lt	04.11.97
			Wilks, Stephen	Lt	27.07.01

V

Name	Rank	Seniority	Name	Rank	Seniority
			Willett, Marion	Lt	21.12.86
			Williams, Alan	Lt Cdr	01.05.84
			Williams, Derek	Lt	13.12.88
Vanns, Jonathan	Lt	04.05.92	Williams, David	Lt	15.03.00
Vaughan, Jeffery	Lt	10.11.95	Williams, Deborah Karen	Lt	04.11.92
Villa, Nina	Lt	08.11.01	Williams, David	Slt	26.03.00
Vincett, Shirley	Lt	12.01.99	Williams, Peter John	Lt	16.11.92
Vokes, Simon	Slt	27.01.02	Williams, Susan	Slt	26.03.00
			Williams, Suzanne	Lt	01.03.80
			Williamson, William	Lt Cdr	26.05.87

W

Name	Rank	Seniority	Name	Rank	Seniority
			Wilson, Edward	Slt	08.05.89
Waddleton, Michael	Lt	17.07.84	Wilson, Ethel	Lt	01.11.98
Wagstaff, Melvin	Slt	21.06.92	Wilson, George	Lt	05.06.96
Wain, Alan	Lt Cdr	01.10.87	Wilson, George	Lt	01.11.95
Wakeham, David	Slt	16.11.99	Wilson, Ian	Lt	21.02.82
Walker, Keith	Lt	05.02.88	Wilson, William	Lt	04.11.85
Walker, Pamela	Lt	05.12.01	Windle, John	Lt	13.07.90
Wall, Margaret	Lt	26.10.84	Wood, Christopher	Lt	27.10.92
Wallace, Iain	Lt Cdr	01.04.95	Wood, Michael	Lt	01.06.84
Walsh, Edward	Lt Cdr	01.06.82	Wood, Norman	Lt Cdr	01.03.90
Ward, John	Lt	02.03.88	Woodrow, Clive	Lt	16.11.01
Ward, Linda	Slt	09.06.00	Woods, Edward Arthur	Lt	04.11.92
Ward, Lesley	Lt	12.05.95	Woodward, Stewart	Lt Cdr	14.11.84
Ward, Simon	Lt RMR	22.11.00	Wooldridge, Donald	Lt	03.02.94
Waring, Peter	Lt	14.11.96	Woolgar, Victor	Lt Cdr	01.01.88
Warner, Peter	Capt RMR	10.03.96	Worrall, Ian	Capt RMR	01.07.99
Warters, David	Slt	10.07.01	Wright, John	Slt	05.12.00

Name	Rank	Seniority	Name	Rank	Seniority
Wrin, Jane Frances	Lt	26.11.92			
Wylie, William	Lt Cdr	05.12.83			
Wynne, David	Lt	21.04.93			

Y

Name	Rank	Seniority
Yeomans, Roy	Lt	10.04.97
Yorke, Barrie	Lt	01.07.87
Young, Steven	Lt	05.05.95

Z

Name	Rank	Seniority
Zaccarini, Jason	Lt	26.03.02

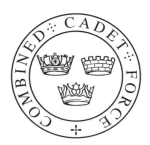

COMBINED CADET FORCE

Name	Rank	Seniority	School/College

A

Abrahams, Ian	Slt	07.03.00	HQCCF Recall
Adams, Mark	Lt	21.07.01	Churchers College
Adams, Thomas	Lt	01.09.81	Cheltenham
Aldridge, Mark	Lt	01.04.95	St Dunstans
Allen, Brian	Slt	28.02.84	Elizabeth College
Allison, Peter	CaptRMR	01.07.99	Charterhouse
Andrews, Jacqueline	Lt	29.11.96	HQCCF Recall
Armitage, David	Slt	01.10.98	Wellington
Armstrong, Ivan	Lt Cdr	31.05.95	Bangor
Ashfield, Noel	Slt	28.11.00	Campbell
Ashton, Stephanie	Slt	13.06.01	HQCCF Recall
Ayers, William	Lt	01.07.00	HQCCF Recall

B

Bader, Brett	Slt	14.08.01	Bournemouth
Bailey, Nicholas	Lt	05.09.00	HQCCF Recall
Baker, Michael	Lt	25.09.97	Plymouth
Baker, Piers	Slt	14.07.86	HQCCF Recall
Barker, Janet	Lt	16.08.01	HQCCF Recall
Barlow, Katrina	Slt	10.11.01	Gordons
Batchelder, Mark	Slt	14.08.00	Berkhamstead
Benson, Leisle	Slt	01.01.02	Tonbridge
Benson, Roger	Lt	01.09.95	Nottingham High
Bird, Elizabeth	Slt	01.07.98	HQCCF Recall
Bird, Jason	Slt	31.07.99	Trinity
Blan, Stuart	Lt RMR	04.11.99	Canford
Bolam, Laura	Slt	25.03.01	Langley
Bond, Edward	Slt	12.03.01	Haileybury
Bone, Robert	Slt	14.08.00	Mill Hill
Boorer, Fiona	Slt	13.03.02	HQCCF Recall
Borking, Graham	Lt	09.01.90	Queen Victoria
Botterill, Marc	Lt	01.09.01	HQCCF Recall
Boughton, Charles	Slt	08.08.95	Royal Hospital
Boulton, Martin	Alt RMR	01.03.99	Sherborne
Bowen-Walker, Peter	Slt	18.11.01	Perse

Name	Rank	Seniority	School/College
Bowles, Michael	Lt	21.09.86	King Williams IO
Bownass, Thomas	Lt	19.09.01	Seaford
Brading, Christopher	Slt	01.03.02	HQCCF Recall
Brazier, Colin	Lt	19.06.97	HQCCF Recall
Briant, Clare	Slt	02.04.01	Bearwood
Bridgeman, Keith	Cdr	01.07.01	MTS Northwood
Brittain, Norman	Lt	01.08.75	Oundle
Brooks, John	Lt Cdr	19.02.80	St Peters C of E
Brown, Anthony	Cdr	26.04.98	HQCCF Recall
Brown, Simon	Lt	01.10.99	Shiplake
Brown, Stephen	Lt	26.07.99	Milton Abbey
Brown, Thomas	Slt	02.04.01	Arnold
Browne, Nialle	Slt	12.10.98	Uppingham
Bryant, Marion	Slt	13.08.01	Bournemouth
Burden, Richard	LtRMR	01.09.01	Harrow
Burns, James	Lt	01.05.74	HQCCF Recall
Burrowes, Christopher	Lt	12.08.91	Winchester
Butt, Robert	Slt	07.02.01	Downside

C

Callow, Martin	CapRMR	01.07.99	Royal Hospital
Cardwell, Alexander	Lt Cdr	20.09.01	Bangor
Carpenter, Richard	Lt	01.09.01	Nottingham High
Carter, Ian	Slt	01.02.88	Cheltenham
Carter, Michael	Lt Cdr	21.06.95	Kelly
Carter, Nicholas	Lt Cdr	20.07.98	Newcastle High
Carter, Steven	Lt Cdr	01.09.93	HQCCF Recall
Cartmell, Keith	Lt	16.11.98	Arnold
Caves, Richard	Lt	21.07.01	Strathallan
Chantler, Micheal	Lt	03.03.02	HQCCF Recall
Chapman, Kenneth	Slt	19.06.84	Stamford
Chetwood, James	Lt	01.09.97	Portsmouth
Clark, Daniel	AltRMR	01.09.01	Bradfield
Clark, Timothy	Slt	11.08.97	HQCCF Recall
Clarke, Rueben	Lt	01.05.96	HQCCF Recall
Clayton, Fiona	Lt	01.08.99	Sutton Valence
Clifford, Karen	Slt	15.01.02	Pangbourne

Name	Rank	Seniority	School/College
Clough, Howard	Lt	01.09.99	Scarborough
Coetzee, Sarah	Slt	27.02.01	Campbell
Collier, Anthony	Slt	08.08.94	HQCCF Recall
Collins, Janet	Slt	21.09.91	RGS Newcastle
Collins, Micheal	Slt	28.02.83	Magdalen
Collins, Wendy	Lt	27.09.93	HQCCF Recall
Cook, Stephen	Lt RMR	01.10.01	Wellingborough
Copleston, Michael	Lt	01.08.01	Taunton
Copp, Alasdair	CapRMR	01.07.99	Canford
Copplestone, Neil	Lt Cdr	01.09.01	Brentwood
Corbould, Leigh	Lt	10.10.99	Canford
Costin, Robert	Slt	11.08.98	Worksop
Cox, Damian	Slt	25.03.01	Prior Park Col
Cox, James	Lt	17.09.97	Birkenhead
Coyle, David	Slt	04.08.01	Framlingham
Coyne, Lucie	Lt Cdr	01.09.01	Brentwood
Crabtree, John	Lt Cdr	01.11.89	Kings Col Taunto
Craig, Alex	2LtRMR	07.04.02	Shrewsbury
Creasey, Peter	Lt	16.06.00	Royal Hospital
Crees, David	Cdr	01.11.92	HQCCF Recall
Crocker, Allan	Slt	11.03.02	Clifton
Crook, Patricia	Slt	28.03.00	Haileybury
Crook, Stephen	Slt	11.02.00	City of London
Curtis, Berwick	Lt	01.09.81	Epsom
CuthbertsonJames	Slt	01.02.97	Kelvinside

D

Name	Rank	Seniority	School/College
Davies, Jonathon	Lt	07.10.99	HQCCF Recall
Delpech, Daniel	Lt	30.01.92	Haberdashers
Dewey, Peter	CapRMR	01.07.99	Rugby
Dickin, James	Slt	05.02.01	HQCCF Recall
Doody, Edwin	Slt	05.02.01	HQCCF Recall
Dore, Karen	Slt	01.09.96	HQCCF Recall
Dubbins, Keith	Lt	17.07.93	Ryde
Dunn, Alexander	Cdr	16.03.95	HQCCF Recall
Durrans, Howard	Lt	13.01.98	Bridlington
Durrant, Robert	Cdr	01.03.92	HQCCF Recall
Duthie, Ruth	Lt	07.07.00	Portsmouth
Dyer, Bridgette	LWRMR	02.11.00	Pangbourne
Dyer, Paul	Slt	12.03.01	Duke of Yorks
Dyster, Sabine	Slt	15.02.99	HQCCF Recall

E

Name	Rank	Seniority	School/College
Eames, Andrew	MaJRMR	01.07.86	Hereford
Eaton, Trevor	Lt	01.09.01	St Dunstans
Ecclestone, Kay	Lt	21.07.00	HQCCF Recall
Edwards, David	Slt	14.10.01	Sherborne
Elbourne, Nicholas	Cdr	01.11.97	Wellingborough
Elkington, Herbert OBE	Cdr	12.01.87	HQCCF Recall
Elliott, Lynnette	Lt	21.07.01	Clifton
Ellis, Timothy	Lt	01.09.94	Prior Park Col
Emms, Peter	Lt	21.07.01	Magdalen
Ettinger, Damian	Lt	01.09.92	Downside
Evans, Richard	Lt Cdr	16.09.96	HQCCF Recall
Everest, Derek	Lt	01.04.74	Kings Edwards
Eyles, Mark	Slt	13.08.01	Colstons
Eyles, Ruth	Slt	08.08.95	HQCCF Recall

F

Name	Rank	Seniority	School/College
Finn, Mark	Lt Cdr	09.11.93	Afloat Trng Officer
Fischer, Andrew	Slt	18.10.99	St Lawrence

Name	Rank	Seniority	School/College
Ford, Peter	Lt	13.01.78	SO Diving
Forey, Sarah	Slt	28.06.01	St Peters C of E
Foulger, Tim	Lt	01.09.97	HQCCF Recall
Fountain, Evan	Lt RMR	01.09.00	Wellington
Fox, Stephen	CapRMR	01.07.99	Shrewsbury
Francis-Jones, Anthony	Lt	01.04.01	Kings Col Taunto
Freedman, Stephen	Lt Cdr	05.09.99	MTS Crosby
Friend, David	Lt	01.10.96	Kings BrutonSch
Frost, Rex	Cdr	01.08.92	Exeter
Fullarton, Ian	Lt	01.09.00	RGSHighWycombe
Fuller, David	Lt	01.08.00	Oundle
Fyleman, Keith	Lt	18.10.01	Cheltenham

G

Name	Rank	Seniority	School/College
Georgiakakis, Nikos	Lt	20.08.90	Charterhouse
Gibson, Alan	Lt	25.06.01	Oratory
Glasbey, Martyn	Slt	05.09.91	Ryde
Glasspoole, Paul	Lt Cdr	04.05.89	Hele's
Glimm, Klaus	ActMajRMR	01.07.99	HQCCF Recall
Gordon, Robin	Slt	07.04.02	Campbell
Gray, John	Slt	18.05.01	Wellingborough
Green, George	Cdr	01.01.94	Brighton
Greenhough, Clive	Lt	01.09.99	HQCCF Recall
Griffin, Paul	Slt	01.01.98	Downside
Guise, Nicola	Lt	01.09.95	Oundle

H

Name	Rank	Seniority	School/College
Hall, Austin	Lt	15.07.88	HQCCF Recall
Hall, Kevin	Slt	25.03.01	Plymouth
Hamilton, Lesley	Lt	01.09.98	Liverpool
Hamon, Christopher	Lt	01.09.96	Sherborne
Harding, Susan	Lt Cdr	07.07.95	Kelly
Hardman, Thomas	Lt	01.09.97	Haberdashers
Harris, David	MajRMR	25.02.85	Kimbolton
Harris, Steven	Lt Cdr	01.08.98	Exeter
Harrison, Anthony	Lt	08.02.94	HQCCF Recall
Harrod, Samantha	Slt	11.08.98	HQCCF Recall
Hartley, George	Lt	01.09.01	Ruthin
Harvey, Peter	Lt Cdr	01.08.97	HQCCF Recall
Harvey, Stephen	CapRMR	17.08.97	Bedford Modern
Hatch, Alastair	CaptRMR	01.09.00	Sherborne
Hawkins, Keith	Lt Cdr	01.04.93	HQCCF Recall
Hellier, Jeremy	Lt Cdr	01.03.90	Wellington
Henderson, Joan	Lt	01.10.98	RGS HighWycombe
Hendry, Alastair	Slt	08.08.94	Reigate
Henry, Thomas	Lt Cdr	23.08.00	George Heriots
Hewitt, Richard	Lt	31.07.83	Durham
Hey, Richard	Lt	01.04.98	Oratory
Hill, Charles	Lt	01.03.77	Winchester
Hill, Peter	Lt	12.03.98	Sevenoaks
Hobbs, Andrew	CaptRMR	01.07.99	Canford
Hocking, Barry	Slt	14.08.00	Royal Hospital
Holland, Clare	Lt	22.07.00	Calday Grange
Holmes, Matthew	Lt Cdr	19.09.01	Langley
Horley, Philip	Slt	14.08.00	Sutton Valence
Horsman, Stefan	Slt	01.10.01	Portsmouth
Houghton, Philip	Slt	07.03.99	Fettes
Hudson, John	Lt Cdr	01.09.95	Kings Col Taunto
Hutchinson, Jeremy	Cdr	12.08.96	HQCCF Recall
Huxtable, Nigel	Lt	31.07.00	HQCCF Recall

Name	Rank	Seniority	School/College

I

Ibbertson-Price,William	LtCdr	14.11.91	HQCCF Recall
Ing, John	MajRMR	01.07.99	Harrow
Iredale, Judy	Slt	01.07.98	Taunton

J

Jacklin, John	Lt Cdr	08.10.99	HQCCF NCFBO
Jackson, Andrew	Slt	01.01.98	HQCCF Recall
Jackson, Howard	Lt	15.07.88	Worksop
Jackson, Robert	Lt	01.06.81	Bedford
Jago, Peter	Lt	21.01.97	RGS Lancaster
James, David	Slt	01.01.02	St Bartholomews
Jeans-Jakobsson, Michael	Lt	01.05.92	HQCCF Recall
Jenkins, David	Lt Cdr	01.09.92	HQCCF Recall
Jethwa, Ashok	Slt	26.01.99	Arnold
Johnson, Marcus	Slt	08.08.95	Exeter
Johnston, Kirsten	Slt	01.09.97	MTS Northwood
Jolliff, Timothy	Slt	18.10.95	Loughborough

K

Kay, Anne	Slt	07.04.96	HQCCF Recall
Kearsey, Peter	Slt	15.09.99	Christs Hospital
Kennedy, Karen	Slt	28.03.99	Plymouth
Kermode, Erica	Slt	08.08.94	HQCCF Recall
Kilbey, Susan	Slt	10.11.98	Cheltenham
Killgren, Carl	Lt Cdr	01.11.98	Stamford
Killgren, Susan	Slt	14.08.01	Stamford
Kirton, Stephanie	Lt	24.07.00	Berkhamsted
Kirwin, Christopher	Cdr	01.02.91	Kelly

L

Larby, John	Lt Cdr	01.09.95	Kelly
Lawson, Edward	Lt Cdr	28.01.97	Arnold
Lawson, Grant	Lt RMR	01.03.00	Shiplake
Lawson, Matthew	Lt Cdr	06.11.00	St Johns
Lee, John	Lt	01.09.90	Ruthin
Leigh, Richard	Slt	14.08.00	King Williams IOM
Lewis, Andrew Robert	Lt	10.08.93	Christ Hospital
Leyshon, Lara	Slt	04.10.01	Haberdashers
Lilford, Jane	Slt	12.03.01	Bridlington
Lingard, David	Cdr	08.03.99	HQCCF Recall
Little, John	Lt Cdr	01.09.91	Eastbourne
Lloyd, Theo	Lt	22.11.99	Churchers College
Loudon, Iain	Slt	18.10.95	Rossall
Lovell, Keith	Lt	15.02.01	Bearwood
Lovell, Stephen	Lt	08.01.92	Royal Hospital
Lucas, Ian	Cdr	26.09.01	Tonbridge
Lucas, Stuart	Slt	27.02.01	Loretto
Lucius-Clarke, David	Lt	01.09.97	HQCCF Recall

M

MacCarthy, Thomas	Slt	06.11.01	Adams Grammar
MacDonald, Fraser	Lt	01.09.71	Trinity
MacIntosh, Colin	Lt RMR	15.07.99	Shrewsbury
Mackie, Alan	Cdr	01.09.01	Bangor
Maddocks, Jane	Slt	14.02.02	HQCCF Recall
Magor, Brian	Cdr	14.10.85	Calday Grange
Marsh, Lesley	Lt Cdr	19.01.93	HQCCF Recall
Martin, Steven	Lt	01.01.87	Kelly

Martindale, Leslie	Lt Cdr	06.08.00	Calday Grange
Matson, Christopher	Lt	26.11.99	HQCCF Recall
May, Edward	Slt	01.07.98	HQCCF Recall
Maynard, Rachel	Slt	01.10.00	Wellingborough
McCann, John	Slt	17.10.00	Strathallan
McConnell, Susan	Lt	31.08.92	HQCCF Recall
McConnell, William	Lt	06.05.92	HQCCF Recall
McDonald, Gary	Lt	21.07.01	Adams Grammar
McDonald, Richard	Lt RMR	01.09.86	Whitgift
McGuff, Neil	Lt	01.09.00	Wellington
McKee, Mark	Slt	10.08.93	Campbell
Melville, Graham	Lt	21.06.01	Birkenhead
Mercer, Jane	Lt	21.07.01	Rossall
Mercer, Louise	Lt	10.09.97	Prior Park Col
Middleton, Craig	2LtRMR	01.07.01	Uppingham
Miles, David	2LtRMR	01.01.02	Royal Hospital
Millard, Michelle	Lt	24.07.00	Victoria College
Mills, Anita	Lt	01.01.00	Monkton Combe
Milne, Stewart	Slt	25.06.97	HQCCF Recall
Milton, Phillippa	Slt	25.06.01	Bedford Sch
Minto, Neil	Lt	01.04.01	HQCCF Recall
Mitchell, Ian	Lt	01.09.99	Wellington
Mitchell, Robert	Lt Cdr	01.09.88	Kings Col Sch Wi
Montgomery, Paul	Lt Cdr	01.04.01	Dean Close
Moody, Susan	Lt Cdr	15.12.95	HQCCF Recall
Moore, Adrian	Slt	04.10.01	HQCCF Recall
Moore, David John	Lt	21.04.85	HQCCF Recall
Moore, Terena	Slt	11.07.83	HQCCF Recall
Morgan, Bryn	Lt	01.01.91	Brentwood
Morgan, Giles	Lt Cdr	09.02.96	HQCCF Recall
Morgan, James	Slt	01.04.96	Sedbergh
Morton, Hilary	Slt	21.01.01	King Williams IOM
Moss-Gibbons, David	Cdr	06.01.00	Bradfield Col
Mytton, Evan	Lt Cdr	01.01.01	HQCCF Recall

N

Newton, John	Lt	01.01.84	HQCCF Recall
Newton, Robert	Lt Cdr	01.01.96	HQCCF Recall
Nicholson, Robert	Cdr	01.03.95	Milton Abbey
Nurser, Graham	Slt	28.11.00	Wellington

O

O`brien, Timothy	Slt	06.11.00	Reading Blue Coat
Ogilvie, Fergus	CaptRMR	01.07.99	Giggleswick
Oldbury, David	Slt	01.01.93	HQCCF Recall
Osmond, Stephen	Cdr	03.12.01	RGS Worcester
Othick, Anthony	Slt	14.08.01	Scarborough
Owen, Elizabeth	Slt	19.01.98	HQCCF Recall
Owen, John	Lt Cdr	01.12.84	HQCCF Recall

P

Packer, Thomas	Lt Cdr	13.01.95	HQCCF Recall
Parker, Ann	Slt	02.09.92	St Bartholomews
Parkinson, Christopher	Lt	01.11.83	Sutton Valence
Parkinson, Ian	Slt	01.06.99	KingsSchRochester
Parkinson, Kenneth	Lt	01.09.90	HQCCF Recall
Paton, Gordon	Lt Cdr	01.01.81	HQCCF Recall
Payne, Anthony	Lt	01.12.73	Loughborough
Pegg, Joanna	Slt	01.01.00	Exeter
Pidoux, John	Slt	01.01.86	Maidstone
Pike, John	Slt	31.01.01	Sandbach

Name	Rank	Seniority	School/College
Pocock, Clare	Slt	18.10.01	St Bartholomews
Poulet, Gerard	Slt	01.05.01	St Margarets
Poulet-Bowden, Geraldine	Lt	21.07.01	St Margarets
Powell, Andrew	Lt Cdr	05.11.01	Reigate
Powell, John	Slt	08.08.95	Pangbourne
Price, Thelma	Slt	28.06.99	Dulwich
Prior, Anthony	Lt	01.08.82	Milton Abbey
Prosser, Nicholas	Lt Cdr	01.09.77	Tonbridge

R

Name	Rank	Seniority	School/College
Raines, David	Lt	05.08.79	Elizabeth Col
Reid, David	Lt RMR	01.09.98	Wellington
Renel, John	Lt	01.08.86	HQCCF Recall
Rennison, Christopher	Lt RMR	01.07.99	Royal Hospital
Reynolds, Christopher	Lt	01.10.73	Bournemouth
Rhodes, Terry	Lt	24.04.00	Kimbolton
Richard, Peter	Lt	01.01.93	HQCCF Recall
Richards, Philip	Lt	16.02.94	Fettes
Ridley Thomas, Michael	Lt	01.09.92	HQCCF Recall
Ripley, Myles	Lt	01.09.83	Sedbergh
Robarts, Paul	Slt	25.06.00	HQCCF Recall
Roberts, Derek	Lt	11.07.94	Brighton
Roberts, Martin	Lt Cdr	01.04.96	HQCCF Recall
Robinson, Simon	Lt Cdr	01.03.01	Trinity Teignmouth
Robinson, Susan	Lt	01.03.01	Trinity Teignmouth
Roby, Ronald	Cdr	01.09.86	HQCCF Recall
Rooms, Lindsay	Cdr	01.12.97	Oundle
Rose, Helen	Slt	13.08.01	Bedford Modern
Rothwell, George	Lt Cdr	06.04.95	HQCCF Recall
Rudall, Anthony	Lt	01.04.01	St Lawrence
Rule, Peter	Cdr	01.06.98	Trinity
Russell, James	ActMajRMR	01.04.00	Malvern

S

Name	Rank	Seniority	School/College
Sanders, Bryant	Cdr	15.11.86	Bournemouth
Sanders, Robert	Lt	16.09.99	Oratory
Sanderson, Guy	Slt	06.11.01	City of London
Savage, Anthony	Cdr	01.01.97	Portsmouth
Savage, Jennifer	Slt	06.11.01	Alleyns School
Schofield, Michelle	Slt	23.11.01	Kings Sch Rochester
Scorgie, Stuart	Lt Cdr	01.09.00	Clifton
Scott, Frances	Lt	27.02.00	Edinburgh
Sell, Roger	Lt	01.09.97	Hereford
Shannon, Tom	Lt	02.09.86	Queen Victoria
Shone, Michael	Lt	01.09.01	HQCCF Recall
Shorrocks, Jonathan	Lt Cdr	01.09.96	RGS Worcester
Sibley, Peter	Lt Cdr	25.02.87	HQCCF Recall
Simister, Alan	Lt	01.05.01	Eastbourne
Simpson, Philip	Lt	01.01.98	Ellesmere
Simpson-Hayes, Gizella	Slt	01.10.01	MTS Crosby
Sissons, Stewart	Lt	09.04.98	HQCCF Recall
Smith, Alison	Lt	21.07.01	Dollar
Smith, John	Lt	01.01.01	HQCCF Recall
Smith, Nicolas	Slt	14.08.01	Woodbridge
Smith, Ronald	Lt Cdr	22.08.00	Kelvinside
Solly, Raymond	Lt	16.05.90	HQCCF Recall
Spall, Christopher	Lt	07.04.02	Loretto
Spence, Donna	Slt	29.07.96	Bangor
Spence, Richard	Lt	01.12.98	Bangor
Spike, Nigel	Slt	04.11.89	Glasgow Academy
Stanley, John	Slt	08.01.02	Sandbach
Stansbury, William	Slt	01.09.96	MTS Northwood
Stapleton, Sonia	Slt	06.11.01	St Dunstans
Sterling, Rebecca	Slt	17.11.01	King Edwards
Stevens, Laurence	Lt	01.09.85	St Bartholomews
Stevens, Peter	Cdr	01.09.93	Plymouth
Stilwell, Valerie	Slt	08.08.94	HQCCF Recall
Stocker, Paul	Lt	21.07.01	Uppingham
Stocks, David	CaptRMR	12.09.00	Bradfield
Stratton-Brown, Colin	Lt Cdr	01.09.90	Maidstone
Streatfeild-James, Adam	CaptRMR	05.09.00	Strathallan
Stringer, Christopher	CaptRMR	01.07.99	Malvern
Sugden, Kara	Slt	08.01.02	Canford
Sutherland, Peter	Lt	22.07.00	Whitgift
Sweeney, Sean	Lt Cdr	03.05.00	HQCCF Recall

T

Name	Rank	Seniority	School/College
Taylor, Liam	CaptRMR	01.07.99	Winchester
Tear, Richard	Lt	01.09.99	Wellington
Telford, Nicola	Slt	14.12.01	HQCCF Recall
Temple, Robert	Lt	08.03.01	HQCCF Recall
Tennant, David	Lt	30.09.92	Tonbridge
Tetley, Neil	Slt	18.10.00	Kings Wimbledon
Thorn, Simon	Slt	17.10.98	Radley
Till-Dowling, Julie	Slt	01.09.01	Ryde
Tinker, Christopher	Cdr	30.05.96	Whitgift
Tiplady, Rodney	Slt	01.09.96	Edinburgh
Todd, Malcolm	Lt Cdr	01.01.93	HQCCF Recall
Tolhurst, Aidan	Lt Cdr	01.09.81	City of London
Trigg, Duncan	Slt	12.07.98	Ruthin
Trundle, Simon	Lt	01.09.94	HQCCF Recall
Tucker, Vivian	Slt	12.10.98	Hereford
Tudor, Catherine	Slt	10.08.93	King Edwards
Turner, Clive	Lt	21.07.01	HQCCF Recall

V

Name	Rank	Seniority	School/College
Van Der Werff, Tanya	Lt	01.09.95	Reading Blue Coat
Van Zwanenberg, Louise	Lt	25.01.99	Woodbridge
Vaughan, Piers	Lt Cdr	05.01.98	Sevenoaks
Vickers, Michael	Lt	01.06.96	Christs College
Vickery, David	Cdr	01.09.00	Monkton Combe
Vigers, Rosemary	Lt	20.07.94	Kings Sch Bruton
Vine, Roger	Lt	21.07.95	Dulwich

W

Name	Rank	Seniority	School/College
Walker, Colin	Cdr	01.01.88	Strathallan
Walker, David	Slt	15.10.01	Woodbridge
Walmsley, Richard	Lt RMR	10.01.01	Strathallan
Walsh, George	Slt	30.09.00	Liverpool
Ward, Sarah	Slt	12.12.00	Mill Hill
Warren, Clive	Lt	01.04.00	Colstons
Waugh, Patrick	Lt	01.12.97	Wellingborough
Webb, Victoria	Slt	01.09.00	Maidstone
Whale, Andrew	Lt	01.04.89	Pangbourne
Wharton, Adam	Slt	25.03.01	Stowe
Whitlock, Scott	Slt	14.08.00	Epsom
Wilding, Karl	Slt	19.09.01	Harrow
Wilkes, Justin	Lt Cdr	29.06.98	Dollar
Wilkinson, Daren	Slt	18.01.02	Bridlington
Williams, Robert	Lt Cdr	01.01.02	Glasgow Academy
Windsor, Michael	Slt	12.10.98	Kings Wimbledon
Woodward, Peter	Slt	12.03.01	Monkton Combe
Worrall, Stuart	Lt RMR	01.09.99	Kings Col Taunton

Name	Rank	Seniority	School/College	Name	Rank	Seniority	School/College
Wylie, John	Lt Cdr	20.09.01	Radley				

Y

Name	Rank	Seniority	School/College
Yates, Christopher	Lt RMR	01.07.99	Winchester
Yorath, Alun	Lt RMR	01.07.99	Pangbourne
Young, Edward	Slt	17.09.01	Uppingham

ROYAL NAVAL RESERVE AND OTHER VESSELS AUTHORISED TO FLY THE BLUE ENSIGN IN MERCHANT VESSELS (FOREIGN OR HOME TRADE ARTICLES) AND FISHING VESSELS.

1. A list of Royal Naval Reserve and other vessels authorised to fly the Blue Ensign will no longer be published in the Navy List.

2. Its inclusion was intended for the information of Captains of Her Majesty's Ships with reference to the provisions of Article 9153 of the Queen's Regulations for the Royal Navy under which they are authorised to ascertain whether British Merchant Ships (including Fishing Vessels) flying the Blue Ensign of Her Majesty's Fleet are legally entitled to do so.

3. However, the usefulness of this list serves only a limited purpose as the list of vessels that could fly the Blue Ensign can change frequently. British merchant ships and fishing vessels are allowed to wear the plain Blue Ensign under the authority of a special Warrant, subject to certain conditions being fulfilled, and which are outlined below.

4. Vessels registered on the British Registry of Shipping may wear a plain Blue Ensign providing the master or skipper is in possession of a warrant issued by the Director of Naval Reserves under the authority of the Secretary of State for Defence, and the additional conditions outlined below are fulfilled. The Blue Ensign is to be struck if the officer to whom the warrant was issued relinquishes command, or if the ship or vessel passes into foreign ownership and ceases to be a British ship as defined by MSA 95.

     a. Vessels on Parts I, II, and IV of the Register. The master must be an officer of the rank of lieutenant RN/RMR or Captain RM/RMR or above in the Royal Fleet Reserve or the maritime forces of a United Kingdom Overseas Territory or Commonwealth country of which Her Majesty is Head of State, or an officer on the Active or Retired Lists of any branch of the maritime reserve forces of these countries or territories.

     b. Vessels on Part II of the Register. This part of the Register is reserved for fishing vessels. The skipper must comply with the same criteria as for sub-Clause 4.a. above, however the crew must contain at least four members, each of whom fulfils at least one of the following criteria:

         Royal Naval or Royal Marines reservists or pensioners
         Reservists or pensioners from a Commonwealth monarchy or United Kingdom Overseas Territory
         Ex-ratings or Royal Marines who have completed twenty years service
         in the Reserves
         Members of the Royal Fleet Reserve

5. Action on sighting a merchant ship wearing a Blue Ensign. The Commanding Officer of one of HM ships on meeting a vessel wearing the Blue Ensign may send on board a commissioned officer to confirm that the criteria outlined above are being met in full. If it is found that the ship is wearing a Blue Ensign, without authority of a proper warrant, the ensign is to be seized, taken away and forfeited

to The Sovereign and the circumstances reported to the Director Naval Reserves, acting on behalf of the Commander in Chief Naval Home Command, who maintains the list of persons authorised to hold such warrants. However, if it is found that, despite the warrant being sighted, the ship is failing to comply with the criteria in some other particular, the ensign is not to be seized but the circumstances are to be reported to the Director Naval Reserves.

OBITUARY
ROYAL NAVAL SERVICE

Commander
Maughan LVO, OBE, J M C   09.04.02

Lieutenant Commander
Woolliams, M F   28.06.01
Stewart, A M   11.05.01
Hawley, S C   19.05.02

Surgeon Lieutenant
Kershaw, D J E   15.05.01

Lieutenant
Skidmore, R P   12.06.02
Suggett, P R   19.06.01
Lewis, J L M   12.06.02
Paton, D W   25.07.01
Christie, D W   14.03.02

ROYAL MARINES

Brigadier
Bowkett, R M   16.07.02

Captain
Rule, S J   05.04.01

ROYAL NAVAL RESERVE

Lieutenant Commander
Houghton, N G   27.03.01

ABBREVIATIONS OF RANKS AND LISTS

A	Acting
A/	Acting
ACT	Acting
ADM	Admiral
ADM OF FLEET	Admiral of the Fleet
ASL	Acting Sub-Lieutenant
AT	Acting Temporary
BRIG	Brigadier
CAND	Candidate
CAPT	Captain
CDT	Cadet
CHAPLAIN-FLT	Chaplain of the Fleet
CDR	Commander
CDRE	Commodore
CNO	Chief Nursing Officer
COL	Colonel
COMDT	Commandant
(CS)	Careers Service
(D)	Dental
E	Engineering
(FS)	Family Service
GEN	General
(GRAD)	Graduate
HON	Honorary
I	Instructor
LOC	Local
LT	Lieutenant
LCDR	Lieutenant-Commander
LT CDR	Lieutenant-Commander
LT COL	Lieutenant-Colonel
LT GEN	Lieutenant-General
MAJ	Major
MAJ GEN	Major-General
MID	Midshipman
(NE)	New Entry
NO	Nursing Officer
OFF	Officer
OFFR	Officer
P/	Probationary
PNO	Principal Nursing Officer
PR	Principal
RADM	Rear-Admiral
REV	Reverend
RM	Royal Marines
S	Supply & Secretariat

(SD)	Special Duties List
(SDT)	Special Duties List Temporary
SG	Surgeon
SURG	Surgeon
(SL)	Supplementary List
SLT	Sub-Lieutenant
SNO	Senior Nursing Officer
SUPT NO	Superintendent Nursing Officer
T	Temporary
T/	Temporary
TLT	Temporary Lieutenant
TSLT	Temporary Sub-Lieutenant
(UCE)	University Cadet Entrant
VADM	Vice-Admiral
X	Seaman
2LT	Second Lieutenant, Royal Marines

ABBREVIATIONS OF SPECIALISATIONS & QUALIFICATIONS

(Eur Ing)	European Engineer
A/TK	Heavy Weapons Anti-Tank
AAWO	Anti Air Warfare Officer
ACC/EM	Accident and Emergency
ACGI	Associate, City and Guilds London Institute
ACIS	Associate of The Institute of Chartered Secretaries and Administrators
ACMA	Associate, Institute of Cost & Management Accountants
ACMI	Associate of The Chartered Management Institute
(AD)	Medical and Dental Administration
ADIPM	Associate, Institute of Data Processing Management
adp	Passed Advanced Adp Course Dadptc
AE	Air Engineering
AE U/T	Air Engineering Under Training
AE(L)	Air Engineering (Electrical)
AE(M)	Air Engineering (Mechanical)
AE(O)	Air Engineering (Observer)
AE(P)	Air Engineering (Pilot)
(AE)	Assault Engineer
AFIMA	Associate Fellow, Institute Mathematics & Its Applications
AFOM	Associate, Faculty of Occupational Medicine
AGSM	Associate of The Guildhall School of Music and Drama
AIL	Associate, Institute of Linguists
AIM	Associate, Institute of Metallurgists
AInstP	Associate, Institute of Physics
AKC	Associate, King's College London
ALCD	Associate, London College of Divinity

AMASEE	Associate Member, Association of Electrical Engineers
AMBCS	Associate Member, British Computing Society
AMBIM	Associate Member, British Institute of Management
AMHCIMA	Associate Member, Hotel Catering & Institutional Management Association
AMIAM	Associate Member, Institute of Administrative Management
AMICE	Associate Member, Institute of Civil Engineers
AMIEE	Associate Member, Institute of Electrical Engineers
AMIERE	Associate Member, Institution of Electronic and Radio Engineers
AMIIE	Associate Member, Institution of Incorporated Engineers
AMIMarE	Associate Member, Institute of Marine Engineers
AMIMarEST	Associate Member Institute Marine Engineers Science & Technology
AMIMechE	Associate Member, Institute of Mechanical Engineers
AMIMechIE	Associate Member of Institute of Mechanical Incorporated Engineers
AMInstP	Associate Member, Institute of Physics
AMINucE	Associate Member, Institution of Nuclear Engineers
AMIPIE	Associate Member, Institution of Plant Engineers
AMNI	Associate Member, Nautical Institute
AMRAeS	Associate Member, Royal Aeronautical Society
AMRINA	Associate Member. Royal Institution of Naval Architects
ARAM	Associate, Royal Academy of Music
ARCM	Associate, Royal College of Music
ARCS	Associate, Royal College of Science
ARCST	Associate, Royal College of Science and Technology (Glasgow)
ARIC	Associate, Royal Institute of Chemistry
ARICS	Professional Asssociate, Royal Institution of Chartered Surveyors
ATC	Air Traffic Control Officer
ATCU/T	Air Traffic Control Officer Under Training
AV	Aviation
AWO(A)	Advanced Warfare Officer(Above Water)
AWO(C)	Advanced Warfare Officer(Communications)
AWO(U)	Advanced Warfare Officer(Underwater)
aws	Qualified Air Warfare College
BA	Bachelor of Arts
BA(OU)	Bachelor of Arts, Open University
BAO	Bachelor of Art of Obstetrics
BAR	Barrister
BCH	Bachelor of Surgery (Bch)
BCh	Bachelor of Surgery
BChD	Bachelor of Dentistry
BChir	Bachelor of Surgery
BComm	Bachelor of Commerce
BD	Bachelor of Divinity
BDS	Bachelor of Dental Surgery
BEd	Bachelor of Education
BEng	Bachelor of Engineering
BM	Bachelor of Medicine
BMedSc	Bachelor of Medical Science

BMS	Bachelor of Medical Science
BMus	Bachelor of Music
BPh	Bachelor of Philosophy
BPharm	Bachelor of Pharmacy
BS	Bachelor of Surgery
BSc	Bachelor of Science
BSC(EH)	Bsc Environmental Health
BSc(Eng)	Bachelor of Science (Engineering)
BTech	Bachelor of Technology
C	Communications
C PHYS	Chartered Physicist
C/T	Clinical Teacher
CA	Caterer
(CA)	Consultant in Anaesthetics
(CA/E)	Consultant in Accident/Emergency
CC	Coronary Care
(CC)	Consultant in Paediatrics
DipAF	The Certified Diploma in Accounting and Finance
(CDO)	Commando Trained
(CE)	Consultant in Otorhinolaryngology
CEng	Chartered Engineer
Cert Ed	Certificate of Education
CertTh	Certificate in Theology
CGIA	Insignia Award of The City & Guilds of London Insitute
(CGS)	Consultant in General Surgery
CHB	Bachelor of Surgery (Chb)
ChB	Bachelor of Surgery
ChM	Chartered Mathematician
(CK)	Consultant in Dermatology
(CL)	Consultant in Pathology
(CM)	Consultant in General Medicine
CMA	Management Accountant
CMarSci	Chartered Marine Scientist
CMath	Chartered Mathematician
(CN/P)	Consultant in Neuro-Psychiatry
(CO)	Consultant in Ophthalmology
(CO/M)	Consultant in Occupational Medicine
(CO/S)	Consultant in Orthopaedic Surgery
(COSM)	Consultant in Oral Surgery/Oral Medicine
CPDATE	This Is A 'pay' Only Sq. It Will Not Be Awarded To Personnel.
CPN	Community Psychiatric Nurse
CQSW	Certificate of Qualification in Social Work
(CU)	Consultant in Urology
(CX)	Consultant in Radiology
D	Direction Officer
DA	Diploma in Anaesthesia
DAppDy	Diploma in Applied Dynamics

CH	Diploma in Child Health
DCHS	Diploma in Community Health Studies
DCL	Doctor of Civil Law
DCP	Diploma in Clinical Pathology
DD	Doctor of Divinity
DDPH	Diploma in Public Dental Health
DEH	Diploma in Environmental Health
df	Qualified Defence Fellowship
DGDP RCS(UK)	Diploma in General Dental Practice Rcs (Uk)
DGDP(UK)	Diploma in General Dental Practice (Uk)
DGDPRCS(Eng)	Diploma General Dental Practice Rcs(Eng)
DHC(PO)	Diploma in Remote Health Care - Polar Option
DHMSA	Diploma in The History of Medicine (Society of Apothecaries)
DIC	Diploma of The Imperial College
DIH	Diploma in Industrial Health
Dip FFP	Diploma of The Faculty of Family Planning
Dip ICN	Diploma in Infection Control Nursing
Dip OHN	Diploma in Occupational Health Nursing
Dip OM	Diploma in Occupational Medicine
Dip SM	Diploma in Sports Medicine
DipA&PPS	Diploma in Academic & Practical Physiotherapy in Sport
DipAvMed	Diploma in Aviation Medicine
DIPCM	Diploma in Clinical Microbiology
DIPCR	Teaching Diploma in Clinical Radiology
DipEd	Diploma in Education
DipEP	Rs Health Diploma in Environmental Protection
DIPH&S	Diploma in Health and Safety
DipHE(Paeds)	Diploma (He)(Paediatrics)
DipIMC RCSED	Diploma in Immediate Medical Care of Royal College Surgeons (Edinburgh)
DIPRP	Post Graduate Diploma in Radiation Protection
DipTh	Diploma in Theology
DLitt	Doctor of Letters
DLO	Diploma in Laryngology and Otology
DM	Doctor of Medicine
DMCMP	Diploma in Medical Centre Practice Management
DMNS	Diploma in Military Nursing Studies
DMRD	Diploma in Medical Radiological Diagnosis
DNE	Diploma in Nursing Education
DNM	Diploma in Nuclear Medicine
DO	Diploma in Ophthalmology
DObstRCOG	Diploma Royal College of Obstetricians and Gynaecologists
DOrth	Diploma in Orthodontics
DP	Diploma in Philosophy
DPH	Diploma in Public Health
DPHC	Dental Public Health - Consultant
DPhil	Doctor of Philosophy
DPhysMed	Diploma in Physical Medicine

DPM	Diploma in Psychological Medicine
DRD	Diploma in Restorative Dentistry
DRRT	Diploma in Remedial & Recreational Therapy
DSc	Doctor of Science
DTM&H	Diploma in Tropical Medicine and Hygiene
E	E
Eur Ing	European Engineer
EW	Electronic Warfare
F	Pilot and Observer
FA	Fleet Analyst
FBCS	Fellow, British Computer Society
FBIM	Fellow, British Institute of Management
FC	Fighter Controller
FCIPD	Fellow of The Chartered Institute of Personnel and Development
FCIS	Fellow, Institute Chartered Secretaries & Administrators
FCMA	Fellow, Chartered Institute of Management Accountants
FCMI	Fellow of The Chartered Management Institute
FDS	Fellow in Dental Surgery
FDS RCPSGlas	Fellow in Dental Surgery Royal College of Physicians & Surgeons (Glasgow)
FDS RCS(Eng)	Fellow in Dental Surgery, Royal College of Surgeons of England
FDS RCS(Irl)	Fellow in Dental Surgery Royal College of Surgeons in Ireland
FDS RCSEdin	Fellow in Dental Surgery Royal College of Surgeons of Edinburgh
FDS(RCS)	Fellow in Dental Surgery, Royal College of Surgeons of England
FFA	Fellow, Institute of Financial Accountants
FFAEM	Fellow of The Faculty of Accident and Emergency Medicine
FFARCS	Fellow, Faculty of Anaesthetists, Royal College of Surgeons of England
FFARCSI	Fellow, Faculty of Anaesthetists, Royal College of Surgeons in Ireland
FFOM	Fellow, Faculty of Occupational Medicine
FHCIMA	Fellow of The Hotel and Catering Management Association
FIAA	Fellow, Institute of Actuaries of Australia
FICS	Fellow of The International College of Surgeons
FIEE	Fellow, Institute of Electrical Engineers
FIEEIE	Fellow of The Institute of Electrical and Electronic Incorporated Engineer
FIEIE	Fellow, Institute of Electrical and Electronic Incorporated Engineers
FIERE	Fellow, Institution of Electronic and Radio Engineers
FIIE	Fellow of The Institution of Incorporated Engineers
FIL	Fellow, Institute of Linguists
FIM	Fellow of The Institute of Metals
FIMA	Fellow, Institute of Mathematics and Its Applications
FIMarE	Fellow, Institute of Marine Engineers
FIMarEST	Fellow Institute Marine Engineers Science & Technology
FIMechE	Fellow, Institution of Mechanical Engineers
FIMS	Fellow, Institute of Management Specialists Or Mathematical Statistics
FInstAM	Fellow Institute of Administrative Management
FINucE	Fellow, Institute of Nuclear Engineers
FIOSH	Fellow of The Institute Occupational Safety & Health
FIPM	Fellow of The Institute of Personnel Management

FISM .... Fellow of The Institute of Supervision and Management
FITE .... Fellow, Institution Electrical & Electronics Technician Engineers
FNI .... Fellow, Nautical Institute
FRAeS .... Fellow, Royal Aeronautical Society
FRAM .... Fellow, Royal Academy of Music
FRC.Psych .... Fellow of The Royal College of Psychiatrists
FRCA .... Fellow of The Royal College of Anaesthetists
FRCGP .... Fellow Royal College General Practioners
FRCOG .... Fellow, Royal College of Obstetricians and Gynaecologists
FRCP .... Fellow, Royal College of Physicians, London
FRCPath .... Fellow, Royal College of Pathologists
FRCPEd .... Fellow, Royal College of Physicians, Edinburgh
FRCPGlas .... Fellow, Royal College of Physicians and Surgeons of Glasgow
FRCR .... Fellow, Royal College of Radioligists
FRCS .... Fellow, Royal College of Surgeons of England
FRCS(ED)A&E .... Fellow of The Royal College of Surgeons (Edinburgh) Accident & Emergency
FRCS(ORL) .... Fellow Royal College of Surgeons - Otorhinology
FRCS(ORTH) .... Fellow Royal College Surgeons (Orthopaedics)
FRCS(Urol) .... Fellow Royal College of Surgeons (Urology)
FRCSEd .... Fellow, Royal College of Surgeons of Edinburgh
FRCSGlas .... Fellow, Royal College of Physicians and Surgeons of Glasgow
FRCSTr&Orth .... Fellowship of The Royal College of Surgeons (Trauma & Orthopaedics)
FRGS .... Fellow, Royal Geographical Society
FRHistS .... Fellow Royal Historical Society
FRICS .... Fellow Royal Institute Chartered Surveyors
FRIN .... Fellow of The Royal Institute of Navigation
FRINA .... Fellow, Royal Institute of Naval Architects
FRMS .... Fellow, Royal Meteorological Society
FRSA .... Fellow, Royal Society of Arts
fsc .... Qualified Foreign Staff College
g .... Gunnery (Mortar Course)
GB .... The Gilbert Blane Medal
GCIS .... Graduate of The Institute of Chartered Secretaries and Administrators
gdas .... General Duties Areo Systems
GISVA .... Graduate Institute of Surveyors, Valuers and Auctioneers
GMP .... Senior House Officer in General Medical Practioner - Under Training
GMPP .... General Medical Practitioner
GradIMA .... Graduate Member, Institute of Mathematics and Its Applications
GradIMS .... Graduate Institute of Management Specialists
GradInstPS .... Graduate Institute of Purchasing and Supply
(GS) ....Specialist in General Surgery
(GS)UT .... Senior Registrar in General Surgery - Under Training
gw .... Guided Weapons Systems Course Rmcs Shrivenham
H CH .... Hydrographer (Charge)
hcsc ....Higher Command & Staff College
HDCR .... Higher Diploma of College of Radiographers
HDIPCR .... Higher Diploma in Clinical Radiology

Hf	Hudson Fellowship
HM	Hydrographer Metoc
HM2	Hydrographer/Metoc (Second Class)
HNC	Higher National Certificate
HND	Higher National Diploma
HULL	Hull Engineering
HW	Heavy Weapons
H1	Hydrographer (First Class)
H2	Hydrographer (Second Class)
I(1)Ab	Interpreter 1st Class Arabic
I(1)Ch	Interpreter 1st Class Chinese
I(1)Da	Interpreter 1st Class Danish
I(1)Du	Interpreter 1st Class Dutch
I(1)Fi	Interpreter 1st Class Finnish
I(1)Fr	Interpreter 1st Class French
I(1)Ge	Interpreter 1st Class German
I(1)Id	Interpreter 1st Class Indonesian
I(1)It	Interpreter 1st Class Italian
I(1)Ja	Interpreter 1st Class Japanese
I(1)Ma	Interpreter 1st Class Malayan
I(1)No	Interpreter 1st Class Norwegian
I(1)Pl	Interpreter 1st Class Polish
I(1)Po	Interpreter 1st Class Portugese
I(1)Ru	Interpreter 1st Class Russian
I(1)Sh	Interpreter 1st Class Swahili
I(1)Sp	Interpreter 1st Class Spanish
I(1)Sw	Interpreter 1st Class Swedish
I(1)Tu	Interpreter 1st Class Turkish
I(1)Ur	Interpreter 1st Class Urdu
I(2)Ab	Interpreter 2nd Class Arabic
I(2)Ch	Interpreter 2nd Class Chinese
I(2)Da	Interpreter 2nd Class Danish
I(2)Du	Interpreter 2nd Class Dutch
I(2)Fi	Interpreter 2nd Class Finnish
I(2)Fr	Interpreter 2nd Class French
I(2)Ge	Interpreter 2nd Class German
I(2)Id	Interpreter 2nd Class Indonesian
I(2)It	Interpreter 2nd Class Italian
I(2)Ja	Interpreter 2nd Class Japanese
I(2)Ma	Interpreter 2nd Class Malayan
I(2)No	Interpreter 2nd Class Norwegian
I(2)Pl	Interpreter 2nd Class Polish
I(2)Po	Interpreter 2nd Class Portugese
I(2)Ru	Interpreter 2nd Class Russian
I(2)Sh	Interpreter 2nd Class Swahili
I(2)Sp	Interpreter 2nd Class Spanish
I(2)Sw	Interpreter 2nd Class Swedish

I(2)Tu	Interpreter 2nd Class Turkish
I(2)Ur	Interpreter 2nd Class Urdu
IC	Intensive Care
IC/CC	Intensive Care and Coronary Care
idc	Qualified Imperial Defence College
IEng	Incorporated Engineer
ifp	Qualified, International Fellows Programme
IS	Information Systems
isc	Initial Staff Course
JCPTGP	Certificate of Prescribed Experience in General Practice
jsdc	Joint Service Defence College
jssc	Joint Services Staff College
LC	Landing Craft
LCIPD	Licentiate of The Chartered Institute of Personnel and Development
LDS	Licentiate in Dental Surgery
LDS RCPSGlas	Licenciate in Dental Surgery Royal College of Physicians & Surgeons (Glasgow)
LDS RCS(Eng)	Licentiate in Dental Surgery, Royal College of Surgeons of England
LDS RCS(Irl)	Licenciate in Dental Surgery Royal College of Surgeons in Ireland
LDS RCSEdin	Licenciate in Dental Surgery Royal College of Surgeons of Edinburgh
LGSM	Licentiate, Guildhall School of Music and Drama
LHCIMA	Licentiate Hotel, Catering and Institutional Management Assn
LICG	Licentiate of City and Guilds Institute
LIEE	Licentiate, Institute Electrical Engineers
LIMA	Licentiate Institute Mathematics & Its Applications
LLB	Bachelor of Law
LLD	Doctor of Laws
LLM	Master of Law
LMCC	Licentiate, Medical Council of Canada
LMHCIMA	Licentiate Member of Hotel,Catering and Institutional Management Assn
LMIPD	Licentiate Member To The Institute of Personnel and Development
LMSSA	Licentiate in Medicine & Surgery, Society of Apothecaries
LRAM	Licentiate, Royal Academy of Music
LRCP	Licentiate, Royal College of Physicians, London
LRCPSGlas	Licentiate, Royal College of Physicians and Surgeons of Glasgow
LRCS	Licentiate, Royal College of Surgeons of England
LRPS	Licentiate, Royal Photographic Society
(LT)	Laboratory Technician
LTh	Licentiate in Theology
M ED	Masters in Education
M.Univ	Master of The University (Ou)
(M) UT	Senior Registrar in General Medicine - Under Training
A	Master of Arts
MA(CANTAB)	Master of Arts Cambridge
MA(Ed)	Master of Arts in Education
MA(OXON)	Master of Arts Oxon
MAPM	Member of The Association of Project Managers
MB	Bachelor of Medicine

MBA	Master of Business Administration
MBCS	Member, British Computer Society
MBIM	Member, British Institute of Management
MCD	Mine Warfare Clearance Diver
MCD/MW	Mine Clearance Diving & Mine Warfare
MCFA	Member of The Catering and Food Association
MCGI	Member of City and Guilds Institiute
MCh	Master in Surgery
MChOrth	Master of Orthopaedic Surgery
MCIEH	Member Chartered Institute in Environmental Health
MCIPD	Chartered Member of The Institute of Personnel and Development
MCIT	Member, Institute of Training Officers
MCMI	Member of The Chartered Management Institute
MD	Doctor of Medicine
MDA	Master of Defence Administration
MDSc	Master of Dental Science
mdtc	Maritime Defence Technology Course
ME	Marine Engineering
ME U/T	Marine Engineering Under Training
ME(L)	Marine Engineering (Electrical)
MEng	Master of Engineering
MESM	Marine Engineering (Submarine)
METOC	Meteorology & Oceanography
MFCM	Member, Faculty of Community Medicine
MFDS,RCS	Membership of The Faculty of Dental Surgery Royal College of Surgeons England
MFGDP(UK)	Membership in Gen Dent Practice, Faculty of General Dental Practitioners (Uk)
MFOM	Member, Faculty of Occupational Medicine
MFPM	Member of Faculty of Pharmaceutical Medicine
MGDS RCS	Member in General Dental Surgery, Royal College of Surgeons of England
MGDS RCSEd	Member in General Dental Surgery, Royal College of Surgeons of Edinburgh
MHCIMA	Member, Hotel Catering & Institutional Management Association
MHSM	Member of The Institute of Health Services Management
MICE	Member, Institution Civil Engineers
MIDPM	Member Institute of Data Processing Management
MIEE	Member, Insitution of Electrical Engineers
MIEEE	Member of The Institution of Electrical and Electronic Engineers
MIEEIE	Member of The Institute of Electrical and Electronic Incorporated Engineers
MIERE	Member, Institution of Electrical & Radio Engineers
MIExpE	Member, Institute of Explosives Engineers
MIIE	Member of Institution of Incorporated Engineers
MIL	Member, Institute of Linguists
MILDM	Member of The Institute of Logistics and Distribution Management
MILog	Member of The Institue of Logistics
MILT	Member of The Institute of Logistics and Transport
MIM	Member, Institute of Metals
MIMA	Member of The Institute of Mathematics and Applications
MIMarA	Member, Institute of Marine Architects

MIMarE .... Member, Institute of Marine Engineers
MIMarEST .... Member Institute Marine Engineers Science & Technology
MIMechE .... Member, Institution of Mechanical Engineers
MIMechIE .... Member of The Institute of Mechanical Incorporated Engineers
MIMS .... Member, Institute of Management Specialists
MInsD .... Member of The Institute of Directors
MinstAM .... Member, Institute of Administrative Management
MInstFM .... Member, Institute of Facilities/Resources Management
MinstP .... Member, Institute of Physics
MInstPS .... Member, Institute of Purchasing and Supply
MINucE .... Member, Institute of Nuclear Engineers
MIOSH .... Member, Institute of Occupational Safety and Health
MIPD .... Member of The Institute of Personnel and Development
MIPlantE .... Member, Plant Engineers
MIPM .... Member, Institute of Personnel Management
MIProdE .... Member, Institute of Production Engineers
MISecM .... Member of The Institute of Security Management
MISM .... Member of The Institute of Supervisory Management
MITD .... Member Institute of Training and Development
MITE .... Member, Institute of Technical Engineers
MLDR .... Mountain Leader
LITT .... Master of Letters
ML2@ .... Mountain Leader 2 (Rm)
MMus .... Master of Music
MNI .... Member, Nautical Institute
MNZIS .... Member of The New Zealand Institute of Surveyors
MOR .... Heavy Weapons Mortar Course
MOrth .... Master of Orthodontics
MOrth,RCS .... Membership in Othodontics Royal College of Surgeons England
MPH .... Master of Public Health
MPhil .... Master of Philosophy
PS .... Member, Pharmaceutical Society
MRAeS .... Member, Royal Aeronautical Society
MRCGP .... Member, Royal College of General Practitioners
MRCOG .... Member, Royal College Obstetricians & Gynaecologists
MRCP .... Member, Royal College of Physicians, London
MRCP(UK) .... Member, Royal College of Physicians
MRCPath .... Member, Royal College of Pathologists
MRCPE .... Member, Royal College of Physicians, Edinburgh
MRCPGlas .... Member, Royal College of Physicians and Surgeons of Glasgow
MRCPI .... Member, Royal College of Physicians of Ireland
MRCPsych .... Member, Royal College of Phsyciatrists
MRCS .... Member, Royal College of Surgeons of England
MRCVS .... Member of The Royal College of Veterinary Surgeons
MRIC .... Member, Royal Institute of Chemistry
MRIN .... Member, Royal Institute of Navigation
MRINA .... Member, Royal Institute of Naval Architects

MS	Master of Surgery
MSc	Master of Science
MSc gw	Master of Science Guided Weapons
MSc(Econ)	Master of Economic and Social Studies
MScD	Master of Dental Science
MSE	Member, Society of Engineers
MSRP	Member of The Society For Radiological Protection
MTh	Master of Theology
MTO	Motor Transport Officer
MW	Mine Warfare
n	Frigate Navigating Officer's Course
N	Navigation
nadc	Nato Defence College Course
NCS(A)	Naval Control Shipping
NCS(B)	Nsc (B)
NCS(C)	Ncs (C)
ndc	National Defence College
NDipM	National Diploma in Management
NInstC	Nuclear Instrument Calibration Course
nrf	Qualified, Nato Research Fellowship
O	Observer
O LYNX	Observer (Lynx)
O MER	Observer (Merlin)
SKW	Observer (Seaking Aew)
O SK6	Observer (Seaking 6)
O U/T	Observer Under Training
ocds(Can)	Qualified Canadian National Defence College
ocds(Ind)	Qualified Indian National Defence College
OCDS(JAP)	Overseas National Defence College Japanese
ocds(No)	Qualified, Norwegian Defence College
ocds(Pak)	Qualified Pakistan National Defence College
ocds(US)	Qualified The United States National War College
ocds(USN)	Qualified, United States Naval War College
odc(Aus)	Qualified Australia Joint Services Staff College
odc(Fr)	Qualified French Cours Superieur Interarmees
ODC(SWISS)	International Training in Security and Arms Control
odc(US)	Qualified United States Armed Forces Staff College
ONC	Orthopaedic Nursing
osc	Qualified Overseas Staff College
osc(Nig)	Qualified Nigerian Command & Staff College
osc(us)	Qualified, Usmc Command & Staff College
OStJ	Order of St. John
OTSPEC	Operating Theatre Specialist
P	Pilot
P LYNX	Pilot (Lynx)
P LYN7	Pilot (Lynx 7)
P MER	Pilot (Merlin)

P SHAR	Sea Harrier Pilot
P SKW	Pilot (Seaking Aew)
P SK4	Pilot (Seaking 4)
P SK6	Pilot (Seaking 6)
P U/T	Pilot Under Training
(P)	Physiotherapist
pce	Passed Command Examinations
pce(sm)	Passed Command Examinations (Sm)
pcea	Passed Command Examinations (Air)
(PD)	Pharmacy Dispenser
pdm	Principal Director of Music
PFOM	President Faculty of Occupational Medicine
PGCE	Post Graduate Certificate of Education
PGDip	Post Graduate
PGDIP	Post Graduate Diploma
PGDIPAN	Post Graduate Diploma in Applied Navigation
PGDRP	Post Graduate Diploma in Radiation Protection
PH	Helicopter Pilot
PhD	Doctor of Philosophy
PI	Photographic Interpreter
PR	Plotting & Radar
psc	Passed Staff Course
psc(a)	Passed Staff Course (Raf)
psc(j)	Passed Staff Course (Joint)
sc(j)(o)	Overseas Staff Colleges Except Ndc Rome
psc(j)o	Overseas Staff Colleges Except Ndc Rome
psc(m)	Passed Staff Course (Army)
PSC(ONDC)	Staff Course (Overseas National Defence College)
psc(or)	Passed Staff Course Overseas Reserves
PT	Physical Training
ptsc	Completed Technical Staff Course at The Rmsc Shrivenham
PWO	Principal Warfare Officer
PWO(A)	Principal Warfare Officer Above Water
PWO(C)	Principal Warfare Officer Communications
PWO(N)	Principal Warfare Officer Navigation
PWO(U)	Principal Warfare Officer Underwater
rcds	Royal College of Defence Studies
RCPS(Glas)	Royal College of Phsicians and Surgeons of Glasgow
RCS	Royal College of Surgeons of England
RCSEd	Royal College of Surgeons of Edinburgh
REG	Regulating
REGM	Registered Midwife
(RGN)	Registered General Nurse
RL	Reconnaissance Leader
RMN	Registered Mental Nurse
RMP1	Pilot 1
RMP2	Pilot 2

NT .... Registered Nurse Tutor
S .... Supply
(S) .... Stores
(SA) .... Senior Specialist in Anaesthetics
SALT .... Salt - Nmmis Only
SBS .... Special Boat Squadron
SCM .... State Certified Midwife
SEC .... Secretarial
(SGS) .... Senior Specialist in General Surgery
SM .... Submariner
SM .... Sm Qualified
SM(n) .... Submarine Navigating Officer
SM(N) .... Submarine (Navigation)
(SM) .... Senior Specialist in General Medicine
SMTAS .... Submarine Torpedo Anti-Submarine
SO(LE) .... Staff Officer Personnel and Logistics
(SO/M) .... Senior Specialist in Occupational Medicine
sondc .... Senior Overseas National Defence College
sowc .... Senior Officer's War Course
sq .... Rm Major Staff Qualified After Holding Two Specified Staff Appointments
tacsc .... Territorial Army Command and Staff Course
TAS .... Torpedo Anti-Submarine
tas .... Torpedo Anti-Submarine Basic
TDCR .... Teachers Diploma College of Radiographers
TEng .... Certificate of Technical Engineering
TM .... Training Management
TM/IS .... Training Management/Information Systems
TMSM .... Training Management (Sm)
tp .... Qualified Test Pilots Course
(W) .... Writer
(X) .... Specialist in Radiology
(X) UT .... Senior Registrar in Radiology - Under Training
WE .... Weapons Engineering
WE U/T .... Weapons Engineering Under Training
WESM .... Weapon Engineering (Submarine)
WTO .... Weapon Training Officer
X X

ABBREVIATIONS OF PLACE WHERE OFFICER IS SERVING WHEN NOT SERVING AT SEA

AACC MID WALLOP .... HQ School of Army Aviation Middle Wallop
ACDS OR (SEA) .... Assistant Chief of Defence Staff Operational Requirement (Sea Sy
ACDS(POL) USA .... Assistant Chief of Defence Staff (Policy and Nuclear) USA
ACE SRGN GIBLTAR .... Allied Forces Southern Europe (Gibraltar)
ACE SRGN TURKEY .... Allied Forces Southern Europe (Turkey)
AFCC .... ARMED FORCES CHAPLAINCY CENTRE
AFPAA HQ .... ARMED FORCES PERSONNEL ADMINISTRATION AGENCY HEADQUARTERS

AFPAA WTHY DOWN	AFPAA (Worthy Down)
AFPAA(CENTURION)	Directorate of AFPAA (CENTURION)
AGRIPPA AFSOUTH	HMS Agrippa (Allied Forces S. Europe (Italy))
AGRIPPA NAVSOUTH	HMS Agrippa (Allied Naval Forces S. Europe (Italy))
AH IPT	Attack Helicopter Integrated Project Team
AMC	Aquisition Management Cell
ASC WATCHFIELD	Joint Service Command and Staff College Watchfield
ASM IPT	Attack Submarine Integrated Project Group
AST(W)	Area Security Team (West)
ATTURM	Amphibious Training & Trials Unit Royal Marines
BDLS AUSTRALIA	British Defence Liaison Staff Australia
BDLS CANADA	British Defence Liaison Staff Canada
BDLS INDIA	British Defence Liaison Staff India
BDMT	Arms CIS Group/Bowman Military Team
BDS WASHINGTON	British Defence Staff Washington
BOWMAN IPT	BOWMAN Integrated Project Team
BRNC BAND	Band of HM Royal Marines Britannia Royal Naval College
BRNC RNSU SOTON	Royal Naval Support Unit - University of Southampton
CALEDONIA DLO	HMS Caledonia
CALLIOPE	Royal Naval Reserve Tyne (RN Staff)
CAMBRIA	Royal Naval Reserve South Wales (RN Staff)
CAMBRIDGE	Her Majesty's Ship CAMBRIDGE
CAPTAIN SM2	Captain Second Submarine Squadron
CASOM IPT	CASOM Integrated Project Team
CDO LOG REGT RM	Commando Logistics Regiment Royal Marines
CESM IPT	CESM Integrated Project Team
CFLT COMMAND SEC	Commander-in-Chief Fleet Command Secretary's Division
CFPS SHORE	Commander Fishery Protection Squadron (Shore)
CHFHQ(SHORE)	CDO Helo Force Headquarters (Shore)
CINCFLEET CIS	Northwood Communications Information Systems
CINCFLEET FIMU	FLEET INFORMATION MANAGEMENT UNIT
CINCFLEET FTSU	Commander-in-Chief (Fleet Technical Support Unit)
CJPS	Allied Forces Europe Reaction Forces Planning Staff
CLYDE MIXMAN1	Her Majesty's Ship NEPTUNE Mixed Manning
CMSG IPT	CMSG Integrated Project Team
CNNRP BRISTOL	Chairman Naval Nuclear Regulatory Panel
CNOCS GROUP	Captain Naval Operational Combat Systems Group
CNSA BRISTOL	Captain Naval Ship Acceptance
COLLINGWOOD	Her Majesty's Ship COLLINGWOOD
COMNA DARTMOUTH	Commodore Naval Aviation (BRNC Dartmouth)
COMSTRIKFORSTH	Commander Strike Force South
CSIS IPT	CSIS Integrated Project Team
CSSE USA	Chief Strategic Systems Executive (USA)
CSST RNSSS	CSST Royal Navy Strategic Systems School
CTCRM	Commando Training Centre Royal Marines
CTCRM BAND	Band of HM Royal Marines Commando Training Centre Royal Marines
CTS	Corporate Technical Services

CV(F) IPT	CVF Integrated Project Team
DA BRIDGETOWN	Defence Attache Bridgetown
DA KIEV	Defence Attache Kiev
DA PEKING	Defence Attache Peking
DA SINGAPORE	Defence Attache Singapore
DA SOFIA	Defence Attache Sofia
DA TBILISI	Defence Attache Tbilisi
DALRIADA	Her Majesty's Ship DALRIADA
DARTMOUTH BRNC	Britannia Royal Naval College Dartmouth
DCSA COMMCEN PLY	DCSA COMMCEN PLYMOUTH
DCSA MSG PORT	DCSA Messaging Portsmouth
DCSA NWD REGION	DCSA NORTHWOOD REGIONAL OFFICE
DCSA RADIO PLY	DCSA RADIO ENGINEERING - SYSTEM CONTROL POINT PLYMOUTH
DCSA RADIOHQ FMR	DCSA RADIO HEADQUARTERS
DCTA	Defence Clothing and Textile Agency
DDA HALTON	Defence Dental Agency Halton
DDA PLYMOUTH	Defence Dental Agency Plymouth
DDA PORTSMOUTH	Defence Dental Agency Portsmouth
DDA TE	Defence Dental Agency Training Establishment
DEF DIVING SCHL	Defence Diving School
DEF EXP ORD SCHL	Defence Ordnance Disposal School
DEF MED TRG CTR	Defence Medical Services Training Centre
DEF SCH OF LANG	Defence School of Languages
DGIA	Defence Geographic and Imagery Intelligence Agency
DHFS	Defence Helicopter Flying School
DHSA	Defence Helicopter Support Authority
DISC	Defence Intelligence & Security Centre
DITMTC SHRIVNHAM	Defence Information Technology and Management Training Centre
DL IPT	Data Links Integrated Project Group
DLO MCBU/DGMIPT	DLO Munitions Corporate Business Unit
DLO/DGDEF LOG SP	DLO/Director General Defence Logistics Support
DMTO HQ	Defence Medical Training Organisation Head Quarters
DNR DISP TEAM	DIRECTOR OF NAVAL RECRUITING DISPLAY TEAM
DNR EC 2	Directorate of Naval Recruiting East Central 2
DNR N IRELAND	Directorate of Naval Recruiting Northern Ireland
DNR NEE 1	Directorate of Naval Recruiting North East England 1
DNR NWE 2	Directorate of Naval Recruiting North West England 2
DNR PRES TEAMS	DIRECTOR OF NAVAL RECRUITING PRESENTATION TEAMS
DNR RCHQ NORTH	DIRECTOR OF NAVAL RECRUITING REGIONAL HEADQUARTERS (NORTH)
DNR RCHQ SOUTH	Director of Naval Recruiting Regional Careers Headquarters (Sou
DNR SCO 2	Directorate of Naval Recruiting Scotland 2
DNR SEE 1	Directorate of Naval Recruiting South East England 1
DNR SWE 1	Directorate of Naval Recruiting South West England 1
DNR SWE 2	Directorate of Naval Recruiting South West England 2
DNR W CENTRAL	Directorate of Naval Recruiting West Central
DNR WROUGHTON	Director of Naval Recruiting, Wroughton
DOSG BRISTOL	Defence Ordnance Safety Group Bristol

DPA BRISTOL	Defence Procurement Agency Bristol
DRAKE CBP(DLO)	Her Majesty's Ship DRAKE - Captain Base Personnel
DRAKE CBS	Her Majesty's Ship DRAKE - Captain Base Safety
DRAKE DPL	Her Majesty's Ship DRAKE - Area Manpower Management Organisation (AM
DRAKE NBC	Her Majesty's Ship DRAKE - Naval Base Commander
DRAKE NBSD	Her Majesty's Ship DRAKE - Naval Base Services Director
DRAKE SFM	Her Majesty's Ship DRAKE - Superintendent Fleet Maintenance
DRYAD	Her Majesty's Ship DRYAD
DSQ ROSYTH	Director Safety & Quality - ROSYTH
DSTL CDA HLS	Defence Science & Tech Labs Centre for Defence Analysis (HLS)
DSTL PORTN DN	Defence Science & Tech Labs Porton Down
EAGLET	Royal Naval Reserve Mersey (RN Staff)
ELANT/NAVNORTH	CinC Eastern Atlantic Area and Commander Naval Forces Northern
ES AIR BRISTOL	Equipment Support (Air) Bristol
ES AIR MASU	Equipment Support (Air) MASU
ES AIR NAML	Equipment Support (Air) Naval Aircraft Materials Laboratory
ES AIR WYTON	Equipment Support (Air) Wyton
ES AIR YEO	Equipment Support (Air) Yeovilton
EUMS	European Union Military Staff
EXC BRISTOL	Her Majesty's Ship BRISTOL
EXCELLENT	Her Majesty's Ship EXCELLENT
EXCH ARMY SC(G)	Exchange Service British Army On the Rhine
EXCHANGE ARMY UK	Exchange Service UK Army Units
EXCHANGE AUSTLIA	Exchange Service Australian Navy
EXCHANGE BRAZIL	Exchange Service Brazilian Navy
EXCHANGE CANADA	Exchange Service Canadian Armed Forces
EXCHANGE DENMARK	Exchange Service Denmark
EXCHANGE FRANCE	Exchange Service France
EXCHANGE GERMANY	Exchange Service German Navy
EXCHANGE ITALY	Exchange Italian Navy
EXCHANGE NLANDS	Exchange Service Netherlands Forces
EXCHANGE NORWAY	Exchange Service Norway
EXCHANGE RAF UK	Exchange Service with the Royal Air Force
EXCHANGE SPAIN	EXCHANGE SPAIN
EXCHANGE USA	Exchange Service United States
FDG	Fleet Diving Group
FDU1	Fleet Diving Unit (1)
FDU2	Fleet Diving Unit (2)
FDU3	Fleet Diving Unit (3)
FLEET ADD NWD	Fleet Additions (Northwood)
FLEET ADD PORTS	Fleet Additons Portsmouth
FLEET AV CRANWEL	Fleet Aviation Cranwell
FLEET AV CU	Fleet Aviation (HMS Seahawk)
FLEET AV SULTAN	Fleet Aviation (SULTAN)
FLEET AV VALLEY	Fleet Aviation (RAF Valley)
FLEET AV VL	Fleet Aviation Yeovilton
FLEET CIS PORTS	Fleet Communication Information Systems Portsmouth

FLEET CMSA UK	Fleet Cruise Missile Support Activity (UK)
FLEET HQ NWD	Fleet Headquarters Northwood
FLEET HQ PORTS	Fleet Headquarters Portsmouth
FLEET HQ PORTS 2	Fleet Headquarters Portsmouth No. 2
FLEET PHOT PORTS	Fleet Photographic Unit Portsmouth
FLEET ROSYTH	Fleet (Rosyth)
FLS1	FORWARD LOGISTIC SITE 1
FLS3	FORWARD LOGISTIC SITE 3
FLS4	FORWARD LOGISTICS SITE 4
FLYING FOX	HMS FLYING FOX
FORT BLOCKHOUSE	Royal Defence Medical College
FORWARD	RNR Communications Training Centre (Birmingham) (RN Staff)
FOSM FASLANE	Flag Officer Submarines (Faslane)
FOSM GOSPORT	Flag Officer Submarines (Gosport)
FOSM NWOOD HQ	Flag Officer Submarines (Northwood) Headquarters
FOSM NWOOD OPS	Flag Officer Submarines (Northwood)
FOSNNI OPS DLO	FOSNNI/Commander Clyde Operations Department
FOSNNI/NBC CLYDE	Flag Officer Scotland & Northern Ireland/Naval Base Commander
FOST CSST DEVPT	FOST Captain Sea & Shore Submarine Training (Devonport)
FOST CSST FSLN	FOST Captain Sea & Shore Submarine Training (Faslane)
FOST DPORT SHORE	Flag Officer Sea Training (Devonport)
FPGRM	Fleet Protection Group Royal Marine
FSC IPT	Future Surface Combatant
FWO DEVONPORT	Fleet Waterfront Organisation (Devonport)
FWO FASLANE	Fleet Waterfront Organisation Faslane
FWO PORTSMOUTH	Fleet Waterfront Organisation Portsmouth
GANNET	Her Majesty's Ship GANNET
GANNET SAR FLT	Gannet SAR Flight
HQ AIRNORTH	Headquarters Air North
HQ ARRC	HQ Ace Rapid Reaction Corps
HQ BAND SERVICE	Headquarters Band Service
HQ DCSA	HQ Defence Communication Services Agency
HQ NORTH	Headquarters North
HQ SOUTHLANT	Headquarters South Atlantic Area
HQ STC	Headquarters Strike Command Ops Support (ATC)
HQ 3 CDO BDE RM	3 Commando Brigade Royal Marines
HQBF CYPRUS	Headquarters British Forces Cyprus
HQ3GP HQSTC	Headquarters 3 Group
HU DERRIFORD	Ministry of Defence Hospital Unit (Derriford)
HU FRIMLEY	Ministry of Defence Hospital Unit Frimley Park
HU PETERBRGH	Ministry of Defence Hospital Unit Peterborough
HU PORTSMOUTH	Ministry of Defence Hospital Unit (Portsmouth)
HUMS IPT	Health & Usage Monitoring Systems Integrated Project Team
IA BRISTOL	Integration Authority Bristol
IMS BRUSSELS	International Military Staff, Brussels
INM ALVERSTOKE	Institute of Naval Medicine
JACIG	Joint Arms Control Implementation Group

JARIC	Joint Air Reconnaissance and Intelligence Centre
JCA IPT UK	Future Carrier Borne Aircraft Integrated Project Team
JCA IPT USA	Future Carrier Borne Aircraft Integrated Project Team USA
JDCC	Joint Doctrine and Concepts Centre
JF HARROLE OFF	Joint Force Harrier Role Office
JFHQ STAFF NWOOD	Joint Force Operations Staff
JHCHQ	JOINT HELICOPTER COMMAND HEADQUARTERS
JHCNI	Joint Helicopter Command (Northern Ireland)
JHQ NORTHEAST	Baltic Approaches
JHQ SOUTHCENT	JOINT HEADQUARTERS SOUTHCENT
JHQSW MADRID	JHQ SOUTHWEST MADRID
JMOTS NORTHWOOD	Joint Maritime Operational Training Staff (Northwood)
JPS UK	Joint Planning Staff UK
JS PHOT SCHOOL	Joint Services Photographic School
JSCSC	Joint Services Command and Staff College
JSSU AY NIK	Joint Service Signal Unit Ayios Nikolaos
JSSU DIGBY	Joint Service Signal Unit - Digby
JSSU OAKLEY	Joint Service Signal Unit - Oakley
JSU NORTHWOOD	Joint Support Unit Northwood
KING ALFRED	Her Majesty's Ship King Alfred Royal Navy Reserve Unit Portsmouth
LAIPT	Area Information Systems (South West)
LANG TRNG(UK)	Language Training (UK)
LN BMATT (CEE)	Loan BMATT (CEE) (Vyskov)
LN BMATT SAFRICA	British Military Advisory and Training Team (South Africa)
LN SIERRA LEONE	Loan Sierra Leone
LOAN ABU DHABI	Loan Service in Abu Dhabi
LOAN BMATT GHANA	Bmatt West Africa
LOAN BMATT(EC)	British Military Advisory Training Team (Eastern Caribbean)
LOAN BRUNEI	Loan Service in Brunei
LOAN DARA	Loan DARA
LOAN DSTL	Loan Defence Science & Tech Labs
LOAN HYDROG	Loan Hydrographer
LOAN JTEG BSC DN	Loan Joint Test Evaluation Group Boscombe Down
LOAN KUWAIT	Loan Service Kuwait
LOAN MALAYSIA	Loan Malaysia
LOAN OMAN	Loan Service Oman
LOAN OTHER SVCE	Loan Other Service
LOAN SAUDI ARAB	Loan Service Saudi Arabia
LPD(R) IPT	Landing Platform Dock (Replacement) Integrated Project Team
MAS BRUSSELS	Military Agency For Standardisation (Brussels)
MCME IPT	MCM Equipment Integrated Project Team
MCTC	Military Corrective Training Centre
MERLIN IPT	Merlin Integrated Project Team
MSA	Medical Supply Agency
MTS IPT	Maritime Trainers and Simulators Integrated Project Team
MWC PORTSDOWN	Maritime Warfare Centre (Portsdown)
MWC SOUTHWICK	Maritime Warfare Centre

NAIC NORTHOLT	Naval Aeronautical Information Cell
NATO DEF COL	Nato Defence College
NATO MEWSG VL	NATO Multi-Service Electronic Warfare Support Group Yeovilton
NBC PORTSMOUTH	Naval Base Commander (Portsmouth)
NC3 AGENCY	NATO C3 Agency
NELSON	Her Majesty's Ship NELSON
NELSON RNSETT	The Royal Naval School of Educational and Training Technology (R
NELSON WF	Her Majesty's Ship Nelson-Waterfront
NEPTUNE DLO	Captain Base Port (Personnel & Support), HMS NEPTUNE
NEPTUNE DSA	HMS Neptune - Director of Safety Assurance
NEPTUNE FD	FACILITIES DEPARTMENT
NEPTUNE NT	Her Majesty's Ship NEPTUNE - Naval Technical Department
NEPTUNE 2SL/CNH	HMS Neptune (NSC)
NEW IPT	Naval EW Integrated Project Team
NMA GOSPORT	Commodore Naval Drafting
NMA PORTSMOUTH	Naval Manning Agency - Portsmouth
NMA WHALE ISLAND	Naval Manning Agency - Whale Island
NORTH DIVING GRP	Northern Diving Group
NP BRISTOL	Nuclear Propulsion Bristol
NP DNREAY	Nuclear Propulsion Dounreay
NP 1002 DIEGOGA	Naval Party 1002 Diego Garcia
NP 1061	Naval Party 1061 - Royal Naval Liaison Officer - Split
NP 1066	NAVAL PARTY 1066
NP 1067 KOSOVO	Naval Party 1067 KOSOVO
NS OBERAMMERGAU	NATO School (SHAPE) Oberammergau
NSE NORTHWOOD	NACOSA SUPPORT ELEMENT NORTHWOOD
NSRS IPT	Nato Submarine Rescue System Integrated Project Team
NW IPT	Nuclear Weapons Integrated Project Team
OCLC BIRM	Officer Careers Liaison Centre, Birmingham
OCLC BRISTOL	OFFICER CAREERS LIAISON CENTRE,BRISTOL
OCLC MANCH	Officer Careers Liaison Centre, Manchester
OCLC ROSYTH	Officer Careers Liaison Centre, Rosyth
OPTAG	Operational Training and Advisory Group (Warminster)
PAAMS PARIS	Principal Anti Air Missile System Paris
PAIT	Project Alexander Implementation Team
PCRS IPT	Primary Casualty Receiving Ship Integrated Project Team
PJHQ	Permanent Joint Headquarters (Northwood)
PJHQ AUGMENTEES	Permanent Joint Headquarters (Northwood)
PRESIDENT	Royal Naval Reserve London (RN Staff)
PRESTWICK	Royal Naval Air Station Prestwick
QHM CLYDE	Queens Harbourmaster(Clyde)
QINETIQ FARN	QINETIQ Farnborough
QINETIQ HASLAR	QINETIQ Haslar
QINETIQ MALVERN	QINETIQ Malvern
QINETIQ PYSTCK	QINETIQ Pyestock
RAF AWC	Air Warfare Centre RAFC Cranwell
RAF COTTESMORE	Royal Air Force Cottesmore

RAF CRANWELL EFS	Royal Air Force College Cranwell (Joint Elementary Flying Tra
RAF HANDLING SQN	Royal Air Force Handling Squadron
RAF LINTN/OUSE	Royal Air Force (Linton On Ouse)
RAF SHAWBURY	Royal Air Force Shawbury
RAF WEST DRAYTON	Royal Air Force West Drayton
RAF WITTERING	Royal Air Force Wittering
RALEIGH	Her Majesty's Ship RALEIGH
RCDM	Royal Centre for Defence Medicine
RCDS	Royal College of Defence Studies
RH HASLAR	The Royal Hospital Haslar
RHQ AFNORTH	Regional Headquarters Allied Forces North
RHQ SOUTHLANT	Regional Headquarters Southern Atlantic
RM BAND PLYMOUTH	Band of HM Royal Marines Plymouth
RM BAND PTSMTH	Band of HM Royal Marines Portsmouth
RM BAND SCOTLAND	Band of HM Royal Marines Scotland
RM CHIVENOR	RM Chivenor
RM CONDOR	Royal Marines Condor
RM NORTON MANOR	Royal Marines Norton Manor
RM SCHOOL MUSIC	Royal Marines School of Music
RM WARMINSTER	Royal Marines Warminster
RMB STONEHOUSE	Royal Marine Barracks Stonehouse
RMC OF SCIENCE	Royal Military College of Science Shrivenham
RMCS SHRIVENHAM	Royal Military College of Science
RMDIV LECONFIELD	Royal Marines Division Army School of Mechanical Transport
RMR BRISTOL	Royal Marines Reserve Bristol
RMR LONDON	Royal Marines Reserve London
RMR MERSEYSIDE	Royal Marines Reserve Merseyside
RMR SCOTLAND	Royal Marines Reserve Scotland
RMR TYNE	Royal Marines Reserve Tyne
RN GIBRALTAR	Royal Navy Gibraltar
RN HM SCHL DRAKE	Royal Naval Hydrographic & Meterological School
RNAS CULDROSE	Royal Naval Air Station Culdrose
RNAS YEOVILTON	Royal Naval Air Station Yeovilton
RNEAWC	Royal Naval Element Air Warfare Centre
RNHMS CULDROSE	Royal Naval Hydrographical & Meterological School
RNLO GULF	Royal Naval Liaison Officer (Gulf)
RNLO JTF4	Royal Naval Liaison Officer for Commander Joint Task Force 4,USN
RNP TEAM	Royal Naval Presentation Team
RNSR BOVINGTON	Royal Naval School of Recruiting, Bovington
RNU RAF DIGBY	Royal Naval Unit RAF DIGBY
RNU ST MAWGAN	Royal Naval Unit St Mawgan
SA ANKARA	Service Attache Ankara
SA ATHENS	Service Attache Athens
SA BERLIN	Service Attache BERLIN
SA BRAZIL	Service Attache Brazil
SA BUENOS AIRES	Service Attache Buenos Aires
SA CAIRO	Service Attache Cairo

SA CARACAS	Service Attache Caracas
SA COPENHAGEN	Service Attache Copenhagen
SA ISLAMABAD	Service Attache Islamabad
SA LISBON	Service Attache Lisbon
SA MADRID	Service Attache Madrid
SA MALAYSIA	Service Attache Malaysia
SA MOSCOW	Service Attache Moscow
SA MUSCAT	Service Attache Muscat
SA OSLO	Service Attache Oslo
SA PARIS	Service Attache Paris
SA RIYADH	Service Attache Riyadh
SA ROME	Service Attache Rome
SA SEOUL	Service Attache Seoul
SA THE HAGUE	Service Attache the Hague
SA TOKYO	Service Attache Tokyo
SABR IPT	SABR Integrated Project Team
SACLANT BELGIUM	Supreme Allied Commander Atlantic, Belgium
SACLANT ITALY	Supreme Allied Commander Atlantic, Italy
SACLANT USA	Supreme Allied Commander Atlantic, USA
SAT IPT	Satellite Communications Integrated Project Team
SAUDI AFPS SAUDI	Saudi Armed Forces Project Sales Saudi
SCH SIG BLANDFD	School of Signals Blandford
SCOTIA	Her Majesty's Ship SCOTIA
SCU LEYDENE ACNS	SCU Leydene ACNS
SDG PORTSMOUTH	Southern Diving Unit 2 (Portsmouth)
SFM PORTSMOUTH	Superintendent Fleet Maintenance (Portsmouth)
SFM ROSYTH	Superintendent Fleet Maintenance (Rosyth)
SHAPE BELGIUM	Supreme Headquarters Allied Powers In Europe (Belgium)
SHERWOOD	RNR Communications Training Centre (Nottingham) (RN Staff)
SIFF IPT	SIFF Integrated Project Team
SONAR 2087 IPT	Defence Procurement Agency Peer Group G
SSA BATH	Ships Support Agency
SSIP IPT	SSIP Integrated Project Team
STG BRISTOL	Sea Technology Group Bristol
STRS IPT	STRS Integrated Project Team
SULTAN	Her Majesty's Ship SULTAN
SULTAN AIB	Admiralty Interview Board
SUPT OF DIVING	Superintendent of Diving
SVHO IPT	Survey Vessels Hydrography and Oceanography Integrated Project Team
TCM IPT	Torpedo Counter Measures Integrated Project Team
TEMERAIRE	Her Majesty's Ship TEMERAIRE
TORPEDO IPT	Torpedo Integrated Project Team
TRAINTEAM BRUNEI	Training Team Brunei
T45 IPT	TYPE 45 DESTROYER INTEGRATED PROJECT TEAM
UKCEC IPT	UK COOPERATIVE ENGAGEMENT CAPABILITY
UKLFCSG RM	United Kingdom Landing Force Command Support Group Royal Marines
UKMFTS IPT	Flt Sim & Synth Trnrs/UK Mil Flying Trg Sys Integrated Project Team

UKMILREP BRUSS	United Kingdom Military Representative Brussels
UKNMR SHAPE	United Kingdom Military Representative SHAPE
UKSU AFSOUTH	United Kingdom Support Unit Allied Forces Southern Europe
UKSU JHQ NORTH	United Kingdom National Support Element Allied Forces Northern
UKSU SHAPE	UK Support Unit Supreme Headquarters Allied Powers In Europe
UKSU SOUTHLANT	United Kingdom Support Unit Southlant
UNOMIG	UN MONITORING IN GEORGIA
URNU NEWCASTLE	University Royal Naval Unit (Newcastle-upon-Tyne)
VICTORY	Her Majesty's Ship VICTORY
VIVID	Her Majesty's Ship VIVID
WILDFIRE	Her Majesty's Ship WILDFIRE
WSA BRISTOL	Warship Support Agency (Bristol)
WSA/CAPT MCTA	Warship Support Agency/Captain Maritime Commissioning Trials & A
1 ASSLT GP RM	1 Assault Group Royal Marines
2SL/CNH	Second Sea Lord/Commander-in-Chief Naval Home Command
2SL/CNH FOTR	Flag Officer Training and Recruiting Headquarters
32(THE ROYAL)SQN	Royal Air Force Northolt - 32 The(The Royal) Squadron
40 CDO RM	40 Commando Royal Marines
42 CDO (RM)	42 Commando Royal Marines
42 CDO RM	42 Commando Royal Marines
45 CDO (RM)	45 Commando Royal Marines
45 CDO RM	45 Commando Royal Marines
702 SQN HERON	702 Naval Air Squadron Her Majesty's Ship Heron
727 NAS	727 Naval Air Squadron
750 SQN (HERON)	Heron Flight
750 SQN SEAHAWK	750 Squadron Seahawk
771 SQN	771 Squadron
792 NAS	Fleet Target Group Squadron Shore Culdrose
815 SQN HQ	815 Headquarters Naval Air Squadron, Her Majesty's Ship Heron
824 SQN	824 Squadron
848 SQN HERON	848 Naval Air Squadron
849 SQN HQ	849 Naval Air Squadron Headquarters
899 SQN HERON	899 Naval Air Squadron Her Majesty's Ship Heron

V

Y

Amendments to Navy List Entry

Editor of the Navy List
Room 115
Victory Building
HMNB Portsmouth
PO1 3LS

Please ensure that you state your Service Number and use the spaces provided next to each incorrect field to insert what you believe to be the correct entry. All potential inaccuracies will be investigated.

The information contained in Sections 2 and 3 of this edition was extracted from the Naval Manpower Management Information System and is corrected to include those promotions, appointments etc. promulgated on or before 9 April 2002 which will be effective on or before 30 June 2002.

Service Number (mandatory) ....

Surname ....

Forenames ....

Titular Address ....

Post-Nominals* ....

Rank ....

Commission ....

Branch ....

Spec ....

Seniority ....

* Please note that documentary evidence (for example, a supporting certificate) will be required if any amendments to your post-nominal details are to be made.

Signed .... Date ....

Once completed, please return this form to the above address, marked for the attention of your Appointer.

Every effort will be made to correct errors and omissions notified to the Editor but regrettably receipt of this form cannot be acknowledged.